The **HUTCHINS**

DIRECTORY OF

WEB SITES

Second edition

The *The* **HUTCHINSON** DIRECTORY OF WEB SITES

The **HUTCHINSON**

DIRECTORY OF

WEB SITES

Second edition

Helicon

First published in Great Britain in 1999

Second edition 2000

Helicon Publishing Ltd
42 Hythe Bridge Street
Oxford OX1 2EP

Typeset by TechType

Printed and bound in Slovenia by
DELO tiskarna by arrangement
with Korotan Ljubljana

ISBN: 1-85986-335-3

British Library Cataloguing in Publication Data

A catalogue record for this book is available from the British Library.

Papers used by Helicon Publishing Ltd are natural recyclable products made from wood grown in sustainable forests. The manufacturing processes of both raw material and paper conform to the environmental regulations of the country of origin.

CONTENTS

STAFF AND CONTRIBUTORS

Project Editor

Graham Bennett

Database Editor

Claire Lishman

Editorial Director

Hilary McGlynn

Production

John Normansell

Art and Design

Terence Caven

Contributors

Sharon Brimblecombe
Gareth Chadwick
Sharon Charity
Susan Cuthbert
Paul Davis
Elisabeth Hallett
Carl Hanson
Sara Jenkins-Jones
Richard Martin
Rachel Minay
Mark McGuinness
Tim Morris
Martin Noble
Stephen Pavlovich
Hal Robinson
Pete Shone
Efrossini Spentzou

INTRODUCTION

In 1998 the Internet generated $301 billion in revenue, according to a report released in June 1999 by researchers at the University of Texas, USA. The Internet also created 1.2 million jobs in 1998. From its specialized beginnings as a military network in the late 1960s the Internet is now a major global source of information, and increasingly of trade.

It is now commonplace for museums, galleries, companies, universities, and public organizations to have their own Web site. These sites are aimed at audiences as different as PhD students and schoolchildren, economists and hobbyists. Some sites have been produced by acknowledged experts in their field, some have been written by dedicated enthusiasts, and some are amateurish and occasionally misleading. There are now millions of places on the Internet where you can find information. Some will entertain, some educate. Some will be reliable and well-researched, others not. But where to begin, when even some of the more powerful search engines on the Web struggle under the weight of all these different sources? For example, some US researchers estimate that search engines in 1999 were indexing only approximately 16% of the 800 million publicly available Web pages when used individually; when the 11 main search engines were combined to conduct a metasearch they still failed to index more than half of the Web pages. In contrast, *The Hutchinson Directory of Web Sites* has been specifically designed to take you straight to the best and most reliable sites on the Internet, across all subjects.

For ease of use the Web sites listed in this book have been divided into 14 major subject areas:

Animals & Plants
Art & Design
History
Literature & Drama
Medicine & Health
Music & Dance
Peoples & Places

Politics, Law & Economics
Science
Society
Sport
Technology & Computing
Thought & Belief
The World

To help locate exactly what you want, each of these subject areas has been further subdivided into subcategories that are listed on the first page of each main subject area, providing a convenient grouping of the sites you are interested in.

In addition, there is a full index at the back of this book to help you find sites on a specific topic.

This book includes a free CD-ROM – a full electronic index of all the sites listed in this book. They are grouped in exactly the same way as explained above, and offer a hassle-free alternative to typing in the address of the site you want to see. Just find the title of the site you want on the CD-ROM and 'point and click' with your mouse to be taken straight there. The other major advantage of using this CD-ROM to access the sites is that **the links on this CD are updated automatically** by our editors. What this means is that the links on this CD-ROM won't be out of date as soon as a specific site closes or moves. You don't have to do anything to see these updates – the CD-ROM has been designed so that you will be taken automatically to the most up-to-date version of the site we know about. If a site closes down permanently, we will even try to find a suitable replacement, covering the same topic!

The following pages provide information on how to use the **free** CD-ROM, a glossary of common terms (for readers who are new to the Internet), and an explanation of what the World Wide Web is and where it came from.

Your FREE Hutchinson Directory of Web Sites CD-ROM

To use the CD-ROM (attached inside the cover of this book), you must have a CD-ROM or DVD drive, a Windows 9x/2000 compliant Internet browser, and a connection to the Internet (a modem and an Internet Service Provider).

If You Are Using a PC

Put the CD-ROM in the drive. Connect to the Internet using your chosen Internet Service Provider. In the space where you would normally type the address of a Web site, type "d:\start.htm", where d is the letter of your CD-ROM/DVD drive.

If you cannot type in the Web address as described above, you can also start the CD-ROM by clicking on "File" and then "Open" in your browser. Use the "Browse" button and the window in the dialog box to find your CD-ROM/DVD drive, and double click on the file "start.htm" to open it.

If You Are Using a Mac

Open your browser. Place the CD-ROM in the drive and, when it appears, double click on the CD-ROM drive icon on the desktop. When the window opens, click and drag the file "start.htm" onto your browser window.

If you experience problems, please do not hesitate to contact our technical support team on 00 44 (0)1865 246448 or email to: support@helicon.co.uk.

GLOSSARY OF COMMON INTERNET TERMS

ActiveX Microsoft's umbrella name for a collection of technologies used to create applications that run on the World Wide Web.

applet mini-software application. Examples of applets include Microsoft WordPad, the simple word processor in Windows 95/98 or the single-purpose applications written in Java which in 1996 were beginning to appear on the World Wide Web. These include small animations such as a moving ticker tape of stock prices.

bookmark facility for marking a specific place in electronic documentation, or a specific site, to enable easy return to it. It is used in several types of software, including electronic help files and tutorials. Bookmarks are especially important on the World Wide Web, where it can be difficult to remember a uniform resource locator (URL) in order to return to it. Most Web browsers therefore have built-in bookmark facilities, whereby the browser stores the URL with the page name attached. To return directly to the site, the user picks the page name from the list of saved bookmarks.

browser or **Web browser** software that allows access to the World Wide Web.

cookie on the World Wide Web, a short piece of text that a Web site stores in a cookies folder or a cookie.txt file on the user's computer, either for tracking or configuration purposes, for example, to improve the targeting of banner advertisements. Cookies can also store user preferences and passwords. The cookie is sent back to the server when the browser requests a new page. Cookies are derived from 'magic cookies', the identification tokens used by some UNIX systems.

cyberspace the imaginary, interactive 'worlds' created by networked computers; often used interchangeably with 'virtual world'. The invention of the word 'cyberspace' is generally credited to US science-fiction writer William Gibson (b. 1948) and his first novel *Neuromancer* (1984).

domain on the Internet, segment of an address that specifies an organization, its type, or its country of origin. Domain names are read backwards, starting at the end. All countries except the USA use a final two-letter code such as ca for Canada and uk for the UK. US addresses end in one of seven 'top-level' domains, which specify the type of organization: com (commercial), mil (military), org (usually a nonprofit-making organization), and so on.

download to retrieve a file from another computer via a network. All Web pages have to be **downloaded** before they can be viewed and larger software applications may also be transferred in this manner.

electronic mail or **e-mail**, messages sent electronically from computer to computer via network connections such as Ethernet or the Internet, or via telephone lines to a host system. Messages once sent are stored on the network or by the host system until the recipient picks them up. As well as text, messages may contain enclosed text files, artwork, or multimedia clips.

e-zine contraction of **electronic magazine** periodical sent by e-mail. E-zines can be produced very cheaply, as there are no production costs for design and layout, and minimal costs for distribution. Like printed magazines, e-zines typically have multiple contributors and an editor responsible for selecting content.

FAQ abbreviation for **frequently asked questions** file of answers to commonly asked questions on any topic. First used on USENET, where regular contributors, or 'posters', to newsgroups got tired of answering the same questions over and over and wrote these information files to end the repetition.

GIF acronym for **Graphics Interchange Format**, popular and economical picture file format developed by CompuServe. GIF (pronounced with a hard 'g') is one of the two most commonly used file formats for pictures on the World Wide Web (the other is JPEG) because pictures saved in this format take up a relatively small amount of space. The term is often used simply to mean 'picture'.

home page opening page on a particular site on the World Wide Web. The term is also used for the page which loads automatically when a user opens a Web browser, and for a user's own personal Web pages.

HTML abbreviation for **Hypertext Markup Language**, standard for structuring and describing a document on the World Wide Web. The HTML standard provides labels for constituent parts of a document (for example headings and paragraphs) and permits the inclusion of images, sounds, and 'hyperlinks' to other documents. A browser program is then used to convert this information into a graphical document on-screen. The specifications for HTML version 4, called Dynamic HTML, were adopted at the end of 1997.

HTTP abbreviation for **Hypertext Transfer Protocol**, in computing, the protocol used for communications between client (the Web browser) and server on the World Wide Web.

hypertext system for viewing information (both text and pictures) on a computer screen in such a way that related items of information can easily be reached. For example, the program might display a map of a country; if the user clicks (with a mouse) on a particular city, the program will display information about that city. A single example of **hypertext** is known as a **hyperlink**.

information superhighway popular collective name for the Internet and other related large-scale computer networks. The term was first used in 1993 by US vice president Al Gore in a speech outlining plans to build a high-speed national data communications network.

Internet Service Provider (ISP), any company that sells dial-up access to the Internet. Several types of company provide Internet access, including online information services such as CompuServe and America Online (AOL), electronic conferencing systems such as the WELL and Compulink Information eXchange, and local bulletin board systems (BBSs). More recently founded ISPs, such as Demon Internet and PIPEX, offer only direct access to the Internet without the burden of running services of their own just for their members.

JavaScript a scripting language commonly used to add interactive elements to Web pages. JavaScript was developed by Netscape Communications as LiveScript (it was not derived from Java) and has been standardized by ECMA as ECMAScript.

JPEG abbreviation for **Joint Photographic Experts Group**, used to describe a compression standard set up by that group and now widely accepted for the storage and transmission of colour images. The JPEG compression standard reduces the size of image files considerably.

MIDI manufacturer's standard allowing different pieces of digital music equipment used in composing and recording to be freely connected.

netiquette derived from **Internet etiquette**, behaviour guidelines evolved by users of the Internet. The rules of netiquette include: no messages typed in upper case (considered to be the equivalent of shouting); new users, or new members of a newsgroup, should read the frequently asked questions (FAQ) file before asking a question; no advertising via USENET newsgroups.

Netscape US software company that supplies Navigator, a World Wide Web browser, which is usually referred to as Netscape. Netscape Communications was founded in 1994 as Mosaic Communications, and called its browser Netscape. The names were changed in deference to the University of Illinois, where the Mosaic browser was written.

network a method of connecting computers so that they can share data and peripheral devices, such as printers. The main types are classified by the pattern of the connections – star or ring network, for example – or by the degree of geographical spread allowed; for example, local area networks (LANs) for communication within a room or building, and wide area networks (WANs) for more remote systems. The Internet is made up from many interconnected networks around the world.

online connected, so that data can be transferred, for example, to a printer or from a network like the Internet. The opposite of offline.

plug-in small add-on file which enhances the operation of an application program, often by enabling it to launch, display, or interpret a file created using another one. The first plug-ins were made for graphics programs in the 1980s, but the practice became very popular in the mid-1990s, when a range of plug-ins became available to enhance the multimedia capabilities of Netscape's Navigator browser. Plug-ins are often created and distributed by independent developers rather than the manufacturer of the program they extend.

RealAudio software system for broadcasting sound over the Internet in real time. Broadcasters use an encoder and a special server to provide content, and members of the 'audience' can listen to live radio or create a customized news broadcast which they can download whenever they wish. RealAudio software is supplied by RealNetworks Inc (formerly called Progressive Networks). Its RealPlayer software plays RealAudio and RealVideo.

search engine remotely accessible program to help users find information on the Internet. Commercial search engines such as AltaVista and Lycos comprise databases of documents, URLs, USENET articles, and more, which can be searched by keying in a key word or phrase. The databases are compiled by a mixture of automated agents (spiders) and webmasters registering their sites.

Shockwave application that enables interactive and multimedia features, such as movies, sounds, and animations, to be embedded in Web pages. Unlike Java, which achieves these effects by using a special programming language, Shockwave allows developers to add items created with conventional authoring tools such as Director or Freehand.

thumbnail a small version of a larger image used for reference. Web sites containing many images often initially present them as thumbnails, in order to save download time. Users may then select and view only the images they want at full size.

URL abbreviation for **Uniform Resource Locator**, series of letters and/or numbers specifying the location of a document on the World Wide Web. Every URL consists of a domain name, a description of the document's location within the host computer and the name of the document itself, separated by full stops and backslashes. The complexity of URLs explains why bookmarks and links, which save the user from the chore of typing them in, are so popular.

USENET contraction of **users' network**, the world's largest bulletin board system, which brings together people with common interests to exchange views and information. It consists of e-mail messages and articles organized into newsgroups. USENET is uncensored and governed by the rules of netiquette.

WAV abbreviation of **Windows WAVeform** audio file format for IBM-compatible PCs, widely used to distribute sounds over the Internet. WAV files, which contain a digitized recording of a sound, bear the suffix .wav.

Webcam any camera connected to the Internet, usually for the purpose of displaying an image on a Web page. Webcams are trained on a wide range of famous sights such as London's Tower Bridge. They have also been placed inside birds' nesting boxes, refrigerators, strip clubs, and bedrooms.

What is the Internet?

The Internet is a global computer network connecting governments, companies, universities, and many other networks and users.

Electronic mail, electronic conferencing, educational, and chat services are all supported across the network, as is the ability to access remote computers and send and retrieve files. For most people this is what is meant by both the 'Internet', the 'World Wide Web', and the 'Web'. It is estimated that there over 150 million Internet users around the world.

The technical underpinnings of the Internet were developed as a project funded by the US Defense Advanced Research Project Agency (DARPA) to research how to build a network that would withstand military attack. The Internet itself began in the mid-1980s with funding from the US National Science Foundation as a means to allow US universities to share the resources of four regional supercomputing centres. The number of users grew quickly, and in the early 1990s access became cheap enough for domestic users to have their own links on home personal computers. As the amount of information available via the Internet grew, indexing and search services such as Gopher, Archie, Veronica, and WAIS were created by Internet users to help both themselves and others.

Since that time, there has been a rapid growth of venture capital invested in companies involved in Internet operations. This totalled $309.1 million in the first quarter of 1997, compared with $7.6 million in the first quarter of 1995 and $148.7 million for the same period of 1996.

How Do I See what is on the Internet?

Browsers are software programs used to access the Internet and to search for and view data. Netscape Navigator/Communicator and Microsoft's Internet Explorer are the leading Web browsers. They usually do not permit the user to edit data, but are sometimes able to convert data from one file format to another.

Browsers act as a graphical interface to information available on the Internet – they read HTML (hypertext markup language) documents and display them as graphical documents which may include images, video, sound, and hypertext links to other documents.

Web pages may also contain dynamic objects and Java applets for enhanced animation, video, sound, and interactivity.

What is a Web Page?

World Wide Web documents ('Web pages') are text files coded using HTML to include text and graphics, and are stored on a Web server connected to the Internet. The Web server can be any computer, from the simplest Apple Macintosh to the largest mainframe, as long as Web server software is available.

Every Web page has a URL (Uniform Resource Locator)–a unique address (usually starting with http://www) which tells a browser program where to find it. An important feature of the World Wide Web is that most documents that contain links enabling readers to follow whatever aspects of a subject interest them most. These links may connect to different computers all over the world. Interlinked or nested Web pages belonging to a single organization or individual are known collectively as a 'Web site'.

The original World Wide Web program was created in 1990 for internal use at CERN, the Geneva-based physics research centre, by Tim Berners-Lee and Robert Cailliau. The system was released on the Internet in 1991, but only caught on in a major way in 1993, following the release of Mosaic, an easy-to-use PC-compatible browser. The exponential growth of the Internet since then has been widely attributed to the popularity of the Web. From the 600-odd Web servers in existence in December 1993, the number grew to around 2,000,000 by the end of 1997 and this growth continues..

ANIMALS & PLANTS

Amphibians & Reptiles

Aldabra Tortoise

http://www.seaworld.org/animal_bytes/aldabra_tortoiseab.html

Illustrated guide to the aldabra tortoise including information about genus, size, life span, habitat, gestation, diet, and a series of fun facts.

F A C T

AXOLOTL (Aztec 'water monster'), aquatic larval form ('tadpole') of the Mexican salamander *Ambystoma mexicanum*, belonging to the family Ambystomatidae. Axolotls may be up to 30 cm/12 in long. They are remarkable because they can breed without changing to the adult form, and will metamorphose into adults only in response to the drying-up of their ponds.

All About Axolotls

http://w3.one.net/~inky/axolotls.html

Personal home page devoted to axolotls. Provides photos, answers to frequently asked questions, a guide to keeping axolotls as pets, and suggestions for further reading in books and on the Web.

American Alligator

http://www.seaworld.org/animal_bytes/alligatorab.html

Illustrated guide to the American alligator including information about genus, size, life span, habitat, gestation, diet, and a series of fun facts.

Caecilians Web Site

http://www.peagreenboat.com/eels/

Many facts about these legless amphibians, especially *Typhlonectes Natans*, an aquatic caecilian often found in aquariums in the USA. Tips on care, health, and breeding can also be found at this site.

Cane Toad

http://share.jcu.edu.au/dept/PHTM/staff/rsbufo.htm

Profile of the world's largest toad, its unwise introduction to Australia, and the damage it has wrought. There's a photo of a cane toad, another of the massive number of eggs it can produce, and a complete bibliography of books and articles written about *Bufo marinus*.

Dr Seward's Gila Monster Web Page

http://www.drseward.com/

Comprehensive guide to *Heloderma suspectum*. The well-arranged contents include a description of the two subspecies, information on habit, behaviour, diet, reproduction in the wild, and the challenges of captive breeding. There are many pictures of gilas.

Frilled Lizard

http://werple.net.au/~areadman/liz.htm

Detailed pages about this Australian lizard. There are descriptions of the reptile's colouring, eating habits, and defence strategies, all accompanied by photos.

Frogland

http://allaboutfrogs.org/

Enthusiastic and informative personal home page devoted to frogs. Provides pictures, a guide to frogs around the world, tips on keeping frogs as pets, jokes, and a colouring book.

Frogs and Toads

http://www.wildlifetrust.org.uk/london/frogs/frogs.html

Information about frogs and toads from the London Wildlife Trust. This online leaflet, accompanied by colour diagrams, explains the difference between the two amphibians and discusses how best to conserve their populations.

Gavial

http://www.sdcs.k12.ca.us/roosevelt/
gavialhome.html

Well-presented information about the gavial. Intended to educate children about this harmless reptile, the site has information on habitat, diet, interaction with humans, and reproduction.

King Cobra

http://www.nationalgeographic.com/features/97/
kingcobra/index-n.html

Cleverly presented National Geographic guide to the king cobra. The behaviour of this ferocious predator is explained by clicking on various parts of a cobra's body entwined through the site. There are a number of stunning photographs.

Rat Snake

http://www.seaworld.org/animal_bytes/
rat_snakeab.html

Illustrated guide to the rat snake including information about genus, size, life span, habitat, gestation, diet, and a series of fun facts.

Seaworld

http://www.seaworld.org

Large Web site containing illustrated information about a variety of creatures. Topics covered for each creature include lifespan, diet, habit and breeding, as well as fun facts.

Somewhat Amusing World of Frogs

http://www.csu.edu.au/faculty/commerce/account/
frogs/frog.htm

Fascinating facts about frogs – did you know, for example, that most frogs will drown eventually if denied access to land?

South American Ornate Horned Frog

http://www.seaworld.org/animal_bytes/frogab.html

Illustrated guide to the South American ornate horned frog. This page gives an insight into the life of this eye-catching amphibian; where and how long it lives, how it breeds and what it eats.

Tappaboy Newt Page

http://www.ultranet.com/~vail/newt/index.html

Everything one could wish to know about these small salamanders can be found here. Contents include still and video footage of newts, newt art, the chance to chat with other newt addicts, practical tips on looking after them, and links to other newt sites.

Whole Frog Project

http://george.lbl.gov/ITG.hm.pg.docs/Whole.Frog/
Whole.Frog.html

US project that provides school students with a three-dimensional imaging tool as an alternative to dissection.

Birds

Answers to Frequently Asked Questions About Lories and Lorikeets

http://students.washington.edu/~nyneve/
loryFAQ.html

Wide-ranging information on lories and lorikeets. Contents include a description of various breeds, their habitat, and efforts to conserve them. This page contains comprehensive advice on their housing and dietary requirements and photos of the most popular breeds. There is also a bibliography of books about these parrots and a list of addresses of lori and parakeet clubs around the world.

Bald Eagle

http://www.seaworld.org/animal_bytes/
bald_eagleab.html

This illustrated guide to the bald eagle covers such topics as genus, size, life span, habitat, gestation, diet, and a series of fun facts.

Bird On!

http://birdcare.com/birdon/welcome_text.html

News and features on the wild birds of Britain and Europe. The site is run by two self-confessed bird enthusiasts and includes information on caring for birds, as well as an extensive library of pictures and photographs.

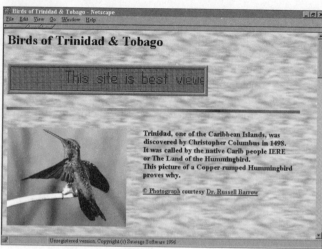

green parrot and tales of the exploits of these alert and opportunistic birds.

Fabulous Kakapo

http://www.kakapo.net/en/index.html

Interesting profile of the solitary flightless parrot, which may live for 60 years, but is now on the verge of extinction. The reasons for the drastic decline in the bird's numbers are explained, together with information on conservation efforts on predator-free islands. The site is frequently updated with news of the fight for survival of this sturdy, but defenceless, bird.

Birds of Trinidad & Tobago

http://www.interlog.com/~barrow/

Selection of tropical bird images from Dr Russell Barrow's collection are posted here. Although the site doesn't contain a great deal in the way of in-depth ornithological information, the pictures are excellent.

California Condor

http://www.fws.gov/r9extaff/biologues/
bio_cond.html

Vital information about the perilous state of the estimated 30 surviving Californian condors. This page offers short descriptions of their physical appearance, eating preferences, reasons for their decline, and scientific attempts to boost the production of the species. It's an important page for all those concerned about the dangers looming over wildlife nowadays.

Canary FAQ

http://www2.upatsix.com/faq/canary.htm

Answers to frequently asked questions about canaries provide a wealth of information on all breeds of these caged birds. Every conceivable aspect of caring for canaries is covered and there are useful links to other canary sites.

Encounters with Mr Kea

http://www.kiwihome.co.nz/magazine/
NZGeographic/Encounters_with_Kea.html

Informative, well-written article on the kea and its troubled relationship with humans. There are many pictures of New Zealand's mischievous

FinchWorld

http://www.finchworld.com/

Huge source of information on finches. Contents include practical advice for those buying a finch for the first time, tips on diet, housing, recreation activities, and avian illnesses. There are links to finch sites around the world and news of ornithological research on these songbirds.

Hummingbirds!

http://www.hummingbirds.net/

Comprehensive source of information on this family of brightly coloured birds. There are good descriptions of natural behaviour, details of migration patterns, a large number of photographs, and latest research findings. The site also offers anecdotes about the bird and links to hummingbird societies.

Journey North

http://www.learner.org/jnorth/

US-based educational site for junior school children on the topic of wildlife migration. As well as the major ongoing project to track the southward migration of Monarch butterflies, there are projects on building garden areas to help migrating animals and the migration stories of a variety of species.

Large Macaw FAQ

http://www2.upatsix.com/faq/lgmacaw.htm

Comprehensive answers to frequently asked questions about the large macaw. There is advice on the housing, dietary, and recreational requirements of these large and demanding birds. The breeds most commonly kept as pets are described, together with information on those listed as endangered species.

Lovebird FAQ

http://www2.upatsix.com/faq/lvbrdfaq.htm

Guide to lovebirds and how to keep and breed them. There are descriptions of the nine breeds of lovebirds and comprehensive advice on diet, housing, and training. This sight also contains a bibliography of recommended books on lovebirds.

Northern Oriole

http://district.gresham.k12.or.us/ghs/nature/ animal/bird/black/noriole.htm

Introduction to the Northern oriole, with information about its physical characteristics and its distribution. There is a link to details about similar species. The page is illustrated with colour photographs.

Parrot

http://www.seaworld.org/animal_bytes/ parrotsab.html

Illustrated guide to the parrot including information about genus, size, life span, habitat, gestation, diet, and a series of fun facts.

Penguin Page

http://www.vni.net/~kwelch/penguins/

Lots of information about penguins – the different species, their behaviour, reproduction, 'Relatives and friends', predators, and fossils.

Poultry Breeds

http://www.ansi.okstate.edu/poultry/

Masses of information on poultry breeds from all over the world, offered by the Department of Animal Science of Oklahoma State University. It includes photos and elaborate descriptions of about a hundred different species of chickens, ducks, geese, turkeys, and other poultry. Other experts on ornithology are invited to contribute textual and visual material.

Rissa Tridactyla (Black Kittiwake)

http://www.oit.itd.umich.edu/bio/doc.cgi/ . Chordata/Aves/Charadriiformes/Laridae/ Rissa_tridactyla.ftl

Good source of information on the black-legged kittiwake. The contents include the bird's geographic range, physical characteristics, behaviour, and economic benefits for humans. Images of the gulls may also be accessed.

Royal Society for the Protection of Birds

http://www.rspb.co.uk/

Europe's largest wildlife conservation charity provides online news and local contact details, as well as a vast amount of information on birds and bird-watching in the UK, with descriptions, sketches and photographs of every common UK birds. The site also holds information on how to join the society, and lists the society's sites and activities around the country.

Secretary Bird

http://www.phillyzoo.org/pz0055.htm

Information about the secretary bird, with concise descriptions of its African habitat, physical characteristics, reproduction, social habits, diet, and conservation status. The page is illustrated with a colour photograph of the bird.

Southern Cassowary

http://www.wildlife-australia.com/cass.html

Good profile of this large flightless ratite. Three species of cassowary are described, but the site concentrates on the southern cassowary: its physical characteristics, diet, and breeding behaviour. The reasons for the decline in cassowary numbers as humans encroach on its habitat are clearly set out.

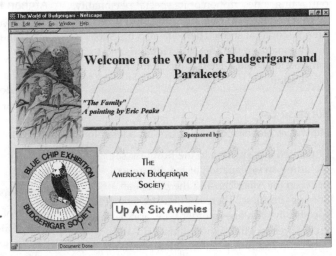

see p 6

Welcome to the World of Budgerigars and Parakeets

http://www2.upatsix.com/abs/

Huge source of information from the American Budgerigar Society. There is comprehensive advice on how to look after and exhibit the world's favourite pet bird. All manner of avian illnesses and their treatment are discussed. There are links to other specialist budgie sites.

F A C T

BURMESE CAT

breed of domestic shorthaired cat of ancient origin. The modern breed is descended from a cat introduced into the USA in 1930 from Burma and crossed with a Siamese. The original Burmese has a sable brown coat with lighter shading on the underside; the medium-length body is muscular and more rounded than a Siamese.

Cats

Abyssinian Cat

http://www.tdl.com/~pattic/abyfaq/

Lots of information about the popular and attractive domestic Abyssinian cat. This illustrated site includes a detailed description of the breed, its characteristics and temperament, its history, health issues, and advice about whether the Abyssinian is the right cat for you. There is also a link to Abyssinian breeders on the Web.

Bengal Cat

http://www.bengalcat.co.uk/pet/beginners/index.htm

Lots of information about this very attractive new breed of domestic cat. The beginner's introduction describes the origins of the breed and its appearance. Click on the home button to access pages about the Bengal's wild ancestor, the Asian leopard cat, pictures of the Bengal's different patterning, a description of its special personality, as well as advice on care, breeding, and how to prepare for a cat show. There are also links to developments in the USA and Holland, and to information about UK breeding standards and registration.

Burmese Cat

http://www.breedlist.com/burmese-breeders.html

Illustrated introduction to the Burmese cat, including an explanation of the differences between the American and the European, or Foreign, Burmese. There are links to sites dealing specifically with one or other type, and to pages giving breeders throughout the world and American and European breeding standards.

CFA Breed Profile: Manx

http://www.cfainc.org/breeds/profiles/manx.html

Page about the tailless Manx cat, created by the Cat Fanciers Association, USA. There is information about the cat's origins, requirements for showing at competitions, appearance, and personality. The site is illustrated with colour photographs of differently marked Manx cats.

CFA Breed Profile: Persian

http://www.cfainc.org/breeds/profiles/persian.html

Page about this popular long-haired cat, created by the Cat Fanciers Association, USA. There is information about the cat's origins, requirements for showing at competitions, appearance, and personality. The site includes links to colour photographs and articles about the seven colour divisions that are recognized at competitions.

Dogs

Afghan Hound Club of America

http://www.akc.org/breeds/recbreeds/afghanhd.cfm

Profile of the Afghan from the American Kennel Club. There is a history of the breed, a description of the ideal breed standard, a note on the dog's temperament, and some quirky facts about Afghans. There is also a high resolution photo of this silky aristocrat.

Akita

http://www.akitaclub.org/

Profile of the Akita from the American Kennel Club. This site contains a history of the breed, a description of the ideal breed standard, advice on the dog's temperament, and some quirky facts about the breed. There is also a high-resolution photo of this large and powerful dog.

American Kennel Club

http://www.akc.org

Large Website containing information on purebred breeds of dog. The site includes a history of each breed, a description of the ideal breed standard, a note on the dog's temperament, and fun facts about the breed. There is usually also a photograph of each breed, and links to clubs connected with the breed and to other related Web sites.

American Bloodhound Club

http://www.bloodhounds.org/

Source of information containing details of the origins of the breed, breed standards, and shows. There are also a large number of photos and links to other bloodhound sites.

American Boxer Club

http://clubs.akc.org/abc/abc-home.htm

Best of many boxer sites. Contents include the history of the breed, the breed standard, veterinary advice, tips for owners, and news of boxer shows. There are extensive links to other boxer sites and a comprehensive bibliography.

American Pointer Club

http://www.akc.org/breeds/recbreeds/pointer.cfm

Profile of the pointer from the American Kennel Club. As well as a history of the breed, a description of the ideal breed standard, and information on the dog's temperament, the site contains fun facts about pointers. Also included is a high-resolution photo of this alert hunting dog.

American Pomeranian Club

http://www.prodogs.com/brn/apc/index.htm

Filled with information about the history of the breed, the breed standard, shows, veterinary advice, and many tips for owners. There is a listing of other Pomeranian sites across the world and information about the bi-monthly *Pomeranian Review*.

American Rottweiler Club

http://www.amrottclub.org/

Information about the history of the breed, the breed standard, shows, veterinary advice, and grooming. The many tips for owners include advice on what to do if your Rottweiler bites someone. There is also a comprehensive listing of other Rottweiler sites across the world and a useful bibliography.

American Shetland Sheepdog Association

http://www.akc.org/breeds/recbreeds/
shetshee.cfm

Profile of the Shetland from the American Kennel Club. There is a history of the breed, description of the ideal breed standard, a note on the dog's temperament, and some interesting facts about the breed. There is also a high-resolution photo of this long-haired working dog.

American Shih Tzu Club

http://clubs.akc.org/astc/index.html

Filled with information about the history of the breed, the breed standard, shows, veterinary advice, grooming and a host of tips for owners. There is a bibliography and links to other shih tzu sites. There is even a Chinese song.

Basset Hound Club of America

http://www.akc.org/breeds/recbreeds/basset.cfm

Profile of the basset hound from the American Kennel Club. There is a history of the breed, description of the ideal breed standard, a note on the dog's temperament, and some quirky facts about bassets. There is also a high-resolution photo of this short-legged dog.

Beagle

http://www.akc.org/breeds/recbreeds/beagle.cfm

Profile of the beagle from the American Kennel Club. A history of the breed, a description of the ideal breed standard, useful notes on the beagle temperament, as well as some quirky facts about beagles, are highlights. There is also a high-resolution photo of this tenacious hunter.

Bulldog

http://www.akc.org/breeds/recbreeds/bulld.cfm

The American Kennel Club's bulldog profile. As well as describing the breed standard and

BULLDOG

British breed of dog of ancient but uncertain origin, formerly bred for bull-baiting. The head is broad and square, with deeply wrinkled cheeks, small folded ears, very short muzzle, and massive jaws, the peculiar set of the lower jaw making it difficult for the dog to release its grip.

outlining its history, this site contains fascinating (and fun) bulldog facts and photos. It also provides advice to owners on cleaning facial wrinkles every day.

Cavalier King Charles Spaniel

http://www.akc.org/breeds/recbreeds/ckcs.cfm

History of the breed, description of the ideal breed standard, a note on the dog's temperament, and some interesting facts about the King Charles spaniel. There is also a high resolution photo of some of these graceful toy gundogs.

Chihuahua

http://www.akc.org/breeds/recbreeds/chihua.cfm

Profile of the Chihuahua from the American Kennel Club. There is a history of the breed, description of the ideal breed standard, a note on the dog's temperament, and some interesting facts about the breed. There is also a high-resolution photo of the diminutive dog.

Chow Chow Club

http://www.chowclub.org/

All there is to know about chow chows. The site is filled with information about the history of the breed, the breed standard, US chow shows, veterinary advice, and many tips for owners. There is a useful bibliography and information on subscribing to *Chow Life*.

Cocker Spaniel

http://www.akc.org/breeds/recbreeds/cockersp.cfm

Profile of the cocker spaniel from the American Kennel Club. There is a history of the breed, description of the ideal breed standard, a note on

the dog's temperament, and some quirky facts about cockers. There is also a high resolution photo of this smallest of sporting dogs.

Collie

http://www.akc.org/breeds/recbreeds/collie.cfm

Profile of the collie from the American Kennel Club. There is a history of the breed, description of the ideal breed standard, a note on the dog's temperament, and some interesting facts about collies. There is also a high resolution photo of this lithe and active dog.

COLLIE

any of several breeds of sheepdog originally bred in Britain. They include the border collie, the bearded collie, and the rough collie and its smooth-haired counterpart.

Dachshund Club

http://www.k9netuk.com/breed/dachclub.html

All you could possibly want to know about dachshunds from the longest-established dachshund club in the world. In addition to the history of the breed, breed specifications, and advice to owners, there is updated information on shows and other events for dachshund owners in Britain. There are also many dachshund pictures.

Dalmatian Club of America

http://www.cet.com/~bholland/dca/

Information about the history of the breed, the breed standard, shows, veterinary advice, and many tips for owners. There is a comprehensive listing of other Dalmatian sites and a useful bibliography. This well-organized site even has a search engine.

Dobermann Pinscher

http://www.akc.org/breeds/recbreeds/dobpinr.cfm

Profile of the Dobermann from the American Kennel Club. There is a history of the breed, description of the ideal breed standard, a note on the dog's temperament, and some surprising facts about Dobermanns. There is also a high-resolution photo of this compact and muscular dog.

Dog Lovers Page

http://www.petnet.com.au/dogs/
dogbreedindex.html

Information on breeds, ranging from the world's smallest breed (the Chihuahua) to the tallest (the Irish wolfhound). This Australian-based site includes photographs and details of over 100 breeds of dog.

English Foxhound

http://www.akc.org/breeds/recbreeds/engfox.cfm

Profile of the foxhound from the American Kennel Club. There is a history of the breed, a description of the qualities demanded by Masters of Foxhounds, a note on the dog's temperament, and some quirky facts about foxhounds. There is also a high-resolution photo of this tenacious hunter.

English Springer Spaniel

http://www.akc.org/breeds/recbreeds/
engsprsp.cfm

The English springer spaniel is the subject of this page from the American Kennel Club. It contains a history of the breed, description of the ideal breed standard, a note on the springer temperament, and some quirky facts about springers. There is also a high-resolution photo of this sturdy sporting dog.

German Shepherd Dog

http://www.akc.org/breeds/recbreeds/
germshep.cfm

Everything there is to know about Alsatians, from the American Kennel Club. There is a history of the breed, agreed breed standards, and some photos. There are links to other German shepherd sites.

Great Dane Club of America

http://www.users.cts.com/king/g/gdca/

Information about the history of the breed, the breed standard, shows, veterinary advice, and many tips for owners. There is a comprehensive listing of other Great Dane sites across the world.

It is slow to load, but there is also a section with Great Danes to watch running across the screen to a musical accompaniment.

Harrier Club of America

http://www.ridgecrest.ca.us/~auborn/harriers/
HCA.html

Details of the origins of the breed, breed standards, and shows. There are a large number of photos, a full bibliography, and links to other harrier sites. Information on the dog is accessed by clicking on the harrier at the bottom of the home page.

Irish Setter

http://www.akc.org/breeds/recbreeds/irishset.cfm

Profile of the best-known breed of setter from the American Kennel Club. There is a history of the breed, description of the ideal breed standard, a note on the dog's temperament, and some quirky facts about Irish setters. There is also a high resolution photo of this aristocratic dog.

Irish Water Spaniel

http://www.akc.org/breeds/recbreeds/irishwas.cfm

Profile of the Irish water spaniel from the American Kennel Club. There is a history of the breed, description of the ideal breed standard, a note on the dog's temperament, and some quirky facts about the breed. There is also a high resolution photo of this strongly built sporting dog.

Irish Wolfhound

http://www.akc.org/breeds/recbreeds/irshwfhd.cfm

The American Kennel Club's profile of the Irish wolfhound. There is a history of the breed, description of the breed standard, a note on the dog's temperament, and some quirky facts about wolfhounds. There is also a high-resolution photo of this awesome hound.

Jack Russell

http://www.akc.org/breeds/recbreeds/jrt.cfm

This American Kennel Club profile of the Jack Russell presents a history, breed standard and photos of this determined terrier among terriers. Fun Jack Russell facts and photos are other features.

Komondor

http://www.akc.org/breeds/recbreeds/
komdor.cfm

Profile of komondors from the American Kennel Club. There is a history of the breed, description of the ideal breed standard, a note on the dog's temperament, and some interesting facts about komondors. There is also a high-resolution photo of this imposing dog.

Labrador Retriever Club

http://thelabradorclub.com/

Information about the history of the breed, the breed standard, shows, veterinary advice, and many tips for owners. There is a listing of other Labrador sites across the world and many photos. The home page, however, is not particularly user-friendly. You need to click on 'Library' to access general information on Labradors rather than club affairs.

Mastiff

http://www.akc.org/breeds/recbreeds/mastif.cfm

Profile of the mastiff from the American Kennel Club. There is a history of the breed, a description of the ideal breed standard, a note on the dog's temperament, and some interesting facts about mastiffs. There is also a high-resolution photo of this massive working dog.

Newfoundland

http://www.akc.org/breeds/recbreeds/newfdld.cfm

Profile of Newfoundlands from the American Kennel Club. The site contains a history of the breed, description of the ideal breed standard, a note on the dog's temperament, and some quirky facts about Newfoundlands. There is also a high-resolution photo.

Official Web Site of the Bichon Frise Club of America

http://members.tripod.com/~BFL/bfca.html

Information about the history of the breed, the breed standard, shows, veterinary advice, and many tips for owners. There is a comprehensive listing of other bichon frise sites across the world and a useful bibliography.

> **F A C T**
>
> **OLD ENGLISH SHEEPDOG**
> breed of herding dog. It is grey or blue-grey, with white on its head, chest, and legs, and is about 62 cm/24 in at the shoulder. Its long, thick, rough hair grows abundantly over its face.

Old English Sheepdog

http://www.akc.org/breeds/recbreeds/
olengshe.cfm

Profile of the Old English sheepdog from the American Kennel Club. There is a history of the breed, description of the ideal breed standard, a note on the dog's temperament, and some quirky facts about the Old English. There is also a high-resolution photo of this loveable dog.

Otterhound Club of America

http://clubs.akc.org/ohca/

A must for otterhound lovers. The site is filled with information about the history of the breed, the breed standard, and tips for owners wanting otterhounds as pets or guard dogs. There is a good bibliography and a comprehensive listing of other otterhound sites across the world.

Papillon

http://www.akc.org/breeds/recbreeds/papp.cfm

Profile of the papillon from the American Kennel Club. As well as a history of the papillon and breed standard, the site contains a note on the dog's temperament, and some quirky facts about papillons. There is also a high-resolution photo of this elegant toy dog.

Pekingese Club of America

http://www.geocities.com/Heartland/3843/

Information about the history of the breed, the breed standard, shows, veterinary advice, and many tips for owners. There is also a comprehensive listing of other Pekingese sites across the world.

Pharaoh Hound

http://www.akc.org/breeds/recbreeds/pharaoh.cfm

Profile of pharaoh hounds from the American

Kennel Club. There is a history of the breed, description of the ideal breed standard, a note on the dog's temperament, and some quirky facts about pharaohs. There is also a high-resolution photo of this graceful hound.

Poodle Club of America

http://www.swdg.com/pca/

Filled with information about the history of the breed, the breed standard, US poodle shows, veterinary advice, and many tips for owners. There is a comprehensive listing of other poodle sites across the world and a useful bibliography.

Pug

http://www.akc.org/breeds/recbreeds/pug.cfm

Profile of the pug from the American Kennel Club. There is a history of the breed, description of the ideal breed standard, a note on the dog's temperament, and some interesting facts about pugs. There is also a high-resolution photo of this long-established breed.

Samoyed Club of America

http://www.samoyed.org/
Samoyed_Club_of_America.html

Information about the history of the breed, the breed standard, shows, veterinary advice, and many tips for owners. There is a comprehensive listing of other samoyed sites across the world.

Scottish Deerhound Club of America.

http://www.deerhound.org/

This site is filled with information about the history of the breed, the breed standard, shows, veterinary advice and many tips for owners. It also lists other Scottish deerhound sites across the world.

Siberian Husky Club of America

http://www.shca.org/

Information about the history of the breed, the breed standard, shows, veterinary advice, and many tips for owners. There is a comprehensive listing of other husky sites across the world and an extensive bibliography.

F A C T

SCHNAUZER

breed of dog originating in Germany and now found in three sizes: miniature, standard, and giant. All have a coarse coat, either all black or pepper and salt in colour, with a strong, square muzzle and bristly hair on the face.

Standard Schnauzer Club of America

http://www.geocities.com/~ssca_club/

A well-designed home page accesses information about the history of the breed, the breed standard, shows, veterinary advice, tips for owners, and a gallery of photos. There is a listing of other schnauzer sites across the world.

St Bernard Club of America Home Page

http://www.akc.org/clubs/saints/

Information about the history of the breed, the breed standard, shows, veterinary advice, and many tips for owners. There are many tales of the dog's heroic deeds and a comprehensive listing of other Saint Bernard sites across the world.

Sussex Spaniel

http://www.akc.org/sussessp.htm

Profile of the Sussex spaniel from the American Kennel Club. There is a history of the breed, description of the ideal breed standard, a note on the dog's temperament, and some quirky facts about the breed. There is also a high-resolution photo of this large field dog.

Terrier Group

http://www.akc.org/terriers.htm

General description of the breeds classified as terriers by the American Kennel Club. There is information on the origins of these feisty and energetic dogs and a complete listing of recognized breeds. Further details of all the breeds are easily accessible.

Tibetan Spaniel Club of America

http://www.tibbies.net/

Filled with information about the history of the breed, the breed standard, shows, veterinary advice, and many tips for owners. There is a comprehensive listing of other Tibetan spaniel sites across the world and a useful bibliography.

Weimaraner Club of America

http://www.geocities.com/~weimclub/

Details of the origins of the breed, breed standards, and shows. There are a large number of photos, Weimaraner stories, details of how to obtain the magazine *Weimaraner Times,* and links to other Weimaraner sites.

Welsh Corgi

http://www.akc.org/breeds/recbreeds/cardiga.cfm

Profile of the Pembroke Welsh corgi from the American Kennel Club. There is a history of the breed, description of the ideal breed standard, a note on the dog's temperament, and some interesting facts about the breed. There is also a high-resolution photo of this small and powerful dog.

Whippets: Born to Run

http://www.sonic.net/~whippet

Everything you always wanted to know about whippets: their relationship to greyhounds, their agility and speed (including a QuickTime movie) and how to rear, care, and race them, together with many links to related sites.

Wonderful World of Border Collies

http://www.bcrescue.org/bc-page.html

The site is filled with information about the history of the breed, the breed standard, shows, veterinary advice, photos and tips for owners. There is a comprehensive listing of other border collie sites across the world and a useful bibliography.

Invertebrates

American Tarantula Society

http://torgo.cnchost.com/ats/

Information on tarantulas, other spiders, and scorpions from the world's largest arachnid society. There are articles on buying, feeding,

looking after, and breeding tarantulas. Tarantula owners exchange experiences and there is a listing of other arachnid sites.

F A C T

ARACHNID (arachnoid)

type of arthropod of the class Arachnida, including spiders, scorpions, ticks, and mites. They differ from insects in possessing only two main body regions, the cephalothorax and the abdomen, and in having eight legs.

Arachnology

http://www.ufsia.ac.be/Arachnology/Arachnology.html

Largely a collection of annotated links, organized under headings such as taxonomy and classification, palaeontology, poison, bites, diseases, pests, and phobia. The site also contains a collection of spider-related myths, stories, poems, songs, and art.

Beetles

http://www.ent.iastate.edu/imagegal/coleoptera/

Colour photographs of numerous beetle species from Iowa State University's Entomology Image Gallery. They include bean beetles, Colorado potato beetles, ladybirds, scarab beetles, and weevils. Click on a link to view each insect and the damage that some of them cause. There is a search engine at the top of the page to look for other species of insect.

B-Eye

http://cvs.anu.edu.au/andy/beye/beyehome.html

Reveals the world through the eyes of a honey bee. Designed by a neuroscientist, this site simulates the optics of a honey bee's eye, pointing out the differences between the way humans and honey bees see patterns. Images can be viewed as fixed patterns or from the vantage point of a bee's hover.

Butterfly Web Site

http://mgfx.com/butterfly/

Useful links page to the world of butterflies, with graphics, articles, and discoveries, as well as information on related topics. As well as a gallery of images and a 'Frequently Asked Questions' page, this site contains sections with educational resources and a 'World watch' of butterfly populations.

Cockroaches

http://www.insect-world.com/main/blatodea.html

General information about the cockroach from its early evolution to the present day. The site includes its life history, information on its relationship with humans, and even how to keep a cockroach as a pet.

Diptera – Flies

http://www.insect-world.com/main/diptera.html

Part of a much larger site on insects, here is an introduction to this important insect order, with sections on flightless flies and all other major groups in this order which contains over 120,000 species.

Flies and Mosquitoes

http://www.ent.iastate.edu/Imagegal/diptera/

Colour photographs of flies and mosquitoes from Iowa State University's Entomology Image Gallery. They include the crane fly and crane fly larva, and several dozen images of different species of mosquito and mosquito parts. Click on a link to view each insect. There is a search engine at the top of the page to look for other species of insect.

Global Entomology Agricultural Research Server

http://198.22.133.109/

Site dedicated to entomology, with the emphasis on bees. Features include the 'Internet classroom' where common questions such as 'Why do bees swarm?' are clearly answered; a selection of recent research papers on the subject; a gallery of images and sounds; and even a collection of entomological computer programs to download.

Hawk Moths of Gibraltar Point

http://www.lincstrust.co.uk/species/ hawkmoths/hawkmoths.html

Good source of information on the species of hawk moth found in Britain.

There are high-resolution images of each species and information on behaviour and breeding patterns observed at a Lincolnshire nature reserve.

Insecta

http://www.insecta.com/

Beautiful illustrations accompany this site which contains information about insects, drawn from the Spencer Entomological Museum at the University of British Colombia, Canada. There is a 'Bug of the Month' feature and a glossary of entomological terms, and the designers hope to cover more areas soon.

Introduction to Insect Anatomy

http://www.insect-world.com/main/anatomy.html

Wealth of colourful facts and illustrations about the anatomy of the insect world. The page is divided into various sections giving detailed information about the basic similarities and differences between various insects. The page begins with an explanation of the main insect body parts – head, thorax, and abdomen – and is illustrated with a useful diagram of a grasshopper.

Louse

http://www.ent.iastate.edu/Imagegal/phthiraptera/

Colour photographs of lice from Iowa State University's Entomology Image Gallery. These include pictures of body, cattle, crab or pubic, and hog lice. Click on a link to view each louse. There is a search engine at the top of the page to look for other species of insect.

Mosquito Bytes

http://whyfiles.news.wisc.edu/016skeeter/ index.html

Part of the Why Files project, published by the National Institute for Science Education (NISE)

F
A
C
T

MOSQUITO

any of a group of flies in which the female has needlelike mouthparts and sucks blood before laying eggs. The males feed on plant juices. Some mosquitoes carry diseases such as malaria. (Family Culicidae, order Diptera.)

and funded by the National Science Foundation, this page provides extensive information about mosquitoes, the diseases they carry, and ways to protect yourself from these tiny bugs that carry a big bite. The highly readable text, laid out over 14 pages, includes information on malaria and why, these days, it's more dangerous than ever. Numerous images and diagrams enhance the text throughout. The more tricky terms are linked to a glossary, and you will find a comprehensive bibliography of sources for further research.

Praying Mantids

http://www.insect-world.com/main/mantids.html

Lots of information on the care of the carnivorous praying mantids (or mantis), with tips on housing, breeding, and suitable species. This illustrated page is part of the Bug Club site and includes links to other bug pets, newsletter, penpals, and books.

Rearing Caterpillars

http://www.ex.ac.uk/bugclub/cater.html

Lots of information about how to rear your caterpillar into a butterfly or moth. There are tips on how to obtain them, housing, feeding, pupation, and emergence. This illustrated page is part of the Bug Club site and includes links to other bug pets, newsletter, penpals, and books.

Weird and Wonderful World of Woodlice

http://www.dryad.demon.co.uk/julies/woodlice.htm

Comprehensive and entertaining guide to woodlice. Information is provided on its history, predators, physiology, reproduction, behaviour, and colour variations. There is a recommended reading list, and there are even tips on keeping them as pets.

Welcome to the Scorpion Emporium

http://wrbu.si.edu/www/stockwell/emporium/emporium.html

Complete source of information on the nippy creepy crawlies. There is an interesting list of frequently asked questions about scorpions. A gallery of photos aids identification of a particular species. There is also advice on looking after scorpions and even what to do if they turn on you.

Worm World

http://www.nj.com/yucky/worm/

Lively guide for children, with information on topics such as worms' bodies, how to make a worm bin, and different types of worm, plus an art gallery and some worm jokes.

Mammals

Aardvark

http://www.oit.itd.umich.edu/bio108/Chordata/Mammalia/Tubulidentata.shtml

Detailed description of this strange-looking, insectivorous mammal. There is information about the aardvark's skeletal and dental structure, and links to explain unfamiliar terms.

Adam's Fox Box III

http://www.foxbox.org/

Beautifully designed site providing an impressive amount of information about foxes: articles, songs, stories, poems, images, and a video clip. The site also provides many pointers to other fox-related sites, including one explaining how to dance the foxtrot!

African Lion

http://www.seaworld.org/animal_bytes/lionab.html

Illustrated guide to the African lion including information about genus, size, life span, habitat, gestation, diet, and a series of fun facts.

Arabian Horse World Wide Guide

http://www.arabianhorseguide.com/

Comprehensive source of information on Arabian horses. A fascinating article traces people's love affair with the breed. There is also a database of US-based breeders and trainers and an 'Arabian Horse Yellow Pages' has links to a large number of commercial and noncommercial Arabian sites around the world.

Asiatic Lion Information Centre

http://wkweb4.cableinet.co.uk/alic/intro.html

General information page about the decline and conservation of the Asiatic subspecies of lion.

Click to find out about the Gir National Park, the lions' last remaining wild habitat, differences between African and Asiatic lions, and methods of conservation. There are also links to a map showing the Asiatic lion's past and present distribution and to a photo gallery.

Australian Koala Page

http://www.aaa.com.au/Koala.shtml

Large source of information on this reclusive marsupial. The behaviour of the animal, its unique physiology, and threats to its habitat are well described. There are also links to a number of koala conservation societies and news of latest koala research.

Badgers.org.uk

http://www.badgers.org.uk/

Complete resource for anyone interested in badgers. There are detailed pages about the conservation of the animals, accompanied by many photos. You can also send a virtual badger postcard, or sign up for your own badger e-mail account.

Bat Conservation International

http://www.batcon.org/

Articles, photographs, and miscellaneous bat trivia, plus sound files of bat echolocation signals. As well as promoting membership of their bat society, this page contains plenty of bat-related information, including US and European species'

lists and tips on photographing these elusive animals.

Bear Den

http://www.nature-net.com/bears/index.html

Invaluable resource for information on all types of bears. As well as general information on the evolution and history of bears in general, there are more specific details on each of the eight species of bear, including habitat, reproduction, food, and much more. The site also has photographs and sound effects.

Bengal Tiger

http://www.seaworld.org/animal_bytes/tigerab.html

Illustrated guide to the Bengal tiger including information about genus, size, life span, habitat, gestation, diet, and a series of fun facts.

Bilby

http://www.anca.gov.au/plants/threaten/information/species/animals/mammals/bilby/bilby.htm

Profile of the rabbit-eared bandicoot. There is a picture of a bilby, a description, details of its habitat, and reasons why it has become an endangered species.

Breeds of Livestock – Horse Breeds

http://www.ansi.okstate.edu/breeds/horses/

Extensive database of horse breeds from all over the world. A typical page offers details on the breed's origin and history, and presents a description of it and a couple of photographs.

Cheetah

http://dialspace.dial.pipex.com/town/plaza/abf90/cheetah.htm

Details about this fast-moving predator. The page contains information about the appearance, breeding habits, and typical height and weight of the animal.

Chimpanzee

http://www.seaworld.org/animal_bytes/chimpanzeeab.html

Illustrated guide to the chimpanzee including information about genus, size, life span, habitat, gestation, diet, and a series of fun facts.

Chipmunk Place

http://www.owca.com/

Extensive guide to the species of ground squirrel. Information available includes facts about chipmunks, their diet and control, and there is also a section on 'Famous Chipmunks'.

Common Marmoset

http://www.club.innet.be/~year1531/

Comprehensive guide to the pleasures and difficulties of keeping a marmoset as a pet. There is information on the dietary, accommodation, recreational, and emotional needs of marmosets. Information on reproduction is enhanced by a picture enabling male and females to be distinguished.

Common Wombat

http://www.tased.edu.au/tot/fauna/wombat.html

Profile of this lumbering herbivorous marsupial, the world's largest burrowing animal. There are pictures of wombats and brief information on their habitat, habits, and diet.

Dromedary Camel

http://www.seaworld.org/animal_bytes/dromedary_camelab.html

Illustrated guide to the dromedary camel including information about genus, size, life span, habitat, gestation, diet, and a series of fun facts.

Echidna and I

http://yoyo.cc.monash.edu.au/~tzvi/Echid_I.html

Quirky but fascinating page devoted to the echidna, which includes images, biological facts, and stories related to this small mammal.

Elephant

http://species.fws.gov/bio_elep.html

Presentation on the Asian and African elephant with details about their physical appearance, food, social life, status of protection, and more. It is a useful, quick reference tool for all those concerned about wildlife and its protection.

Ferret Central

http://www.ferretcentral.org/

Huge source of information on ferrets. There is an interesting account of people's long relationship with this domesticated polecat. There is comprehensive advice on all aspects of keeping a ferret (including several articles on litter training). Other contents include photos, latest updates of ferret events around the world, and links to the World Ferret Union and other ferret sites.

Giant Panda Facts

http://www.wwfcanada.org/facts/panda.html

Information about the giant panda from the World Wildlife Fund, Canada. Descriptions of the behaviour of the animals, as well as details of the threats to the existence of the species, are included, as well as a bibliography.

Giraffe

http://www.seaworld.org/animal_bytes/giraffeab.html

This illustrated guide to the giraffe contains information about genus, size, life span, habitat, gestation, diet, as well as a series of fun facts.

Gorilla

http://www.seaworld.org/animal_bytes/gorillaab.html

Guide to the gorilla, with illustrations. It contains information about genus, size, life span, habitat, gestation, diet, and a series of fun facts.

Grevy's Zebra

http://www.seaworld.org/animal_bytes/grevysab.html

> **F A C T**
>
> **ZEBRA**
> black and white striped member of the horse genus *Equus* found in Africa; the stripes serve as camouflage or dazzle and confuse predators. Zebras live in family groups and herds on mountains and plains, and can run at up to 60 kph/40 mph.

Details about the Grevy's zebra can be found in this illustrated guide. Contents cover genus, size, life span, habitat, gestation, and diet.

GWF Felis Concolor Cougar (Eastern Cougar)

http://www.gwf.org/library/wildlife/ani_cougar.htm

Good profile of *Felis concolor,* the largest cat in the USA. The contents include information on its habitat, diet, hunting technique, reproduction, and survival threats. There is also an extensive list of references.

Hippopotamus

http://www.seaworld.org/animal_bytes/ hippopotamusab.html

Guide to the hippopotamus, with pictures. This site contains information about genus, size, life span, habitat, gestation, diet, and a series of fun facts.

Jaguar

http://dialspace.dial.pipex.com/town/plaza/ abf90/jaguar.htm

Details about the largest species of cat in the Americas, the jaguar. The page contains information about the appearance, breeding habits, and typical height and weight of the animal.

Leadbeter's Possum Page

http://cres20.anu.edu.au/possum/possum.html

Well-written article on attempts to save the rare Leadbeter's possum from extinction in Victoria. The behaviour of the animal is described together with threats to its survival. There is an audio clip of the possum's alarm call and a video.

Lemur

http://www.seaworld.org/animal_bytes/ lemurab.html

Information on the lemur. Contents include information about genus, size, life span, habitat, gestation, diet, illustrations and a series of fun facts.

Lynx Rufus – Bobcat

http://www.sbceo.k12.ca.us/~mcssb/ sbpanda/bobcat.html

Good profile of the bobcat. Contents include details of physical characteristics, behaviour, geographic range, and reproduction. There is also a photo of a bobcat.

Marsupial Cooperative Research Centre

http://www.newcastle.edu.au/marsupialcrc/

Interesting details of latest research into marsupial preservation issues in Australasia. This site examines efforts to preserve endangered species, while scientifically culling those in excess numbers and restricting introduced predators. For further information there is a link to Australia's Genome Research Network.

National Wild Horse and Burro Program

http://www.blm.gov/whb/

Sponsored by the US Bureau of Land Management, this site offers information, news items, a photo archive, statistics, and more about wild horses and burros and the government programme that seeks to protect them and their habitat in the American West. This site includes adoption information.

Ocelot – *Felis pardalis*

http://ananke.advanced.org/2878/tx_ocelot.html

Brief profile of the endangered wild cat. There is a description of the animal, its habitat and distribution, and the reasons why it is on the verge of extinction.

Orang-utan – Quintessential Forest Dweller

http://www.lpzoo.com/ark/orang_article.html

Well-written profile of the orang-utan. Among the interesting facts in this account of the behaviour, diet, and social life of the orang-utan is that they eat some four hundred different kinds of food, and that they are not solitary browsers but need to know that the company of other orang-utans is available. There is a picture, a map of the orang-utan's range, and a bibliography.

Paulson's Rabbit World - Netscape

File Edit View Go Window Help

Paulson's
Rabbit World

Michael Betz's
Bunny Award For
Best Web Page

"Rabbits just sit there and do nothing all day" is what one of my best friends told me when I informed her that I lived with

Document Done

distribution. There is a high-resolution photo of the USA's fastest native mammal.

Raccoons

http://www.loomcom.com/raccoons

Compiled with obvious enthusiasm, this site brings facts to life with images, sounds, and animations. It also includes a section on raccoons in the media, links to other sites of interest, and an interactive bulletin board for raccoon-related discussion.

Paulson's Rabbit World

http://www.rabbitworld.com/

Comprehensive guide to keeping these active and gregarious animals as pets. If you are contemplating getting a bunny, this is the site to visit. There is advice on providing accommodation (while giving the rabbit the run of the house), protecting rabbits from household dangers, toilet training, diet, and common rabbit ailments. There are useful links to the House Rabbit Society and other rabbit sites.

Pine Marten

http://www.anglianet.co.uk/pinemarten/pm_marte.html

Lots of information about pine martens – habitat, diet, and behaviour. The site also provides a rather dubious audio clip of 'some martens going about their business'.

Prairie Dog

http://ngp.ngpc.state.ne.us/wildlife/pdogs.html

Well-written profile of this sociable burrowing rodent from the Nebraskan wildlife. In addition to information on its diet and habitat, it looks at the ecological importance of preserving prairie dog towns.

Pronghorn

http://www.geocities.com/Athens/Forum/3807/features/pronghorn.html

Profile of the pronghorn, its characteristics, and

F A C T

RACCOON

any of several New World species of carnivorous mammals of the genus *Procyon*, in the family Procyonidae. The common raccoon *P. lotor* is about 60 cm/2 ft long, with a grey-brown body, a black-and-white ringed tail, and a black 'mask' around its eyes.

Red Hartebeest

http://www.iwwn.com.na/napha/red.html

Short profile of Namibia's red hartebeest. There is a picture of the antelope and details of its appearance, behaviour, habitat, diet, and reproduction.

Remarkable Platypus

http://www.anca.gov.au/plants/manageme/platintr.htm

Comprehensive information on this shy monotreme presented by the Australian Natural Conservation Agency. Findings of latest research into platypuses is presented, together with recommendations to help preserve the species.

Rhinoceros

http://planetpets.simplenet.com/plntrhno.htm

Page about the ecological plight of the rhinoceros, with text and pictures describing the various rhinoceroses, and the factors threatening them with extinction. There is also a quiz and projects to get involved in.

Black Rhinoceros

http://www.seaworld.org/animal_bytes/
black_rhinocerosab.html

Illustrated guide to the black rhinoceros including information about genus, size, life span, habitat, gestation, diet, and a series of fun facts.

Royal Society for the Prevention of Cruelty to Animals

http://www.rspca.co.uk/

Great site for animal lovers, featuring a selection of interactive quizzes and puzzles for children, as well as information about how to deal with anyanimal problems you may have.

Shrew(-ists) Site

http://members.vienna.at/shrew/index.html

Splendid site for the shrew enthusiast that includes images, details of current research, a newsletter, and facts, stories and myths about this animal. There is even a shrew gift shop!

Skunk and Opossum Page

http://granicus.if.org/~firmiss/m-d.html

Lively site providing all the information you could possibly want about skunks and opossums – photos, a guide to identifying their tracks, common misconceptions, advice on keeping them as pets, stories featuring the animals, and even a recipe!

Snow Wolves

http://www.pbs.org/kued/snowwolves/

Companion to a US Public Broadcasting Service (PBS) television programme, this site follows the reintroduction of wolves into Yellowstone National Park from their initial placement in 1995 to the autumn of 1996. It includes a section on the filmmaker's diary, sound and image galleries, and the script to the television programme that was first shown in August 1997. You can also find links to wolf resources and a trivia quiz.

Spotted Hyenas

http://www.csulb.edu/~persepha/hyena.html

Facts about hyenas illustrated by a number of photos. There is also a highly informative 'Frequently Asked Questions' section dealing with questions such as 'Do they really laugh?' and 'Will they eat people?', as well as a folklore section dealing with the depiction of hyenas through history.

Springbok

http://www.iwwn.com.na/napha/spring.html

Information on this endangered South African antelope. There is a photo, description of the springbok, and information about its social and mating habits.

Squirrel Place

http://www.squirrels.org/

Comprehensive resources about squirrels, including a history of the species, a selection of videos from the BBC's *Daylight Robbery II,* and a list of 'Frequently Asked Questions'.

Tasmanian Devil

http://www.schoolworld.asn.au/species/
tasdevil.html

Profile of the largest of Australia's surviving marsupial carnivores. There is a picture of a devil, details of its appearance and behaviour, and an explanation of how it became extinct on the Australian mainland. There is an accompanying note about the demise of the Tasmanian tiger.

Tiger Basics

http://www.5tigers.org/allabout.htm

This page offers descriptions of the five sub-species of tiger with details of their anatomy, hunting methods, habitats, the pressures they are under, and the measures taken to protect them. There is also a 'Multimedia' section with pictures and sounds, and even a 'Tigers in the news' section.

Walrus

http://www.seaworld.org/animal_bytes/
walrusab.html

Guide to the walru, with illustrations. This site provides details of genus, size, life span, habitat, gestation, diet, and a series of fun facts.

Warthog

http://www.seaworld.org/animal_bytes/
warthogab.html

Information on the warthog, covering genus, size,

life span, habitat, gestation, diet, and a series of fun facts.

Wild Wolves

http://www.pbs.org/wgbh/nova/wolves/

'What's in a wolf's howl – a calling card, a warning, or an invitation?' This site includes information about the relationship between wolves and dogs, lets you hear a wolf howl, and also includes a quiz.

Pets & Keeping Animals

Anemones

http://www.actwin.com/fish/species/anemone.html

Article on keeping anemones in an aquarium environment. The site offers information on species, feeding, and tank maintenance practices to help these creatures thrive in captivity.

Chameleons

http://www.skypoint.com/members/mikefry/chams.html

Guide to the expensive and time-consuming business of looking after a pet chameleon. Would-be owners are warned not to support the trade in endangered species. Dietary and housing requirements are well explained, together with advice on what to do if your lizard is stressed, goes on hunger strike, has parasites, or does not get enough unfiltered sunlight. There are links to a number of specialist sites related to chameleons in the wild or in captivity.

Cichlid Home Page

http://cichlidresearch.com/index.html#Contents

Comprehensive source of information on *cichlidae*, their habitats, and how to keep them in an aquarium. There are a large number of photographs. Fish can be searched for by scientific or common names.

Complete Guide to Keeping Giant Green Iguanas in Captivity

http://www.baskingspot.com/iguanas/igbook/igbookbody.html

All there is to know about the many difficulties of keeping a giant iguana. This site contains information on behaviour, diet, housing, and common veterinary problems. There is a bibliography and listings of reptile veterinarians and other iguana sites around the world.

Cyber-Pet

http://www.cyberpet.com/

Lively US site, with information about choosing your dog or cat, health and nutrition, breeding and exhibiting, and pet products and services. It also includes some audio clips explaining various sections of the site.

Guinea Pig Care

http://www.aracnet.com/~seagull/Guineas/#Care

From housing to health, this site contains lots of useful information for guinea-pig lovers, including a health chart to help you diagnose illnesses.

Heather's Wild World

http://members.primary.net/~heather/

All you need to know about having a monkey as a pet. The challenges of meeting the complex social needs of these high-care, high-need pets (prone to smearing faeces and splattering urine) are frankly presented. There's a huge amount of practical advice and a photo gallery of monkeys.

Slithering Snakes

http://www2.excite.sfu.ca/pgm/students/alex_reid/snakes/MAINPAGE.HTM

Guide attempting to take the fear factor out of snakes. Emergency guidelines in case of being bitten by a snake are given, and light relief is provided in the form of an ode to snakes. This site also includes sections on such topics as 'Snakes in mythology', 'Record snakes', 'Helpful snakes', and even a bibloigraphy. The site is illustrated throughout.

Stick Insect

http://www.ex.ac.uk/bugclub/sticks.html

Loads of information on the care of your stick insects – how to house them, what to feed them on, how to handle them, and how to encourage breeding. This illustrated page is part of the Bug Club site and includes links to other bug pets, plus a newsletter, penpals, and books.

Tortoise Guide

http://easyweb.easynet.co.uk/~slowcoach/slow/slocoach.html

Essential site for tortoise enthusiasts and owners. It contains a history of tortoises in the UK, a comprehensive selection of 'Care sheets' covering different areas of keeping and caring for tortoises, and tips for the less experienced tortoise owner. There's also a picture gallery of the many varieties that can be found throughout the world and a summary of the Convention on International Trade in Endangered Species that governs trade in tortoises. You can also keep up to date with tortoise-related events via the 'What's On' page.

Welcome to the Bigchelon Turtle Page

http://members.aol.com/bigchelon/bigc.htm

Good source of advice on keeping turtles from an experienced owner. Contents include tips on how to buy a turtle as well as on housing, dietary requirements, hygiene, and other needs of turtles. There is a bibliography and links to other turtle sites.

Sea Creatures

Angelfish

http://www.actwin.com/fish/species/angelfish.html

This site includes details of angelfish breeds, feeding, keeping in an aquarium, and possible diseases. Images and multimedia clips are also downloadable from this site.

Atlantic Cod

http://www.ncr.dfo.ca/communic/ss-marin/atlantic/acod.htm

Information on the atlantic cod's life cycle, migration patterns, and feeding habits. This site also includes a history of the northwest Atlantic cod fishing industry, from the discovery of the New World to the collapse of the fish stocks in the 1980s.

Basking Shark Project

http://www.isle-of-man.com/interests/shark/index.htm

All about the basking shark – the second-largest fish in the sea but very little understood. As well as pertinent facts and an image gallery, this site also includes sections on current research, and opportunities to see the basking shark around the world.

Bottlenose Dolphin

http://www.seaworld.org/animal_bytes/dolphinab.html

Illustrated guide to the bottlenose dolphin including information about genus, size, life span, habitat, gestation, diet, and a series of fun facts.

California Sea Lion

http://www.seaworld.org/animal_bytes/sea_lionab.html

Guide to the California sea lion, with illustrations. This site contains information about genus, size, life span, habitat, gestation, diet, and a series of fun facts.

Carpet Python

http://www.seaworld.org/animal_bytes/
carpet_pythonab.html

This illustrated guide to the carpet python provides information about genus, size, life span, habitat, gestation, diet, and a series of fun facts.

Cephalopod Page

http://is.dal.ca/~ceph/TCP/index.html

Introduction to the world of cephalopods, the class that includes the squids, cuttlefish, and octopuses. As well as some images of marine life, this site also contains biological information about each subgroup.

Classification of Whales

http://ourworld.compuserve.com/homepages/jaap/
cetacea.htm

Description of the two suborders of cetaceans: the baleen whales or *Mysticeti* and the toothed whales or *Odontoceti*. A chart shows the main differences between the two suborders.

Dugong

http://werple.mira.net/~areadman/dugong.htm

Good profile of this rotund marine mammal. There is information on the habit, physical characteristics, diet, and breeding behaviour of the dugong, as well as pictures of the animal. Estimates of remaining populations in Pacific, Gulf, and Red Sea waters indicate the endangered status of the dugong.

> **F A C T**
>
> **DUGONG**
>
> marine mammal *Dugong dugong* of the order Sirenia (sea cows), found in the Red Sea, the Indian Ocean, and western Pacific. It can grow to 3.6 m/11 ft long, and has a tapering body with a notched tail and two fore-flippers.

Elephant Seals

http://ourworld.compuserve.com/homepages/jaap/
elepseal.htm

Descriptions and images of northern and southern elephant seals. This site includes information about their appearance, distribution, feeding habits, and life history. There are also two useful bibliographies.

Endangered Species Home Page

http://www.fws.gov/r9endspp/endspp.html

US Fish and Wildlife site with full details of its ongoing conservation programmes. The site also contains a 'Kids' Corner', a gallery of images, and a link to the latest edition of its *Endangered Species Bulletin.*

FINS – Fish Information Service

http://www.actwin.com/fish/index.cgi

Huge source of practical information on all aspects of keeping fish in aquariums. The needs of all manner of tropical and temperate fish, marine, and freshwater fish are covered in detail. There is a good listing of frequently asked questions and a comprehensive picture library of just about every fish in the world. With the help of FINS you can learn whatever you want about ichthyology.

Fish FAQ

http://www.wh.whoi.edu/faq/botRfaq.html

Answers to hundreds of questions about fish and shellfish. Unfortunately the questions are not grouped, or searchable, in any way, but they do include answers to such things as 'Do fish sleep?' and 'Are Hawaiian monk seals coming back?'.

History of Koi Carp

http://www.netpets.org/fish/reference/
freshref/nishi.html

Origin and development of the Koi (*Nishikigoi*) carp in Japan, including the history of breeding them in captivity.

In Search of Giant Squid

http://seawifs.gsfc.nasa.gov/
OCEAN_PLANET/HTML/
squid_opening.html

Exhibition about the world's largest invertebrates presented by the Smithsonian's National Museum of Natural History. It includes a large number of photos, discussion of stories and myths surrounding giant squid, a fascinating comparison of squid and snails, and informative sections on anatomy, food, movement, and defence systems.

Killer Whales

http://www.seaworld.org/killer_whale/
killerwhales.html

Pictures and videos of this sea creature. There is also a lot of detailed biological information concerning, for example, the habitat, behaviour, and communication of killer whales. There are also plenty of activities and ideas to keep younger children entertained.

North Pacific Fur Seal

http://www.yoto98.noaa.gov/books/
seals/seals6.htm

Biology, distribution, and the effect of humans on the population of North Pacific fur seals. Once hunted to near extinction, the seals' greatest threat now is pollution.

Salmon Page

http://www.riverdale.k12.or.us/
salmon.htm

Comprehensive source of information on salmon that introduces itself: 'How to catch them, cook them, buy them, and save them...'. In addition to these four areas there are videos to download, links to school projects on salmon which are available on the Web, and links to newsgroups to put you in contact with other salmon enthusiasts.

Save the Manatee Club

http://www.objectlinks.com/manatee/

Good source of information about the three species of manatee, with particular emphasis on the West Indian. The habitat, behaviour, and reproductive habits of the aquatic herbivore are

well described with readable text and pictures. There is a guide on where to see manatees in the wild and reports on conservation efforts in Florida and elsewhere.

Sea Otter

http://www.seaworld.org/animal_bytes/
sea_otterab.html

Illustrated guide to the sea otter including information about genus, size, life span, habitat, gestation, diet, and a series of fun facts.

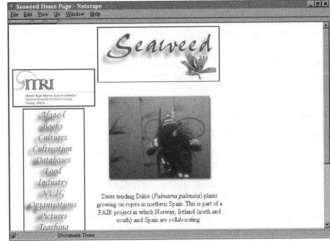

Diver tending Dulse (*Palmaria palmata*) plants growing on ropes in northern Spain. This is part of a FAIR project in which Norway, Ireland (north and south) and Spain are collaborating.

Seaweed Home Page

http://seaweed.ucg.ie/seaweed.html

Notes on the seaweed species of the British Isles, plus information on the Irish seaweed industry, a seaweed recipe, and links to algal databases. The site also includes a growing selection of education resources.

Shark Research Institute

http://www.njscuba.com/Sharks/

Shark Research Institute's Web site detailing research projects and online resources. The site includes information about whale shark sightings, shark attacks, and the behavioural patterns of different shark species.

Turtles

http://www.turtles.org

Site full of information about turtles. There are pictures, information on current

---

F A C T

MANATEE

any of a group of plant-eating aquatic mammals found in marine bays and sluggish rivers, usually in thick, muddy water. They have flippers as forelimbs, no hindlimbs, and a short rounded and flattened tail used for swimming.

research programmes, a kids' corner, and stills from an underwater video camera.

UK Underwater Wildlife

http://www.gla.ac.uk/~gbza62/
contents.html#Echinodermata

Gallery of photographs of all kinds of wildlife that can be found in British waters, organized according to formal species classification.

Ultimate Shark Page

http://www.ncf.carleton.ca/~bz050/
HomePage.shark.html

Lots of links to shark sites and resources, plus information about shark classification and 'weird and wonderful' sharks such as the cookie-cutter shark and the giant nurse.

Underwater Photography

http://staff.washington.edu/scotfree/

Personal site dedicated to pictures, nearly all of which were taken in the northwest Pacific. As well as being very aesthetically pleasing, the pictures are all labelled and the site includes technical information about how they were taken.

Welcome to Coral Forest

http://www.blacktop.com/coralforest/

Site dedicated to explaining the importance of coral reefs for the survival of the planet. It is an impassioned plea on behalf of the world's endangered coral reefs and includes a full description of their biodiversity, maps of where coral reefs are to be found (no less than 109 countries), and many photos.

Whales – Endangered Species

http://www.wwf.org/species/species.cfm?sectionid
=121&newspaperid=21

Home page of the endangered species of whales in both the North Atlantic and North Pacific regions. Further pages describe the biology, distribution, and threat to each of the endangered species in turn.

Whale Songs

http://whales.ot.com

Developed by teachers and funded by the International Fund for Animal Welfare, here is a site based on an expedition researching into whale song. One teacher joined a research vessel and you can follow his experience of the search for whales. There are also sections on 'Song of the Whale' (the IFAW research ship), 'Educational resources', and 'Cetacean info'.

Miscellaneous Animals

Electronic Zoo

http://netvet.wustl.edu/e-zoo.htm

Vast collection of links to animal Web sites and images (there is even a section devoted to fictional animals, from Animaniacs to Wile E Coyote), plus NetVet – animal welfare information and links to veterinary sites.

Etosha: Africa's Untamed Wilderness

http://www.pbs.org/edens/etosha/

Companion to the US Public Broadcasting Service (PBS) television programme *The Living Edens,* this page concerns the flora and fauna of southern Africa's Etosha National Park. Learn about the drastic changes that the wet and dry seasons bring to the park. Read brief descriptions of the predators and prey that thrive in this sanctuary; take a behind-the-scenes look at the filming of the television programme; and read about the history of the park. Then, after you have browsed the various sections, test your knowledge with the trivia quiz. There is also a list of resources and links for further research.

Kangaroo Australian A – Z Animal Archive

http://www.aaa.com.au/A_Z/

When Australia's first European explorers saw a strange animal as tall as a human, leaping around like giant grasshoppers, they couldn't believe their eyes! Here is a site with images and descriptions of Australian wildlife, from Antechinus to Zyzomys.

Noah's Exotic Menagerie

http://www.teleport.com/~cos/noah/noah.html

US-based nonprofit organization that aims to look after endangered animals without homes and also educate the public about them. As well as information on the organization, the site also contains a photo album of some animals they have helped.

People for the Ethical Treatment of Animals – PETA Online

http://www.peta-online.org/

Well-organized home of the world's largest animal rights organization. PETA's mission, history, and role are described together with reports of campaigns, a comprehensive listing of resources, and a children's section. The Activist's Library has a huge selection of photos, articles, and fact sheets chronicling PETA's endeavours to raise the status of animals.

Zoonet Image Archives

http://www.mindspring.com/~zoonet/gallery.html

Comprehensive collection of indexes to zoo galleries, with or without detailed text, and links to other animal pictures.

Botany & Gardening

Angiosperm Anatomy

http://www.botany.uwc.ac.za:80/sci_ed/std8/anatomy/

Good general guide to angiosperms (flowering plants). The differences between monocotyledons and dicotyledons are set out here. The functions of roots, stems, leaves, and flowers are explained by readily understandable text and good accompanying diagrams.

ANGIOSPERM

F A C T

flowering plant in which the seeds are enclosed within an ovary, which ripens into a fruit. Angiosperms are divided into monocotyledons (single seed leaf in the embryo) and dicotyledons (two seed leaves in the embryo). They include the majority of flowers, herbs, grasses, and trees except conifers.

Ascomycota

http://phylogeny.arizona.edu/tree/eukaryotes/fungi/ascomycota/ascomycota.html

Good source of information on this large group of fungi. A colourful home page shows photos of baker's yeast, penicillium, and other well-known ascomycetes. Among the interesting and well-presented facts about these fungi is that they have more than one reproductive option open to them. The text is supported with diagrams and photos. Further sources of information from professional plant pathologists are indicated.

Banks, Sir Joseph

http://www.nhm.ac.uk/info/banksarchive/banks.html

Profile of the life and voyages of the 18th-century British botanist Joseph Banks. The page includes information about James Cook, Botany Bay, and the *banksia* species of plant which was named after him.

Bonsai FAQ

http://home.maine.rr.com/michaelj/bonsai/faq/part1.html

Well-arranged noncommercial introduction to the art of bonsai. There is comprehensive practical advice for bonsai beginners, news from bonsai associations and suppliers, and links to a huge range of bonsai sites around the world. This site has everything you need to start growing your own bonsai and to get in touch with other enthusiasts.

British Lawnmower Museum

http://dspace.dial.pipex.com/town/square/gf86/

Only in the British Isles can you find a museum that is dedicated to grass-cutting machines. This online museum has a section on the deranged sport of lawnmower racing, as well as 'Lawnmowers of the rich and famous', and many pictures of museum exhibits.

Cole Crops or Brassicas

http://www.ext.vt.edu/pubs/envirohort/426-403/426-403.html

Informative guide to this group of vegetables from the Virginia Cooperative Extension. There is a guide to planting them as well as the types of soil and sunlight that yield best results. This site also features solutions to common problems and information about harvesting and storage.

Compost

http://www.ext.vt.edu/pubs/envirohort/general/compost.html

Informative guide to compost from the Virginia Cooperative Extension. It first describes exactly what compost is and what its benefits are. Then it gives detailed information about making your own compost.

Fertilizing the Garden

http://www.ext.vt.edu/pubs/envirohort/general/fertilizer.html

Information on fertilizer from the Virginia Cooperative Extension. There is a description of both the major and trace elements in fertilizer. Also included is information on applying dry fertilizers, manures, liquid fertilizers, and foliar feeding. As well as this, there are notes on nutrient requirements for various vegetables, vegetable tolerance to soil acidity, and the symptoms of nutrient deficiency.

Fun With Lichens

http://mgd.nacse.org/hyperSQL/lichenland/

Thorough guide to these unique fungus-alga combinations. Written by a lichen enthusiast at the University of Oregon, this is a good introduction to the subject. The textual content is well supported with photographs. There are sections suitable for the general reader, schoolchildren, and professional botanists, ecologists, and foresters.

GardenWeb Glossary of Botanical Terms

http://www.gardenweb.com/glossary/

Searchable, text-only glossary of well over 2,000 botanical terms. There is a brief explanation of how the search engine works and a selection of criteria on with which to refine your search, including 'terms' or 'definitions', as well as a basic and/or boolean search.

Growing Sunflowers

http://jstait.addr.com/~jstait/sunflowers/howto.htm

Comprehensive guide to growing sunflowers, one of the easiest flowers to grow, and one of the most

vibrant. The instructions include planting, germination, and soil considerations, and are accompanied by explanatory photographs.

Growing Waratahs

http://155.187.10.12/telopea/telopea.html

Page dedicated to the beautiful waratah plant, with numerous colour photographs of the different species. The site includes information about their propagation and cultivation, and there is also a reading list.

Insect Control FAQ

http://res.agr.ca/lond/pmrc/faq/insect.html

Table of frequently asked questions about all kinds of insect control, including the Colorado potato beetle and aphids. The questions answered on this site include 'What are the most common insect pests?' and 'What alternatives are there to insecticides to control insects?'.

Linnaeus, Carolus

http://www.ucmp.berkeley.edu/history/linnaeus.htm

Profile of the life and legacy of the Swedish 'father of taxonomy'. A biography traces how his childhood interest in plants led to his becoming the greatest observational biologist of his day. There is also a discussion as to whether this son of a priest was an evolutionist.

Micropropagation at Kew

http://www.rbgkew.org.uk/ksheets/microprop.html

Report of the work of the Micropropagation Unit at Britain's prestigious Kew Gardens. It contains descriptions of how endangered species are cultured *in vitro* from seed or vegetative material. There are details of Kew's online publication *Micropropagation News*.

Pete's Pond Page

http://reality.sgi.com/peteo/

Site run by a garden-pond enthusiast which is full of images of fish, waterplants, and even the surrounding garden. There is also a lot of useful information and hints for those trying to create a pond of their own.

Royal Botanic Gardens, Kew

http://www.rbgkew.org.uk/

Kew Gardens' home page, with general visitor

information, a history of the gardens, a guide to the main plant collections, and a searchable database.

Royal Horticultural Society

http://www.rhs.org.uk/

Large source of information on horticulture in the UK. The contents include a guide to RHS gardens, the Society's scientific and educational work, RHS publications, and information about the annual Chelsea Flower Show and other events.

Seeds of Life

http://www.vol.it/mirror/SeedsOfLife/home.html

Wealth of information about seeds and fruits, including the basic structure of a seed, fruit types, how seeds are dispersed, seeds and humans, plus a mystery seed contest.

Soil pH – What It Means

http://www.esf.edu/pubprog/brochure/soilph/soilph.htm

Explanation of soil pH. The Web site also describes how to measure the pH of soil using simple experimental equipment, and goes on to describe methods that may be used to modify the acidity of alkalinity of your soil.

Survey of the Plant Kingdoms

http://www.mancol.edu/science/biology/plants_new/intro/start.html

Systematic guide to the nonanimal kingdoms

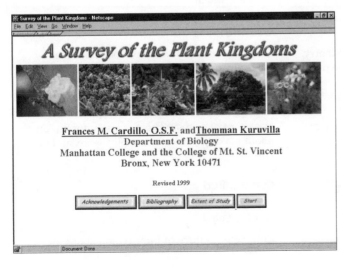

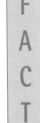

BOTANY (Greek *botane* 'herb'),

the study of living and fossil plants, including form, function, interaction with the environment, and classification.

(plants, fungi, protista, and monera) – their major groups, classification, and anatomy.

Vegetables, Nuts & Fruit

Almonds

http://www.botanical.com/botanical/mgmh/a/almon026.html

Detailed information about the almond tree and its habitat. The place of the almond tree in history and mythology is discussed in detail, as is the tree itself. There are notes on its cultivation and even a selection of recipes in which it is used. It also features information about sweet and bitter almonds, including details of their constituents and, where relevant, uses in medicine.

Apple

http://www.botanical.com/botanical/mgmh/a/apple044.html

Large source of information relating to apples. Included here are a detailed description of the tree and its habitat, as well as a brief introduction to the role of the apple in history. Also featured are details of the tree's constituents and of the many uses of the apple tree – not only in cooking, but also in aiding digestion, curing constipation, and cleaning teeth.

Apricot

http://www.botanical.com/botanical/mgmh/a/apric050.html

Detailed information about the apricot tree, including notes on its history, its habitat, and the tree itself. It also features sections about the tree's constituents and its numerous uses in cosmetics and perfumes.

Artichoke, Globe

http://www.botanical.com/botanical/mgmh/a/artic066.html

Contains detailed information about this plant. This site includes a description of the artichoke and its place in history. There are also notes on the different ways of cultivating artichokes. This page forms part of a larger site which also has information on the Jerusalem artichoke.

Asparagus

http://www.ext.vt.edu/pubs/envirohort/426-401/426-401.html

Informative guide to asparagus from the Virginia Cooperative Extension. There is a guide to planting asparagus, as well as the types of soil and sunlight that yield best results. This site also features solutions to common problems and information about harvesting and storage.

Beans

http://www.ext.vt.edu/pubs/envirohort/426-402/426-402.html

Informative guide to beans from the Virginia Cooperative Extension. There is a guide to planting beans, as well as the types of soil and sunlight that yield best results. This site also features solutions to common problems and information about harvesting and storage. There are also extensive notes on the different types of beans, such as soybeans, dry beans, and lima beans.

Bilberry

http://www.botanical.com/botanical/mgmh/b/bilber37.html

Contains detailed information about the bilberry, including an informative description of the plant, its constituents, and its habitat. It also features notes on the uses of the plant, which include treating scurvy and diabetes. There is also information about making bilberry jam – one of the other better known uses.

Blackberry

http://www.botanical.com/botanical/mgmh/b/blaber49.html

A detailed guide to the bilberry, including an informative description of the plant, its history,

and its habitat. This site also features notes on the uses of the blackberry, which include treating dysentery and diarrhoea. There is also information about making blackberry wine and vinegar.

Cashew Nut

http://www.botanical.com/botanical/mgmh/c/casnut29.html

Informative resource relating to the cashew tree and nut. It contains a detailed description of the tree, its habitat, and its constituents. There are also notes on the many uses of the tree, which include treating skin conditions and acting as a diuretic. There is even information on other species of the cashew tree.

Coconut

http://www.rbgkew.org.uk/ksheets/coconut.html

Interesting information about coconuts from Britain's prestigious Kew Gardens. This account of 'God's greatest gift to man' looks at the many products derived from coconuts.

Cucumbers, Melons, and Squash

http://www.ext.vt.edu/pubs/envirohort/426-406/426-406.html

Informative guide to melons, squash, and cucumbers from the Virginia Cooperative Extension. There is a guide to planting them, as well as the types of soil and sunlight that yield best results. This site also features solutions to common problems and information about harvesting and storage.

Currant, Black

http://www.botanical.com/botanical/mgmh/c/curbl131.html

Complete source of information about the blackcurrant. Contained here are informative descriptions of the plant and its habitat. This site also features notes on the uses of the plant, which include the preparation of lozenges and the treatment of dropsy. There is also information about making blackcurrant jelly, wine, and even cheese!

Currant, Red

http://www.botanical.com/botanical/mgmh/c/currd132.html

Complete resource of information about the

redcurrant. Contained here are an informative description of the plant and its habitat. This site also features notes on the uses of the plant, which include the preparation of an antiseptic and the treatment of fevers.

Edible and Poisonous Mushrooms

http://www.conservation.state.mo.us/nathis/ flora/mushroom/mushroom.html

Well-presented guide to mushrooms. The site assists those new to the joys of recreational mushroom hunting, advises where to find wild mushrooms, identifies poisonous varieties, and gives useful cooking tips. Identification is made easier by drawings of a large variety of mushrooms.

Exotic Varieties Add to Popularity of America's Favourite Fruit

http://www.sunherald.com:80/living/docs/ nanas012898.htm

Comprehensive article on the banana, with more-or less-known facts about this tropical and most popular fruit. It includes exhaustive nutritional information, and extended presentation of the properties and cooking of several 'Boutique bananas', that is, a series of uncommon kinds of bananas from all over the world.

Fig, Common

http://www.botanical.com/botanical/mgmh/f/ figcom12.html

Informative resource relating to the common fig tree. It contains a detailed description of the tree, its habitat, and its cultivation. There are also notes on the constituents of the tree, as well as information on the possible medicinal uses of the common fig tree, which include acting as a laxative and treating warts.

Garden Peas

http://www.gardenguides.com/Vegetables/ peas.htm

Contains extensive information on the garden pea. There are notes on the different varieties, and there is also a guide to planting peas, taking account of soil, temperature, and sunlight.

Onions, Garlic, and Shallots

http://www.ext.vt.edu/pubs/envirohort/ 426-411/426-411.html#L1

Informative guide to these closely related

vegetables from the Virginia Cooperative Extension. There is a guide to planting them, as well as the types of soil, sunlight, and moisture that yield best results. This site also features solutions to common problems and information about harvesting and storage.

Pomegranates in California

http://fruitsandnuts.ucdavis.edu/pomeg.html

In-depth guide to this fruit which contains images and 'Fruit facts'. It also indexes a host of more complex information on growing pomegranates and help with the common problems related to growing pomegranates.

Real Cranberry Home Page

http://www.scs.carleton.ca/~palepu/cranberry.html

Whilst containing much information about the cranberry, this site also links to other places in the Internet, each offering information about the plant. There is a very large list of recipes making use of the cranberry, from cranberry wild rice salad to cranberry beer. There is also a large amount of information about how cranberries can help to fight urinary tract infections.

Rhubarb Compendium

http://www.metalab.unc.edu/rhubarb/

Pictures, history, recipes: the list of information included at this site goes on an on; it even includes a section on rhubarb being a possible key to CFC(chlorofluorocarbon) control. It is impossible to believe you would need to know something about rhubarb that this site doesn't tell you.

Root Crops

http://www.ext.vt.edu/pubs/envirohort/ 426-422/426-422.html

Informative guide to these vegetables from the Virginia Cooperative Extension. There is a guide to planting and fertilizing them, as well as the types of soil, sunlight, and moisture that yield best results. This site also features solutions to common problems and information about harvesting and storage.

Super Food – Kiwi Fruit

http://www.leggs.com/articles/health/july96/ kiwi.html

Good source of information on this fruit, also

known as the Chinese gooseberry. There are details of the chemistry of the fruit and cultivation techniques. The site also includes recipes, serving suggestions, and guides for kiwi purchasers.

Sweet Corn
http://www.ext.vt.edu/pubs/envirohort/
426-405/426-405.html

Informative guide to sweetcorn from the Virginia Cooperative Extension. There is a guide to planting and fertilizing them, as well as the types of soil, sunlight, and moisture that yield best results. This site also features solutions to common problems and information about harvesting and storage.

Tomatoes
http://www.homegrowntomatoes.com/tomato.htm

Describes the different varieties of tomato available, and the best uses for each variety. It also includes notes on growing tomatoes and keeping them free from disease.

Flowers

Amaranths
http://www.botanical.com/botanical
/mgmh/a/amara030.html

Detailed information about different types of amaranths, including love-lies-bleeding and prince's feather. Their habitat is described, as are their constituents. There are also notes on the various medicinal uses of the plants as diuretics and anthelmintics.

Anemones
http://www.botanical.com/botanical/mgmh/
a/anemo034.html

Contains detailed information about the anemone, including an informative description of the plant itself as well as of its habitat. There are also extensive notes on the cultivation of anemones, including tips on the soil, propagation, and planting.

Asphodel
http://www.botanical.com/botanical/mgmh/a/
aspho080.html

A guide to this plant, including a detailed description of both the asphodei itself and its habitat. The site also features details of the constituents of asphodel, as well as notes on its medicinal uses. There is also a brief introduction to other species of this plant.

Barberry, Common
http://www.botanical.com/botanical/mgmh/b/
barcom12.html

Large amount of information about the common barberry, including a detailed description of the plant and its habitat. There is an account of the history of the plant, as well as details of its constituents and cultivation. This site also features notes on the plant's medicinal uses, which include treating jaundice and diarrhoea. There are even a number of recipes which include barberries as a main ingredient.

Bluebell
http://www.botanical.com/botanical/mgmh/b/
bluebe60.html

Informative guide to the bluebell, or harebell. This site contains an informative description of the plant and its habitat. It also features notes on the bluebell's constituents and many uses, which include acting a substitute for starch and being used as a styptic.

Broom

http://www.botanical.com/botanical/mgmh/b/broom-70.html

Large resource of information about this type of shrub. This site also contains an informative description of the plant, its history, and its habitat. It also features notes on the plant's constituents and many medicinal uses, which include treating kidney and bladder complaints as well as dropsy. There are also notes on the cultivation of broom.

Bugle, Common

http://www.botanical.com/botanical/mgmh/b/buglec82.html

Detailed resource relating to this plant. It contains an informative description of the plant and its habitat. There are also notes on the possible medicinal uses of the common bugle, which include arresting haemorrhages and allaying irritation.

Buttercup, Bulbous

http://www.botanical.com/botanical/mgmh/b/butcup97.html

Informative site containing a detailed description of the plant and its characteristics. There are also notes on the possible medicinal uses of the bulbous buttercup, which include treating gout and rheumatism and curing certain headaches.

Callistemon (Bottlebrushes)

http://155.187.10.12/callistemon/callistemon.html

Facts about the *callistemon*, or bottlebrush. The page includes information and a map relating to its distribution, a description and a drawing of the plant, advice on propagation, and commonly grown species. There is also a reading list.

Celandine, Greater

http://www.botanical.com/botanical/mgmh/c/celgre43.html

This site contains a detailed description of the greater celandine, its history, and its habitat. There are also notes on the constituents and

possible medicinal uses of the plant, which include acting as a diuretic and treating warts and ringworm. This page forms part of a larger site that also contains information about the lesser celandine.

Clematis

http://www.botanical.com/botanical/mgmh/c/clemat73.html

In addition to a detailed description of the plant, its habitat, and other related species, there are also extensive notes on the possible medicinal uses of clematis, which include acting as a diuretic and diaphoretic. As the plant is poisonous, there are details of possible antidotes.

Coltsfoot

http://www.botanical.com/botanical/mgmh/c/coltsf88.html

Informative resource relating to coltsfoot. It contains a detailed description of the plant, its constituents, and its habitat. There are also extensive notes on the possible medicinal uses of coltsfoot, which include treating coughs and acting as a demulcent.

Cornflower

http://www.botanical.com/botanical/mgmh/c/cornf102.html

Detailed information about the cornflower, including a description of the plant and its habitat. There are also extensive notes on the possible uses of cornflower, which include making ink and potpourri and treating bruises.

Cowslip

http://www.botanical.com/botanical/mgmh/c/cowsl112.html

Informative resource relating to this European plant. It contains a very detailed description of the plant, including information about its habitat, constituents, and even its medicinal uses, which include acting as a sedative or antispasmodic. There are also links to information about related plants, including the primrose.

Cranesbill Root, American

http://www.botanical.com/botanical/mgmh/c/crane115.html

This Web site contains a detailed description of the American cranesbill root, including information about its habitat, constituents, and even its medicinal uses, which include acting as a styptic and treating piles. There is also information about related species.

Crowfoot, Upright Meadow

http://www.botanical.com/botanical/mgmh/c/croup120.html

Informative resource relating to this plant. It contains a very detailed description of the upright meadow crowfoot, including information about its habitat. There are also notes on its medicinal uses, which include treating gout and warts. This page forms part of a larger site that also includes information about celery-leaved crowfoot.

Cuckoo-Pint

http://www.botanical.com/botanical/mgmh/c/cucko122.html

Detailed analysis of this plant and its habitat. There are extensive notes on the plant's constituents, and there are even details of its many medicinal uses. It also features descriptions of other species.

Daffodil

http://www.botanical.com/botanical/mgmh/d/daffod01.html

Detailed resource relating to this popular plant, including a description of the plant and its habitat. There are also notes on the constituents and possible medicinal uses of the daffodil, which include treating burns and stiff joints.

Dahlias

http://www.botanical.com/botanical/mgmh/d/dahlia02.html

Detailed description of the plant and its habitat.

F
A
C
T

DAHLIA

any of a group of perennial plants belonging to the daisy family, comprising 20 species and many cultivated forms. Dahlias are stocky plants with tuberous roots and showy flowers that come in a wide range of colours.

There are also helpful notes on the constituents and possible uses of dahlias.

Daisy, Common

http://www.botanical.com/botanical/mgmh/d/daisyc03.html

Informative resource relating to the English common daisy. It contains a description of the plant as well as notes on its possible medicinal uses, which include treating fevers, wounds, and liver disorders.

Dandelion

http://www.botanical.com/botanical/mgmh/d/dandel08.html

Detailed information about the dandelion, its habitat, and even its place in history. There are also notes on the constituents, cultivation, and possible medicinal uses of the dandelion, which include acting as a diuretic and treating piles. There is also a recipe for dandelion tea.

Foxglove

http://hortweb.cas.psu.edu/vegcrops/herbs/digitalispurpurea.html

Wealth of information about this plant from the Department of Horticulture at Pennsylvania State University, USA. There is a description of the plant itself, as well as details about when and how it blooms. There are also notes on the best way of planting it, and what sorts of soil and light it needs.

Fritillary, Common

http://www.botanical.com/botanical/mgmh/f/fritil33.html

Detailed introduction to the common fritillary, including information on the plant itself, its habitat, and its propagation methods.

Gertrude Jekyll: *Roses for English Gardens*

http://www.rosarian.com/jekyll/roses/

Complete text of this work by the English landscape designer and gardener Gertrude Jekyll. The books focuses on a number of topics, such as new and old garden roses, Brier and Pompon roses, and rose arches, arbours, screens, hedges, and trellises.

Goldenrod

http://www.botanical.com/botanical/mgmh/g/golrod26.html

Analysis of this North American plant. There is a detailed description of the plant and its habitat, as well as notes on its constituents. There is also an informative description of the possible medicinal uses of the plant and an introduction to species.

Guelder Rose

http://www.botanical.com/botanical/mgmh/g/gueros44.html

Informative resource relating to the guelder rose. It contains a detailed description of the plant and its habitat. There are also notes on the constituents of the plant, as well as information on the possible medicinal uses of the guelder rose, which include acting as an antispasmodic.

Hellebore, False

http://www.botanical.com/botanical/mgmh/h/helfal15.html

Detailed information about this poisonous plant. There is a description of the plant's history, from Greek mythology to more recent times. It also features notes on the plant's constituents, and on the preparation of an infusion made from the plant.

Hollyhocks – Tall and Graceful

http://www.gardenguides.com/flowers/annuals/ hollyhocks.htm

Contains an image of hollyhocks, as well as a detailed description of the plant. There are also notes on growing hollyhocks, taking account of pests and problems, and the amount of sunlight and moisture that they require.

Kangaroo Paws

http://155.187.10.12/anigozanthos/index.html

Page devoted to the kangaroo paw plant, and the genus *Anigozanthos* to which it belongs. The site includes a description and colour photograph, information about propagation, pests and diseases, and a list of commonly grown species – some of which are illustrated. There is also a related reading list.

Lavender

http://hortweb.cas.psu.edu/vegcrops/herbs/Lavandulaangustifolia.html

Highly informative site from the Department of Horticulture at Pennsylvania State University, USA. There is a description of the plant itself, as well as details about when and how it blooms. There are also notes on the best way of cultivating it, and when it should be harvested.

Orchid House

http://sciserv2.uwaterloo.ca/orchids.html

Everything you could ever want to know about orchids can be found here. There is a very good introductory 'Frequently Asked Questions' section, as well as information for the more experienced horticulturist. There is even an orchid-related short story and some pictures of orchids accompanied by soothing music.

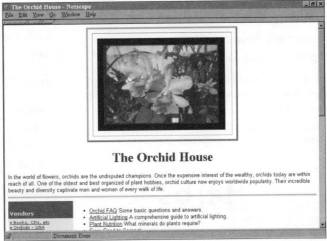

Peonies – Glorious in Bloom

http://www.munchkinnursery.com/gardenclip_peony.htm

Image of a peony, as well as a detailed description of the plant. There are also notes on growing peonies, taking account of the acidity of the soil and the amount of sunlight and moisture that they require.

Phloxes

http://www.digmagazine.com/96/56-96/phloxe.cfm

Contains images of different varieties of the wildflower family phlox, as well as detailed descriptions of each plant. There are also notes and tips on growing creeping phlox, taking account of the amounts of both sunlight and moisture that it requires.

Primrose

http://www.botanical.com/botanical/mgmh/p/primro69.html

Contains detailed information about the primrose, including an informative description of the plant and its habitat. This site also features details of the plant's constituents, as well as notes on the medicinal uses of the primrose, which range from being used as a sedative to treating muscular rheumatism.

Tulip Book

http://www.bib.wau.nl/tulips/

Online version of P Cos's manuscript catalogue of tulips, published in 1637.

Yesterday's Rose

http://www.country-lane.com/yr/

Information on over one hundred varieties of old garden rose. The site has many photographs of different kinds of rose, as well as details on the scent, flower, growth, and care of the popular plants.

Herbs

Algy's Herb Page

http://www.algy.com/herb/index.html

Dedicated to all things connected with herbs. This site is divided into a number of sections, allowing swift retrieval of information. 'The apothecary' contains links to articles about the preparation of medicinal herbs and how caution should be exercised. 'The kitchen' is a large collection of recipes involving herbs. 'The garden' describes the best way of growing your own herbs, including information about weather, harvesting, and geography. There is also an online library with books about herbs, a page containing the latest news in the herb world, and finally 'The greenhouse', where visitors to the site can discuss their herb-related problems and tips.

Allspice

http://www.botanical.com/botanical/mgmh/a/allsp025.html

Detailed information about allspice, including notes on the tree *Pimento officinalis* and its habitat. There are notes on the constituents of the tree and on its uses and preparations in medicine.

Aloes

http://www.botanical.com/botanical/mgmh/a/aloes027.html

Contains a detailed text-only description of a number of types of aloes and their habitat. Their constituents are also described in detail, as are their medicinal uses. There are even notes on the preparation of the tincture made from the plant.

Anise

http://hortweb.cas.psu.edu/vegcrops/herbs/Pimpinellaanisum.html

Information about the Mediterranean plant, including its herbal uses, its propagation method, and notes on how to plant anise seeds successfully. This wealth of information is provided from the Department of Horticulture at Pennsylvania State University, USA.

Arrowroot

http://www.botanical.com/botanical/mgmh/a/ arrow064.html

Contains detailed information about this plant. This site includes a description of the plant, its history, and its habitat. There are also extensive notes on its medicinal uses, which include acting as an antidote for certain poisons, arresting gangrene, and as food for convalescents. It also features details of other species of this plant.

Bergamot

http://hortweb.cas.psu.edu/vegcrops/herbs/ Monardadidyma.html

Wealth of information about this evergreen tree from the Department of Horticulture at Pennsylvania State University, USA. Information is included on the plant's herbal uses, propagation method, and the pests and diseases it is susceptible to. There are also notes on how and where it should be planted.

Betony, Wood

http://www.botanical.com/botanical/mgmh/b/ betowo35.html

Detailed information about this plant, including an informative description of the plant, its history, and its habitat. It also features notes on the medicinal uses of the plant, which range from relieving headaches to treating rheumatism.

Borage

http://www.botanical.com/botanical/mgmh/b/ borage66.html

Large source of information about this European plant. This site contains an interesting description of the plant, its history, and its habitat. It also features notes on borage's constituents and many medicinal uses, which include treating fevers and acting as a diuretic. There are also notes on the cultivation of borage.

Burdock

http://www.botanical.com/botanical/mgmh/b/ burdoc87.html

Informative resource relating to this plant. It contains a detailed description of the plant, its

constituents, and its habitat. There are also notes on the cultivation of burdock, as well as on the possible medicinal uses of the plant, which include relieving inflammation and acting as a diuretic.

Caraway

http://hortweb.cas.psu.edu/vegcrops/herbs/ Carumcarvi.html

Wealth of information about this herb from the Department of Horticulture at Pennsylvania State University, USA. The origins of caraway are described, as is the herb itself. There are also notes on its uses and the best ways of growing it.

Cassia (Cinnamon)

http://www.botanical.com/botanical/mgmh/c/ cassia31.html

Informative resource relating to cassia. It contains a detailed description of the plant, its constituents, and its habitat. There are also notes on the possible medicinal uses of the plant – such as acting as a stimulant or treating uterine haemorrhage – and on the dosages required.

Castor-oil Plant

http://www.botanical.com/botanical/mgmh/c/ casoil32.html

Detailed description of this plant and its history. There are notes on the cultivation and preparation of the castor-oil plant. Also included here are a detailed analysis of the constituents of the plant, as well as its uses in both medicine and picture restoration.

Catechu, Black

http://www.botanical.com/botanical/mgmh/c/ catbla35.html

Informative resource relating to black catechu. It contains a detailed description of the plant and its habitat. There are also notes on the possible medicinal uses of the plant, which range from stopping nosebleeds to treating gonorrhoea.

Chervil

http://hortweb.cas.psu.edu/vegcrops/herbs/ Anthriscuscerefolium.html

Wealth of information about this plant from the Department of Horticulture at Pennsylvania State University, USA. There is a description of the plant itself, as well as its details about when and how it blooms. There are also notes on the best way of planting it, and what sorts of soil and light it needs.

Chickweed

http://www.botanical.com/botanical/mgmh/c/chickw60.html

This Web site contains a detailed description of the plant and its habitat. There are also notes on the possible medicinal uses of chickweed, which include treating ulcers and external abscesses. Hydrophobia and scurvy are two other conditions the plant is said to treat.

Chicory

http://www.botanical.com/botanical/mgmh/c/chicor61.html

In addition to a detailed description of the plant, its history, and its habitat, this site also includes extensive notes on the cultivation of chicory, as well as on its constituents and possible medicinal uses, which include acting as a laxative and diuretic.

Chive

http://hortweb.cas.psu.edu/vegcrops/herbs/Alliumschoenoprasum.html

Wealth of information about this plant from the Department of Horticulture at Pennsylvania State University, USA. Information is included on its herbal uses, its propagation method, and notes on how to plant it successfully.

Cloves

http://www.botanical.com/botanical/mgmh/c/cloves76.html

Informative resource relating to cloves. This site contains a detailed description of the clove tree, its constituents, and its habitat. There are also extensive notes on the possible medicinal uses of cloves, which include relieving nausea, acting as an antiseptic, and treating bronchial troubles.

Coca, Bolivian

http://www.botanical.com/botanical/mgmh/c/cocobo78.html

Information on the Bolivian coca. Contents includedetailed description of the plant, its constituents, and its habitat. There are also

extensive notes on the possible medicinal uses of Bolivian coca, which include acting as a stimulant and local anaesthetic. However, as the site points out, the dangers of the drug far outweigh its benefits.

Columbine

http://www.botanical.com/botanical/mgmh/c/columb89.html

Information on the plant columbine, including a detailed description of the plant and its habitat. There are also extensive notes on the possible medicinal uses of columbine, which include acting as an astringent (although it should be noted that the plant can be poisonous).

Comfrey

http://www.botanical.com/botanical/mgmh/c/comfre92.html

Page of information on the comfrey plant. It contains a detailed description of the plant, its constituents. and its habitat. There are also extensive notes on the cultivation of comfrey, as well as on its possible medicinal uses, which include treating coughs and acting as an astringent.

Coriander

http://hortweb.cas.psu.edu/vegcrops/herbs/Coriandrumsativum.html

Fact sheet from the Department of Horticulture at the Pennsylvania State University, USA with a wealth of information on the appearance, cultivation, harvesting, and diseases of coriander.

Cumin

http://www.botanical.com/botanical/mgmh/c/cumin127.html

Informative resource relating to this herb. It contains a detailed description of the plant, its habitat, and even its place in history. There are also notes on the cultivation, constituents, and possible medicinal uses of cumin, which include acting as an antispasmodic and carminative.

Dill

http://hortweb.cas.psu.edu/vegcrops/herbs/Anethumgraveolens.html

Fact sheet from the Department of Horticulture at the Pennsylvania State University, USA, with a variety of information on the cultivation, harvesting, and uses of dill.

Fennel

http://hortweb.cas.psu.edu/vegcrops/herbs/
Foeniculumvulgare.html

Fact sheet from the Department of Horticulture at
the Pennsylvania State University, USA with
plenty of details on the appearance, cultivation,
harvesting, diseases, and uses of fennel.

Garlic

http://hortweb.cas.psu.edu/vegcrops/herbs/
Alliumsativum.html

Wealth of information about this plant from the
Department of Horticulture at Pennsylvania State
University, USA. There is a description of the plant
itself, as well as its details about when and how it
blooms. There are also notes on the best way of
planting it, and when it should be harvested.

Ginger

http://www.botanical.com/botanical/mgmh/g/
ginger13.html

Informative resource relating to ginger. It contains
a detailed description of the plant and its habitat.
There are also notes on the constituents of the
plant, as well as information on the possible
medicinal uses of ginger, which include acting as
a stimulant.

F
A
C
T

GINGER
southeast Asian reedlike perennial plant; the
hot-tasting spicy underground root is used as
a food flavouring and in preserves. (*Zingiber
officinale*, family Zingiberaceae.)

Ginseng

http://www.botanical.com/botanical/mgmh/g/
ginsen15.html

Extract from the *Modern Herbal* by Mrs M Grive,
first published in 1931. This site gives a thorough
description of the ginseng plant, its cultivation,
harvesting, and the uses to which it is put. Some
substitutes for the plant are also described.

Goldenseal

http://www.botanical.com/botanical/mgmh/g/
golsea27.html

Contains a detailed analysis of this plant and its
habitat. There are extensive notes on the plant's

cultivation and constituents, and there are even
details of the plant's many medicinal uses and the
preparation of the drugs in which it is used.

Horseradish

http://hortweb.cas.psu.edu/vegcrops/herbs/
Armoraciarusticana.html

Wealth of information about this plant from the
Department of Horticulture at Pennsylvania State
University, USA. The origins of horseradish are
described, as is the plant itself. There are also
notes on its uses and the best ways of growing it.

Lemon Balm

http://hortweb.cas.psu.edu/vegcrops/herbs/
Melissaofficinalis.html

Wealth of information about this plant from the
Department of Horticulture at Pennsylvania State
University, USA. There is a description of the
plant and the diseases to which it is prone. There
are details about when and how it blooms, and
also notes on the best way of cultivating it and
when it should be harvested.

Oregano

http://hortweb.cas.psu.edu/vegcrops/
herbs/Origanumvulgare.html

Detailed information about oregano from
the Department of Horticulture at
Pennsylvania State University, USA.
There is a description of the plant itself, as
well as its details about when and how it
blooms. There are also notes on the best
way of planting it, and when it should be
harvested.

Parsley

http://hortweb.cas.psu.edu/vegcrops/
herbs/Petroselinumcrispum.html

Information about this much-loved culinary herb,
from the Department of Horticulture at
Pennsylvania State University, USA. There is a
description of the plant, its propagation method,
and which types of light and soil it requires. There
are also notes on its uses in decoration, medicine,
cosmetics, and cooking.

Peppermint

http://hortweb.cas.psu.edu/vegcrops/herbs/
Menthaxpiperita.html

Considerable information about this plant from
the Department of Horticulture at Pennsylvania

State University, USA. There is a description of the plant, its propagation method, and which types of light and soil it requires. There are also notes on how to grow it, as well as its uses in medicine, cosmetics, and cooking.

Red Clover

http://www.botanical.com/botanical/mgmh/c/clovrd75.html

Informative resource relating to red clover. It contains a detailed description of the plant and its habitat. There are also extensive notes on the possible medicinal uses of red clover, which include acting as an antispasmodic and treating whooping cough.

Rosemary

http://hortweb.cas.psu.edu/vegcrops/herbs/Rosmarinusofficinalis.html

Wealth of information about this plant from the Department of Horticulture at Pennsylvania State University, USA. There is a description of the plant itself and its place in mythology. There is also information on when and how it should be planted, and notes on its uses.

F A C T

ROSEMARY

evergreen shrub belonging to the mint family, native to the Mediterranean and western Asia, with small, narrow, scented leaves and clusters of pale blue or purple flowers. It is widely cultivated as a herb for use in cooking and for its aromatic oil, used in perfumery and pharmaceuticals. (*Rosemarinus officinalis*, family Labiatae.)

Rue

http://hortweb.cas.psu.edu/vegcrops/herbs/rutagraveolens.html

Informative resource relating to this herb from the Department of Horticulture at Pennsylvania State University, USA. There is a description of the plant and the ways it should be harvested and cultivated. It also includes notes on the many uses of the herb in decoration, cookery, and medicine.

Sage

http://hortweb.cas.psu.edu/vegcrops/herbs/Salviaofficinalis.html

Information about this plant from the Department of Horticulture at Pennsylvania State University, USA. There is a description of the plant and its place in history. There is also information about its propagation method, the pests and diseases it is susceptible to, and which types of light and soil it requires.

Spearmint

http://hortweb.cas.psu.edu/vegcrops/herbs/Menthaspicata.html

Detailed resource relating to this herb from the Department of Horticulture at Pennsylvania State University, USA. There is a description of the plant, its place in history, and the ways it should be harvested and cultivated. It also includes notes on the many uses of the herb in medicine, cosmetics, and cookery.

Sweet Basil

http://hortweb.cas.psu.edu/vegcrops/herbs/Ocimumbasilicum.html

Wealth of information about this plant from the Department of Horticulture at Pennsylvania State University, USA. The origins of basil are described, as is the plant itself. There are also notes on the uses of basil and the best ways of growing it.

Tarragon

http://hortweb.cas.psu.edu/vegcrops/herbs/Artemesiadracunculus.html

Considerable information about this plant from the Department of Horticulture at Pennsylvania State University, USA. There is a description of the plant and its propagation method. There is also information about its bloom, the pests and diseases it is susceptible to, and which types of light and soil it requires.

Thyme

http://hortweb.cas.psu.edu/vegcrops/herbs/Thymusvulgaris.html

Detailed resource relating to this herb from the Department of Horticulture at Pennsylvania State University, USA. There is a description of the plant, its place in history, and the ways it should be harvested and cultivated. It also includes notes on the many uses of the herb in decoration, medicine, cosmetics, and cookery.

Watercress

http://www.botanical.com/botanical/mgmh/w/
watcre09.html

This detailed page on watercress contains an informative description of the plant and its habitat. There are also notes on the constituents and possible medicinal uses of watercress.

Woad

http://www.botanical.com/botanical/mgmh/w/
woad--28.html

Fascinating resource on this historic herb, includes a description of the plant and its habitat. There are also notes on the cultivation and possible medicinal uses of woad, which include acting as an astringent.

Trees

Alder, Common

http://www.botanical.com/botanical/mgmh/a/
alder019.html

Contains much detailed information on the common alder, or *Alnus glutinose.* The plant itself is described, as is its habitat. There is also a detailed description of the constituents of the plant, and there are even notes on its uses as a dye and as a cure for rheumatism.

Ancient Bristlecone Pine

http://www.sonic.net/bristlecone/intro.html

All about the bristlecone pines of California, thought to be the world's oldest living inhabitants. This site is a good starting point for information about dendrochronology (the study of tree rings to date past events or to establish past climatic conditions).

Angostura (True)

http://www.botanical.com/botanical/
mgmh/a/angos039.html

Notes on the tree that is used in the preparation of angostura bitters. There is a description of the tree itself, as well as of its constituents and of the medicinal uses of the bark. Also featured here is a description of the way to prepare an infusion made from the bark.

Arbutus (Strawberry Tree)

http://www.botanical.com/botanical/mgmh/a/
arbut053.html

Detailed information about this shrub. Contained here are detailed notes on its habitat and characteristics, as well as notes on many uses which range from wine production to tanning.

Ash

http://www.botanical.com/botanical/mgmh/a/
ash--073.html

Contains detailed information about the ash. This site also features an extensive description of the different types of this tree, as well as notes on its constituents. There is also information about its medicinal uses, which include treating dropsy and jaundice, as well as gout and rheumatic complaints.

Beech

http://www.botanical.com/botanical/mgmh/b/
beech-27.html

Large source of information about this tree. Included here are a description of the tree itself, its habitat, and its history. There are notes on its constituents and also on its medicinal uses, which include producing antiseptic and treating skin conditions. There are also brief descriptions of the many species of beech tree.

Birch, Common

http://www.botanical.com/botanical/mgmh/b/
bircom43.html

Detailed information about this tree, including an informative description of the common birch, its history, and its habitat. This site also features notes on the constituents and medicinal uses of the common birch, which range from acting as an astringent to treating skin conditions.

F A C T

TREE

perennial plant with a woody stem, usually a single stem (trunk), made up of wood and protected by an outer layer of bark. It absorbs water through a root system.

British Trees Home Page

http://www.u-net.com/trees/p3.htm

Introductory guide to native British trees. The site can be searched by common name or Latin name, and there is a photographic collection of the mature trees, as well as seeds and flowers in various stages of their development.

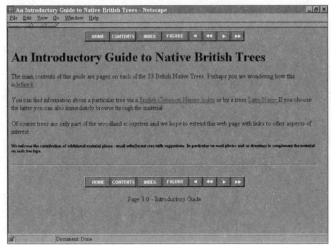

Cacao

http://www.botanical.com/botanical/mgmh/c/cacao-02.html

Informative resource relating to this tree. It contains a detailed description of the plant, its habitat, and its history. There are also notes on the many uses of cacao, which include making cocoa, preparing suppositories, and acting as a diuretic.

Cedar, Yellow

http://www.botanical.com/botanical/mgmh/c/cedyel41.html

Informative resource relating to the yellow cedar tree. It contains a detailed description of the tree, its constituents, and its habitat. There are also notes on the possible medicinal uses of the plant – such as acting as a diuretic or treating rheumatism – and on the dosages and poisonous effects.

Chestnut, Horse

http://www.botanical.com/botanical/mgmh/c/chehor58.html

Informative resource relating to the horse chestnut. It contains a detailed description of the tree, its constituents, and its habitat. There are also notes on the cultivation of the tree, as well as on its possible medicinal uses, which include treating fevers, rheumatism, and haemorrhoids.

Chestnut, Sweet

http://www.botanical.com/botanical/mgmh/c/cheswe59.html

This site contains information relating to the sweet chestnut. It contains a detailed description of the tree, its propagation methods, and its habitat. There are also notes on the many uses of the sweet chestnut, which include making stuffing for turkeys and whitening linen. The possible medicinal uses of the tree are also featured.

Elder

http://www.botanical.com/botanical/mgmh/e/elder-04.html

Immensely informative resource relating to the elder. It contains a detailed description of the plant, as well as its place in history. There are also notes on the constituents and uses of the bark, leaves, and flowers of the elder. There are even a number of recipes that make use of the elder, including elderberry chutney.

Elm, Common

http://www.botanical.com/botanical/mgmh/e/elmcom08.html

Informative resource relating to the common elm, containing a detailed description of the tree and its habitat. There are also notes on the uses and constituents of the tree, as well as information on Dutch elm disease.

Eucalyptus

http://www.botanical.com/botanical/mgmh/e/eucaly14.html

Information on the eucalyptus tree, its appearance and habitat. There are also notes on the constituents of the tree, as well as information on the possible medicinal uses of the eucalyptus, which include acting as an antiseptic.

Frankincense

http://www.botanical.com/botanical/mgmh/f/franki31.html

Informative resource relating to frankincense. The site contains a detailed description of the tree and its habitat. There are also notes on the constituents of the plant, as well as information on the possible medicinal uses of frankincense, which include acting as a stimulant.

Leptospermum

http://155.187.10.12/leptospermum/index.html

Page devoted to the *leptospermum* genus of plant, commonly known as the 'tea tree', with a description of its distribution, history, and cultivation. Also included are links to colour photographs and information about more than 30 different species of the tea tree plant.

Today's Christmas Trees

http://www.esf.edu/pubprog/brochure/xmastree/xmastree.htm

The origins of the traditions of the Christmas tree are dealt with here. The site also describe types of pine that are commonly used as Christmas trees, and discusses the environmental impact the yearly crop has on forest ecosystems.

University of Delaware Botanic Gardens – Trees

http://bluehen.ags.udel.edu/gopher-data2/.botanic_garden/trees.html

Key facts about the trees in these botanic gardens – their botanical name, pronunciation, foliage, growth habits, landscape uses, pests, and so on – plus a glossary of terms can be found at this site.

American Bamboo Society World Wide Web Page

http://www.bamboo.org/abs/

Good central source of information about bamboo. There is much information about different giant grasses, their decorative and practical uses, how to grow them, and keep them healthy. Though the site provider is primarily a horticultural organization, the contents also include information on how to make a variety of objects from bamboo, news of conservation projects, and further written and online sources of information about bamboo.

Buckwheat

http://www.botanical.com/botanical/mgmh/b/buckwh81.html

Detailed information about buckwheat. Included here are detailed descriptions of the plant, its habitat, and its cultivation. This site also features notes on the plant's constituents and possible medicinal uses. There is also an introduction to other species, including false and climbing buckwheat.

Cactus and Succulent Plant Mall

http://www.cactus-mall.com/index.html

Huge source of information on cacti and how to grow them. There are also reports on conservation of cacti and succulents. There are links to a large number of international cacti associations.

Miscellaneous Plants

Adder's Tongue, English

http://www.botanical.com/botanical/mgmh/f/ferns-08.html#add

In-depth information about this fern, including a detailed description of the plant and its habitat. It also features notes on the possible medicinal uses of the plant, including extensive information about the preparation of a treatment for wounds.

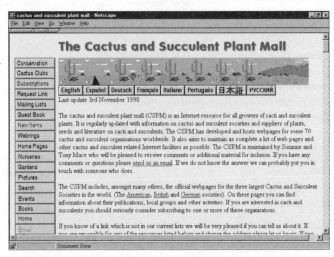

Carnivorous Plants FAQ

http://www.sarracenia.com/faq.html

Well-written source of general information about carnivorous plants. Each genus is presented with good text and pictures. There is advice on planting, growing, and feeding carnivorous plants. The site contains information on the effort to conserve endangered species.

Convolvulus, Field

http://www.botanical.com/botanical/mgmh/c/convol96.html

Informative resource relating to field convolvulus, or field bindweed. It contains a detailed description of the plant, including information about its blooming pattern, its habitat, and its propagation methods. Also included here are links to information about related plants, including the jalap bindweed.

Docks

http://www.botanical.com/botanical/mgmh/d/docks-15.html

Features a brief introduction to dock plants, as well as descriptions of a number of different species, including patience dock, great water dock, and sharp-pointed dock. The possible medicinal uses of these plants are also described, where relevant.

Fern Resource Hub

http://www.inetworld.net/sdfern/

Huge source of fern-related information for the fern hobbyist. Organized by the San Diego Fern Society (USA), this is a clearing house of information for fern societies across the world. There is general information on ferns and how to grow them, and a range of sources of further information. If you have queries about ferns, there are experts to be e-mailed. There is also news of upcoming fern events all over the world.

Flax

http://www.botanical.com/botanical/mgmh/f/flax--23.html

Informative resource relating to flax. It contains detailed descriptions of the plant, its habitat, and

even its history. There are also notes on the constituents of the plant, as well as information on its possible medicinal uses, which include acting as a laxative and treating burns.

Fungi

http://www.herb.lsa.umich.edu/kidpage/factindx.htm

University-run network of hyperlinked pages on fungi, from their earliest fossil records to their current ecology and life cycles, from how they are classified systematically to how they are studied. Although this page is not shy of technical terms, there are clear explanations and pictures to help the uninitiated.

Grasses

http://www.botanical.com/botanical/mgmh/g/grasse34.html

Informative resource relating to various types of grass, such as couch grass and darnel. It contains detailed descriptions of the plants, including, where relevant, information about the plants' habitats, their constituents, and even their medicinal uses, which, in the case of couch grass, include treating rheumatism and acting as a diuretic.

Moss, Common Club

http://www.botanical.com/botanical/mgmh/m/mosccl48.html

Informative resource relating to common club moss. It contains a detailed description of the plant and its habitat. There are also extensive notes on the possible medicinal uses of common club moss, which include acting as a diuretic and treating diarrhoea, eczema, and rheumatism.

Nettles

http://www.botanical.com/botanical/mgmh/n/nettle03.html

Complete guide to nettles, covering six types of this plant: greater, lesser, white dead, purple dead, and yellow dead. There are detailed descriptions of all these types of nettles, including, where relevant, recipes that include them as an ingredient, notes on their constituents, and also information about medicinal uses.

Nightshade, Deadly

http://www.botanical.com/botanical/mgmh/n/nighde05.html

Extensive resource of information about deadly nightshade, or belladonna. Included here are detailed descriptions of this poisonous plant and its habitat. There is information about the cultivation of belladonna, and even notes on the possible medicinal uses of the plant, which range from treating eye diseases to acting as an antispasmodic.

Nightshade, Woody

http://www.botanical.com/botanical/mgmh/n/nighwo06.html

Detailed information about woody nightshade, including an informative description of the plant, its constituents, and its habitat. This site also features notes on the medicinal uses of the plant, which range from treating skin conditions to asthma.

Properties of the Hemp Plant

http://www.cats-eye.com/cannabis/hemp.html

'Hemp' in this archive is used to describe what is actually a large range of plants. These plants consist of three main variations: *Cannabis sativa*, *Cannabis indica*, and *Cannabis ruderalis*.

Teazles

http://www.botanical.com/botanical/mgmh/t/teazle09.html

In-depth information about teazles, or teasels. There is an informative description of the plant itself, and there are even detailed notes on a number of its uses: for curing jaundice and fleecing wool. It also includes information on the different types of teazles.

Thornapple

http://www.botanical.com/botanical/mgmh/t/thorna12.html

Informative resource relating to the thornapple, or datura. It contains a detailed description of this poisonous plant and its habitat. There are also notes on the constituents, cultivation, and possible medicinal uses of the thornapple, which include acting as an antispasmodic and narcotic.

Agriculture

Biological Control

http://www.nysaes.cornell.edu:80/ent/biocontrol/

University-based site on the various methods of biological control used by farmers in the USA. This includes sections on parasitoids, predators, pathogens, and weed feeders. Each sections contains images and sections on 'Relative effectiveness' and 'Pesticide susceptibility'.

Fisheries

http://www.fao.org/WAICENT/FAOINFO/FISHERY/FISHERY.HTM

Web site of the Fisheries Department of the United Nations Food and Agriculture Organization. This is a comprehensive report on the state of the world's fisheries and how to manage them for future generations. Information can be accessed via species and by country and there are links to a large number of international and scientific bodies concerned with fishing.

International Federation of Organic Farming Movements

http://ecoweb.dk/ifoam/

Site of an international organization working to promote sustainable organic agriculture. There are a clear summary of the organization's goals, reports of international campaigns on food and farming issues, press releases, contacts for the hundreds of affiliated organizations, and details of related publications.

Potatoes, Peppers, and Eggplants

http://www.ext.vt.edu/pubs/envirohort/
426-413/426-413.html

Informative guide to these vegetables from the Virginia Cooperative Extension. There is a guide to planting them, as well as the types of soil, sunlight, and moisture that yield best results. This site also features solutions to common problems and information about harvesting and storage.

Royal Agricultural Society of England

http://www.rase.org.uk/

Information on the work of the association established by Royal Charter to promote the agricultural industry in England. There are full details of the structure of RASE, the annual Royal Show, and other events.

Seeds of Change Garden

http://horizon.nmsu.edu/garden/welcome.html

Inspirational tutorial by the Smithsonian Institution, USA, on cultural exchange, food crops, and gardens. The site has masses of information about Old World and New World foods and detailed instructions on creating Old World and New World recipes. This educational site also includes separate clickable teacher/parent notes offering additional information as well as an extensive bibliography on Columbus, Thanksgiving, food, and cultural diversity.

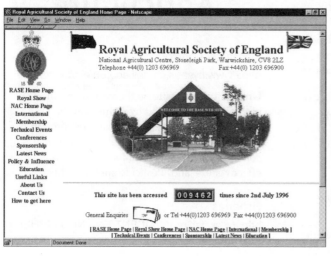

Sustainable Agriculture Network

http://www.sare.org/san/

US-government-funded organization dedicated to the global exchange of information on sustainable farming systems. This well-organized site highlights the issues through interesting profiles of individual farming families who have moved away from conventional cultivation techniques. Findings of research projects are presented and there are links to a number of US sustainable agriculture sites.

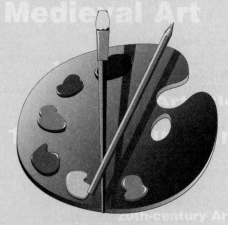

ART & DESIGN

Medieval Art

Angelico, Fra

http://www.oir.ucf.edu/wm/paint/auth/angelico/

Site at the WebMuseum, Paris, devoted to Fra Angelico.

F A C T

ANGELICO, FRA (c. 1400–1455)

Italian painter. He was a monk, active in Florence, and painted religious scenes. His series of frescoes at the monastery of San Marco, Florence, was begun after 1436. He also produced several altarpieces in a style characterized by a delicacy of line and colour.

Bellini, Giovanni

http://www.oir.ucf.edu/wm/paint/auth/bellini/

Site at the WebMuseum, Paris, devoted to Giovanni Bellini.

Bouts, Dirk

http://www.oir.ucf.edu/wm/paint/auth/bouts/

Site at the WebMuseum, Paris, devoted to Dirk Bouts.

Broederlam, Melchior

http://www.oir.ucf.edu/wm/paint/auth/broederlam/

Site at the WebMuseum, Paris, devoted to Melchior Broederlam.

Cavallini, Pietro

http://www.oir.ucf.edu/wm/paint/auth/cavallini/

Site at the WebMuseum, Paris, devoted to Pietro Cavallini.

Christus, Petrus

http://www.oir.ucf.edu/wm/paint/auth/christus/

Site at the WebMuseum, Paris, devoted to Petrus Christus.

Daddi, Bernardo

http://www.mega.it/eng/egui/pers/daddi.htm

Profile of the Florentine painter. There is a summary of the main events of his life and the development of his style. This site also includes photographs of two of his best-known works.

Drawings of Sandro Botticelli

http://sgwww.epfl.ch/cgi-bin/Webdriver?MItab=sandro&MIcol=object&MIval=frame0&CODEHTML1=allegory&CODEHTML2=frontispice&BABEL=english

Detailed information about the Florentine painter Sandro Botticelli. Included here is a detailed biography, as well as a large amount of information about his paintings. Part of the site also focuses on his drawings rather than his paintings, discussing his drawing style and his legacy in this area. A large selection of his works are used throughout the site, to illustrate the text and help understanding of the issues discussed.

Eyck, Jan van

http://www.oir.ucf.edu/wm/paint/auth/eyck/

Site at the WebMuseum, Paris, devoted to Jan van Eyck.

Fouquet, Jean

http://www.oir.ucf.edu/wm/paint/auth/fouquet/

Site at the WebMuseum, Paris, devoted to Jean Fouquet.

Ghirlandaio, Domenico

http://www.oir.ucf.edu/wm/paint/auth/ghirlandaio/

Site at the WebMuseum, Paris, devoted to Domenico Ghirlandaio.

Giotto

http://198.62.75.1/www1/francis/

Profile of the life and achievements of the Italian who transformed European art. There are also over two hundred stunning images of Giotto's work.

Goes, Hugo van der

http://www.oir.ucf.edu/wm/paint/auth/goes/

Site at the WebMuseum, Paris, devoted to Hugo van der Goes.

Mantegna, Andrea

http://www.oir.ucf.edu/wm/paint/auth/mantegna/

Site at the WebMuseum, Paris, devoted to Andrea Mantegna.

Piero della Francesca

http://www.oir.ucf.edu/wm/paint/auth/piero/

Site at the WebMuseum, Paris, devoted to Piero della Francesca.

WebMuseum, Paris

http://www.oir.ucf.edu/wm/paint/auth/

Large site containing information on some of the world's greatest artists. This site provides biographical details, photographs, critical discussion of the artist's works, and hyperlinks to related artists.

Weyden, Rogier van der

http://www.oir.ucf.edu/wm/paint/auth/weyden/

Site at the WebMuseum, Paris, devoted to Rogier van der Weyden.

16th-century Art

Albrecht Dürer – An Exhibit of Four of Our Favourite Prints

http://glyphs.com/art/durer/

Contains a selection of prints by the German artist Albrecht Dürer, as well as a brief amount of information about each one. There is the option to download the large-size images, such as *The Knight, Death, and the Devil.*

Altdorfer, Albrecht

http://www.oir.ucf.edu/wm/paint/auth/altdorfer/

Site at the WebMuseum, Paris, devoted to Albrecht Altdorfer.

Baldung Grien, Hans

http://www.oir.ucf.edu/wm/paint/auth/baldung/

Site at the WebMuseum, Paris, devoted to Hans Baldung Grien.

Barocci, Federico

http://www.oir.ucf.edu/wm/paint/auth/barocci/

Site at the WebMuseum, Paris, devoted to Federico Barocci.

Bosch, Hieronymus

http://www.oir.ucf.edu/wm/paint/auth/bosch/

Site at the WebMuseum, Paris, devoted to Hieronymus Bosch.

Bronzino, Agnolo

http://www.oir.ucf.edu/wm/paint/auth/bronzino/

Site at the WebMuseum, Paris, devoted to Agnolo Bronzino.

Brueghel, Pieter the Elder

http://mexplaza.udg.mx/wm/paint/auth/bruegel/

Profile of the greatest 16th-century Flemish artist. There is a biography of Pieter Brueghel the Elder, notes on his paintings, and high-resolution images of his best-known works. The site also includes biographical details of his two sons.

Burgkmair, Hans the Elder

http://www.oir.ucf.edu/wm/paint/auth/burgkmair/

Site at the WebMuseum, Paris, devoted to Hans Burgkmair the Elder.

Caravaggio, Michelangelo Merisi da

http://www.oir.ucf.edu/wm/paint/auth/caravaggio/

Site at the WebMuseum, Paris, devoted to Michelangelo Merisi da Caravaggio.

Carracci

http://www.oir.ucf.edu/wm/paint/auth/carracci/

Site at the WebMuseum, Paris, devoted to the Carracci family.

Cellini, Benvenuto

http://sunserv.kfki.hu/~arthp/html/c/cellini/index.html

Profile of the Florentine sculptor, engraver, and goldsmith. A biography provides a flavour of the escapades and intrigues that dominated his life. There are also high-resolution images of five of his best-known works.

Clouet

http://www.oir.ucf.edu/wm/paint/ auth/clouet/

Site at the WebMuseum, Paris, devoted to the Clouet family.

Correggio

http://www.oir.ucf.edu/wm/paint/auth/correggio/

Site at the WebMuseum, Paris, devoted to Correggio.

Cranach, Lucas the Elder

http://www.oir.ucf.edu/wm/paint/auth/cranach/

Site at the WebMuseum, Paris, devoted to Lucas Cranach the Elder.

David, Gerard

http://www.oir.ucf.edu/wm/paint/auth/davidg/

Site at the WebMuseum, Paris, devoted to Gerard David, providing biographical details, hyperlinks to related artists, photographs, and critical discussion of his work.

Dossi, Dosso

http://www.oir.ucf.edu/wm/paint/auth/dossi/

Site at the WebMuseum, Paris, devoted to Dosso Dossi, providing biographical details, hyperlinks to related artists, photographs, and critical discussion of his work.

Greco, El

http://www.oir.ucf.edu/wm/paint/auth/greco/

Site at the WebMuseum, Paris, devoted to El Greco, providing biographical details, hyperlinks to related artists and movements, photographs, and critical discussion of his work.

F A C T

GRECO, EL (1541–1614)

Spanish painter called 'the Greek' because he was born in Crete. He painted elegant portraits and intensely emotional religious scenes with increasingly distorted figures and unearthly light.

Hilliard, Nicholas

http://www.oir.ucf.edu/wm/paint/auth/hilliard/

Site at the WebMuseum, Paris, devoted to Nicholas Hilliard.

Holbein, Hans, the Younger

http://www.oir.ucf.edu/wm/paint/auth/holbein/

Site at the WebMuseum, Paris, devoted to Hans Holbein the Younger.

Leonardo da Vinci

http://www.oir.ucf.edu/wm/paint/auth/vinci/

Site at the WebMuseum, Paris, devoted to Leonardo da Vinci.

Leonardo da Vinci Drawings

http://banzai.msi.umn.edu/leonardo/

Fifteen of Leonardo da Vinci's drawings including *Vitruvian Man*, *Self Portrait*, and *Five Characters in a Comic Scene*.

Michelangelo

http://www.oir.ucf.edu/wm/paint/auth/michelangelo/

Site at the WebMuseum, Paris, devoted to Michelangelo.

Raphael

http://www.oir.ucf.edu/wm/paint/auth/raphael/

Site at the WebMuseum, Paris, devoted to Raphael.

Tintoretto

http://www.oir.ucf.edu/wm/paint/auth/tintoretto/

Site at the WebMuseum, Paris, devoted to Tintoretto.

Titian

http://www.oir.ucf.edu/wm/paint/auth/titian/

Site at the WebMuseum, Paris, devoted to Titian.

Veronese, Paolo (Caliari)

http://www.ringling.org/veron.html

Profile of the sumptuous Venetian painter. It traces his contribution to the Venetian art tradition and describes his major works. There is a reproduction of his celebrated *Rest on the Flight into Egypt*.

WebMuseum, Paris

http://www.oir.ucf.edu/wm/paint/auth/

Large site containing information on some of the world's greatest artists. This site provides biographical details, photographs, critical discussion of the artist's works, and hyperlinks to related artists.

17th-century Art

Artemisia Gentileschi and the Age of Baroque

http://rubens.anu.edu.au/student.projects/artemisia/Artemisia.html

Full biography of the Italian artist. The influence of the traumatic events of her life on her art are related. This site includes a good introduction to her art and style and also discusses the influence of Rubens and Caravaggio.

Avercamp, Hendrick

http://www.oir.ucf.edu/wm/paint/auth/avercamp/

Site at the WebMuseum, Paris, devoted to Hendrick Avercamp.

Bernini, Gianlorenzo

http://www.sinclair.edu/sec/artman263/ma263be1.htm

Biography of the Italian artist. It traces his career and contribution to the development of the Baroque style. There are several photos of his work as sculptor and architect.

Beyeren, Abraham van

http://www.oir.ucf.edu/wm/paint/auth/beyeren/

Site at the WebMuseum, Paris, devoted to Abraham van Beyeren.

Cano, Alonso

http://www.oir.ucf.edu/wm/paint/auth/cano/

Site at the WebMuseum, Paris, devoted to Alonso Cano.

Cuyp, Aelbert

http://www.oir.ucf.edu/wm/paint/auth/cuyp/

Site at the WebMuseum, Paris, devoted to the Cuyp family.

Dyck, Sir Anthony van

http://www.oir.ucf.edu/wm/paint/auth/dyck/

Site at the WebMuseum, Paris, devoted to Sir Anthony van Dyck.

Elsheimer, Adam

http://www.oir.ucf.edu/wm/paint/auth/elsheimer/

Site at the WebMuseum, Paris, devoted to Adam Elsheimer.

Giordano, Luca

http://www.oir.ucf.edu/wm/paint/auth/giordano/

Site at the WebMuseum, Paris, devoted to Luca Giordano.

Hals, Frans

http://www.oir.ucf.edu/wm/paint/auth/hals/

Site at the WebMuseum, Paris, devoted to Frans Hals.

Heda, Willem Claesz

http://www.oir.ucf.edu/wm/paint/auth/heda/

Site at the WebMuseum, Paris, devoted to Willem Claesz Heda.

Heem, Jan Davidsz de

http://www.oir.ucf.edu/wm/paint/auth/ heem/

Site at the WebMuseum, Paris, devoted to Jan Davidsz de Heem.

Hobbema, Meindert

http://www.oir.ucf.edu/wm/paint/auth/hobbema/

Site at the WebMuseum, Paris, devoted to Meindert Hobbema.

Hooch, Pieter de

http://www.oir.ucf.edu/wm/paint/auth/hooch/

Site at the WebMuseum, Paris, devoted to Pieter de Hooch.

Le Brun, Charles

http://www.oir.ucf.edu/wm/paint/auth/le-brun/

Site at the WebMuseum, Paris, devoted to Charles Le Brun.

Murillo, Bartolomé Esteban

http://www.oir.ucf.edu/wm/paint/auth/murillo/

Site at the WebMuseum, Paris, devoted to Bartolomé Esteban Murillo.

Rembrandt

http://amsterdam.park.org:8888/Netherlands/pavilions/culture/rembrandt/

**F
A
C
T**

DUTCH ART

The Netherlands became effectively independent, with approximately the boundaries it has today, in the early 17th century. Among the many Dutch masters of this period were Rembrandt; Willem Kalf, who excelled at still lifes; and Adriaen van Ostade, who painted Flemish peasant scenes.

Art historians and Rembrandt buffs will bask in this splendid page, dedicated to the Dutch painter's work and sponsored by the Rembrandt Research Project.

Rubens, Peter Paul

http://www.oir.ucf.edu/wm/paint/auth/rubens/

Site at the WebMuseum, Paris, devoted to Peter Paul Rubens.

Velázquez (or Velásquez) Diego

http://sunsite.unc.edu/wm/paint/auth/velazquez/

Good introduction to the life, work, and legacy of Spain's greatest painter. His life as a Madrid court painter and his two trips to Italy are described. The skills of the master of realism known as 'the painter's painter' are analysed. There are also high-resolution photos of fifteen of his best-known compositions.

Vermeer, Jan

http://www.oir.ucf.edu/wm/paint/auth/vermeer/

Site at the WebMuseum, Paris, devoted to Jan Vermeer.

WebMuseum, Paris

http://www.oir.ucf.edu/wm/paint/auth/

Large site containing information on some of the world's greatest artists. This site provides biographical details, photographs, critical discussion of the artist's works, and hyperlinks to related artists.

18th-century Art

Blake, William

http://www.oir.ucf.edu/wm/paint/auth/blake/

Site at the WebMuseum, Paris, devoted to William Blaker.

Boucher, François

http://www.oir.ucf.edu/wm/paint/auth/boucher/

Site at the WebMuseum, Paris, devoted to François Boucher.

Canaletto

http://www.oir.ucf.edu/wm/paint/auth/canaletto/

Site at the WebMuseum, Paris, devoted to Canaletto.

Chardin, Jean-Baptiste-Siméon

http://www.oir.ucf.edu/wm/paint/auth/chardin/

Site at the WebMuseum, Paris, devoted to Jean-Baptiste-Siméon Chardin.

Copley, John Singleton

http://www.oir.ucf.edu/wm/paint/auth/copley/

Site at the WebMuseum, Paris, devoted to John Singleton Copley.

David, Jacques-Louis

http://www.oir.ucf.edu/wm/paint/auth/david/

Site at the WebMuseum, Paris, devoted to Jacques-Louis David.

Desportes, Alexandre-François

http://www.oir.ucf.edu/wm/paint/auth/desportes/

Site at the WebMuseum, Paris, devoted to Alexandre-François Desporte.

Feke, Robert

http://www.oir.ucf.edu/wm/paint/auth/feke/

Site at the WebMuseum, Paris, devoted to Robert Feke.

Fragonard, Jean-Honoré

http://www.oir.ucf.edu/wm/paint/auth/fragonard/

Site at the WebMuseum, Paris, devoted to Jean-Honoré Fragonard.

Fuseli, Henry

http://www.oir.ucf.edu/wm/paint/auth/fuseli/

Site at the WebMuseum, Paris, devoted to Henry Fuseli.

Gainsborough, Thomas

http://www.oir.ucf.edu/wm/paint/auth/gainsborough/

Site at the WebMuseum, Paris, devoted to Thomas Gainsborough.

Greuze, Jean-Baptiste

http://www.oir.ucf.edu/wm/paint/auth/greuze/

Site at the WebMuseum, Paris, devoted to Jean-Baptiste Greuze.

Guardi, Francesco

http://www.oir.ucf.edu/wm/paint/auth/guardi/

Site at the WebMuseum, Paris, devoted to Francesco Guardi.

Kauffmann, Angelica

http://www.knight.org/advent/cathen/08609b.htm

Profile of the Swiss-born painter. It traces her precocious talent in music and art, the artistic recognition she won during her years in London, and the salon she established in Italy. Her portraits are praised on this site but her historical pictures are declared to be overly sentimental.

Troy, Jean-François de

http://www.oir.ucf.edu/wm/paint/auth/troy/

Site at the WebMuseum, Paris, devoted to Jean-François de Troy.

Watteau, Jean-Antoine

http://www.oir.ucf.edu/wm/paint/auth/watteau/

Site at the WebMuseum, Paris, devoted to Jean-Antoine Watteau.

WebMuseum, Paris

http://www.oir.ucf.edu/wm/paint/auth/

Large site containing information on some of the world's greatest artists. This site provides biographical details, photographs, critical discussion of the artist's works, and hyperlinks to related artists.

West, Benjamin

http://www.oir.ucf.edu/wm/paint/auth/west/

Site at the WebMuseum, Paris, devoted to Benjamin West.

Wright, Joseph

http://www.oir.ucf.edu/wm/paint/auth/wright/

Site at the WebMuseum, Paris, devoted to Joseph Wright.

19th-century US Art

Cassatt, Mary

http://www.oir.ucf.edu/wm/paint/auth/cassatt/

Site at the WebMuseum, Paris, devoted to Mary Cassatt.

Chase, William Merritt

http://www.oir.ucf.edu/wm/paint/auth/chase/

Site at the WebMuseum, Paris, devoted to William Merritt Chase.

Eakins, Thomas

http://www.oir.ucf.edu/wm/paint/auth/eakins/

Site at the WebMuseum, Paris, devoted to Thomas Eakins.

LaFarge, John

http://www.knight.org/advent/cathen/16050b.htm

Biography of the US painter, decorator, and writer. His artistic interests and his innovations in the design of stained glass and murals are described. The full breadth of the interests of this pious man is traced.

Sargent, John Singer

http://www.oir.ucf.edu/wm/paint/auth/sargent/

Site at the WebMuseum, Paris, devoted to John Singer Sargent.

WebMuseum, Paris

http://www.oir.ucf.edu/wm/paint/auth/

Large site containing information on some of the world's greatest artists. This site provides biographical details, photographs, critical discussion of the artist's works, and hyperlinks to related artists.

Whistler, James Abbott McNeill

http://www.oir.ucf.edu/wm/paint/auth/whistler/

Site at the WebMuseum, Paris, devoted to James Whistler.

19th-century British Art

Beardsley, Aubrey

http://www.stg.brown.edu/projects/hypertext/
landow/victorian/decadence/ab/beardsleyov.html

Profile of the Victorian aesthete. His brief decadent life, his prodigious output, and his friendship with Oscar Wilde are described. Many of his works of art can be seen at this site.

Brown, Ford Madox

http://www.oir.ucf.edu/wm/paint/auth/brown/

Site at the WebMuseum, Paris, devoted to Ford Madox Brown.

Burne-Jones, Sir Edward Coley

http://sunsite.unc.edu/wm/paint/auth/burne-jones/

Profile of the English Pre-Raphaelite painter, designer, and illustrator. It traces his friendship with William Morris and their shared interest in the revival of medieval applied arts. There are also examples of Burne-Jones' best-known works.

Constable, John

http://www.oir.ucf.edu/wm/paint/auth/constable/

Site at the WebMuseum, Paris, devoted to John Constable.

Rossetti Archive

http://jefferson.village.virginia.edu/rossetti/
rossetti.html

Multimedia site archiving much of the work of this Pre-Raphaelite painter and poet. There is an extensive biography, as well as a database including his poems, prose, translations, and artwork. This includes some original digitized manuscripts as well as reviews and commentaries.

Ruskin, John

http://www.stg.brown.edu/projects/hypertext/
landow/victorian/ruskin/ruskinov.html

Extensive material on the life, works, and legacy of the English critic. There is a detailed biography, extracts from his writing, and comprehensive analyses of his engagement with the work of Turner and the Pre-Raphaelite Brotherhood. This site also includes examples of Ruskin's early writing, his denunciation of the elite classes, and the inspiration he provided to other intellectuals.

Ruskin on Turner

http://art-bin.com/art/oruskincontents.html

Ruskin was a passionate advocate of J M W Turner's paintings, whose work he catalogued, and this unusual site is devoted to both the artist and his critic. It includes the full texts of all Ruskin's articles with Turner's paintings and biographical information on both.

Turner, Joseph Mallord William

http://www.oir.ucf.edu/wm/paint/auth/turner/

Site at the WebMuseum, Paris, devoted to Joseph Mallord William Turner.

19th-century European Art

Bonheur, Rosa

http://www.nmwa.org/legacy/bios/bbonheur.htm

Profile of the life and works of the pioneering French painter of animals. Her unorthodox life style is described. It is related that it was the support of Queen Victoria which established her commercial success. There is a bibliography and guide to permanent collections of her works.

Boudin, Eugène

http://www.oir.ucf.edu/wm/paint/auth/boudin/

Site at the WebMuseum, Paris, devoted to Eugène Boudin.

Bouguereau, Adolphe-William

http://www.oir.ucf.edu/wm/paint/auth/bouguereau/

Site at the WebMuseum, Paris, devoted to Adolphe-William Bouguereau.

Cézanne, Paul

http://www.oir.ucf.edu/wm//paint/auth/cezanne/

Contains an extensive biography and gallery dedicated to the French painter. This site contains writings on his paintings and his relationship with Impressionism, Classicism, and Cubism.

Corot, Jean-Baptiste-Camille

http://www.oir.ucf.edu/wm/paint/auth/corot/

Site at the WebMuseum, Paris, devoted to Jean-Baptiste-Camille Corot.

Courbet, Gustave

http://www.oir.ucf.edu/wm/paint/auth/courbet/

Site at the WebMuseum, Paris, devoted to Gustave Courbet.

Couture, Thomas

http://www.oir.ucf.edu/wm/paint/auth/couture/

Site at the WebMuseum, Paris, devoted to Thomas Couture.

Daumier, Honoré

http://www.oir.ucf.edu/wm/paint/auth/daumier/

Site at the WebMuseum, Paris, devoted to Honoré Daumier.

Degas, Edgar

http://www.oir.ucf.edu/wm/paint/auth/degas/

Site at the WebMuseum, Paris, devoted to Edgar Degas.

Delacroix, Eugène

http://www.oir.ucf.edu/wm/paint/auth/delacroix/

Site at the WebMuseum, Paris, devoted to Eugène Delacroix.

Friedrich, Caspar David

http://www.oir.ucf.edu/wm/paint/auth/friedrich/

Site at the WebMuseum, Paris, devoted to Caspar David Friedrich.

Gauguin, Paul

http://www.oir.ucf.edu/wm/paint/auth/gauguin/

Site at the WebMuseum, Paris, devoted to Paul Gauguin.

Goya, Francisco de

http://www.oir.ucf.edu/wm/paint/auth/goya/

F A C T

GOYA, FRANCISCO JOSÉ DE GOYA Y LUCIENTES (1746–1828),

Spanish painter and engraver. One of the major figures of European art, Goya depicted all aspects of Spanish life – portraits, including those of the royal family, religious works, scenes of war and of everyday life.

Site at the WebMuseum, Paris, devoted to Francisco de Goya.

Gros, Antoine-Jean

http://www.oir.ucf.edu/wm/paint/auth/gros/

Site at the WebMuseum, Paris, devoted to Antoine-Jean Gros.

Hiroshige, Ando

http://www.oir.ucf.edu/wm/paint/auth/hiroshige/

Site at the WebMuseum, Paris, devoted to Ando Hiroshige.

Hokusai, Katsushika

http://www.oir.ucf.edu/wm/paint/auth/hokusai/

Site at the WebMuseum, Paris, devoted to Katsushika Hokusai.

Ingres, Jean-Auguste-Dominique

http://www.oir.ucf.edu/wm/paint/auth/ingres/

Site at the WebMuseum, Paris, devoted to Jean-Auguste-Dominique Ingres.

Jongkind, Johan-Barthold

http://www.oir.ucf.edu/wm/paint/auth/ jongkind/

Site at the WebMuseum, Paris, devoted to Johan-Barthold Jongkind.

Legros, Alphonse

http://www.oir.ucf.edu/wm/paint/ auth/legros/

Site at the WebMuseum, Paris, devoted to Alphonse Legros, providing biographical details, hyperlinks to related artists and movements, photographs, and critical discussion of his work.

Manet, Edouard

http://www.oir.ucf.edu/wm/paint/auth/ manet/

Site at the WebMuseum, Paris, devoted to Edouard Manet.

Millet, Jean-François

http://www.oir.ucf.edu/wm/paint/auth/millet/

Site at the WebMuseum, Paris, devoted to Jean-François Millet.

Monet, Claude

http://www.oir.ucf.edu/wm/paint/auth/monet/

Site at the WebMuseum, Paris, devoted to Claude Monet.

Moreau, Gustave

http://www.oir.ucf.edu/wm/paint/auth/moreau/

Site at the WebMuseum, Paris, devoted to Gustave Moreau.

Morisot, Berthe

http://www.oir.ucf.edu/wm/paint/auth/morisot/

Site at the WebMuseum, Paris, devoted to Berthe Morisot.

Munch, Edvard

http://www.oir.ucf.edu/wm/paint/auth/munch/

Site at the WebMuseum, Paris, devoted to Edvard Munch.

Pissarro, Camille

http://www.oir.ucf.edu/wm/paint/auth/ pissarro/

Site at the WebMuseum, Paris, devoted to Camille Pissarro.

Puvis de Chavannes, Pierre

http://www.oir.ucf.edu/wm/paint/auth/puvis/

Site at the WebMuseum, Paris, devoted to Pierre Puvis de Chavannes.

Redon, Odilon

http://www.oir.ucf.edu/wm/paint/auth/redon/

Site at the WebMuseum, Paris, devoted to Odilon Redon.

Renoir, Pierre-Auguste

http://www.oir.ucf.edu/wm/paint/auth/renoir/

Site at the WebMuseum, Paris, devoted to Pierre-Auguste Renoir.

Rodin, Auguste

http://www.oir.ucf.edu/wm/paint/auth/rodin/

Site at the WebMuseum, Paris, devoted to Auguste Rodin.

Rousseau, Henri

http://www.oir.ucf.edu/wm/paint/auth/rousseau/

Site at the WebMuseum, Paris, devoted to Henri Rousseau.

Seurat, Georges

http://www.oir.ucf.edu/wm/paint/auth/seurat/

Site at the WebMuseum, Paris, devoted to Georges Seurat.

> **F A C T**
>
> **POINTILLISM (Divisionism),**
> technique in oil painting developed in the 1880s by the Neo-Impressionist Georges Seurat. He used small dabs of pure colour laid side by side to create form and an impression of shimmering light when viewed from a distance.

Signac, Paul

http://www.oir.ucf.edu/wm/paint/auth/signac/

Site at the WebMuseum, Paris, devoted to Paul Signac.

Sisley, Alfred

http://www.oir.ucf.edu/wm/paint/auth/sisley/

Site at the WebMuseum, Paris, devoted to Alfred Sisley.

Tissot, James

http://www.oir.ucf.edu/wm/paint/auth/tissot/

Site at the WebMuseum, Paris, devoted to James Tissot.

Toulouse-Lautrec, Henri de

http://sunsite.unc.edu/wm/paint/auth/toulouse-lautrec/

Images of work and information about the 19th-century French painter Henri de Toulouse-Lautrec.

Vincent Van Gogh Exhibition Gallery

http://www.vangoghgallery.com/

Impressively comprehensive database of the life and works of Vincent van Gogh.

20th-century Art

Andy Warhol Museum Home Page

http://www.usaor.net/warhol/

Samples of Warhol's art from the museum devoted to preserving his work. The online exhibition available here includes most of his famous works. The site also contains a museum calendar, details of special exhibitions, education resources, and information about Warhol's films and videos.

Art Deco Erté

http://www.webcom.com/ajarts/erte.html

Full profile of the life and work of Romain de Tirtoff. A biography of Erte is accompanied by numbers of high resolution gouaches, stage sets, and graphics, illustrating the variety of creative themes of his long life.

Bacon, Francis (artist)

http://www.oir.ucf.edu/wm/paint/auth/bacon/

Site at the WebMuseum, Paris, devoted to Francis Bacon, providing biographical details and photographs of his work, including *Head VI* and *Man with Dog*.

Benton, Thomas Hart

http://sheldon.unl.edu/HTML/ARTIST/Benton_TH/AS.html

This site features several images of US artist Thomas Hart Benton's paintings. You will also find a brief description of Benton and his work. Click on 'the object' to view a larger image of the art.

Cornell, Joseph

http://www.oir.ucf.edu/wm/paint/auth/cornell/

Site at the WebMuseum, Paris, devoted to Joseph Cornell.

Davis, Stuart

http://www.oir.ucf.edu/wm/paint/auth/davis/

Site at the WebMuseum, Paris, devoted to Stuart Davis.

Dobell, William – The Painter's Progress

http://www.artgallery.nsw.gov.au/exhibits/dobell.html

Profile of the controversial Australian figurative artist. The career, personality, and interests of Dobell are described. Two portrits (one a self portrait) are included.

Encounter with Marcel Duchamp

http://www.freshwidow.com/duchamp-aug96.html

Web site on Marcel Duchamp, including extensive background information, audio samples of Duchamp's voice, and original music inspired by Duchamp. Also featured is an extensive listing of sources and references, along with a detailed timeline of Duchamp's life and work (eight pages with images), and a page 'Calling all Duchampians'.

Freud, Lucian

http://www.oir.ucf.edu/wm/paint/auth/freud/

Site at the WebMuseum, Paris, devoted to Lucian Freud.

Gris, Juan

http://www.oir.ucf.edu/wm/paint/auth/gris/

Site at the WebMuseum, Paris, devoted to Juan Gris.

Haring.Com

http://www.haring.com/

Colourful Web site dedicated to the US artist Keith Haring.

Hockney, David

http://www.oir.ucf.edu/wm/paint/auth/hockney/

Site at the WebMuseum, Paris, devoted to David Hockney.

Hofmann, Hans

http://sgal-server.unl.edu/HTML/ARTIST/Hofmann_H/SSII.html

Profile of the modern painter in which Hofmann describes his motivation for painting. A biography traces the influence of Matisse, Picasso, and Braque on the young German and the extraordinary influence of his teaching in the USA. His influence on the New York School is also analysed.

Hopper, Edward

http://www.oir.ucf.edu/wm/paint/auth/hopper/

Site at the WebMuseum, Paris, devoted to Edward Hopper.

Kandinsky, Wassily

http://www.oir.ucf.edu/wm/paint/auth/ kandinsky/

Site at the WebMuseum, Paris, devoted to Wassily Kandinsky, providing biographical details, hyperlinks to related artists and movements, photographs, and critical discussion of his work.

Kiefer, Anselm

http://www.oir.ucf.edu/wm/paint/auth/kiefer/

Site at the WebMuseum, Paris, devoted to Anselm Kiefer.

Kitaj, R B

http://www.oir.ucf.edu/wm/paint/auth/kitaj/

Site at the WebMuseum, Paris, devoted to Ron B Kitaj.

Klee, Paul

http://www.oir.ucf.edu/wm/paint/auth/klee/

Site at the WebMuseum, Paris, devoted to Paul Klee.

Klimt, Gustav

http://www.oir.ucf.edu/wm/paint/auth/klimt/

Site at the WebMuseum, Paris, devoted to Gustav Klimt, providing biographical details.

Roy Lichtenstein Foundation

http://www.lichtensteinfoundation.org/

Brief biography and photograph of the US Pop artist. This beautifully laid-out Web site is most valuable for the well-described links it provides to Web site resources containing over 130 Lichtenstein images in their galleries. Also to be found here are references to the artist's obituaries in a variety of newspapers, and a forum for discussion of his work.

Magritte Art Gallery

http://www.magritte.com/

Dozens of colour reproductions of Magritte's work, displayed in alphabetically arranged clickable 'rooms'. The titles of each work are given in French – click on each to expand the image.

Malevich, Kasimir

http://www.oir.ucf.edu/wm/paint/auth/malevich/

Site at the WebMuseum, Paris, devoted to Kasimir Malevich.

Marc, Franz

http://www.oir.ucf.edu/wm/paint/ auth/marc/

Site at the WebMuseum, Paris, devoted to Franz Marc.

Matisse, Henri

http://www.oir.ucf.edu/wm/paint/auth/matisse/

Site at the WebMuseum, Paris, devoted to Henri Matisse.

Modigliani, Amedeo

http://www.oir.ucf.edu/wm/paint/auth/modigliani/

Site at the WebMuseum, Paris, devoted to Amedeo Modigliani.

Moholy-Nagy, Laszlo

http://seurat.art.udel.edu/UDGallery/ TEXT/MN.html

Full profile of the writer, experimental artist, and Bauhaus leader. It traces the Hungarian's World War I service and the influence of Gropius, Dadaism, and German Expressionism on his work. The conflicts within the Bauhaus movement and his role in the US Bauhaus school are described.

Mondrian, Piet

http://www.oir.ucf.edu/wm/paint/auth/mondrian/

Site at the WebMuseum, Paris, devoted to Piet Mondrian, providing photographs of his work, including *Composition with Red, Yellow, and Blue* and *Broadway Boogie Woogie*.

F A C T

POP ART

movement in modern art that took its imagery from the glossy world of advertising and from popular culture such as comic strips, films, and television; it developed in the 1950s and flourished in the 1960s, notably in Britain and the USA.

Morandi, Giorgio – The Master of 20th-Century Italian Painting

http://www.artgallery.nsw.gov.au/exhibits/morandi.html

Profile of the Italian painter. A description of his ordered provincial life in Bologna is accompanied by an analysis of his art and his legacy. There are samples of three of his best-known still-life paintings.

Motherwell, Robert

http://www.godardgallery.toronto.on.ca/mother.htm

Contains a selection of paintings by the US artist Robert Motherwell, including two from his *Elegies to the Spanish Republic* series.

Norman Rockwell Gallery

http://www.paonline.com/zaikoski/rockwell.htm

Ten thumbnail reproductions of American artist Norman Rockwell's *Saturday Evening Post* covers. There is no biographical information here, but the site does include the title and date of each cover as well as the file size so you can prepare yourself for the download time.

O'Keeffe, Georgia

http://www.ionet.net/~jellenc/okeeffe1.html

Well-written biography of the US abstract painter. It describes her career as teacher, and the flower motifs and austere architectural themes recurring in her work. The elemental vistas of her New Mexico period are analysed. A bibliography is also included.

Picasso Official Web Site

http://www.clubinternet.com/picasso/

Introduced by Pablo Picasso's son Claude, this site is dedicated to the Picasso exhibition at the Museum of Modern Art in New York City. Not only does it contain a number of reproductions from the exhibition itself, but it also provides information about Picasso events around the world.

Pollock, Jackson

http://www.oir.ucf.edu/wm/paint/auth/pollock/

Site at the WebMuseum, Paris, devoted to Jackson Pollock.

Salvador Dalí Art Gallery

http://www.daliweb.com/index.htm

Dalí resource that includes many images as well as biographical information, analyses of his works, and a collection of essays about Dalí's influences and the surrealist movement.

Schiele, Egon

http://www.oir.ucf.edu/wm/paint/auth/schiele/

Site at the WebMuseum, Paris, devoted to Egon Schiele.

Tanguy, Yves

http://www.artsnetmn.org/inner/tanguy2.html

Profile of Yves Tanguy. Contents include a biography, hyperlinks to related movements, photographs, and a critique of the artist's work.

WebMuseum, Paris

http://www.oir.ucf.edu/wm/paint/auth/

Large site containing information on some of the world's greatest artists. This site provides biographical details, photographs, critical discussion of the artist's works, and hyperlinks to related artists.

World of Escher

http://www.WorldOfEscher.com/

Good profile of the Dutch artist. The paradoxes and spatial illusions for which M C Escher became famous are richly illustrated by a series of low- and high-resolution images of his best-known work. Contents include a biography, many articles assessing Escher's work, entertaining Escher anecdotes, a complete bibliography, and links to other Escher sites.

Photography

Abbott, Berenice

http://www.nmwa.org/legacy/bios/ babbott.htm

Biography of the US photographer. Her wide range of artistic and scientific interests are described. There is a photo of Abbott, a bibliography, and a listing of her works in public collections.

Adams, Ansel

http://www.book.uci.edu/ AdamsHome.html

Introduction to this famous US photographer run by the University of California, including a selection of images, essays, biographical information, sound clips, and a chronology of his life.

Alfred Stieglitz and the Photo-Secessionists

http://www.cwrl.utexas.edu/~slatin/20c_poetry/projects/stieglitz2.html

Article on US photographer Alfred Stieglitz and the formation of the photo-secessionists who defined the demarcation between the journalistic and artistic aesthetic in photography. This page also notes the influence of Stieglitz and the photo-secessionists on the literary world. There is also a brief list of reference books.

Arbus, Diane

http://elsa.photo.net/arbus1.htm

Review of a book on the life and legacy of the US photographer. The power of Arbus' bizarre photos of giants, midgets, freaks, transvestites, nudists, and the disabled is ascribed to her use of a square camera. The role of her daughter in protecting her reputation after her suicide is described.

Around the World in the 1890s

http://lcweb2.loc.gov/ammem/wtc/wtchome.html

Part of the American Memory presentation of the US Library of Congress, this page features hundreds of images by US photographer William Henry Jackson and is part of the World's Transportation Commission Photograph Collection. Found here are images taken during Jackson's travels through North Africa, Asia, Australia, and Oceania – including photos of the local inhabitants; city, street, landscape, and harbour scenes; plus all manner of transportation types, including elephants, sleds, camels, sedan chairs, horses, rickshaws, and railways. The collection can be browsed by keyword and subject, or you can select a country from the trip itinerary. Click on the images to increase their size.

Atget, Eugene

http://www.kbnet.co.uk/rleggat/photo/history/atget.htm

Profile of Atget and the 30 years he spent chronicling Parisian life. The Surrealist influences, the myths he wove around himself, and his death in obscurity are described.

Avedon, Richard

http://www.ocaiw.com/avedon.htm

Biography and most famous work of the former merchant marine who rose to eminence in fashion photography. There is a photo of Avedon and descriptions of the stark black and white images of the great and good in the USA, many of which can be viewed at this site.

Beaton, Cecil

http://www.harrowschool.org.uk/harrow/beaton.htm

Lengthy profile of the life and career of the English photographer Cecil Beaton. It traces the development of the young Harrovian's aesthetic interests in theatre, art, and beautiful women. The role of Edith Sitwell in establishing his reputation, his war photographs, and his success as a society and royal photographer are uncritically described.

Brassaï

http://its2.ocs.lsu.edu/guests/lsuprss/spr-sum-96/warehime.htm

Review of a book on the life and legacy of the influential Hungarian-born photographer. The reputation he gained as 'the eye of Paris', his engagement in intellectual life, and the paradoxical pursuit of Surrealism and realism in his work are described.

Bravo, Manuel Alvarez

http://www.arts-history.mx/mab/bravo2.html

Good account of the life and work of the Mexican photographer. The rise to fame of the self-taught artist is described. His subsequent career is presented with some of his well known sombre pictures.

Cameras: The Technology of Photographic Imaging

http://www.mhs.ox.ac.uk/cameras/
index.htm

General presentation of the camera collection at the Museum of the History of Science, Oxford, UK. Of the many highlights, perhaps the most distinguished are some very early photographs, the photographic works of Sarah A Acland, and the cameras of T E Lawrence.

Cartier-Bresson, Henri

http://www.esinet.net/personal/eric/ hcb/bio.html

Biography of the French photojournalist. It traces Cartier-Bresson's bourgeois upbringing, refusal to join the family business, discovery of Surrealism, journey to Africa, role in founding the Magnum agency, and the success which led to him being hailed as the 'master of the Leica'.

Cityscapes: Panoramic Photographs, 1851–1991

http://lcweb2.loc.gov/cgi-bin/query/r?ammem/
pan:field(SUBJ+band(Cityscape+photographs+))

Part of the Panoramic Photo Collection of the US Library of Congress, this page features some 1,000 panoramic photographs of cityscapes from around the world, taken between 1851 and 1991. To find images of a specific city, click on New Search and enter the name of the city. The images include brief notes. Click on the images to increase their size.

Coburn, Alvin Langdon

http://photocollect.com/bios/coburn.html

Biography of the Bostonian who found fame as a photographer in Britain. It traces his early interest in photography, his role in the Linked Ring Brotherhood of fellow photography pioneers, the success he won with his photogravures, his symbolist period and his later engagement with mystic abstraction.

Daguerreian Society

http://www.daguerre.org/

Information about the process involved in this early form of photography, 19th- and 20th-century texts about it, an extensive bibliography of related literature, plenty of daguerreotypes to look at, and information about the society itself can be found here.

F
A
C
T

DAGUERREOTYPE

in photography, a single-image process using mercury vapour and an iodine-sensitized silvered plate; it was invented by Louis Daguerre in 1838.

Demachy, Leon Robert

http://www.kbnet.co.uk/rleggat/photo/history/dema
chy.htm

Profile of the French photographer noted for his innovative printing techniques. His use of soft focus lenses is described. There are quotes from Demachy denouncing 'straight print' and justifying his 'manipulations'.

Eadweard Muybridge of Kingston upon Thames

http://www.kingston.ac.uk/muytext0.htm

Introduction to this pivotal figure in the early history of the cinema. The site includes a well-illustrated biography, broken into easy-to-read sections, on such topics as 'Early years' and 'The zoopraxiscope'. There is also a separate index of all the images on the site and information about the Muybridge Museum in Kingston.

Emerson, Peter Henry

http://www.kbnet.co.uk/rleggat/photo/history/
emerson.htm

Profile of the exponent of 'naturalistic photography'. Emerson's theory that good photos should not be in focus, and the reaction this aroused, is set out. Emerson's egotism and arrogance are described alongside his contributions to landscape photography.

Evans, Walker

http://xroads.virginia.edu/~UG97/fsa/welcome.html

Tribute to the US photographer who established the documentary photoessay. In addition to biographical details, there are many of the haunting images of southern sharecroppers in the Great Depression which made Evans's reputation.

Exposure: A Beginners Guide to Photography

http://www.88.com/exposure/index.htm

Introduction to the world of photography including a 'Crash course', as well as sections with 'A few easy tricks to jazz up your pictures' and an explanation of exposure theory. To help out with the latter, there is a 'sim-cam', allowing you to experiment with f-number and shutter speed for an image and see the results without wasting a lot of film.

Fox Talbot Museum

http://www.r-cube.co.uk/fox-talbot/

Site of the museum dedicated to the memory of the multi-talented pioneer of photography. A biography of Talbot is accompanied by photos. There is information of exhibitions and the museum's photo collection.

Frank, Robert

http://www.filmpicker.com/greats/frank.htm

Biography of the Swiss-born photographer. It describes Frank's turning away from fashion photography to chronicle the life of his adopted USA. His role in the development of realist documentaries is analysed.

History of Photography

http://www.kbnet.co.uk/rleggat/photo/index.htm

From the early pioneers to the establishment of photography as we know it, this site provides a thorough account of the gradual development of photography. There are numerous internal links

to important characters, techniques, and descriptions of important processes and styles. It also provides a useful bibliography and information on the Royal Photographic Society.

Kertész, André

http://www.stedelijk.nl/eng/archief/100foto/kertesz.html

Profile of the self-taught Hungarian photographer, André Kertész, who was among the first to exploit the possibilities of compact cameras. It traces his career in Paris and the USA. The absurd, poetic, and tragicomic aspects of life, and the graphic quality of his work are highlighted here.

Photo.net

http://photo.net/photo/

Useful site for those interested in photography. As well as a series of exhibitions, this site includes advice on buying a camera, what film to use, and lots of technical advice to help you achieve the results you want.

Ray, Man

http://www.icp.org/exhibitions/man_ray/mr_bio.htm

Contains an article by the photographer Man Ray entitled 'Photography can be Art'. There are also reproductions of Ray's photographs each with a brief amount of information.

F
A
C
T

RAY, MAN (1890–1976),
US photographer, painter, and sculptor. He was active mainly in France and was associated with the Dada movement and then surrealism.

Requiem – Robert Capa

http://digitaljournalist.org/issue9711/req2.htm

Tribute to the war photographer. It features the last pictures taken by Capa moments before stepping on the land mine in Vietnam which killed him. A fellow photojournalist describes what it was about Capa that inspired his colleagues.

Siskind, Aaron

http://dizzy.library.arizona.edu/branches/ccp/
sisyavgd/sischrn.htm

Chronology of the main events in the life of the US photographer, Aaron Siskind. His family life, his frequent travels abroad, his activities to popularize his theories of photography, and the honours he won are described.

Timeline of Photography

http://www.eastman.org/5_timeline/5_index.html

Created by the George Eastman International Museum of Photography & Film, this page provides a detailed timeline of the history of photography and film, which begins as far back as the 5th century BC with Aristotle's description of optical principles. You can scroll the timeline or jump to specific periods of interest. Underlined text will take you to more involved descriptions. The bottom of the page contains a list of sources used to create the timeline.

Galleries & Exhibitions

Art Guide – The Art Lover's Guide to Britain and Ireland

http://www.artguide.org/

Regularly updated guide to the art world in Britain and Ireland. There is a searchable database of exhibitions, a clickable region-by-region directory, a listing of gallery Web sites, information about 1,900 artists, and a special section for children.

(Art)ⁿ Laboratory – Virtual Photography

http://www.artn.nwu.edu/index.html

Exhibitions of online artists who are experimenting with high-end computers and the Internet to create new forms of visual art. Virtual snapshots of the rendered scene are photographed by the computer's virtual camera and the (Art) ⁿ Laboratory features more than 1,200 such intriguing HTML pages.

Art Nouveau Alphonse Mucha Museum

http://www.webcom.com/ajarts/mucha.html

Profile of the life and work of the Czech Art Nouveau pioneer. A detailed biography of Mucha is supported by a number of high-resolution images of his best-known posters and panels.

Art Room

http://www.arts.ufl.edu/art/rt_room/
@rtroom_doorway.html

Lively, interactive site for younger children suggesting various art-orientated activities. There are several clearly-explained projects to try, things to think about, and an exhibition of work by children from Iceland.

Art Watchers

http://www.xterna-net.de/~r.strasser/

Bilingual (English and German) art site that offers a little bit more than just a gallery of online images. It also includes sections on art theory and tips for both beginners and more advanced artists.

Brooklyn Museum of Art

http://wwar.com/brooklyn_museum/index.html

Illustrated guide to the Brooklyn Museum. The site includes an exhibition calendar, and information about the museum's painting, sculpture, textile, and photography exhibits from around the globe.

Centre Georges Pompidou

http://www.cnac-gp.fr/english/

Official home page of the famous French arts centre. This is a bilingual site and along with practical information and a selection of photos of artworks on display, there is also some explanation of the building's history and architecture.

Detroit Institute of Arts

http://www.dia.org/

Search the Detroit Institute of Arts' online database which contains over 1,000 images from the permanent collection. Have a sneak preview of current exhibits and get advance word on what's coming to the museum.

Electric Gallery: About Haitian Art

http://www.egallery.com/about.html

Illustrated essay about Haitian art featuring paintings by Philomé Obin, Andre Pierre, and Wilson Bigaud. Links are provided to a bibliography and the Electric Gallery Home Page.

El Prado Museum

http://www.cyberspain.com/passion/prado.htm

Guide to the celebrated art gallery in Madrid. There is a good history of the Prado's collection of Spanish art and the buildings housing it. This site also includes practical information for visitors, together with latest news of exhibitions.

Finnish Contemporary Art

http://www.uiah.fi/internetguide/navfin.html

Interesting overview of the basic directions and trends in Finnish contemporary art. The site discusses the main concepts behind Finnish contemporary creations, offers an analysis of the 'visual idiom' used by the artists, presents a series of female and male artists that have marked the recent Finnish art scene with their gender-specific creations, and explores the role of new media in contemporary Finnish art.

First Impressionist Exhibition, 1874

http://www.artchive.com/74nadar.htm

This site is a partial recreation of the first exhibition by the Impressionists in Paris on 15 April 1874. Included here are images of some of the works exhibited by Renoir, Monet, Degas, Pissaro, Cézanne, Sisley, Boudin, and Morisot, along with the contemporary criticisms that appeared in Parisian newspapers following the exhibit, most of which were negative. Click on 'zoom' to see larger versions of the paintings.

**F
A
C
T**

IMPRESSIONISM

movement in painting that originated in France in the 1860s and had enormous influence in European and North American painting in the late 19th century. The Impressionists wanted to depict real life, to paint straight from nature, and to capture the changing effects of light.

Gallery Walk

http://www.ECNet.Net/users/mfjfg/galwalk.html

Visual excursion through the works of some of the top galleries in Europe and the USA. The site is divided into sections dedicated to commercial, independent, non-profit, and academic galleries and also includes a 'Monthly feature'.

Getty

http://www.getty.edu/

Home page of the Getty Institute in California. The Institute houses one of the largest art collections in the world, and this Web site allows visitors a glimpse of many of the works of art. Also to be found here are details of the Getty conservation programme, the Getty Grant programme, and the research and conservation activities of the Getty institute. The Web site is highly graphics-based, and can be slightly confusing to navigate around.

Hayward Gallery

http://www.hayward-gallery.org.uk

Images and information about current exhibitions at the South Bank's Hayward Gallery. There are also links to the Gallery's Arts Council Collection, education and talks, national touring exhibitions, publications, and booking information.

Kidlink Worldwide Computer Art Exhibition

http://blues.fd1.uc.edu/~kidart/kidart.html

Computer art online exhibition presenting computer graphics created by children between the ages of 10 and 15 years as part of their participation in the KIDLINK global dialogue. The site includes files from Brazil, Denmark, the Netherlands, Russia, Slovenia, Sweden, Uruguay, and the USA. Pictures are grouped by country and information about the artists and the software used to create the graphics can also be accessed.

Kids' International Gallery

http://www.kids-space.org/gallery/gallery.html

Fun and interactive gallery for kids to share their artwork and stories, and to chat with one another. Contributions may concern a wide range of topics such as people, animals, fantasy, landscapes, transportation, and science – all mapped out in a big introductory drawing. The stories are interactive and pictures are clickable. Children can view pictures drawn by kids all over the world and send them their thoughts and comments.

Louvre Museum and Palace

http://mistral.culture.fr/louvre/louvrea.htm

Comprehensive guide to the Louvre Museum and Palace, Paris, France. It gives the historical background to the palace and its continued development over the centuries, including the current development programme and plans for the future. There are floor plans showing where to find different collections and synopses of the various collections and departments, including pictures and details of major works. There is also a host of practical information, such as admission charges, opening hours, directions, and group visit arrangements.

Metropolitan Museum of Art, New York

http://www.metmuseum.org/

Well arranged site of New York's premier art gallery. Contents include a plan of the building, details of current exhibitions, an online archive, and information about educational activities. There are regularly changed profiles of leading artists.

Musée d'Art Moderne

http://www.cofrase.com/artforum/mamparis/
indexfr.htm

Bilingual guide to Paris's premier museum of modern art. There are practical details for visitors, together with constantly updated news of exhibitions.

Museum of Modern Art

http://www.moma.org/

As you would expect, a very well designed site from one of the world's most famous museums of modern art, in New York City. You can view online exhibits here, as well as learn full details of the current exhibitions and more practical information about the museum's opening times.

National Gallery, London

http://www.nationalgallery.org.uk/

Comprehensive guide to the National Gallery in London. This site includes full details about the gallery, as well as containing information about current and future exhibitions. There is also a 'Puzzling pictures' section which looks at works with an unusual history.

National Gallery of Art, Washington

http://www.nga.gov/home.htm

Well-designed guide to the National Gallery of America that includes information about opening hours, a history of the gallery, and a calendar of events. There are also virtual tours through selected artist's works and special features on artistic themes.

National Portrait Gallery

http://www.npg.org.uk/index.htm

Information on this UK gallery, comprising floor plans, details of all the paintings on display in the various collections, information on current and future exhibitions and events, plus general information on such topics as opening hours and facilities. There is also a sound guide which takes you on an oral tour of the gallery.

Royal Academy of Arts

http://www.royalacademy.org.uk/

Official guide to the oldest fine arts institution in Britain. There is a brief history of the Royal Academy (RA). In addition to details of exhibitions, there is practical information for visitors, users of the RA library, and would-be artists wishing to enrol on RA courses.

State Hermitage Museum

http://www.hermitagemuseum.org/html_En/
index.html

Official site of the world-famous Hermitage art museum in St. Petersburg, Russia. This site offers a history, reviews, and details of tours and lectures, as well as hundreds of high-quality images from the wide-ranging collection.

Tate Gallery

http://www.tate.org.uk/home/index.htm

Home of the leading gallery of British art. This site contains comprehensive news of displays, exhibitions, and events at the main London gallery and those in Liverpool and St Ives.

Uffizi Gallery

http://www.televisual.it/uffizi/

Guided tour through different rooms in this online gallery of the Uffizi in Florence, supported by commentary and background to each painting.

Wallace Collection

http://www.the-wallace-collection.org.uk/

Collection of online art from the Wallace Collection in London. As well as the opportunity to view some of the works, there is a large amount of biographical information about many of the artists whose work is displayed.

Artistic Movements & Styles

Abstract Expressionism

http://sunsite.unc.edu/wm/paint/tl/20th/abs-expr.html

Introduction to this art movement from the WebMuseum, Paris. Many of the movement's main protagonists – such as Pollock and Rothko – are discussed, and there is a brief essay entitled 'Jackson Pollock: Breaking the Ice to Action Painting'. This page forms part of a much larger site which includes descriptions of numerous Abstract Expressionist artists, as well as examples of their work.

African Art: Aesthetics and Meaning

http://www.lib.virginia.edu/dic/exhib/93.ray.aa/African.html

Introduction to African art and its contexts, through the electronic catalogue of an exhibition hosted by the Bayly Art Museum at the University of Virginia, USA. The site offers online images accompanied by illuminating text and linked to larger photos of African artefacts. This is a superb example of the potential of professional online museums.

Art Deco

http://orathost.cfa.ilstu.edu/students/pcfare/deco.html

Well-designed introduction to Art Deco covering not only architecture and design, but also the relevance of music and film. Numerous Art Deco images can be downloaded, and profiles of some of the key figures in the movement are also available.

Art Detective

http://www.visi.com/~eduweb/pintura/

Novel approach to art history, encouraging viewers to follow the path of a detective story to discover the identity of a mystery painting by comparing it with examples by Raphael, Titian, Millet, Van Gogh, Gauguin, and Picasso. In short, an interactive introduction for kids to some of the major figures in this field.

Art History: A Preliminary Handbook

http://www.arts.ouc.bc.ca/ fiar/hndbkhom.html

Introduction to the whys and wherefores of studying art history at university level, compiled by a professor at Okanagan University College, USA. The site includes sections on 'What is art?', 'Basic questions to ask yourself about the work', and even 'Some points for writing any essay'.

Art History Resources

http://witcombe.sbc.edu/ARTHLinks.html

Enormous collection of art history links covering periods from prehistoric times to late 20th-century art movements.

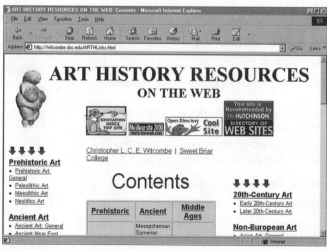

Art Nouveau

http://www.tulane.edu/lester/text/1890-Present/Art.Nouveau/Art.Nouveau.html

Photographic collection of architecture and Art Nouveau, featuring façades, entrances, doors, couches, benches, vases, lamps, and other fine examples of the style.

Art Studio Chalkboard

http://www.saumag.edu/art/studio/chalkboard.html

Well-organized site that contains practical advice on drawing and painting. The site contains detailed descriptions of perspective, shading, and preparing canvases, all accompanied by helpful diagrams.

Conceptual Art

http://www2.awa.com/artnetweb/views/tokartok/tokcon/tokcon0.html

Discusses conceptual art in a series of articles, which include 'so what is conceptual art?', 'ideational forms', and 'classic conceptual art'.

> **F A C T**
>
> **CONCEPTUAL ART (Concept art, Conceptualism),**
> type of modern art in which the idea or ideas that a work expresses are considered its essential point, with its visual appearance being of secondary (often negligible) importance. It is, as a result, a highly controversial type of art.

Cubism

http://udgftp.cencar.udg.mx/ingles/Pintura/pintura20/tempe.html

Brief explanation of Cubism and how it 'presents objects just as they are conceived by the mind and how they exist, not the way they are seen'. It includes a gallery of pictures by famous Cubists.

Dadaism

http://dept.english.upenn.edu/~jenglish/English104/tzara.html

Excerpts from *Dada Manifesto* 1918 and *Lecture on Dada* 1922, translated from the French by Robert Motherwell.

> **F A C T**
>
> **STIJL, DE (Dutch 'the style'),**
> influential movement in art, architecture, and design founded 1917 in the Netherlands. Attempting to bring art and design together in a single coherent system, the members of De Stijl developed an austere simplification of style, based on simple geometrical shapes and primary colour.

De Stijl – The Magazine

http://www.earth.ruu.nl/~keijzer/destijl/magazine_index.html

Introduces the reader to the art movement De Stijl, and also describes in detail its development between 1917 and 1931. Photographs of artwork are used to aid understanding of this movement, as are quotations from the artists themselves.

Die Brücke (The Bridge) – German Expressionist Artists' Group 1905–13

http://www.lacma.org/Exhibits/Bible/BRUCKE.HTM

Image of the title page from the *Brücke* manifesto. The image is accompanied by a brief text description of the group and a timeline of their activities.

Futurism Menu

http://www.milanoweb.com/mazzotta/futurismo/ingindex.html#future

Introduction to futurism, one of the most important 20th-century avant-garde movements in literature and art. It includes short essays on the main principles of the futurists, pages on their literary groups and theatrical performances, and excerpts from their manifestos.

Gothic Painting (1280–1515)

http://metalab.unc.edu/wm/paint/tl/gothic/

Introduction to Gothic painting from the WebMuseum, Paris. The subject is divided into three areas: international Gothic style, innovation in the north, and late Gothic painting. Within each category there is information about both the style and the painters, with links to selections of their works.

Icon Gallery

http://www.christusrex.org/www1/lviv/Gallery/Gallery.Entrance.html

Presented by the Ukrainian Greek Catholic Archdiocese of Lviv, this site is an exhibit of Russian religious icons painted from the 11th through 16th centuries. There are 25 images in all. Each image is accompanied by in-depth information on its location, history, and meaning, and there is a general introduction to Russian icon painting.

International Constructivism Home Page

http://www.rci.rutgers.edu/~eliason/ ichp.htm

Includes an informative introduction to Constructivism, as well as a brief bibliography, and a selection of links to related pages.

Detroit Institute of Arts – Permanent Collection

http://www.dia.org/collections/index.html

Rich selection of artefacts representing different stages in the history of art across the world. Visitors are given contextual information about each item, specific details about it, and an option for a larger image. The collections are divided geogrpahically and thematically, and include such sections as 'Graphic arts' and 'Asian art'.

Italian Renaissance (1420–1600)

http://metalab.unc.edu/wm/paint/tl/it-ren/

Introduction to the style and painters of the Italian Renaissance from the WebMuseum, Paris. The subject is divided into two categories – the Early and the High Renaissance – each containing further information. A number of artists are featured to illustrate the information, including Giotto, Botticelli, and Tintoretto.

Painting Without a Brush

http://users.hsonline.net/kidatart/htdoc/lesson27.htm

Simple and clear introduction to the work of Jackson Pollock and the style of painting called 'action painting'. There is an description of Pollock's art, as well as notes on the way he created it. A guide to creating your own action painting is also included, giving tips on the best ways to paint 'in the style of Jackson Pollock'.

Pre-Raphaelite Critic

http://www.engl.duq.edu/servus/ PR_Critic/

Personal guided tour around the Pre-

Raphaelite movement. As you would expect, the site contains an extensive archive of paintings, but also has reviews, parodies, and modern emulations of Pre-Raphaelite work.

Pure Abstraction

http://sunsite.unc.edu/wm/paint/tl/ 20th/pure-abs.html

Discusses abstract art and the role played by Mondrian and Malevich in its development. A further essay is included here – 'Malevich and Russian Suprematism' – offering a deeper insight into Malevich's theories and techniques. Numerous examples of these artists' works are used to aid understanding of the concepts described.

Surrealism

http://www.surrealist.com/home.html

Bewildering tour of the surrealist world. Contents include surreal games, sounds, and images, automatic writing, critical paranoia, and objects and delusions. There are links to other sites associated with the surrealist movement.

Towards Abstraction

http://sunsite.unc.edu/wm/paint/tl/20th/ abstract.html

Introduction to abstract art from the WebMuseum, Paris. There is a description of a number of the key figures in this movement, such as Kandinsky, Franz Marc, and August Macke. There is also an essay entitled 'Kandinsky and Abstraction', as well as numerous examples of abstract works of art.

see p 67

RENAISSANCE (Revival of Learning),

period in European cultural history that began in Italy around 1400 and lasted there until the end of the 1500s. A central theme of the Renaissance was humanism, the belief in the active rather than the contemplative life, and a faith in the republican ideal.

Virtual Renaissance

http://renaissance.district96.k12.il.us/

Travel back to Renaissance times, find out how customs, language, and dress differed, and let characters as diverse as Cosimo the Alchemist and Henry the Helpless (a guard at the Tower of London) tell you about their lives.

WebMuseum: Classicism

http://www.oir.ucf.edu/wm/paint/glo/classicism/

Informative description of Classicism as an artistic style. Its relationship with Romanticism is also discussed.

'Le salon des refusés', 'The 1870 war', and 'The opinion of the public'.

What Do You Understand by The Term 'Mannerism'?

http://www.jngo.demon.co.uk/mannerism.html

Informative, text-only essay on Mannerism, including an explanation of the origin of this style, as well as a number of descriptions of key paintings.

World Art Treasures

http://sgwww.epfl.ch/BERGER/

Extensively illustrated Web site, the aim of which is 'to promulgate the discovery and love of art'. Drawing from a wealth of visual resources, the site offers themed guides to art from Egypt, China, Japan, India, and Europe. Specific programs include 'Pilgrimage to Abydos (Egypt)' and 'The enchanted gardens of the Renaissance'.

FAUVISM (French *fauve*, 'wild beast'),

movement in modern French painting characterized by the use of very bold, vivid colours. The name is a reference to the fact that the works seemed to many people at the time to be crude and untamed.

WebMuseum: Fauvism

http://sunsite.doc.ic.ac.uk/wm/paint/glo/fauvism/

Guide to the Fauvist style of painting, including links to related articles about protagonists of this movement, including Vincent Van Gogh, Paul Gauguin, and Paul Cézanne.

WebMuseum: Impressionism

http://mexplaza.udg.mx/wm/paint/glo/impressionism/

Illustrated site from the WebMuseum, linked to pages on principal painters. It also includes an explanation of the development of the movement, broken down into these sections: 'The founders',

Ancient Architecture

Aztec Architecture

http://library.advanced.org/10098/aztec.htm

Part of a larger site on architecture, this page explains how the Aztecs built their temples, houses, and the Emperor's palace. This site provides some insight into Aztec culture, and there is a small bibliography.

AZTEC

member of an American Indian people who migrated south into the valley of Mexico in the AD 1100s, and in 1325 began reclaiming lake marshland to build their capital, Tenochtitlán, on the site now occupied by Mexico City. Under their emperor Montezuma I, who reigned from 1440, the Aztecs created an empire in central Mexico.

Chetro Ketl Great Kiva

http://sipapu.ucsb.edu/html/kiva.html

Painstaking reconstruction of a 337-room, four-storey building that was constructed between AD 1010 and AD 1109 by the Chaco Anasazi of the American Southwest. As well as a tour of the house, there is also detailed archaeological information and images of objects found during the excavation of the house.

Colonnades

http://www.ncsa.uiuc.edu/SDG/Experimental/split/colonnades.html

Illustrated overview of the use of colonnades in Hellenistic and Roman architecture. The site includes several links to related material on the Web.

Mayan Architecture

http://library.advanced.org/10098/mayan.htm

Part of a larger site on architecture, this page delves into the broad range of Mayan buildings. Learn how the Mayans constructed everything from simple hay huts to elaborate stone temples. Also discussed are style and artistic elements. A GIF displays several views of a Maya Kingdom. The text offers some insight into Mayan culture, and there is a brief bibliography.

'Palace' of Diocletian at Split

http://sunsite.unc.edu/expo/palace.exhibit/intro.html

Library of Congress exhibit based around the city of Spalato in former Yugoslavia, founded by Emperor Diocletian. There is an interactive plan of the palace as well as additional background information on the culture, history, and architecture of the period.

Parthenon

http://homer.reed.edu/Parthenon.html

Introduction to the main features of the Parthenon on the Acropolis of Athens. Visitors will find short descriptions of the architecture and sculpture of the famous building, with illustrations. The site also offers several links to other art collections and classical sites.

British Architecture

Buckingham Palace

http://www.royal.gov.uk/palaces/bp.htm

Official guide to the London residence of the British queen. In addition to a history of the palace, there are sections on the Royal Mews, the State Coach, the State Room, the Queen's Gallery, and current art exhibitions. Information is provided on entry to those parts of the palace open to the public.

Castles of Wales

http://www.castlewales.com/home.html

Outstanding bilingual site on over 170 medieval castles in Wales. The site offers marvellous photos, an overview of Welsh medieval history, a glossary of castle terms, technical details, and a rich reference list. There is even a separate index of the castles accompanied by more than five photos.

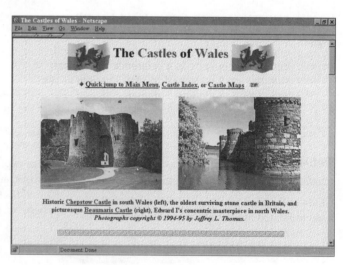

Historic Chepstow Castle in south Wales (left), the oldest surviving stone castle in Britain, and picturesque Beaumaris Castle (right), Edward I's concentric masterpiece in north Wales. *Photographs copyright © 1994-95 by Jeffrey L. Thomas.*

Hampton Court Palace

http://www.the-eye.com/hcintro.htm

Colourful guide to the historic royal residence. An informative tour of the attractions of the palace is accompanied by a variety of photographs of the palace, Henry VIII, and Cardinal Wolsey. Text accompanying the photographs describes the scene as it must have been in the 16th century.

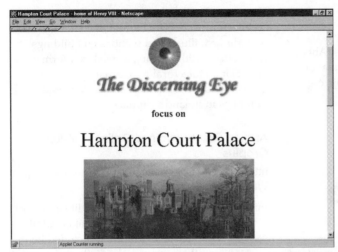

There is also advice for tourists planning a visit to Hampton Court and nearby attractions.

Lighthouse Society of Great Britain

http://www.lsgb.co.uk/

Site providing information on the many lighthouses around the coast of Great Britain and Ireland. In addition to a listing of all British and Irish lighthouses, the site describes the history of the lighthouse, lighthouse builders, and 20th-century changes to lighthouses. A section of educational material for younger users is also provided, probably the best feature of which is a virtual visit to Eddystone Light.

Medieval Castle Page

http://www.radix.net/~mfeinberg/castles/castles.htm

Detailed information on medieval castles in

Britain. This site includes an examination of the different types of castle and the construction methods used. There are numerous photographs and a explanation of siege warfare, which the castles were generally built to defend against.

Medieval Church Architecture

http://www.chass.utoronto.ca:8080/~sjames/medieval/medieval.htm

Lovingly researched page on medieval churches in the UK. Each church currently featured has a photo gallery and an illustrated essay on the findings about the history of the building. These essays give detailed written and stylistic evidence to back up the researcher's conclusions about the origins of the church.

Online Scotland: Castles and Historic Houses

http://www.ibmpcug.co.uk/~ecs/culture/cult02.htm#Brodie Castle

Illustrated guide to castles and historic houses in Scotland. The site offers historical information about the buildings, details of opening hours for visitors, and access directions.

Pugin, Augustus

http://www.hubcom.com/pugin/

Profile of the English architect and designer, tracing his passions for the Gothic and for Roman Catholicism. There is a detailed biography, photos, and descriptions of all the buildings with which he was associated. There are additionally details of the tiles, fabrics, gargoyles, wallpaper, furniture, and stained glass which he designed.

Tower of London

http://www.tower-of-london.com/

Guided tour of the tower's and surroundings of the London landmark. This elaborate site include a virtual tour that requires Macromedia Shockwave (freely available to download at this site), and many of the other sections are supported by images and music.

Westminster Abbey

http://www.westminster-abbey.org/

Regularly updated Web site of Westminster Abbey. There are 65 pages of well presented information for visitors and churchgoers. Also, the choir, organ, and bells can be heard in audio clips.

European Architecture

Alvar Aalto Museum

http://192.102.40.8/aalto/

Dedicated to the architect Alvar Aalto, this site features a chronology of his life and details and photographs of his work in Finland and elsewhere. A bibliography is also provided, and there is information about the Viipuri Library.

Ancient Art and Architecture

http://www.geocities.com/Athens/Crete/9169/index.html

Images of architecture and architectural sculpture from the Mediterranean basin, with particular emphasis on Classical and Hellenistic architecture from Rome and Greece. There are also images of art and architecture from Egypt.

Architectural Dublin

http://www.archeire.com/archdublin/

Very aesthetically-pleasing site on the architectural variety of Dublin. It contains hyperlinked, illustrated sections on buildings from 17th to 20th century, as well as information on major architectural figures, city planning, derivation of street names, and endangered buildings in Ireland's capital.

Artifice Great Buildings Online – Walter Gropius

http://www.artifice.com/cgi-bin/gbc-architect.cgi/Walter_Gropius.html

Informative resource relating to the life and work of the German architect Walter Adolf Gropius. A biography is included here, and there are also detailed articles on many of his works, including Bauhaus, Harvard Graduate Center, and Gropius House.

Baroque Architecture of St Petersburg

http://russia.uthscsa.edu/St.Peterburg/

Part of a larger site on Russian architecture, this page includes a brief architectural history of St Petersburg with images of impressive 18th-century buildings of the Baroque style. Images are accompanied by the dates of construction and the architects' names.

F A C T

BAUHAUS

German school of art and design founded in 1919 in Weimar by the architect Walter Gropius in an attempt to fuse art, design, architecture, and crafts into a unified whole. In 1925, under political pressure, it moved to Dessau (where it was housed in a building designed by Gropius), and in 1932 it made another forced move to Berlin, where it was closed by the Nazis the following year.

Capella Sistina (Sistine Chapel)

http://www.christusrex.org/www1/sistine/0-Tour.html

Extensively illustrated guide to the artwork that adorns the Sistine Chapel. The site also includes a master-plan of the chapel and numerous links to news bulletins and articles published by the

Christus Rex Information Service. Information is available in a number of languages including English, French, German, Italian, Portuguese, and Spanish.

Corbusier, Le

http://studwww.rug.ac.be/~jvervoor/architects/corbusier/corbusier.html

Tribute to the modernist architect, artist, theorist, and painter. In addition to biographical details, there are descriptions and pictures of his buildings. There are also examples of his graphic art, lithographs, etchings, engravings, and furniture, and an analysis of his theories.

From Human Architecture to Architectural Structure

http://www.mcm.acu.edu/academic/galileo/ars/arshtml/arch1.html

Illustrated online essay exploring the work of the Florentine architect and engineer Filippo Brunelleschi and the origin of linear perspective in architecture.

Gardens, Villas, and Social Life in Renaissance Florence

http://www.arts.monash.edu.au/visarts/diva/kent.html

Brief essay on the role of countryside villas and gardens in the life of upper-class Renaissance Florentines. The discussion is an interesting case study of historical geography and also of the sociological concerns involved in environmental studies.

Gaudí Central

http://futures.wharton.upenn.edu/ ~jonath22/gaudi.html

Short biography of the renowned Catalonian architect together with a wide selection of photographs and information on his most celebrated buildings, all of them in or around the city of Barcelona. For those who would like to visit the buildings, the site includes the addresses of many of them and a link to a map of the metro system.

Guimard, Hector

http://www.etca.fr/Users/Sylvain%20Meunier/Guimard/ baladepseizeAGL/

Unusual biographical site that guides the viewer through the French architect's work by way of a virtual tour through the suburbs of Paris. The detailing of the images is very good which means, however, that load time can be slow.

Morten Online

http://www.danbbs.dk/~nyboe/

Dedicated to the Dutch architect Gerrit Thomas Rietvelt, this site contains a brief biography, as well as photographs of both the architect and a number of his designs.

Neumann, Johann Balthasar

http://www.knight.org/advent/cathen/10773a.htm

Profile of the artist and decorator associated with the development of Rococo. In addition to biographical details there are descriptions of the best-known buildings he designed.

Palladio, Andrea

http://www.knight.org/advent/cathen/11423c.htm

Profile of the poor carpenter's son who gave his name to a classic architectural tradition. The site describes Palladio's apprenticeship as a sculptor, his travels, and the main buildings he designed. There is an account of the subsequent revival of his legacy in Britain and the USA as a result of the enthusiasm of Inigo Jones.

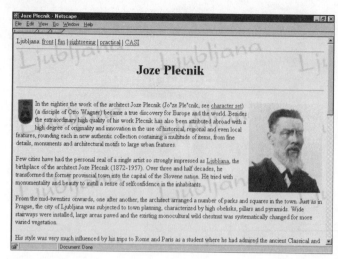

In the eighties the work of the architect Joze Plecnik (Jo°ze Ple°cnik, see character set) (a disciple of Otto Wagner) became a true discovery for Europe and the world. Besides the extraordinary high quality of his work Plecnik has also been attributed abroad with a high degree of originality and innovation in the use of historical, regional and even local features, rounding each in new authentic collection containing a multitude of items, from fine details, monuments and architectural motifs to large urban features.

Few cities have had the personal seal of a single artist so strongly impressed as Ljubljana, the birthplace of the architect Joze Plecnik (1872-1957). Over three and half decades, he transformed the former provincial town into the capital of the Slovene nation. He tried with monumentality and beauty to instill a sense of selfconfidence in the inhabitants.

From the mid-twenties onwards, one after another, the architect arranged a number of parks and squares in the town. Just as in Prague, the city of Ljubljana was subjected to town planning, characterized by high obelisks, pillars and pyramids. Wide stairways were installed, large areas paved and the existing monocultural wild chestnut was systematically changed for more varied vegetation.

His style was very much influenced by his trips to Rome and Paris as a student where he had admired the ancient Classical and

Plecnik, Joze

http://www.ijs.si/slo/ljubljana/plecnik.html

Profile of the Slovenian architect. Focusing on his role in the transformation of Ljubljana, it contains descriptions and photos of the many public buildings and churches he designed.

Renaissance Art

http://www.shu.edu/academic/arts_sci/modlang/sites/italian/artists/outline.html

Informative guide to the life and works of the Italian architect and theorist Leon Battista Alberti. A detailed biography is included here, with much attention being given to his education. There is also a large amount of information on Alberti's work, including numerous images to accompany the text.

Russian Attractions

http://russia.uthscsa.edu/attract.html

Tour of Russian architectural styles. The tour comprises photographic visits to Moscow, the baroque architecture of St Petersburg, the museum of wooden architecture in Karelia, and the Trinity-St Sergiy Lavra in Zagorsk. The images in each section are shown as thumbnails that may be expanded by clicking on them. Also briefly examined here is the Russian lacquer art form of Palekh, again with several photographed examples.

Saarinen, Eoro

http://www.scandinaviandesign.com/eero_saarinen/index.htm

Profile of the Finnish-born architect. There is a

photograph, biography, and information and photographs of the buildings he designed.

Tour Eiffel

http://www.paris.org/Monuments/Eiffel/

History, technical details, and practical information about the Eiffel Tower. There are also some bizarre facts about the Tower. Visitors are warned of the prohibitive cost of dining atop the Tower.

Wren, Sir Christopher

http://www-groups.dcs.st-and.ac.uk/history/Mathematicians/Wren.html

Part of an archive containing the biographies of the world's greatest mathematicians, this site is devoted to the life and contributions of architect Christopher Wren. In addition to biographical information, you will find a list of references about Wren and links to other essays in the archive that reference him. The text of this essay includes hypertext links to the essays of those mathematicians and thinkers who influenced Wren. You will also find an image of Wren, which you can click on to enlarge, and a map of his birthplace.

US Architecture

All-Wright Site

http://www.geocities.com/SoHo/1469/flw.html

Dedicated to the life and work of US architect Frank Lloyd Wright, this Web page includes a biography, a guide to literary and electronic resources on Wright, quotations, and an architectural guide arranged geographically.

Architecture and Interior Design for 20th-Century America, 1935–55

http://lcweb2.loc.gov/ammem/gschtml/gotthome.html

Part of the Gottscho-Schleisner Collection of the US Library of Congress, this page is a record of achievements in US architecture during the 20th century. It includes numerous images of the interiors and exteriors of homes, stores, offices, factories, historic buildings, and other structures. The photos in this collection were taken by Samuel Gottscho and William Schleisner. There are also watercolour images of the 1939–40 New York World's Fair. You may browse the images by keyword or subject.

Arcosanti Project

http://www.arcosanti.org/

Introduction to architect Paolo Soleri's theory of 'arcology' – a combination of architecture and ecology in urban design. As well as hyperlinked information about the theory and the man, this site contains a virtual tour of a city which is currently being built following these principles in Arizona, USA.

Buckminster Fuller Virtual Institute

http://gate.cruzio.com/~joemoore/index.html

Site of the institute pledged to continue the ideas of the visionary US architect. There is a full biography of Fuller, an animation of Fuller's Dymaxion projection of Spaceship Earth, images of domes he inspired, and articles about him.

Frank O Gehry and Associates

http://www.louisiana.dk/approac21/appr2.html

Site of the innovative US architect Gehry, including a biography and details of his career. There are descriptions, photos, and diagrams of the residential and commercial buildings which established his reputation.

Historic American Buildings Survey and Engineering Record

http://lcweb2.loc.gov/ammem/hhhtml /habshome.html

Preview of the Historic American Buildings Survey and the Historic American Engineering Record collections of the US Library of Congress Prints and Photographs Division. This page is a record of architectural and engineering accomplishments in the USA and its territories, and features images of building types and engineering technologies that range from a one-room schoolhouse to the Golden Gate Bridge. The images include brief notes. Click on the images to increase their size.

F A C T

KAHN, LOUIS ISADORE (1901–1974),

US architect. A follower of Mies van der Rohe, he developed a classically romantic style, in which functional 'servant' areas such as stairwells and air ducts feature prominently, often as towerlike structures surrounding the main living and working, or 'served', areas.

Kahn, Louis

http://www.noguchi.org/kahn.html

Profile of the innovative Estonian-born US architect and urban planner. There is a photo of Kahn, a biography, and details of his most famous buildings.

Los Angeles: Revisiting the Four Ecologies

http://www.cf.ac.uk/uwcc/archi/jonesmd/la/

This page offers a stroll through four distinct 'ecologies' of contemporary Los Angeles architecture. This photographic narrative, the work of a Welsh architecture student, serves as both tribute and update to Reyner Banham's 1971 book about Los Angeles architecture, *Los Angeles: The Architecture of Four Ecologies*. As such, the same four ecologies that Banham explored in 1971 are revisited some twenty years later. The four ecologies are defined as surfopia, downtown, foothills, and autopia. Text from Banham's book describing each of the ecologies is interspersed with fresh perspectives, and there are several thumbnail images of modern architecture in each of the sections.

Mission Churches of the Sonoran Desert

http://dizzy.library.arizona.edu/images/swf/ mission.html

History of Spanish missions in the Sonoran Desert region of northern Mexico and southern Arizona. The site includes an image map of the area and a list of suggested readings. Click on a particular mission for photos and further information.

National Building Museum

http://www.nbm.org/Great_Hall.html

Online version of the National Building Museum in Washington DC, USA. As well as being an architectural archive of many previous exhibitions, this site includes some of the museum's permanent collections, education programmes, publications, job opportunities, and even an online museum shop.

Pei Buildings

http://www.mit.edu/people/bei/ www/page4.html

Tribute to the work of the innovative US modernist architect I M Pei, including a photo and biography. There are also photos of the large number of public buildings in the USA and China for which he has won renown.

Philip Johnson Profile

http://www.achievement.org/autodoc/page/joh0pro-1

Description of the life and work of US architect Philip Johnson. The Web site contains not only a profile and biographical information, but also holds a lengthy interview with Johnson, accompanied by a large number of photographs, video sequences, and audio clips.

Raymond Hood – The New York Skyscraper

http://ccwf.cc.utexas.edu/~rcm/hood.html

Tribute to the pioneering architect of skyscrapers Raymond Hood. There are descriptions and many photos of his most famous buildings and details of the competitions and awards won by Hood.

Richardson, H H

http://www.hhrichardson.com/

Tribute to the memory of the US Romanesque architect H H Richardson. His life, times, and legacy are lovingly explored. There are photos of the buildings he designed and news of efforts to conserve them.

Asian & Middle Eastern Architecture

Chinese Architecture

http://library.advanced.org/10098/china1.htm

Part of a larger site on architecture, this page touches on the basic idea and structure of Chinese architecture and discusses the construction of

Buddhist temples, walled Chinese cities, intricate roof designs, and the buildings of the Forbidden City and Great Wall of China. A GIF shows changing views of the Forbidden City.

Islamic Architecture in Isfahan

http://isfahan.anglia.ac.uk:8200

Illustrated architectural guide to the Iranian city of Isfahan. This site also includes a bibliography and links to additional Iranian sites.

New Jerusalem Mosaic

http://www1.huji.ac.il/njeru/open_screen2.htm

Online tour of the city of Jerusalem throughout the ages. It is a well organized site, with comprehensive information accessible both by subject and by era. See the people, the places, and the costumes of Jerusalem and even taste the food (each age in the timeline has its own recipes and background information on the dietary habits of the period).

Taj Mahal

http://www.erols.com/zenithco/tajmahal.html

Guide to the famed 'elegy in marble'. In addition to a history of the building, there is a floor plan, general photograph, and images of several of the inlaid designs for which the Taj is renowned.

Templenet – The Ultimate Source of Information on Indian Temples

http://www.indiantemples.com/encyclo.html

Comprehensive well-organized source of information on India's temples. Architectural, archaeological, and historical articles are accompanied by detailed descriptions of thousands of temples. There is also practical information for those planning visits.

Miscellaneous Architecture

Architecture: A Virtual Tour

http://archpropplan.auckland.ac.nz/virtualtour/

Tour, organized by the New Zealand School of Architecture, around some important world sites, both contemporary and historical. The site also has a section on architectural innovations,

ARCHITECTURE

art of designing structures. The term covers the design of the visual appearance of structures; their internal arrangements of space; selection of external and internal building materials; design or selection of natural and artificial lighting systems, as well as mechanical, electrical, and plumbing systems; and design or selection of decorations and furnishings.

including a fully sustainable house. The entire site is highly illustrated, so beware of the possibility of a lengthy load time.

Castles on the Web

http://www.castlesontheweb.com/

Well-presented guide to castles, palaces, and abbeys around the world, with lots of pictures in the image archive. It includes collections of tour sites where numerous castles can be visited, as well as specific information about individual castles.

Gargoyles in Cyberspace

http://www.geocities.com/Paris/2069/garglink.html

Gargoyle-dedicated Web site, offering a history of the gargoyle in architecture, images of gargoyles, links to gargoyle sculptors, gargoyle cartoons, and gargoyle fan clubs.

Gothic Dreams

http://www.elore.com/el-ti-04.html

Homage to the glories of Gothic architecture. Filled with stunning images from the great Gothic churches, this site illustrates the various Gothic styles, with particular emphasis on Chartres Cathedral. A Virtual Cathedral Project explains the techniques involved in creating these magnificent buildings.

Harmony and Proportion: Sound Design

http://www.aboutscotland.co.uk/harmony/harmony.html

Introduction to the theory of harmony and proportion in space that offers insight into two of the aesthetic principles governing architecture and design. Links within the site explore the theories of Plato, Pythagoras, Alberti, and Palladio.

Late Gothic Architecture

http://www.tulane.edu/lester/text/Gothic/Late.Gothic/Late.Gothic.html

Extensive photographic gallery with specimens of late Gothic architecture. The site offers a large number of façade-and interior-shots from churches in Italy, as well as a few from elsewhere around Europe.

Sustainable Architecture: Eco Design and Landscaping

http://www.aloha.net/~laumana/

This site is an archive of information about sustainable architecture, which includes ecological planning, design, integrated architecture, landscaping for tropical, sub-tropical, or temperate climates, and there is an introduction to sustainable development theory. You will find tips on conservation of resources and renewable energy, and information on how to build efficient, livable housing by applying the techniques of sustainable architecture. There is also a list of resources for further research.

World's Tallest Buildings

http://www.worldstallest.com/

These pages contains a wealth of photographs, illustrations, and diagrams of the tallest buildings in the world, including drawings of some proposed buildings. Click on the images to increase their size and to read information regarding the buildings and the areas in which they are situated.

Craft, Design & Printing

All About Carpets

http://www.carpetinfo.co.uk/pages/aboutfrm.htm

Good source of information on carpets. The site includes a history of the craft, guide to various carpets, how carpets are made and carpet makers trained, and information on natural and synthetic fibres.

Arts and Crafts Society

http://www.arts-crafts.com/

Online community dedicated to the spirit and philosophy of the Arts and Crafts Movement. The site provides a wide range of information and enables you to network with others interested in this area.

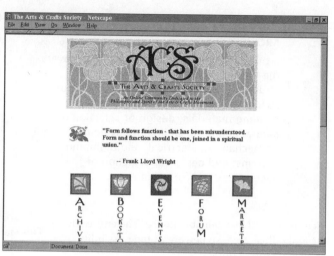

Bayeux Tapestry

http://www.ealdormere.sca.org/university/btapestry/bayeux-s.html

Entire tapestry, electronically captured in a collection of 35 files, plus a number of miscellaneous close-ups on such areas as the stitching and the reverse side of the tapestry.

Bookbinding – A Tutorial

http://www.cs.uiowa.edu/~jones/book/

Step-by-step guide to learning how to save those tatty old paperbacks by rebinding them. Written with the assistance of preservation librarians, this takes you through all the stages involved in saving a crumbling book by photocopying it and skilfully putting the pages together to make a distinguished looking tome complete with cover and dust jacket.

Build it and Bust it: A Web Site Construction Zone

http://library.advanced.org/11686/

Interactive structural engineering site. Learn the theory, then build and test practically any two-dimensional structure made from beam and joints online. Please note: you will need a Java-enabled browser to get the most out of this site.

Candle Making

http://users.wantree.com.au/~campbell/candles.htm

Mainly text-based guide to making and designing your own candles. There are few general pictures of the finished product, but the text is very instructive.

Carlos' Colouring Book

http://coloring.com/

One of the most restful sites on the Internet – just choose from a list of outline images, click on a colour with your mouse and 'paint' the picture any way you like. A site suitable for kids of all ages.

Giugiaro

http://jyanet.com/cap/1998/0213fe3.htm

Examination of the career of the Italian automotive designer. The 'folded paper school of design' and other trends with which he has been associated are described. There are photos of some of Giugiaro's best-known cars and a listing of the work he has done for a number of manufacturers.

History of Printing

http://www.digitalcentury.com/encyclo/update/print.html

Global history of printing, with links to a biography of William Caxton and further links to examples of his work, his early type, and to other typographic visionaries.

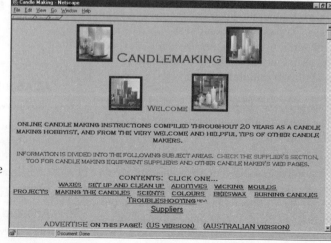

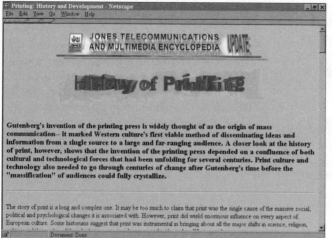

about the different types of quills, as well as the different techniques used to make decorations and jewelry.

Printworks Magazine

http://eyelid.ukonline.co.uk/print/works.htm

Contains illustrated essays by printmakers about their art. There are also details of exhibitions and workshops, a gallery of artists' work, as well as information on the materials and techniques used in printmaking.

Information on Origami

http://www.origami.vancouver.bc.ca/

Good introduction to the Japanese art of paperfolding. There is a brief history of this 2,000-year-old art form. A section on 'washi', Japanese handmade paper, has a long glossary of origami terms, and there are practical guides for beginners.

> **F A C T**
>
> **PRINTMAKING**
>
> creating a picture or design by printing from a plate (woodblock, stone, or metal sheet) that holds ink or colour. The oldest form of print is the woodcut, common in medieval Europe, followed by line engraving (from the 15th century), and etching (from the 17th century); coloured woodblock prints flourished in Japan from the 18th century.

Let's Begin Ikenobo

http://www.asianmall.com:80/ikenobo/

Full source of information on the leading school of Japanese ikebana flower arrangement. The long history of the art is traced with informative text and photographs. There is information about the Ikenobo Ikebana Society of America and the Japanese headquarters.

Textile Dictionary

http://www.ntgi.net/ICCFD/textile.htm

Dictionary produced by the Internet Centre for Canadian Fashion and Design. Divided into seven categories of fibres, each section includes information about hundreds of different fibres, and details each one's characteristics and uses.

Masks.org

http://www.masks.org/

Dedicated to masks, this site houses a wide-ranging exhibition of masks by international artists, as well as links to other mask sites.

Welcome to the Story of Spode

http://www.spode.co.uk/

Profile of the life of Josiah Spode and his perfection of the process of blue underglazing transfer printing which ensured his reputation. This site also includes information for visitors wishing to tour the pottery he founded, which is now the oldest in Britain.

NativeTech: Native American Technology and Art

http://www.nativeweb.org/NativeTech/quill/index.html

Section from a much larger site devoted to the many different types and uses of porcupine quills in Native American art. There is information

Woolworks – The Online Knitting Compendium

http://www.woolworks.org/

Source of information for knitters. There are over 200 free patterns for all varieties of garments and information is provided on resources for knitters which include books, stockists, and other knitting sites. If you are proud of something you have knitted you can even add a photo to the gallery.

World Wide Quilting Page

http://ttsw.com/MainQuiltingPage.html

Comprehensive information for anybody interested in quilt making. In addition to practical advice for beginners, there are details of competitions, a bulletin board for exchange of information, quilting mysteries to solve, and a history of quilting around the world.

You Can Make Paper

http://www.beakman.com/paper/paper.html

Fun and environmentally conscious project aiming to teach children about paper and how to make their own home-made paper. Friendly chat follows the step-by-step instructions. The site also offers interactive demonstrations on cellular phones, gravity, smoking and our lungs, relativity, magnets, and more. Children (and adults) can post their questions to a query box.

HISTORY

Archaeology

Amphoras Project

http://www.epas.utoronto.ca/amphoras/project.html

Canadian archaeological project to bring together knowledge about amphoras. This is an unparalleled source of all that is known about the use of these unglazed, ceramic containers in the ancient world. In addition to a good general introduction to the subject, there is a bibliography of scholarly work on amphoras, translation of references to amphoras in Greek texts, a search engine, and links to other amphora sites.

F A C T

CERAMICS

objects made from clay, hardened into a permanent form by baking (firing) at very high temperatures in a kiln. Ceramics are used for building construction and decoration (bricks, tiles), for specialist industrial uses (linings for furnaces used to manufacture steel, fuel elements in nuclear reactors, and so on), and for plates and vessels used in the home.

Archaeology

http://www.archaeology.org/

Online edition of the prestigious journal of the Archaeological Institute of America. The well-written articles give a glimpse of the range of archaeological research being done around the globe. The full texts of short articles are available online, together with abstracts (and often the full text) of a large number of longer articles. Two years of back issues can be accessed.

Archaeology Field Techniques – University of Memphis

http://www.people.memphis.edu/~anthropology/fldsch99.html

Page designed to show various aspects of archaeological field techniques. This Web site, run by the Anthropology Department at the University of Memphis, USA, includes photographic and text descriptions of archaeological excavation, mapping, photography, and surveying.

Archaeology in Luxembourg

http://www.cpu.lu/gka/sitemap.htm

Unusual home page dealing with the archaeology of Luxembourg. The Web site specifically illustrates Celtic and Gallo-Roman archaeology in Luxembourg, and is run by a non-profit organization. The contents of the Web site include excavation reports, finds, and lists of related online publications.

ArchNet – Featured Web Site

http://www.lib.uconn.edu/ArchNet/News/Feature.html

Virtual library for archaeology with information classified by geographical region and by subject. This is an immense resource on worldwide archaeology. This page is a regularly changed 'Featured Web site' and is a very good place to start.

Buried Secrets

http://www.turknet.com/atlas/97april/catalhoyuk/index.html

Interesting account of recent archaeological research at this Turkish Neolithic site. Written by the head of the team from Cambridge University working at the site, the informative text is accompanied by photographs.

Discovering the Past at Santa Cruz

http://www.blm.gov/education/santa_cruz/

Sponsored by the US Bureau of Land Management, this site explores the confluence of Native American and European cultures at Santa Cruz de Terrenate, a Spanish presidio located in present-day southern Arizona. Some of the articles include the 'Story of Santa Cruz', 'Setting the world stage', and 'Artifacts in context'. There is also an area that examines the science of archaeology. Text is enhanced by images and illustrated maps.

Giza Plateau Computer Model

http://www-oi.uchicago.edu/OI/DEPT/COMP/GIZ/MODEL/Giza_Model.html

Lengthy account by archaeologists from the Oriental Institute of Chicago, accompanied by photographs. It is quite a brain-stretching site with a wealth of state-of-the-art computer graphics, suitable for all those interested in the latest and most exciting developments in the field of archaeology.

Glossary of Archaeological Terms

http://www.smu.edu/~anthrop/glossary.html

Extensive glossary of key words listed alphabetically, useful to teachers and students dealing with school modules with archaeological, prehistoric, and widely anthropological concerns.

Guide to Historic Wreck Sites

http://www.st-and.ac.uk/institutes/sims/deswreck.html

Fact sheet with the complete list of the historical shipwreck sites around the UK. It provides background information on the Protection of Wrecks Act (1973) and a brief description of each of the 45 designated underwater sites.

How Does Stonehenge Work?

http://faculty.washington.edu/wcalvin/bk6/bk6ch2.htm

Chapter from William H Calvin's book *How the Shaman Stole the Moon*. The Web site features a lengthy text accompanied by several diagrams describing how the layout of the stones at Stonehenge works as a calendar. Also featured are several quotes regarding the stones.

Iowa Office of the State Archaeologist

http://www.uiowa.edu/~osa/

Not the usual tourist guide to this US state, but a guide to its prehistory. Based at the University of Iowa, it contains many pages of information about Iowa's cultural heritage from the early palaeoindian period to the historic period, including current research and educational programmes.

Lieutenant-General Pitt Rivers's Collection and the Early History of the Pitt Rivers Museum in Oxford.

http://units.ox.ac.uk/departments/prm/RESEARCH-AT-PRM/PRproject.detail-1.html

Profile of the life and legacy of this British soldier who unexpectedly inherited an estate, which enabled him to further his pioneering work in archaeology. His collecting and intellectual interests are presented together with information about his establishment of the Pitt Rivers Ethnographic Museum of the University of Oxford, UK.

Lost City of Arabia

http://www.pbs.org/wgbh/nova/ubar/

Companion to the US Public Broadcasting Service (PBS) television programme *Nova*, this page tells the story of an archaeological expedition in the Arabian Desert seeking the legendary Lost City of Arabia. It includes an artefact gallery, an interview with the lead archaeologist, a map of Arabia, and information about remote-sensing instruments that allow archaeologists to locate structures buried beneath layers of sand. There is also a list of resources for further research.

Mercury Project

http://cwis.usc.edu:80/dept/raiders/

Intriguing presentation of what claims to be the first World Wide Web experiment with tele-robotics. Web users took part in a seven-month (September 1994–March 1995) artificial excavation of an experimental terrarium in Los Angeles, with the help of a tele-robot remotely controlled through a simple Web interface. This site is a must-see for technology enthusiasts. It features descriptions of all phases of the experiment, explanations of the buried artefacts and the user interface, a QuickTime movie from the excavations, and excerpts from the log kept during the experiment.

Mysterious Mummies of China

http://www.pbs.org/wgbh/nova/chinamum/

Companion to the US Public Broadcasting Service (PBS) television programme *Nova*, this page tells the remarkable story of the 3,000-year-old mummies with European features which were retrieved from the Takla Makan Desert in China. It includes numerous photographs and brief notes about the recovered bodies, plus a crash-course on mummification called 'Mummies 101' and a section on linguistics. You can download a transcript

---

F A C T

PITT-RIVERS, AUGUSTUS (1827–1900) adopted name of Augustus Henry Lane-Fox

English archaeologist. He made a series of model archaeological excavations on his estates at Rushworth in Dorset, England, and developed the concept of stratigraphy (identifying layers of soil within a site with successive archaeological stages).

of the television programme, and there is a list of resources for further research.

Mystery of the Mesa: A Science Detective Story

http://www.blm.gov/education/mesas/mesa.html

Sponsored by the US Bureau of Land Management, this site explores an archaeological discovery on a remote Alaskan mesa and explains how scientists study artefacts and draw conclusions about the ancient inhabitants of this land. Articles highlight the essential role of scientists in writing the earliest chapters of the USA's history.

Piltdown Man

http://www.tiac.net/users/cri/piltdown.html

Who committed the greatest anthropological hoax in history? Examine the case against all the potential perpetrators at this official home page of Piltdown Man. The site also contains a description of the 'discovery' and a chronology of events.

Prehistoric Art of the Pyrenees

http://www.culture.fr/culture/app/eng/artprepy.htm

Exhibition of the prehistoric art of the Pyrenees Mountains. The site offers a brief introduction to the Magdalenians, the prehistoric hunter-gatherers who, already extinct by the end of Ice Age, left behind about 450 samples of the art that died with them. Visitors are given the choice either to view the exhibits as they come or to follow an itinerary of the exhibition first.

Pyramids – The Inside Story

http://www.pbs.org/wgbh/nova/pyramid/

Intricately designed site that allows you to wander through the chambers and passageways of the Egyptian pyramids. Hosting extensive interviews with specialists, the site attempts to address a number of famous riddles concerning the pyramids. Those with engineering minds will find plenty of information on the scale and construction of the pyramids, and those with the appropriate plug-ins will enjoy virtual tours of areas usually closed to visitors.

Radiocarbon WEB-info

http://www2.waikato.ac.nz/c14/webinfo/index.html

Information about radiocarbon dating that includes the basis of the method, its applications, and submission of samples for testing, plus links to related sites.

Remote Sensing in History

http://observe.ivv.nasa.gov/nasa/exhibits/history/history_0.html

Brief timeline with some often overlooked landmarks in the history of remote sensing, as well as an engaging investigation into the long-held desire of people to see what is 'unseen'.

Schliemann, Heinrich

http://kroeber.anthro.mankato.msus.edu/information/ biography/pqrst/schliemann_heinrich.html

Biography of the controversial German archaeologist. This Web site includes a photograph of Schliemann and describes his works, including his excavations at Hissarlik, the city that he believed (correctly) to be Troy.

Stonehenge

http://www.anima.demon.co.uk/stones/england/ stonehen/index.html

Concise review of the current state of confusion regarding the origins and reasons behind the existence of Stonehenge. The site presents a number of the attempts to reconstruct the history of the legendary stone circle and define its mathematical and astronomical significance, but lets the visitors decide for themselves!

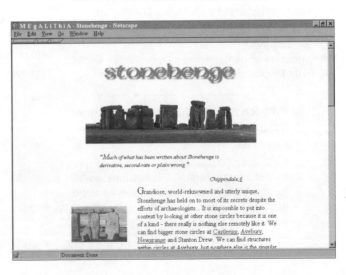

Stones of England

http://www.stonepages.com/England/England.html

Extensive reference guide with photographs of stone circles, dolmens, burrows, hill forts, and other megalithic sites from around England.

Stones of Ireland

http://www.stonepages.com/Ireland/Ireland.html

Reference guide with impressive photos from a variety of stone circles, dolmens, court and passage tombs, cairns, and stone forts from around Ireland.

Stones of Scotland

http://www.stonepages.com/Scotland/Scotland.html

Reference guide with marvellous photographic material from a variety of megalithic sites in Scotland.

Ancient History, 3000–401 BC

Ancient Paths through Texts and Image: The Fall of Troy

http://cti.itc.Virginia.EDU/~mpm8b/fall_of_troy/falltroy.htm

Extensively illustrated and user-friendly 'multimedia path' through the famous tale of the Trojan War as it has survived on vases, manuscripts, statues, paintings, and other forms of art throughout the centuries. Each picture is accompanied by details of the particular event that is being depicted.

A–Z Of Ancient Ireland

http://www.atlanticisland.ie/atlanticisland/arts/flatoz.html

A–Z listing of the features of ancient Irish history and mythology. This site is comprehensive in its descriptions of the people, places, things, and events that make up Irish legends and history. However, the site is not big on multimedia content.

Eleusinian Mysteries

http://www.erols.com/nbeach/eleusis.html

Part of the Ecole Initiative maintained by the University of Evansville, this page provides an in-depth look at the sacred Eleusinian Mysteries. The text examines the history and cultural influences of the Mysteries, discusses the importance of Demeter, reveals the people who were permitted to participate in the rituals, describes the ceremonies performed, and touches on the conflicting views of scholars who have studied the Eleusinian Mysteries. You will also find a translation of the 'Hymn to Demeter', which includes a list of notes to aid comprehension. Several of the names included in the text are linked to the Ecole Initiative's glossary. At the bottom of the page you will find a list of over two dozen sources.

Empedocles

http://www.utm.edu/research/iep/e/empedocl.htm

Profile of the Sicilian philosopher, poet, scientist, and statesman. It recounts how his exploits as a healer won him fame. Empedocles' most important poetry is described together with a detailed summary of his theory of elements.

Epic of the Peloponnesian War: Historical Commentary

http://www.warhorsesim.com/epw_hist.html

Comprehensive overview of the Athenian–Spartan war. The three phases of the war and their precipitating events are chronicled. All the twists and turns, alliances, and betrayals of this conflict are detailed.

History of Herodotus by Herodotus

http://classics.mit.edu/Herodotus/history.html

Translation by George Rawlinson of the nine books of Herodotus. Each of the nine books may be downloaded separately from this site, or there is an option to bundle them all into a single file for downloading. The site includes a discussion section where various academics have passed comment on the books.

Minoan Civilization

http://www.dilos.com/region/crete/min_cul.html

Comprehensive source of information concerning Minoan civilization, which covers the history of

Minoan Crete from the pre-palace period of 2,600 BC to the Sub-Minoan period of 1,000 BC. You will find articles on Sir Arthur Evans and the excavations at Knossos; the legend of King Minos; the story of the labyrinth, which includes the tale of Theseus and his battle with the Minotaur; and more. The articles include photographs, drawings, and diagrams. There is also an image gallery of Knossos and Minoan Crete.

Mycenae

http://www.tulane.edu/lester/text/Ancient.World/My cenae/Mycenae.html

Virtual tour of the ancient Greek city of Mycenae. Click on the links for a brief description and colour photograph of key sites and artefacts, including the citadel, the Lion Gate, various tombs, a death mask, a gold tiara, and a decorated gold cup.

F A C T

MYCENAE

ancient Greek city in the eastern Peloponnese, which gave its name to the Mycenaean (Bronze Age) civilization. Its peak was 1400–1200 BC, when the Cyclopean walls (using close-fitting stones) were erected.

Peloponnesian War

http://history.idbsu.edu/westciv/peloponn/

Part of a larger site on the history of Western civilization maintained by Boise State University, this page provides an introductory look at the historical figures and events of the Peloponnesian War. Information is organized into 17 brief articles, each concerning a specific aspect of the war, such as the Delian League, Pericles' war strategy, the Sicilian Expedition, the later war years, and the results of the war. You can start at the beginning and work your way through the articles in chronological order or go directly to a page that interests you. Tricky words are introduced with an audio icon to assist with pronunciation. A list of references includes links to several full-length texts including Thucydides' *History of the Peloponnesian War.*

Persian Wars

http://history.idbsu.edu/westciv/persian/

Part of a larger site on the history of western civilization maintained by Boise State University,

this page provides an introduction to the historical figures and events of the Persian Wars. Information is organized into 22 brief articles, each concerning a specific aspect of the wars, such as the Ionian Revolt, Darius I, the Battle of Marathon, and the Battle of Thermopylae. Each battle includes pages dealing with its preparation and its aftermath. You can start at the beginning and work your way through the articles in chronological order or go directly to a page that interests you. Tricky words are introduced with an audio icon to assist with pronunciation. A list of references includes a link to the full-text of *The Persian Wars* by Herodotus.

Plague in Athens During the Peloponnesian War

http://www.indiana.edu/~ancmed/plague.htm

Part of a larger site concerning ancient medicine, this article investigates the plague that ravaged Athens during the Peloponnesian War. In addition to background information about the war and information about the outbreak of the plague and its effect on the city, this article attempts to arrive at a diagnosis of the disease based on Thucydides' detailed description.

Thucydides and the Ancient Simplicity

http://www.perseus.tufts.edu/~gcrane/ thuc.HC_ToC.html

Thoughtful in-depth analysis of the work of the Athenian historian. The reasons for the ongoing interest in Thucydides on the part of historians of human conflict is analysed. Parallels are drawn between the Gulf and Vietnam wars and the Peloponnesian War. The author speculates why Thucydides abandoned his great work – did he come to realize his account of events did not correspond with reality? For anybody interested in international relations this is a thought-provoking site.

Trojan War

http://www-lib.haifa.ac.il/www/art/troyan.html

This intriguing site tells the story of the Trojan War through art, and features various media spanning the 5th to 19th centuries. The major events of the war are arranged in chronological order, such as the Abduction of Helen, Achilles and Hektor, The Wooden Horse, the Fall and

Burning of Troy, and Leaving Troy, with hypertext descriptions of the related artworks listed under each heading. Click on the descriptions to view the art and see how artists from a number of eras, employing a variety of styles, have represented aspects of the war. Among the artworks, you will find vase and canvas paintings, a Roman wall painting, and more.

Works by Thucydides

http://classics.mit.edu/Browse/
browse-Thucydides.html

Thucydides' work *The History of the Peloponnesian War*, written *c.* 431 BC and in this case translated into English by Richard Crawley, is available to download as a text file from this Web site. The file is a full and complete version of the work and as such will take some time to download.

Ancient History, 400 BC–AD 99

Alexander's First Great Victory

http://www.thehistorynet.com/MilitaryHistory/articl
es/1997/12972_text.htm

Engaging analysis of the Battle of Granicus between the Persian forces and the army of Alexander the Great, with details on the tactics employed by the Greek commander during his first major military action in Asia.

Alexander the Great Home Page

http://wso.williams.edu/~junterek/

Life story of Alexander the Great, with biographies of his parents, graphics, and lively links.

Augustus

http://www.geocities.com/Athens/Aegean/9982/rep
ort.html

Detailed biography of the long life of Julius Caesar's great-nephew, who introduced constitutional monarchy to Rome. It traces Octavian's rise to power, his participation in the Second Triumvirate, his adoption of the title that

was to be used by the emperors who followed him, and the acquisition of more lands than any Roman leader before him.

Battle of Actium

http://myron.sjsu.edu/romeweb/ROMARMY/
art21.htm

Informative introduction to the Battle of Actium. The reasons for the battle are discussed, as are its consequences. Predominantly text-based, this page also contains links to biographies of two key protagonists in this battle: Marc Antony and Octavian.

Biography of Horace and Annotated Bibliography

http://www.uky.edu/ArtsSciences/Classics/
horawillbio.html

Profile of the life of the Roman poet, listing of his works, and a full bibliography. It traces Horace's rise from humble origins, his strict upbringing, the support for Brutus which led to the loss of his estates, the subsequent commencement of his literary career, and the prosperity he found thanks to the patronage of Augustus.

Cicero Home Page

http://www.utexas.edu/depts/classics/documents/
Cic.html

Essential source of information on Cicero. There is the complete text of Plutarch's biography, images of Cicero, and an extensive bibliography. A large number of Latin texts are included, in addition to an English translation of Cicero's musings on the genres of rhetoric.

Epicurus and Epicurean Philosophy

http://www.creative.net/~epicurus/

Discussion of Epicurus' philosophy, including its history, beliefs, and relationship with other philosophies. Several of his letters and doctrines are reproduced, and there is a guide to further study.

First Caesars

http://history.idbsu.edu/westciv/julio-cl/

Part of a larger site on the history of Western civilization maintained by Boise State University, this page provides a fascinating look at the

Roman emperors from Augustus to Nero. Information is organized into 27 brief articles, each concerning a specific emperor or an aspect of his reign. The story begins with Octavian's triumphant return from Egypt to Rome in 31 BC and ends with the death of Nero and an assessment of the Julio-Claudian emperors. Tricky words are introduced with an audio icon to assist with pronunciation. There is also a list of references including links to the full text of Vergil's *Aeneid* and Tacitus' *Annals of Imperial Rome.*

Gaius (Caligula)

http://www.salve.edu/~romanemp/gaius.htm

Interesting account of the turbulent life of the crazed and capricious megalomaniac. The main events of his life are well related and there is discussion as to whether the judgement of contemporaries and historians was correct. Was Caligula mad or was he simply acting the role of tyrant to which he had been doomed by a brutalizing childhood?

Gallic Wars by Julius Caesar

http://classics.mit.edu/Caesar/gallic.html

Full text of Julius Caesar's commentaries on his Gallic campaigns. This translation by W A McDevitte and W S Bohn is linked to texts of Caesar's other histories.

Histories by P Cornelius Tacitus

http://classics.mit.edu/Tacitus/histories.html

Full text of Tacitus's most famous history. This translation by Alfred John Church and William Jackson Brodribb is linked to a number of comments on the *Histories* and to information about the other works of the famous Roman historian.

Josephus, Flavius

http://www.knight.org/advent/cathen/08522a.htm

Profile of the life and work of the aristocratic Jewish historian. It traces his priestly background, role in the Jewish revolt against Roman rule, and his subsequent rapprochement with Rome. The significance of his writings for an understanding of Jewish and early Christian history is examined.

Landings of Caesar in Britain, 55 and 54 BC

http://www.athenapub.com/caesar1.htm

Description of Caesar's two invasions of Britain, illustrated with maps. Also included is a photograph of Deal beach in Kent, where it is believed Caesar first set foot in Britain.

Nero

http://www.salve.edu/~romanemp/nero.html

Details of the brutal and dissolute life of Nero. It traces his adoption by Claudius, succession as emperor, the burning of Rome, and his fall from power. There is a forgiving historical assessment of Nero, a man propelled to power by manipulative figures in turbulent times.

Punic Wars

http://history.idbsu.edu/westciv/punicwar/

Part of a larger site on the history of Western civilization maintained by Boise State University, this page provides an introduction to the historical figures and events of the Punic Wars. Information is organized into 18 brief articles, each concerning a specific aspect of the wars, such as Hannibal's crossing of the Alps. There is also information about the history of Carthage and Rome in 146 BC, and a list of supplemental references.

Roman Revolution

http://history.idbsu.edu/westciv/romanrev/

Part of a larger site on the history of Western civilization maintained by Boise State University, this page provides an informative look at the historical figures and events surrounding the Roman land reform revolution and its aftermath. Read about the brothers Gracchi who led the way toward agrarian reform, learn about the conditions that led to revolution, and the results. This site includes information on the First and Second Triumvirates, the assassination of Julius Caesar, and the failures of the Roman Republic. Information is organized into 39 brief articles. Tricky words are introduced with an audio icon to assist with pronunciation. There is also a list of references.

Titus Flavius Vespanius

http://www.salve.edu/~romanemp/titus.htm

Biography of the classically educated son of Vespasian. It traces his rise to power, and the extensive public works and economic reforms of this competent paternalistic autocrat. It suggests that the reputation he enjoyed after his death may have been the result of his early demise.

Works by P Cornelius Tacitus

http://classics.mit.edu/Browse/browse-Tacitus.html

Tacitus's two works *The Annals* and *The Histories*, which were written in *c.* 109 AD and have been translated by Alfred John Church and William Jackson Brodribb, are available to download as text files from this Web site. The files are full and complete versions of the works and as such will take some time to download.

Ancient History, AD 100–399

Caracalla

http://www.knight.org/advent/cathen/03328c.htm

Profile of the Roman emperor remembered by history through his derisive nickname, rather than his title. It traces his rise to power, the bloody events unleashed by the murder of his brother, Geta, and how his brother's death shaped the course of Caracalla's five-year rule and led to his assassination.

Christian Catacombs

http://www.catacombe.roma.it/welcome.html

Multilingual site dedicated to the Christian catacombs, mainly found in Italy. This is a well-designed site with pictures and information about the history and the importance of these places. It also includes a map of their locations and an examination of the symbols early Christians used in their carvings.

Constantine I

http://www.salve.edu/~dimaiom/conniei.html

Profile of the life of the emperor who, by his adoption of Christianity, foundation of Constantinople, and belief in absolute monarchy,

FACT

CONSTANTINE THE GREAT (*c.* AD 285–337),

first Christian emperor of Rome and founder of Constantinople. He defeated Maxentius, joint emperor of Rome AD 312, and in 313 formally recognized Christianity. As sole emperor of the west of the empire, he defeated Licinius, emperor of the east, to become ruler of the Roman world 324.

shaped the course of European civilization. This account deals with his struggles against his brothers-in-law, his support of Christianity, and the feuds that followed his death. There is also a bust and an icon of Constantine at this site.

Cyril of Alexandria, St

http://www.knight.org/advent/cathen/04592b.htm

Extended biography of the Doctor of the Church. It traces Cyril's tumultuous career as an enemy of Jews and Nestorians, his many theological works, and the legacy he left of monophysitism (a belief in the human and divine nature of Jesus).

Diocletian

http://myron.sjsu.edu/romeweb/empcont/e176.htm

Portrait of the military despot whose reforms ensured the continuity of the eastern Roman empire for a 1,000 years. It traces his rise from humble origins to military leadership at a time of intense turmoil. The military, economic, and administrative reforms Diocletia implemented before his abdication are described.

Hadrian's Wall

http://www.northumbria-tourist-board.org.uk/hadrian/

This site provides historical information, photographs and diagrams of Hadrian's Wall, as well as descriptions of its features. You can also learn the latest 'news from the wall' and pick up tourist tips, including information on where to stay when visiting the wall.

Jovian

http://myron.sjsu.edu/romeweb/empcont/e211.htm

Biography of the soldier who became Roman emperor, fought in Persia, and restored Christianity. There is a discussion of the theories that Jovian was murdered or died from overeating.

Licinius

http://www.salve.edu/~romanemp/licinius.html

Profile of the life of the peasant who became Roman emperor. His struggles against Christianity and full details of his wars with Constantine the Great are related here.

Vaballathus and Zenobia

http://www.salve.edu/~romanemp/zenobia.htm

Detailed and thoughtful analysis of the rise of the Palmyran city state, its struggle against Rome, and the role of its energetic queen, Zenobia, and her son, Vaballathus. The reasons for Zenobia's ill-timed revolt are analysed and ascribed to commercial as much as political motives.

Valens

http://www.salve.edu/~romanemp/valens.htm

Detailed account of the life of the eastern Roman emperor. It traces his rise to power and the military struggles against the Goths and Persians which led to the disastrous loss of the Battle of Adrianople and the inglorious death for which he is mostly remembered.

Why Rome Fell

http://history.idbsu.edu/westciv/fallrome/

Part of a larger site on the history of Western civilization maintained by Boise State University, this page, though currently a work in progress, nevertheless provides a fascinating, if incomplete, look at the causes of the fall of the Roman Empire. Information is organized into 11 brief articles, each concerning a specific aspect of Rome's decline, such as the city of Rome, religious and economic changes, and social transformation. You can start at the beginning and work your way through the articles in chronological order or go directly to a page that interests you.

Works of Julius Caesar

http://classics.mit.edu/Browse/browse-Caesar.html

English translations of Caesar's campaign descriptions' written, allegedly, by Caesar himself, although some have given credit to a lesser known diarist. They are available for downloading in text file format, and provide an interesting insight into the life of probably the greatest of the Roman emperors. The accounts included are: The Gallic Wars (which few dispute was written by Caesar), The Civil Wars, The African Wars, The Alexandrian Wars, and The Spanish Wars.

Miscellaneous Ancient History

All Souls School British Museum Ancient Greeks Virtual Tour

http://www.rmplc.co.uk/eduweb/sites/allsouls/bm/ag1.html

Virtual tour of the British Museum's ancient Greece exhibit, run by a teacher from a primary school near the museum. This site, although aimed primarily at other teachers, features a wealth of photographs and other information concerning the objects on display in the museum.

Ancient Egypt Site

http://www.geocities.com/~amenhotep/index.html

Exploration of ancient Egypt, offering, among many other things, historical accounts and an overview of the Egyptian languages. Navigating the site is made easier with the help of an extended glossary. 'More serious students' are advised to consult the bibliographical section and there is a long list of readings for all levels of interest.

Attila the Hun and the Battle of Chalons

http://www.msstate.edu/Archives/History/scholarship/attila.art

Description of one of the most important battles in history. Many historians say that the Battle of Chalons was the saviour of Western civilization from the marauding and barbaric Huns. The two protagonists at the battle were Aetius from the Western Roman Empire, known as the last of the Romans, and Attila the Hun, both of whom are briefly described here along with the battle itself. The Web site is in the format of a text-only file.

Dead Sea Scrolls

http://sunsite.unc.edu/expo/deadsea.scrolls.exhibit/
intro.html

Online resource designed to supplement an
exhibit at the Library of Congress, Washington
DC, entitled 'Scrolls from the Dead Sea: The
Ancient Library of Qumran and Modern
Scholarship'. The site is illustrated and offers
historical information about the scrolls, their
discovery 2,000 years after they were hidden, and
the Qumran community who, it is believed, were
responsible for both their production and
concealment.

Deep in the Tombs

http://members.aol.com/Egyptkids/Tombs.html

Lively, unpredictable site about the tombs of
ancient Egypt for young archaeologists. The site
offers endless fun combined with masses of
important information about the pyramids,
hieroglyphics, the Rosetta stone, the mummy's
curse, the pharaohs, and the tomb robbers. If you
survive your fall into a deep shaft just inside a
temple entrance, you can enjoy a Pharaoh's
challenge online quiz!

Diotima: Women and Gender in the Ancient World

http://www.uky.edu/ArtsSciences/Classics/
gender.html

Well-written piece on an often neglected topic.
Women played a crucial role in the ancient world
which has often been overlooked in more
traditional studies. This essay goes some way to
opening up a rewarding area of study.

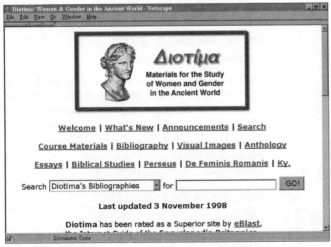

Great Gallery of Horseshoe Canyon

http://www.apogeephoto.com/mag1-6/
mag2-4rh.shtml

Article and several photographs of ancient
pictographs found on canyon walls in
Canyonland National Park, Utah, USA. The
article includes tourist information.

Great Temple of Abu Simbel

http://www.ccer.ggl.ruu.nl/abu_simbel/

Fascinating tour of the Great Temple of Abu
Simbel, dedicated to Ramses II. Clicking on the
heads of the various statues takes you to more
detailed photographs and if you click on the
entrance you will go inside. A map of the temple
is also available.

Historical Library

http://www.perseus.tufts.edu/cgi-bin/text?
lookup=Diod.+init.

Part of the Perseus Project at Tufts University, this
site includes the text of this work by the Greek
historian Diodorus Siculus. Hyperlinks help to
guide the reader, explaining the relevance of
people and places throughout the work. The text
itself is available in both English and Greek.

History of Persia

http://www.fordham.edu/halsall/ancient/asbook05.
html

Substantial introduction to the history of Persia
from the Achamaenid kings of 500 BC to the 18th-
century Zand dynasty. There are numerous links
to images and text about related people,
places, and monuments.

Inca Empire

http://www.sscf.ucsb.edu/~ogburn/
inca/inca.htm

Multimedia site dedicated to the history
of the Inca people. The Web site features
many images of the Andean Indian
people, along with texts and histories
relating to the conquest and subjugation
of the area by the Spanish. Also featured
are music samples from the area, and
several pieces of fantasy art with the
Incas as the subject.

Mesopotamia

http://saturn.sron.ruu.nl/%7Ejheise/akkadian/mesopotamia.html

What was life like between the Tigris and Euphrates rivers 5,000 years ago? Find out at this site, which contains information about the climate, people, economy and beliefs of the ancient Sumerians.

Nehemiah

http://www.knight.org/advent/cathen/10737c.htm

Account of the book associated with the Hebrew governor Nehemiah. It traces Nehemiah's role in rebuilding the walls of Jerusalem, his actions to protect the poor, and to prevent Jews from marrying outside the faith. Various theories relating the book of Nehemiah to that of Ezra are discussed.

Odyssey in Egypt

http://www.website1.com/odyssey/

Interactive archaeological dig, recorded and arranged week by week during the excavation of a 4th-century Coptic monastery at Wadi Natrun, Egypt. Learn about daily life on the dig, as well as science, archaeology, and Egyptian history and culture.

Perseus Art and Archaeology

http://www.perseus.tufts.edu/artarch.html

Massive library of classical art objects, sites, and buildings maintained by the Perseus Project at Tufts University, Medford, Massachusetts. Each section a description of the object and its context, as well as images. The catalogues currently contain over 500 coins, 1,400 vases, 350 sculptures, 150 sites, and 350 buildings.

Perseus Project Home Page

http://www.perseus.tufts.edu/

Digital library on ancient Greece, with an overview of archaic and classical Greek history; Greek works in English translation; thousands of images and descriptions of vases, coins, buildings, and sites, as well as Greek dictionaries.

Philistine

http://www.knight.org/advent/cathen/12021c.htm

Profile of the ancient inhabitants of the maritime plain of Palestine. The possible piratical origins of these seafaring people are discussed. The conflicts with the Jews, Egyptians, and Assyrians, which eventually led to the Philistine loss of identity, are traced.

Roman Military Sites in Britain

http://www.morgue.demon.co.uk/index.htm

Complete guide to the Roman military presence in the British Isles. There are many maps and descriptions of Roman sites, a brief history of the Roman occupation, a guide to the Roman armies and their composition, and photographs of many of the sites as they stand today.

Seven Wonders of the World

http://ce.eng.usf.edu/pharos/wonders/

Pictures and information about all of the seven wonders of the ancient world. The site includes the location, history, and a quite detailed description of each of these important historical monuments.

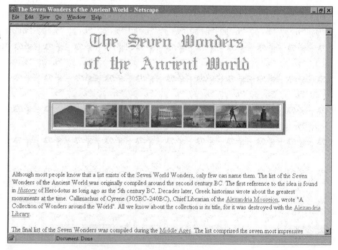

Theban Mapping Project

http://www.kv5.com/intro.html

Site for the project whose aim is the archaeological mapping of the ancient city of Thebes. The site features a virtual tour of the largest tomb ever discovered and a clickable map of the Valley of the Kings. It also includes a behind-the-scenes look at the work of Egyptologists and a tour of the major Theban monuments at Luxor.

Treasures of the Sunken City

http://www.pbs.org/wgbh/nova/sunken/

Companion to the US Public Broadcasting Service

(PBS) television programme *Nova*, this page follows French archaeologist Jean Yves Empereur and his team as they discover the Pharos lighthouse, one of the Seven Wonders of the ancient world. Learn about the high-tech tools Empereur used to map these ancient ruins, explore a piece of the map yourself, and watch video clips of various phases of the recovery. You can also read a transcript of an interview with Jean Yves Empereur, as well as a transcript of the television programme, and learn what other treasures have since been discovered. There is a special section on the Seven Wonders of the World.

Welcome to Egypt: The Valley of the Kings

http://www.geocities.com/TheTropics/2815/

Illustrated guide to the Egyptian Valley of the Kings offering historical information on the ancient pharaohs Tut-Ankh-Aman, or Tutankhamen, Ramses II, and Amenhotep II. The site also includes an hieroglyphic alphabet chart and links to related sites on the Web.

Welcome to Persepolis

http://www.iranonline.com/iran/Fars/persepolis/

Guide to the glories and history of Persepolis. There is a description of the site, details of its most important buildings, and accompanying photographs.

Who Was Who Among the Royal Mummies

http://www-oi.uchicago.edu/OI/IS/WENTE/NN_Win95/NN_Win95.html

Illustrated essay by Prof E F Wente which details research recently conducted to determine the precise identities of the royal Egyptian mummies.

Medieval British History

Alcuin of York

http://www-groups.dcs.st-and.ac.uk/history/Mathematicians/Alcuin.html

Part of an archive containing the biographies of the world's greatest mathematicians, this site is devoted to the life and contributions of Alcuin of York. In addition to biographical information, you will find a list of references about Alcuin and links to other essays in the archive which reference him. The text of this essay includes hypertext links to the essays of those mathematicians and thinkers who influenced Alcuin. You will also find an image of him, which you can click on to enlarge, and a map of his birthplace.

Angelcynn – At Weststow Anglo-Saxon Village

http://www.geocities.com/Athens/2471/weststow.html

Online reconstruction of life on an Anglo-Saxon village. Fully illustrated throughout, there is also a map and sections on such topics as 'The reconstruction', 'Everyday life', and 'The economy'. This is part of a much larger site on Anglo-Saxon England.

Anglo-Saxon England

http://bay1.bjt.net/~melanie//anglo-sa.html

Good background information about Anglo-Saxon England, with notes about key writings (including *Beowulf*, the Lindisfarne Gospels and the Anglo-Saxon Chronicle), brief biographies of the Anglo-Saxon kings, maps, a timeline, bibliographies, and annotated links to other sites.

Anglo-Saxon Invasion of Britain

http://www.geocities.com/Athens/2471/invade.html

Brief but illuminating introduction to the Anglo-Saxon invasion of Britain, with extracts from chronicles of the period and a few illustrations.

Arthur of Britain

http://www.angelfire.com/ak/auden/arthur.html

Colourful and concise site detailing possible explanations of several Arthurian legends, namely: the Holy Grail, the sword in the stone, and the location of Arthur's tomb. It also provides the text of some modern versions of the legend of King Arthur.

Battle of Bosworth

http://www.r3.org/bosworth/index.html

Extensive Web site on the last battle of the War of the Roses. This site contains maps and texts from the Tudor government of the time, as well as documents from other observers at the battle, such as the Spanish report by Diego de Valera, a Castillian courtier.

Battle of Hastings

http://battle1066.com/index.html

Incredibly detailed and well-designed account of the battle of 1066 which is divided into sections on the various claimants to the English throne at the time, followed by an account of the battle itself. The site also includes a glossary, timeline, and details about the Bayeux Tapestry.

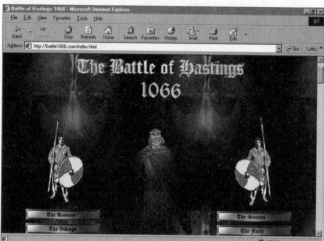

Camelot Project

http://www.lib.rochester.edu:80/camelot/CPHOME.stm

Database of Arthurian texts, images, bibliographies, and basic information, with sections on the knights and ladies of his realm – such as Guinevere, Galahad, and Morgan Le Fay – and key symbols and motifs – such as the Holy Grail and Excalibur.

Conquest of Ireland

http://www.fordham.edu/halsall/source/geraldwales1.html

Excerpt from Giraldus Cambrensis's 12th-century account of the Norman conquest of Ireland, taken from the Internet Medieval Library.

Domesday Book

http://www.fordham.edu/halsall/source/domesday1.html

From the Internet Medieval Sourcebook come two extracts from the Domesday Book: instructions

---

F A C T

DOMESDAY BOOK

record of the survey of England carried out in 1086 by officials of William the Conqueror in order to assess land tax and other dues, ascertain the value of the crown lands, and enable the king to estimate the power of his vassal barons.

---

issued to the commissioners who were to obtain the records, and an excerpt from the Domesday survey of the county of Norfolk.

Feudal Terms of England

http://eserver.org/history/feudal-terms.txt

Dictionary of terms relating to feudalism, including explanations of obligations, the hierarchy, and even related matters such as the parts of a castle. Although the terms and their meanings mainly focus on England, other parts of the world are covered too.

History of the Britons

http://www.fordham.edu/halsall/source/nennius.html

Excerpts from an English translation of Nennius's *Historia Britonum/History of the Britons,* taken from the Internet Medieval Sourcebook.

Kells, Book of

http://www.geocities.com/Heartland/Park/6748/kells.html

Central source of information about the famous Irish manuscript, including stunning high-resolution images. There are links to research about the manuscript and further sources of information about Celtic knotwork and other Celtic and Anglo-Saxon manuscripts.

King Richard III Found Not Guilty

http://www.r3.org/trial/trial2.html

Part of a larger site on Richard III, this page follows the mock trial held at the University of Indiana Law School in October 1996, in which a three-judge panel, including Chief Justice of the US Supreme Court William Rehnquist, found Richard III not guilty of the murders of the

Princes in the Tower. This page includes a summary of both parties' arguments, links to audio of the mock trial, and a link to the results of the second mock trial held at the US Supreme Court in July 1997.

Laws of William the Conqueror

http://www.fordham.edu/halsall/source/will1-lawsb.html

From the Internet Medieval Sourcebook, a translation of the ten laws that William put into place after the Norman conquest of England; for example, forbidding the sale of men and the sale of cattle outside cities.

Lollards

http://www.knight.org/advent/cathen/09333a.htm

Comprehensive history of the Lollards, followers of English religious reformer John Wycliffe. The corruption within the English church, which created fertile ground for Wycliffe's movement, is described prior to an analysis of the many beliefs subsequently described as Lollard. The efforts to suppress Lollardy are outlined.

Magna Carta

http://www.yale.edu/lawweb/avalon/magframe.htm

Full text of this historic document with hypertext definitions of key words and phrases and an index to facilitate specific searches.

Medieval Sourcebook – Corpus Iuris Civilis: Marriage

http://www.fordham.edu/halsall/source/cjc-marriage.html

Extensive extracts on marriage from a document of central importance for modern European civil and canon church laws, namely Justinian's 'Corpus Iuris Civilis'. This site offers a mixture of laws, imperial decrees, senatorial consults, and opinions of famous lawyers dating back to Roman times, and concentrates especially Augustus's famous family reforms.

Murder of Thomas Becket, 1170

http://www.ibiscom.com/becket.htm#TOP

Illustrated account of the events surrounding the murder of Thomas Becket, the then Archbishop of Canterbury, allegedly on the orders of King Henry II, on the altar steps of Canterbury Cathedral in 1170.

Paris, Matthew

http://www.knight.org/advent/cathen/11499a.htm

Profile of the Benedictine monk and chronicler. It traces how the humble monk spent most of his life at St Albans Abbey and how his friendships with English and Norwegian royalty provided access to the information he used to write his chronicles. His skills as an illustrator are set out alongside an assessment of his achievements as an historian.

Ricardian Studies Primer

http://www.r3.org/basics/index.html

Part of a Richard III and Yorkist history site, this section contains brief articles and notes concerning the background, major events, and principal players associated with Richard III during the period of English history which includes the Wars of the Roses, the fall of the House of Lancaster and rise of the House of York, as well as the life and reign of Richard III. Information is contained in nine browsable sections. This site includes a medieval dictionary.

Richard III Society Home Page

http://www.r3.org/intro.html

Home page of the US branch of the Richard III Society providing a wealth of information about the king – as a figure in both history and literature. Here are reviews of stage and film versions of Shakespeare's *Richard III*; an online library of primary texts and secondary sources, and a hypertext edition of Shakespeare's play with links to appropriate sections of a recent biography.

Secrets of the Norman Invasion

http://www.cablenet.net/pages/book/index.htm

Detailed hypertext document exploring the Norman invasion of Britain. The site is extensively illustrated and includes a number of images from the Bayeux Tapestry in addition to a series of aerial surveys of the Hastings region.

St Edward the Confessor

http://www.knight.org/advent/cathen/05322a.htm

Profile of the English king. It traces his exile, his accession to the throne, and the reign of this unambitious and deeply pious monarch.

Timeline of Arthurian Britain

http://www.britannia.com/history/timearth.html

Part of a larger site on British history, this page features a chronology of Arthurian and 5th-century history, blended with information about the many legends of Arthur and his court. The timeline includes hypertext links to additional information. The text of the timeline is enhanced by images of colourful paintings and illustrations.

Warfare in Anglo-Saxon England

http://www.geocities.com/Athens/2471/warfare.html

Concise information on the army, weapons, and war tactics of the early Anglo-Saxons, with extracts from Roman writers and *Beowulf*, as well as a few illustrations and a bibliography.

16th- & 17th-century British History

Bacon, Francis (philosopher)

http://www.luminarium.org/sevenlit/bacon/index.html

Very aesthetic site with biographical details, famous quotes, essays, and links to many works by this famous philosopher, politician, and essayist. As well as looking very good, this site also includes a timeline of Bacon's life and some contemporary background music.

Battle of Naseby 1645

http://easyweb.easynet.co.uk/~crossby/ECW/ battles/naseby.html

Introduction to the background to this decisive battle in the English Civil War, a detailed account of the battle itself, and copies of three contemporary accounts of the actual fighting written by leading parliamentarians at the scene. There are also pictures of some of the types of soldier involved, as well as information on the battle site as it exists today and its archaeological significance.

Dee, John

http://www-history.mcs.st-and.ac.uk/history/Mathematicians/Dee.html

Biography and portrait of the English 16th-century mathematician, astrologer, alchemist, and magician. This site also includes a brief description of Dee's works.

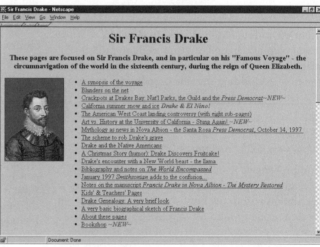

Drake, Sir Francis

http://www.mcn.org/2/oseeler/drake.htm

Network of pages on this Elizabethan explorer, focusing mainly on his circumnavigation of the globe. As well as a synopsis of the voyage and plenty of background information on the man himself, this site also includes a 'Kids' and teachers' page'.

Elizabeth I

http://www.luminarium.org/renlit/eliza.htm

Biography of the queen, plus the text of some of her

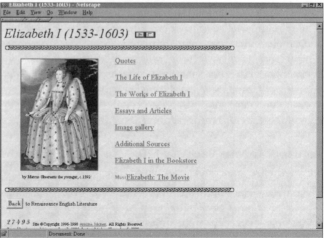

poems and speeches, letters, and essays about her life. The site also contains an audio clip of contemporary music.

English Civil War

http://history.idbsu.edu/westciv/english

Part of a larger site on the history of Western civilization maintained by Boise State University, this page provides an introduction to the English Civil War and the historical figures who played prominent roles in it. Information is organized into 23 brief articles, each concerning a specific aspect of the conflict and its origins, such as religion and the Scottish question, the execution of Charles I, parliament and Oliver Cromwell, the restoration, and final resolution. You can start at the beginning and work your way through the articles in chronological order or go directly to a page that interests you. There is also a list of references for further study.

Extracts from the Declaration of Rights (February 1689)

http://history.hanover.edu/early/decright.htm

Excerpts from the Declaration of Rights statement of the 17th century. This Hanover University-run site is a scanned version of the original and it has links to other historical British documents.

Food in Tudor England

http://tudor.simplenet.com/life/food/

Educational resource which discusses the changing nature of food during the Tudor era in Britain. Also included are a selection of authentic Tudor recipes, and a glossary of terms.

Glorious Revolution of 1688

http://www.lawsch.uga.edu/~glorious/

Web site intended to serve as a permanent collection of materials covering the period in English history known as the Glorious Revolution. This site features a chronology, an encyclopedia, Internet links, and literature references.

Gunpowder Plot Pages

http://www.bcpl.lib.md.us/~cbladey/guy/html/main.html

Extensive site on the Gunpowder Plot, detailing the history and events. It contains many maps,

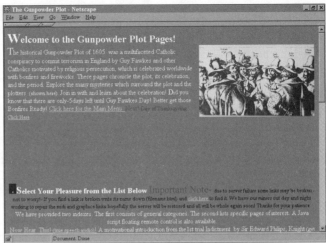

pictures, and also some contemporary music. There is also information on other aspects of contemporary life, such as clothing and food.

Henry VIII

http://tudor.simplenet.com/henry8/

Illustrated site introducing the most famous of the Tudor kings. A brief biography is followed by links to Henry's six wives, with pictures. There is also a link to the Henry VIII gallery, with numerous period portraits of the monarch and his contemporaries. Click to enlarge each portrait.

Lady Jane Grey

http://ladyjane.iinet.net.au/

Story of Lady Jane Grey and her nine days as Queen of England in the 16th century. There are many pictures on this site, which covers her family background and early life, through her marriage and events leading up to her enthronement, and then her execution for treason. It includes contemporary correspondence surrounding the event and there is also a chart of all the kings and queens of England.

Mary I

http://www.camelotintl.com/heritage/maryi.html

Picture of the English queen, as well as a brief biography and links to articles on related subjects, including her husband Philip, her father Henry VIII, and her successor Elizabeth I.

Raleigh, Sir Walter

http://www.luminarium.org/renlit/ralegh.htm

Devoted to the life and works of the 16th-century English writer and courtier Sir Walter Raleigh.

Click links to read about his life and access his works. There are quotes, essays, an extensively hyperlinked biography, a portrait, and a selection of both his poetry and prose.

Spanish Armada

http://www.nmm.ac.uk/ei/fact/armada.htm

Fact file produced by the National Maritime Museum on the Spanish Armada. The historical background to the invasion and details of the Spanish retreat are described.

Thomas More Web Site

http://www.d-holliday.com/tmore/

Biography and chronology of the English politician and author. His family, writings, and travels are also described, and there is information on Thomas More societies and resources.

Tudor and Renaissance Music

http://tudor.simplenet.com/music/

Educational resource which discusses the importance of music during the Tudor era in Britain. Sacred and secular music is covered, and there is also an 'Instruments' section which shows images of instruments of the period. MIDI files of period music can also be downloaded.

United Kingdom

http://www.crwflags.com/fotw/flags/gb.html

Detailed discussion pages with historical information about the Union Jack, its design, and uses.

18th-century British History

Bolingbroke, Henry St John

http://socserv2.socsci.mcmaster.ca/~econ/ugcm/3l l3/bolingbroke/index.html

Part of the Archive for the History of Economic Thought at McMaster University, this page features the text of four essays, letters, and dissertations written by Henry St John Bolingbroke: 'A Dissertation Upon Parties', written between 1733 and 1734 in a series of letters to Sir Walter Walpole; 'The Idea of a Patriot King', which seeks to outline the duties of a king to his country; 'Letters on the Study and Use of History'; and 'On the Spirit of Patriotism', in which he discusses the responsibilities of freedom.

Culloden Moor and Story of the Battle

http://www.queenofscots.co.uk/culloden/cull.html

Excerpts from the book of the same title by the late Peter Anderson of Inverness, Scotland. Details of events leading up to, during, and after the battle are described in depth on this Web site. The odd burst of poetic lament is also thrown in for good measure.

Daniel Defoe: 'Giving Alms No Charity'

http://socserv2.socsci.mcmaster.ca/~econ/ugcm/3ll3/defoe/index.html

Part of the Archive for the History of Economic Thought at McMaster University, this page features the text of an address before English Parliament given in 1704 by Daniel Defoe, in which he first lays out the history of England's rise to manufacturing and trade superiority, and then asserts that the workhouses and other social programmes that were designed to provide for and employ the poor have actually increased their number and have had a detrimental effect on the nation and its prosperity. Defoe concludes by dissecting the causes of poverty in England and the 'ruine of our poor' and warns of the destruction of England's prosperity should the problem of the poor go unaddressed by Parliament.

Edmund Burke: Speech on Conciliation with America

http://odur.let.rug.nl/~usa/D/1751-1775/libertydebate/burk.htm

Part of a larger site on historical documents, this page is the text of a speech given on 22 March 1775 by the English statesman and political thinker Edmund Burke, in which he calls for a peaceful handling of the crisis in America. The site includes a link to a brief biography of Edmund Burke.

King George III – Proclamation of Rebellion, 1775

http://douglass.speech.nwu.edu/proc_a52.htm

Text of King George III's proclamation at the outbreak of the American Revolution, in which he states that the American colonies are in open rebellion to the Crown and declares that British soldiers and colonists alike are expected to aid in the suppression of this uprising.

King's Rangers

http://www.cam.org/~dmonk/index.html

History of the King's Rangers, otherwise known as Rogers' Rangers. The Web site describes the role of the rangers in the American War of Independence and the Indian and French Wars. Run by a group of re-enactors, the Web site lists the history of the rangers up to their disbanding in 1783.

Mutiny on the *HMS Bounty*

http://www.visi.com/~pjlareau//bounty1.html

Biographical details on all the crew members of this infamous ship, including some pictures. There is even a list of people who should have been on the ship but weren't, and a summary of the story of the mutiny.

Objections to the Taxation of the American Colonies

http://odur.let.rug.nl/~usa/D/1751-1775/stampact/object.htm

Part of a larger site on historical documents, this page is the text of a pamphlet written by Soame Jenyns, a member of English Parliament, in which he supports Parliament's right to tax the American colonies and describes the theory of virtual representation. A brief introduction provides historical context.

F A C T

IMPERIALISM

policy of extending the power and rule of a government beyond its own boundaries. A country may attempt to dominate others by direct rule and settlement – the establishment of a colony – or by less obvious means such as control of markets for goods or raw materials.

Resolutions of the Stamp Act Congress

http://odur.let.rug.nl/~usa/D/1751-1775/stampact/sa.htm

Part of a larger site on historical documents, this page is the text of resolutions drawn up on 19 October 1765, which declare the rights and liberties of the American colonists and air their grievances against the imposition of stamp duties. A brief introduction provides historical context.

South Sea Bubble

http://is.dal.ca/~dmcneil/sketch.html

Extensively linked account of the main events of the South Sea Bubble – the first stock market crash in England in

1720. The site contains contemporary quotes and pictures.

Speech Delivered by King William of England to Parliament

http://odur.let.rug.nl/~usa/D/1701-1725/england/french.htm

Part of a larger site on historical documents, this page is the text of a speech delivered by King William of England to Parliament on 31 December 1701, regarding his concern over French expansion in Europe and the Americas. A brief introduction provides historical context.

Tyburn Tree Home Page

http://www.bouldernews.infi.net/~charliem/index.htm

Information on public executions in England in the 16th and 17th centuries. This site contains the dying speeches of some prominent unfortunates, the historical background to the period, a picture gallery, and links to extracts from contemporary sources.

William Pitt: Speech on the Stamp Act

http://odur.let.rug.nl/~usa/D/1751-1775/stampact/sapitt.htm

Part of a larger site on historical documents, this page is the text of a speech delivered to the English Parliament by William Pitt, in which he denies Parliament's right to tax the American colonies. A brief introduction provides historical context.

19th-century British History

Battle of Trafalgar

http://www.compulink.co.uk/~flagship/battle.htm

Informative article about the Battle of Trafalgar, including the text of the prayer that Nelson wrote before the battle. There are also links to related articles, including a detailed biography of Nelson himself.

Commemoration of the Great Famine

http://www.toad.net/~sticker/nosurrender/PotatCom.html

Comprehensive account of the potato famine and its consequences for Ireland. The disaster is traced through examination of contemporary accounts as well as through historical articles placing the famine within the broader history of Ireland. There are a large number of photos. This well-written site is of interest to anybody studying the history of Ireland.

Corn Laws by T R Malthus

http://www.yale.edu/lawweb/avalon/econ/corframe.htm

Text of 'Observations on the Effects of the Corn Laws', a document written and published in 1814 by the Rev T R Malthus. The document describes the effect the ancient laws were having on the price of grain at the start of the 19th century, and in particular the way the laws supported the corrupt market system taking advantage of the rapidly expanding urban population of the time.

F A C T

CORN LAWS

in Britain until 1846, laws used to regulate the export or import of cereals in order to maintain an adequate supply for consumers and a secure price for producers. They were repealed because they became an unwarranted tax on food and a hindrance to British exports.

Disraeli, Benjamin

http://dialspace.dial.pipex.com/town/terrace/adw03/peel/bdchron.htm

Timeline about this prime minister, particularly in relation to his purchase of the Suez Canal. There is information about his early life and political career, alongside some of his famous quotes and details about the Suez Canal.

Duke of Wellington's Correspondence

http://www.wtj.com/pl/pages/welling2.htm

This page features the dispatches of the Duke of Wellington during the Peninsula and Waterloo campaigns of the Napoleonic Wars. The correspondence is divided into two sections: the first, concerning the Peninsula campaigns, includes dispatches regarding preparations for the battles of Talavera, Busaco, and Salamanca; the second focuses on the mobilization and campaign of Waterloo, and includes letters written to the families of dead officers after the battle. Some of the letters, those issued to officers of foreign armies, are presented here in French, the language in which they were originally penned.

Industrial Revolution: A Trip to the Past

http://members.aol.com/mhirotsu/kevin/trip2.html

Web site containing a brief history of the Industrial Revolution, as well as an essay. There is also information about developments in medicine, transportation, and art, and an essay about the change from cottage industry to the factory system.

F A C T

INDUSTRIAL REVOLUTION

sudden acceleration of technical and economic development that began in Britain in the second half of the 18th century. The traditional agricultural economy was replaced by one dominated by machinery and manufacturing, made possible through technical advances such as the steam engine.

Learning Curve – Power, Politics, and Protest

http://www.pro.gov.uk/learningcurve/politics/default.asp

Public Record Office Web site dedicated to presenting information about 19th-century politics in Britain, using real documents. This well-designed site would be of interest to history students of all ages, but was written with the national curriculum in mind, and includes a timeline of events in the 19th century.

Life of the Industrial Worker in 19th-century England

http://applebutter.freeservers.com/worker/

This site examines the conditions under which industrial labourers toiled during the Industrial Revolution in early 19th-century England. It

features the results of the Sadler Committee on textile factories and Chadwick's Report on Sanitary Conditions, plus testimony from Ashley's Mine Commission. Included in these reports are a number of testimonials from labourers. There are hyptertext links to further information on child labour, textile factories, as well as to relevant Parliamentary papers. Brief explanatory notes accompany most articles and provide historical context.

Peel, Sir Robert

http://madhatter.chch.ox.ac.uk/chch/people/peel.html

Profile of the British prime minister from his alma mater, Christ Church, Oxford. His privileged family background as a textile magnate is set out. Peel's long association with Oxford, from his workaholic undergraduate days, to the outrage caused by his support for Catholic Emancipation, is related here.

Philosophy of the Manufacturers, 1835

http://www.fordham.edu/halsall/mod/1835ure.html

This page offers a defence of the manufacturing system as it was developing during the 19th century. It was written in 1835 by Andrew Ure, a professor at the University of Glasgow, and represents the viewpoint of the factory owner during the Industrial Revolution.

Victorian Web

http://www.stg.brown.edu/projects/hypertext/landow/victorian/victov.html

Information on social context, economics, religion, philosophy, and literature in Victorian times, including a section dedicated to the Pre-Raphaelites.

'Wages Theory of the Anti-Corn Law League, The'

http://leftside.uwc.ac.za/Archive/1881-ls/ls07.htm

Complete text of this essay by Friedrich Engels, which has been reproduced here complete with notes.

20th-century British History

Abdication Crisis

http://web.bham.ac.uk/maddendp/abdicatn.htm

This site includes the text of Edward VIII's announcement of abdication, which was read by the Speaker in the House of Commons and the Earl of Onslow in the House of Lords in December 1936. You will also find an excerpt from a biography of Elizabeth II which describes the impact that the abdication had on Edward VIII's reluctant successor, the Duke of York.

Chamberlain, Sir Joseph Austen

http://www.nobel.se/laureates/peace-1925-1-bio.html

Full biography of the half-brother of Neville Chamberlain. It traces his education, which trained him for political life, the role of his father in shaping his career, his 45 years in the House of Commons, and Chamberlain's work with French and German foreign ministers which led to his sharing of the Nobel Peace Prize.

Chronicle of the Falkland Islands History and War

http://www.yendor.com/vanished/falklands-war.html

Chronicle of the history of the Falkland Islands, from their discovery in 1592 to the British capture of the islands from Argentina in 1982. The main focus of this site is the detailed account it gives of the 1982 conflict between the UK and Argentina, including a photograph of the declaration of surrender of the island of South Georgia being signed by the Argentine commander.

Great Haig Debate

http://raven.cc.ukans.edu/~kansite/ww_one/comment/haig-debate.html

Part of a larger site concerning World War I documents, this page profiles the debate over the military fitness and conduct of General Douglas Haig, who planned what would become one of the bloodiest and costliest battles of the war. It includes several articles written by military historians offering opposing opinions of Haig's personality and behaviour.

Gulf War Frontline

http://www2.pbs.org/wgbh/pages/frontline/gulf/index.html

Highly informative Web site associated with the US–UK co-produced television series, broadcast in 1996. It includes transcripts of interviews with key figures – decision-makers, commanders, and analysts – maps, and a chronology.

F A C T

GULF WAR

war 16 Jan–28 February 1991 between Iraq and a coalition of 28 nations led by the USA. The invasion and annexation of Kuwait by Iraq on 2 August 1990 provoked a build-up of US troops in Saudi Arabia, eventually totalling over 500,000. The UK subsequently deployed 42,000 troops, France 15,000, Egypt 20,000, and other nations smaller contingents.

International Churchill Societies Online

http://www.winstonchurchill.org/

Site fostering interest in the life and the philosophical and literary heritage of Sir Winston Churchill. It includes short features, questions and answers, timelines, and links to related sites.

Liberation of Ireland

http://homepages.iol.ie/~dluby/history.htm

Introduction to modern Irish history, from the Easter rising of 1916 to the present day. It includes biographies and pictures on important figures involved in the struggle for independence. There's a chart of all Irish prime ministers and presidents and it even plays the national anthem if you have the correct plug-in.

Lord Boyd Orr of Brechin

http://www.nobel.se/laureates/peace-1949-bio.html

Good portrait of the Scottish peace campaigner. It traces his early interest in the socially disadvantaged, his medical career, his pioneering work in nutrition research, his leadership of the World Food Organization, his Nobel Peace Prize, and his untiring efforts to promote world government.

Master Lend-Lease Agreement, 23 February 1942

http://www.yale.edu/lawweb/avalon/decade/decade04.htm

Part of the Avalon Project at the Yale Law School, this page is the text of the Lend-Lease Agreement of 23 February 1943, made between the UK and the USA, which established the terms and conditions for the USA to provide the UK with implements of war.

Neville Chamberlain WAVS

http://earthstation1.simplenet.com/Chamberlain.html

Audio clips from Chamberlain's speeches. Of the dozen clips included, perhaps the most famous are the 'This piece of paper' speech on returning from a meeting with Hitler, and of course Chamberlain's 'This country is at war with Germany' declaration of war. The clips are mostly WAV type files, but several are also available in Real Audio format. Note that the files are quite large and may take some time to download.

1956 – The Suez Crisis and the Peacekeeping Debut

http://www.screen.com/mnet/eng/med/class/teamedia/peace/Part1/P1_11.htm

Account of the 1956 Suez Crisis adapted from the book *Discovering Canada*. It also includes a brief article entitled 'The Peacekeeping Debut – A Different Perspective'.

Speeches of Winston Churchill Sounds Page

http://earthstation1.simplenet.com/churchil.html

Speeches of Winston Churchill. This Web site is subdivided into three sections: Pre-War Speeches, Complete WWII Broadcasts, and Post War & Iron Curtain Speeches. Each section contains a large archive of true speech WAV format files which may be either downloaded or played by your browser software (with the aid of the appropriate plug-in).

Thatcher, Margaret

http://www.pathfinder.com/time/time100/leaders/profile/thatcher.html

Part of a larger archive from *Time* exploring the most influential people of the 20th century, this article highlights the life and work of former British prime minister Margaret Thatcher. The profile also features a timeline of her life and career.

British Royal Family

Althorp

http://www.althorp.com/intro/welcome.shtml

Full details of the Spencer family home, which is now the last resting place of Diana. There is practical information for visitors on how to find Althorp. Facilities available to visitors, including the gift shop selling goods 'inspired by Diana but not cheapening her memory', are described.

British Monarchy

http://www.royal.gov.uk/

The official site of the British monarchy includes reviews of its history, its present role and character, and details on the formal order of accession, coronation, and succession that applies to each monarch. There are sections on the royal palaces and parks, the life of Princess Diana, and a guest book for visitors to sign.

Directory of Royal Genealogical Data

http://www.dcs.hull.ac.uk/public/genealogy/royal/catalog.html

Extensive guide to the royal families of Europe and how they are related to each other. There are 30,000 individuals listed on this vast searchable genealogy. The site monitors visits to compile a list of the ten most popular monarchs. William the Conqueror comes out on top.

Duke of York

http://www.royal.gov.uk/family/york.htm

Official biography of the second son of the British queen, presented by the British monarchy Web site.

There are full details of the Duke of York's education, military career, sporting, and charitable interests. The site contains images of the Duke but none of his daughters or former wife.

Funeral of Diana, Princess of Wales

http://earthstation1.simplenet.com/ Princess_Diana.html

Sound recordings and pictures from the funeral of Diana, Princess of Wales. The WAV format audio clips include the rendition of 'England's Rose' by Elton John and the funeral addresses of Tony Blair, Earl Spencer and the Archbishop of Canterbury among others. There are over seventy JPEG format images of the funeral and procession also available from this Web site.

Her Majesty Queen Elizabeth the Queen Mother

http://www.royal.gov.uk/family/mother.htm

Official biography of the Queen Mother, presented by the British monarchy Web site. The Queen Mother's long life is comprehensively chronicled.

Her Majesty the Queen

http://www.royal.gov.uk/family/hmqueen.htm

Official biography of the British queen, presented by the British monarchy Web site. There are full details of the queen's life and interests and links to other members of her family.

Prince Edward

http://www.royal.gov.uk/family/edward.htm

Official biography of the youngest son of the British queen, presented by the British monarchy Web site. There is a general account of the Prince's education, theatrical, sporting, and charitable interests.

Prince of Wales

http://www.royal.gov.uk/family/wales.htm

Official biography of the heir to the British throne, presented by the British monarchy Web site. There are full details of the Prince's education, military career, interests and overseas' visits. There are images of Charles and his family (but none of his late wife, Diana, Princess of Wales).

Prince Philip, Duke of Edinburgh

http://www.royal.gov.uk/family/philip.htm

Official biography of the husband of the British queen, presented by the British monarchy Web site. There are full details of the Duke's career as sailor and royal consort, and details of his charitable and sporting interests.

Princess Royal

http://www.royal.gov.uk/family/royal.htm

Official biography of the daughter of the British queen, presented by the British monarchy Web site. There are full details of the Princess Royal's life, her equestrian achievements, and her extensive charitable work.

Prince's Trust

http://www.princes-trust.org.uk/

Home page of the charity established by Charles, Prince of Wales, out of his concern for social and environmental issues. There is extensive information on the role of the Trust in providing training and encouraging small business enterprises in disadvantaged areas of Britain.

Queen of Hearts

http://www.royalnetwork.com/rnn/dibio.html

Memorial site to the Princess of Wales in the form of an illustrated biography. This site also contains remembrance prayers for a wide variety of faiths and many personal tributes from people across the world.

St James's Palace

http://www.royal.gov.uk/palaces/stjamess.htm

Official guide to St James's Palace and the Court to which London-based ambassadors are accredited. This history of the official residence of the Prince of Wales is part of the Web site of the British royal family.

Windsor Castle

http://www.hotelnet.co.uk/windsor/home.htm

Learn about Queen Elizabeth II's residence at this informative site. A brief history of the castle is provided, together with descriptions and photographs of several of the interior rooms.

There's also a map for those who want to visit and details of opening hours and admission charges.

History of Oceania

Australian History

http://www.austemb.org/history.htm

Interactive online guide to Australian History from 1788 to the present. This site includes a detailed timeline of events since 1901.

Bruce, Stanley Melbourne

http://www.virtualaustralia.com.au/people/prime_ministers/stanley_bruce.html

Portrait of the Anglophile, spat-wearing prime minister of Australia in the 1920s. This is a good account of his political career and his role in the building of Canberra as Australia's capital.

Chifley, Ben

http://www.virtualaustralia.com.au/people/prime_ministers/chifley.html

Biography of the self-effacing train driver who rose to become Labor Prime Minister of Australia. This well-written account traces Chifley's rise to the leadership of the Labor Party in 1945 and the post-war reconstruction and encouragement of immigration that characterized his four years as prime minister.

Curtin, John

http://www.virtualaustralia.com.au/people/prime_ministers/curtin.html

Sympathetic account of the career of Australia's leader during World War II. It traces Curtin's evolution from an opponent of conscription in World War I to his dynamic leadership of Australia from 1941 to 1945 and his premature death.

Deakin, Alfred

http://www.virtualaustralia.com.au/people/prime_ministers/deakin.html

Good account of the career of Australia's second prime minister. It charts his career as lawyer, journalist, and exponent of Australian federation before examining the claim that he was Australia's greatest leader.

Eureka Stockade

http://users.netconnect.com.au/~ianmac/eureka.html

Account of this act of civil insurrection and its role in forging Australia's national identity. The events leading up to the historic clash between diggers and troopers are outlined, together with recent historical evidence reassessing what took place.

Fraser, Malcolm

http://www.virtualaustralia.com.au/people/prime_ministers/fraser.html

Profile of the former Australian prime minister. This is a comprehensive summary of his career as an Australian politician and subsequently as a campaigner for the ending of apartheid.

Hughes, William

http://www.virtualaustralia.com.au/people/prime_ministers/billy_hughes. htm

Good account of the turbulent life of the Australian prime minister who served as leader of three different parties. This biography of 'The Little Digger' traces his life as a poor immigrant, a trade unionist, the wartime prime minister who took Australia into the League of Nations, and the more than fifty years he spent as a federal parliamentarian.

Macquarie, Lachlan

http://www.virtualaustralia.com.au/people/prime_ministers/macquari.html

Brief biography of the dynamic Scot who shaped the future of the colony of New South Wales. It traces his military service in India and the impetus he gave to the creation of public institutions in Sydney.

Lyons, Joseph

http://www.virtualaustralia.com.au/people/prime_ministers/lyons.html

Sympathetic account of the life of Joseph Lyons. It traces his humble origins in Tasmania, his rise through the Labor Party, and his formation of the United Australia Party. The first Australian prime minister to die in office, his legacy was maintained by his wife.

Menzies, Sir Robert

http://www.virtualaustralia.com.au/people/
prime_ministers/menzies.html

Profile of Australia's longest-serving
prime minister. This is a comprehensive
account of the lengthy career of the only
Australian prime minister ever to retire of
his own accord.

Mr Ned – The Man With a Bucket on his Head

http://www.lonelyplanet.com.au/dest/aust/vic2.htm

Description of the elevation of the common horse
thief Ned Kelly into iconic Australian folk hero.
This cynical article debunks the myth-makers,
ranging from Mick Jagger to the acclaimed artist,
Sidney Nolan, who, it claims, have distorted the
sordid facts of the petty criminal and his
vainglorious death.

Our Modern Commonwealth

http://www.rhouse.co.uk/rhouse/rcs/modcom/

Useful general guide to the Commonwealth
organized by the Royal Commonwealth Institute.
The notes for teachers and worksheets for
children are designed to be used by schools in all
Commonwealth countries. The material on foods,
games, and oral traditions in a large number of
countries is interesting and well prepared.

Scullin, James

http://www.virtualaustralia.com.au/people/prime_
ministers/scullin.html

Brief biography of the Australian prime minister
in the early 1930s. This is a good account of
Scullin's unsuccessful attempts to deal with the
consequences of the Great Depression and the
events which caused the Labor Party to lose
power.

Parkes, Henry

http://www.virtualaustralia.com.au/people/prime_
ministers/parkes.html

Biography of the Australian politician who
became known as the 'Father of Federation' and
coined the phrase, 'Commonwealth of Australia'.
This account also examines the repeated failures
in business which brought Parkes ridicule.

F A C T

WAITANGI, TREATY OF

treaty negotiated in New Zealand in 1840
between the British government and the
indigenous Maori. The treaty guaranteed the
Maori their own territory and gave them
British citizenship.

Treaty of Waitangi

http://aotearoa.wellington.net.nz/back/quick.htm

Introduction to the Treaty of Waitangi, an
agreement negotiated in 1840 between the British
government and the indigenous Maori of New
Zealand. The pages describe the background to
the Treaty, and present both its English and Maori
versions. There is also a discussion of the
consequences of the Treaty, and its implications
for New Zealanders today.

Whitlam, Gough

http://www.virtualaustralia.com.au/people/prime_
ministers/whitlam.html

Profile of the career of the former Australian
prime minister. This site contains a good
summary of the turbulent events that led to the
dismissal of this modernizing Labor leader.

Early & Medieval European History

Avignonese Papacy and the Great Schism

http://history.idbsu.edu/westciv/babylon

Part of a larger site on the history of Western
civilization maintained by Boise State University,
this page provides an introduction to the
weakening of the papacy during the 14th and
early 15th centuries, the confrontation between
King Philip IV of France and Pope Boniface VIII,
and the Great Schism. Information is organized
into 19 brief articles, each concerning a specific
aspect of the conflicts in the Church. You can start
at the beginning and work your way through the
articles in chronological order or go directly to a

page that interests you. There is also a list of references for further study.

Battle of Yarmuk and After

http://www.fordham.edu/halsall/source/yarmuk.html

This page concerns an account of the Battle of Yarmuk in Syria in 636, a decisive battle at which the army of Byzantine emperor Heraclius was defeated and Syria was won by the Muslims. This 9th-century description, translated from its original Arabic text, emphasizes the hostility that Syrians felt toward Byzantium.

Byzantium

http://www.bway.net/~halsall/byzantium.html

History of Byzantium and the Byzantine Empire that begins with a general overview and then leads to sections on architecture, the military, geography, and religion.

Charlemagne and the Carolingian Era

http://history.idbsu.edu/westciv/charles/

Part of a larger site on the history of Western civilization maintained by Boise State University, this page provides an introduction to Charlemagne and the Carolingian era. Information is organized into 23 brief articles, each concerning a specific aspect of the era, such as a summary of Charlemagne's conquests, Carolingian culture, law, and administration. You can start at the beginning and work your way through the articles in chronological order or go directly to a page that interests you. There is also a list of references for further study.

Chronicles of Froissart, The

http://etext.lib.virginia.edu/cgibin/browse-mixed?id=FroChro&tag=public&images=images/modeng&data=/lv1/Archive/eng-parsed

Text of Berners' famous translation of 14th-century historian and poet Froissart's *Chronicles*. The site also includes an introduction to the piece.

Clovis

http://www.knight.org/advent/cathen/04070a.htm

Biography of the Merovingian king. It attempts to disentangle the facts from the myths and popular poetry about the leader, who made Paris his capital and built a Frankish kingdom from the ruins of the Roman Empire.

Comnena, Anna

http://home.earthlink.net/~womenwhist/heroine5.html

Concise presentation of the life and works of Anna Comnena, one of the most influential women of Byzantine times, who is often considered to be the world's first female historian.

Crusade

http://www.ukans.edu/kansas/medieval/108/lectures/first_crusade.html

Essay which introduces the First Crusade and outlines its causes and consequences.

Crusaders' Journeys to Jerusalem

http://www.christusrex.org/www2/cruce/

Part of a larger site, this page presents excerpts of manuscripts written in the 11th, 12th, and 13th centuries concerning the Oriental crusades. The original pages appear in Latin or Medieval French, with translations in English and Italian. The information is divided into three major volumes, from which numerous excerpts are taken: the Times of the First Holy Wars, the Times of the Frankish Kings (1100–1187), and the Times of the Reconquest of the Holy Lands.

F A C T

CRUSADE (French *croisade*)
European war against non-Christians and heretics, sanctioned by the pope; in particular, the Crusades, a series of wars undertaken 1096–1291 by European rulers to recover Palestine from the Muslims.

El Cid

http://www.knight.org/advent/cathen/03769a.htm

Biography of this Spanish hero, which tries to disentangle his legendary reputation from his activities as a mercenary soldier. El Cid's campaigns with and against the Moors, and his depiction in literature, are also well chronicled.

F A C T

Cid, El, Rodrigo Díaz de Vivar (c. 1043–1099),

Spanish soldier, nicknamed **El Cid** ('the lord') by the Moors. Essentially a mercenary, fighting both with and against the Moors, he died while defending Valencia against them, and in subsequent romances became Spain's national hero.

Female Heroes: Eleanor of Aquitaine

http://home.earthlink.net/~womenwhist/heroine2.html

Part of the Women in World History Curriculum, this page explores the life and times of Eleanor of Aquitaine. The site includes an illustration of Eleanor of Aquitaine entering Constantinople in AD 1147.

Female Heroes: The Women Left Behind During the Crusades

http://home.earthlink.net/~womenwhist/heroine3.html

Part of the 'Women in World History Curriculum', this page gives information about the lives of women who were left behind as their husbands, sons, or guardians left for the Crusades. This site includes samples of the lyrics to two French troubadour songs of the period and a list of resources for further study.

Gallery: Byzantine Images

http://www.bway.net/~halsall/images.html

Panorama of Byzantine art from Mount Athos, Meteora in Thessaly, Mistra in the Peloponnese, Ravenna in South Italy, Ohrid in Serbia, Toplou monastery in Crete, and Byzantine Constantinople.

Henry II, St

http://www.knight.org/advent/cathen/07227a.htm

Profile of the energetic life of the pious German king who became Holy Roman Emperor. There are details of his many military campaigns and a conclusion that he bolstered the authority of the church in order to further his own. The legends which became attached to Henry after his canonization are refuted.

Hospitallers of St John of Jerusalem

http://www.knight.org/advent/cathen/07477a.htm

Extensive history of the ancient military religious order also known as the Knights of Malta. The few known facts about the 12th-century origins of the Hospitallers are related, prior to describing details of the development of the military, religious, and medical functions of the order during the Crusades. The modern functions of the Catholic and Protestant branches of the order are set out.

Ill-Fated Crusade of the Poor People

http://www.thehistorynet.com/MilitaryHistory/articles/1998/0298_text.htm

Account of the less well known and ill-fated 'crusade of the poor people' that was organized by Pope Urban II and the Byzantine emperor Alexius in the summer of AD 1096, preceding the famous four crusades to the Holy Land by Europeans during the 12th and 13th centuries.

Joan of Arc, St

http://www.knight.org/advent/cathen/08409c.htm

Full biography of Jeanne D'Arc. It traces the familiar story of her teenage visions and the mission they inspired. Charles VII is condemned for not doing more to save the Maid of Orléans from her fate at the hands of the English and their allies. The process of her beatification and canonization is also outlined.

Leo I the Great, St

http://www.knight.org/advent/Popes/pple01.htm

Biography of the 5th-century Pope. It traces his bitter disputes with those asserting the monophysite (single nature) of Christ, and his campaigns against Attila the Hun.

Llull, Ramon

http://www-groups.dcs.st-and.ac.uk/history/Mathematicians/Llull.html

Part of an archive containing the biographies of the world's greatest mathematicians, this site is devoted to the life and contributions of Ramon Llull. In addition to biographical information, you will find a list of references about Llull and links to other essays in the archive which refer to him. The text of this essay includes hypertext links to the essays of those mathematicians and thinkers who influenced Llull. You will also find a map of his birthplace.

Louis IX, St

http://www.knight.org/advent/cathen/09368a.htm

Comprehensive biography of the French king. It highlights his commitment to the Crusader cause, the territorial concessions to the English for which he was much criticized, and the support that the judicious and pious monarch gave to the church.

Medieval Domestic Life

http://www.millersv.edu/~english/homepage/duncan/medfem/domestic.html

Extensive hypertext on a wide range of aspects of medieval domestic life, mainly as it relates to the role of women. The site deals with matters such as the concerns of girls and maidens, marriage ceremonies, childbirth, contraceptive methods, rape, women and brewing, widowhood, women and sports, and cooking.

Medieval Faith and Religion

http://www.millersv.edu/~english/homepage/duncan/medfem/religion.html

Hypertext on a wide range of aspects of medieval religious life, mainly as it relates to women. The site includes concise sections on medieval healers and nurses, women in the clergy, virginity, the cult of Virgin Mary, the female body, anorexia, marriage and the church, and life in medieval nunneries.

Medieval Glossary

http://www.geocities.com/Athens/2471/glossary.html

Exhaustive and very useful glossary of the names of kings, warriors, people, areas, and very many other terms of significance for students of medieval culture.

Mongol Invasion of Europe

http://www.thehistorynet.com/MilitaryHistory/articles/1997/06972_text.htm

Full text description of the Mongol invasion of Europe in 1241. The site describes the day that Polish people still celebrate (April 9), when they repulsed an Asiatic invasion of Europe in 1241. Their Mongol enemies saw things differently; at Liegnitz, Poland, they won their third victory in a row over a European army, all with a diversionary force of only 20,000 warriors.

Regia Anglorum

http://www.regia.org/

Collection of articles and images providing an interactive experience for those interested in medieval history, and Anglo-Saxon and Viking Britain in particular. The site includes information on the Battle of Hastings, braid weaving, Church organization, contemporary food and drink, and monastic life among several other topics.

Sack of Constantinople, 1204

http://www.fordham.edu/halsall/source/choniates1.html

Account of Byzantine historian Nicetas Choniates concerning the sacking of Constantinople during the Fourth Crusade, which includes a description of the pillaging of the Hagia Sophia. There is also an interesting, brief introduction that provides context.

Urban II: Speech at the Council of Clermont, 1095

http://www.fordham.edu/halsall/source/urban2-fulcher.html

Account of the address given by Pope Urban II at the Council of Clermont, in which he calls for a crusade to recover Palestine from Muslim rule. The account by Fulcher of Chartres, who witnessed Urban II's speech, is preceded by a brief introduction.

Wars of Religion

http://www.lepg.org/wars.htm

Historical look at the religious wars between Catholics and Protestants that plagued France for over 35 years before the Edict of Nantes in 1598. The site investigates the dynastic, social and religious tensions that permeated French society and which belied the phrase *une foi, un loi, un roi* (one faith, one law, one king). Split into two pages, this site includes information on the various wars that were fought, including the St Bartholomew's Day Massacre, the War of the Three Henries, and the Wars of the League. You will also find a map of the territorial divisions in France drawn along religious and political lines.

World of the Vikings

http://www.pastforward.co.uk/vikings/index.html

Well-presented resource of pages from around the world on all things Viking. This includes sections on ships, mead, museums, runes, and sagas. Many of these pages are illustrated and there are also academic and schools pages, filled with ideas on how to study this field.

17th- & 18th-century European History

Battle of Cape St Vincent – February 14th 1797

http://www.stvincent.ac.uk/1797/

Commemorative Web site for the bicentenary of the Battle of Cape St Vincent. The site has a shot-by-shot account of the battle, biographies of some of the major characters, and listings of ships taking part. A virtual tour of Nelson's Royal Navy flagship *HMS Victory* is also accessible from this Web site.

Fouquet, Nicolas

http://www.kipar.org/menu.html

Biographical Web site on the French nobleman. A portrait of Fouquet opens the site, together with an appeal for lookalikes. The text of the site then goes on to describe his life and related historical details. A picture of Fouquet's chateau is included here, along with several other related images.

French Revolution Home Page

http://members.aol.com/agentmess/frenchrev/index.html

Collection of documents and essays relating to the French Revolution including the text of 'The

F
A
C
T

FRENCH REVOLUTION

the period 1789–1799 that saw the end of the monarchy in France. The revolution began as an attempt to create a constitutional monarchy, but by late 1792 demands for long-overdue reforms resulted in the proclamation of the First Republic.

Declaration of the Rights of Man and of the Citizen' and 'The Declaration of the Rights of Woman and of the Citizen'.

Glossary of the French Revolution

http://www.warwick.ac.uk/fac/arts/History/teaching/french-rev/glossary.html

This page is a glossary of French terms and phrases associated with the French Revolution. Browsing the list is a worthwhile history lesson in itself. The list includes definitions for such words and phrases as *accapareur*, a monopolist, hoarder (especially of grain); *salut et fraternité*, a greeting frequently used in correspondence; *tricoteuses*, the 'knitter women' who attended sessions of the National Assembly, etc; and *Vainqueurs de la Bastille*, a title given to those who actively participated in the capture of the Bastille.

L'Age D'Or – The Age of the Sun King

http://www.geocities.com/Paris/Rue/1663/index.html

Website on the baroque period of French history. The site features images of baroque costumes, baroque art, and a history of baroque music, along with a brief description of 'L'Age D'Or'.

Letters and Dispatches of Lord Horatio Nelson

http://www.wtj.com/pl/pages/nelson2.htm

Featured here are the letters and dispatches of Admiral Horatio Nelson during the years 1797–1805. The correspondence includes such topics as the search for the French fleet prior to the Battle of the Nile, the aftermath of that battle, and several aspects of the Trafalgar campaign, including a photograph of Admiral Nelson's last letter to Lady Hamilton.

Maximilien Robespierre: Justification of the Use of Terror

http://www.fordham.edu/halsall/mod/robespierre-terror.html

This page provides excerpts of a speech delivered on 5 February 1794 by Maximilien Robespierre, leader of the Committee for Public Safety during the Reign of Terror, in which he justifies terror as a legitimate means toward successfully achieving the ends of the French Revolution. A brief introduction provides context.

Montcalm and Wolfe

http://www.digitalhistory.org/wolfe.html

Comprehensive Web site on the French and Indian War. The site features details of the men and resources available to both sides in the conflict, and also describes the forts around which much of the war was fought. A bibliography is also included, as is a description of the major battles.

Peter the Great

http://www.dana.edu/~dwarman/showie.htm

Essay covering the life and reign of Peter the Great. The essay is divided up into four areas: the background to his life and reign, his childhood and early life, his rule, and his death and legacy. Throughout the text there are hyperlinks to articles on related topics, such as the Great Northern War, the Russian navy, and St Petersburg. While there is no graphical content, this is compensated for by the clear and concise presentation.

'Reflections on the Revolution In France'

http://english-www.hss.cmu.edu/18th/burke.txt

Text of Burke's essay in which he denounced the French Revolution.

Texts and Documents: Europe

http://history.hanover.edu/europe.html

Collection of pivotal documents on Europe from the Stone Age to the Cold War via the Greek Polis, the Courtly Culture, the Crusades, the Enlightenment, the French Revolution, the Holocaust, and many other landmarks in the development of Europe. The visitor can browse through the individual periods as a continuum, or choose to focus on the literature, politics, theology, or philosophy of each one.

Thomas Paine National Historical Association

http://www.mediapro.net/cdadesign/paine/

Full texts of the major works of Thomas Paine, including *Common Sense*, *The Rights of Man*, and

The Age of Reason. There are details of the work of the museum honouring his legacy and links to further sources of Paine information.

Treaty of Paris, 1763

http://odur.let.rug.nl/~usa/D/1751-1775/7yearswar/paris.htm

Part of a larger site on historical documents, this page is the full text of the Treaty of Paris of 1763 which ended conflict between England, Spain, and France.

19th-century European History

Battle of the Nations

http://www.geocities.com/TimesSquare/Alley/2187/leipzig.htm

War-gamer's view of the Battle of the Nations at Leipzig in 1813. The Web site is divided up into a variety of pages, one a detailed map of the area; others describe each day of the battle in turn. Each day of the battle page has information sub-pages providing maps and details of troop movements for that day.

Bourgeois, Léon Victor Auguste

http://www.nobel.se/laureates/peace-1920-bio.html

Portrait of the clockmaker's son, his long career in French politics, and his role as 'the spiritual father of the League of Nations'. It traces his interests in music and art, his period as prime minister, his drafting of the statutes of the League of Nations, and the Nobel Peace Prize it won him.

Briand, Aristide

http://www.nobel.se/laureates/peace-1926-1-bio.html

Good portrait of the French orator and his lifelong antiwar activities. It traces his childhood friendship with Jules Verne, his careers as journalist, lawyer, and politician, his periods as prime minister, and the Nobel Peace Prize he won for his untiring efforts, as foreign minister in the second half of the 1920s, to establish peace and reconciliation in Europe.

Bridges that Éblé Built

http://www.wtj.com/artdocs/berezina.htm

This site concerns the hasty construction of two bridges across the icy Beresina River to assist in the retreat of Napoleon's tattered and freezing Grand Army from Russia in November 1812. You will find information about the engineers responsible for constructing the bridges, as well as the pandemonium that ensued once they were completed and the troops became desperate to cross them. The text is complimented by a number of illustrations, paintings, a computer simulation, and quotes from eyewitnesses attesting to the conditions at the Beresina River crossing. You will also find a list of primary and secondary resources.

Kropotkin, Prince Peter

http://www.pitzer.edu/~dward/Anarchist_Archives/kropotkin/Kropotkinarchive.html

Biographical information about Peter Kropotkin, the 'anarchist prince'. You will also find the texts of his collected works, including such essays as 'Appeal to the Young', 'Fields, Factories, and Workshops', 'The Spirit of Revolt', 'War!', 'Anarchist Morality', and more. There are also four essays providing commentary on Kropotkin's philosophy and a section of photographs and drawings.

Marshal Louis Davout's Correspondence

http://www.wtj.com/pl/pages/davout.htm

This site presents letters and reports issued by French General Marshal Davout's headquarters during the campaigns against Prussia of September and October 1806. The majority of the correspondence features communications from Marshal Davout to his superiors, but you will also find internal reports from Davout's officers.

The letters are grouped into sets of ten and are presented in French and English.

Memoirs of General Savary, the Duke of Rovigo

http://www.wtj.com/pl/pages/savary.htm

This page features English translations of select chapters from the memoirs of General Savary, the trusted chief of intelligence to Napoleon. Divided into four sections, the chapters provide a firsthand account of Napoleon's Egyptian campaign and the European campaigns of 1805, 1809, and 1813. Some of the topics discussed here include the Battle of the Pyramids, the capitulation of Marshal Mack and the Austrian army at Ulm, the Battle of Wagram, the Battle of Dresden, and the beginnings of fortune's ceasing to favour the French. A brief introduction provides some context.

Memoirs of Prince Metternich

http://www.h-net.msu.edu/~habsweb/sourcetexts/mettsrc.htm

This page features a selection from the memoirs of Prince Metternich. The topics include 'censorship', 'renewal of the Carlsbad Decrees', 'Metternich on the diet at Pressburg', and 'the death of Emperor Francis II of Austria'. There is also a brief introduction that includes a caveat concerning the veracity and historical value of Metternich's memoirs.

Muslims in the 19th-century Russian Empire

http://www.uoknor.edu/cybermuslim/russia/rus_home.html

Photographic narrative of the Turks and Tatars of central Asia and the Caucasus and their clash with an expanding Russian Empire. This site includes photographs and maps, and hypertext links lead you to additional information, including a link to a page with images of all the flags of the Russian Federation.

'Napoleon and England'

http://www.napoleon.org/us/us_cd/bib/articles/textes/SN400/us_SN400_napoleon_anglet.html

Detailed essay on the subject of Napoleon and England. This two-part essay covers such topics as the English navy, Egypt and the Battle of Aboukir Bay, and the peace of Amiens. Throughout the essay are a number of illustrations, making this site a complete and well-presented guide to the relationship between Napoleon and England.

Napoleon Series – Life and Times of Napoleon Bonaparte

http://www.historyserver.org/napoleon.series/

Meeting point for everybody interested in Napoleon Bonaparte and his times. The site offers a virtual visit to Napoleonic battlefields, details about Napoleon's marshals, an overview of his (in)famous last 100 days as emperor, a full calendar of Napoleonic events, and a series of articles by visitors on the Napoleonic period.

sketches, caricatures, pamphlets, and posters associated with the Siege of Paris and the Paris Commune.

Spanish-American War Centennial Web Site

http://www.spanam.simplenet.com/

Celebration of the centenary of the Spanish-American War. The Web site features a chronology of the war, profiles of both the arms and manpower of each side, and several texts written by both participants and journalists. The Web site is still under construction, but it already contains a very large amount of information on the war.

20th-century European History

Revisiting the Battle of Marengo

http://www.wtj.com/artdocs/marengo.htm

This site investigates the meeting of the French and Austrian armies at the Battle of Marengo in June 1800, the last battle of the French Revolutionary Wars. The description of the battle is divided into two parts: the first part looks at the battle as a whole and features a number of colourful illustrations and maps of the changing battlefield; the second part concerns specifically the decisive role of Kellerman's Charge in determining the outcome. Another section is devoted to the uniforms of the French and Austrian infantrymen. You will also find a list of primary and secondary resources.

Siege and Commune of Paris

http://www.library.nwu.edu/spec/siege/

From the Northwestern University Library, USA, an online collection of hundreds of photographs,

Annotated Memoirs of Admiral Miklós Horthy, Regent of Hungary

http://www.msstate.edu/Archives/
History/hungary/horthy/

Autobiography of the man who dominated Hungarian politics in the interwar years. Annotations to the text clarify the original. A foreword, written 30 years after Horthy's death and from a post-Cold-War vantage point, seeks to rescue the reputation of a leader vilified for his alliance with Hitler. There is additionally a brief biography and photo of Horthy.

Armenian Research Centre Home Page

http://www.umd.umich.edu/dept/armenian/

Concise set of resources from the University of Michigan's Armenian Research Centre, with features on Armenia today, the Armenian massacres 1915–23, and excerpts from the works of key authors.

Assassination of Archduke Franz Ferdinand, 28 June 1914

http://raven.cc.ukans.edu/~kansite/ww_one/
comment/sarajevo.html

Part of a larger site concerning World War I documents, this page provides a wealth of information regarding the assassinations of the Archduke and Duchess of Austria-Hungary in Sarajevo. In addition to presenting the details of the assassination, including a photograph and map, this page provides critical background information on the political tensions in the Balkans. You will also find links to the biographies of the principal figures involved and a history of the Black Hand, the secret Serbian terrorist society.

Balkan Crisis, 1913

http://www2.theatlantic.com/atlantic/atlweb/flashbks/balkans/usherf.htm

Text of an article that first appeared in the January 1913 issue of *Atlantic Monthly*. This article, written by Roland Usher, explores the ethnic rivalries and strife in the Balkans and the region's historically strategic importance, and presages the outbreak of World War I, less than two years after this article was published.

Brezhnev, Leonid Ilyich

http://artnet.net/~upstart/brezhnev.html

Timeline that follows the major events in the life of Leonid Brezhnev, from his birth in the Ukraine through his years as leader of the USSR. The text of the timeline includes several hypertext links, including a link to the text of the Constitution of the USSR adopted in 1977. Following the timeline, there is a brief summation and additional information about Brezhnev, including the books he wrote and the medals he earned. There are also links to audio clips of Brezhnev speaking.

Civil War in Moscow, October 1993

http://www.cs.toronto.edu/~mes/russia/period/october93.html

Photographic history of events in Moscow that culminated in the attempted coup of 1993. Photographs of most of the principle players are included.

Clicking Anastasia

http://www.lostsecrets.com/

Interactive game where the aim is to uncover the lost treasure of the Romanov Tsars. As well as playing the game, you can discover more about

the history of the mysterious Russian Grand Duchess Anastasia.

Collins, Michael

http://www2.cruzio.com/~sbarrett/mcollins.htm

Full details of the turbulent life of the Irish nationalist hero. It traces his childhood and role in the Easter Rising, the war of independence, and civil war. There is a poem in tribute to 'the Big Fella'.

Estonian History

http://www.ibs.ee/history/index.html

This page, produced by Estonia's Institute of Baltic Studies, offers a brief history and chronology of the country, plus essays on Soviet occupation, the restoration of independence, and Baltic nationalities.

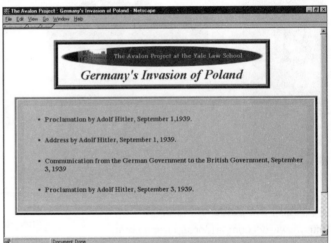

Germany's Invasion of Poland

http://www.yale.edu/lawweb/avalon/wwii/gpmenu.htm

Part of the Avalon Project at the Yale Law School, this page features three proclamations by Adolf Hitler and a communication between the German government and the UK, all of which are attempts to justify Germany's attack on Poland. Hitler's address to the Reichstag, on 1 September 1939, includes hypertext links to the texts of the Versailles Treaty of 1919 and the Munich Agreement.

Hammarskjöld, Dag

http://www.nobel.se/laureates/peace-1961-bio.html

Biography of the Swedish winner of the Nobel

Peace Prize. The influence of Hammarskjöld's father on his political convictions is set out. There is a description of his career as a civil servant and his role in defusing Cold War crises during his tenure as UN secretary-general.

Internal Workings of the Soviet System

http://sunsite.unc.edu/expo/soviet.exhibit/intro1.html

Guided exhibit from the Soviet Archives of the Library of Congress, focusing on the internal workings and development of the Soviet hierarchy and its political agenda, from Lenin's revolutionary days through to Gorbachev's *perestroika*.

J Stalin Internet Archive

http://www.marxists.org/reference/archive/stalin/index.htm

Biographical information on Joseph Stalin that includes an extensive biography and historical information. Although written from an unabashed marxist perspective, this site does include some differing points of view in the 'Reference archive'.

Kosova

http://albanian.com/main/countries/kosova/index.html

Albanian nationalist perspective on Serbia's troubled province. There is a good description of Kosovo (or Kosova), its economy, places of interest, and the major cities. The site also provides updated news of human rights abuses and demonstrations for an end to Serb rule.

Kosovo and Metohija

http://www.kosovo.com/

Polemical Web site of the Serbian Orthodox Church in the troubled Kosovo region of Yugoslavia. The case that Kosovo is an integral part of Serbia and must remain so is strongly put, with a wealth of historical argument. The text is well supported by photographs. For an understanding of the deeply felt passions behind the Serbian attempt to retain control of the ethnic Albanian province, this site is essential.

Munich Pact

http://www.yale.edu/lawweb/avalon/imt/munich1.htm

Part of the Avalon Project at the Yale Law School, this page features the text of the Munich Agreement concluded on 29 September 1938 between Germany, Italy, France, and Great Britain, which ceded the Sudetenland to Germany. You will also find related documents, including the minutes of nine meetings of the International Commission which convened to facilitate the transfer of territory.

Nazi Gold

http://www.pbs.org/wgbh/pages/frontline/shows/nazis/

Companion to the US Public Broadcasting Service (PBS) television programme *Frontline*, this page is a frank inquiry into Switzerland's role during World War II, exploring charges that it funnelled the lost assets of Holocaust victims into the country. This site includes up-to-date information on Swiss and foreign investigations into Switzerland's actions during and after the war. There is also information concerning the recent allegation that Jews were transported by train through Switzerland to death camps inside Germany. Read transcripts from a Swiss television programme that provided a forum for Swiss historians, journalists, officials, and others to discuss these disturbing issues. This site also includes information critical of other supposedly neutral countries that profited from dealings with Nazi Germany. Transcripts of the *Frontline* programme are also available for downloading, and there is a list of further readings.

NAZISM

ideology based on racism, nationalism, and the supremacy of the state over the individual. The German Nazi party, the *Nationalsozialistische Deutsche Arbeiterpartei* (National Socialist German Workers' Party), was formed from the German Workers' Party (founded in 1919) and led by Adolf Hitler from 1921 to 1945.

Nazi-Soviet Relations, 1939–1941

http://www.yale.edu/lawweb/avalon/nazsov/nazsov.htm

Translations of documents recovered in 1945 from the archives of the German Foreign Office. Most significantly, this site features the translation of the Treaty of Non-aggression made between Germany and the USSR on 23 August 1939, including the Secret Additional Protocol of the same date which set the boundaries of Poland 'in the event of a territorial and political rearrangement'. This site is currently under construction.

Nicholas and Alexandra Romanov

http://www.geocities.com/Vienna/9463/

Biographical details of the last of the Romanov Tsars of Russia, Nicholas II, his wife, and children. The Web site features brief pages for each of the children, which include a photograph and a short text description. In addition to the family details there is a quiz section, and also details of Yekaterinburg, where the family was murdered by Bolsheviks.

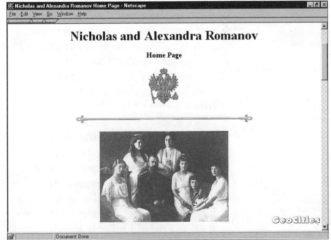

Nizkor Project – the Joseph Goebbels Diaries: Excerpts 1942–43

http://www.nizkor.org/hweb/people/g/goebbels-joseph/goebbels-1948-excerpts-01.html

Excerpts from the diaries of the German Nazi leader, Joseph Goebbels, revealing his chilling ponderings on the 'Jewish question'. Click on each date for an expanded diary entry.

Nuremberg War Crimes Trials

http://www.yale.edu/lawweb/avalon/imt/imt.htm

Part of the Avalon Project at the Yale Law School, this site is a comprehensive source of official documentation regarding the Nuremberg Trials. Some of the documents include official court papers and rules for procedure, testimony of witnesses, and key documents cited during the trial, including the notorious 'Night and fog' decree, the Stroop Report on the Nazi's quashing of the 1943 Jewish uprising in the Warsaw Ghetto, and Hitler's first directive for the conduct of war, in which he sets the date and time for the attack on Poland. There are a number of other documents concerning Nazi conspiracy and aggression.

Rasputin

http://www.halcyon.com/demiurge/rasputin.html

Essay exploring the influence of Rasputin during the last days of the Russian empire. The site also includes a brief bibliography.

Rise of Hitler

http://www.historyplace.com/worldwar2/riseofhitler/index.htm

Account of Hitler's rise to power, from his birth to the burning of the Reichstag.

Royal Household

http://www.DocuWeb.ca/SiSpain/english/politics/royal/king.html

Biography of the present Spanish king and his role in the restoration of constitutional democracy, which is part of the official site of the Spanish royal family. There is a high-resolution photo of Juan Carlos and biographies of Queen Sofia and their three children.

Russian Empire: 1895–1910

http://cmp1.ucr.edu/exhibitions/russia/russia.html

Selection of the California Museum of Photography's collection of original stereoscopic negatives, depicting Russian architecture before Stalin's destructive 'urban renewal' program laid waste to many of these important landmarks.

Russian Revolution

http://www.barnsdle.demon.co.uk/russ/rusrev.html

Key quotations, a concise chronology of the Revolution, maps, photographs, and links to other pages on the Russian Revolution and Russian history in general.

> **F**
> **A**
> **C**
> **T**
>
> **RUSSIAN REVOLUTION**
>
> two revolutions of February and October 1917 (Julian calendar) that began with the overthrow of the Romanov dynasty and ended with the establishment of a communist soviet (council) state, the Union of Soviet Socialist Republics (USSR).

Soviet Archives Exhibit

http://sunsite.unc.edu/expo/soviet.exhibit/soviet.archive.html

Library of Congress Soviet Archive exhibition contains hitherto highly secret internal records of communist Soviet rule, now available for public study for the first time.

Spanish Government and the Axis

http://www.yale.edu/lawweb/avalon/wwii/spain/spmenu.htm

Part of the Avalon Project at the Yale Law School, this page features telegrams, notes, letters, and memoranda dispatched between representatives of the Spanish government, including several by General Francisco Franco, and representatives of the Axis powers, including Adolf Hitler and Benito Mussolini, mostly concerning the conditions for Spain's entry into World War II. Included here is a secret protocol between the Spanish and German governments, stipulating Spanish military resistance to any attempted allied landings on Spanish territory.

Treaty on European Union

http://europa.eu.int/en/record/mt/top.html

Full text of the 1992 treaty of Maastricht, which brought the European Union into existence, in place of the European Community.

Trial of Adolf Eichmann

http://www.pbs.org/eichmann/

Companion to a US Public Broadcasting Service (PBS) television programme, this comprehensive site covers the war-crimes trial of Nazi SS Lieutenant Colonel Adolf Eichman. The section on Eichmann 'In his own words' features a biography, timeline, photographs, and Eichmann's final statement following sentencing. Another section takes an in-depth look at the trial proceedings and features a transcript of the 15 charges against Eichmann as read by the court, brief biographies and photographs of the key participants, plus a transcript of the sentence handed down by the presiding judge. There is also information on the documentary that aired in April 1997.

Understanding the Balkan Conflict

http://library.advanced.org/2860/index.htm

Useful site which explains the background behind the conflict in the Balkans. There are also interviews with people from the regions discussed, and a picture gallery.

Vladimir Ilyich Lenin Internet Archive

http://csf.colorado.edu/psn/marx/Other/Lenin/

Internet Archive dedicated to Lenin. It features a wide selection of his articles on Marx, the Revolution, and the West, as well as numerous photographs of Lenin.

Yugoslavia at the Crossroads, 1962

http://www2.theatlantic.com/atlantic/atlweb/flashbks/balkans/nealf.htm

Text of an article that first appeared in the December 1962 issue of *Atlantic Monthly*. This article, written by Fred Neal, explores the effects that communism under Marshal Tito had on the Yugoslavian economy.

World War I

Analysis of the Schlieffen Plan

http://www.lib.byu.edu/~rdh/wwi/1914m/
schlieffen.html

Part of a larger site concerning World War I
documents, this page features an assessment of
the German attack plan originally devised in 1905
by Chief of the German General Staff Alfred von
Schlieffen and later modified for the 1914 attack
on the Western Front.

Battle of Jutland

http://www.magweb.com/sample/sconflic/
co03wese.htm

Full account of the World War I naval battle.
There are sections entitled 'Survivors' (interviews
with people who fought in the battle) and 'Essay'
(the background and events), as well as 'Material
losses' and a 'Photo gallery'.

Bryce Report on German Atrocities

http://raven.cc.ukans.edu/~kansite/ww_one/
comment/bryce.html

Part of a larger site concerning World War I
documents, this page provides a detailed
introduction to the Bryce Report, as well as a
hypertext link to the report itself, which presents
the conclusions of an inquiry into claims of
German atrocities committed during World War I,
particularly those against civilians during the
invasion of Belgium. The introduction to the
report offers important background information
and historical context.

Death of an Air Ace, 1918

http://www.ibiscom.com/luf.htm

This site features a first-hand account of a World
War I air battle that claimed the life of US pilot
Major Raoul Lufbery. This harrowing story is
related by Captain Eddie Rickenbacker, who
finished the war as the USA's top ace. You can
also find out why fighter planes were first
developed and why pilots wore silk scarves.
There is a list of references.

Dicta Boelcke: Rules of Success in Air Combat

http://raven.cc.ukans.edu/~kansite/ww_one/comm
ent/dicta-b.html

Part of a larger site concerning World War I
documents, this page features German airman

Oswald Boelcke's principles for becoming a
successful fighter pilot. It includes an introduction
that explains the uncertain role of the aeroplane
in combat at the beginning of the war. The text of
the *Dicta Boelcke* includes helpful comments from
the editor.

Eastern Front, 1914–1917

http://www.wtj.com/artdocs/ww1sum2.htm

This page offers a summary of the fighting and
the circumstances that resulted from the fighting
on the Eastern Front during World War I. The text
is enhanced by a number of photos and maps of
the changing front. Click on the thumbnail
images of maps to increase their size. You can also
view images of the uniforms worn by those
fighting at the Eastern Front.

Fighting the Flying Circus

http://www.wtj.com/pl/pages/rick.htm

This page features the first 32 chapters of US ace
fighter pilot Captain Edward Rickenbacker's
memoirs of fighting the Red Baron's vaunted
'Flying Circus' during World War I. Some of the
chapters featured here include 'Downing My First
Hun', 'A Victory and a Narrow Escape', 'Down in
Flames', and 'A Regular Dogfight'. The index
page features a number of photographs and a
fascinating diagram of World War I flight
manoeuvres, which you can click on to enlarge.

Gallipoli 1915

http://www.focusmm.com.au/~focus/anzac_01.htm

Illustrated historical account of the 1915 events at
Gallipoli during World War I.

Great War and the Shaping of the 20th Century

http://www.pbs.org/greatwar/

Companion to a co-production of the BBC and US
Public Broadcasting Service (PBS), this site is a
comprehensive multimedia exploration of the
history and effects of World War I. An interactive
timeline lets you examine the events leading up
to and during World War I, as well as its
aftermath. Other features include an interactive
gallery of maps and locations; interviews from
respected World War I historians covering a
variety of topics; synopses; and programme
excerpts from each of the eight television
episodes. There is also a list of related Web sites

and research materials. This site includes numerous images and maps.

Great War Statistics

http://www.d-n-a.net/users/dnetDkjs/figures.htm

Part of a larger site about World War I, this site includes numerous tables and statistics relating to soldiers, casualties, ammunitions and materials, and the financial costs of the war.

Maps and Pictures of the Western Front

http://www.d-n-a.net/users/dnetDkjs/maps_pix.htm

This site includes several maps and photographs relating to the war on the Western Front. Part of a larger site on World War I, it contains a useful general overview map; the images include one of the Ulster Tower war memorial.

Medical Front, World War I

http://raven.cc.ukans.edu/~kansite/ww_one/medical/medtitle.htm

Part of a larger site concerning World War I documents, this page features all manner of medical-related documents from the Great War, including articles on military surgery and on the treatment of influenza and trench fever. You will also find information regarding sanitation and hygiene, field dentistry, pharmacology, hospitals and nurses, veterinary services, and the medical aspects of gas warfare. Excerpts of diaries written by military doctorsare included, as well as a gallery of photographs.

Red Fighter Pilot: Memoirs of the Red Baron

http://www.richthofen.com/

This page features the English translation of the first six chapters of famous German flying ace Manfred von Richthofen's memoirs of World War I. A brief introduction provides interesting details about the book and its publication during the war. Some of the chapters featured here include the 'Outbreak of War', 'Boredom Before Verdun', 'In the Air', and 'I Fly In a Thunderstorm'. There is also an interesting, slightly jingoistic preface to the book, written by a British editor in 1918.

Report on the Marne

http://www.lib.byu.edu/~rdh/wwi/1914/joffre.html

Part of a larger site concerning World War I documents, this page features the text of the official French report of Marshal Joseph Joffre regarding events of August and September 1914 at the Marne. Marshal Joffre's report analyzes the successes and failures of the French armies engaged in the first battle of the Marne.

Static Front

http://raven.cc.ukans.edu/~kansite/ww_one/comment/crane.htm

Part of a larger site concerning World War I documents, this page features an essay regarding the stalemate that developed on the Western Front during the Great War and explores why there was no breakthrough. It investigates the strategy, technology, specific battles, and leadership of the war.

Trenches on The Web

http://worldwar1.com/

Extensive site on World War I that is regularly updated with new features. These include themed tours, a discussion forum, and a reference library.

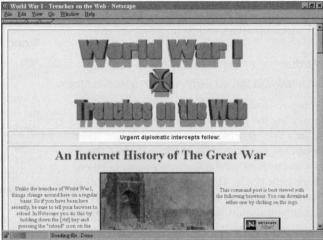

U-Boat Attack, 1916

http://www.ibiscom.com/sub.htm

This site explains the origin of Germany's policy of unrestricted submarine warfare and features an excerpt from the diary of a U-boat commander, in which he describes, in detail, the attack and sinking of a cargo ship in 1916. This site includes several interesting photographs documenting such scenes as a crew escaping their sinking ship and a group of captured U-boat sailors being led into a Georgia prison camp. There is also a list of references.

U-Boat Net

http://uboat.net/

German submarine archive featuring listings of all 1,168 U-boats, and details of the men who sailed in them. The fates of the U-boats, including losses and captures, are described here. There are also maps of operational regions, details of the technology used in the submarines, and many colour photographs of the boats themselves.

Use of Poison Gas on the Western Front

http://www.lib.byu.edu/~rdh/wwi/1915/chlorgas.html

Part of a larger site concerning World War I documents, this page features two articles written by the New York *Tribune*'s war correspondent Will Irwin, in which he describes the German army's poison gas attack at Ypres in April 1915. The second article provides a detailed description of the insidious attack and its lingering effects.

Verdun

http://www.lib.byu.edu/~rdh/wwi/1916/verdun.html

This page features the report of Lord Northcliffe regarding the German assault on Verdun in March 1916. It provides a wealth of information regarding the disastrous attack, including the perspectives of several German prisoners taken during the battle. This highly critical report also seeks an answer as to why the German High Command should undertake such a hopeless offensive. The page is part of a larger site containing Wold War I documents.

Versailles Treaty Contents

http://ac.acusd.edu/History/text/versaillestreaty/vercontents.html

Full text, maps, cartoons, photos, and suggested reading on the Treaty of Versailles, the main peace treaty after World War I.

> **F**
> **A**
> **C**
> **T**
>
> ## WORLD WAR I (1914–18)
>
> war between the Central European Powers (Germany, Austria-Hungary, and allies) on one side and the Triple Entente (Britain and the British Empire, France, and Russia) and their allies, including the USA (which entered 1917), on the other side. An estimated 10 million lives were lost and twice that number were wounded.

Western Front, 1914–1918

http://www.wtj.com/artdocs/ww1sum.htm

This page offers a summary of the brutal fighting on the Western Front during World War I and explores the new tactics that were employed there. The text is enhanced by a number of photographs and maps of the offensives. Click on the thumbnail images of maps to increase their size.

World War I Document Archive

http://www.lib.byu.edu/~rdh/wwi/

Archive of primary documents from World War I, including conventions, treaties, official papers, and memorials and personal reminiscences; plus an image archive, a biographical dictionary, and links to other related resources.

World War I: The War at Sea

http://www.ukans.edu/~kansite/ww_one/naval/n0000000.htm

A comprehensive look at the role of the navy in the first world war, from a larger resource of World War I documents.. You will find numerous images and information regarding ships, weapons, tactics, statistics, methods of communication, battles and campaigns, including Rudyard Kipling's account of the Battle of Jutland. You will also find biographies of admirals and other important naval figures of World War I.

World War II

A-Bomb WWW Museum

http://www.csi.ad.jp/ABOMB/index.html

Commemorative and awareness-raising site of the nuclear catastrophe in Hiroshima and Nagasaki in 1945. A rich display offers scientific data about the bomb, chilling descriptions of the atomic disaster, survivors' narrations, children's memories of the event, evidence retained in its original state in order to commemorate the tragedy, the problems and opinions of the second generation, a walk through contemporary Hiroshima, and tours around the Peace Memorial Museum and the Peace Park.

Atlantic Charter

http://www.yale.edu/lawweb/avalon/wwii/atlantic.htm

Part of the Avalon Project at the Yale Law School, this page provides the text of the agreement made between Prime Minister Churchill and President Roosevelt on 14 August 1941, in which they assert 'common principles in the national policies of their respective countries on which they base their hopes for a better future for the world'.

Atomic Bomb: Decision

http://www.dannen.com/decision/index.html

Rich source of documentation regarding the US government's decision to drop atomic bombs on Japan in August 1945. Some of the documents include the minutes of the target committee; international law regarding the bombing of civilians; results of the Trinity tests conducted in Nevada during July 1945; the official bombing order issued by President Truman; several reports, warnings, and petitions against dropping the bomb, or for first demonstrating its potency before Japan and the United Nations; a transcript of the telephone conversation between General Leslie Groves and Dr Robert Oppenheimer following the detonation at Hiroshima; and a number of other documents. There is also an audio clip of Truman's radio address on 9 August 1945.

Atomic Bombings of Hiroshima and Nagasaki

http://www.yale.edu/lawweb/avalon/abomb/mpmenu.htm

Part of the Avalon Project at the Yale Law School,

this page contains the report of the Manhattan Engineer District of the United States Army describing the effects of the atomic bombs dropped on Hiroshima and Nagasaki in August 1945. As stated in the report's foreword, it 'summarizes all the authentic information that is available on damage to structures, injuries to personnel, morale effect, etc., which can be released at this time without prejudicing the security of the United States.' The report is divided into more than two dozen chapters, including those on damage and injuries, propaganda, selection of targets, the nature of an atomic explosion, characteristics of various types of injuries, and an eyewitness account.

Battle of Britain

http://www.geocities.com/Pentagon/4143/

Informative tribute site on the Battle of Britain. A history of the battle is included, with details of many of the key people and technology. There are also detailed notes on the pilots, the aircraft, and the aircraft losses. A photo gallery of people, aircraft, and landscapes complete this site.

Canonesa, Convoy

http://home.onet.co.uk/~canonesa/

Web site maintained by a descendant of one of the crew of the *Canonesa*, whose ancestor died when the freighter was torpedoed by the *U100*. This site provides a snapshot into the early part of the Battle of the Atlantic in World War II, with biographical details of the crew of both the submarine and the freighter available. A good deal of background information surrounding the convoy and the sinking is also provided.

D-Day

http://www.pbs.org/wgbh/pages/amex/dday/index.html

Companion to the US Public Broadcasting Service (PBS) television programme *The American Experience*, this page tells the story of the allied invasion of Normandy during World War II. This site includes a special feature on the daring paratrooper drop behind enemy lines. You can also read the text of actual newspaper stories covering the invasion and the text of letters written by soldiers at the front. Browse a list of resources for further reading.

Enola Gay Perspectives

http://www.glue.umd.edu/~enola/welcome.html

History of the plane and the atomic bomb it dropped on Hiroshima, up to and including the controversy that took place over the recent Enola Gay exhibition at the Smithsonian Institution in Washington DC, USA. This site deals with almost every aspect of the bombing, from technical specifications of the aircraft to the moral questions surrounding the decision to bomb the Japanese into surrender.

German Surrender Documents – WWII

http://www.msstate.edu/Archives/History/USA/WWII/german-surrender

Full and complete English transcript of the German surrender documents from World War II. This is a text-only archive site and as such the contents are presented in a no-frills format.

Japanese-American Internment

http://scuish.scu.edu/SCU/Programs/Diversity/exhibit1.html

Historical account of the US government's internment of Japanese Americans living on the West Coast during World War II. In addition to explanatory text, you will find maps, photos, a copy of the official apology delivered by President George Bush, and other images. There are close-up photographic narratives of several of the Santa Clara Valley camps.

Japanese Surrender Documents

http://www.yale.edu/lawweb/avalon/wwii/jmenu.htm

Part of the Avalon Project at the Yale Law School, this page contains seven documents regarding the surrender of Japanese forces during World War II. It includes several instruments of surrender and a translation of Emperor Hirohito's receipt of the surrender documents.

Loose Lips Sink Ships

http://www.ibiscom.com/lslips.htm

Excerpts from a document issued by the US government to soldiers entering into battle during World War II, instructing them on ways to avoid tipping off the enemy. It includes a list of the ten subjects that soldiers are prohibited to mention in letters home, discusses the benefits of reticence among the ranks, and offers advice on how to conduct themselves if captured.

Nazi Occupation of Poland

http://www.ibiscom.com/poland.htm

Information on the German invasion of Poland in 1939 featuring excerpts from the journal of Dr Zygmunt Klukowski, chief physician of a small hospital in the village of Szczebrzeszyn, in which he describes the brutality of Nazi occupation. This site includes photographs and sidebars containing facts about the war and the Nazi occupation of Poland. There is also a list of references.

Pearl Harbor

http://www.execpc.com/~dschaaf/mainmenu.html

Short account of the attack on Pearl Harbor, plus maps, a timeline of events, a list of casualties, and a survivor's story.

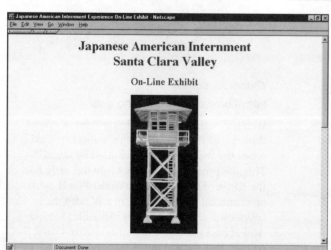

Pearl Harbor: Relevant Documents

http://www.yale.edu/lawweb/avalon/wwii/
pmenu.htm

Part of the Avalon Project at the Yale Law School,
this page includes several messages sent between
the governments of the USA and Japan just prior
to the bombing of Pearl Harbor. The first is a US
State Department document delivered to the
Japanese ambassador on 26 November 1941, in
which US Secretary of State Hull outlines US
policy concerning the Far East and proposes a
basis for agreement between the two countries.
The second is a note that President Roosevelt
dispatched to Emperor Hirohito on 6 December
1941. The final message, delivered by the
Japanese ambassador on 7 December 1941, is the
Japanese response to the US Secretary of State's
document of 26 November 1941. This document
includes a brief note regarding Secretary of State
Hull's angry response to the Japanese
ambassador's message.

Potsdam Conference

http://www.yale.edu/lawweb/avalon/decade/
decade17.htm

Part of the Avalon Project at the Yale Law School,
this page features the text of conclusions arrived
at by Truman, Churchill, and Stalin during the
Berlin Conference, held from 17 July to 2 August
1945. This document concerns preparations for
peace settlements, the principles that should
govern the post-war treatment of Germany, war
reparations, Nazi war criminals, and other
matters related to the defeat of Nazi Germany.

Private Art

http://www.private-art.com/

Collection of letters written by a US soldier and
his relations during World War II. The site has
been compiled by the wife of the soldier
concerned and, as well as being a well-designed
site, it offers an interesting source of primary
historical evidence for students of the period.

Radio Broadcast of the D-Day Landing at Normandy

http://www.otr.com/hicks.html

Part of a larger site paying homage to the glory
days of radio, this site features incredible audio of
George Hicks's on-the-scene news report of the D-
day invasion of Normandy, including the exciting

account of a German air attack on the *USS Ancon*
during which the furious sounds of war nearly
drown out the sound of Hicks' report. In addition
to audio, there is a brief article that provides
context and a photograph.

Radio Broadcasts on the Eve and End of War

http://www.otr.com/kaltenborn.html

Part of a larger site paying homage to the glory
days of radio, this page features audio of two H V
Kaltenborn news broadcasts, the first from
London on the eve of World War II and the other
from New York following Japan's surrender. In
addition to the audio, you will find biographical
information on Kaltenborn and a photograph of
the newsman.

Glory Days of Radio

http://www.otr.com/index.shtml

Extensive Web site paying homage to the glory
days of radio. This site offers audio clips of radio
broadcasts throughout World War II. In addition
to the audio clips, there are brief articles
providing context, photographs, and biographical
information.

Radio Report on the Fall of Paris

http://www.otr.com/sevareid.html

Part of a larger site paying homage to the glory
days of radio, this page features audio of the Eric
Severeid news broadcast announcing the fall of
Paris during World War II. In addition to the
audio, you will find biographical information on
Severeid and a photograph of the newsman.

Radio Reports of William L Shirer from Berlin During World War II

http://www.otr.com/shirer.html

Part of a larger site paying homage to the glory
days of radio, this page features audio of three
William Shirer radio broadcasts from the World
War II era, one coming from Berlin just before,
and one just after, Germany's invasion of Poland,
and the last announcing the formal surrender of
France. In addition to the audio, you will find
biographical information on Shirer and a
photograph of the newsman.

World War Electronic Passport

http://www.mrdowling.com/706wars.html

Concise accounts of World Wars I and II. The
material is provided by a teacher and so is written

in a straightforward and readable style, condensing all the facts into small sections.

World War II Images

http://earthstation1.simplenet.com/wwiipics/wwiipics.html

Images of World War II. Over a hundred pictures are shown here as thumbnails; clicking on one will load the full-size image. Subjects covered include many aspects of the war, from snapshots of ordinary people to the bombing of Hiroshima. The vast majority of the pictures are in monochrome, but several colour shots are also included.

World War II Posters: Powers of Persuasion

http://www.nara.gov/exhall/powers/powers.html

Propaganda posters from World War II. The posters shown here are US examples, but could equally have come from any nation taking part in the fighting. A wartime song may also be downloaded in both WAV and MAC formats.

World War II Timeline

http://www.historyplace.com/worldwar2/timeline/ww2time.htm

Large and detailed chronology of World War II, as well as the major interwar events leading up to it. It is divided by year and includes links to subsidiary pages with more details of all major events.

Yalta Conference

http://www.yale.edu/lawweb/avalon/wwii/yalta.htm

Part of the Avalon Project at the Yale Law School, this page features the text of agreements reached at the Yalta Conference of 1945 between President Roosevelt, Prime Minister Churchill and Generalissimo Stalin. Among other topics considered, this document outlines decisions of the Big Three concerning world organization, the dismemberment of Germany, war reparations, and a declaration of liberated Europe.

Holocaust

Holocaust Glossary

http://www.wiesenthal.com/resource/gloss.htm

Full explanations of terminology used when discussing the legacy of the Holocaust. This page is part of a site founded by Simon Wiesenthal, a survivor of the Holocaust.

Holocaust Timeline

http://www.historyplace.com/worldwar2/holocaust/timeline.html

Timeline containing all the key information and links to associated sites. Although the root page seems to contain only the barest of details, many of the links take you to primary documents and pictures.

Shtetl: Righteous Gentiles

http://www.pbs.org/wgbh/pages/frontline/shtetl/

Companion to the US Public Broadcasting Service (PBS) television programme *Frontline,* this page provides information into Polish citizens, 'righteous gentiles', who risked their lives to rescue Jews during World War II. There are sections concerning the historical relationship between Poles and Jews, which includes a timeline and article; stories of individual Poles who rescued Jews; and detailed information regarding the German death camp Treblinka, which includes a bibliography for further research. You can also read an excerpt from Eva Hoffman's book *Shtetl: The Life and Death of a Small Town and the World of Polish Jews* and download a transcript of the television programme.

US Holocaust Memorial Museum

http://www.ushmm.org/

Created and maintained by the Holocaust Memorial Museum in Washington DC, USA, this site includes a series of detailed online exhibitions. In the museum library you can also find information on how to trace people who were involved in the Holocaust.

Yad Vashem

http://www.yad-vashem.org.il/

Israeli monument to the Jewish people killed by the Nazis in the Holocaust. This site can simultaneously induce sorrow, anger, and, most importantly, hope, in its visitors. There are also many links to other Holocaust-related sites.

African History

African History Timeline

http://www.fordham.edu/halsall/africa/africasbook.
html

Timeline beginning with the appearance in Africa of *homo habilis* 2.5 million years ago to the present day. Along the way there are links to significant people, places, events, and organizations from the Nubian civilization and the slave trade to the Ku Klux Klan and Marcus Garvey.

F
A
C
T

ANCIENT AFRICA

Africa is probably the continent in which humans originated. However, one of Africa's earliest external contacts was with the Romans, who gave the name Africa to their African provinces with the city of Carthage. Classical writers called this continent Libya, and both Herodotus and Ptolemy wrote about it.

Anglo-Boer War Museum

http://www.anglo-boer.co.za/

Comprehensive site providing an account the second of the South African Wars 1899–1902. There is a background to the causes of the Boer War, as well as a chronology of the major battles. Also of interest is a collection of war photographs, and a large section on Boer prisoners of war from both sides, accompanied by maps and poems.

Battle of Adwa Centennial

http://www.ethiopians.com/adwa.html

Site marking the centenary of the Italian defeat at Adwa in 1896. It includes background information and details of the peace treaty that ended the battle. It should be noted that this site is written from the Ethiopian perspective.

Great African Kings

http://www.swagga.com/king.htm

Features profiles of 24 great African kings, creators of some of the world's first known high civilizations. The text provides dates when these kings ruled, as well as detailing their greatest achievements. Some are accompanied by images.

Great African Queens

http://www.swagga.com/queen.htm

Features profiles of 13 great African queens, including Cleopatra and Makeda, Queen of Sheba. Some of the information is accompanied by images, and there is a quiz section. This page is part of a larger site concerning African history.

Kingdoms of the Medieval Sudan

http://www.xula.edu/~jrotondo/Kingdoms/

Provides a historical overview of Sudanic Africa before the modern era. Key themes are the rise of the Islamic religion, and how trading helped to shape Sudanese empires such as Mali and Songhai. There is also an impressive photo gallery, illustrating daily life in the region as well as West African traditions and beliefs.

Lutuli, Albert John

http://www.nobel.se/laureates/peace-1960-bio.html

Profile of the Nobel Peace Prize laureate and African National Congress leader. His determination to obtain an education and his subsequent career as a teacher are traced. His appointment as a Zulu chief and magistrate, his increasing concern for all non-white South Africans, and his role in the ANC are set out. The repeated bans on his activities and his death are also described here.

Operation Bonito May 1978

http://www.geocities.com/TimesSquare/
Alley/2187/legion.htm

Description of the actions taken by the French Foreign Legion in May 1978 to free hostages in the city of Kolwezi, Democratic Republic of Congo (former Zaire). The Web site describes the unit and its arrival, tactics, and withdrawal from the area after the fighting had ceased. Also included is a transcript of the parachutists' prayer, which differs slightly in form from the standard type of message to the almighty.

Slavery

Address Adopted by a Convention of Negroes in Alexandria, Virginia, from 2–5 August 1865

http://odur.let.rug.nl/~usa/D/1851-1875/slavery/addres.htm

Part of a larger site on historical documents, this page is the text of an address delivered to the US Congress that notes the loyalty of blacks to the Union cause during the US Civil War, and anticipates harsh conditions for newly freed slaves in the South following Reconstruction.

Confessions of Nat Turner

http://odur.let.rug.nl/~usa/D/1826-1850/slavery/confesxx.htm

Part of a larger site on historical documents, this page is the full text of the confessions of a Virginia slave who led a rebellion in 1831. The confessions are broken into seven chapters, including an introduction that provides historical context.

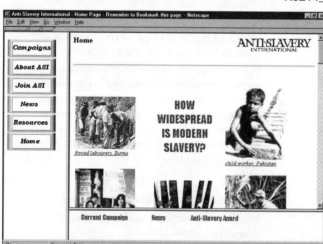

Frederick Douglass: Autobiography

http://odur.let.rug.nl/~usa/B/fdouglas/dougxx.htm

Part of a larger site of historical documents, this page concerns chapters four, five, and six of the 1883 edition of Frederick Douglass's autobiography. The chapters are divided into five parts

including 'A General Survey of a Slave Plantation', 'A Slaveholder's Character', 'A Child's Reasoning', 'Luxuries at the Great House', and a brief introduction that provides historical context.

Fugitive Slave Act of 1850

http://odur.let.rug.nl/~usa/D/1826-1850/ slavery/act.htm

Part of a larger site of historical documents, this page is an excerpt from the Fugitive Slave Act of the USA, which mandated that escaped slaves be returned to the state or territory from which they fled.

Journal of John Woolman

http://etext.lib.virginia.edu/etcbin/browse-mixed-new?id=WooJour&tag=public&images=images/modeng&data=/texts/english/modeng/parsed

Complete text of US Quaker John Woolman's *Journal*.

Phillis Wheatley – Precursor of American Abolitionism

http://www.forerunner.com/forerunner/X0214_Phillis_Wheatley.html

Profile of the self-taught African slave whose literary gifts, piety, and intelligence brought her fame in 18th-century USA and Britain. There is an extract of her poetry and an account of the dismal old age of the first prominent black US writer.

Slavery

http://www.charitynet.org/~asi/

Site of the leading organization campaigning to end the last vestiges of slavery. There are full details of Anti-Slavery International's work to assist bonded labourers, abused working children, and the trafficking of women

---

F A C T

SLAVERY

slavery goes back to prehistoric times but during the imperialism of Spain, Portugal, and Britain in the 16th to 18th centuries and in the American South in the 17th to 19th centuries, the slavery of Africans became a mainstay of the agricultural factory economy.

for sexual exploitation. The suffering chronicled on these pages makes it clear that slavery is not a thing of the past.

Slave Voices

http://scriptorium.lib.duke.edu/slavery/

Online exhibition from the Duke University Special Collections Library, covering the history of slavery in America, including sections on forced migration, plantation America, the problems of freedom, and the slave community in the Old South.

Studies in the World History of Slavery, Abolition and Emancipation

http://h-net2.msu.edu/~slavery/

Occasional online publication on the subject of slavery, abolitionism, and emancipation. A number of essays on these subjects are included and a database of images and documents is also being developed. The site is aimed at a global audience, hence essays are sometimes written in languages other than English.

Supreme Court Decision: The Dred Scot Case

http://odur.let.rug.nl/~usa/D/1851-1875/dredscott/dredxx.htm

Part of a larger site on historical documents, this page concerns the opinion of the US Supreme Court in the Dred Scott case, as written by Chief Justice Taney, as well as the concurring and dissenting opinions of each of the Justices. Includes a syllabus and information on the case as it was presented to the US Supreme Court.

Thomas Jefferson on Slavery

http://odur.let.rug.nl/~usa/P/tj3/writings/slavery.htm

Part of a larger site on historical documents, this page is an excerpt from a text called Notes on the State of Virginia. This section is Thomas Jefferson's appeal to end slavery and colonize former American slaves in Africa. A brief introduction provides historical context.

Truth, Sojourner

http://www.nisto.com/wct/who/sojourn.html

Profile and photo of the US anti-slavery pioneer. It traces the religious commitment of the ex-slave and her rise to national prominence.

Up from Slavery: An Autobiography

http://sunsite.unc.edu/docsouth/washington/washing.html

Full text of the autobiography of the celebrated US black educator Booker T Washington.

Asian History

MAO ZEDONG (Mao Tse-tung, 1893–1976), Chinese communist politician and theoretician, leader of the Chinese Communist Party (CCP) 1935–76. He organized the Long March 1934–35 and the war of liberation 1937–49, following which he established a People's Republic and communist rule in China.

Badges of Chairman Mao Zedong

http://www.cnd.org/CR/maobadge/index.html

History of the badges of Chairman Mao Zedong, which became an integral part of the Mao cult. There is a brief summary of the importance of the badges, followed by the full text of an article about them with a few links to relevant issues of *Beijing Review*.

Beauty and Darkness: Cambodia in Modern History

http://users.aol.com/cambodia

Essays, oral histories, and photos relate the recent history of Cambodia, particularly the Khmer Rouge period. The site is divided into several sections, including 'The Banyan tree: untangling Cambodian history' and 'Cambodia and the media: two opposing viewpoints'.

Chang Ch'ien and Han Conquest

http://www.thehistorynet.com/MilitaryHistory/articles/04964_text.htm

Lengthy text only Web site describes the full known history of Chang Ch'ien and also lists the military conquests of the Han dynasty. The site describes how Chang Ch'ien's far-ranging diplomacy laid the groundwork for Han dynasty conquests, but as a side effect formed the foundations of the silk road link between East and West.

Condensed China

http://asterius.com/china/

As the site says, this is more of a 'Cliff Notes' history of China. However it does stretch across the entirety of known history: from the origins of Chinese civilization to the modern People's Republic. It is divided into four main sections: 'The origins of Chinese civilization', 'The early empire', 'The second empire', and 'The birth of modern China'.

Emergence of Modern China

http://www-chaos.umd.edu/history/modern2.html

Authoritative summary of the importance of the rebellion in the history of modern China, as part of a comprehensive suite of Web sites about Chinese history.

Envisioning Yuan Ming Yuan

http://www.cs.ubc.ca/spider/wang/

Fascinating site dedicated to the Chinese palace that was burned down in 1860. The palace has been recreated online by means of multimedia technology to create a site that is rich in both images and information. The entire history of the garden's construction is described in detail, and the extensive gallery has been divided into a number of areas, such as statues, plants, and weapons.

Fundamentals Of National Reconstruction

http://acc6.its.brooklyn.cuny.edu/~phalsall/texts/sunyat.html

Background to the Chinese revolution, and to the views of the first president of the Republic of China, Sun Zhong Shan, in particular.

History of Korea

http://violet.berkeley.edu/~korea/history.html

Large and comprehensive introduction to the history of Korea, divided into six main clickable parts: 'ancient history', 'Koryô dynasty', 'Chosôn dynasty', 'colonial period', 'liberation and the Korean War', and 'contemporary Korea'. Each

section has links to further information and many are illustrated.

History of Thailand

http://www.escati.com/history.htm

History of Thailand from the prehistoric cultural development of the people, to the legacy of Rama I. The site also contains detailed information about the Thai principalities, both historically and today, accompanied by many pictures.

History of the Japanese Samurai

http://www.geocities.com/Tokyo/Temple/9577/report.html

Informative, text-only history of the Japanese *samurai*. As well as discussing such themes as how the *samurai* class came about, what their role was, and how they developed over the years, the author also includes a detailed bibliography, which serves as a useful guide to further study.

Ho Chi Minh

http://www.pathfinder.com/time/time100/leaders/profile/hochiminh.html

Part of a larger archive from *Time* exploring the most influential people of this century, this article highlights the life and work of the North Vietnamese communist politician Ho Chi Minh. The profile also features a timeline and a quiz about his life.

Hong Kong 97: Lives in Transition

http://www.pbs.org/pov/hongkong/

Companion to the US Public Broadcasting Service (PBS) television programme *POV*, this page features a fascinating insight into the lives of Hong Kong residents as their city transferred from British back to Chinese rule in July 1997. This page consists of a number of diary entries written between May and October of 1997, plus an interactive timeline detailing Hong Kong's history from the Opium Wars to the last British Governor. There is also a section that examines through text, images, and maps the 'living city' of Hong Kong as it has existed through the ages.

Hong Kong Handover

http://www.hongkong97.com.hk/

Site run by the *South China Morning Post* on the 1997 handover of the British colony to China. It contains a timeline from 1711, details of the joint agreement, and some expected changes. This is by no means an unbiased view, but it does contain some interesting information, notably in opinion columns taken from the newspaper.

India-Pakistani War of 1971

http://freeindia.org/1971war/

Information on the conflict that culminated in the creation of a new country, Bangladesh. The site includes a discussion of the roots of discord and the war itself in detail, with photos and maps supporting the text. Features of specific aspects of the war are updated every week. This site includes an archive of photographs and interviews with Indian military officers who took part in the war.

Japanese History

http://www.japan-guide.com/e/e641.html

Detailed chronology of Japanese historical events, from 8,000 BC to modern times. It has a separate section for each major historical period, from the Jomon period to the post-war era. It also includes sections on the effect of the atomic bomb on the country, as well as details of Japanese religion, and also includes a selection of links to related sites.

Mahatma Gandhi Ashram

http://www.nuvs.com/ashram/

Extensive information about Gandhi's life and philosophy, including photos, timelines, and quotes. There is also a useful introduction, a section for students and researchers, and a new multimedia page, containing a film clip of the man in both Mac and Windows formats.

Mao Zedong: On Practice

http://www.cis.yale.edu/amstud/inforev/practice.html

Part of a lecture delivered in 1937 by Chinese leader Mao Zedong at the Anti-Japanese Military and Political College in Yenan. The text of this lecture concerns the relationship 'between knowledge and practice, between knowing and doing'. At the bottom of the page you will find editor's notes from a 1977 edition of the lecture and a list of footnotes.

Mohandas A Gandhi: Indian Home Rule (1909)

http://www.wsu.edu:8080/~wldciv/world_civ_reader/world_civ_reader_2/gandhi.html

Essay on Indian Home Rule – an imaginary dialogue with Gandhi in which he answers questions from an interviewer about what to do about those who agitate for independence from Britain. There are links to footnotes.

Mughal Legacy

http://edweb.cnidr.org/india/mughals.html

Brief biographies of all six Mogul, or Mughal, emperors, as well as plenty of images. There are also pages giving historical context to this Asian empire. Throughout the text there are hyperlinks to articles providing further information on related topics and several of the pages include notes on the emperors' various architectural legacies.

Sorghaghtani Beki

http://home.earthlink.net/~womenwhist/heroine8.html

Interesting portrait of an influential woman and mother of kings, from the Genghis Khan period of Mongolia. The site is also a source of information on less well known aspects of a little-understood period of Asian history.

Spratly Islands Dispute

http://www.reedbooks.com.au/heinemann/hot/sprat.html

Background on the contested island group and the potential for war between the six states claiming ownership. There is a map of the islands and a history of the dispute. Designed for school classes in international affairs, there are a number of suggested classroom activities.

Taiping Rebellion 1851–64

http://www-chaos.umd.edu/history/ modern2.html#taiping

Account of the causes and effects of the Taiping Rebellion, and other influences that weakened the already ailing Qing dynasty. The names of key players and places are given with their Chinese-character equivalent (no special software necessary).

Who Were the Shoguns?

http://www.jinjapan.org/kidsweb/japan/ i/q8.html

Description of the introduction of shoguns as well as their usurpation of power and role in the history of Japan. An image of the founder of the shogunate is also included.

F A C T

SHOGUN

Japanese term for military dictator and abbreviation for '*seii tai shogun*' – 'great barbarian-conquering general'. Technically an imperial appointment, the office was treated as hereditary. The shogun held legislative, judicial, and executive power.

WWW Memorial Hall of the Victims in the Nanjing Massacre (1937–38)

http://www.arts.cuhk.edu.hk/ NanjingMassacre/ NM.html

Dedication to the memory of the victims of Japanese atrocities in the city of Nanjing. This very extensive site provides links to photographs of the massacre (some of these are disturbing), accounts of Chinese, Japanese, and Western witnesses, maps and statistics, Japanese attitudes to the massacre, textbook censorship in Japan, and much more about Japanese attitudes to World War II from the Chinese point of view.

Latin American History

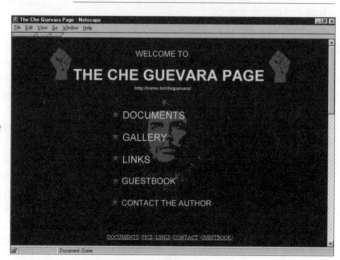

Che Guevara Page

http://www.nadir.org/nadir/initiativ/che/

English, German, and Spanish biographies of the Latin American revolutionary Che Guevara. Also featured on this site is an extract from his book *Guerilla Warfare,* and a link to a recording of one of his speeches. Several articles are included on the site, as well as a large gallery of images.

Cinco de Mayo

http://latino.sscnet.ucla.edu/demo/ cinco.html

This page provides a historical perspective of the yearly *Cinco de Mayo* celebration that commemorates the Mexican victory over the French at the Battle of the Pueblo in 1862. You will also find images of traditional Mexican dresses that might be worn at such a celebration.

Cuba: Historical Text Archive

http://www.msstate.edu/Archives/History/ Latin_America/cuba.html

General and historical information on Cuba, including coverage of the Missile Crisis of 1962.

There are also other sections, including 'The Cuban nation, 1898–1959' and 'Spanish-Cuban-American War'. Please note that some of the information is only available in Spanish.

Early History of Haiti

http://pasture.ecn.purdue.edu/~agenhtml/agenmc/haiti/history.html

Essay on the history of Haiti that includes images and hyperlinks to related sites. It is a personal viewpoint and covers the period from AD 450 to the beginning of the 19th century.

Hidalgo, Miguel

http://www.knight.org/advent/cathen/16045a.htm

Profile of the turbulent life of the Mexican priest who spearheaded the struggle for Mexican independence. It traces his training for the priesthood, the influence of French philosophy, and the circumstances that led him to take command of the wave of revulsion against Spanish rule in 1810. There are details of the military campaigns that ultimately led to Hidalgo's capture and execution.

Historical Text Archive – Cuban Missile Crisis

http://www.msstate.edu/Archives/History/Latin_America/crisis.html

Documents and essays related to the Cuban missile crisis, including Soviet leader Krushchev's letter to US president John Kennedy, Kennedy's address to the nation, Britain's response to the crisis, recollections, and a bibliography.

Latin America: Historical Text Archive

http://www.msstate.edu/Archives/History/Latin_America/latam.html

Wide-ranging collection of information on Latin America, including its 'discovery' and conquest by European explorers, the cultures of the Andes, and links to images and many other resources.

Maya Adventure

http://www.sci.mus.mn.us/sln/ma/index.html

Guide to the lost world of the Mayan civilization, introduced by the Science Museum of Minnesota. The site contains information about the sites of the various Mayan communities, maps of the settlements, and activities designed by the

FACT

MAYA
member of an American Indian civilization originating in the Yucatán Peninsula in Central America about 2600 BC, with later sites in Mexico, Guatemala, and Belize, and enjoying a classical period AD 325–925.

education division of the museum. There is also an extensive photo archive.

Papa Toussaint

http://www.towson.edu/~richard/papa.html

Papa Toussaint is a hypertext edition of an historical novel by C Richard Gillespie which chronicles the last five years in the life of Toussaint L'Ouverture, the liberator of Haiti.

Zapata, Emiliano

http://www.cs.utk.edu/~miturria/project/zapata.html

Biography of the Mexican revolutionary Emiliano Zapata. The page also includes two essays 'Thunder over Mexico (The Legacy of Emiliano Zapata)', and 'The Story of the Questions – the Real Story of Zapata'. There is also an appeal from the Zapatista National Liberation Army.

Middle Eastern History

Abbasids

http://www.islam.org/Mosque/ihame/Sec6.htm

History of the Abbasid dynasty, with links to aspects of Islam, and Islamic and Middle Eastern history. The page is illustrated with colour photographs of period architecture.

Begin, Menachem

http://www.nobel.se/laureates/peace-1978-2-bio.html

Portrait of the Zionist leader who won a Nobel Peace Prize. It traces his youth in Poland, hisincreasing involvement in Zionism, his clandestine emigration to Palestine, his role as leader of the Irgun terrorist organization, and his role in Israeli politics.

Camp David Accords

http://sunsite.unc.edu/sullivan/CampDavid-Accords-Intro.html

Multimedia guide to the 1978 Camp David Accords presided over by US president Jimmy Carter. This site contextualizes the Accords in relation to subsequent developments in the Middle East.

Chronology of Afghan History

http://www.afghan-web.com/history/achron.html

Detailed and clearly presented chronology of the history of Afghanistan from its Stone Age beginnings in 50,000 BC to the Taliban's capture of Kabul in 1996. There are links to the Ghaznavid Dynasty and to Ahmad Shah Durrani's empire. A link at the bottom of the page leads to more information about the country and its people.

Empires Beyond the Great Wall: The Heritage of Genghis Khan

http://vvv.com/khan/khan.html

Provided by the Royal British Columbia Museum, this site includes a brief biography of the Mongol ruler Genghis Khan, with additional sections on Mongol culture, and descriptions of artefacts from Inner Mongolia that were part of the museum's exhibit.

Fatimids

http://www.islam.org/Mosque/ihame/Sec8.htm

Brief history of the Fatimid dynasty, with links to aspects of Islam, and Islamic and Middle Eastern history. The page is illustrated with a colour photograph of the mosque of al-Azhar in Cairo.

From the Queen of Saba to a Modern State

http://www.gpc.org.ye/Ancient0.htm

Comprehensive account of the history of Yemen. The site includes the myths surrounding the Queen of Sheba, the emergence of the kingdom of Saba, and details of subsequent South Arabian civilizations. The rise of Islam and the subsequent development of the modern Yemeni state are also set out here. The site is provided by the political party currently ruling the country.

History of Palestine

http://www.interx-me.com/jerusalem/palestine.htm

Brief account of the main events in 20th-century Palestine. It should be noted that this history of Israeli-Palestinian relations is written from a Palestinian perspective.

History of Palestine

http://www.israel-mfa.gov.il/mfa/go.asp?MFAH00kt0

Brief account of the main events in 20th-century Palestine. It should be noted that this history of Israeli-Palestinian relations is written from a Israeli perspective.

History of the Shrine of Imam Ali

http://www.al-islam.org/shrines/mashad.htm

Guide for Shi'ite pilgrims to Mashhad. There is a description of the city and its history. All the Islamic buildings for which the city is noted are described in detail.

Intifada Diary – Ten Years After

http://www.birzeit.edu/diary/intifada/

Reflections on the Palestinian uprising against Israeli occupation by those who took part. Organized as part of the tenth anniversary of the *intifada*, there are interesting personal reminiscences, well supported with photographs.

Israeli Declaration of Independence, 1948

http://www.yale.edu/lawweb/avalon/israel.htm

Part of the Avalon Project at the Yale Law School, this page is text of the declaration of Israel's independence, issued from Tel Aviv on 14 May 1948. The document includes hypertext links to texts of the Balfour Declaration of 2 November 1917 and the Charter of the United Nations.

Israel-PLO Agreement, 1993

http://www.yale.edu/lawweb/avalon/isrplo.htm

Part of the Avalon Project at the Yale Law School, this page is the text of the Isreal-PLO Agreement of 1993, which sets forth principles to 'put an end to decades of confrontation and conflict.' The document includes hypertext links to the text of several UN Security Resolutions.

Khomeini, Ayatollah Ruhollah

http://www.pathfinder.com/time/time100/leaders/profile/khomeini.html

Part of a larger archive from *Time* exploring the most influential people of this century, this article highlights the life and work of the Iranian Shiite Muslim leader Ayatollah Khomeini. The profile also features a timeline and a quiz about his life.

Knesset

http://www.knesset.gov.il/knesset/engframe.htm

Comprehensive guide to the functions of Israel's parliament. There are profiles of the 120 members, information on the Israeli constitution, a description of the complex Israeli electoral system, and a guide to other Israeli government sites. There is practical information for visitors to the Knesset.

Meir, Golda

http://www.israel-mfa.gov.il/facts/state/gmeir.html

Fulsome official biography of the Israeli foreign minister and prime minister. It traces her rise through the Histadrut trade union movement to political prominence, her diplomatic work, her leadership of Israel, and her resignation after the 1973 Yom Kippur war.

Out There News Explores the Middle East Conflict

http://www.megastories.com/mideast/index.htm

Details of the wars of the Arab–Israeli conflict, as well as information about the key players in the conflict. There are also descriptions of the relevance of parts of Jerusalem in the conflict.

Stern Gang

http://www.codoh.com/zionweb/zizad/zizad26.html

History of the extreme Zionist anti-British terrorist organization founded by Avraham Stern. It recounts how the movement was dismissed as the fanatic fringe of Zionism until the rise to leadership of Israel of its former head, Menachem Begin.

Suez 1956

http://ac.acusd.edu/History/text/suez.html

Detailed essay about the Suez crisis that includes and examination of British prime minister Benjamin Disraeli's involvement in the purchase of the Canal. There are extensive footnotes and a bibliography.

Umayyads

http://www.islam.org/Mosque/ihame/Sec4.htm

History of the Umayyad dynasty, with links to aspects of Islam, and Islamic and Middle Eastern history. The page is illustrated with line drawings and photographs of period architecture.

Zionist Leaders – David Ben-Gurion

http://www.israel-mfa.gov.il/mfa/zionism/bgur.html

Fulsome biography of Israel's first prime minister. It traces his early commitment to Zionist ideals in Poland through to his leadership during the war to establish the Israeli state. There are several pictures of Ben-Gurion.

FACT

ARAB–ISRAELI CONFLICT

series of wars and territorial conflicts between Israel and various Arab states in the Middle East since the founding of the state of Israel in May 1948. These include the war of 1948–49; the 1956 Suez War between Israel and Egypt; the Six-Day War of 1967, in which Israel captured territory from Syria and Jordan; the October War of 1973; and the 1982–85 war between Israel and Lebanon.

Rabin, Yitzhak

http://194.90.199.197/knesset/rabin/ebio.htm#7

Tribute to the assassinated Israeli leader. It traces Rabin's long career with informative text and a large number of pictures.

American Indian History

Cankpe Opi – Wounded Knee Home Page

http://www.dickshovel.com/WKmasscre.html

Comprehensive Web site putting the American Indians' side of the story of the massacre of Wounded Knee. The Web site describes the history of the massacre and goes on to cover the insults, propaganda, and anger that have surrounded the incident, right up to the present day.

Chief Geronimo: His Own Story

http://odur.let.rug.nl/~usa/B/geronimo/geronixx.htm

Part of a larger site of historical documents, this page is text from the Apache leader's autobiography. It is broken into five sections with several articles in each section. Articles include 'Origin' and 'Early life of the Apache Indians', 'Geronimo's mightiest battle', 'Coming of the white man', 'The final struggle' , and 'Hopes for the future'.

History of the Northwest Coast

http://www.hallman.org/indian/.www.html

Chronology of American Indians of the Pacific Northwest area of the USA and Canada and their contact with whites. The chronology begins in 1774 and features hypertext links to pages with more in-depth information. The site includes maps and other images.

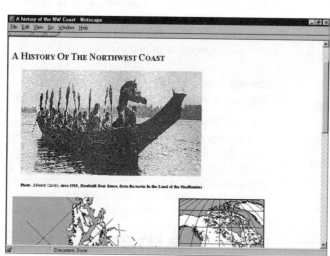

My Son, Pass By Me

http://www.dickshovel.com/DwyBrd.html

Harrowing account of the massacre at Wounded Knee of American Indians by US soldiers. The account is given by a survivor of the massacre, and will be upsetting for many to read.

Native American Conquest

http://www.FloridaHistory.com/

History lesson about the Spanish conquest of southeastern USA, which contains maps, contemporary illustrations and a useful summary page, in addition to more detailed sections such as 'Who conquered native America' and 'Where conquistadors went in America'.

Native American Maps

http://indy4.fdl.cc.mn.us/~isk/maps/mapmenu.html

Staggering collection of maps related to American Indian issues in the USA and Canada. They demonstrate, pictorially, such things as the variety of tribes in California, judicially established Indian lands in 1978, and federally owned lands. Many of the maps are 'clickable', leading to further information and images.

Relations Between the USA and Native Americans

http://www.yale.edu/lawweb/avalon/natamer.htm

Part of the Avalon Project at the Yale Law School, this page includes a comprehensive collection of treaties and statutes made between the USA and American Indian nations from 1789 to 1887. The statutes are arranged chronologically; the treaties are arranged chronologically or by Indian tribe. You will also find the text of a federal court case brought by a American Indian against a Brigadier-General of the US Army.

Role of the Indians in the Conflict between France, Spain, and England, 1761

http://odur.let.rug.nl/~usa/D/1751-1775/indians/glen.htm

Part of a larger site on historical documents, this page is the text of a document written by South Carolina Governor Glen, in which he details the need for the English to align themselves with the Cherokee Indians in order to ensure peace and a balance of power in South Carolina. A brief introduction provides historical context.

Sitting Bull – In Memory

http://www.dickshovel.com/sittingbull.html

Obituary of the Sioux tribal chief killed at Wounded Knee. The text of this page gives some surprising information on the character of the chief, for example, one of his white American captives describes him as 'uniformly gentle, and kind to his wife and children and courteous and considerate in his [interactions] with others'.

American Civil War

American Civil War

http://www.historyplace.com/civilwar/index.html

Extensive site dedicated not only to the events, but also the people involved in this US conflict. There is a detailed timeline scattered with thumbnail images. As well as being able to view these images at full size, there are also plenty of links to other pictures from the root page.

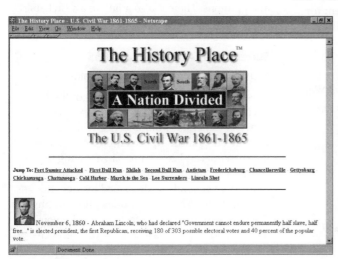

Battle of Fredericksburg, 1862

http://www.nps.gov/frsp/fredhist.htm

Detailed account written by a ranger of the park that now occupies the site of the battle. The account is illustrated by several photographs and drawings, and also has hypertext links to biographical information on the main protagonists.

Battle of Gettysburg Home Page

http://www.militaryhistoryonline.com/gettysburg/

Battle of Gettysburg home page. The US Civil War battle is described in detail here, with sections covering each of the three days the battle lasted. The information is comprehensive and concise, and each day of the battle is accompanied by a tactical map.

Carnage at Antietam, 1862

http://www.ibiscom.com/antiet.htm

Documents Confederate General Robert E Lee's gamble to take the war to the North, an offensive that culminated in the bloodiest day in US military history at the Battle of Antietam. The furious fighting at 'Bloody Lane' is described through the first-hand account of Lieutenant Frederick Hitchcock of the 132nd Pennsylvania volunteers. David Thompson of the 9th New York volunteers describes the murderous attack on Confederate positions across Antietam Creek. This site includes photographs, maps, sketches, and sidebars of interesting facts about the battle. There is also a list of references.

Civil War Medicine

http://www.powerweb.net/bbock/war

Useful information about medicine in the US Civil War. It describes the state of medicine at the start of the war, and also technology, transport, and even amputations during the war itself. There is also a bibliography, and 'When Johnny Comes Marching Home' is played in the background as you explore the site.

From Manassas to Appomattox: Memoirs of Confederate General James Longstreet

http://www.wtj.com/pl/pages/longstreet.htm

This page features seven chapters of Confederate General James Longstreet's recollections of the US Civil War. Included here are General Longstreet's firsthand accounts and analyses of the Battles of Bull Run, Antietam, Gettysburg, and Chickamauga. Three chapters are devoted to the Battle of Gettysburg, one for each day of the battle, and include Longstreet's ideas on the reason for the Confederate defeat there. A brief introduction provides interesting information about Longstreet and the smear campaign against him following the war.

General George A Custer Home Page

http://www.garryowen.com/

Clearing house of information for Custer buffs. Click on 'Custer review topics' for comprehensive accounts of the life of the controversial general and the Battle of Little Big Horn. There are a huge number of links to other Custer sites.

Images of the US Civil War

http://jefferson.village.virginia.edu/vshadow2/cwimages.html

Part of a larger site on the US Civil War, this page is a searchable database of over 600 images of the US Civil War. Photos and drawings can be searched by date, specific battle, or keyword.

Lee, Robert Edward

http://www.stratfordhall.org/rel.htm

Portrait and biography of the confederate general. The site run by the Robert E Lee Memorial Association includes a Lee family tree, a chronology of Lee's life, details of the horses Lee used in the Civil War, and a copy of Lee's general order number nine, the surrender document for the end of the war. There is also a link to the Stafford Hall Plantation site: birthplace and family home of Lee.

Letters from an Iowa Soldier in the Civil War

http://www.ucsc.edu/civil-war-letters/home.html

Selections from letters written by Newton Roberts, a private in the Union troops, provide vivid impressions of the Civil War and of conditions in the Union camps.

Letters from the US Civil War

http://jefferson.village.virginia.edu/vshadow2/cwletters.html

Part of a larger site on the US Civil War, this page is an archive of letters, memoirs, and reminiscences written during the conflict. The documents are written from or addressed to (or contain references to) communities in two counties, one located in the North and one in the South. Personal papers are searchable by date, subject, or keyword.

Maps of the US Civil War

http://Jefferson.village.virginia.edu/vshadow2/pics/ormaps.html

Part of a larger site on the US Civil War, this page features maps of the Shenendoah Valley, drawn before and during the war, showing main roads and railroads, Sheridan's valley campaigns of 1864–65, the geography of Staunton and Augusta, and more. A section of photographs of the 1864 burning of Chambersburg includes official records about the burning and a brief history. There are also drawings and lithographs.

Newspapers during the US Civil War

http://jefferson.village.virginia.edu/vshadow2/cwnewspapers.html

Part of a larger site on the US Civil War, this page is an archive of newspaper reports during the war. Featured newspapers are from cities in Augusta county in the South and Franklin county in the North. Users can view an index of articles on a given topic, such as politics or selected battles, or customize a search using keywords. Users are warned that the content of these newspapers has not been edited for potentially offensive language and opinions. There is also a link to a searchable database of the census of 1860.

Surrender at Appomattox, 1865

http://www.ibiscom.com/appomatx.htm

This page documents the final days of the US Civil War. It includes a series of dispatches sent between Generals Grant and Lee which led to their meeting at the Appomattox Courthouse and the surrender of Lee's army. The meeting at the courthouse, including the dialogue between the two weary generals, is described by General Horace Porter. This site includes photographs and sidebars with interesting facts about the war and the surrender. There is also a list of references.

17th-century American History

Anne Hutchinson – American Jezebel or Woman of Courage?

http://cpcug.org/user/billb/hutch.html

Full account of the life of the US religious leader whose beliefs led to conflict with Massachusetts Puritanism. Hutchinson is hailed by many as a pioneer feminist. There are quotations from her writings and her trial and a good bibliography.

Charter of Massachusetts Bay

http://odur.let.rug.nl/~usa/D/1601-1650/massachusetts/mchart.htm

Part of a larger site on historical documents, this page is the text of a document written in 1629 granting the Massachusetts Bay Company rights of self-government in America. A brief introduction provides historical context.

Declaration in the Name of the People

http://odur.let.rug.nl/~usa/D/1651-1700/bacon_rebel/bacon.htm

Document written by Nathaniel Bacon on 30 July 1676, which challenges the authorized government and lays the blame for Virginia's failures on the shoulders of Governor William Berkeley. A brief introduction to the page, part of a larger site containing historical texts, provides historical context.

First Virginia Charter

http://odur.let.rug.nl/~usa/D/1601-1650/virginia/chart01.htm

Part of a larger site on historical documents, this page is the text of the first of three charters granting the Virginia Company the authority to govern its own colony. The original charter was written on 10 April 1606. A brief introduction provides historical context.

Governor William Berkeley on Nathaniel Bacon's Rebellion

http://odur.let.rug.nl/~usa/D/1651-1700/bacon_rebel/berke.htm

The text of a document written on 19 May 1676 by Virginia Governor William Berkeley, which defends his position and accuses Nathaniel Bacon of treason. Part of a larger resource of historical documents, this page contains a brief introduction providing historical context.

Instructions for the Virginia Colony

http://odur.let.rug.nl/~usa/D/1601-1650/virginia/instru.htm

This page contains the text of instructions written in 1606 by a council in England advising the Virginia Company of the proper methods of colonizing in America. A brief introduction provides historical context.

John Winthrop – First Governor of Massachusetts

http://www.forerunner.com/forerunner/X0526_Bios-_John_Winthrop.html

Profile of the Puritan and his determination to make New England 'a city set on a hill'. This Christian account of his life stresses the religious basis of his commitment to good government.

Mayflower Compact

http://odur.let.rug.nl/~usa/D/1601-1650/plymouth/compac.htm

Part of a larger site on historical documents, this page is the text of a document written in November of 1620 for the purpose of establishing self-rule and protecting the rights of the settlers of the English colony of Plymouth. The page includes the names of those who signed the document.

Ordinance and Constitution of the Virginia Company in England

http://odur.let.rug.nl/~usa/D/1601-1650/virginia/ordi.htm

Issued on 24 July 1621 by the Virginia Company council in England, this is the text of a document authorizing the establishment of a self-governing assembly in colonial Virginia. A brief introduction provides historical context.

Plan of Union

http://odur.let.rug.nl/~usa/D/1651-1700/union/penn.htm

Written by William Penn in 1697, this is a document addressing the need for unifying the English colonies in America and calls for a yearly meeting of representatives. A brief introduction to the page, part of a larger site, provides historical context.

Second Virginia Charter

http://odur.let.rug.nl/~usa/D/1601-1650/virginia/chart02.htm

The second of three charters granting the Virginia Company the authority to govern its own colony. The second charter was written on 23 May 1609 and includes a 'sea to sea' provision not found in the first charter. A brief introduction to this page, part of a larger site providing full text versions of historical documents provides historical context.

Third Virginia Charter

http://odur.let.rug.nl/~usa/D/1601-1650/virginia/chart03.htm

Part of a larger site on historical documents, this page is the text of the last of three charters granting the Virginia Company the authority to govern its own colony. The third charter was written on 12 March 1612, and includes a provision extending the jurisdiction of the Virginia Company. A brief introduction provides historical context.

William Bradford – Governor of Plymouth Colony

http://www.forerunner.com/forerunner/ X0534_Bios-_William_Bradfo.html

Profile of the Mayflower pilgrim. It traces his role as Governor of Plymouth Colony in forging a government based on conventalism, the belief that men could form compacts in the sight of God without the consent of a higher authority.

18th-century American History

Albany Plan of Union, 1754

http://odur.let.rug.nl/~usa/D/1751-1775/7yearswar/ albany.htm

Part of a larger site on historical documents, this page is the text of a document calling for an act of English Parliament to permit the formation of a single general government in America to rule the colonies.

Archiving Early America

http://earlyamerica.com/earlyamerica/index.html

Astonishing collection of archive material from 18th-century America, paying equal respect to everyday life and landmark events. The Constitution and Declaration of Independence go in hand with pamphlets and excerpts from newspapers of the period, and portraits of early Americans. As well as offering valuable information, the site also captures the feel of the period by offering digitized versions of the documents in their original format as well as in full text version.

Articles of Confederation

http://odur.let.rug.nl/~usa/D/1776-1800/ constitution/confart.htm

Part of a larger site on historical documents, this page contains the full text of the document that outlined the national government formed by the thirteen original states of the USA, and includes the names of all the signatories.

F
A
C
T

FRANKLIN, BENJAMIN (1706–1790)
US scientist, statesman, writer, printer, and publisher. He proved that lightning is a form of electricity, distinguished between positive and negative electricity, and invented the lightning conductor.

Benjamin Franklin: His Autobiography

http://odur.let.rug.nl/~usa/B/bfranklin/frankxx.htm

Part of a larger site on historical documents, this page is devoted to the full text of Benjamin Franklin's autobiography. It is indexed into 12 chapters, or it can be viewed as one large file. There is also a timeline of the important events of his life.

Betsy Ross Home Page

http://libertynet.org/iha/betsy/

Learn the facts behind Betsy Ross and the making of the first US flag. Poets, authors, politicians, and others chime in about the meaning of the flag. This site includes a section on flag etiquette, flag facts and trivia, a timeline, frequently asked questions, and a picture gallery of US flags during various periods in history.

Captain Thomas Preston's Account of the Boston Massacre

http://odur.let.rug.nl/~usa/D/1751- 1775/bostonmassacre/prest.htm

Part of a larger site on historical documents, this page is an account of the Boston Massacre of 5 March 1770, written by Thomas Preston, a captain in the English 29th Regiment stationed in Boston.

Daniel Boone: Myth and Reality

http://xroads.virginia.edu/~HYPER/HNS/Boone/ smithhome.html

Scholarly examination of the different ways in which Boone has been portrayed by different biographers and commentators – both as a mythic hero and as a 'real' person – plus a chronology of Boone's life.

Declaration and Resolves of the First Continental Congress, October 1774

http://odur.let.rug.nl/~usa/D/1751-1775/independence/decres.htm

Part of a larger site on historical documents, this page is the text of a document which lists the colonists' grievances against the English Crown and Parliament, announces the formation of the First Continental Congress in Philadelphia, and declares the rights and liberties of American colonists.

Declaration of Independence

http://www.nara.gov/exhall/charters/declaration/decmain.html

Links to the history of the Declaration of Independence, and to the full text of the Constitution's first ten amendments, known as the Bill of Rights, and amendments 11–27.

Declaring Independence – Drafting the Documents

http://lcweb.loc.gov/exhibits/declara/declara1.html

Full account of the preparation of the US Declaration of Independence. This US Library of Congress site lists all the drafts and highlights the individuals behind the writing of this famous document.

Federalist Papers

http://odur.let.rug.nl/~usa/D/1776-1800/federalist/fedxx.htm

Part of a larger site on historical documents, this page features all 85 of the influential Federalist Papers, written by Alexander Hamilton, James Madison, and John Jay. Each paper can be viewed separately. This site includes links to brief biographies of Hamilton, Jay, and Madison, and an introduction provides critical historical context.

Historic Valley Forge

http://www.ushistory.org/valleyforge/index.html

Source of very detailed information regarding the six-month encampment of the Continental Army at Valley Forge during the difficult winter of 1777.

Read the story of Valley Forge, learn who was quartered there, and find out if the weather that winter was as unforgiving as legend reports. For additional context, this site also features a timeline of the American Revolution, a special section on George Washington, and the stories of critical French assistance during the conflict and the fledgling spy system of the Continental Army.

Letters to the Inhabitants of Massachusetts Bay

http://odur.let.rug.nl/~usa/D/1751-1775/libertydebate/leon.htm

Part of a larger site on historical documents, this page is the text of letters that Daniel Leonard submitted to the *Massachusetts Gazette* in January of 1775, in which he warns of the consequences of opened rebellion against the English. The text includes links to point-by-point responses by John Adams. A brief introduction provides historical context.

Manifest Destiny

http://odur.let.rug.nl/~usa/E/manifest/manifxx.htm

Part of a larger site on historical documents, this page is an essay that provides an in-depth look at the 'philosophy that created a nation'. Information is indexed into five sections which discuss the philosophy, components, and many shades of manifest destiny, including its influence on US imperialism, yellow journalism, and the Monroe Doctrine.

Memoir on the French Colonies in North America, 1750

http://odur.let.rug.nl/~usa/D/1726-1750/7yearswar/galis.htm

Part of a larger site on historical documents, this page is a section of Marquis de la Galissoniere's memoirs, in which he anticipates conflict between the French and English in North America and calls for construction of fortifications in the French territories. A brief introduction provides historical context.

North Carolina Biennial Act

http://odur.let.rug.nl/~usa/D/1701-1725/northcarolina/ba.htm

Part of a larger site on historical documents, this page is the text of the Biennial Act of 1715, passed by the North Carolina Assembly to encourage the continuation of colonial self-rule. A brief introduction provides historical context.

Northwest Ordinance

http://odur.let.rug.nl/~usa/D/1776-1800/ohio/norwes.htm

Part of a larger site on historical documents, this page is the text of a document establishing government in the US territory northwest of the Ohio River.

Proposed Amendments to the US Constitution

http://odur.let.rug.nl/~usa/P/jm4/speeches/amend.htm

Part of a larger site on historical documents, this page is the text of a document written by James Madison on 8 June 1789, in which he calls for changes and amendments to the US Constitution.

Second Continental Congress: Declaration of the Causes and Necessity of Taking up Arms

http://odur.let.rug.nl/~usa/D/1751-1775/war/causes.htm

Part of a larger site on historical documents, this page is the text of a document prepared by the Second Continental Congress, which convened in May 1775 and whose delegates agreed to continue with armed resistance against the English. A brief introduction provides historical context.

Virginia Declaration of Rights

http://odur.let.rug.nl/~usa/D/1776-1800/independence/ virdor.htm

Part of a larger site on historical documents, this page is the text of a document drafted by George Mason and adopted on 12 June 1776 by the Virginia Convention of Delegates.

World of Benjamin Franklin

http://sln.fi.edu/franklin/rotten.html

Life and times of Benjamin Franklin. The site includes exhaustive biographical details, a family tree of Franklin and his family, and comprehensive information on his achievements in the many fields in which he was prominent. There is a video clip on the front page and certain other pages have audio clips attached to the articles.

19th-century US History

Abraham Lincoln's Assassination

http://members.aol.com/RVSNorton/Lincoln.html

Comprehensive information on the life and death of John Wilkes Booth, the assassination of President Lincoln, and its aftermath. You can trace the events of Lincoln's last day, read the texts of Booth's diary and John Surratt's 1870 lecture on the conspiracy, as well as biographical sketches of those tried by a military commission in 1865 and of the soldier who shot Booth. Conspiracy theories are outlined and there are numerous photos and quotes.

African American Perspectives, 1818–1907

http://lcweb2.loc.gov/ammem/aap/aaphome.html

Part of the American Memory presentation of the US Library of Congress, this site is the Daniel A P Murray Pamphlet Collection, which provides a broad review of African-American history and culture from the early 19th to the early 20th centuries. Some of the authors included here are Frederick Douglass, Booker T Washington, Ida B Wells-Barnett, Benjamin W Arnett, Alexander Crummel, and Emanuel Love. There are three timelines of African-American history from 1852 to 1925.

Buffalo Bill

http://www.comp-unltd.com/~rodeo/billcody.html

Sympathetic profile of the colourful life of Buffalo Bill. Written by the town which bears his name, this account of Cody traces his evolution from tracker and army scout to the Wild West Show which made him one of the best-known men in the world in the late 19th century. Cody's efforts to raise the status of native Americans and women are also highlighted here.

Burr–Hamilton: Was The Duel Rigged?

http://www.geocities.com/TimesSquare/Alley/2187/burr.html

Debate on the outcome of the duel between Aaron Burr and Alexander Hamilton. The Web site presents possible evidence that the duel wasn't rigged after all, and that Burr's weapons were fitted with a hair trigger. Images of both of the protagonists, the weapons in question, and an engraving of an image of the duel are all shown on this Web site.

California as I Saw It: First-Person Narratives of California's Early Years, 1849–1900

http://lcweb2.loc.gov/ammem/cbhtml/cbhome.html

Part of the American Memory presentation of the US Library of Congress, this site features the eyewitness accounts of pioneers living in California during the years between the Gold Rush and the turn of the 20th century. The collection includes text and illustrations, covering such topics as the encounters between pioneers and those already established in California; the effects of mining, ranching, agriculture, and urban development on the land; the arrival of statehood; and the myth and mystique of California. This site includes an historical introduction for context and a regional map. The collection can be browsed by keyword, subject, author, or title.

'Case of the Negro, The'

http://etext.lib.virginia.edu/etcbin/browse-mixed-new?id=WasCase&tag=public&images=images/modeng&data=/texts/english/modeng/parsed

Complete text of US educator Booker T Washington's article, first published in *Atlantic Monthly*.

Chicano!

http://www.pbs.org/chicano/index.html

Companion site to a US Public Broadcasting Service (PBS) television programme, this page provides a timeline history of Mexican-Americans and their civil rights movement in the USA, focusing on the plight of the migrant farm workers. The timeline reaches back to 1840 and is divided into sections, each of which deals with increments of 20 years, or you can view the timeline overview that summarizes major events. This site also features over 100 brief biographies of notable figures in the civil-rights movement referred to on the PBS programme, such as César Chávez. The bulk of the site is only in English, but selected pages have Spanish-language versions.

Constitution of the Confederate States of America

http://odur.let.rug.nl/~usa/D/1851-1875/constitution/css.htm

Part of a larger site on historical documents, this page is the text of the constitution adopted by the Congress of Confederate States on 11 March 1861. It includes the names of all signatories and the states they represented.

Death of John Wilkes Booth, 1865

http://www.ibiscom.com/booth.htm

Documents the final days of US President Abraham Lincoln's assassin, John Wilkes Booth. It features a first-hand account of Booth's last moments, including his final words, as related by the officer in charge of capturing him. This site includes photographs, a map of Booth's escape route, and sidebars with interesting facts about the aftermath of Lincoln's assassination. There is also a list of references.

Democracy in America by Alexis de Tocqueville

http://xroads.virginia.edu/~HYPER/DETOC/home.html

Full text of de Tocqueville's celebrated analysis of US society. A perceptive introduction looks at the context in which the Frenchman wrote and the continuing relevance of the work for an understanding of the processes of US democracy today.

Gettysburg Address

http://lcweb.loc.gov/exhibits/gadd/

Full text of the historic speech given by Abraham Lincoln on 19 November 1863. This US Library of Congress site also has extensive information concerning the various drafts of the speech prepared by Lincoln. The speech is translated into no less than 29 languages.

Gold Rush

http://www.pbs.org/goldrush/

Companion to a US Public Broadcasting Service (PBS) television programme, this site embraces the adventure story that was the California Gold Rush. Here you will find detailed information on the first discovery of gold and the wild fever that followed. Some of the many subjects explored here include women of the Gold Rush, success stories, the effects of different cultures coming together, the rise of San Francisco, the terrible environmental destruction brought on by mechanized mining, and the creation of the enduring California myth that has come to define the American Dream. There are also classroom resources and a section of fun facts.

Great Chicago Fire

http://www.chicagohs.org/fire/

Commemorative exhibit created by the Chicago Historical Society and Northwestern University, this comprehensive site provides an illustrated look at the fire that devastated the city of Chicago in 1871. The information is divided into two sections, which again are divided into chapters. The first section concerns the conflagration and the city's recovery. The second section is devoted to how the century-old fire has been remembered and features eyewitness and contemporary journalists' accounts, illustrations and paintings, plus fictional accounts such as the legend of Mrs O'Leary and her cow. Both sections feature a number of image galleries, essays, and a library of relevant texts.

Hawaii's Last Queen

http://www.pbs.org/wgbh/pages/amex/hawaii/ index.html

Companion to the US Public Broadcasting Service (PBS) television programme *The American Experience,* this page tells the story of Hawaii's last native ruler, Queen Lili'uokalani, including the events that led to her surrender of the Hawaiian kingdom to US marines in 1893 and subsequent statehood for Hawaii. This site includes a timeline of her life and an audio clip of one of many native songs written by Queen Lili'uokalani. You can also read the text of the programme transcript. There is also a quiz on Hawaii and a list of sources for further reading.

Impeachment – Andrew Johnson

http://www.historyplace.com/unitedstates/impeachments/johnson.htm

Details of President Andrew Johnson's impeachment hearings in 1868. The first US president to undergo an impeachment trial, Johnson's biographical details are also included,

as well as the background to the trial, the argument over the reconstruction of the South after the American civil war.

Louisiana Purchase and Associated Documents

http://www.yale.edu/lawweb/avalon/diplomacy/fr1803m.htm

Part of the Avalon Project at the Yale Law School, this page contains a number of documents related to the Louisiana Purchase of 1803. In addition to the text of the treaty itself and the two conventions between the USA and France, you will find texts of three of President Thomas Jefferson's annual messages to Congress, notes regarding the Louisiana Purchase treaty, four statutes relating to the treaty, plus the text of the Treaty of San Ildefenso which ceded the Louisiana Territory from Spain to France in 1800.

**F
A
C
T**

LOUISIANA PURCHASE

purchase by the USA from France in 1803 of an area covering about 2,144,000 sq km/828,000 sq mi, including the present-day states of Louisiana, Missouri, Arkansas, Iowa, Nebraska, North Dakota, South Dakota, and Oklahoma.

Mark Twain on the Philippine-American War

http://www.msc.edu.ph/centennial/filam4.html

Broad source of information on the Philippine-American War and the battle between imperialist and anti-imperialist forces. Read numerous articles by Mark Twain, who emerged as the foremost literary opponent of imperialism and the war in the Philippines. You can also read contemporary editorial criticism of Mark Twain and the anti-imperialists' position, as well as Anti-Imperialist League texts and other documents. The introductory article on Mark Twain's opposition to the war includes photographs, cartoons, and illustrations.

Monroe Doctrine

http://odur.let.rug.nl/~usa/D/1801-1825/jmdoc.htm

Part of a larger site on historical documents, this page is the text of the declaration by President James Monroe in 1823 concerning the threat of

European intervention and ambitions in the Western hemisphere.

Negro Self-Help

http://etext.lib.virginia.edu/etcbin/browse-mixed-new?id=WasNegr&tag=public&images=images/modeng&data=/texts/english/modeng/parsed

Complete text of this work by the US educator Booker T Washington. Included here are the illustrations from the original edition.

Old Sturbridge Village – Where Early America Comes Alive

http://www.osv.org/

Introduction to Old Sturbridge Village in Massachusetts, one of the first communities of pilgrims from Europe in the 17th century. After a brief overview of the village today and the ongoing exhibits and special events, the site offers a virtual tour that begins at the centre of the village and then moves to the countryside exhibits. Visitors can enjoy sights and sounds of the past – of farming activities, militia musters, and music and merriment. The kids have their own pages with puzzles, craft projects, and other contests.

Overthrow of the Molly Maguires

http://www.history.ohio-state.edu/projects/coal/MollyMaguire/mollymaguires.htm

This page features the text of an 1894 *McClure's* magazine article concerning the secret order of Molly Maguires, its infiltration by an agent of the Pinkerton Detective Agency, and the subsequent trials that brought the Molly Maguires to an end. It includes several photographs, including an image of 'coffin notices', the threatening messages that Molly Maguires sent to coal mine superintendents.

F A C T

THE MOLLY MAGUIRES

in US history, a secret Irish coalminers' organization in the 1870s that staged strikes and used violence against coal-company officials and property in the anthracite fields of Pennsylvania, prefiguring a long period of turbulence in industrial relations.

Pig's Eye Notepad

http://www.wavefront.com/~pjlareau/pep1.html

History of St Paul, capital of Minnesota, USA. The Web site's information is in the form of an alphabetical encyclopedia of the history of St Paul, 1830–50, from its first European settler (Pierre 'Pig's Eye' Parrant) to its incorporation as a city.

Pony Express Home Station

http://www.ccnet.com/~xptom/

Comprehensive information about the Pony Express. There is a history of this unique postal service, biography of riders, description of routes, a collection of contemporary and modern newspaper articles on the Pony Express, and a quiz section. The site is of interest for those interested in the development of the American West.

Symbolism of Freemasonry

http://www.umdl.umich.edu/cgi-bin/moa/sgml/moa-idx?notisid=AHK6822

Nineteenth-century work by Albert Gallatin Mackey on the legends, myths, and symbols connected with freemasonry. This site is fully searchable and contains the original scanned text of the original work.

Thaddeus Stevens: Speech of 18 December 1865

http://odur.let.rug.nl/~usa/D/1851-1875 reconstruction/steven.htm

Part of a larger site on historical documents, this page is the text of a speech concerning the seceded states' constitutional relationship to the Union following the US Civil War.

The US–Mexican War 1846–1848

http://www.pbs.org/kera/usmexicanwar/

Attractive and detailed history of the US–Mexican War. The illustrated pages include a timeline of events and a series of essays which discuss related concepts such as manifest destiny.

Tombstone – The Town Too Tough To Die

http://www.clantongang.com/old west/tombmap.html

Guide to the town made famous by the fight at the OK Corral. Among the interesting nuggets are the fact that Wyatt

Earp and Doc Holliday did not actually shoot it out in a corral. There is a good history of the town and extensive information about current tourist facilities.

True Story Of Casey Jones

http://www.taco.com/roots/caseyjones.html

Excerpt from 'Erie Railroad Magazine' Vol. 24 (April 1928), No 2, pp. 13, 44. This site describes the events surrounding the fatal crash the made Casey Jones a folk legend. The site includes photographs of Jones, his engine (638), and finally his tombstone.

Wade-Davis Manifesto

http://odur.let.rug.nl/~usa/D/1851-1875/reconstruction/wdmani.htm

Part of a larger site on historical documents, this page is a response directed at US president Abraham Lincoln following his rejection of the Wade-Davis Bill.

War of 1812 and Associated Documents

http://www.yale.edu/lawweb/avalon/diplomacy/br1814m.htm

Part of the Avalon Project at the Yale Law School, this page includes the text of the declaration of war between the UK and the USA in 1812 and a number of documents related to the War of 1812, including provisions for the exchange of naval prisoners of war, a number of acts of US Congress, and the text of the Treaty of Ghent of 1814 which ended the conflict.

West

http://www.pbs.org/weta/thewest/

Companion to a US Public Broadcasting Service (PBS) television programme, this site features extensive information about the American West. An interactive timeline follows the course of events from pre-Columbian times to the early 20th century; an interactive map includes information on the territory and the times; brief biographies reveal the facts about historical figures. In addition, you'll find an archive of memoirs, journals, letters, photos, and transcripts, plus links to Internet resources on the history of the American West. A search engine allows you to track down information from all sections of the site.

AMERICAN WEST

western frontier of the USA. Specifically the term refers to the period between 1850, when westward expansion began, and 1890, when the west coast region was settled.

Wild Wild West

http://www.gunslinger.com/west.html

While containing a brief history of the American Wild West, this illustrated site focuses on stories about the outlaws and marshals of the times. There are several such stories, together with numerous photographs, and also many links to sites where further information can be found.

20th-century US History

Abbie Hoffman (Steal This Web Page)

http://www.oz.net/~hayduke/Abbie/AbbieHoffman.html

Huge source of information on the hippie counterculture icon. There are details, and original cover illustrations, of all of Hoffman's books. Others contents include sound clips, photographs, and articles by and about Hoffman. There are also a large number of links to other sources of information on the US counterculture and the history of the 1960s.

Al Capone and Friends

http://www.acsp.uic.edu/iasoc/crim_org/Vol10_3/art_5a.htm

Detailed account of the life of Alphonse Capone. There are blow-by-blow accounts of his most infamous deeds and substantial details on his accomplices and victims.

American Leaders Speak: Recordings from World War I and the 1920 Election

http://lcweb2.loc.gov/ammem/nfhome.html

Part of the American Memory presentation of the

US Library of Congress, this site includes 59 sound recordings of speeches by US leaders, including Warren G Harding, James Cox, Calvin Coolidge, Franklin D Roosevelt, Samuel Gompers, Henry Cabot Lodge, and John J Pershing. Speeches range from one to five minutes and focus on issues related to World War I and the presidential election of 1920. Transcriptions and images of the speakers accompany each speech.

American Life Histories, 1936–1941

http://lcweb2.loc.gov/ammem/wpaintro/wpahome.html

Part of the American Memory presentation of the US Library of Congress, this collection includes 2,900 documents representing over 300 writers who were part of the Federal Writers' Project of the US Works Progress Administration (WPA) during the Great Depression. Documents include drafts and revisions, interviews, narratives, dialogues, and more. Excerpts of interviews include audio clips with dialogue read by modern actors. There is information on the WPA and Federal Writers' Project and numerous images.

> **F A C T**
>
> **DEPRESSION**
>
> in economics, a period of low output and investment, with high unemployment. Specifically, the term describes two periods of crisis in the world economy: 1873–96 and 1929 to the mid-1930s.

Baker, Philip J Noel

http://www.nobel.se/laureates/peace-1959-bio.html

Biography of the Quaker pacifist and the work for disarmament that won him a Nobel Peace Prize. His involvement in the Labour Party and in the formation of both the League of Nations and United Nations is traced.

Black Thursday: October 24, 1929

http://sac.uky.edu/~msunde00/hon202/p4/nyt.html

Description of the day Wall Street crashed in 1929 leading to the Great Depression. This Web site

> **F A C T**
>
> **WALL STREET CRASH (1929)**
>
> panic selling on the New York Stock Exchange following an artificial boom from 1927 to 1929 fed by speculation. On 24 October 1929, 13 million shares changed hands, with further heavy selling on 28 October and the disposal of 16 million shares on 29 October.

illustrates historical events by the use of headlines from the *New York Times* of the period.

Bunche, Ralph

http://www.nobel.se/laureates/peace-1950-bio.html

Good biography of the Black barber's son who played a key role in the foundation of the United Nations and won a Nobel Peace Prize. It traces his rise from childhood poverty, his distinguished academic and sporting career, his engagement in the US civil rights movement, and his role as UN mediator in Palestine and on subsequent peacekeeping missions.

Civil Rights Movement: Fraud, Sham, and Hoax, The

http://etext.lib.virginia.edu/etcbin/browse-mixed-new?id=WalCivi&tag=public&images=images/modeng&data=/texts/english/modeng/parsed

Complete text of this speech by the US politician George Corley Wallace in which he aired his anti-integration views.

Colour Photographs from the Farm Security Administration and Office of War Information, 1938–44

http://lcweb2.loc.gov/ammem/ fsowhome.html

Part of the American Memory presentation of the US Library of Congress, this page includes hundreds of colour photographs produced by photography units of the US Farm Security Administration (FSA) and the Office of War Information (OWI). The FSA photographs depict life in the USA and its territories, with special attention given to rural areas and farm labour. The OWI photographs focus on the home front during World War II and include factories and female employees, railroads, military training, and other aspects of mobilization. The collections can be browsed by keyword or subject. Click on the images to increase their size. This site also includes information on the FSA and OWI.

Dawes, Charles Gates

http://www.nobel.se/laureates/peace-1925-2-bio.html

Profile of the career of the US politician and winner of the Nobel Peace Prize. It traces his privileged background, his career as a lawyer and financier, his long and distinguished service for the US government, and his role in fixing the level of German reparations after World War I.

Desert-Storm.Com

http://www.desert-storm.com/index.html

Archive Web site 'created by a student to honour those who participated in Operation Desert-Storm'. The Web site features hoards of information, media clips, articles, and other related details of the war. The Web master of the site seems only vaguely aware that more than one country took part in the war – being a US site you can guess where the bias lies. The section on the US soldiers missing in action or killed in action serves as a reminder of just how one-sided the war actually was; it seems unlikely that the Iraqis could even count their dead let alone list them on a single page of a Web site.

Federal Arts Projects of the 1930s

http://lcweb2.loc.gov/ammem/fedtp/ftcole00.html

Part of a larger site on the Federal Arts Project, this site provides a wealth of historical information and images concerning US President Franklin D Roosevelt's New Deal programmes to support artists and encourage the arts in the USA during the Great Depression. This site includes images of Works Progress Administration Posters, numerous photographs, memorabilia, and more.

Fight for America – Senator Joseph McCarthy

http://www.sirius.com/~mcjester/writings/joemccarthy.html

Biographical essay on the now discredited senator. It is divided into historical sections beginning in 1909 and ending in 1957. The essay contains many useful footnotes.

Fighting for Equality

http://www.seattletimes.com/mlk/movement/Seatimeline.html

Timeline of the civil rights movement in the USA, featuring short essays, photos, and excerpts from

famous speeches and other important documents, signalling some major turning points in the development of the movement.

Hull, Cordell

http://payson.tcs.tulane.edu/cordellhull/prod04.htm

Detailed biography of the backwoods Tennesseean who became a leading Democratic politician and winner of the Nobel Peace Prize. This site traces his career as a lawyer and politician, his tenure as US secretary of state, and the concern with international issues which led Roosevelt to describe him as 'the father of the United Nations'.

Inside a Factory, 1904

http://lcweb2.loc.gov/ammem/papr/west/westhome.html

Part of the American Memory presentation of the US Library of Congress, this site contains 21 motion pictures shot in 1904 featuring the interiors and exteriors of three Westinghouse factories. Should you not wish to download the entire film, each title contains sample still-frames. Many of the films include brief notes. There is also a special presentation of the 'Westinghouse world: the company, the people, and the places'.

Just David

http://tom.cs.cmu.edu/cgi-bin/book/lookup?num=440

Complete text of this novel by Eleanor Porter, first published in 1916.

Kellogg, Frank Billings

http://www.nobel.se/laureates/peace-1929-bio.html

Biography of the farm boy who rose to international prominence and won the Nobel Peace Prize. It traces Kellogg's sketchy formal education, his success in business, the fame he achieved as a Republican trustbuster, and the activities as secretary of state which led to his Nobel award.

Kennedy Assassination

http://mcadams.posc.mu.edu/home.htm

Hundreds of pages of elaborate reconstruction of the events of the fateful day in Dallas. There is comprehensive treatment of all the manifold

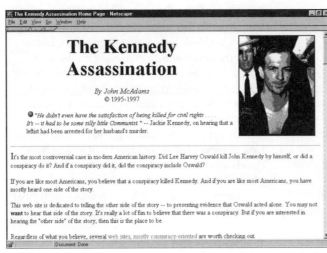

progress in extending the availability of birth control.

Marshall Plan

http://www.loc.gov/exhibits/marshall/

Site containing an outline of the post-war economic aid programme. Two complete pages of the original document are available to read, and a picture of George C Marshall is also available.

Martin Luther King Jr Papers Project

http://www.stanford.edu/group/King/

Archive of documents associated with Martin Luther King, with a biography, detailed chronology, and feature articles. The documents held here are mainly transcripts of speeches he gave, and include the famous 'I have a dream' speech.

theories explaining the assassination of JFK but sympathy for the view that Lee Harvey Oswald acted alone. Among the many links are those to the specialist newsgroups pondering the merits of the various explanations of events.

King, Coretta Scott

http://www.triadntr.net/~rdavis/mlkwife.htm

Well-written biography of the wife of the US civil-rights leader Martin Luther King. It describes her determination to overcome discrimination in her native Alabama, training as a musician, abandonment of her career on marriage, and support for her husband's ideals before and after his assassination. There is a summary of Coretta King's campaign to re-investigate the circumstances of Martin Luther King's murder.

Monkeying with the Scopes 'Monkey' Trial

http://www.associate.com/ministry_files/Other_Electronic_Texts/Christian_Distribution_Network/17_The_Scopes_Monkey_Trial

Informative, text-only essay on the Scopes 'monkey' trial by Dr David N Menton. The essay provides the background to the trial, profiles of both the cases of the defence and the prosecution, and details of the trial and its outcome. The essay is written from a Christian point of view.

Malcolm X – An Islamic Perspective

http://www.colostate.edu/Orgs/MSA/docs/m_x.html

Concise biography, adapted from the pamphlet 'Malcolm X: Why I Embraced Islam' by Yusuf Siddiqui. The site includes quotes taken from *The Autobiography of Malcolm X* as told to Alex Haley.

Margaret Sanger Papers Project

http://www.nyu.edu/projects/sanger/

Huge source of information on the life and legacy of the US birth-control pioneer. There are biographical details and extracts from her letters, writings, and speeches. There are also details of a newsletter chronicling her achievements and

> **FACT**
>
> **SCOPES MONKEY TRIAL**
>
> trial held in Dayton, Tennessee, USA, 1925. John T Scopes, a science teacher at the high school, was accused of teaching, contrary to a law of the state, Charles Darwin's theory of evolution. He was fined $100, but this was waived on a technical point.

New Deal Network

http://newdeal.feri.org/

Devoted to the public works and arts projects of the New Deal, this site is sponsored by the Franklin and Eleanor Roosevelt Institute. It includes several current feature stories and access to past features, plus a massive database of photos, political cartoons, and numerous texts (speeches, letters, and other historic documents) from the New Deal era.

Oklahoma Bombing Trial

http://denver.digitalcity.com/bombing/

Extensive source of information regarding the bombing of a US federal building in Oklahoma City and the subsequent trial of Timothy McVeigh. This site features investigative articles and reports, full texts of court records, trial exhibits and other important papers, plus an audio file of the actual bombing and video clips of the aftermath. You will also find the US Justice Department's report on the FBI's handling of the evidence.

Parks, Rosa

http://www.horizonmag.com/1/parks.htm

Informative biography of Rosa Parks who is sometimes known as the 'mother' of the civil-rights revolution in the USA due to her refusal to give up her seat on an Alabama bus, which sparked the bus boycott. This page also contains suggestions for further reading.

President William Jefferson Clinton

http://vcepolitics.com/usa/clinton.htm

The scandals in the Clinton presidency are detailed here, from Whitewater to Lewinsky, with an explanation of the impeachment trials. There is also a selection of links to the full text of relevant political documents, including the four articles of impeachment.

Root, Elihu

http://www.nobel.se/laureates/peace-1912-bio.html

Profile of this Republican politician and winner of the Nobel Peace Prize. Root's career in law and finance, the reforms he instituted as secretary of war after the Spanish-American war, and his subsequent activities as Secretary of State and US senator are described. His dedication to the cause of international dispute arbitration is highlighted.

Surviving the Dust Bowl

http://www.pbs.org/wgbh/pages/amex/dustbowl/

Companion to the US Public Broadcasting Service (PBS) television programme *The American*

Experience, this page tells the story of the decade-long drought that devastated the southern plains of the USA during the Great Depression. Learn about the conditions that brought on the dust storms and discover how people survived through ten years of drought and dust. Read a firsthand account taken from a survivor's memoirs, learn about New Deal programmes that attempted to remedy some of the suffering and destruction, and look at remarkable photographs of rolling dust clouds as they advanced ominously across the plains. You can also listen to audio clips of interviews and browse a list of sources for further reading.

Temperance and Prohibition

http://www.cohums.ohio-state.edu/history/projects/prohibition/Contents.htm

Site run by Ohio State University chronicling the history of the temperance movement and prohibition in the USA. To the accompaniment of a MIDI rendition of the theme from the TV series *Cheers*, the site describes the background of prohibition and contains biographies of many of the main characters involved with the temperance movement.

Washington As It Was: Photographs, 1923–59

http://lcweb2.loc.gov/ammem/thchtml/thhome.html

Part of the American Memory presentation of the US Library of Congress, this page features the Theodor Horydczak collection of photographs, which offer a comprehensive look at the architecture and social life of the Washington DC area from the 1920s to the 1940s. Some of the photos include street and neighbourhood scenes and the exteriors and interiors of commercial, residential, and government buildings. Numerous Washington events are represented, including the 1932 Bonus Army encampment, the 1933 World Series, and the World War II preparedness campaigns. This site also features a special presentation: 'Discovering Theodor Horydczak's Washington'. The images can be browsed by keyword or subject.

Watergate

http://vcepolitics.com/wgate.htm

Account of the Watergate scandal, with sections on such topics as its political context, the Watergate burglary, casualties and convictions resulting from Watergate, and its aftermath.

Woodrow Wilson: War Message

http://www.lib.byu.edu/~rdh/wwi/1917/wilswarm.html

Part of a larger site on historical documents, this page is the text of US President Woodrow Wilson's speech before Congress on 2 April 1917, in which he asked that Congress pass a war resolution to bring the USA into World War I.

Cold War

Bay of Pigs Invasion

http://www.parascope.com/articles/1296/bayofpigs.htm

Scholarly account of the failed US invasion of Cuba at the Bay of Pigs. It is illustrated with photos and a map, and includes plentiful bibliographic footnotes. The site also includes links to some updated information on Cuban–US relations.

Bikini Atoll

http://www.bikiniatoll.com/

Informative site funded from reparations paid to the people of Bikini by the US government. There is comprehensive information on the history and culture of the atoll, ongoing radiation cleanup activities, local government, and facilities available to deep-sea fishermen and other visitors. Details are provided of how to get to Bikini.

Cold War Policies 1945–91

http://ac.acusd.edu/History/20th/coldwar0.html

Illustrations, short features, and notes on the Cold War years from the Yalta Conference to the dissolution of the Soviet Union. This site contains

---

**F
A
C
T**

COLD WAR

ideological, political, and economic tensions 1945–89 between the USSR and Eastern Europe on the one hand and the USA and Western Europe on the other. The Cold War was fuelled by propaganda, undercover activity by intelligence agencies, and economic sanctions; and was intensified by signs of conflict anywhere in the world.

'Outline notes' for each US president and major event and gives more detailed, timeline-style information on other central topics, such as the nuclear arms race.

Cuban Missile Crisis

http://www.hpol.org/jfk/cuban/

Comprehensive and dramatic account of the crisis which brought the world close to nuclear war. You can experience the escalating tension by loading the recordings of conversations in the White House between JFK and his staff.

Gorbachev, Mikhail

http://www.pathfinder.com/time/time100/leaders/profile/gorbachev.html

Part of a larger archive from *Time* exploring the most influential people of this century, this article highlights the life and work of the former Soviet president Mikhail Gorbachev, and his role in introducing reform to the communist Russia. The profile features a timeline and audio clips.

Hollywood Blacklist

http://dept.english.upenn.edu/~afilreis/50s/blacklist.html

Story of the anticommunist crusade directed against the US film industry during the late 1940s and early 1950s, which ruined the careers of many Hollywood directors, screenwriters, and actors. Find out how Hollywood responded to the Red Scare and how individuals coped with being blacklisted. You will also find information concerning the legacy of the Hollywood blacklisting. The text includes a number of hypertext links to additional information.

Images of My War

http://www.ionet.net/~uheller/vnbktoc.html

Illustrated memories and a personal history offered by Ron H, a Vietnam War veteran. The site also includes his brief and succinct descriptions of the 'mind-numbing work with interludes of intense fear' that he experienced for almost three years in the region.

Inspector General's Survey of the Cuban Operation

http://www.seas.gwu.edu/nsarchive/latin_america/cuba/ig_report/index.ht ml

Full text of the US Central Intelligence Agency's scathing, self-critical, internal inquest into the 1961 Bay of Pigs debacle. This report of the Inspector General, recently released under the Freedom of Information Act, is one of the most secret documents of the Cold War era. The full report is available zipped for downloading, or can be viewed in its original form online.

Korean War Veterans National Museum and Library

http://www.theforgottenvictory.org/

Multifaceted Web site on the Korean War. The Web site features many images and texts on the war, including maps, memorials, veterans group listings, and much more among the comprehensive information held here.

Observations on Life at the Khe Sanh Combat Base

http://sunsite.unc.edu/pub/academic/history/marshall/military/vietnam/khe_sanh.txt

Personal account of life at the Khe Sanh base in the Vietnam war. The Web site is in text only, and consists of an excerpt from the book *Vietnam Generation* by Peter Brush. The account begins with the first arrivals at Khe Sanh in 1962 and details its history up to its abandonment in 1968.

Soviet Union and the United States

http://sunsite.unc.edu/expo/soviet.exhibit/intro2.html

Guided tour through the Soviet Archives of the Library of Congress, following the major developments in the relationships between the USSR and USA, from the early days of cooperation in the 1920s through World War II and the Cold War and up to the collapse of the communist system in the early '90s.

Spies in the Sky

http://www.pbs.org/wgbh/pages/amex/spy/ index.html

Companion to the US Public Broadcasting Service (PBS) television programme *The American Experience*, this page tells the illustrated story of the crash of a US spy plane over the Soviet Union in 1960 and the fate of its pilot, Gary Powers. You can learn recently

declassified details about the U-2 spy plane, and find out about the revolutionary cameras that snapped clear, detailed pictures from way up in the stratosphere. Once you have browsed the site, test your knowledge with a quiz. The programme transcript is available for downloading and there is a list of sources.

START II Treaty Fact Sheet

http://www.state.gov/www/regions/nis/russia_start2_treaty.html

Site published by the US Bureau of Public Affairs explaining the START II treaty of 1993 which was designed to further reduce and limit strategic offensive weapons.

Tonkin Gulf Incident

http://www.yale.edu/lawweb/avalon/tonkin-g.htm

Part of the Avalon Project at the Yale Law School, this page features US President Lyndon Johnson's message to Congress on 5 August 1954, in which he reports that North Vietnamese forces had made 'deliberate attacks against US Naval vessels' in the Gulf of Tonkin. It also includes a joint resolution of Congress that supports widening the scope of US involvement in the Vietnam War.

War at Home and Abroad

http://icdweb.cc.purdue.edu/~phealy/mccarthy.html

Illustrated account of the Cold War from the perspective of the USA's home and foreign policy. It contains links expanding on a number of issues raised in the account, such as the Marshall Plan, the Manhattan Project, and Sputnik.

Wars for Vietnam: 1945–1975

http://students.vassar.edu/~vietnam/

Substantial chronicle of the Vietnam Wars from 1945 to 1975 that also captures the Cold War ambience which dominated post-World War II America. The detailed overview of the events provides links to all major political and historical events connected with developments in Vietnam and in the USA. The site also offers a wealth of central documents spanning the whole period of the crisis.

Yalta & Hiroshima – The Causes of the War

http://icdweb.cc.purdue.edu/~phealy/yalta.html

Detailed and illustrated essay about the causes of the Cold War. It contains links to further information on topics raised in the essay, such as the text of a treaty.

US Presidents & First Ladies

Abraham Lincoln: Proclamation on the Wade-Davis Bill

http://odur.let.rug.nl/~usa/P/al16/writings/wdveto.htm

Part of a larger site on historical documents, this page concerns a proclamation written by US president Abraham Lincoln and delivered on 8 July 1864 concerning the restoration of state government in the southern states of the USA following the end of Civil War.

Abraham Lincoln – Sixteenth President 1861–1865

http://www.whitehouse.gov/WH/glimpse/presidents/html/al16.html

Biography and presidential record of the sixteenth president of the USA. The Web site contains a brief biography and portrait of both Lincoln and his first lady, Mary Todd Lincoln. Also included are transcripts of both of Lincoln's inaugural addresses, and a selection of familiar quotations.

Abraham Lincoln: The President's Last Speech

http://odur.let.rug.nl/~usa/P/al16/speeches/last.htm

Part of a larger site on historical documents, this page is the text of the last speech by US President Abraham Lincoln, delivered on 11 April 1865.

Adams, Abigail

http://www.whitehouse.gov/WH/glimpse/firstladies/html/aa2.html

Biography of the first first lady of the USA. It traces her privileged New England upbringing, childhood illness, the determination with which she became one of the best self-educated US women of her era, and her long marriage to John Adams.

Andrew Jackson – Seventh President 1829–1837

http://www.whitehouse.gov/WH/glimpse/presidents/html/aj7.html

Portrait and biography of the seventh president of the United States. The site features Jackson's inaugural speech and several other quotations by him. Details of Jackson's wife, Rachel Donelson Jackson, are also available via a hypertext link.

Andrew Johnson – Seventeenth President 1865–1869

http://www.whitehouse.gov/WH/glimpse/presidents/html/aj17.html

Biography and presidential record of the 17th president of the USA. The Web site contains a brief biography and portrait of both Johnson and his first lady, Eliza McCardle Johnson. Also included is a transcript of Johnson's inauguration.

Ask Thomas Jefferson!

http://spidey.sfusd.k12.ca.us/schwww/sch773/zimmerman/jefferson.html

Large collection of quotations by Thomas Jefferson, carefully arranged by subject.

F
A
C
T

LINCOLN, ABRAHAM (1809–1865)

16th president of the USA 1861–65, a Republican. In the American Civil War, his chief concern was the preservation of the Union from which the Confederate (Southern) slave states had seceded on his election.

You are encouraged to select a topic and 'Ask Thomas Jefferson' his opinion.

Autobiography by Thomas Jefferson

http://www.bibliomania.com/NonFiction/Jefferson/Autobiography/chap00.html

Full text of the autobiography of the third president of the USA, written at the age of 77 and published in 1821.

Benjamin Harrison – Twenty-third President 1889–1893

http://www.whitehouse.gov/WH/glimpse/presidents/html/bh23.html

Biography of Benjamin Harrison, the only president of the USA to be a descendant of a former president. The Web site includes a brief text biography of Harrison and his first lady, Caroline Lavinia Scott Harrison, complete with portraits of both. A full transcript of Harrison's inaugural speech is also available from this Web site, as are various quotes from the former president.

Calvin Coolidge – Thirtieth President 1923–1929

http://www.whitehouse.gov/WH/glimpse/presidents/html/cc30.html

Biography and presidential record of the 30th president of the USA. The Web site contains a brief biography and portrait of both Coolidge and his first lady, Grace Anna Goodhue Coolidge. Also included is a transcript of Coolidge's inaugural address.

Chester A Arthur – Twenty-first President 1881–1885

http://www.whitehouse.gov/WH/glimpse/presidents/html/ca21.html

Biography and presidential record of the 21st president of the USA, and the second to inherit the presidency after the assassination of his predecessor. The Web site contains a brief biography and portrait of both Arthur and his first lady, Ellen Lewis Herndon Arthur. Also included is a transcript of Arthur's inauguration address.

Clinton, Hillary Rodham

http://www.whitehouse.gov/WH/EOP/First_Lady/html/HILLARY_Bio.html

Descriptive biography of the controversial first lady. This biography details her childhood, her marriage, and explains the ways in which she has used her position in the Whitehouse to promote social change. The page also includes a list of further reading.

Dwight D Eisenhower Library, Abilene, Texas

http://redbud.lbjlib.utexas.edu/eisenhower/ddehp.htm

Everything there is to know about Ike and Mamie Eisenhower from the official presidential archive. In addition to comprehensive details of Eisenhower's life and career, the site contains a host of official and unofficial papers from his years in the White House, transcripts of key speeches, and photos.

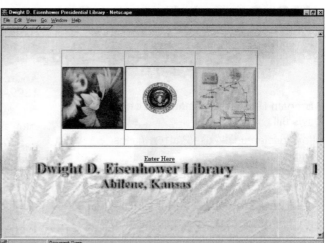

Franklin D Roosevelt Cartoon Collection

http://www.wizvax.net/nisk_hs/fdr/index.html

Archive of political cartoons from the presidency of Franklin D Roosevelt. The cartoons are divided into ten sections, with titles such as 'Waiting for the New Deal', 'The war years', 'The first 100 days', and 'The road to Pennsylvania Avenue'. Text accompanies the cartoons and provides context.

Franklin D Roosevelt: Fireside Chats, 1933–1944

http://www.mhrcc.org/fdr/fdr.html

Part of a larger site on historical documents, this

page is the text of 30 of US president Franklin D Roosevelt's radio broadcasts to the US public, most of which concern the effects of the Great Depression, his administration's attempts to turn the economic tide, and issues regarding World War II. Some of the speeches include 'On the bank crisis', 'On the work relief program', 'On drought conditions', and 'On the declaration of war with Japan'.

Franklin D Roosevelt: Pearl Harbor Speech

http://odur.let.rug.nl/~usa/P/fr32/speeches/ph.htm

Part of a larger site on historical documents, this page is the text of the speech that US president Franklin D Roosevelt delivered to US Congress on 8 December 1941, following the Japanese attack on the US naval base at Pearl Harbor, Hawaii.

Franklin D Roosevelt – Thirty-second President 1933–1945

http://www.whitehouse.gov/WH/glimpse/presidents/html/fr32.html

Biographical guide to F D Roosevelt, the 32nd US president. The site also includes the texts of all four of his inaugural addresses, a biography of his wife Anna Eleanor Roosevelt, and a link to the Franklin D Roosevelt Presidential Library.

Franklin Pierce – Fourteenth President 1853–1857

http://www.whitehouse.gov/WH/glimpse/presidents/html/fp14.html

Biography and presidential record of the 14th president of the USA. The Web site contains a brief biography and portrait of both Pierce and his first lady, Jane Means Appleton Pierce. Also included is a transcript of Pierce's inaugural address.

George Washington – First President 1789–1797

http://www.whitehouse.gov/WH/glimpse/presidents/html/gw1.html

Biography and presidential record of the first president of the USA. The Web site contains a brief biography and portrait of both George Washington and his first lady, Martha Dandridge Washington. Also included are transcripts of both

WASHINGTON, GEORGE (1732–1799)

Commander of the American forces during the American Revolutionary War and 1st president of the USA 1789–97; known as 'the father of his country'.

of Washington's inaugural addresses, and a few familiar quotations.

George Washington's Farewell Address

http://odur.let.rug.nl/~usa/P/gw1/speeches/gwfar.htm

Part of a larger site on historical documents, this page is the text of the farewell address given on 17 September 1796 by the first president of the USA on the occasion of his leaving office. Images of stamps bearing George Washington's likeness are included.

Gerald R Ford Library and Museum

http://www.lbjlib.utexas.edu/ford/

All you could want to know about Gerald and Betty Ford, from the official US presidential archive. In addition to biographical details, this large site contains a wealth of information on all aspects of the Ford Administration. A hundred photos of the ex-president can be downloaded. There is a search engine and links to related sites.

Grover Cleveland – Twenty-second President 1885–1889, Twenty-fourth President 1893–1897

http://www.whitehouse.gov/WH/glimpse/presidents/html/gc22.html

Web site on the only US president elected to two non-consecutive terms of office. The Web site features brief text biographies of both Cleveland and his first lady, Frances Folsom Cleveland, complete with portraits of both. Also shown are full transcripts of both of his inaugural addresses and several familiar quotations.

Harry S Truman Presidential Library & Museum

http://www.trumanlibrary.org/

Collections of papers documenting Truman's life and career before and after the presidency, as well as collections of audio-visual materials, books, articles and other printed items, oral history interviews, and museum objects.

Herbert Hoover Presidential Library and Museum

http://www.nara.gov/nara/president/hoover/

Official presidential archive of Herbert Hoover. This site has a series of biographies of Hoover, written for audiences ranging from primary school children to professional historians. A huge number of official and unofficial documents from his administration can be accessed. There is also a quiz.

Inaugural Addresses of the Presidents of the USA

http://www.bartleby.com/124/index.html

Text of the inaugural addresses made by all the US presidents, arranged chronologically.

James A Garfield – Twentieth President 1881

http://www.whitehouse.gov/WH/glimpse/presidents/html/jg20.html

Biography and presidential record of the 20th president of the USA, and the second to be assassinated. The Web site contains a brief biography and portrait of both Garfield and his first lady, Lucretia Rudolph Garfield. Also included is a transcript of Garfield's inaugural address.

James Buchanan – Fifteenth President 1857–1861

http://www.whitehouse.gov/WH/glimpse/presidents/html/jb15.html

Biography and presidential record of the 15th president of the USA. The Web site contains a brief biography and portrait of both Buchanan and his first lady, Harriet Lane. Also included is a transcript of Buchanan's inaugural address.

James K Polk – Eleventh President 1845–1849

http://www.whitehouse.gov/WH/glimpse/presidents/html/jp11.html

Biography of the 11th president of the USA. The Web site contains a brief biography and portrait of both Polk and his first lady, Sarah Childress Polk. Also included is a transcript of Polk's inaugural address.

James Madison – Fourth President 1809–1817

http://www.whitehouse.gov/WH/glimpse/presidents/html/jm4.html

Biography of the fourth president of the USA. The Web site contains a brief biography and portrait of both James Madison and his first lady, Dolley Payne Todd Madison. Also included are transcripts of Madison's inaugural addresses.

James Monroe – Fifth President 1817–1825

http://www.whitehouse.gov/WH/glimpse/presidents/html/jm5.html

Biography of the fifth president of the USA. This site includes a portrait of Monroe, along with brief biographies of both Monroe and his first lady, Elizabeth Kortright Monroe. It also features transcripts of both of Monroe's inaugural speeches.

Jimmy Carter Library

http://carterlibrary.galileo.peachnet.edu

Comprehensive official archive of the former US president. A huge range of official and unofficial documents, transcripts, and tapes from the Carter White House can be accessed with the help of a search engine. Among the interesting facts of this extensive account of Carter's life is that he was the first US president to be born in a hospital. You can even check the regularity of Carter's church attendance while in the White House. The site includes a large number of photographs and a 'Kid's corner' has a child-focused approach to Carter's achievements and interests.

John Adams – Second President 1797–1801

http://www.whitehouse.gov/WH/glimpse/presidents/html/ja2.html

Biography of the second president of the USA. Along with a portrait and brief biography of Adams, this Web site contains the full text of Adams's inaugural speech and various quotes from other sources. Also shown here is a portrait of Adams's first lady, Abigail Smith Adams, of whom the site also features a brief biography.

John Quincy Adams – Sixth President 1825–1829

http://www.whitehouse.gov/WH/glimpse/presidents/html/ja6.html

Biography of the sixth president of the USA. The Web site contains a brief biography and portrait of both Adams and his first lady, Louisa Catherine Johnson Adams. Also included is a transcript of Adams's inaugural address, and some familiar quotations.

John Tyler – Tenth President 1841–1845

http://www.whitehouse.gov/WH/glimpse/presidents/html/jt10.html

Biography of the tenth president of the USA. The Web site contains a brief biography and portrait of both Tyler and his two first ladies, Letitia Christian Tyler, who died in his first year in office, and Julia Gardiner Tyler, whom he married while in office. Also included is a transcript of Tyler's inaugural address, which he gave despite inheriting the presidency on the death of William Henry Harrison.

Kennedy, John F

http://www.geocities.com/~newgeneration/

Tribute to John F Kennedy, in which the user can – among other things – browse transcripts of his speeches, take a tour of the White House with Mrs Kennedy, see and hear photos and sound clips from memorial services, and take part in a virtual press conference with the president.

Kennedys

http://www.geocities.com/CapitolHill/Senate/1968/

History of the US family of politicians. The Web site follows the Kennedys through their political aspirations and their scandals, to their unfortunate tragedies. A family photograph album is also included on the site, as is a family tree, a chatroom, a discussion board, and a fun section on quizzes and puzzles.

Last Days of a President: Films of McKinley and the Pan-American Exposition, 1901

http://lcweb2.loc.gov/ammem/papr/mckhome.html

Collection of 28 motion pictures from the Paper Print Collection of the US Library of Congress. This site includes footage of President William McKinley at his second inauguration and at the Pan-American Exposition, as well as images of President McKinley's funeral. Should you not wish to download the entire film, each title contains sample still-frames. There is also

background information regarding President McKinley and the Pan-American Expo, and a section of selected bibliography.

Lyndon B Johnson Library and Museum

http://www.lbjlib.utexas.edu/

Comprehensive biographies of LBJ and his wife Lady Bird, photos of Johnson with key figures in his administration, a mass of official and unofficial documents from his administration, and transcripts and recordings of phone calls. A search engine accesses the vast resources available on this site.

Martin Van Buren – Eighth President 1837–1841

http://www.whitehouse.gov/WH/glimpse/presidents/html/mb8.html

Biography of the eighth president of the USA, and the first to be born under the US flag. The Web site contains a brief biography and portrait of both Van Buren and his first lady, Hannah Hoes Van Buren. Also included is a transcript of Van Buren's inaugural address.

Millard Fillmore – Thirteenth President 1850–1853

http://www.whitehouse.gov/WH/glimpse/presidents/html/mf13.html

Biography of the 13th president of the USA, Millard Fillmore. The Web site contains a brief biography and portrait of both Fillmore and his first lady, Abigail Powers Fillmore. Also included on the Web site is a transcript of Fillmore's inauguration.

Ronald Reagan – Fortieth President 1981–1989

http://www.whitehouse.gov/WH/glimpse/presidents/html/rr40.html

Biographical information about the 40th US president Ronald Reagan. The site includes his two inaugural addresses, a biography of his wife Nancy, and a link to the Ronald Reagan Presidential Library.

Roosevelt, Eleanor

http://www.udhr50.org/history/Biographies/bioer.htm

Informative biography of this US humanitarian and first lady. It describes how the shy young girl

ROOSEVELT, (ANNA) ELEANOR (1884–1962)

US social worker, lecturer, and first lady. She influenced New Deal policies, especially those supporting desegregation. She was a delegate to the United Nations general assembly and chair of the UN commission on human rights 1946–51, and helped to draw up the Declaration of Human Rights at the UN 1945.

blossomed at finishing school in England. Her support of Franklin D Roosevelt's New Deal and her lifelong commitment to social justice and nuclear disarmament, which won her acclaim at home and abroad, are described. For further information there is also a bibliography.

Rutherford B Hayes – Nineteenth President 1877–1881

http://www.whitehouse.gov/WH/glimpse/presidents/html/rh19.html

Biography and presidential record of the 19th president of the USA. The Web site contains a brief biography and portrait of both Hayes and his first lady, Lucy Ware Webb Hayes. Also included is a transcript of Hayes's inaugural address, and a selection of familiar quotations.

Thomas Jefferson – Third President 1801–1809

http://www.whitehouse.gov/WH/glimpse/presidents/html/tj3.html

Biography of the third president of the USA. The Web site contains a brief biography and portrait of both Thomas Jefferson and his first lady, Martha Wayles Skelton Jefferson. Also included on the Web site is a transcript of Jefferson's inaugural address, and a few familiar quotations.

'TR' Sounds & Pictures Page

http://earthstation1.simplenet.com/TR.html

Picture and sound archive of Theodore Roosevelt. Of the dozen or so images of Roosevelt on this page, most are political caricatures, and the remainder are photographs. The Web site also features 'a rare recording of TR during a Presidential campaign speech as a Bull Moose candidate on the platform of his party.'

TR: The Story of Teddy Roosevelt

http://www.pbs.org/wgbh/pages/amex/tr/index.html

Companion to the US Public Broadcasting Service (PBS) television programme *The American Experience*, this page tells the story of US president Theodore Roosevelt. It includes a timeline of events that took place in the USA during his presidency from 1901 to 1909; audio clips of interviews discussing a variety of topics; and a section on the legacy of Theodore Roosevelt which features information on the history and construction of the Panama Canal and which honours his commitment to conservation. You can also browse a list of sources for further reading.

Ulysses S Grant – Eighteenth President 1869–1877

http://www.whitehouse.gov/WH/glimpse/presidents/html/ug18.html

Biography and presidential record of the 18th president of the USA. The Web site contains a brief biography and portrait of both Grant and his first lady, Julia Dent Grant. Also included are transcripts of both of Grant's inaugural addresses, and a selection of familiar quotations.

Warren G Harding – Twenty-ninth President 1921–1923

http://www.whitehouse.gov/WH/glimpse/presidents/html/wh29.html

Biography and presidential record of the USA's 29th president. A brief biography and portrait of both Harding and his first lady, Florence Kling Harding are features of this page. Also included is a transcript of Harding's inaugural address.

William Henry Harrison – Ninth President 1841

http://www.whitehouse.gov/WH/glimpse/presidents/html/wh9.html

Biography of the ninth president of the USA, the first to die in office. The Web site contains a brief biography and portrait of both Harrison and his wife, Anna Tuthill Symmes Harrison. Also included on the Web site is a transcript of Harrison's inaugural address.

William Howard Taft – Twenty-seventh President 1909–1913

http://www.whitehouse.gov/WH/glimpse/presidents/html/wt27.html

Biography and presidential record of the 27th president of the USA. The Web site contains a brief biography and portrait of both Taft and his first lady, Helen Herron Taft. Also included is a transcript of Taft's inaugural address.

William McKinley – Twenty-fifth President 1897–1901

http://www.whitehouse.gov/WH/glimpse/presidents/html/wm25.html

Biography and presidential record of the 25th president of the USA. The Web site contains a brief biography and portrait of both McKinley and his first lady, Ida Saxton McKinley. Also included are transcripts of both of McKinley's inaugural addresses.

Woodrow Wilson – Twenty-eighth President 1913–1921

http://www.whitehouse.gov/WH/glimpse/presidents/html/ww28.html

Biography and presidential record of the 28th president of the USA. The Web site contains a brief biography and portrait of both Wilson and both his first ladies, Ellen Louise Axson Wilson and Edith Bolling Galt Wilson. Also included are transcripts of both of Wilson's inaugural addresses.

Works of Abraham Lincoln

http://libertyonline.hypermall.com/Lincoln/Default.htm

Speeches of Abraham Lincoln, including his two inaugural addresses, the Emancipation Proclamation, and the Gettysburg Address.

Zachary Taylor – Twelfth President 1849–1850

http://www.whitehouse.gov/WH/glimpse/presidents/html/zt12.html

Biography of the 12th president of the USA. The Web site contains a brief biography and portrait of both Taylor and his first lady, Margaret Mackall Smith Taylor. Also included is a transcript of Taylor's inaugural address.

Miscellaneous History & Chronologies

Anatolia Throughout the Ages

http://www.focusmm.com.au/civi_mn1.htm

Chronology of the Asian part of Turkey, from the Neolithic Age to the end of the Ottoman Empire. There are over 20 sections and each one is in the form of a brief, illustrated essay.

F
A
C
T

OTTOMAN EMPIRE

Muslim empire of the Turks from 1300 to 1920, the successor of the Seljuk Empire. It was founded by Osman I and reached its height with Suleiman in the 16th century.

Deeper Shade of Black

http://www.ai.mit.edu/~isbell/HFh/black/bhcal-toc.html

Large database of information on the history of African-American people. There is a weekly updated news feature, a full search engine for past news and pages on literature and films, too. There is some international information, but most of it is focused on the USA.

1524–1998: From New France to Modern Quebec

http://www3.sympatico.ca/cousture/HIST2.HTM

Substantial itinerary through the history of Quebec from a francophone's point of view. It includes facts connected with Canada, nationalism, and the relationship between English- and French-speakers.

Historic Audio Archives

http://www.webcorp.com/sounds/nixon.htm

Collection of extracts from key speeches of various famous people, mainly politicians, throughout history. It includes sections by Nixon, Chamberlain, Hitler, Quayle, and Clinton.

Hyper History

http://www.hyperhistory.com/online_n2/
History_n2/a.html

Project that attempts to provide an interactive
account of the history of the world. This very
detailed site contains timelines of events from
prehistoric times to 1998, and is divided into
colour-coded categories.

Images from World History

http://www.hp.uab.edu/image_archive/index.html

Extended visual archive of digitized photographs
and maps to help with history teaching, mainly
oriented towards courses dealing with the pre-
modern world. The areas covered include ancient
Asia, Iron-Age Europe, Mediterranean cultures
up to the late Roman empire, ancient and feudal
Africa, and medieval Europe up to the 15th
century.

Irish History on the Web

http://wwwvms.utexas.edu/~jdana/irehist.html

Well-organized source of information about Irish
history, including issues regarding Home Rule.
There are sections on general Irish history, the
Irish famine, timelines, key documents, suggested
reading, and genealogical research links.

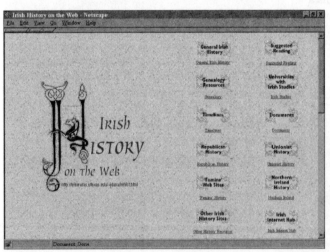

Irish in America: Long Journey Home

http://www.pbs.org/wgbh/pages/irish/

Companion to a US Public Broadcasting Service
(PBS) television programme, this site chronicles
the significant role that Irish immigrants have had
in shaping the USA. It is divided into five sections
covering Irish genealogy, music, language, and
notable Irish Americans. Here you can learn how
to trace immigrant ancestors; hear how Irish
surnames sound in the native language, hear the
Irish roots of some common US English words,
and learn about the history of the Irish language;
read about the instruments and music used in the
series' soundtrack; listen to an Irish poem about
the Great Famine; and read brief biographies of
some of the many important Irish Americans.

Media History Timeline

http://www.mediahistory.com/time/century.html

Timeline with key events in media history by era,
century, or decade, starting as far back as 3500 BC.
Each fact sheet is accompanied by thumbnail
images illustrating pertinent events, technologies,
or people.

1900 v. Now

http://www.pathfinder.com/time/time100/timewarp/t
imewarp.html

Part of a larger archive from *Time* that explores
the new millennium, this well-designed page
allows you to compare statistics from 1900 with
currently available figures.

Past Features – Britain

http://www.buckinghamgate.com/events/
features/past_features.html

Tour through the landmarks of British
tradition. Featured sections include
Stonehenge, Shakespeare's Globe
Theatre, Edinburgh International
Festival, the Proms, Henley Royal
Regatta, and Dickens's Annual Festival.
The site also contains valuable tips and
crucial details about Britain's living
tradition – a must for every
sophisticated tourist.

Pedagogy of History

http://daemon.ilt.columbia.edu/k12/
history/pedagogy.html

Engaging reflections on the pedagogy of history
and the use of primary sources in the teaching of
the subject, written by a history student at
Columbia University, USA.

Russian History

http://www.departments.bucknell.edu/russian/history.html

Overview of Russian history including a chronology of major events, a gallery of images, and a virtual tour of the Kremlin.

Selection of Events and Documents on the History of Finland

http://www.clinet.fi/~pkr01/historia/history.html

Multilingual, illustrated pages with links to source materials and events in Finnish history, from medieval times to World War II. These include a 14th-century 'letter of protection' by King Birger Magnusson for women in Karelia; the first newspaper printed in Finland in the 18th century; documents produced under Russian rule, and later, at the time of Finnish independence; maps; treaties; telegrams; and acts of parliament.

Slovakia Document Store

http://slovakia.eunet.sk/

Collection of resources in Slovak and English, including a traveller's guide and information about the country's geography, natural resources, history, culture, and religion.

Society of Genealogists Information Leaflets

http://www.sog.org.uk/leaflets/index.html

Useful range of leaflets from the Society of Genealogists for those interested in tracing their family history. Included here is information about the significance of last names when researching your family tree, and a list of useful addresses.

Texts and Documents: The United States of America

http://history.hanover.edu/usa.htm

Impressive collection of primary documents about the United States of America from the time of the first colonists to the War of the Gulf in the 1990s, via the Western Frontier, 19th-century immigration, the suffragists, the Cold War, and much more. The visitor can browse through the individual periods as a continuum, or choose to focus on the literature, politics, theology, or philosophy section of each one.

F A C T

UNITED STATES OF AMERICA (USA),

country in North America, extending from the Atlantic Ocean in the east to the Pacific Ocean in the west, bounded north by Canada and south by Mexico, and including the outlying states of Alaska and Hawaii.

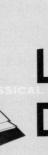

LITERATURE & DRAMA

Classical Literature, 3000–1 BC

Aeschines: *Against Ctesiphon*

http://www.perseus.tufts.edu/cgi-bin/text?lookup=Aeschin.+3.init.

English and Greek versions of Aeschines's famous speech.

Aesop's Fables

http://www.pacificnet.net/~johnr/aesop/

Full text of 398 of the most popular of Aesop's fables. Several have pictures to illustrate the story and some also have sound effects.

F A C T

AESOP

by tradition, a writer of Greek fables. According to the historian Herodotus, he lived in the mid-6th century BC and was a slave. The fables that are ascribed to him were collected at a later date and are anecdotal stories using animal characters to illustrate moral or satirical points.

Ancient Paths Through Text and Image: Aeneas in the Underworld

http://cti.itc.Virginia.EDU/~mpm8b/underworld/hades.home.htm

Illustrated and user-friendly 'multimedia path' through ancient Hades as it has survived in vases, manuscripts, sculptures, paintings, and other forms throughout the centuries. Each picture is accompanied by details of the particular event in the story which is being depicted.

Demosthenes *Against Leptines*

http://www.perseus.tufts.edu/cgi-bin/text?lookup=Dem.+20.init.

Complete translation of Demosthenes' work.

Demosthenes *On the Crown*

http://www.perseus.tufts.edu/cgi-bin/text?lookup=dem.+18.1&vers=English|none

Complete translation of Demosthenes' work.

Vergil Project

http://vergil.classics.upenn.edu/

Academic resource dedicated to the study and appreciation of Roman poet Virgil (Vergil is an alternative spelling). The site includes texts and commentaries, an image archive, a search tool, and links to other relevant sites.

Works By Aeschylus

http://classics.mit.edu/Browse/browse-Aeschylus.html

Seven of Aeschylus' works are available for download in English translation from this site. The files which are in text format are generally large, but the server is very fast so downloads take a minimal amount of time.

Works by Euripedes

http://classics.mit.edu/Browse/browse-Euripides.html

Nineteen of Euripedes's works translated into English are available to download as text files from this Web site. The text files are full and complete versions of the works and as such the files are relatively large and will take some time to download.

Works by Homer

http://classics.mit.edu/Browse/browse-Homer.html

Downloadable translations of Homer's works. The three files here are the complete works: *The Iliad, The Odyssey,* and the lesser-known work *Hymn to Dionysus.* The latter of these also includes some other miscellaneous writings.

Classical Literature, AD 1–399

Golden Ass, The

http://eserver.org/books/apuleius/

Adlington's translation of the famous adventure of Lucius Apuleius. A glossary explains the meanings of now unfamiliar words used by the 16th-century translator.

Metamorphoses by Ovid

http://classics.mit.edu/Ovid/metam.html

Downloadable version of the epic poem by Ovid.

F A C T

OVID (Publius Ovidius Naso, 43 BC–AD 7)
Latin poet. His poetry deals mainly with the themes of love (*Amores* 20 BC, *Ars amatoria/The Art of Love* 1 BC), mythology (*Metamorphoses* AD 2), and exile (*Tristia* AD 9–12).

Ovid

http://geocities.com/Athens/Acropolis/6681/ovidb.htm

Profile of the poet. It traces his education, his fast life in Augustan Rome, and his banishment to the Black Sea. There is also a listing of Ovid's works.

Pharsalia by Lucan

http://sunsite.berkeley.edu/OMACL/Pharsalia/

Full text of Sir Edward Ridley's 1896 translation of Marcus Annaeus Lucanus's epic poem of the civil wars of Caesar and Pompey.

Works by Marcus Aurelius Antoninus

http://classics.mit.edu/Browse/browse-Antoninus.html

The Meditations of Marcus Aurelius Antoninus, written *c.* 167 AD , translated by George Long. The complete work is available to download in twelve separate books, or in one large file which may take some time.

Works by Plutarch

http://classics.mit.edu/Browse/browse-Plutarch.html

Sixty-seven of Plutarch's works translated into English by John Dryden are available to download as text files from this Web site. Plutarch wrote biographies of many of the leading figures of late Grecian and early Roman culture, many of which are included here. The files are full and complete versions of the works and will take some time to download.

Old English Literature

Anglo-Saxon Chronicle

http://sunsite.berkeley.edu/OMACL/Anglo/

Complete text of the *Anglo-Saxon Chronicle* from the Online Medieval and Classical Library.

'Battle of Maldon'

http://www.georgetown.edu/labyrinth/library/oe/texts/a9.html

Complete text of the 325-line fragment of the anonymous Old English poem, 'The Battle of Maldon'. The poem, which appears in the original Anglo-Saxon language, is divided into five-line stanzas.

'Beowulf'

http://etext.lib.virginia.edu/cgibin/browse-mixed?id=AnoBeow&tag=public&images=images/modeng&data=/lv1/Archive/eng-parsed

Complete text of this Anglo-Saxon poem. This online edition from the University of Virginia includes annotations to aid understanding.

'Caedmon's Hymn': Northumbrian version

http://www.georgetown.edu/labyrinth/library/oe/texts/a32.1.html

Complete text of 'Caedmon's Hymn' written by the earliest known English Christian poet, Caedmon. The poem, which appears in its Northumbrian version, is divided into five-line stanzas.

'Dream of the Rood'

http://www.georgetown.edu/labyrinth/library/oe/texts/a2.5.html#n4

Complete text of the Old English poem 'The Dream of the Rood'. The poem is divided into five-line stanzas, and some of the words in the text have links to footnotes containing alternative forms, or additions.

'Seafarer, The'

http://www.georgetown.edu/labyrinth/library/oe/texts/a3.9.html

Complete 125-line text of the Old English elegy, 'The Seafarer'. The poem, which is divided into five-line stanzas, is presented in the original Anglo-Saxon language.

Middle English Literature

Chaucer's *Canterbury Tales*

http://www.canterburytales.org/canterbury_tales.html

Comprehensive site dedicated to the study and enjoyment of Chaucer's *Canterbury Tales*. The text is presented in both the orginal Middle English, and as a modern-day translation. The text is also fully searchable.

'Confessio Amantis'

http://etext.lib.virginia.edu/cgibin/browse-mixed?id=GowConf&tag=public&images=images/mideng&data=/lv1/Archive/mideng-parsed

Complete text of John Gower's famous poem.

Gower, John

http://icg.fas.harvard.edu/~chaucer/special/author/gower/

Profile of the life and work of Chaucer's friend and fellow poet. It relates how he switched from writing in Latin and French to English at the command of Richard II, and how he acquired an international reputation. There are extracts from all of his best-known works, complete with a guide to words unfamiliar to the modern reader.

Labyrinth Library: Middle English Bookcase

http://www.georgetown.edu/labyrinth/library/me/me.html

Online access to a collection of Middle English texts including works by Geoffrey Chaucer, *Sir Gawain and the Green Knight*, and the York plays. The site includes search and download facilities.

'Owl and the Nightingale, The'

http://etext.lib.virginia.edu/etcbin/browse-mixed-new?id=AnoOwlJ&tag=public&images=images/modeng&data=/lv1/Archive/mideng-parsed

Complete text of this early Middle English poem from the University of Virginia.

Selected Poetry of John Lydgate (1370?–1449)

http://library.utoronto.ca/www/utel/rp/authors/lydgate.html

Contains an excerpt from the poem 'The Testament of John Lydgate'.

Selected Poetry of John Skelton (1460?–1529)

http://library.utoronto.ca/www/utel/rp/authors/skelton.html

Includes the text of several of Skelton's poems, such as *Phyllyp Sparowe* and *The Tunnyng of Elynour Rummynge*.

Selected Poetry of Robert Henryson (1424?–1506?)

http://library.utoronto.ca/www/utel/rp/authors/henryson.html

Contains the text of several poems by Robert Henryson, including 'Robin and Malkin' and an excerpt from 'The Testament of Cressida'.

Selected Poetry of William Dunbar (1456?–1513?)

http://library.utoronto.ca/www/utel/rp/authors/dunbar.html

Contains the text of several poems by William Dunbar, including *Lament For The Makers*.

Thomas Malory's 'Morte d'Arthur'

http://www.hti.umich.edu/bin/me-idx?type=header&idno=MaloryWks2

Site devoted to the Middle English text of

MALORY, THOMAS (c. 1410–1471)

English author. He is known for the prose romance *Le Morte D'Arthur* (*c.* 1470), printed in 1485, which relates the exploits of King Arthur's knights of the Round Table and the quest for the Holy Grail.

Malory's great prose work. Caxton's preface is also included.

Troilus and Criseyde

http://etext.lib.virginia.edu/cgibin/browse-mixed?id=ChaTroi&tag=public&images=images/mideng&data=/lv1/Archive/mideng-parsed

Full text of Geoffrey Chaucer's *Troilus and Criseyde*, tagged in SGML by the University of Virginia Electronic Text Centre and converted 'on the fly' to browsable HTML. Details are also given of the first edition and the printed critical edition on which the electronic version is based, as well as of the revisions made to it.

Vision of Piers Plowman

http://etext.lib.virginia.edu/cgibin/browse-mixed?id=LanPier&tag=public&images=images/mideng&data=/lv1/Archive/mideng-parsed

Full text of William Langland's poem *Piers Plowman*, tagged in SGML by the University of Virginia Electronic Text Centre and converted 'on the fly' to browsable HTML. Details are also given of the first edition and the printed critical edition on which the electronic version is based, as well as of the revisions made to it.

16th-century British Literature

Complete Works of Christopher Marlowe

http://www.perseus.tufts.edu/Texts/Marlowe.html

Attractive and well organized site with links to plays including *Dr Faustus,* poetry, translations, and miscellaneous works in both their original and modern forms.

Donne, John

http://www.luminarium.org/sevenlit/donne/index.html

Good-looking site with biographical details, famous quotes, essays, and links to many works by this famous poet. This site also offers a glossary of some of the more obscure metaphysical phrases used by Donne, and includes some contemporary background music.

Edmund Spenser Home Page

http://darkwing.uoregon.edu/~rbear/

Comprehensive site devoted to the life and works of the 16th-century English poet Edmund Spenser. The numerous works include *The Faerie Queene,* which comes with its own search engine. The site has been created by Renascence Editions at the University of Oregon, USA, and is edited by Richard Bear. There are also links to Spenser texts from other sites, and to resource sites, which include the Spenser Society.

SPENSER, EDMUND (c. 1552–1599)

English poet. His major work is the allegorical epic *The Faerie Queene*, of which six books survive (three published in 1590 and three in 1596).

Everyman

http://etext.lib.virginia.edu/cgibin/browse-mixed?id=AnoEver&tag=public&images=images/mideng&data=/lv1/Archive/mideng-parsed

Full text of the famous medieval play *Everyman*, tagged in SGML by the University of Virginia Electronic Text Centre and converted to browsable HTML. Details of the first and current printed edition as well as the revisions made to the electronic one are also given.

Selected Poetry of Edmund Spenser (1552–1599)

http://library.utoronto.ca/www/utel/rp/authors/spenser.html

Features a brief note on the life and works of the poet Edmund Spenser. The text of a large selection of his poetry is included here, such as an annotated version of 'Epithalamion' and excerpts from 'The Faerie Queene'.

Selected Poetry of Elizabeth I

http://library.utoronto.ca/www/utel/rp/authors/
1eliz.html

Hypertext edition of selected poetry by Queen Elizabeth I. The edition has incorporated notes, where necessary, and detailed guidelines related to the encoding of the texts.

Selected Poetry of Francis Quarles (1592–1644)

http://library.utoronto.ca/www/utel/rp/authors/
quarles.html

Contains poems by Francis Quarles, including selections from his collections 'Emblemes' and 'Divine Fancies'.

Selected Poetry of Fulke Greville, Baron Brooke (1554–1628)

http://library.utoronto.ca/www/utel/rp/authors/
fulkgrev.html

Features a selection of Greville's poetry, including excerpts from 'Caelica' and 'Mustapha'.

Selected Poetry of Gabriel Harvey (c. 1550–1631)

http://library.utoronto.ca/www/utel/rp/authors/
harveyga.html

Contains the text of several of Harvey's poems, including 'Gorgon or the Wonderful Year'.

Selected Poetry of George Chapman (1559?–1634)

http://library.utoronto.ca/www/utel/rp/authors/
chapman.html

Contains a selection of works by the poet George Chapman.

Selected Poetry of George Gascoigne (c. 1534–1577)

http://library.utoronto.ca/www/utel/rp/authors/
gascoign.html

Contains the text of several of Gascoigne's poems, several of which come from his collection 'The Steele Glas'.

Selected Poetry of George Peele (1556–1596)

http://library.utoronto.ca/www/utel/rp/authors/
peele.html

Contains an annotated example of Peele's poetry taken from 'Polyhymnia'.

Selected Poetry of Henry Howard, Earl of Surrey (1517?–1547)

http://library.utoronto.ca/www/utel/rp/authors/
surrey.html

Features a brief note on the life and works of the English courtier and poet Henry Howard. Several of his poems are included here, along with annotations to aid understanding.

Selected Poetry of Henry VIII (1491–1547)

http://library.utoronto.ca/www/utel/rp/authors/
henry8.html

Contains a brief note on the life and works of Henry VIII. The text of a number of his poems have also been included here, such as 'Lusty Youth Should us Ensue'. Many of the poems have been annotated to aid understanding.

Selected Poetry of John Lyly (1554–1606)

http://library.utoronto.ca/www/utel/rp/authors/
lyly.html

Contains an annotated version of Lyly's 'Cupid and my Campaspe play'd'.

Selected Poetry of Michael Drayton (1563–1631)

http://library.utoronto.ca/www/utel/rp/authors/
drayton.html

Contains a brief note about the poet Michael Drayton, as well as the text of many of his poems, including excerpts from 'Nymphidia, The Court Of Fairy'.

Selected Poetry of Robert Greene (1560–1592)

http://library.utoronto.ca/www/utel/rp/authors/
greene.html

Selection of Greene's poetry, including excerpts from 'Menaphon'.

Selected Poetry of Sir Edward Dyer (1543–1607)

http://library.utoronto.ca/www/utel/rp/authors/dyer.html

Contains the text of Dyer's poem 'My mind to me a kingdom is'.

Selected Poetry of Sir Thomas Wyatt (1503–1542)

http://library.utoronto.ca/www/utel/rp/authors/wyatt.html

Features a detailed biography and an image of the English poet. In addition, a large number of his poems have been included here, such as 'They flee from me that sometime did me seek'. Several of the poems have been annotated to aid understanding.

Selected Poetry of Sir Walter Raleigh (c. 1552–1618)

http://library.utoronto.ca/www/utel/rp/authors/ralegh.html

Contains a number of poems by Sir Walter Raleigh, including 'As You Came from the Holy Land', 'The Nymph's Reply', and 'The Passionate Man's Pilgrimage'. Several of these poems have been annotated to aid understanding.

Selected Poetry of Thomas Lodge (1558–1625)

http://library.utoronto.ca/www/utel/rp/authors/lodgetho.html

Includes a selection of excerpts from Lodge's 'Rosalind'.

Selected Poetry of Thomas Morley (1557/58–1602)

http://library.utoronto.ca/www/utel/rp/authors/morleyth.html

Contains a selection of poetry by the composer Thomas Morley, including 'On a Fair Morning as I Came by the Way'.

Selected Poetry of Thomas Nashe (1567– 1601)

http://library.utoronto.ca/www/utel/rp/authors/ nashe.html

Features a selection of poems by Nashe, including an annotated excerpt from 'Summer's Last Will and Testament'.

Selected Poetry of Thomas Sackville, Earl of Dorset (1536–1608)

http://library.utoronto.ca/www/utel/rp/authors/sackvilt.html

Contains the text of Sackville's 'The Mirror for Magistrates: The Induction', which is accompanied by a large number of notes to aid understanding.

'Shepheardes Calendar'

http://etext.lib.virginia.edu/etcbin/browse-mixed-new?id=SpeShep&tag=public&images=images/modeng&data=/texts/english/modeng/parsed

Guide to this work by the English poet Edmund Spenser. Not only is the complete text of the work provided, but also the introduction by Spenser himself. Furthermore, there is an essay on the work itself, an introduction to the life and works of Spenser, as well as a number of images scanned from a facsimile of the 1579 edition.

Sidney, Sir Philip

http://www.luminarium.org/renlit/sidney.htm

Brief biography of the poet, plus a number of his works, some of his famous quotes, essays, articles, and some contemporary music.

17th-century British Literature

Aphra Behn Page

http://lit-arts.com/rmn/behn/index-ab.htm

Introduction to the first professional woman prose writer and dramatist in the English language. The site includes a chronology of her life and works, and primary sources and articles. There are also links to information about other Restoration writers.

F A C T

BEHN, APHRA (1640–1689)

English novelist and dramatist. She was the first woman in England to earn her living as a writer. Her works were criticized for their explicitness; they frequently present events from a woman's point of view.

Compleat Angler, or the Contemplative Man's Recreation, The

http://www.ulib.org/webRoot/Books/_Gutenberg_Etext_Books/etext96/tcang10.txt

Complete text of Izaak Walton's classic fishing compendium.

Herbert, George

http://www.luminarium.org/sevenlit/herbert/index.html

Very aesthetic site with biographical details, famous quotes, essays, and links to many works by this famous poet. As well as looking very good, this site also includes a timeline of his life and some contemporary background music.

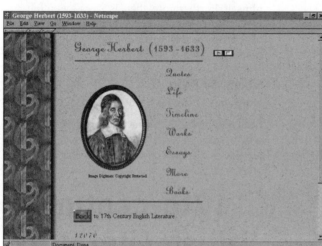

John Arbuthnot: 'An Argument for Divine Providence'

http://panoramix.univ-paris1.fr/CHPE/Textes/Arbuthnot/Arbuthnot.html

This page features the text of John Arbuthnot's 1710 essay 'An Argument for Divine Providence Taken from the Constant Regularity Observed in Both Sexes', in which Arbuthnot uses examples of mathematical probabilities to suggest that the consistent balance in the number of births of boys and girls is proof of divine providence, from which he concludes that polygamy is against the laws of nature. The screen is split into French and English translations of this essay.

Marvell, Andrew

http://www.luminarium.org/sevenlit/marvell/index.html

Very aesthetic site with biographical details, famous quotes, essays, and links to many works by this famous poet. As well as looking very good, this site also includes a timeline of Marvell's life and some contemporary background music.

Milton, John

http://www.luminarium.org/sevenlit/milton/index.html

Very aesthetic site with biographical details, famous quotes, essays, and links to many works by this famous poet. As well as looking very good, this site also includes some contemporary background music.

New Atlantis, The

http://etext.lib.virginia.edu/etcbin/toccer-new?id=BacAtla&tag=public&images=images/modeng&data=/texts/english/modeng/parsed&part=0

Text of Francis Bacon's unfinished fable.

Oroonoko

http://library.adelaide.edu.au/etext/b/behn/oroonoko.html

Text of Aphra Behn's novel which attacked slavery.

Pilgrim's Progress

http://ccel.wheaton.edu/b/bunyan/pilgrims_progress/title.html

Complete text of John Bunyan's powerful allegory.

Selected Poetry and Prose by John Dryden

http://library.utoronto.ca/www/utel/rp/authors/dryden.html

Selected poetry and a piece of prose in hypertext form by John Dryden, from the Department of English at the University of Toronto, Canada, accompanied by notes and encoding information.

Selected Poetry and Prose of Alexander Pope (1688–1744)

http://library.utoronto.ca/www/utel/rp/authors/pope.html

Contains a biography of the poet, as well as a large selection of Pope's poetry, including 'Pastorals', 'The Rape of the Lock', and 'An Essay on Criticism'. The preface to his translation of Homer's *Iliad* is also featured here.

Selected Poetry and Prose of Edward Young (1683–1765)

http://library.utoronto.ca/www/utel/rp/authors/youngedw.html

Features a large selection of Young's poetry, including excerpts from 'Night Thoughts on Life, Death and Immortality' and 'The Love of Fame, the Universal Passion'. Also included here is the text of his essay 'Conjectures on Original Composition'.

Selected Poetry of Abraham Cowley (1618–1667)

http://library.utoronto.ca/www/utel/rp/authors/cowley.html

Contains a selection of the poetry of Abraham Cowley, including an excerpt from 'Davideis: A Sacred Poem Of The Troubles Of David'.

Selected Poetry of Aphra Behn (1640–1689)

http://library.utoronto.ca/www/utel/rp/authors/behn.html

Contains the text of several works by the English novelist and dramatist.

Selected Poetry of Edmund Waller (1606–1687)

http://library.utoronto.ca/www/utel/rp/authors/waller.html

Contains a large selection of poems by Edmund Waller, including 'Self-Banished' and 'Go, Lovely Rose!'.

Selected Poetry of Francis Beaumont (1584–1616) and John Fletcher (1579–1625)

http://library.utoronto.ca/www/utel/rp/authors/beauflet.html

Contains a selection of the poetry of the two collaborators, including 'Lay a garland on my hearse'.

Selected Poetry of George Wither (1588–1667)

http://library.utoronto.ca/www/utel/rp/authors/wither.html

Contains examples of Wither's poetry, taken from three of his collections: 'Fidelia', 'Fair-virtue, the Mistresse of Philarete', and 'A collection of emblems, ancient and moderne, quickened with metricall illustrations'.

Selected Poetry of Giles Fletcher The Younger (1585?–1623)

http://library.utoronto.ca/www/utel/rp/authors/fletchgy.html

Contains excerpts from Fletcher's poem 'Christ's Triumph after Death'.

Selected Poetry of Henry Vaughan (1621?–1695)

http://library.utoronto.ca/www/utel/rp/authors/vaughan.html

Features a brief note on the life and works of the poet Henry Vaughan, as well as a large selection of his poetry, including 'The Retreat', 'They are all Gone into the World of Light', and 'The World'. Several of the poems have been annotated to aid understanding.

Selected Poetry of James Shirley (1596–1666)

http://library.utoronto.ca/www/utel/rp/authors/shirley.html

Contains several poems by Shirley, including an excerpt from 'The Triumph of Beauty'.

Selected Poetry of Phineas Fletcher (1582–1650)

http://library.utoronto.ca/www/utel/rp/authors/fletchpi.html

Contains excerpts from Fletcher's poem 'The Purple Island'.

Selected Poetry of Richard Barnfield (1574–1627)

http://library.utoronto.ca/www/utel/rp/authors/barnfiel.html

Contains the text of several works by the English poet Richard Barnfield.

Selected Poetry of Richard Crashaw (1613–1649)

http://library.utoronto.ca/www/utel/rp/authors/crashaw.html

Contains a number of poems by Richard Crashaw, including 'A Hymn to the Name and Honour of the Admirable Saint Teresa' and an excerpt from 'The Flaming Heart'. Many of the poems are linked to explanatory notes.

Selected Poetry of Richard Lovelace (1618–1657)

http://library.utoronto.ca/www/utel/rp/authors/lovelace.html

Features a number of poems by Richard Lovelace, including 'To Althea, from Prison' and 'To Lucasta, Going to the Wars', both of which have been annotated to aid understanding.

Selected Poetry of Robert Herrick (1591–1674)

http://library.utoronto.ca/www/utel/rp/authors/herrick.html

Contains the text of a number of poems by Robert Herrick, including 'Delight in Disorder', 'To Anthea, who may Command him Anything', and 'Upon Julia's Clothes'. Many of the poems include explanatory notes.

Selected Poetry of Samuel Butler (1613–1680)

http://library.utoronto.ca/www/utel/rp/authors/butlersa.html

Features an excerpt from Butler's poem 'Hudibras'.

Selected Poetry of Samuel Daniel (1563?–1619)

http://library.utoronto.ca/www/utel/rp/authors/daniel.html

Contains a selection of the poetry of Samuel Daniel, including excerpts from 'Delia' and 'Musophilus'. Several of the poems include notes to aid understanding.

Selected Poetry of Sir Henry Wotton (1568–1639)

http://library.utoronto.ca/www/utel/rp/authors/wotton.html

Includes the text of two poems by Henry Wotton: 'The Character of a Happy Life' and 'You Meaner Beauties Of The Night'.

Selected Poetry of Sir John Suckling (1609–1642)

http://library.utoronto.ca/www/utel/rp/authors/suckling.html

Contains a number of Suckling's poems, including 'Why so Pale and Wan Fond Lover?' and an excerpt from 'A Ballad Upon A Wedding'.

Selected Poetry of Thomas Campion (1587–1620)

http://library.utoronto.ca/www/utel/rp/authors/campion.html

Contains the text of a number of poems by Thomas Campion, including 'There Is A Garden In Her Face'.

Selected Poetry of Thomas Carew (1595?–1640)

http://library.utoronto.ca/www/utel/rp/authors/carew.html

Contains a brief introduction to the English poet, as well as a number of his poems, such as 'An Elegy upon the Death of the Dean of St Paul's, Dr John Donne'.

Selected Poetry of Thomas Parnell (1679–1718)

http://library.utoronto.ca/www/utel/rp/authors/parnell.html

Includes several of Parnell's most important poems, including 'The Hermit', 'A Hymn to Contentment', and 'A Night-Piece on Death'.

Selected Poetry of Thomas Sprat (1635–1713)

http://library.utoronto.ca/www/utel/rp/authors/sprat.html

Includes the complete text of Sprat's 'An Account of the Life and Writings of Mr Abraham Cowley'.

Selected Poetry of Thomas Traherne (1636–1674)

http://library.utoronto.ca/www/utel/rp/authors/traherne.html

Contains a note on the life and works of English cleric and poet Thomas Traherne. A selection of his poetry is also featured here, including 'Wonder'.

Selected Poetry of William Drummond of Hawthornden (1585–1649)

http://library.utoronto.ca/www/utel/rp/authors/drummond.html

Contains a selection of poems by William Drummond, including 'For the Baptist'.

Selected Poetry of William Habington (1605–1654)

http://library.utoronto.ca/www/utel/rp/authors/habingto.html

Contains the text of Habington's poem 'Nox Nocti Indicat Scientiam', taken from his collection *Castara*.

Selected Prose of Sir William D'avenant (1606– 1668)

http://library.utoronto.ca/www/utel/rp/authors/davenant.html

Contains the text of the poet and dramatist's *Preface to Gondibert*.

Silva by John Evelyn

http://www.british-trees.com/p10.htm

Devoted to John Evelyn's 1664 work on the cultivation of trees, subtitled 'A Discourse Of Forest-Trees, and The Propagation of Timber In His Majesties Dominions'. There are extensive notes, a picture of John Evelyn, and an image of the frontispiece of the original publication.

Coleridge Companion: An Introduction to the Major Poems and the *Biographia Literaria*

http://virtual.park.uga.edu/232/stc/ccomp.htm

E-text version of a 278-page guide to the life and work of the Romantic poet. There are extensive biographical details, in addition to long and thoughtful analyses of his poems and critical works.

Dr Johnson and Fanny Burney

http://etext.lib.virginia.edu/etcbin/browse-mixed-new?id=BurJohn&images=images/modeng&data=/lv1/Archive/eng-parsed&tag=public

Complete text by the English novelist and diarist Fanny Burney.

Guide to Samuel Johnson

http://andromeda.rutgers.edu/~jlynch/Johnson/Guide/

Thorough source of information on Dr Johnson. There is a biography, complete bibliography, and description of his best-known works. There is also a good summary of ongoing academic interest in Johnson and his world.

18th-century British Literature

F
A
C
T

JOHNSON, SAMUEL (1709–1784)
English lexicographer, author, and critic. He was also a brilliant conversationalist and the dominant figure in 18th-century London literary society. His *Dictionary* (1755), provided in its method the pedigree for subsequent lexicography and remained authoritative for over a century.

Arbuthnot, John

http://www-history.mcs.st-and.ac.uk/history/Mathematicians/Arbuthnot.html

Brief biography and portrait of the Scottish mathematician and satirist John Arbuthnot. In addition, this Web site offers a brief history of Arbuthnot's work and a link to details of his contemporary, Huygens, whose work on probability Arbuthnot translated. A brief publication list is included for further reference.

Castle of Otranto, The

http://www.ulib.org/webRoot/Books/_Gutenberg_Etext_Books/etext96/cotrt10.txt

Complete text of Horace Walpole's Gothic novel, which first appeared in 1764.

Gulliver's Travels

http://english-server.hss.cmu.edu/fiction/gulliver.txt

Text of Jonathan Swift's satirical novel.

History of Tom Jones, a Foundling by Henry Fielding

http://english-www.hss.cmu.edu/fiction/tom-jones.txt

Full text of Fielding's epic tale which set the standards for the modern novel.

Inchbald, Elizabeth

http://www.knight.org/advent/cathen/07717b.htm

Profile of the life and work of the novelist, dramatist, and actress. Her theatrical success, the difficulties she faced when her husband died, and her late success as a novelist are covered. There is an emphasis on the Catholic faith which grew so strong in old age that it led her to destroy the memoirs she had prepared for publication.

Jane Austen Information Page

http://uts.cc.utexas.edu/~churchh/janeinfo.html

Provides biographical details on Austen and her family, background information on the society of the time, the full text of many of her works, including a hypertext version of *Pride and Prejudice*, and some pieces of literary criticism. Also included are lists of film and TV adaptations of her works, and a small collection of Jane Austen jokes.

F A C T

AUSTEN, JANE (1775–1817)

English novelist. She described her raw material as 'three or four families in a Country Village' and she observed contemporary speech and manners with wit and precision. Her penetrating observation of human behaviour results in insights that transcend period. Many of her works have been successfully adapted for film and television.

Jane Austen: *Pride and Prejudice*

http://www.bibliomania.com/Fiction/Austen/Pride/index.html

Hypertext edition of Jane Austen's *Pride and Prejudice*.

Jonathan Swift Essays

http://socserv2.socsci.mcmaster.ca/~econ/ugcm/3ll3/swift/index.html

Part of the Archive for the History of Economic Thought at McMaster University, this page features the text of two essays by Jonathan Swift: 'On Lowering the Coins', from an address Swift made to an assembly of merchants in 1736 opposing the devaluation of coins, and 'Proposal to Pay Off the Debt of the Nation' (1932), in which Swift suggests that Parliament pay off the national debt without taxing its subjects.

Letters of Jane Austen – Brabourne Edition

http://www.pemberley.com/janeinfo/brablets.html

Large selection of Jane Austen's letters, complete with notes and a search facility.

Life and Opinions of Tristram Shandy, Gent, The

http://www.gifu-u.ac.jp/~masaru/TS/contents.html#start

Complete text of Laurence Sterne's bawdy novel.

Love and Friendship

http://www.pemberley.com/janeinfo/lovfrend.html

Both the text of Jane Austen's burlesque, epistolary novel and notes on its characters and themes.

'Modest Proposal, A'

http://english-server.hss.cmu.edu/18th/swift-modest.txt

Text of Jonathan Swift's satirical pamphlet.

Northanger Abbey

http://www.bibliomania.com/Fiction/Austen/Northanger/index.html

Complete text of Jane Austen's novel.

Robinson Crusoe

http://www.bibliomania.com/Fiction/defoe/robin/index.html

Hypertext edition of Daniel Defoe's novel *Robinson Crusoe*.

Selected Poetry and Prose Of Samuel Johnson (1709–1784)

http://library.utoronto.ca/www/utel/rp/authors/johnson.html

Contains the text of a number of poems by Samuel Johnson, as well as his preface to his edition of Shakespeare's plays.

Selected Poetry Edited by Thomas Percy (1728–1811)

http://library.utoronto.ca/www/utel/rp/authors/percy.html

Contains several examples of Percy's poetry, including many poems from 'Reliques of Ancient English Poetry'. Several of these poems have been annotated to aid understanding.

Selected Poetry of Allan Ramsay (1686–1758)

http://library.utoronto.ca/www/utel/rp/authors/ramsayal.html

Features a selection of works by the poet Allan Ramsay, including 'Give Me a Lass with a Lump of Land' among others.

Selected Poetry of Anna Laetitia Barbauld (1743–1825)

http://library.utoronto.ca/www/utel/rp/authors/barbauld.html

Features an image of the poet, as well as the text of a number of her poems.

Selected Poetry of Augustus Montague Toplady (1740–1778)

http://library.utoronto.ca/www/utel/rp/authors/toplady.html

Includes a brief note on the life and works of Toplady, as well as the text of his hymn 'Rock of Ages'.

Selected Poetry of Charles Churchill (1732–1764)

http://library.utoronto.ca/www/utel/rp/authors/churchil.html

Contains excerpts from Charles Churchill's poem 'The Ghost'.

Selected Poetry of Charles Wesley (1707–1788)

http://library.utoronto.ca/www/utel/rp/authors/wesleyc.html

Contains the text of several of Wesley's poems, including 'For Christmas Day' and 'Morning Hymn'.

Selected Poetry of Christopher Smart (1722–1771)

http://library.utoronto.ca/www/utel/rp/authors/smart.html

Contains excerpts from Smart's poems 'Jubilate Agno' and 'A Song to David'.

Selected Poetry of George Crabbe (1754–1832)

http://library.utoronto.ca/www/utel/rp/authors/crabbe.html

Contains the text of two of Crabbe's poems: 'The Village' and an excerpt from 'The Borough'.

Selected Poetry of Isaac Watts (1674–1748)

http://library.utoronto.ca/www/utel/rp/authors/watts.html

Features a biography and image of Isaac Watts, as well as a selection of his poetry. Included here is the text of 'Man Frail and God Eternal' and 'Against Evil Company'.

Selected Poetry of James Beattie (1735–1803)

http://library.utoronto.ca/www/utel/rp/authors/beattie.html

Includes excerpts of Beattie's poem 'The Minstrel'.

Selected Poetry of James Macpherson (1736–1796)

http://library.utoronto.ca/www/utel/rp/authors/macphers.html

Contains the text of Macpherson's poem 'The Songs of Selma', taken from his collection *Fingal*.

Selected Poetry of James Thomson (1700–1748)

http://library.utoronto.ca/www/utel/rp/authors/thomson.html

Features the text of a number of Thomson's poems, including 'Rule, Britannia' and excerpts from 'The Seasons: Summer'.

Selected Poetry of John Gay (1685–1732)

http://library.utoronto.ca/www/utel/rp/authors/gay.html

Contains several poems by John Gay, including 'Sweet William's Farewell to Black-Eyed Susan' and excerpts from 'The Beggar's Opera'.

Selected Poetry of John Wesley (1703–1791)

http://library.utoronto.ca/www/utel/rp/authors/wesleyj.html

Contains the text of the Methodist preacher's hymn 'Thou Hidden Love of God'.

Selected Poetry of Jonathan Swift (1667–1745)

http://library.utoronto.ca/www/utel/rp/authors/swift.html

Features the text of a number of poems by Jonathan Swift, including 'Stella's Birthday March

13, 1719'. Several of the poems have been annotated to aid understanding.

Selected Poetry of Joseph Addison

http://library.utoronto.ca/www/utel/rp/authors/addison.html

Selections from Addison's best-known poetry. There is additionally a link to Addison's poetry and prose in Latin.

Selected Poetry of Joseph Warton (1722–1800)

http://library.utoronto.ca/www/utel/rp/authors/wartonj.html

Features a selection of Warton's poetry, including an excerpt from 'The Enthusiast: or, the Lover of Nature'.

Selected Poetry of Lady Mary Wortley Montagu (1689–1762)

http://library.utoronto.ca/www/utel/rp/authors/montagu.html

Features a number of poems by the English society hostess, including excerpts from her 'Town Eclogues' series.

Selected Poetry of Matthew Prior (1664–1721)

http://library.utoronto.ca/www/utel/rp/authors/prior.html

Contains a selection of works by the English poet and diplomat, including 'A Simile' and 'To a Lady'.

Selected Poetry of Oliver Goldsmith (1730?–1774)

http://library.utoronto.ca/www/utel/rp/authors/goldsmit.html

Features several of Goldsmith's poems, including an annotated version of 'The Deserted Village, A Poem' and an excerpt from 'The Traveller; or, A Prospect of Society'.

Selected Poetry of Richard Brinsley Sheridan (1751–1816)

http://library.utoronto.ca/www/utel/rp/authors/sheridan.html

Features a selection of Sheridan's poetry, including 'Here's to the Maiden of Bashful Fifteen', an excerpt from *School for Scandal*.

Selected Poetry of Robert Blair (1699–1746)

http://library.utoronto.ca/www/utel/rp/authors/blair.html

Contains an excerpt from Blair's poem 'The Grave'.

Selected Poetry of Robert Burns

http://library.utoronto.ca/www/utel/rp/authors/burns.html

Hypertext presentation of a selection of poems by Robert Burns, the famous 18th-century Scottish poet. The hypertext is accompanied by textual and other notes, and detailed information on the encoding principles of the electronic edition.

F
A
C
T

BURNS, ROBERT (1759–1796)

Scottish poet. He used a form of Scots dialect at a time when it was not considered suitably 'elevated' for literature. In addition to his poetry, Burns wrote or adapted many songs, including 'Auld Lang Syne'.

Selected Poetry of Robert Fergusson (1750–1774)

http://library.utoronto.ca/www/utel/rp/authors/fergussn.html

Contains several poems by Robert Fergusson, including 'The Daft Days'.

Selected Poetry of Thomas Chatterton (1752–1770)

http://library.utoronto.ca/www/utel/rp/authors/chattert.html

Features a selection of the poems of Thomas Chatterton, several of which have been annotated to aid understanding.

Selected Poetry of Thomas Gray (1716–1771)

http://library.utoronto.ca/www/utel/rp/authors/gray.html

Contains a number of poems by Thomas Gray. Among them are 'The Bard: A Pindaric Ode', 'Elegy Written in a Country Churchyard', and 'Ode on a Distant Prospect of Eton College'.

Several of these poems have been annotated to aid understanding.

Selected Poetry of Thomas Warton The Younger (1728–1790)

http://library.utoronto.ca/www/utel/rp/authors/wartontj.html

Features a selection of the critic's poetry, among them being an excerpt from 'The Pleasures of Melancholy'.

Selected Poetry of William Collins (1721–1759)

http://library.utoronto.ca/www/utel/rp/authors/collins.html

Features a number of poems by William Collins, including 'Ode to Evening' and 'An Ode on the Popular Superstitions of the Highlands of Scotland'.

Selected Poetry of William Cowper (1731–1800)

http://library.utoronto.ca/www/utel/rp/authors/cowper.html

Reproductions of a number of Cowper's poems, including 'The Castaway' and excerpts from 'The Task'. Many of the poems contain explanatory notes to aid understanding.

Selected Poetry of William Lisle Bowles (1762–1850)

http://library.utoronto.ca/www/utel/rp/authors/bowles.html

Contains the text of several works by the English poet William Bowles.

Selected Poetry of William Shenstone (1714–1763)

http://library.utoronto.ca/www/utel/rp/authors/shenston.html

Contains the text of several poems by Shenstone, including an excerpt from 'The Schoolmistress'.

Sentimental Journey through France and Italy, A

http://darkwing.uoregon.edu/~rbear/sterne.html

Complete text of the novel by Laurence Sterne, author of *Tristram Shandy,* considered by many to be the very first novel.

Vicar of Wakefield, The

http://etext.lib.virginia.edu/cgibin/browse-mixed?id=GolVica&tag=public&images=images/modeng&data=/lv1/Archive/eng-parsed

Text of Oliver Goldsmith's famous novel.

William Blake Archive

http://jefferson.village.virginia.edu/blake/

Sample images from a project engaged in compiling a digital archive of Blake's illuminated books, paintings, and drawings.

19th-century British Literature

'Ballad of Reading Gaol, The'

http://www.bibliomania.com/Fiction/wilde/ReadingGaol/index.html

E-text copy of Oscar Wilde's 'The Ballad of Reading Gaol'. From this index page you have a choice of viewing either the full or the shorter version of the ballad.

Bride of Lammermoor, The

http://www.catawba.k12.nc.us/books/brlam10.txt

Complete text of this work by Walter Scott that formed part of his series of historical novels.

Brontë, Branwell

http://www.incompetech.com/authors/bbronte/

Light-hearted biography of 'The forgotten'

Brontë, Branwell. As well as a history of his life, his poetry is also discussed.

Brontë Sisters

http://www2.sbbs.se/hp/cfalk/bronteng.htm

Extensive collection of information on each of the Brontë sisters, including online novels and poems, literary criticism and interpretation, biographies, bibliographies, and mailing lists.

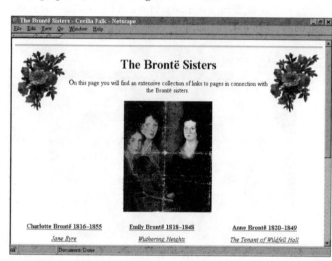

Can You Forgive Her?

http://etext.lib.virginia.edu/etcbin/browse-mixed-new?id=TroForg&tag=public&images=images/modeng&data=/texts/english/modeng/parsed

Complete text of this novel by Anthony Trollope.

Captain Frederick Marryat – A Biography

http://www.cronab.demon.co.uk/mary.htm

Extensive biography of the English naval officer and writer. Marryat's naval career and his frequent acts of courage in adversity are described in detail. His literary career, together with the financial difficulties which forced him to turn to writing children's books, are traced.

Case Book of Sherlock Holmes, The, by Arthur Conan Doyle

http://wiretap.spies.com/ftp.items/Library/Classic/casebook.dyl

Complete text of this novel featuring the detective Sherlock Holmes.

'Charge of the Light Brigade'

http://etext.lib.virginia.edu/britpo/tennyson/TenChar.html

Full text of Tennyson's most famous work 'Charge of the Light Brigade'. As well as the text, this site also includes photos of each page of the original manuscript of the poem.

'Chimes, The'

http://etext.lib.virginia.edu/cgibin/browse-mixed?id=DicChim&tag=public&images=images/modeng&data=/lv1/Archive/eng-parsed

Illustrated text of one of Charles Dickens's Christmas stories.

Christmas Carol, A

http://etext.lib.virginia.edu/cgibin/browse-mixed?id=DicChri&tag=public&images=images/ modeng&data=/lv1/Archive/eng-parsed

Illustrated version of Charles Dickens's novel.

Complete Collection of Poems by Robert Louis Stevenson

http://library.utoronto.ca/www/utel/rp/authors/stvnsnrl.html

A selection of poems by Robert Louis Stevenson, a complement to his well-known stories, plus links to other related Web sites.

Complete Collection of Poems by Rudyard Kipling

http://www.geocities.com/Athens/Aegean/1457/

Full text of many of the published poems of Rudyard Kipling, together with a short biography (containing hypertext links to other related sites).

Complete Poetical Works of Percy Bysshe Shelley

http://www.bartleby.com/139/index.html

Online edition of Shelley's complete poetical works.

Complete Poetical Works of William Wordsworth

http://www.bartleby.com/145/index.html

Wordsworth's complete poetical works are available here. Poems are indexed chronologically and by first line, and include hyperlinked footnotes.

Complete Shorter Fiction of Oscar Wilde

http://www.bibliomania.com/Fiction/wilde/stories/index.html

Index page to electronic editions of *The Complete Shorter Fiction* and Poems in *Prose of Oscar* Wilde. All items are available in HTML format. The *Shorter Fiction* is also available in PDF (portable document format) for those with an Adobe Acrobat reader.

Conan Doyle's *The Memoirs of Sherlock Holmes:* electronic edition

http://www.hti.umich.edu/bin/pd-idx?type=header&id=DoyleMemoi

Electronic edition of the *The Memoirs of Sherlock Holmes* by Sir Conan Doyle, distributed by the Oxford Text Archive with information on the encoding procedure.

Cricket on the Hearth, The

http://www.ulib.org/webRoot/Books/_Gutenberg_Etext_Books/etext96/tcoth10.txt

Complete text of one of Charles Dickens's Christmas novels.

Diary of a Nobody by George Grossmith and Weedon Grossmith

http://tom.cs.cmu.edu/cgi-bin/book/lookup?num=1026

Full text of the comic novel detailing the life of literature's best-known nonentity, Charles Pooter.

Dickens, Charles

http://landow.stg.brown.edu/victorian/dickens/dickensov.html

Biographical page from the Victorian Web – including a chronology of Dickens's life, features on his working methods and his affair with Ellen Ternan, and overviews of *Little Dorrit* and *Great Expectations*.

Dickens House Museum

http://www.rmplc.co.uk/orgs/dickens/DHM/DHM2/index.html

Charles Dickens lived at this house (which is now a museum) during two of the most significant years of his career. This site gives the history of the family at the time, a virtual tour (including pictures of some of the objects and possessions in the main rooms), plus some more practical information about admission and opening times.

Dodgson, Charles Lutwidge

http://www-groups.dcs.st-and.ac.uk/history/Mathematicians/Dodgson.html

Part of an archive containing the biographies of the world's greatest mathematicians, this site is devoted to the life and contributions of Charles Dodgson. In addition to biographical information, you will find a list of references about Dodgson and links to other essays in the archive that reference him. The text of this essay includes hypertext links to the essays of those mathematicians and thinkers who influenced Dodgson. You will also find an image of him, which you can click on to enlarge, and a map of his birthplace.

Dombey and Son

http://www.bibliomania.com/Fiction/dickens/Dombey/index.html

Online hypertext edition of *Dombey and Son* by Charles Dickens.

Don Juan

http://eserver.org/poetry/don-juan.txt

Text of George Byron's epic satire.

Dr Jekyll and Mr Hyde

http://www.bibliomania.com/Fiction/stevensn/drjekyll/index.html

Hypertext copy of *Dr Jekyll and Mr Hyde* by Robert Louis Stevenson.

Elizabeth Barrett Browning: An Overview

http://landow.stg.brown.edu/victorian/ebb/browningov.html

Part of the Victorian Web, this extensive site features a number of articles about the poet's life, relationships, and self-portrayal in her work. There are also several articles about the social, political, scientific, and religious context of her work, and the themes, symbolism, and genre of her poetry is also discussed.

Elizabeth Gaskell – *The Life of Charlotte Brontë*

http://lang.nagoya-u.ac.jp/~matsuoka/EG-Charlotte-1.html

Complete text of Elizabeth Gaskell's affectionate autobiography of her friend Charlotte Brontë.

BROWNING, ELIZABETH (MOULTON) BARRETT (1806–1861)

English poet. In 1844 she published *Poems* (including 'The Cry of the Children'), which led to her friendship with and secret marriage to Robert Browning in 1846. She wrote strong verse about social injustice and oppression in Victorian England.

Eothen by A W Kinglake

http://www.catawba.k12.nc.us/books/eothn10.txt

Full text of Kinglake's account of his travels in the Middle East.

Ernest Dowson Page

http://www.nothnbut.net/~jakramer/EDowson/

Dedicated to the poet Ernest Dowson, this page includes the text of many of his poems, such as *Verses* and 'Villanelle of the Poet's Road'. Also featured here are an illustrated biography and timeline, a bibliography, and a guide to criticism of his work.

Far from the Madding Crowd

http://www.bibliomania.com/Fiction/hardy/crowd/index.html

Online copy of *Far from the Madding Crowd* by Thomas Hardy.

Frankenstein

http://etext.lib.virginia.edu/etcbin/browse-mixed-new?id=SheFran&tag=public&images=images/modeng&data=/texts/english/modeng/parsed

Complete text of this Gothic horror novel by Mary Shelley. It also includes an introduction to the novel by the author herself.

Gaskell Web

http://lang.nagoya-u.ac.jp/~matsuoka/Gaskell.html

Contains information about the writer Elizabeth Gaskell, including a chronology of her life, a detailed bibliography, and information about Gaskell societies. Also included are the texts of many of her novels and short stories, including *North and South* and *Mary Barton*, and there are links to essays and articles about her works.

'George Eliot' by Virginia Woolf

http://www.cs.cmu.edu/People/mmbt/women/VW-Eliot.html

Perceptive article on the life and work of Mary Ann Evans by Virginia Woolf. This essay was first published in The Times Literary Supplement in 1919. Woolf praises the daring of a woman who overcame the many obstacles placed in her path to literary greatness.

George Gissing, New Grub Street

http://lang.nagoya-u.ac.jp/~matsuoka/GG-NGS.html

Text of the novel *New Grub Street* by George Gissing.

Gissing, George

http://landow.stg.brown.edu/victorian/gissing/gissingov.html

Full resource of information on Gissing, his life and times, and the continuing interest in his work. The full text of almost every work written by Gissing is provided. There is also a biography, critical essays, bibliography, and information about a journal devoted to Gissing studies.

Golden Key: The George MacDonald WWW Page

http://dspace.dial.pipex.com/town/plaza/ev90481/md_index.htm

Features a large amount of information about the Scottish novelist George MacDonald. There are details of his life, theology, and writings, complete with a number of photographs. There are articles and essays about him, as well as a list of recommended reading and links to the texts of several of his works including *At the Back of the North Wind*.

Great Expectations

http://www.bibliomania.com/Fiction/dickens/greatexp/index.html

Online edition of *Great Expectations* by Charles Dickens.

Heather on Fire: A Tale of Highland Clearances by Mathilde Blind

http://www.indiana.edu/~letrs/vwwp/blind/heather.html#Text

Full text of Mathilde Blind's celebrated denunciation of the Highland Clearances.

His Last Bow by Arthur Conan Doyle

http://www.geocities.com/~soucek/canon/8-last.htm

Complete text of this detective novel by Arthur Conan Doyle.

Hood, Thomas

http://lang.nagoya-u.ac.jp/~matsuoka/Hood.html

Poems and well-known quotations of the English poet and humorist. There is also a portrait and a detailed chronology of his life.

Hopkins, Gerald Manley

http://www.knight.org/advent/cathen/16045b.htm

Biography of the Jesuit poet from the *Catholic Encyclopedia*. His studies, ordination, work among the poor in Liverpool, and subsequent academic career are described. The lyric quality and daring metaphors of his poetry are also set out here.

Hound of the Baskervilles, The

http://www.bibliomania.com/Fiction/Doyle/Hound/index.html

Complete text of Arthur Conan Doyle's novel.

Hunting of the Snark – An Agony in Eight Fits, The

http://www.math.hr/~urbiha/LewisCarroll/eng-parsed.html

Electronic version of the full text of *The Hunting of the Snark – An Agony in Eight Fits* by Lewis Carroll.

Invisible Man, The

http://etext.lib.virginia.edu/etcbin/browse-mixed-new?id=WelInvi&tag=public&images=images/modeng&data=/texts/english/modeng/parsed

Complete text of one of H G Wells's famous 'scientific romances'.

Ivanhoe

http://etext.lib.virginia.edu/etcbin/browse-mixed-new?id=Scolvan&tag=public&images=images/modeng&data=/texts/english/modeng/parsed

Complete text of Walter Scott's classic novel, together with an introduction. Included in this online edition are a number of images taken from an early print edition.

Jane Austen: Emma

http://www.bibliomania.com/Fiction/Austen/Emma/index.html

E-text of Jane Austen's novel *Emma*.

John Clare Page

http://human.ntu.ac.uk/clare/default.html

Features the text of several of Clare's poems, information about forthcoming events related to the poet, and details of the John Clare Society. A chronology is included here, as is an extensive bibliography. There are also several essays about his work.

Jude the Obscure

http://www.bibliomania.com/Fiction/hardy/Jude/index.html

Complete text of Thomas Hardy's classic novel.

Keats, John

http://www.bartleby.com/126/index.html

Online edition of the poetical works of John Keats, indexed by title and by first line.

'Lady of Shalott, The'

http://www.webmagick.co.uk/prcoll/poetry/lady1.htm

Complete text of this poem by the English poet Alfred Tennyson.

Lady Susan

http://www.pemberley.com/janeinfo/ladysusn.html

Text of Jane Austen's unfinished novel, complete with notes.

Lancelot and Elaine

http://etext.lib.virginia.edu/etcbin/browse-mixed-new?id=TenLanc&tag=public&images=images/modeng&data=/texts/english/modeng/parsed

Text of this work by Lord Alfred Tennyson. Featured throughout the text are illustrations from a manuscript of the work belonging to the University of Virginia.

Last Man, The

http://etext.lib.virginia.edu/etcbin/browse-mixed-new?id=SheLast&tag=public&images=images/modeng&data=/texts/english/modeng/parsed

Complete text of this novel by Mary Shelley, the author of *Frankenstein*. This site also includes a number of images taken from a first edition of the novel.

Lewis Carroll Home Page

http://www.lewiscarroll.org/carroll.html

Large site dedicated to Lewis Carroll as a writer, photographer, and mathematician. There is a large amount of information about studies of Carroll, together with information about his place in popular culture.

Life of Nelson

http://tom.cs.cmu.edu/cgi-bin/book/lookup?num=947

Complete text of Robert Southey's famous biography of Nelson.

Life of Robert Browning

http://www.ulib.org/webRoot/Books/_Gutenberg_Etext_Books/etext96/shabr10.txt

Complete text of William Sharp's biography of the English poet Robert Browning and criticism of his work. This online edition has been edited to correct some of the errors.

F
A
C
T

BROWNING, ROBERT (1812–1889)

English poet. His work is characterized by the accomplished use of dramatic monologue (in which a single imaginary speaker reveals his or her character, thoughts, and situation) and an interest in obscure literary and historical figures. He was married to Elizabeth Barrett Browning.

Life of Scott by J G Lockhart

http://eng.hss.cmu.edu/fiction/life-of-scott.txt

Full text of a biography of Walter Scott written in 1871. This site also includes a long autobiographical memoir written by the novelist.

Life of Thomas Telford Civil Engineer with an Introductory History of Roads and Travelling in Great Britain, The

http://tom.cs.cmu.edu/cgi-bin/book/lookup?num=939

Complete text of this work by the Scottish writer Samuel Smiles about the Scottish civil engineer Thomas Telford. Topics covered in this book include early roads and means of transportation, as well as a detailed biography of Telford, covering such topics as his youth, the Caledonian Canal, and his work as a roadbuilder.

Lorna Doone: A Romance of Exmoor by R D Blackmore

http://tom.cs.cmu.edu/cgi-bin/book/lookup?num=840

Full text of R D Blackmore's classic romance.

MacCarthy, Denis

http://www.knight.org/advent/cathen/09484c.htm

Biography of the Irish poet. It traces his abandonment of the law for a lifelong study of the roots of Irish culture. The interest in Spain as the mythical cradle of the Irish, and the translations of Spanish literature which won him renown, are outlined together with his own poetry.

Mansfield Park

http://www.ulib.org/webRoot/Books/_Gutenberg_Etext_Books/etext94/mansf10.txt

Complete text of Jane Austen's famous novel.

Martin Chuzzlewit

http://www.bibliomania.com/Fiction/dickens/Chuzzlewit/index.html

Hypertext copy of *Martin Chuzzlewit* by Charles Dickens.

Master of Ballantrae, The

http://tom.cs.cmu.edu/cgi-bin/book/lookup?num=864

Complete text of this famous novel by Robert Louis Stevenson.

Mayor of Casterbridge, The

http://www.bibliomania.com/Fiction/hardy/mayor/index.html

E-text edition of Thomas Hardy's *The Mayor of Casterbridge*.

Meredith, George

http://landow.stg.brown.edu/victorian/authors/meredith/meredithov.html

Comprehensive biography of the Victorian man

of letters. It describes his meagre education, his abandonment of the legal profession, his failed first marriage, and his growing literary success. His major novels are summarized. It is suggested that his fiction contains insights which he denied in real life.

Meredith's *The Ordeal of Richard Feverel*

http://www.ul.cs.cmu.edu/books/MeredFever/ordeal.txt

E-text of the psychological novel by the 19th-century English novelist, George Meredith.

Middlemarch, A Study of Provincial Life

http://etext.lib.virginia.edu/cgibin/browse-mixed?id=EliMidd&tag=public&images=images/modeng&data=/lv1/Archive/eng-parsed

Complete text of George Eliot's famous novel.

Mill on the Floss, The

http://www.bibliomania.com/Fiction/eliot/mill/index.html

Hypertext edition of *The Mill on the Floss* by George Eliot.

Moonfleet

http://www.bibliomania.com/Fiction/mfalkner/mnfleet/index.html

Complete text of John Falkner's popular novel.

Moonstone, The

http://www.bibliomania.com/Fiction/collins/Moonstone/index.html

Online edition of Wilkie Collins's *The Moonstone.*

New Arabian Nights, The

http://tom.cs.cmu.edu/cgi-bin/book/lookup?num=839

Complete text of this famous volume of stories by Robert Louis Stevenson.

Nicholas Nickleby

http://www.bibliomania.com/Fiction/dickens/Nickleby/index.html

E-text of Charles Dickens's novel *Nicholas Nickleby.*

Norton, Caroline

http://www.cs.cmu.edu/afs/cs.cmu.edu/user/mmbt/www/women/norton/nc-biography.html

Included here are an informative account of her life, paying attention to her role both as a writer and a social reformer. There is also a detailed bibliography, containing information about her poetry, fiction, plays, and pamphlets.

Pair of Blue Eyes, A

http://tom.cs.cmu.edu/cgi-bin/book/lookup?num=224

Complete text of Thomas Hardy's novel which first appeared in 1872–73. Hardy's 1899 preface is included with this online edition.

Persuasion

http://www.bibliomania.com/Fiction/Austen/Persuasion/index.html

Text of Jane Austen's novel *Persuasion.*

Phineas Finn

http://etext.lib.virginia.edu/etcbin/browse-mixed-new?id=TroFinn&tag=public&images=images/modeng&data=/texts/english/modeng/parsed

Complete text of this novel by Anthony Trollope.

Pickwick Papers, The

http://www.bibliomania.com/Fiction/dickens/Pickwick/index.html

Online version of *The Pickwick Papers* by Charles Dickens.

Picture of Dorian Gray

http://www.bibliomania.com/Fiction/wilde/DorianGray/index.html

Hypertext electronic edition of Oscar Wilde's *The Picture of Dorian Gray.*

Poems of Gerard Manley Hopkins

http://www.bartleby.com/122/index.html

Online edition of Hopkins's poems with illustrations and editorial notes. Poems are indexed by title and by first line.

Poems of Oscar Wilde

http://www.bartleby.com/143/index.html

Online edition of Wilde's poems, indexed by title and by first line.

Prince Otto

http://www.bibliomania.com/Fiction/stevensn/Otto

Complete hypertext edition of Robert Louis Stevenson's *Prince Otto.*

Princess, The

http://diamond.idbsu.edu/GaS/other_gilbert/
princess/index.htm

Complete text of this celebrated epic by the
English poet Alfred Tennyson. This site also
includes some commentary on the work.

Prisoner of Zenda by Anthony Hope

http://www.ulib.org/webRoot/Books/_Gutenberg_
Etext_Books/etext93/zenda10.txt

Full text of Hope's famous tale of derring-do in
the imaginary kingdom of Ruritania.

Quest of the Golden Girl

http://etext.lib.virginia.edu/cgibin/toccer?id=
GalQues&tag=public&images=images/modeng&
data=/texts/english/modeng/parsed&part=0

Full text of Le Gallienne's romantic novel. The
book may be loaded as a whole or accessed
chapter by chapter.

Return of the Native

http://www.ulib.org/webRoot/Books/_Gutenberg_
Etext_Books/etext94/nativ10.txt

Complete text of Thomas Hardy's novel.

Rose and the Ring, The

http://tom.cs.cmu.edu/cgi-bin/book/lookup?num=897

Complete downloadable text of this fairy tale by
William Thackeray.

Rudyard Kipling: 'The White Man's Burden'
and Its Critics

http://www.boondocksnet.com/kipling/index.html

Part of a larger site concerning anti-imperialism
in the USA, this page investigates the stir that
Kipling's poem 'The White Man's Burden' created
there. In addition to the text of the poem, which
inspired many US imperialists, you can read a
number of essays, editorials, interviews, satirical
poems, and cartoons from anti-imperialists in
response. A brief introduction provides historical
context.

Selected Poetry and Prose of Leigh Hunt
(1784–1859)

http://library.utoronto.ca/www/utel/rp/authors/
huntleig.html

Contains the text of several poems by Leigh Hunt,
including 'A Thought of the Nile'.

Selected Poetry and Prose Of Matthew
Arnold (1822–1888)

http://library.utoronto.ca/www/utel/rp/authors/
arnold.html

Contains a selection of 30 of Arnold's poetry and
prose writings, including 'The Forsaken
Merman', 'Sohrab and Rustum', and 'The
Scholar-Gipsy'.

Selected Poetry and Prose of Thomas Love
Peacock (1785–1866)

http://library.utoronto.ca/www/utel/rp/authors/
peacock.html

Contains the text of several poems by Thomas
Peacock, as well as his essay 'The Four Ages of
Poetry'.

Selected Poetry of Algernon Charles
Swinburne (1837–1909)

http://library.utoronto.ca/www/utel/rp/authors/
swinburn.html

Includes the text of many of Swinburne's poems,
such as 'A Forsaken Garden', 'The Garden of
Proserpine', and excerpts from 'Atalanta in
Calydon'.

Selected Poetry of Alice Meynell (1847–
1922)

http://library.utoronto.ca/www/utel/rp/authors/
meynella.html

Contains the text of two poems by the English
poet and essayist Alice Meynell.

Selected Poetry of Arthur Hugh Clough
(1819–1861)

http://library.utoronto.ca/www/utel/rp/authors/
clough.html

Contains a number of poems by Arthur Clough,
including 'Say not the struggle nought availeth'.
Several of the poems have notes, giving details
of publication and also a brief criticism.

Selected Poetry of Charles Kingsley (1819–
1875)

http://library.utoronto.ca/www/utel/rp/authors/
kingsley.html

Contains a selection of poetry by the English
author Charles Kingsley.

Selected Poetry of Charles Wolfe (1791–1823)

http://library.utoronto.ca/www/utel/rp/authors/wolfec.html

Contains the text of Wolfe's well-known poem *The Burial of Sir John Moore at Corunna*.

Selected Poetry of Christina Rossetti (1830–1894)

http://library.utoronto.ca/www/utel/rp/authors/rossettc.html

Contains an image of the poet, as well as a large selection of her poetry, including *A Birthday, Remember,* and *Up-Hill*.

Selected Poetry of Coventry Patmore (1823–1896)

http://library.utoronto.ca/www/utel/rp/authors/patmore.html

Contains excerpts from *The Angel in the House* and 'The Unknown Eros' by the poet and critic Coventry Patmore.

Selected Poetry of Dinah Maria Mulock Craik (1826–1887)

http://library.utoronto.ca/www/utel/rp/authors/craik.html

Contains both a brief biography of the poet and the text of a number of her works, including several poems from the collection *Poems*.

Selected Poetry of Edith Nesbit (1858–1924)

http://library.utoronto.ca/www/utel/rp/authors/nesbit.html

Includes a selection of poetry from the children's writer and author of *The Railway Children*.

Selected Poetry of Edward Fitzgerald (1809–1883)

http://library.utoronto.ca/www/utel/rp/authors/fitzgera.html

Contains the annotated text of Fitzgerald's version of the poem 'Rubáiyát of Omar Khayyám'.

Selected Poetry of Edward Thomas (1878–1917)

http://library.utoronto.ca/www/utel/rp/authors/thomas.html

Contains a selection of Thomas's poetry, including 'Lights Out' and 'The Word'.

Selected Poetry of Elizabeth Barrett Browning

http://library.utoronto.ca/www/utel/rp/authors/brwneliz.html

Hypertext presentation of selected poetry by Elizabeth Barrett Browning from the Department of English at the University of Toronto, Canada. The presentation is accompanied by notes and detailed information on the encoding of the texts.

Selected Poetry of Ernest Dowson (1867–1900)

http://library.utoronto.ca/www/utel/rp/authors/dowson.html

Contains the text of several of Dowson's poems, including 'Non Sum Qualis Eram Bonae sub Regno Cynarae' and 'Vitae Summa Brevis Spem nos Vetet Incohare Longam'.

Selected Poetry of Felicia Dorothea Hemans (1793–1835)

http://library.utoronto.ca/www/utel/rp/authors/hemans.html

Includes the text of her poem 'The Landing of the Pilgrim Fathers in New England'.

Selected Poetry of Francis Thompson (1859–1907)

http://library.utoronto.ca/www/utel/rp/authors/thompsfr.html

Features the text of several poems by Francis Thompson, including 'The Hound of Heaven'.

Selected Poetry of George Meredith (1828–1909)

http://library.utoronto.ca/www/utel/rp/authors/meredith.html

Contains the text of several poems by George Meredith, including annotated versions of 'Love in the Valley', 'Lucifer in Starlight', and excerpts from 'Modern Love'.

Selected Poetry of James Thomson (1834–1882)

http://library.utoronto.ca/www/utel/rp/authors/thomson9.html

Contains excerpts from two of Thomson's poems, 'The City of Dreadful Night' and 'Sunday up the River'.

Selected Poetry of John Davidson (1857–1909)

http://library.utoronto.ca/www/utel/rp/authors/davidson.html

Contains a brief biography of the poet as well as the text several of his poems, including 'Thirty Bob a Week'. Many of the poems also include explanatory notes.

Selected Poetry of John Henry Newman (Cardinal; 1801–1890)

http://library.utoronto.ca/www/utel/rp/authors/newman.html

Features a brief biography of the theologian and poet, as well as a drawing and a selection from 'The Dream of Gerontius'.

Selected Poetry of Letitia Elizabeth Landon (1802–1838)

http://library.utoronto.ca/www/utel/rp/authors/landon.html

Features an image of the English poet, as well as a biography and the text of her *Revenge*.

Selected Poetry of Richard Harris Barham (1788–1845)

http://library.utoronto.ca/www/utel/rp/authors/barham.html

Features the text of the poem 'The Jackdaw of Rheims'.

Selected Poetry of Robert Browning (1812–1889)

http://library.utoronto.ca/www/utel/rp/authors/browning.html

Contains an image of the poet, as well as a large selection of his poetry which includes, among others, 'My Last Duchess' and 'Rabbi Ben Ezra'.

Selected Poetry of Robert Southey (1774–1843)

http://library.utoronto.ca/www/utel/rp/authors/southey.html

Contains a selection of Southey's poems, including 'The Battle of Blenheim' among others.

Selected Poetry of Sabine Baring-Gould (1834–1924)

http://library.utoronto.ca/www/utel/rp/authors/gould.html

Contains the text of the poem 'Onward, Christian Soldiers'. There is also a brief description of his life and works.

Selected Poetry of Sir Walter Scott (1771–1832)

http://library.utoronto.ca/www/utel/rp/authors/scott.html

Includes a number of examples of Scott's poetry, including excerpts from 'The Lady of the Lake' and 'Marmion'.

Selected Poetry Of Thomas Babington Macaulay (1800–1859)

http://library.utoronto.ca/www/utel/rp/authors/macaulay.html

Contains the text of several poems by the poet, historian, and politician Thomas Macaulay.

Selected Poetry of Thomas Campbell (1777–1844)

http://library.utoronto.ca/www/utel/rp/authors/campbell.html

Contains the text of several poems by Thomas Campbell, including 'Hohenlinden', 'Ye Mariners of England', and an excerpt of 'The Pleasures of Hope'.

Selected Poetry of Thomas Edward Brown (1830–1897)

http://library.utoronto.ca/www/utel/rp/authors/brownte.html

Contains the text of several poems by Manx poet Thomas Brown, including 'I bended unto me a Bough'.

Selected Poetry of Thomas Hood (1799–1845)

http://library.utoronto.ca/www/utel/rp/authors/hood.html

Contains the text of several poems by Thomas Hood, including 'Faithless Sally Brown', 'I Remember, I Remember', and 'The Song of the Shirt'.

Selected Poetry of Thomas Lovell Beddoes (1803–1818)

http://library.utoronto.ca/www/utel/rp/authors/beddoes.html

Contains the text of several works by the English poet Thomas Beddoes.

Selected Poetry of Thomas Moore (1779–1852)

http://library.utoronto.ca/www/utel/rp/authors/moore.html

Contains the text of a number of the Irish poet's works, including 'Lalla Rookh' and 'Time I've Lost in Wooing'.

Selected Poetry of Walter Savage Landor

http://library.utoronto.ca/www/utel/rp/authors/landor.html#notes

Text of fourteen of Landor's best-known poems.

Selected Poetry of William Barnes (1801–1886)

http://library.utoronto.ca/www/utel/rp/authors/barnes.html

Contains a selection of Barnes's poetry, including 'Woak Hill'.

Selected Poetry of William Ernest Henley (1849–1903)

http://library.utoronto.ca/www/utel/rp/authors/henley.html

Contains a large selection of works by the English poet William Henley, taken from the collection 'Poems'.

Selected Poetry of William Johnson Cory (1823–1892)

http://library.utoronto.ca/www/utel/rp/authors/ cory.html

Features a brief biography and introduction to the works of poet William Cory. Also included is the text of *Heraclitus*, which contains explanatory notes.

Selected Poetry of William Morris (1834–1896)

http://library.utoronto.ca/www/ utel/rp/authors/morris.html

Contains a large number of poems by the English designer William Morris, including annotated excerpts from 'Earthly Paradise' and 'Love is Enough'.

Selected Poetry of Winthrop Mackworth Praed (1802–1839)

http://library.utoronto.ca/www/utel/rp/authors/praed.html

Includes the text of Praed's *The Vicar*.

Self Help: With Illustrations of Conduct and Perseverance

http://tom.cs.cmu.edu/cgi-bin/book/lookup?num=935

Complete text of Samuel Smiles's didactic work that first appeared in 1859.

She

http://www.bibliomania.com/Fiction/Haggard/She/

Complete text of one of H Ryder Haggard's romantic adventure tales.

Mary Shelley Resource Page

http://www.desert-fairy.com/maryshel.shtml

Resource on this English writer, most famed for her creation of *Frankenstein*. There is illustrated hypertext on her life, the literary sources of *Frankenstein*, and the events of the pivotal summer of 1816. The site also includes wide-ranging information about her contemporaries and parents, including Lord Byron, Percy Shelley, and Mary Wollstonecraft.

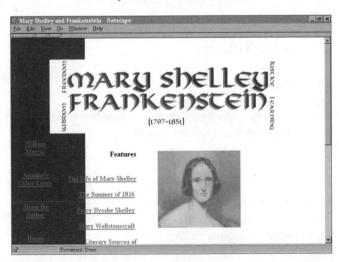

Sherlockian HolmePage

http://www.geocities.com/Athens/Acropolis/8950/holmes.htm

Resource based on the famous fictional detective. It includes essays about Sherlock Holmes, information about Conan Doyle, pictures, and links to other related sites.

Shropshire Lad, A

http://www.bartleby.com/123/index.html

Online edition of Housman's *A Shropshire Lad.*

Silas Marner

http://www.inform.umd.edu/EdRes/ReadingRoom/Fiction/Eliot/SilasMarner/

Text of George Eliot's novel.

Sir Walter Scott: *Heart of Mid-Lothian*

http://www.ul.cs.cmu.edu/books/ScottLothi/heart-lothian.txt

E-text of Sir Walter Scott's popular thriller and romance, based on the Centenary Edition of the Waverley novels published in 1870 by Adam and Charles Black in Edinburgh, Scotland.

Sir Walter Scott: *Waverley*

http://english-www.hss.cmu.edu/fiction/waverley.txt

E-text of Sir Walter Scott's popular romance, based on the Centenary Edition of the Waverley novels published in 1870 by Adam and Charles Black of Edinburgh, Scotland.

Sons and Lovers by D H Lawrence

http://www.bibliomania.com/Fiction/dhl/Sons/index.html

Full text of D H Lawrence's semi-autobiographical tale of Paul Morel.

Study in Scarlet, A

http://etext.lib.virginia.edu/cgibin/browse-mixed?id=DoyScar&tag=public&images=images/modeng&data=/lv1/Archive/eng-parsed

Complete text of Arthur Conan Doyle's detective novel.

Swinburne, Algernon Charles

http://www.stg.brown.edu/projects/hypertext/landow/victorian/decadence/swinburne/acsov.html

Profile of the masochistic aristocratic poet. There is a good biography with an account of his career, his addictions, and mastery of poetic metre. There are samples of his poems and reviews of his work.

Tale of Two Cities

http://www.bibliomania.com/Fiction/dickens/TaleOf2Cities/index.html

Online version of *Tale of Two Cities* by Charles Dickens.

Tenant of Wildfell Hall, The

http://www.bibliomania.com/Fiction/Bronte/Tenant

Online version of Anne Brontë's *The Tenant of Wildfell Hall.* The site also includes a link to further information about the author.

Tennyson, Alfred Lord

http://www.stg.brown.edu/projects/hypertext/landow/victorian/tennyson/tennyov.html

Introduction to Tennyson from the Victorian Web. The site presents his work, with separate essays on its themes, symbolism, and structure. It also offers an overview of the political and social context in which Tennyson wrote, and examines his relation with the visual arts, and his position within the literary circles of the period.

Tess of the D'Urbervilles

http://www.bibliomania.com/Fiction/hardy/tess/index.html

Hypertext copy of Thomas Hardy's novel *Tess of the D'Urbervilles.*

Tess of the D'Urbervilles

http://www.prestigeweb.com/hardy/critiques/tess.html

Critique of Hardy's most famous novel. This is thought-provoking analysis for those seeking the deeper meaning of Tess's plight.

Thomas Hardy Resource Library

http://pages.ripco.com/~mws//hardy.html

Aimed at both the academic scholar and the casual reader interested in the works of Thomas Hardy. The site includes several of Hardy's novels which can be downloaded in plain-text format, a bibliography, articles, book and film reviews, maps, photos, audio clips, a chronology of Hardy's life and works, and links to other relevant sites.

Three Men in a Boat by Jerome K Jerome

http://tom.cs.cmu.edu/cgi-bin/book/lookup?num=308

Full text of Jerome's humorous account of a boating trip on the Thames.

Time Machine, The

http://www.inform.umd.edu/EdRes/ReadingRoom/
Fiction/Wells/TimeMachine/

Text of H G Wells's science-fiction novel.

Trollope's *Lady Anna:* electronic edition

http://www.hti.umich.edu/bin/pd-
idx?type=header&id=TrollLadyA

Complete text in electronic form of *Lady Anna* by
Anthony Trollope distributed by the Oxford Text
Archive.

Vanity Fair

http://www.catawba.k12.nc.us/books/vfair10.txt

Complete text of this celebrated novel by William
Thackeray.

War of the Worlds, The

http://www.fourmilab.ch/etexts/www/warworlds/
warw.html

Text of H G Wells's science-fiction novel.

Watsons, The

http://www.pemberley.com/janeinfo/watsons1.html

Includes the text of Jane Austen's unfinished
novel, as well as a brief explanation as to why
Jane Austen did not complete the work.

Wessex poems and Other Verses

http://www.bartleby.com/121/index.html

Online edition of Thomas Hardy's *Wessex Poems
and Other Verses.*

Wilkie Collins Appreciation Page

http://www.rightword.com.au/writers/wilkie Features
an introduction to the novelist and an account of
his life. There is information about his novels, as
well as a guide to books about his life and work.
Attention is also paid to film and television
adaptations of his novels, and there are details of
Wilkie Collins societies and home pages.

Woman in White, The

http://www.bibliomania.com/Fiction/collins/
WomanInWhite/index.html

Online copy of Wilkie Collins's *The Woman in
White.*

Woodlanders, The

http://www.catawba.k12.nc.us/books/woodl10.txt

Complete text of Thomas Hardy's novel which
was first published in 1887.

Wuthering Heights

http://www.bibliomania.com/Fiction/Bronte/
Wuthering/index.html

Hypertext edition of *Wuthering Heights* by Emily
Brontë.

Yeats, W B

http://www.lit.kobe-u.ac.jp/~hishika/yeats.htm

Appreciation of the life and work of the Irish poet
as well as links to more than 300 poems, class
notes for teaching on the poet, newsletters, and
Yeats fan clubs.

20th-century British Literature (Pre-war)

American Chesterton Society

http://www.chesterton.org/

The sociey's website aims to promote 'an interest
in his writings, primarily among a new
generation of readers unfamiliar with the
man and his work'. This is achieved by
including a biography, as well as artwork by,
about, and influenced by G K Chesterton. A
selection of his poetry is reproduced, a research
service provided, allowing readers to put their
questions to the Society's directors and members.
Essays and articles are featured as part of the
Gilbert! magazine, and there is also information
about events and organizations relating to
Chesterton.

Christie, Agatha

http://members.aol.com/mg4273/chris1.htm

Detailed biographical information on Agatha
Christie's writing career, including a full list of
her novels, details of her short stories, and the
film adaptations of her novels.

Collected Poems of Rupert Brooke

http://tom.cs.cmu.edu/cgi-bin/book/lookup?num=262

Complete text of all of Brooke's poems. There is a
good introduction and biographical note about

the poet of 'the lost generation'.

de la Mare, Walter

http://www.columbia.edu/acis/bartleby/mbp/48.html

Introduction to the life and work of the English poet who 'wrote as much for antiquity as for posterity'. There is an appreciation of his work and the text of five of his best-known poems.

Dubliners

http://www.bibliomania.com/Fiction/joyce/dublin/index.html

Hypertext edition of James Joyce's *Dubliners*.

Eliot, T S

http://www.bartleby.com/201/index.html

Online edition of selected poetry and prose by T S Eliot, including 'The Wasteland' and 'Prufrock and Other Observations'.

Fairies and Fusiliers

http://www.bartleby.com/120/index.html

Online edition of Robert Graves's *Fairies and Fusiliers*. The poems are indexed by title and by first line.

Forster's A Room with a View

http://www.hti.umich.edu/bin/pd-idx?type=header&id=ForstRoomV

Complete electronic text of E M Forster's famous *A Room with a View*, distributed by the Humanities Text Initiative at the University of Michigan, USA.

Forster's Howard's End

http://www.hti.umich.edu/bin/pd-idx?type=header&id=ForstHowar

Full electronic edition of E M Forster's *Howard's End*, distributed by the Humanities Text Initiative at the University of Michigan, USA.

George Gissing, The Private Papers of Henry Ryecroft

http://lang.nagoya-u.ac.jp/~matsuoka/GG-PPHR.html

Text of the semi-autobiographical novel *The Private Papers of Henry Ryecroft* by George Gissing.

Heretics

http://ccel.wheaton.edu/c/chesterton/heretics/heretics.html

Includes a biography of G K Chesterton, as well as the text of his philosophical work *Heretics*.

History of Sir Richard Calmady

http://www.indiana.edu/~letrs/vwwp/malet/calmady.html

Complete text of this novel by Lucas Malet from Indiana University. This online edition also includes an image from an earlier print edition.

James Joyce Web Site

http://www.2street.com/joyce

Dedicated to the appreciation and analysis of the literary works of Irish writer James Joyce. The site includes articles, e-texts, maps, links to both online and offline Joycean resources, a timeline, multimedia, and the online journal *Hypermedia Joyce Studies*.

Joyce: the Critical Background

http://www.ucet.ufl.edu/~kershner/crita.html

Extended essay on Joycean criticism. The site includes discussions of the reception of Joyce's early works, the reaction of reviewers and public after *Ulysses*, examples of pioneering Joycean writing, the impact of structuralism, post-structuralism, and deconstruction on Joyce studies after the 70s, the repositioning of Joyce's work within popular writing of the late 19th century, and the rise of feminist criticism on Joyce.

Kim

http://www.bibliomania.com/Fiction/kipling/kim/index.html

Hypertext copy of Rudyard Kipling's *Kim*.

Lady Chatterley's Lover

http://www.bibliomania.com/Fiction/dhl/chat/index.html

Online hypertext edition of D H Lawrence's *Lady Chatterley's Lover*.

Lawrence, D H

http://web.ukonline.co.uk/rananim/lawrence/

Substantial amount of biographical information and many photographs, from Lawrence's early years in Nottingham to his unhappy expulsion from Cornwall and death in France. There are also a number of essays on certain aspects of his work and the full text of many can be

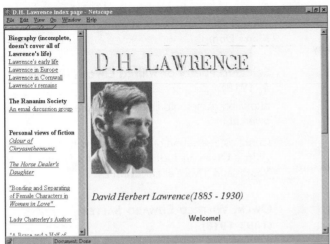

downloaded. A recording of Kenneth Branagh reading an extract of the poem 'Violets' is also available if you have the correct plug-in.

Lewis, C S

http://cslewis.DrZeus.net/

Introduction for anyone wishing to find out about C S Lewis. It includes, among other things, a daily quote, a list of literary works, pictures, audio clips, and papers written about this famous man of letters.

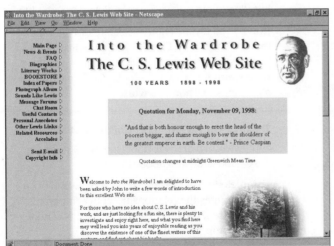

Lord Jim

http://www.bibliomania.com/Fiction/
conrad/LordJim/index.html

Hypertext edition of Joseph Conrad's novel *Lord Jim*.

Moon and Sixpence by W Somerset Maugham

http://tom.cs.cmu.edu/cgi-bin/book/
lookup?num=222

E-text of the novel by the popular English writer. There is a choice of locations to download texts from.

Nostromo

http://www.bibliomania.com/Fiction/
conrad/Nostromo/index.html

Online version of *Nostromo* by Joseph Conrad.

Of Human Bondage

http://www.bibliomania.com/Fiction/
Maugham/Human/index.html

Online hypertext edition of W Somerset Maugham's book *Of Human Bondage*.

Orthodoxy

http://ccel.wheaton.edu/c/chesterton/
orthodoxy/orthodoxy.html

Text of G K Chesterton's philosophical work *Orthodoxy*.

Orwell, George

http://www.k-1.com/Orwell/

Dedicated to the English writer George Orwell. This site contains summaries of his major works, a very detailed biography, a collection of Orwell's essays, and a 'Gallery' of photos, poems, and letters.

Pearse, Patrick

http://wwwvms.utexas.edu/~jdana/
pearsehist.html

All-text biography of the turn-of-the-century Irish poet and nationalist.

P G Wodehouse Fan Club

http://www.serv.net/~camel/wodehouse/

Fan club collection of Plumisms and links to Jeevesiana.

Poems of D H Lawrence

http://www.bartleby.com/128/index.html

Online edition of Lawrence's poems, indexed by title and by first line.

Poems of Siegfried Sassoon

http://www.bartleby.com/135/index.html

Online edition of Sassoon's poems, indexed by title and by first line.

'Politics of T S Eliot, The'

http://www.townhall.com/hall_of_fame/kirk/kirk182.html

Text of a fascinating lecture given by Russell Kirk on the subject of T S Eliot. Throughout the lecture Kirk makes extensive use of both Eliot's poetry and his critical works.

Portrait of the Artist as a Young Man, A

http://www.bibliomania.com/Fiction/joyce/artist/index.html

E-text of James Joyce's novel *A Portrait of the Artist as a Young Man.*

Sassoon, Siegfried

http://www.geocities.com/CapitolHill/8103/index.html

Short biography of the poet with links to some well-known contemporaries. There is also a virtual exhibition of many of his poems, illustrated with images depicting the themes he covers.

Scarlet Pimpernel, The

http://www.cs.cmu.edu/People/rgs/ scarp-table.html

Text of Baroness Orczy's historical novel.

Secret Agent, The

http://www.bibliomania.com/Fiction/conrad/agent/index.html

Hypertext edition of Joseph Conrad's novel *The Secret Agent.*

Secret Sharer, The

http://wiretap.spies.com/ftp.items/Library/Classic/sharer.txt

Complete text of Joseph Conrad's novel.

Selected Poetry of Isaac Rosenberg (1890–1918)

http://library.utoronto.ca/www/utel/rp/authors/rosenberg.html

Contains several poems by the English poet. Among them are 'Louse Hunting' and 'Dead Man's Dump'.

Selected Poetry of Wilfred Owen (1893–Nov. 4, 1918)

http://library.utoronto.ca/www/utel/rp/authors/owen.html

Contains a selection of poetry by the English poet Wilfrid Owen, including 'Anthem for Doomed Youth' and 'Dulce et Decorum Est'.

F A C T

OWEN, WILFRED EDWARD SALTER (1893–1918)

English poet. His verse, owing much to the encouragement of Siegfried Sassoon, is among the most moving of World War I poetry; it shatters the illusion of the glory of war, revealing its hollowness and cruel destruction of beauty.

Thirty-Nine Steps, The

http://www.bartleby.com/149/index.html

Online edition of John Buchan's *The Thirty-Nine Steps.*

Thomas, Dylan

http://pcug.org.au/~wwhatman/dylan_thomas.html

Run by the Dylan Thomas Society of Australia, this site includes a brief biography, some poems, pictures, a list of short stories, and a page on his wife, Caitlin. It also includes links to some audio recordings of Thomas's work.

Treatise on Parents and Children, A

http://www.ulib.org/webRoot/Books/_Gutenberg_Etext_Books/etext97/topac10.txt

Complete text of George Bernard Shaw's work that examines the relationship between parents and children, considering such issues as school, laziness, and punishment.

TSEbase: The Online Concordance to T S Eliot's Collected Poems

http://web.missouri.edu/~tselist/tse.html

Allows online searching of T S Eliot's 'Collected Poems 1909–1962'. After you have entered a search-word, the program swiftly returns the lines containing that word, organized by the poem in which they appear.

Ulysses

http://www.bibliomania.com/Fiction/joyce/ulysses/index.html

Hypertext edition of James Joyce's modernist classic *Ulysses*.

Virginia Woolf and the Bloomsbury Group

http://www.lm.com/~kaydee/Bloomsbury.html

Project by a PhD student at Dublin City University on the Bloomsbury Group, and in particular Virginia Woolf. The Web site contains a history of the group, a list of its members, and many hypertext links to related topics.

Virginia Woolf Chronology

http://www.cygneis.com/woolf/vwchrono.htm

Chronology of the life and works of English writer Virginia Woolf, featuring links to further information on her family, friends, and colleagues and to various extracts from her books that can be found elsewhere on the Web.

Voyage Out, The

http://wiretap.spies.com/ftp.items/Library/Classic/voyage.vw

Complete text of Virginia Woolf's first novel.

Women in Love

http://www.bibliomania.com/Fiction/dhl/Women/index.html

Hypertext copy of D H Lawrence's *Women in Love.*

20th-century British Literature (Post-war)

W H Auden's Poetry

http://www.sat.dundee.ac.uk/~arb/speleo/auden.html

Contains the text of two of Auden's poems: 'Three Short Poems' and 'In Praise of Limestone'.

A S Byatt's *Possession*

http://www.sjsu.edu/depts/jwss.old/possession/

Site devoted to the study of A S Byatt's *Possession*. The page contains a brief biography, bibliography, annotations, and essays.

Ballard, J G

http://www.geocities.com/Area51/Corridor/4085/ballard.html

Dedicated to the English novelist, this site features detailed information about his short story collections and plot synopses of many of his novels. There is a large amount of information about the book *Crash!* and the subsequent film, including links to articles, reviews, interviews, and photographs.

Barnes, Julian

http://www.library.uiuc.edu/egx/barnes/home.html

Julian Barnes bibliography and other information. The contents of this Web site are centred around three bibliographies of Barnes-related material, covering his books, articles, and reviews. Also included is a mini biography and a well researched links section, the latter featuring links to obscure Web resources such as interviews taken from the press, etc.

Betjeman, John

http://www.jbetjeman.freeserve.co.uk/index.htm

Tribute to the life and works of the English poet. There are examples of his work, photographs, a bibliography, transcripts of television programmes, and details of the John Betjeman Society. There are also several links to further sources of information.

Drabble, Margaret

http://tile.net/drabble/

Comprehensive source of information on the English writer. The contents include a photo, biography, interviews, and articles about Drabble. There are full details of her books and summaries of their plots and themes. There is also a guide to Drabble Internet discussion groups.

Fleming, Ian

http://www.mcs.net/~klast/www/fleming.html

Web site dedicated to the author of the James

Bond books and other novels. A biography of Fleming is included here, along with reviews of his books. Other bits and pieces on the Web site range from a photograph of Fleming taken by Sean Connery to Fleming's own ideas on 'How to write a thriller'. It also features many Bond-related facts, figures, and trivia mainly connected to the films.

Gormenghast (Castle) Page

http://www.gate.net/~zacharyp/gormenghast/

Dedicated to Peake's work *Gormenghast*, this Web site takes you on a tour of the book, including descriptions of characters, critical assessments, details of the trilogy, and poetry from the book. Personal details on Peake are also featured, including both a brief biography and bibliography.

Graham Swift: An Overview

http://www.stg.brown.edu/projects/hypertext/landow/post/uk/gswift/gsov.html

Web site describing many aspects of the writer's life and works. The majority of the information published here focuses on Swift's work, in particular relation to religion, science, politics, and history. Biographical and bibliographical information is also provided.

Hypertextualised Tolkien FAQ

http://www.daimi.aau.dk/~bouvin/tolkienfaq.html

Valuable introduction to the world of JRR Tolkien's cult fiction. The site answers basic questions about Tolkien's world and offers a wealth of hyperlinked information about the creatures, the time, and the settings of these extraordinary fantasies. The site also hosts a section on the films inspired by Tolkien's stories and strongly encourages contributions and comments.

Lowry, Malcolm

http://www.interlog.com/~merlinds/volcano/

Full source of information on the turbulent life of the alcoholic novelist. There are a large number of critical reviews of his novels and of events celebrating the fiftieth anniversary of the publication of *Under the Volcano*. For Lowry fans there is a crossword to test knowledge of his best-known work.

L-Space Web – a Terry Pratchett Web Site

http://www.au.lspace.org/

Dedicated to the creator of the Discworld, this site

includes a biography of Pratchett, the 'Annotated Pratchett File' (which contains explanations of all the parodies and in-jokes within the Discworld series), and lots of information about conventions and other fan-related events.

Martin Amis Web

http://martinamis.albion.edu

Site devoted to the British contemporary novelist, with links to biographical information, interviews, criticism, and bibliographies.

May We Borrow Your Husband?

http://www.wh1.tu-dresden.de/~andy/englisch/literature/greene/HusbandIndex.html

Contains a selection of short stories by the English writer Graham Greene, including 'A Shocking Accident', 'Awful When You Think of It', and 'The Root of All Evil'.

Roald Dahl Home Page

http://www.roalddahl.org/index2.htm

Dedicated to Roald Dahl, the author of children's favourites such as *Matilda* and *The Witches*. There is a detailed biography, a timeline that allows you to see the works into the context of his life, photographs of his early years, and a series of articles about the man and his literature.

Rowling, J K

http://harrypotter.okukbooks.com/rowling.htm

Biography of J K Rowling, the creator of the phenomenally successful *Harry Potter* series of children's books. The pages are part of a larger site dedicated to Harry Potter.

Rushdie, Salman

http://www.crl.com/~subir/rushdie.html

General source of information about Salman Rushdie's published works, with quotations, interviews, and articles about him. It maintains hyperlinks to information pertinent to the 'death sentence' he was given in 1989.

Seamus Heaney Page

http://sunsite.unc.edu/dykki/poetry/heaney/heaney-cov.html

Nobel prizewinning poet Seamus Heaney has this site dedicated to his life and works. It includes a biography, bibliography, and many quotations taken from his works. The quotations are available in the form of text or as audio clips.

Spy Who Came in From the Cold, The

http://www.leadership.co.za/issues/july/articles/lecarre.html

Insightful interview with John Le Carré, the author who wrote many spy novels including *The Spy Who Came in From the Cold* (1963).

Ted Hughes Obituary

http://easyweb.easynet.co.uk/~pato/ne/76/hughes.html

Obituary that contains biographical information about Ted Hughes, the poet laureate 1984–98. Hughes's poetic style is also analysed and his work is compared with that of John Betjeman and Philip Larkin.

Tribute to William Golding

http://www.geocities.com/Athens/Forum/6249/index.html

Dedicated to the life and works of English novelist William Golding. The information on this Web site ranges from biographical details and a bibliography to reviews of his books and links to online sources for the texts.

Weldon, Fay

http://tile.net/weldon/index.html

Comprehensive information on the popular English writer. The contents include a biography, guide to her writing, a complete bibliography, book jacket summaries of her novels and short story collections, interviews with the writer, and articles about her. There are also several photos.

British Children's Literature

Alice's Adventures in Wonderland by Lewis Carroll

http://www.cs.cmu.edu/People/rgs/alice-table.html

Project Gutenberg e-text of *Alice's Adventures in Wonderland* by Lewis Carroll.

Black Beauty by Anna Sewell

http://tom.cs.cmu.edu/cgi-bin/book/lookup?num=271

Project Gutenberg e-text of *Black Beauty.* Download the text in text or zip format.

Blue Fairy Book, The

http://etext.lib.virginia.edu/etcbin/browse-mixed-new?id=LanBlue&images=images/modeng&data=/texts/english/modeng/parsed&tag=public

Full text of the first of Andrew Lang's noted tales for children. The book may be accessed as a complete text or chapter by chapter.

Dream Days

http://etext.lib.virginia.edu/cgibin/browse-mixed?id=GraDrea&tag=public&images=images/modeng&data=/lv1/Archive/eng-parsed

Complete text of one of Kenneth Grahame's first novels.

Golden Age, The

http://etext.lib.virginia.edu/cgibin/browse-mixed?id=GraGold&tag=public&images=images/modeng&data=/lv1/Archive/eng-parsed

Complete text of this novel by Kenneth Grahame.

Jungle Book

http://etext.lib.virginia.edu/etcbin/toccer-new?id=KipJung&images=images/modeng&data=/texts/english/modeng/parsed&tag=public

Electronic illustrated copy of *The Jungle Book* by Rudyard Kipling.

Kidnapped

http://tom.cs.cmu.edu/cgi-bin/book/lookup?num=421

Complete text of this famous novel by Robert Louis Stevenson.

King Solomon's Mines

http://www.bibliomania.com/Fiction/Haggard/Solomon/index.html

Plain-text electronic copy of *King Solomon's Mines* by H Rider Haggard.

Little Lord Fauntleroy by Frances Hodgson Burnett

http://www.ulib.org/webRoot/Books/_Gutenberg_Etext_Books/etext96/fntlr10.txt

Full text of Burnett's celebrated children's tale.

The whole book may be downloaded or each chapter read as a single file.

Little Princess, A

http://www.ulib.org/webRoot/Books/_Gutenberg_Etext_Books/etext94/lprss11.txt

Complete text of Frances Burnett's children's novel.

Page at Pooh Corner

http://chaos.trxinc.com/jmilne/Pooh/

Large site containing a detailed biography of the creator of Winnie the Pooh, A A Milne. Also included are photographs of the writer, a biography of Christopher Milne, better known as Christopher Robin, a page about the illustrations used in his novels, and information about Winnie the Pooh.

Peter and Wendy by J M Barrie

http://www.hoboes.com/html/FireBlade/Peter/chapter1.html

Complete text of a US public domain version of Barrie's classic children's fantasy about the boy who wouldn't grow up.

Peter Rabbit Web Site

http://www.peterrabbit.co.uk/

Contains a large amount of information on both Beatrix Potter and the adventures of one of her creations, Peter Rabbit. There are a number of graphics used throughout the site, as well as several games and puzzles based on the world of Beatrix Potter.

Princess and Curdie, The

http://tom.cs.cmu.edu/cgi-bin/book/lookup?num=709

E-text by Project Gutenberg of the Scottish novelist George Macdonald's popular fantasy for children.

Secret Garden, The

http://www.ulib.org/webRoot/Books/_Gutenberg_Etext_Books/etext94/gardn10.txt

Text of the mystical children's novel by Frances Burnett.

Sylvie and Bruno

http://www.bibliomania.com/Fiction/Caroll/Sylvie

E-text of *Sylvie and Bruno* by Lewis Carroll.

Tales From Shakespeare

http://eldred.ne.mediaone.net/cml/tfs.html

Full text of Charles and Mary Lamb's celebrated book. Arthur Rackham's original illustrations are also included.

Through the Looking Glass by Lewis Carroll

http://www.literature.org/authors/carroll-lewis/through-the-looking-glass/

Complete electronic text of *Through The Looking-Glass And What Alice Found There* by Lewis Carroll.

Treasure Island

http://www.bibliomania.com/Fiction/stevensn/island/index.html

E-text of the Robert Louis Stevenson classic *Treasure Island*.

Voyages of Dr Dolittle by Hugh Lofting

http://tom.cs.cmu.edu/cgi-bin/book/lookup?num=1154

Full text of Lofting's classic tale of the man who could talk to animals.

Water Babies, The

http://tom.cs.cmu.edu/cgi-bin/book/lookup?num=1018

Full text of Kingsley's classic fantasy of an orphan child.

Wind in the Willows, The

http://etext.lib.virginia.edu/etcbin/browse-mixed-new?id=GraWind&images=images/modeng&data=/lv1/Archive/eng-parsed&tag=public

Complete text of the classic children's fantasy by Kenneth Grahame. The entire work can be loaded or the tale of Rat, Mole, Badger, and Toad can be accessed chapter by chapter.

17th- & 18th-century American Literature

An elegy, sacred to the memory of the great divine, the Reverend and learned Dr Samuel Cooper...

http://etext.lib.virginia.edu/etcbin/browse-mixed-new?id=WheCoop&tag=public&images=images/modeng&data=/texts/english/modeng/parsed

Complete text of this poem by the American poet Phyllis Wheatley.

Poems of Edward Taylor

http://www.puritansermons.com/poetry/taylor.htm

Profile of the English-born US Puritan poet and theologian. It reveals that the committed Calvinist wrote a poem before each supper. The site includes examples of some of his best-known verse.

Poems on Various Subjects, Religious and Moral

http://digilib.nypl.org/dynaweb/digs/wwm9728/@Generic__BookView

Complete text of this collection of poems by the US poet Phyllis Wheatley. Well over 30 poems have been reproduced here, and the 1772 preface has also been included.

Selected Poetry of Anne Bradstreet (c. 1612–72)

http://library.utoronto.ca/www/utel/rp/authors/abrad.html

Contains a biography of the poet, as well as a picture of her from a painted-glass window. There is also a wide selection of her poetry.

Some Fruits of Solitude

http://etext.lib.virginia.edu/cgibin/browse-mixed?id=PenSoli&tag=public&images=images/modeng&data=/lv1/Archive/eng-parsed

Complete text of this work by the English Quaker William Penn.

19th-century US Literature

Anti-Slavery Poems: Songs of Labor and Reform

http://www.hti.umich.edu/bin/amv-idx.pl?type=header&id=WhittAntis

Complete text of this work by the US poet and opponent of slavery John Greenleaf Whittier.

Awakening, The by Kate Chopin

http://etext.lib.virginia.edu/etcbin/browse-mixed-new?id=ChoAwak&tag=public&images=images/modeng&data=/texts/english/modeng/parsed

Brief analysis and full-text of Chopin's controversial novel. There are details of the artistic and literary influences that shaped Chopin's creativity and the furore of criticism aroused by publication of *The Awakening*.

Bartleby, the Scrivener

http://www.bartleby.com/129/index.html

Online edition of Melville's story *Bartleby, the Scrivener: A Story of Wall-street*.

Billy Budd

http://www.bibliomania.com/Fiction/Melville/BillyBudd

Online copy of Herman Melville's novel *Billy Budd*.

Brick Moon, and Other Stories, The

http://etext.lib.virginia.edu/cgibin/browse-mixed?id=HalBric&tag=public&images=images/modeng&data=/lv1/Archive/eng-parsed

Selection of short stories by the US Unitarian minister and writer Edward Everett Hale.

Children of the Night by Edwin Arlington Robinson

http://www.hti.umich.edu/bin/amv-idx.pl?type=header&id=RobinChild

Full text of the volume which established the reputation of the Pulitzer prize-winning poet.

'Civil Disobedience'

http://www.cs.indiana.edu/statecraft/civ.dis.html

Text of Thoreau's influential essay.

Connecticut Yankee at King Arthur's Court, A

http://etext.lib.virginia.edu/etcbin/toccer-new?id=TwaYank&tag=public&images=images/modeng&data=/texts/english/modeng/parsed&part=0

Complete text of this satire by Mark Twain.

Custer and other Poems by Ella Wheeler Wilcox

http://www.hti.umich.edu/bin/amv-idx.pl?type=header&id=WilcoCuste

Collection of the best-known works of the sentimental US poet.

Emily Dickinson Page

http://userweb.interactive.net/~krisxlee/emily/

Life and works of US poet Emily Dickinson. Resources include an illustrated biography, several hundred of her poems online, links to discussion groups and the Emily Dickinson International Society, and further links to numerous related sites.

'Fall of the House of Usher, The' – Edgar Allan Poe

http://www.andover.edu/faculty/pkalkstein/words/usherset.html

Full text of 'The Fall Of The House Of Usher', one of the most famous short stories of Edgar Allan Poe, the man who is often seen as one of the first modern short story writers.

George Washington, the Cherry-Tree, and Mason Locke Weems

http://home.earthlink.net/~ninianne/ writings/mlw-gw.html

Biography and portrait of the American novelist credited with the creation of many of the myths surrounding George Washington. This site gives full background to the man and the story he helped to create. The aftermath of his publication of Washington's biography is also examined here.

Girlhood of Harriet Beecher Stowe

http://etext.lib.virginia.edu/etcbin/browse-mixed-new?id=StoGirl&tag=public& images=images/modeng&data=/texts/ english/modeng/parsed

E-text of a book about the girlhood of the US suffragist and author Harriet Beecher Stowe written by her son Charles Edward Stowe and her grandson Lyman Beecher Stowe. The original print version was published by McClure's Magazine in 1911. The text contains a number of photographs of members of the Beecher family.

Harriet Jacobs, *Incidents in the Life of a Slave Girl*

http://digilib.nypl.org/dynaweb/digs/ wwm97255/@Generic__BookView

Complete text of this novel from the black American writer Harriet Jacobs. This page is part of an extensive collection about black American women writers, from the New York Public Library Web site.

Harte, Bret

http://www.sehs.lane.edu/sehs/infos/menwomen/ Harte/Harte.html

Profile of the impulsive plain-speaking US poet. It traces his youth in the Californian gold fields and the many occupations he had before turning to writing. Extracts from his poems illustrate the lively nature of his style.

Hawthorne, Nathaniel

http://eldred.ne.mediaone.net/nh/hawthorne.html

Nathaniel Hawthorne resource featuring full editions of a number of his works. The site also includes extensive information about Hawthorne's life and his work, and offers numerous links to other related sites.

Herman Melville: Life and Works

http://www.melville.org/

Comprehensive Web site dedicated to the life and works of Herman Melville. Online resources include biography, bibliography, links to electronic editions of Melville's texts, reviews, text excerpts, Melville criticism, letters, and links to other relevant sites.

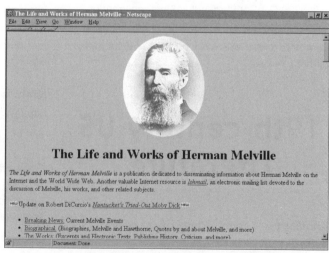

Howells, William Dean

http://eldred.ne.mediaone.net/wdh/howells.html

Texts of Howells's best-known novels and essays.

There is a photo of Howells and details of his encouragement of other writers and opposition to US imperialism. An obituary written shortly after his death puts his life in context.

Humour of Edgar Allan Poe

http://odur.let.rug.nl/~usa/E/poe_humor/poexx.htm

Part of a larger site on historical documents, this page is an essay examining the extent and nature of US writer Edgar Allan Poe's humour, indexed into six sections that offer historical, critical, and psychological perspectives of the man and his works. There are full-text versions of a selection of his stories and a link to biographical information.

'In the Depths of a Coal Mine' by Stephen Crane

http://www.history.ohio-state.edu/projects/coal/CraneDepths/CraneDepths.htm

This page features the text of a magazine article written by US novelist Stephen Crane which appeared in *McClure's* in August 1894. In this article, Crane describes the many unpleasantnesses associated with working in the coal mines during the late 19th century. The text of Crane's article is enhanced by numerous sketches.

John Burroughs – America's Most Beloved Nature Writer

http://english.ttu.edu/kairos/archives/1.1/carroll/jb.htm

Comprehensive source of information on the influential best-selling US poet. A picture of Burroughs emerges from a biography and extracts in which the writer describes himself. There is a selection of quotations on topics related to nature.

Kate Chopin Project

http://www.ee.calpoly.edu/~thoang/chopin.html

Detailed biography of the US novelist. It traces the formative influence of Black, Creole, and Cajun culture on her writing and the turbulent effect of the publication of *The Awakening* (the full text of which may be accessed). A bibliography and photos of Chopin are also provided.

Leaves of Grass by Walt Whitman

http://www.bartleby.com/142/index.html

Full text of Walt Whitman's best-known collection of poems. There are pictures of the poet, Whitman's handwritten biographical note, and an index to the poems and their first lines.

Life and Times of Henry D Thoreau

http://www.library.ucsb.edu/depts/thoreau/bexhibit.html

Comprehensive source of information on the pioneer US conservationist and advocate of civil disobedience. Thoreau's life as Harvard student, teacher, surveyor, and pencil manufacturer is described prior to an analysis of the influence of transcendentalism on his spiritual development. There are extracts from his major works and a guide to further sources of information on Thoreau.

Life on the Mississippi

http://tom.cs.cmu.edu/cgi-bin/book/lookup?num=245

Access to the complete text of this Mark Twain novel, which first appeared in 1883.

Mark Twain in His Times

http://etext.virginia.edu/railton/index2.html

In-depth look at the life and work of Mark Twain. This site contains many photographs and illustrations from his most popular works, not to mention detailed copies of original editions. All this is placed in the context of the period, with illuminating information on stage adaptations and the unusual marketing techniques he used to sell his books.

'Masque Of The Red Death, The'

http://www.poedecoder.com/Qrisse/works/masque.html

Text of Edgar Allan Poe's short story.

Melville's *Moby Dick*: electronic edition

http://www.hti.umich.edu/bin/pd-idx?type=header&id=MelviMoby2

Complete electronic edition of *Moby Dick* by Herman Melville distributed by the Oxford Text Archive.

Message To Garcia, A

http://www.eng.uci.edu/~mpontius/hartley/217-218_.html

Text of Elbert Green Hubbard's chief work.

Murders in the Rue Morgue, The

http://www.poedecoder.com/Qrisse/works/murders.html

Text of Edgar Allan Poe's celebrated short story.

Poems of Emma Lazarus

http://www.hti.umich.edu/bin/amv-idx.pl?type=header&id=LazarPoem1

Large selection of the best-known poems of Emma Lazarus. This 1889 edition of her poems, published two years after her death, has a long introduction to the life and work of the US poet.

Poems of Sidney Lanier

http://www.hti.umich.edu/bin/amv-idx.pl?type=header&id=LaniePoems

Complete text of the 1885 edition of Sidney Lanier's *Poems*.

Poems, William Vaughn Moody

http://www.hti.umich.edu/bin/amv-idx.pl?type=header&id=MoodWPoems

Selection of the best-known poems of William Vaughan Moody.

Poganuc People: Their Loves and Lives

http://etext.lib.virginia.edu/etcbin/browse-mixed-new?id=StoPoga&tag=public&images=images/modeng&data=/texts/english/modeng/parsed

Complete text of this work by Harriet Beecher Stowe. It also includes a number of images scanned from print editions of the book.

Red Badge of Courage, The

http://www.cs.cmu.edu/People/rgs/badge-table.html

Full text of Stephen Crane's epic novel of the US Civil War.

Rip Van Winkle Site

http://www.cwrl.utexas.edu/~daniel/amlit/rvw/rvw.html

Complete text of Washington Irving's account of the legendary sleeper. There are in addition several analyses of the significance of the work and its place in the development of US literature.

Selected Poetry of Edgar Allan Poe (1809–1849)

http://library.utoronto.ca/www/utel/rp/authors/poe.html

Features a number of poems by Edgar Allan Poe, including 'Annabel Lee', 'The Raven', and 'To Helen'.

Selected Poetry of Eugene Field (1850–95)

http://library.utoronto.ca/www/utel/rp/authors/field.html

Contains a brief note about the life and works of Eugene Field, as well as the texts of many of his poems, including *Little Boy Blue* and *Wynken, Blynken, and Nod*.

Selected Poetry of Helen Hunt Jackson (1830–1885)

http://library.utoronto.ca/www/utel/rp/authors/jacksonh.html

Features a brief biography of the US writer, as well as a photograph and a selection of her poetry.

Selected Poetry of Joseph Howe (1804–1873)

http://library.utoronto.ca/www/utel/rp/authors/howe.html

Features a brief biography, as well as the text of several poems by the Canadian politician Joseph Howe. Many of these poems have been annotated to aid understanding.

Selected Poetry of Julia Ward Howe (1819–1910)

http://library.utoronto.ca/www/utel/rp/authors/howejulia.html

Contains a biography of Julia Howe, as well as the text of several of her poems, including 'Battle Hymn of the Republic'. Many of the poems have been annotated to aid understanding.

Selected Poetry of Paul Laurence Dunbar (1872–1906)

http://library.utoronto.ca/www/utel/rp/authors/dunbarp.html

Contains a brief biography and photograph of the poet, as well as the text of many of his poems, several of which include explanatory notes.

'Song of Hiawatha' by Henry Wadsworth Longfellow

http://www.hti.umich.edu/bin/amv-idx.pl?type=header&id=LongfSongH

Full text of Longfellow's most famous poem.

Stephen Crane: Man, Myth & Legend

http://www.cwrl.utexas.edu/~mmaynard/Crane/crane.html

Maintained by the English department at the University of Texas, this site features a brief biography of the US writer Stephen Crane, audio clips of introductory passages from several of his works including *The Red Badge of Courage*, and a gallery of images of the author. This site also explores the themes, issues, and literary techniques that are present in Crane's work. There are links to related sites and research materials.

'The Gold Bug'

http://www.poedecoder.com/Qrisse/works/goldbug.html

Text of Edgar Allan Poe's short story.

Uncle Tom's Cabin

http://etext.lib.virginia.edu/etcbin/toccer-new?id=StoCabi&tag=public&images=images/modeng&data=/texts/english/modeng/parsed&part=0

Full text of the powerful novel which helped galvanize US sentiment against slavery.

Walden, or Life in the Woods

http://www2.cybernex.net/~rlenat/walden00.html

Text of Thoreau's classic work.

Washington Square

http://www.newpaltz.edu/~hathaway/washsq.html

Text of Henry James's novel.

20th-century US Literature (Pre-war)

Adventures and Letters of Richard Harding Davis

http://etext.lib.virginia.edu/cgibin/browse-mixed?id=DavAdve&tag=public&images=images/modeng&data=/lv1/Archive/eng-parsed

Illustrated version of Richard Harding Davis's work.

Age of Innocence, The

http://etext.lib.virginia.edu/etcbin/browse-mixed-new?id=WhaAgeo&tag=public&images=images/modeng&data=/texts/english/modeng/parsed

Complete text of Edith Wharton's Pulitzer prizewinning novel.

Alice Adams

http://etext.lib.virginia.edu/etcbin/browse-mixed-new?id=TarAlic&tag=public&images=images/modeng&data=/texts/english/modeng/parsed

Complete text of this novel by the US writer Booth Tarkington. Also featured here are a number of images and illustrations from the print editions.

Ambrose Bierce Appreciation Society

http://idt.net/~damone/gbierce.html

Introduction to the master of the sardonic short story. The site provides a portrait, an account of Bierce's life, summaries of his major works, lists of TV and film adaptations, and a bibliography.

Babbitt

http://etext.lib.virginia.edu/etcbin/browse-mixed-new?id=LewBabb&tag=public&images=images/modeng&data=/texts/english/modeng/parsed

Complete text of Sinclair Lewis's famous novel, first published in 1922. This online edition from the University of Virginia includes a number of images from an earlier print edition.

Buttered Side Down

http://etext.lib.virginia.edu/cgibin/browse-mixed?id=FerButt&tag=public&images=images/modeng&data=/lv1/Archive/eng-parsed

Complete text of Edna Ferber's novel. This edition includes the foreword as well as the original illustrations from the book.

Complete Works of Robert Frost

http://www.bartleby.com/155/index.html

Online edition of Frost's complete works up to 1920. Audio clips are available of readings of selected poems, and the poems can be looked up by title or by first line.

Cornhuskers

http://www.bartleby.com/134/index.html

Online edition of Sandburg's collection *Cornhuskers*. The poems are indexed both by title and by first line.

Dawn O'Hara, The Girl who Laughed

http://etext.lib.virginia.edu/cgibin/browse-mixed?id=FerDawn&tag=public&images=images/modeng&data=/lv1/Archive/eng-parsed

Complete text of this novel by the US writer Edna Ferber.

Devil's Dictionary, The

http://rabi.phys.columbia.edu/~matmat/html/devils.html

Complete text of Ambrose Bierce's ironic dictionary.

Dorothy Parker Pages

http://userwww.sfsu.edu/~mandelyn/

Tribute to the US writer famed for her ironic wit. The contents include a biography of Parker's career as poet and screenwriter, photos, a selection from her poems, and a bibliography.

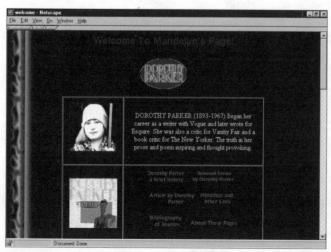

Edgar Lee Masters – *Spoon River Anthology*

http://www.outfitters.com/illinois/fulton/masters.html

Biographical facts about the US poet and details of his provocative best known volume of verse. The links between the haunting graveyard reminiscences and the real lives of the inhabitants of the Illinois towns which inspired Masters are traced.

Edith Wharton – Literature and Politics of her Time

http://www.npg.si.edu/exh/wharton/whar3.htm

Biography of the US novelist and analysis of the formative influences on her work. It traces her New York upbringing, her turbulent married life, her friendship with Henry James, and the years of exile broken only by a return to the USA to collect a Pulitzer prize. There is also a bibliography and a guide to further sources of information.

Edith Wharton's *The House of the Dead Hand*

http://www.hti.umich.edu/bin/pd-idx?type=header&id=WharEHouse

Complete electronic version of Edith Wharton's *The House of the Dead Hand,* distributed by the Humanities Text Initiative at the University of Michigan, USA.

Education of Henry Adams, The

http://xroads.virginia.edu/~HYPER/HADAMS/ha_home.html

Complete text of this autobiography from the University of Virginia. As well as the text itself, there are also a number of images to accompany this online edition as well as the editor's preface.

Fanny Herself

http://etext.lib.virginia.edu/cgibin/toccer?id=FerFann&tag=public&images=images/modeng&data=/lv1/Archive/eng-parsed&part=0

Complete text of Edna Ferber's novel. This edition includes the original illustrations from the book.

F Scott Fitzgerald Home Page

http://www.sc.edu/fitzgerald/

Extensive introduction to F Scott Fitzgerald from the University of South Carolina, USA. It includes a chronology,

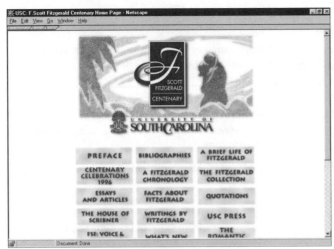

facts about the writer, quotations by and about him, voice and film clips, essays and articles about him, online presentations of his writings, and visual material on his life.

Hartford Friends of Wallace Stevens

http://www.wesleyan.edu/wstevens/stevens.html

Links to selected writings, a recording of Stevens reading 'Not Ideas About the Thing But the Thing Itself', an illustrated tour of his favourite daily haunts, and pictures of his grave site.

Harvester, The

http://etext.lib.virginia.edu/etcbin/browse-mixed-new?id=StrHarv&tag=public&images=images/modeng&data=/texts/english/modeng/parsed

Complete text of this novel by Gene Stratton Porter, first published in 1911. This online edition is from the University of Virginia and comes complete with a selection of images from earlier print editions.

Hemingway, Ernest

http://www.lostgeneration.com/hrc.htm

Large and detailed biography of the author Ernest Hemingway. There are several galleries dedicated to three aspects of Hemingway's life: as a hunter, soldier, and writer. Also included are a bibliography, a list of quotations, and reproductions of some of the paintings he liked.

Hilda Doolittle's Home Page

http://www.cichone.com/jlc/hd/hd.html

Guide to the life and work of the Imagist poet. It traces her personal tragedies and the influence of Ezra Pound (who gave Doolittle her pen name, H D). There are also extracts from her best-known poems.

H P Lovecraft Archive

http://www.hplovecraft.com/

Fulsome tribute to H P Lovecraft, considered by many to be the father of modern terror literature. There is a biography of this impoverished writer of the supernatural who achieved cult status after his death. This site also contains a wealth of other supporting material about the author – writings about Lovecraft, an extensive collection of his letters, and details of some of his more memorable characters.

Hurston, Zora Neale

http://pages.prodigy.com/zora/index.htm

Chronology and biography of this writer. There is a gallery containing photographs and paintings of Hurston, plus a number of essays about her and her works, and a detailed bibliography. There is also a video clip taken from a documentary profile, and a selection of extracts from Hurston's works.

Jack London Collection

http://sunsite.berkeley.edu/London/

Biography of the author Jack London, including a gallery and audio file. There is a large resource of documents relating to his life and work, including letters, postcards, telegrams, manuscripts, and other papers. The text of many of his novels, short stories, essays, and newspaper articles are reproduced, and there is a detailed bibliography too.

Laddie

http://etext.lib.virginia.edu/etcbin/browse-mixed-new?id=StrLadd&tag=public&images=images/modeng&data=/texts/english/modeng/parsed

Complete text of this novel by Gene Stratton Porter, first published in 1913. This online edition is from the University of Virginia.

Langston Hughes Boulevard

http://myhero.com/poets/hughes.asp

Tribute to the US man of letters. There is a large selection of his poems, biographical detail, and pictures of the poet.

Life of Helen Keller

http://www.rnib.org.uk/wesupply/fctsheet/keller.htm

Profile of the inspiring life of the US author. Presented by Britain's Royal National Institute for the Blind, it traces the determination which led Keller to overcome her disabilities to become a world renowned author and public speaker.

Lindsay, Vachel

http://www.hti.umich.edu/bin/amv-idx.pl?type=header&id=LindsBooth

Texts of Vachel Lindsay's volume of verse, *General William Booth Enters into Heaven*. As well as the full HTML text of the poems, this site also includes the original note on the author by Alan Light.

Lowell, Amy

http://www.sappho.com/poetry/historical/a_lowell.html

Full biography of the US Imagist poet. It traces her intense dedication to the art of poetry, her assistance to other poets, and the lesbian content which became increasingly explicit as her career developed. There are extracts from a number of her poems and a photograph.

MacLeish, Archibald

http://www.rothpoem.com/duk_am.html

Profile of the poet, playwright, and three time Pulitzer prizewinner. There is a brief biography and a photo of MacLeish. MacLeish's commitment to the view that intellectuals should engage with social and political issues is stressed.

Mad King, The

http://etext.lib.virginia.edu/etcbin/browse-mixed-new?id=BurMadk&images=images/modeng&data=/lv1/Archive/eng-parsed&tag=public

Illustrated version of Edgar Rice Burroughs's novel.

Main Street

http://etext.lib.virginia.edu/etcbin/browse-mixed-new?id=LewMain&tag=public&images=images/modeng&data=/texts/english/modeng/parsed

Complete text of Sinclair Lewis's best-selling novel, first published in 1920. This online edition from the University of Virginia includes a number of images from an earlier print edition.

Millay, Edna St Vincent

http://members.aol.com/MillayGirl/millay.htm

Good source of information on Millay. There is a biography and extracts from a large number of her poems.

Mrs Protheroe

http://www.softdisk.com/comp/naked/htmltext/prothero.html

Complete text of Booth Tarkington's novel.

Penrod

http://etext.lib.virginia.edu/cgibin/browse-mixed?id=TarPenr&tag=public&images=images/modeng&data=/lv1/Archive/eng-parsed

Complete text of Booth Tarkington's much loved tale of a boy and his dog. There are illustrations from a 1915 version of the novel.

Philosophy 4

http://world.std.com/~dpbsmith/phil4contents.html

Complete text of this work by the US novelist Owen Wister.

Poems

http://www.catawba.k12.nc.us/books/seegr10.txt

Complete text of Alan Seeger's collection *Poems*. This online edition contains work from his youth, his later poems, and his translations. There is also a detailed introduction by the Scottish dramatist William Archer.

Pound, Ezra

http://www.lit.kobe-u.ac.jp/~hishika/pound.htm

Central source of information on the life, works, and legacy of the influential US poet. The contents include biographical information, a comprehensive bibliography, a guide to other Pound resources, and regularly updated news of seminars and research.

Renascence and Other Poems

http://www.bartleby.com/131/index.html

Online edition of Edna St Vincent Millay's *Renascence and Other Poems*.

Selected Poetry of Carl Sandburg (1878–1967)

http://library.utoronto.ca/www/utel/rp/authors/sandburg.html

Contains a brief biography of the poet Carl Sandburg, as well as a large selection of his poetry, including several from the *Chicago Poems* collection.

Sinclair Lewis Home Page

http://www.ilstu.edu/~separry/lewis.html

Large source of information on the US writer. The contents include a biography, an excerpt from *Main Street,* a quiz, and details of latest research and seminars organized by the Sinclair Lewis Society. There is even a recipe for Lewis's favourite cookies.

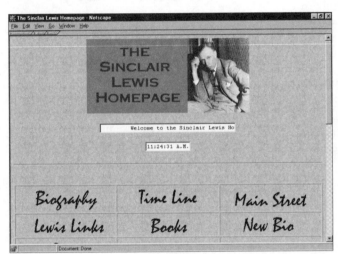

Six Poems by William Carlos Williams

http://etext.lib.virginia.edu/etcbin/browse-mixed-new?id=WilDial&tag=public&images=images/modeng&data=/texts/english/modeng/parsed

Contains the text of six poems from *The Dial* as well as several of the illustrations from the original edition.

Souls of Black Folk, The

http://www.bartleby.com/114/index.html

Online edition of *The Souls of Black Folk* by W E B DuBois.

Steinbeck Centre

http://www.steinbeck.org/world/biograph.html

Exploration of human values through universal ideas found in the works of John Steinbeck, providing access to information about the writer, his works, and contemporary thought.

Stein, Gertrude

http://dept.english.upenn.edu:80/~afilreis/88/stein-bio.html

Biography of the avant-garde, eccentric, self-styled genius. It traces her passion for Cubism, the role of her Paris salon in shaping the careers of the 'lost generation' of writers and artists, and her long relationship with Alice B Toklas. There are also details of her best-known works and a bibliography.

Tender Buttons

http://www.bartleby.com/140/index.html

Online edition of Gertrude Stein's *Tender Buttons.*

Thomas Wolfe Collection

http://www.lib.unc.edu/ncc/wolfe/index.html

Founded by a gift from the author's brothers and sisters, this collection, housed at North Carolina University, USA, includes 'correspondence, manuscripts, legal documents, family memorabilia, printed material by and about Wolfe, photographs, clippings, and recorded materials'. A selection of this material is available freely online, but this site also includes details of who to approach to gain access to the full collection for more serious study.

Three Poems by William Carlos Williams

http://etext.lib.virginia.edu/etcbin/toccer-new?id=WilPoem&tag=public&images=images/modeng&data=/texts/english/modeng/parsed&part=0

Contains the text of three poems from *The Dial* as well as several of the illustrations from the original edition.

Thurber's World (and Welcome To It!)

http://home.earthlink.net/~ritter/thurber/index.html

Information about the life, works, and legacy of the US humorist. There is a listing of his works, the films and TV shows inspired by them, a collection of his most famous aphorisms, and links to other 'Thurberabilia' pages.

Unofficial *e e* cummings Starting Point

http://members.tripod.com/~DWipf/cummings.html

Introduction to the US poet and novelist. There are biographical details, a portrait of the poet, and a bibliography. There is a discussion of whether cummings wanted to have his own name capitalized.

Upton Sinclair – Prophet of Social Justice & Prince of the Proletariat

http://www.kirjasto.sci.fi/sinclair.htm

Comprehensive source of information about the life and prolific output of the US socialist writer. Written by a US student inspired by reading Sinclair, it contains a biography and details of his literary and political endeavours. Sources of further information include a link to the full text of *The Jungle,* his celebrated exposé of the meat-packing industry.

What Every Girl Should Know

http://www.lib.msu.edu/spc/digital/radicalism/hq57.s281920.htm

Facsimile version of *What Every Girl Should Know* from the Radicalism Collection of the Michigan State University Libraries, USA. Click on each number to turn the page.

Willa Cather Page

http://icg.harvard.edu/~cather/

Comprehensive site with a biography, bibliography, and photo gallery. Also included are several critical articles, links to the text of her writings, and details of events relating to her life.

William Faulkner on the Web

http://www.mcsr.olemiss.edu/~egjbp/faulkner/faulkner.html

Large and detailed site about the American writer, including a biography, family tree, and chronology. There are also commentaries, plot synopses, and character studies, together with an extensive bibliography.

Young Adventure: A Book of Poems

http://www.hti.umich.edu/bin/amv-idx.pl?type=header&id=BenetYoung

Complete text of one of Benét's best-known volumes of verse.

Zane Grey Museum

http://www.nps.gov/upde/zgmuseum.htm

Site of the museum honouring the memory of 'the father of the Western novel'. A biography traces Grey's love of the outdoors, his baseball prowess, the persistence with which he pursued a desire to write despite rejection by publishers, and the wealth he obtained through his prolific output of Westerns and screenplays.

20th-century US Literature (Post-war)

Aiken, Conrad

http://members.pgonline.com/~iankluge/aiktitle.htm

Guide to the life and work of the 'philosophical Gothic' US man of letters. There is a biography and bibliography, selection of his works, sources of further information, and details of the Conrad Aiken Studies Journal.

Amy Tan Profile

http://www.achievement.org/autodoc/page/tan0pro-1

Description of the life and work of the best selling novelist Amy Tan. The Web site contains not only a profile and biographical information, but also holds a lengthy interview with Tan from 1996 accompanied by a large number of photographs, video sequences, and audio clips.

Angelou, Maya

http://www.geocities.com/Athens/1523/maya_b.html

Tribute to the US writer, highlighting her inspirational role for women and the powerless. There are extracts from Angelou's poems, pictures, and links to other sources of information.

Auden, W H

http://audensociety.org/

Appreciation of the work and life of W H Auden. There are also links to some of his poems, including 'Funeral Blues', made famous in the film *Four Weddings and a Funeral.*

Baldwin, James

http://www.bridgesweb.com/baldwin.html

Profile of the writer who forcibly articulated to a
white audience the reality of being black in the
USA. There is a biography of Baldwin, and a
small bibliography and an examination of the
controversy surrounding his play *Blues for Mr
Charlie.*

Bananafish Home

http://slf.gweep.net/~sfoskett/jds/

J D Salinger home page. Within these pages you
will find a bibliography, information on Salinger's
characters, opinions on his works, anecdotes, and
more. The Web site is subdivided into small
sections, the titles of which are often slightly
misleading in nature.

Bellow, Saul

http://www.emanuelnyc.org/bulletin/archive/36.html

Biographical sketch designed to assist readers to
understand the works of Saul Bellow. It stresses
the importance of Bellow's trilingual heritage of
English, Yiddish, and French, and the formative
influence of anthropological theory on his work.
The recurring themes of alienation and quest for
knowledge in his oeuvre are summarized.

Biographical Information on Toni Morrison

http://www.cwrl.utexas.edu/~mmaynard/Morrison/
biograph.html

Details of the career of the Nobel prizewinning
US novelist. The contents include a biography,
quotations from Morrison, extracts from reviews,
her Nobel Prize citation, a detailed study of
Beloved, and summaries of her other major works.

Bly, Robert

http://www.wnet.org/archive/lol/bly.html

Selection of some of Bly's best-known poems.
There are brief biographical details and a listing
of some of his books.

Bret Easton Ellis Page

http://www.geocities.com/Athens/Forum/8506/
index.html

Features information about the author and his
novels. There is a biography, as well as recent
news. His books are described and there are links

to both reviews and articles. The site is well
illustrated with photographs of the author and
scans of the covers of the books.

Candy is Dandy, but Liquor is Quicker – Ogden Nash Online

http://www.westegg.com/nash/

Comprehensive searchable online collection of the
pithy verse of the US poet and wit. There is a link
to some of Nash's famous aphorisms.

Carver, Raymond

http://world.std.com/~ptc/

Maintained by a student of Raymond Carver's life
and work, this Web site contains various
information on the contemporary American
writer. As well as an admittedly incomplete
bibliography and some biographical details, the
pages also feature several photographs of Carver
and an interview from 1978.

Catcher in the Rye Guide

http://www.euronet.nl/users/los/tcitr.html

Useful guide for students reading Salinger's
classic novel. The stream of consciousness
technique with which Salinger illustrates the
world of Holden Cauldfield is analysed. There is
a summary of the plot and critical reviews in
addition to a biography of Salinger.

Celestial Timepiece: A Home Page For Joyce Carol Oates

http://storm.usfca.edu/~southerr/jco.html

Title page for a large and comprehensive site on
Joyce Carol Oates. Clicking on the central image
calls up a contents page, which covers topics as
diverse as Joyce Carol Oates on Mike Tyson and a
list of her recent theatre productions.

Cheever, John

http://www.kirjasto.sci.fi/cheever.htm

Profile of the US novelist and short story writer.
There are biographical details, a list of his
publications, and sources of articles about
Cheever.

Don DeLillo's America – A Don DeLillo Page

http://perival.com/delillo/delillo.html

Large source of information on the life and work

of the US novelist. A biography examines the creative influences on his life through a series of extracts from interviews. There is a listing and summary of his novels, plus interviews, profiles, and reviews.

Further Travels With Ken Kesey

http://www.Key-Z.com/

Ken and the Prankster's own site with biographical details of Kesey and other seminal figures of the US beatnik and hippie movements. There are summaries of all of Kesey's novels, and latest news of Kesey and the further adventures of his famous psychedelic bus, Further.

Ginsberg, Allen

http://www.charm.net/~brooklyn/People/AllenGinsberg.html

Provides a lively biography of Ginsberg, including hyperlinks to people and movements of relevance, and to summaries and discussions of major works. The page discussing the poem 'Howl' is particularly impressive, including lengthy quotations from the poem, a critical analysis, and details of the obscenity trial which the poem provoked.

Gore Vidal Index

http://www.pitt.edu/~kloman/vidalframe.html

Very detailed pages dedicated to the controversial US author and critic, written and maintained by a fan. Included here are a number of essays and reviews about Vidal's writing, as well as a number of interviews.

Great Books: *Catch 22*

http://school.discovery.com/spring97/programs/greatbooks-catch22/

Discovery Channel Web site aimed at school students studying Joseph Heller's novel. The information here is centred around a television programme broadcast on the Discovery Channel, but much of what is contained in this site is capable of standing on its own. A glossary of terms used in the book is included, and several key questions on the book are listed and answered.

Great Thompson Hunt

http://www.tekknowledge.com/gonzo/

Must for gonzo journalism fans. Contents include several biographies of Hunter S Thompson, details of his work, critiques, perceptive analyses

of his place in American literature, pictures of the man himself, and news of his latest jousts with authority.

Gwendolyn Brooks Page

http://www.math.buffalo.edu/~sww/brooks/brooks.html

Tribute to the black American poet. Brief biographical details and a photo are accompanied by a selection of her poems, including 'The Good Man' and 'The Ballad of Rudolph Reed'.

Heller, Joseph

http://www.levity.com/corduroy/heller.htm

Profile of the satirical novelist. It traces his consistent opposition to the military-industrial complex. There is a photo of the author and a list of further information resources.

Henry Miller Library

http://www.henrymiller.org/

Information about the exuberant US writer from a library in Big Sur, California. There is a biography of Miller, a complete listing of his works, and an extract from *Tropic of Cancer* to illustrate the passions which drove the controversial writer.

Interview With Allen Ginsberg

http://www.bigtable.com/primer/0007b.html

Interview with Ginsberg by George Petros. The interview is not dated and referenced, but then neither is the work of Ginsberg. This lengthy text-only interview covers details of Ginsberg's life and works ranging from his literary influences to his views on drugs. The politics of the beat generation are also discussed, and Petros makes a long contextual introduction to the background and works of Ginsberg.

Interview with William Gibson

http://www.ulib.org/webRoot/Books/_Gutenberg_Etext_Books/etext95/wmgib10.txt

Complete text of Giuseppe Salza's interview with the US writer William Gibson, famed for writing the novel *Neuromancer* and also for his work on films such as *Johnny Mnemonic*.

Isaac Asimov FAQ

http://www.clark.net/pub/edseiler/WWW/asimov_FAQ.html

Extensive list of 'Frequently Asked Questions' about Isaac Asimov, one of the most celebrated science-fiction writers of our day. The site provides a useful introduction to the writer, as well as specific information on Asimov's life and literary career. Discussions are also included of the contradictions within the *Foundation* and *Robot* books, the relation of Asimov's plots to *Star Trek,* and the legendary three laws of Robotics.

James Dickey – A Memory

http://entropy.me.usouthal.edu/harbinger/xvi/971007/clark.html

Tribute to the US man of letters written shortly after his death in 1997. It examines Dickey's place within American literature and provides biographical details. Recollections of Dickey running a poetry workshop provide an intimate glimpse of the poet.

John Grisham Profile

http://www.achievement.org/autodoc/page/gri0pro-1

Description of the life and work of the US best-selling author John Grisham. This Web site contains not only a profile and biographical information, but also a lengthy interview with Grisham from 1995 accompanied by a large number of photographs, video sequences, and audio clips.

Katherine Anne Porter Page

http://www.accd.edu/sac/english/bailey/porterka.htm

Information on the life and literary output of the US short story writer. There is a photo, brief biographical details, a review of a book on Porter, and a listing of her major works.

Kerouac, Jack

http://www.charm.net/~brooklyn/People/JackKerouac.html

Detailed biography of Kerouac with many useful hyperlinks to sections on people and movements of relevance, and to summaries and discussions of his works.

King, Stephen

http://w3.tyenet.com/lepage/

News for fans of the popular novelist. The Web site features details of King's latest releases, offering progress reports on projects such as books, films, and television programmes. It contains regularly updated information on Stephen King's books and films, short stories, and even a chat room.

Leonard, Elmore

http://www.fusiondesign.com/books_unbound/elmorbio.htm

Biography of the US author. This Web site contains a biography of Leonard and links to details of a recent author tour around the USA.

Levertov, Denise

http://www.poets.org/lit/poet/dlevefst.htm

Good source of information about the life and work of the poet. It traces her childhood interest in literature, the legacy of her family's Jewish ancestry, the letter she wrote to T S Eliot at the age of 12, her emigration to the USA, her association with the Black Mountain Poets, and her outpouring of rage at the US involvement in the Vietnam War. There are also links to her best-known poems and essays.

Maxine Hong Kingston – Teacher Resource Guide

http://falcon.jmu.edu/schoollibrary/kingston.htm#A

Comprehensive information on the US writer. Designed to assist literature teachers, the contents explore Oriental culture through examination of the work of Kingston. There is a biography, complete listing of her works, critical reviews, interviews, and suggested study topics.

Maya Angelou and the African-American Tradition

http://www.usinternet.com/users/bdbourn/maya.htm

Discussion regarding the works of the African-American writer. The Web site takes the form of an essay, and focuses in particular on the African-American influences that according to the writer, Bryan D Bourn, added to her books but detracted from her poetry.

Maya Angelou's *On the Pulse of Morning*

http://www.hti.umich.edu/bin/pd-idx?type=header&id=AngelPulMo

Electronic edition of *On the Pulse of Morning* by

Maya Angelou, distributed by The Humanities Text Initiative at the University of Ann Arbor, Michigan, USA.

Michael Crichton Web Site

http://www.globalnets.com/crichton/left/frames.html

Biographical Web site dedicated to the US author and director Michael Crichton. The Web site combines biographical information with a comprehensive bibliography. Many of Crichton's works are reviewed briefly, and the site also polls visitors to find out their favourite Crichton book This Web site is the 'Left Brain' version with a frames-type format; a 'Right Brain' version is also available based around an elaborate image map.

Moore, Marianne

http://www.cwrl.utexas.edu/~slatin/20c_poetry/projects/lives/mm.html

Chronology of the US poet Marianne Moore. The text of several of her poems is also provided, including 'The Steeple Jack' and 'The Fish'.

Nicholson Baker Fan Page

http://www.j-walk.com/nbaker/

Tribute to the US novelist. The contents include a photo, summaries of the six books he has written, interviews, and a large selection of reviews of his work and analysis of his place in US literature.

Norman Mailer: His Life and Works

http://www.iol.ie/~kic/

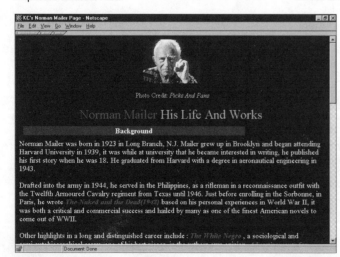

Profile of the long career of the US man of letters. In addition to biographical details and photos, there is a bibliography and a selection of Mailer's pungent observations on US life.

Objectivism: The Philosophy of Ayn Rand

http://www.aynrand.org/entry.html

This site explores Objectivism and the life and ideas of Ayn Rand. Divided into three sections, the first part deals with Objectivism and includes a synopsis of the philosophy, a bibliography of Objectivist writings, essays that apply the philosophy to current events, a list of suggested readings, and questions and answers. The second section concerns the Objectivist writer herself, and includes a short biography, a timeline covering the major events in the writer's life, plus photo and video archives. The third section provides information regarding the Ayn Rand Institute. There is also a section concerning items of special interest, such as campus events, commentaries on current events, news of essay contests, and more.

O'Connor, Flannery

http://www.geocities.com/Athens/3966/

Assessment of the life and work of the Georgian author. It stresses the formative influence of the psychology of the Deep South on O'Connor's upbringing and literary style. There is also a biography, a bibliography, and a photo.

Olson, Charles

http://wings.buffalo.edu/epc/authors/olson/

Good source of information on the innovative Post-modern poet. There are details of all of Olson's major collections of poems and essays. Other contents include a selection of his poems, news of events celebrating his legacy, essays and reviews, and information of the Charles Olson Society.

Paul Bowles Page

http://www.lemmus.demon.co.uk/bowles.htm

Brief autobiographical details of Paul Bowles. There are listings of his novels, short story collections, autobiographical notes, and biographies. Sources of information on Bowles and his influence on the literary scene in his adopted home of Tangier are indicated.

Plath, Sylvia

http://www.poets.org/lit/poet/splatfst.htm

Comprehensive information about the life, poetic works, and legacy of the US poet. The contents include photos of Plath, a large selection of poems, a biography, a bibliography, literary reviews, and resources for scholars.

Poetry of Allen Ginsberg

http://www.geocities.com/SoHo/Cafe/1281/poetry.html

Contains a large selection of Ginsberg's poetry, including 'Howl' and 'A Supermarket in California'.

Practising Post-modernism: The Example of John Hawkes

http://jefferson.village.virginia.edu/~jmu2m/contemporary.literature.32:1.html

Critical analysis of the work of the Post-modernist author. The metaphors used by Hawkes, his interaction with critics, and the formative influences on his work are analyzed. This long and thoughtful essay also summarizes the plots of his novels.

Pynchon, Thomas

http://pete.pomona.edu/pynchon/

Biography and appreciation of the reclusive novelist. The known facts of his life and the formative influences on his work are presented. There are also descriptions of his major books, a bibliography, and audio clips.

Ralph Ellison's *Invisible Man*

http://www.english.upenn.edu/~afilreis/50s/ellison-main.html

Selection of articles on or by US writer Ralph Ellison. The Web site also includes a chapter summary of Ellison's novel *Invisible Man*, in addition to a couple of reviews of the book. The articles are fairly biographical, and focus on Ellison's struggle to be recognized as a black writer.

Raymond Chandler Web Page

http://www.geocities.com/Athens/Parthenon/3224

Features a chronology of the life of novelist Raymond Chandler, together with essays and criticism, a gallery, and a bibliography. This site also contains the text of some of Chandler's early works.

Rich, Adrienne

http://www.wnet.org/archive/lol/rich.html

Short selection of poems by the US feminist thinker and political analyst. The site also contains a listing of Rich's collections of poetry and essays.

Richard Ford: He Champions Ordinary Experiences

http://www.examiner.com/celebs/ford.html

Intimate profile of the Pulitzer-prizewinning author. There is a summary of the plot and themes of *Independence Day* and a photo of Ford. Revealing extracts from interviews with Ford indicate his restless nature, inviting comparison with that of his main character, Frank Bascombe.

Richard Wright – *Black Boy*

http://www.pbs.org/rwbb/rwtoc.html

Tribute to the US novelist. A biography traces the turbulent upbringing of the sharecropper's son, his interest in literature, his experience of racism, and his exile in France. There is also a bibliography.

Roethke, Theodore Huebner

http://www.thebrothers.com/eraaz/roethke1.html

Good source of information about the lyrical poet. The contents include a biography, frequently asked questions, a list of works, and a bibliography.

Roth, Philip

http://www.ngc.peachnet.edu/Academic/Arts_Let/
LangLit/dproyal/roth.htm

Philip Roth research home page. The content of the Web site consists primarily of very lengthy lists of Roth's work and critical reviews, but also included is a brief biography and a photograph portrait of the writer.

Salon Interview: John Updike

http://www.salon1999.com/08/features/updike.html

Interview with the US writer John Updike. The interview covers topics as diverse as the fall of modern literature and the behaviour of President Clinton. The interview also covers parts of Updike's work, and discusses his attitude to women in his novels.

Stillman's Maze

http://www.bluecricket.com/auster/auster.html

Dedicated to the contemporary US writer Paul Auster. Most famous for *The New York Trilogy*, Auster is also the author of several other groundbreaking novels. Images of most of the major book covers are included, as well as a picture of the man himself. Access to both a biography and a bibliography is also available, and some of the other features of the Web site include an Auster news section and a few media articles featuring the writer and his works.

Tan, Amy

http://www.achievement.org/autodoc/page/
tan0bio-1

Full source of information on the US writer. A biography traces her difficult relationship with her mother and the discovery of her family's Chinese roots which ended her career as a business speechwriter and propelled her into a successful literary career. There are photos, details of her novels, and a revealing interview with the author which contains some audio clips.

Thinking of Anaïs Nin

http://www.anaisnin.com/

Site dedicated to the memory of the French-born Catalan-Danish writer and diarist. Three long reminiscences by those who knew Nin highlight the main events of her life and artistic career. There are photos of Nin and details of books about her.

Thornton Wilder: The Centennial

http://www.thornton-wilder.com/novels/
heaven_nr.html

Comprehensive information about the life and works of the US man of letters. There are plot summaries of all his novels and plays, a sample of his essays, and a biography.

Truman Capote – A Black and White Tribute

http://www.ansoniadesign.com/capote/

Celebration of the work of Truman Capote. Revealing extracts from Capote's best-known works and interviews are accompanied by photographs of the author.

Unofficial Ursula K Le Guin Page

http://www.wenet.net/~lquilter/femsf/authors/leguin/

Tribute to the US science-fiction novelist, short story writer, and poet. There are interviews with Le Guin, several reviews and critical studies of her work, and a good bibliography. Other related Internet sources are indicated.

Updike, John Hoyer

http://www.users.fast.net/~joyerkes/

Information and forum for discussion about Updike's life and works. The site includes a biography, bibliography, and selections from his writings.

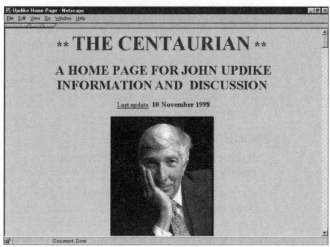

see p 208

Voices From The Gaps : Alice Walker

http://voices.cla.umn.edu/authors/AliceWalker.html

Biographical Web site about US author and civil-rights campaigner Alice Walker. The Web site gives a short biography of Walker including a photograph, and goes on to provide a selected bibliography of her works.

Vonnegutweb

http://www.duke.edu/~crh4/kv/

Huge source of information about the cult US writer. The contents include summaries and analyses of his many novels and short story collections, extensive biographical and personal information, interviews, and a guide to sources of further information.

Welcome to the HomeBrew Charles Bukowski Page

http://www.btinternet.com/~homebrew/

Intimate portrait of the self-abusing drifter and his literary output. Bukowski's life is charted through letters, interviews, pictures, and extracts from his poetry.

William Gaddis Page

http://www.mrsite.com/gaddis/

Good source of information on the US novelist. There is a detailed reader's guide to his best-known novel, *The Recognitions,* information about his other three novels, and assistance to those wishing to explore further the complex world of Gaddis's work.

William S Burroughs (1914–1997)

http://www.bigtable.com/

All things Burroughs. This very large Web site features many pieces of information on William S Burroughs which go far beyond the merely biographical. The primer section, for example, contains dozens of lengthy files that are certainly more than a mere primer, covering as they do almost every aspect of his life and works. The Web site also features a memorial section published since the writer's death in 1997.

Wolfe, Gene

http://world.std.com/~pduggan/wolfe.html

Home page dedicated to the US science-fiction writer Gene Wolfe. The Web site includes several interviews, an incomplete bibliography, images of Wolfe's book covers, and a news section. A well-researched links section is also included.

Zembla – the Nabokov Butterfly Net

http://www.libraries.psu.edu/iasweb/nabokov/nsintro.htm

Extensive site devoted to the life and works of Vladimir Nabokov created by Pennsylvania State University, USA. It includes a biography, photographs of his birthplace, and critiques of his writings.

US Children's Literature

Adventures of Huckleberry Finn, The

http://www.lm.com/~joseph/finn/finntitl.html

Hypertext copy of *The Adventures of Huckleberry Finn* by Mark Twain.

Adventures of Tom Sawyer, The

http://www.bibliomania.com/Fiction/MarkTwain/TomSawyer-Adventures

Electronic edition of Mark Twain's *The Adventures of Tom Sawyer.*

Biography of Joel Chandler Harris

http://xroads.virginia.edu/~UG97/remus/bio.html

Biography of the US folklorist. It traces the role of Harris in introducing the patterns and rhythms of southern African-American speech into US literature through the medium of the character Uncle Remus. With his adroit ear for the subtleties of dialect, Harris is compared with Aesop and Chaucer.

Good Wives

http://www.bibliomania.com/Fiction/alcott/GoodWives/index.html

Online hypertext edition of the novel *Good Wives* by Louisa May Alcott.

Horatio Alger Society

http://www.ihot.com/~has/

Contains a bibliography of the works of Horatio Alger, together with scans of the bindings, illustrations, and dust jackets of several of his books. Also provided are links to e-text versions of his writings and details about joining the Horatio Alger Society.

Little Women

http://www.bibliomania.com/Fiction/alcott/littlew/index.html

Hypertext edition of *Little Women* by Louisa May Alcott.

Marvelous Land of Oz, The

http://www.cs.cmu.edu/People/rgs/ozland-table.html

The first sequel to L Frank Baum's *The Wonderful Wizard of Oz.*

Paul Prescott's Charge

http://etext.lib.virginia.edu/etcbin/browse-mixed-new?id=AlgPaul&images=images/modeng&data=/lv1/Archive/eng-parsed&tag=public

Illustrated text of this novel by Horatio Alger.

Ragged Dick

http://etext.lib.virginia.edu/etcbin/toccer-new?id=AlgRagg&tag=public&images=images/modeng&data=/texts/english/modeng/parsed&part=0

Online plain-text copy of Horatio Alger's *Ragged Dick.*

Rebecca of Sunnybrook Farm

http://etext.lib.virginia.edu/etcbin/toccer-new?id=WigRebe&tag=public&images=images/modeng&data=/texts/english/modeng/parsed&part=0

Complete text of Kate Douglas Wiggin's children's classic. The text may be read as a single file or accessed chapter by chapter.

Remus Tales: Selected Text

http://xroads.virginia.edu/~UG97/remus/selections.html

Selections from the best-known tales of Brer Rabbit and Brer Fox. Each story is accompanied by an analysis of the plot and its didactic purpose.

Tarzan of the Apes by Edgar Rice Burroughs

http://www.cs.cmu.edu/People/rgs/tarz-ftitle.html

Full text of the novel which introduced Tarzan to the world. There are links to many of the sequels and to Burroughs's other works.

What Katy Did Next

http://www.bibliomania.com/Fiction/coolidge/next/index.html

E-text of *What Katy Did Next* by Susan Coolidge.

Wonderful Wizard of Oz by L Frank Baum

http://www.cs.cmu.edu/People/rgs/wizoz-ftitle.html

Full public-domain version of Baum's famous fantasy, together with Baum's original preface.

Canadian Literature

Davies, Robertson

http://www.tceplus.com/davies.htm

Profile of the Canadian man of letters. It traces his interests in the theatre, academic life, Jungian psychology, and Canadian culture. There is also a bibliography and photo of Davies.

Leacock, Stephen

http://www.tceplus.com/leacock.htm

Good profile of the multi-talented Canadian. The main events of Leacock's life and his literary, economic, and political pursuits, are outlined.

There is a portrait, a list of his main books, and a useful bibliography.

Margaret Atwood Information Web Site

http://www.web.net/owtoad/copy.html

Comprehensive Web site on the Canadian author. The pages here contain reams of information on Atwood, including a biography and bibliography, transcripts of recent lectures, photographs, excerpts from her books, and even a section on her partner, Graham Gibson.

Margaret Laurence Society Home Page

http://quarles.unbc.edu/kbeeler_html/laurence/laurencetitle.html

Site of the society working to preserve the memory of the Canadian writer. In addition to details of her life, novels, and short stories, there is information about the Margaret Laurence Society and ongoing academic interest in her work.

Montgomery, Lucy Maude

http://www.upei.ca/~lmmi/cover.html

Biography of the Canadian novelist. Also included is a chronological list of her writings. There are also links to the text of several of her novels, including *Anne of Green Gables, Anne of Avonlea, Anne of the Island,* and *Anne's House of Dreams.*

Richler, Mordecai

http://www.tceplus.com/richler.htm

Profile of the Canadian novelist, scriptwriter, and journalist, containing a photo of Richler and a summary of his career. This site also contains a full listing of his main works and interesting analysis of his comic style.

Selected Poetry of Bliss Carman (1861–1929)

http://library.utoronto.ca/www/utel/rp/authors/carman.html

Features a biography and photograph of the Canadian poet, as well as a note on his works. The text of a number of his poems is included here, including *Low Tide on Grand Pré.*

Selected Poetry of Robert W Service (1874–1958)

http://library.utoronto.ca/www/utel/rp/authors/service.html

Contains a number of poems by Robert Service, including 'The Shooting of Dan McGrew'.

Asian Literature

Analects of Confucius, The

http://eawc.evansville.edu/anthology/analects.htm

Anonymous translation of the ancient Chinese philosophical text: *The Analects of Confucius.*

Book of Five Rings, The

http://www.GojuRyuKarateDo.Com/

Complete text of this book by the Japanese *samurai* Miyamoto Musashi. This online edition includes Musashi's introduction.

Classical Chinese Literature

http://zhongwen.com/gudian.htm

This site contains Chinese classics with each character hyperlinked to its definition and etymology. Works include the *Tao Te Ching, The Art of War,* and *Tang Poems.* There are links to English translations. No Chinese software is necessary.

'Gitanjali'

http://etext.lib.virginia.edu/etcbin/browse-mixed-new?id=TagGita&tag=public&images=images/modeng&data=/texts/english/modeng/parsed

Complete translation of this verse by the Bengali Indian writer Rabindranath Tagore. Also included on this page is an introduction to the work by the poet W B Yeats.

Japanese Text Initiative

http://etext.lib.virginia.edu/japanese/index.html

Collaborative online project by the University of Virginia and the University of Pittsburgh to make texts of classical Japanese literature available on the Web. The first text to have been made available is *Ogura Hyakunin Isshu/100 Poems by 100 Poets.*

Kagekiyo

http://etext.lib.virginia.edu/etcbin/browse-mixed-new?id=StoKage&tag=public&images=images/modeng&data=/texts/english/modeng/parsed

Complete text of this Japanese Noh play, translated by the eugenics campaigner Marie Stopes.

Kenzaburo Oé Home Page

http://www.imsa.edu/~ender/oe.html

Tribute to the Japanese winner of the Nobel Prize for Literature. There is a biography of the novelist, a listing of his works translated into English, and a guide to other Internet resources.

Mishima Gallery

http://www.bea.hi-ho.ne.jp/nbst/mishima.html

Tribute to the passionate Japanese novelist. The site contains details of all his novels translated into English and plot summaries. There are also photos of his house and the shrine kept in his honour.

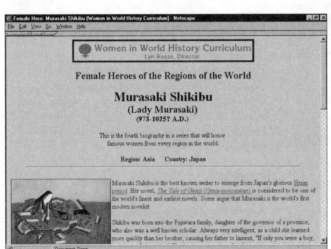

Murasaki Shikibu

http://home.earthlink.net/~womenwhist/heroine9.html

Portrait of Murasaki Shikibu, the best-known writer of Japan's Heian period and one of the earliest modern novelists. The short presentation is of particular interest to historians of literature and those interested in Japan's unique cultural heritage.

Sotoba Komachi

http://etext.lib.virginia.edu/etcbin/browse-mixed-new?id=WalSoto&tag=public&images=images/modeng&data=/texts/english/modeng/parsed

Text of this work by the orientalist Arthur Waley.

Tang Dynasty Poems

http://zhongwen.com/tangshi.htm

Over three hundred Tang dynasty poems. The poems are presented in both Chinese and English

texts, with the Chinese text characters in the readings hyperlinked – clicking on any character will call up its definition and etymology in a separate frame on the Web site.

Three Kingdoms by Luo Guanzhong (1300–1400)

http://www.geocities.com/Hollywood/Academy/8100/index.htm

Huge and lovingly prepared site devoted entirely to the Chinese classic romance *The Three Kingdoms*. The story, racily translated into English, is preceded by several maps, an outline of Chinese history, a section on the making of the Three Kingdoms, two prefaces by the authors, and two introductions. Click through each preface and chapter to gain access. There are also a number of wood-block illustrations accompanying the text.

Early International Literature

'Best' of Edward Gibbon's *Decline and Fall of the Roman Empire*

http://www.his.com/z/gibbon.html

Lengthy key excerpts from Gibbon's classic history of the Roman empire. There is a separate section of famous short quotes from the work which illustrate the cadences and timing of Gibbon's prose.

Conde Mansion

http://www.geocities.com/Athens/Acropolis/7362/

Life, times, and works of the Marquis de Sade. Included is a complete chronology, excerpts from works such as *Aline et Valcour* and *101 Days of Sodom,* and the complete *Dialogue Between A Priest And A Dying Man.*

Digital Dante Project

http://www.ilt.columbia.edu/projects/dante/index.html

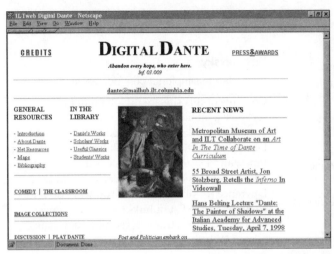

Devoted to the ideas and essays of French writer Michel de Montaigne. It features the text of 21 of Montaigne's essays of self exploration, arranged by title. The database containing the essays can be searched by word or phrase. You will also find a brief biography, including a timeline and a link to an external site for additional biographical information.

Philosophical Dictionary by Voltaire

http://history.hanover.edu/texts/voltaire/volindex.htm

Full text of H I Woolf's translation of Voltaire's celebrated *Dictionnaire Philosophique.*

Polish Poets

http://www.okcom.net/~ggao/Europe/Poland/poland.html

Poems in English by three 16th–17th-century Polish poets: Kochanowski, Szymonowicz, and John Gawinski.

Prince, The

http://www.fordham.edu/halsall/source/prince-excerp.html

Excerpts from Machiavelli's classic work, taken from the Internet Medieval Sourcebook.

Not just the *Divine Comedy,* of which, incidentally, there is a choice of no less than six different annotated translations, but a whole study resource on Dante. It includes related images, a discussion group, and a search facility, as well as a library of related resources.

Don Quixote Exhibit

http://milton.mse.jhu.edu:8006/

Imaginative and instructive interactive exhibit of translations and illustrations of Cervantes's novel *Don Quixote.* There are two versions of the 'tour' through this site – one graphical, the other text-based.

B*History of the Thirty Years' War*

http://www.catawba.k12.nc.us/books/1jcfs10.txt

Translation of this work by the German dramatist, poet, and historian Friedrich Schiller. This online edition comes complete with preface.

Marie Madeleine Pioche de la Vergne, Comtesse de la Fayette

http://www.knight.org/advent/cathen/08738b.htm

Biography of the innovative French novelist. It describes the fame won by her wit and literary talents, and the work which led to her being regarded as the writer of the first French psychological novel.

Montaigne, Michel Eyquem de

http://www.orst.edu/instruct/phl302/philosophers/montaigne.html

19th-century International Literature

Alciato's *Book of Emblems*

http://www.mun.ca/alciato/e001.html

English translations of Alciato's emblems. There are links to the Latin versions and to a commentary on each. The site uses the Latin text and images from the illustrated 1621 edition. It was created by the Department of English, Memorial University of Newfoundland, Canada.

Anna Karenina

http://ccel.wheaton.edu/t/tolstoy/karenina/karenina.txt

Complete text of the Constance Garnett translation of Tolstoy's epic of passion, adultery, and death. The entire book can be downloaded as a single file.

Around the World in 80 Days

http://www.bibliomania.com/Fiction/verne/world/index.html

Online hypertext edition of the Jules Verne classic *Around the World in 80 Days*.

Baudelaire, Charles

http://www.geocities.com/Paris/Metro/1301/

Contains the text of several poems by Baudelaire, including 'Consecration', 'Beauty', and 'Get Drunk!'

F A C T

SYMBOLISM

late 19th-century movement in French poetry, which inspired a similar trend in French painting. The Symbolist poets used words for their symbolic rather than concrete meaning.

Brothers Karamazov, the

http://ccel.wheaton.edu/d/dostoevsky/karamozov/karamozov.txt

Complete text of the Constance Garnett translation of Dostoevsky's famous novel. The entire book can be downloaded as a single file.

Carducci, Giosuè

http://www.nobel.se/laureates/literature-1906-1-bio.html

Biography of the Italian poet. His grounding in classical literature is described prior to a description of Carducci's poetry, his translations, and his active political life.

Crime and Punishment

http://ccel.wheaton.edu/d/dostoevsky/crime/crime.txt

Full text of the Constance Garnett translation of

Dostoevsky's epic novel. The complete novel can be downloaded as a single file.

Dostoevsky

http://stange.simplenet.com/dostoevsky/

Contents of this site are divided into three sections: a bibliography of Dostoevsky's published works, which includes books about Dostoevsky; a timeline of his tumultuous life and times; and Dostoevsky in the words of others, which includes quotes by everyone from D H Lawrence to Albert Einstein. You will also find a comprehensive list of links to critical essays, study guides, electronic texts, and numerous related Web sites.

Dramatist Björnstjerne Björnson

http://odin.dep.no/ud/nornytt/uda-444.html

Extensive profile of the man of letters from the Norwegian Foreign Ministry. His varied literary output is described, alongside a full account of his life. The question is raised of why Björnson received a Nobel Prize for Literature when his compatriot, Henrik Ibsen, did not.

Faust

http://eserver.org/drama/faust.txt

Complete translation of Goethe's classic play.

German Stories from the 19th Century

http://www.fln.vcu.edu/menu.html

Selection of stories in their original form and in translation. Many of them contain related information and original illustrations. Some also have audio and video clips.

Germinal

http://eldred.ne.mediaone.net/ez/germinal.html

Complete text of the Vintage Classics paperback translation of Emile Zola's best-known novel. This is a public domain version that may be freely used.

How a Russian Maupassant Was Made in Odessa

http://www.econ.uiuc.edu/~slavrev/upenn/fall94/al.zh.html

Long and thoughtful analysis of the themes in the work of Isaak Babel. There is particular emphasis on the influence of Tolstoy and Maupassant on the evolution of the literary style of the Oddessa-born Jewish writer. The differences between Babel's Nietzschean aestheticism and Tolstoyan moralism are stressed.

Hugo's *Les Miserables* (Fantine, Cosette, Marius)

http://www.hti.umich.edu/bin/pd-idx?type=header&id=HugoVMiser

Complete electronic edition of Victor Hugo's *Les Miserables* offered by the Humanities Text Initiative at the University of Michigan, USA.

Journey to the Centre of the Earth

http://www.math.technion.ac.il/~rl/JulesVerne/vt/c_earth

Text of Jules Verne's classic novel.

'Living Mummy, The'

http://etext.lib.virginia.edu/etcbin/browse-mixed-new?id=TouLivi&tag=public&images=images/modeng&data=/texts/english/modeng/parsed

Complete translation of this story by the Russian author Ivan Turgenev.

Man in the Iron Mask, The

http://www.hoboes.com/html/FireBlade/Dumas/IronMask/

Complete text of Dumas's classic novel.

Maupassant's *Short Stories of the Tragedy and Comedy of Life*

http://etext.lib.virginia.edu/etcbin/browse-mixed-new?id=MauStor&images=images/modeng&data=/texts/english/modeng/parsed&tag=public

Twenty-seven stories by Guy de Maupassant from the Electronic Text Centre of the University of Virginia Library, USA. The stories are accompanied by a preface by Paul Bouget and an introduction by Robert Arnot, with illustrations from the three volumes of stories published in 1903 by Walter Dunne.

Mistral, Frédéric

http://www.nobel.se/laureates/literature-1904-1-bio.html

Biography of the Nobel-prizewinning Provençal poet. It traces his privileged upbringing and his lifelong commitment to establishing Provençal as a recognized literary language. There is a summary of his best-known epic and lyrical poetry.

Reminiscences of Tolstoy

http://etext.lib.virginia.edu/etcbin/browse-mixed-new?id=TolRemi&tag=public&images=images/modeng&data=/texts/english/modeng/parsed

Complete translation of this work about Leo Tolstoy by his son Ilyá. Also featured here are illustrations from the print editions.

Sienkiewicz, Henryk

http://www.nobel.se/laureates/literature-1905-1-bio.html

Profile of the life of the popular Polish nationalist writer. It traces Sienkiewicz's education, his early satirical writings, his trip to the USA, and the enormous literary output resulting from his dedication to writing about the history of Poland.

Tolstoy Library

http://www.tolstoy.org/

Dedicated to the collection and dissemination of critical and literary works by and about the life and work of Leo Tolstoy.

Twenty Thousand Leagues Under the Sea

http://www.geocities.com/Vienna/1414/20000.html

Full text of Jules Verne's account of the adventures of Captain Nemo.

Twenty-Three Tales

http://etext.lib.virginia.edu/etcbin/browse-mixed-new?id=TolTale&tag=public&images=images/modeng&data=/texts/english/modeng/parsed

Large selection of stories by Leo Tolstoy, written between 1872 and 1903.

20th-century International Literature

Anna Akhmatova Page

http://dybka.home.mindspring.com/jill/akhmatova/

Site featuring a biography of Anna Akhmatova and a bibliography, along with a number of paintings of the poet. It also contains links to other sites about Akhmatova, her contemporaries, and places where further research can be carried out.

Anne Frank Online

http://www.annefrank.com/

Story of Anne Frank's diary, its publishing history, and how the diary's authenticity was established. A photo scrapbook of her life complements brief entries from the diary. A short history of the Holocaust with links and related information is currently under construction.

Beauvoir, Simone de

http://people.delphi.com/gkemerling/ph/beav.htm

This page begins with a biography of the French novelist and existential thinker, and then provides an overview and analysis of Beauvoir's seminal feminist work *The Second Sex*. The text includes a number of quotes from Beauvoir and several hypertext links. At the bottom of the page, you will find a bibliography and a list of sources.

Binchy, Maeve

http://www.readireland.ie/aotm/Binchy.html

Detailed biography of the Irish writer. There is also an analysis and description of some of her writing.

Blanchot, Maurice

http://ivory.lm.com/~kalin/blanchot.html

Profile of the life and work of the French novelist. There is a listing of the main writings translated into English and revealing short extracts from two of them.

Camus, Albert

http://members.aol.com/KatharenaE/private/Philo/ Camus/camus.html

Biography and photograph of the writer and philosopher Albert Camus, as well as translations of a number of his writings. There are also a number of links to essays about his life and work.

Chinua Achebe: An Overview

http://www.stg.brown.edu/projects/hypertext/ landow/post/achebe/achebeov.html

Detailed information about this Nigerian novelist. There is a brief biography and a detailed bibliography, however, the main focus of this site is naturally on his works. Many aspects of his work are considered, including politics and religion, as well as more exclusively literary issues, such as theme, characterization, and narrative structure.

Constructing Franz Kafka

http://info.pitt.edu/~kafka/intro.html

Very large Web site at the University of Pittsburgh's German department. A biography and a bibliography feature prominently here, but there are also many other subject areas available to the visitor, such as the section on teaching Kafka, or the list of texts available on the Web. The site is at least partly bilingual, mostly in English, but much of Kafka's work is reproduced in its original German.

Eluard, Paul

http://ivory.lm.com/~kalin/eluard.html

Brief introduction to Paul Eluard, the famous French Surrealist writer, with biographical information, a selection of his work in English translation, and characteristic excerpts from his poetry and prose.

Eva is Inside her Cat – Gabriel García Márquez

http://www.bnl.com/shorts/stories/eva.html

Full text of 'Eva Is Inside Her Cat', by Gabriel García Márquez – one of the most celebrated short-story writers of the 20th century.

Franz Kafka Photo Album

http://www.cs.technion.ac.il/~eckel/Kafka/ kafka.html

Selection of eighteen photographs of the celebrated Czech author and his family and friends, ranging from pictures of Kafka as a child to one of his gravestone in Prague.

see p 216

Garden of Forking Paths, The

http://www.rpg.net/quail/libyrinth/borges/

Information about the Argentine author Jorge Luis Borges, including biography, bibliography, images, analysis and criticism, and a guide to other relevant Web sites.

Gordimer, Nadine

http://nobel.sdsc.edu/laureates/literature-1991-1-bio.html

Profile of 'the doyenne of South African letters'. It traces her literary career, her commitment to free speech, and the background to the award of the Nobel Prize for Literature. There is also a listing of her books and short stories and a picture.

Greek Literature – Nikos Kazantzakis

http://www.interkriti.org/culture/kazantzakis/kazantz2.htm

Large source of information on the celebrated Cretan writer. Kazantzakis's interest in religion is stressed. There is also a discussion of how two of his books illustrate his desire to merge the Dionysian and Apollonian sides of the Greek heritage.

In a German Pension

http://www.buffnet.net/~starmist/kmansfld/german_pension/german_p.htm

Katherine Mansfield's first published work with links to each short story and an introduction by John Middleton Murray.

Joseph Brodsky (1940–1996): In Memoriam

http://www.sharat.co.il/nosik/brodsky/

Founded as a memorial to the late poet, this site contains an obituary of Brodsky as well as numerous examples of his work. There are also several links to other sites where further information about Brodsky can be found.

Keneally, Thomas

http://www.book.uci.edu/Keneally.html

Very brief biography and summaries of Keneally's books. Although Keneally most famous for his Booker-prizewinning novel *Schindler's List*, this site also features short descriptions of 11 of his other novels, including *The Chant of Jimmie Blacksmith*.

'Life of the Bee'

http://eldred.ne.mediaone.net/mm/b.html

Philosophical essay by the Belgian poet and dramatist Maurice Maeterlinck, translated into English from French.

Literary Calendar – An Almanac of Literary Information

http://litcal.yasuda-u.ac.jp/LitCalendar.shtml

Calendar of information that provides literary births, deaths, and noteworthy events for every day of the year. The site is also searchable so you can look for a particular author or title. The site includes pictures, and links to other related Web pages.

Macondo

http://www.rpg.net/quail/libyrinth/gabo

Dedicated to Colombian Nobel prizewinning writer Gabriel García Márquez. This Web site contains a biography, a bibliography and numerous other information pages, including criticism, essays, and many images of the writer, his book covers, and various other topics.

Mahfouz, Naguib

http://www.sis.gov.eg/egyptinf/culture/html/nmahfouz.htm

Long profile of the Egyptian novelist and winner of the Nobel Prize from the Egyptian Ministry of Culture, which once banned his works. In addition to comprehensive details of his life and career, Mahfouz's place within the traditions of Arab literature is analysed. There are several pictures of Mahfouz and the areas of Cairo that have inspired him.

Mansfield, Katherine

http://www.buffnet.net./~starmist/kmansfld/kmansfld.htm

Substantial source of information on the life and work of the New Zealand writer. The contents include a biography, photos, and bibliography. There are complete texts of *In a German Pension* and many of her best-known stories.

Milan Kundera, *The Unbearable Lightness of Being,* and Prague

http://www.georgetown.edu/irvinemj/english016/kundera/kundera.html

Featuring a bibliography of Milan Kundera and a tour of his home city of Prague. There is also a partial listing of critical works about his writing, and information on the film version of *The Unbearable Lightness of Being.* The tour of Prague section of the site is mostly in the form of links to other resources.

Milosz, Czeslaw

http://www.kirjasto.sci.fi/milosz.htm

Tribute to Poland's best-known writer. A biography traces Milosz's disillusionment with communism and his years of exile.

Naipaul, V S

http://www.kirjasto.sci.fi/vnaipaul.htm

Biography of the Trinidadian-born writer who lives and works in Britain. This essay covers Naipaul's childhood and discusses some of his novels.

Paz, Octavio

http://www.nobel.se/laureates/literature-1990-1-bio.html

Biography of the prolific Mexican man of letters.

It traces his career as a diplomat, his resignation after the massacre of students in 1968, and his subsequent work as editor, poet, and essayist. There is a complete bibliography of books by and about Paz in English and Spanish.

Poems by Adam Lindsay Gordon

http://tom.cs.cmu.edu/cgi-bin/book/lookup?num =258

Best-known works of the Australian poet of the outback. The contents include *Sea Spray and Smoke Drift, Bush Ballads and Galloping Rhymes,* and other less well-known verse.

Saint-Exupéry, Antoine Marie Roger de

http://www.westegg.com/exupery/

Numerous quotations from Saint-Exupéry's works, including *The Little Prince,* a bibliography, and a link to information about Saint-Exupéry's friend Emmanuel Bove.

Solzhenitsyn, Alexander

http://members.aol.com/KatharenaE/private/Alsolz/alsolz.html

Huge source of information on the Russian epic novelist. There is comprehensive biographical and autobiographical information. There are a number of reviews of his novels and analyses of his place in modern literature. Solzhenitsyn's views on the state of modern Russia are also set out here.

Walcott, Derek

http://www.almaz.com/nobel/literature/1992a.html

Extensive source of information on the St Lucian winner of the Nobel Prize for Literature. There is a biography of the poet and playwright, a listing of books by and about Walcott, and extracts from his poems and plays.

Welcome Prophet!

http://www.tcp.ca/Joshua/welcomeprophet.html

Complete hypertext of *The Prophet* by Khalil Gibran, the Lebanese philosopher highly acclaimed for his alluring and mystical-philosophical writing on life.

Zhou Shuren, pen name Lu Xun (1881–1936)

http://www.griffe.com/projects/worldlit/china/luxun.html

Chronological list of the collected works of the great Chinese short story writer and essayist Lu Xun. Works available in e-text are 'A Madman's Diary', 'A Small Incident', and 'The New Year Sacrifice'. There is also a link to other texts in Chinese.

International Children's Literature

Andersen, Hans Christian

http://www.math.technion.ac.il/~rl/Andersen/

All of Hans Christian Andersen's fairy tales can be accessed here, listed in chronological order of their publication and marked as to their perceived popularity. The site also boasts an extensive archive of portraits and photographs of the Danish storyteller.

Children's Authors

http://coe.west.asu.edu/students/dcorley/authors/authors.htm

Information about the authors of a range of best-selling children's literature from around the world, from Janet and Allan Ahlberg to Dr Seuss. Included is biographical details, bibliographies, and relevant links.

'Cinderella, or the Little Glass Slipper'

http://www-dept.usm.edu/~engdept/cinderella/cind5.html

Full electronic text of Cinderella, the famous folk tale, from an illustrated edition published in London as early as 1729. The text is accompanied by transcriptions of the manuscripts pages and is part of the Cinderella Project at the University of Mississippi.

Grimm's Fairy Tales

http://www.cs.cmu.edu/~spok/grimmtmp/

Full text of all 209 fairy tales originally collected by the Swiss Brothers Grimm. It includes such classics as 'Cinderella', 'Rapunzel', 'Hansel and Gretel', and 'Rumpelstiltskin'.

'Little Red Riding Hood'

http://www-dept.usm.edu/~engdept/lrrh/lrrhd.htm

Full text of the popular 'Little Red Riding Hood' from John Marshall's edition of the story which was published in 1823 in London, UK. The presentation, which is part of the Little Red Riding Hood Project at the University of Southern Mississippi, USA, is accompanied by transcriptions of the manuscript pages.

Swiss Family Robinson, The by Johann Wyss

http://ccel.wheaton.edu/wyss/swiss/swiss.html

Full text of William H G Kingston's translation of Wyss's famous adventure story.

Literary Criticism & Theory

Beat Generation

http://www.charm.net/~brooklyn/Topics/BeatGen.html

Lovingly-compiled project on the background and major figures of this literary movement. Includes biographies of major writers, summaries and analysis of major works, and background information on related movements.

King's English, The by Henry Fowler

http://www.bartleby.com/116/

Classic reference book to grammar. Part I deals with vocabulary, syntax, airs and graces, and punctuation; Part II with quotation, grammar, euphony, ambiguity and style. Click through the contents page to access sections. There are also links to a preface and a bibliography.

Stephen, Leslie

http://www.utm.edu/research/iep/s/stephen.htm

Biography of the British philosopher and man of letters. It traces the growing doubt which led him to abandon the priesthood for literary endeavours. His fame as an agnostic writer and editor is described.

Magic Realism

http://artcon.rutgers.edu/artists/magicrealism/magic.html

Essay discussing the concept of magic realism, the term used to describe the fantastic writing of authors including Angela Carter, Gabriel García Márquez, and Jorge Luis Borges.

Mencken, H L

http://www.bomis.com/cgi-bin/ring?page=1&ring=mencken

Tribute to the acerbic social commentator and defender of freedom of conscience and human rights. Examples of his writing include an extensive collection of Mencken's pithy observations on US puritanism and self-righteousness.

Pater, Walter

http://www.crl.com/~subir/pater/

Detailed biography of the scholar, essayist, and art critic. There is information about his works published both during his life and posthumously, and there is a critical biography too. Links are provided to the texts of many of his works.

Romanticism on the Net

http://users.ox.ac.uk/~scat0385/

Online journal dedicated to Romantic studies, which contains articles, reviews, announcements, and links to other related Web sites.

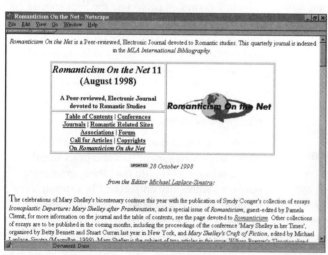

Selected Prose of John Dennis (1657–1734)

http://library.utoronto.ca/www/utel/rp/authors/dennis.html

Contains the text of Dennis's critical essay entitled 'The Grounds of Criticism in Poetry'.

Selected Prose of Walter Horatio Pater (1839–1894)

http://library.utoronto.ca/www/utel/rp/authors/pater.html

Contains a selection of essays by Walter Pater, including those on Wordsworth, Coleridge, and style.

Snow White

http://www.scils.rutgers.edu/special/kay/snowwhite.html

Huge source of information on the well-known fairy tale. Designed for students and teachers of fairy tales, it examines the meaning to be extracted from thirty-seven widely varying versions. There are illustrations, information about film adaptations of the story, and several articles from different authors analysing what *Snow White* is all about.

Stalinism and *Nineteen Eighty-Four*: Oceania and the Soviet Union

http://www.siue.edu/~aho/musov/oceania/1984.html

This essay compares features of Stalinist Russia with those of the fictional totalitarian state Oceania created by George Orwell in the book *Nineteen Eighty-Four*. It examines the characters and events in the book and compares them with real figures and real events in the USSR during the time of Stalin.

Symons, Arthur (1865–1945)

http://homepages.nildram.co.uk/~simmers/symons1.htm

Reproduces several poems by Symons, and features an illustrated chronology, which includes quotations from his life and poetry to build up a vivid impression of the poet. There is also a detailed bibliography.

Twists, Slugs, and Roscoes: Glossary of Hardboiled Slang

http://www.vex.net/~buff/slang.html

From *ameche* to *zotzed*, this page provides definitions for the occasionally incomprehensible street-slang spoken by the gumshoes, grifters, droppers, buttons, snoopers, wise heads, sharpers, tomatoes, trouble boys, twists, pro skirts, bindle punks, and wrong numbers who spice up the crime novels of Raymond Chandler, Dashiell Hammet, and Mickey Spillane. Next to the definitions, in parentheses, you will find abbreviated references to the novels from which the slang is derived. Look at the bottom of the page for the full titles and authors of the referenced books.

University of Victoria Writing Guide

http://webster.commnet.edu/HP/ pages/darling/original.htm?

Originally designed for English students at the University of Victoria, Canada, this site provides a wealth of information for aspiring novelists, poets, or students. The essay-writing section contains sample essays, step-by-step instructions to researching, writing, and proofing an essay, and a discussion of common problems. There is also a complete glossary of literary terms and a grammar guide.

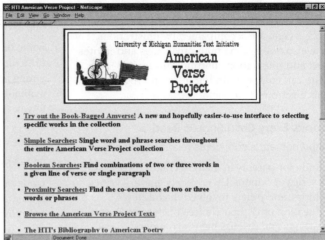

Miscellaneous Literature & Publishing

American Verse Project

http://www.hti.umich.edu/english/ amverse/

Continually expanding (and already immense) electronic archive of American poetry prior to

1920, searchable by various means including word, phrase, and proximity searches. Includes a bibliography of American poetry. Create a poem of your own by taking a random sampling of all the lines in the collection.

Arabic Literature

http://www.islam.org/Mosque/ihame/Ref5.htm

Substantial text-only account of the development of Arabic literature, from the primary document of Islamic faith – the Koran – which greatly influenced the course of Arabic literature, to the literary movements of the 20th century. The site includes links to aspects of Islam, and Islamic and Middle Eastern history.

Bartlett's Familiar Quotations

http://www.bartleby.com/99/index.html

Text of Bartlett's famous work which can be either browsed or searched.

BBC A–Z of authors

http://www.bbc.co.uk/education/ bookcase/az.shtml

A–Z list of authors who have been featured in the BBC Education Web pages. All the entries have either a brief biography, audio clips to download, or links to relevant articles.

Bed-Time Story

http://the-office.com/bedtime-story/

Resource for the busy parent offering a wide range of bedtime readings. The selection includes pet, dragon, bear, and monster stories, holiday stories, or

simply whimsical and adventurous fun stories. Every story is introduced by a helpful summary and several are accompanied by illustrations. The site also offers some midi music files and invites text and illustration contributions from people who can comply with the spirit and regulations of this electronic text book.

Books Every Child Should Read

http://homearts.com/depts/relat/bookintr.htm

Guide for parents to the best children's literature. A series of famous US novelists, literary critics, editors, and others involved in children's education offer their choices of children's readings and discuss their recommendations.

Burning Press

http://www.burningpress.org/bphome.html

Very much in-progress site collecting together various attempts by writers to make use of the new possibilities of Web publishing. You can browse online poetry here or view a gallery of what is known here as 'Vizlit' and 'Audioart'. It is also interactive in the sense that contributions are actively encouraged from visitors.

Celebration of Women's Writers

http://www.cs.cmu.edu/People/mmbt/women/writers.html

Very extensive site, still under development and dedicated to all aspects of women's contribution to literature. There is extensively linked biographical information here, as well as essays about, and text by, the various authors.

Children's Literature Web Guide

http://www.wre.liverpool.k12.ny.us/htmlpages/Whacked/textindex.html

Short on elegance, but not on information. This site was written by a specialist in the field and it includes information about recommended titles, reviews of children's books, lists of book awards and bestsellers, and a host of links to children's literature online.

Classics Archive

http://the-tech.mit.edu/Classics/

Searchable collection of hundreds of Greek and Roman texts in English translation or original plain form with commentary. Hyperlinks to other relevant sites are also available.

Classics for Young People

http://www.acs.ucalgary.ca/~dkbrown/storclas.html

Some of the most popular and increasingly difficult-to-find classic stories for children and young adults, now out of copyright and therefore available on the Web without complications. A few of these stories also come with illustrations.

Comics Page

http://www.comicspage.com/

Updates, news, events, reviews, online presentations, and much more archival and other engaging information about several classic comic titles. As a proper electronic community, the Comics Page also has its own bulletin board, chat room, contests, and trophies for fans.

Creative Quotations

http://www.bemorecreative.com/home-cq.htm

Find an inspiring quote from a vast database of famous people. The database is fully searchable theme, profession, or person.

Cyfarwydd – Storyteller

http://snowcrash.cymru.net/~nwi/cfarwydd.htm

Collection of tales retold from *The Mabinogion* and from Welsh folklore, including 'The changeling of Llanfabon' and 'Pryderi son of Pwyll'.

English Literature Main Page

http://vos.ucsb.edu/shuttle/english.html

Impressive base site if you are searching for works of literature written in English. It begins with resources on Anglo-Saxon literature, but also deals very well with literature written in English but outside the main UK-America axis. The site also includes resources on related fields such as cultural studies and creative writing.

Fairy Tales – Origins and Evolution

http://www.darkgoddess.com/fairy/

Exploration of the origins and the evolution of fairy tales. The presentation describes how fairy tales were not originally destined for children and investigates their gruesome elements, the tellers, and their intended audiences. It then examines how some of the most popular tales were modified and sanitized in order to become children's reading. The site also includes a 'Bookshelf' for further reading.

Haiku for People

http://www.toyomasu.com/haiku/

Extensive information about haiku. The pages introduce their history and form, how to write them, as well as haiku poems by Basho, Buson, Issa, and many others. You can also look at haiku written by less well-known individuals – these are arranged according to theme. There are also links to other Haiku sites.

History of Brazilian Literature

http://www.crl.com/~brazil/lit.htm

Pages devoted to the development of Brazilian literature, from the colonial period beginning in 1500, to the present day. The site is illustrated with photographs of Graciliano Ramos, Machado de Assis, Carlos Drummond de Andrade, and Jorge Amado. There is a link at the bottom of the page to aspects of Brazilian culture.

InterText

http://www.etext.org/Zines/InterText/

Not very visually spectacular, but this site contains about 200 stories across many genres. It is possible to access back issues of the magazine and to search and read the stories by author and title. If the choice is overwhelming, there's an editor's recommended list to help you out. If all that is too passive, there are also guidelines here for submitting stories for future editions.

KidPub

http://www.ehche.ac.uk/~wiredue/kidpub/

Site concerned not with underage drinking, but with publishing – with over 11,000 stories written by children around the world available to read here. What makes it special is the ability for children to submit new stories to the page, to add to the already impressive database.

Master Works of Western Civilization

http://www.eskimo.com/%7Emasonw/gwwc.htm

Essential reading list containing what are considered to be the most important works of Western civilization. It has been compiled from various sources: publishers, writers, and thinkers, and includes links to online versions of some of the texts.

Mother Goose Pages

http://pubweb.acns.nwu.edu/~pfa/dreamhouse/nursery/rhymes.html

Vast numbers of nursery rhymes divided into neat groups and accompanied with performance tips on reading them by children of varying ages. The site also offers a long list of books to read with children, while among its (future) attractions are musical notes and the historical background for each entry.

Online Medieval and Classical Library

http://sunsite.berkeley.edu/OMACL/

Online archive of medieval and classical texts including *Song of Roland* and *Orlando Furioso*. The site includes both search and download facilities, and offers a link to the Medieval Studies Web sites page.

Oxford Text Archive

http://sable.ox.ac.uk

Major archive of electronic texts with over 2,000 titles from a wide variety of sources and in many languages. The professionally designed site offers a catalogue of texts in plain text, HTML (sorted by language), and SGML with clear indications of the availability of the texts and their size, as well as details on how to order or contribute a text. There is also some useful material on SGML, the

Standard Generalized Markup Language used to encode the whole archive.

Poetry Zone

http://www.poetryzone.ndirect.co.uk/index2.htm

Designed and maintained by a travelling poet, Roger Stevens, this site aims to make poetry interesting and accessible for children. You are invited to contribute your own poetry, and there is a section for teachers and parents which includes worksheets and activities.

Tales of Wonder

http://darsie.ucdavis.edu/tales/index.html

Extensive collection of folk tales and fairy tales from around the world. They are divided into geographical areas and are published in large, colourful fonts which should make it easier for children to read them. There are stories from as diverse locations as Africa and Siberia.

Ultimate Electronic Publishing Resource

http://desktoppublishing.com/

Includes reviews of a number of DTP packages, as well as a large library of clip art and a number of links to sites on related topics, including Java, fonts, and graphics programs.

Welsh Literature: Introduction

http://www.britannia.com/wales/lit/intro.html

Introduction to the antiquity and continuity of the literature of Wales. The site provides numerous links to essays on chronologically arranged topics from the heroic poetry of the 6th century AD to 20th-century writing. There is also a recommended reading list.

Films

Alien

http://www.godamongdirectors.com/scripts/alien.shtml

Complete text of this film, directed by Ridley Scott, which set actress Sigourney Weaver on the road to stardom.

Annie Hall

http://www.godamongdirectors.com/scripts/annie.shtml

Complete script of Woody Allen's critically acclaimed film, made in 1977.

Battle over *Citizen Kane*

http://www.pbs.org/wgbh/pages/amex/kane2/index.html

Companion to the US Public Broadcasting Service (PBS) television programme *The American Experience*, this page tells the fascinating story of newspaper magnate William Randolph Hearst's efforts to prevent the classic film *Citizen Kane* from being released, because it reflected negatively on him. There are additional sections on Orson Welles's filmography and resources for further reading about Hollywood and the principal players in the *Citizen Kane* controversy.

Blade Runner

http://www.godamongdirectors.com/scripts/bladerunner_incomp.shtml

Script of this visually spectacular film, starring Harrison Ford, directed by Ridley Scott, and based on the novel *Do Androids Dream of Electric Sheep?* by Philip K Dick.

Braveheart

http://bay1.bjt.net/~melanie/bravehea3.html

Home page dedicated to the film version of the story of William Wallace. The Web site includes all sorts of information on the film, including a cast list, historical background to the story, quotes from the script, and audio clips in WAV format from the soundtrack. The page also includes a section of interesting facts; for example, the film was largely made in Ireland and the English army in the film was actually the Irish reserve force!

Carry Online

http://www.carryonline.com/

Fulsome tribute to the *Carry On* films and their cast. This site contains page after page of information on each of the films, biographies of cast members, and sound clips of memorable moments. The site is frequently updated.

Casablanca Home Page

http://users.aol.com/VRV1/index.html

Personal homage to one of the most memorable films from Hollywood's 'Golden Age'. It includes pictures, posters, an extensive cast list, reviews, and essays, as well as audio and video clips from the film.

Death Wish

http://www.geocities.com/Hollywood/Set/5040/

Comprehensive source of information on the films of Charles Bronson. There are plot summaries and reviews of the five *Death Wish* films and most of Bronson's other films, and a large selection of photographs. A quiz is included for Bronson fans.

Easy Rider

http://us.imdb.com/Reviews/84/8464

Review of the cult counter-culture movie, describing the progress of motorcycle riding drug dealers through small-town USA. The spare dialogue and cinematographic techniques are described.

Gone With the Wind – Forever and Always

http://members.aol.com/GoneWiWind/index.html

Tribute to the epic film of Margaret Mitchell's bestseller. The plot is summarized with profiles of the leading protagonists. There are pictures, sound clips, and details of the secrets used by Scarlett O'Hara to catch men.

Graduate, The

http://www.geocities.com/Hollywood/8200/graduate.txt

Complete script of this cult film starring Dustin Hoffman.

It's a Wonderful Life

http://www.geocities.com/Hollywood/Makeup/8156/

Dedicated to Frank Capra's classic film *It's a Wonderful Life*. Included here are details about the film's history, a copy of the script, facts about the film, and a trivia quiz.

James Bond, Agent 007

http://www.mcs.net/~klast/www/bond.html

Information, articles, and photographs of every actor who has played James Bond. There are also numerous reviews and articles about all the Bond films, together with the photographs and posters used to promote them. In addition, there is a large amount of trivia about the Bond films and the opportunity to download several audio clips.

Jurassic Park

http://www.informatik.uni-oldenburg.de/~indiana/mv/scrpls/jurassic.park.html

Complete script of Steven Spielberg's record-breaking film about a dinosaur theme park.

Monty Python and the Holy Grail

http://www.intriguing.com/mp/scripts/mp-holy.txt

Complete script of this cult comedy.

Raiders of the Lost Ark

http://www.informatik.uni-oldenburg.de/~indiana/mv/scrpls/raiders.html

Script of Steven Spielberg's film about an adventurous archaeologist, starring Harrison Ford. This is the first of the trilogy of Indiana Jones films.

Stanley Kubrick's *A Clockwork Orange*

http://www.aclockworkorange.co.uk/mainheaderhtm.htm

Dedicated to the highly controversial film of Anthony Burgess's book by Stanley Kubrick. This site contains both photos and audio clips from the film, as well as a section on the cast, the script, and three versions of the original trailer to download and play. This site is part of a larger guide to many of Kubrick's films.

Star Wars

http://www.starwars.com/

Official Web site of George Lucas's *Star Wars* films. This site provides you with information about the films that have been released, including details about the cast and crew, and has features on the technology involved in creating the films.

Sweet Hereafter, The

http://www.flf.com/sweet/cmp/sweethereafter.txt

Complete script of this film, directed by Atom Egoyan from the novel by Russell Banks.

2001: A Space Odyssey

http://www.krusch.com/kubrick/script.txt

Complete transcript of this 1960s science fiction film directed by Stanley Kubrick and based on a story by Arthur C Clarke.

British Cinema Actors

Audrey Hepburn Page

http://www.geocities.com/Hollywood/Boulevard/4452/audrey.html

Tribute to the British actress from a fan. There are extensive biographical details, photos, interviews, and a number of articles about and by Hepburn. This site also includes links to many other Hepburn appreciation sites.

Bonham Carter, Helena

http://entertainment.go.com/people/helenabonhamcarter/content/Bio.html

Biography and information on the actor famed for her period dramas. This site contains links to her acting credits and to recent news stories about her professional and private life.

Caine, Michael

http://www.mrshowbiz.go.com/people/michaelcaine/content/Bio.html

Featuring a detailed biography of the actor, with links to similar sites on actors to whom Michael Caine has been connected, this site also contains links to general movie news.

Carlyle, Robert

http://www.geocities.com/Hollywood/Hills/4603/

Pictures, facts, biography, and reviews of the Scottish actor, particularly focusing on *The Full Monty,* and Carlyle's roles on British television and in his Scottish theatre company, Raindog.

Connery, Sean

http://www.mcs.net/~klast/www/connery.html

Oodles of regularly updated information about Scotland's most famous actor. In addition to a full biography and filmography there is a large selection of articles and interviews. After browsing all these pages, what more could you possibly need to know about Sean Connery?

danielday

http://www.danielday.org/

Web site for fans of the English actor Daniel Day-Lewis. The contents include a biography, a large selection of photos, latest on- and off-screen news and gossip, interviews, and film reviews. There are many links to further sources of information on Day-Lewis and his films.

Darla's Peter Sellers Tribute Page

http://members.aol.com/damsel16/sellers.html

Pink Panther theme music plays as the text displays full details of the career of the British comic genius. There's a complete list of Sellers' films, records, and television appearances. There are also a host of links to several Goon Show and Pink Panther sites.

Dirk Bogarde Homepage

http://members.aol.com/Alpheratz9/dirkbogarde.html

Informative site, containing a biography and sensitive personal reviews and character analysis of almost all of Bogarde's films. There is also a picture gallery, and a section containing quotations about and by Dirk Bogarde.

Eccleston, Christopher

http://www.geocities.com/Hollywood/Heights/5978/ChristopherEccleston.html

Detailed pages about the English television and cinema actor Christopher Eccleston. His career and life is traced, and there is an archive of articles about the actor. A photo gallery is another feature.

Fiennes Site

http://members.tripod.com/~ncampos/fienneses/index.html

Profile of the British actor and other members of his distinguished family. A home page photo of Fiennes and his family leads to biographies of 'Rafe' and other Fiennes and a selection of photographs. There is also frequently updated news of Ralph Fiennes's career.

Grant, Hugh

http://mrshowbiz.go.com/people/hughgrant/content/bio.html

Profile of the British actor. Every aspect of Grant's on- and off-screen life is covered. There are articles about Grant and an interview with Liz Hurley, in addition to a number of photographs and links to other Grant sites.

Harrison, Rex

http://www.reelclassics.com/Actors/Rex/rex.htm

Tribute to film star Rex Harrison. You will find numerous film stills, a full-colour film poster, plus a special section of images, quotes, and information about the musical *My Fair Lady*. The bottom of the page includes a list of additional Rex Harrison links.

Jeremy Irons and the Web

http://www.geocities.com/Paris/Rue/1824/irons.html

Features a biography, pictures, filmography, news, and reviews of the actor. Written by an enthusiastic fan, this site gives you a personal homage to Irons's talents, a mailing list, a readers' poll in which you can express your own opinion of Irons, and links to other similar sites.

Kenneth Branagh Page

http://www.geocities.com/~realbillie/ken.html

Profile of the dynamic Irish actor and director.

There is a listing of the television, stage, and film productions in which Branagh has been involved. A 'Frequently Asked Questions' section provides biographical details. There is also regularly updated news of Branagh's latest projects, plus links to other related sites, and photos.

Kerr, Deborah

http://www.reelclassics.com/Actresses/Kerr/kerr.htm

Tribute to Scottish actress Deborah Kerr. You will find two pages of information about Kerr's career, plus film stills and full-colour film posters. The brief text includes links to some of Kerr's co-stars, including Cary Grant and Montgomery Clift. The second page includes a list of additional Deborah Kerr links.

Leigh, Vivien

http://www.dycks.com/vivienleigh/

Tribute to the English actress. A detailed biography, supported by photographs, describes her childhood and sets her career within the history of the golden age of Hollywood. There is information about all her film and stage performances. Interviews, articles, and a bibliography complete a full picture of the talented actress.

Miranda Richardson Appreciation Page

http://www.senet.com.au/~sarneyc/miranda.html

Designed to 'fill a gap' left on the Internet on the subject of Miranda Richardson, this site offers basic biographical and career information on the actor, as well as numerous stills from her films, and some video and audio clips.

Moore, Roger

http://www.mcs.net/~klast/www/moore.html

Comprehensive source of information on the British actor. It traces how the policeman's son worked as a model and salesman before being propelled to fame by his role in *The Saint* and various James Bond movies. There are profiles of his films and a constantly updated selection of news items, interviews, and television appearances, as well as articles about Moore and his work for UNICEF.

Neeson, Liam

http://mrshowbiz.com/people/liamneeson/

Interesting profile of the Irish actor. It traces his childhood interest in boxing, his training as a teacher, interest in amateur dramatics, growing experience in cinema, promotion to lead status, and fame won through the title role in *Schindler's List*. There are also sections on recent show business news and a more fullsome biography.

Official Sir Anthony Hopkins Page

http://www.nasser.net/hopkins/

Tribute to Welsh actor Anthony Hopkins. In addition to a brief biography, you will find Hopkins's complete filmography (some of the films are linked to the Internet Movie Database), an extensive photo gallery with thumbnail images of Hopkins both on and off the job, and links to other Hopkins-related sites. You can also sample music from the soundtracks of a handful of Hopkins' films, listen to clips of dialogue, read magazine articles, and view film posters.

O'Toole, Peter

http://www.reelclassics.com/Actors/O'Toole/otoole.htm

Tribute to actor Peter O'Toole. You will find numerous film stills and full-colour film posters, famous quotes from several of his films, plus a special section of images, quotes, and audio clips from O'Toole's 1962 film *Lawrence of Arabia*. There is also a list of additional Peter O'Toole links.

Thompson, Emma

http://www.tsdesign.com/mulder/emma/index.html

Tribute to English actress Emma Thompson. Here you will find a biographical timeline; a filmography that includes texts of her humorous acceptance speeches at the Academy and Golden Globe Awards; an image gallery of photographs and film stills; and audio and video clips. There is also a section of links to related sites.

Tim Roth: Officially Unofficial Webpage

http://www.geocities.com/Hollywood/Lot/3753/main.html

Information about the English actor and his films, with little-known facts about Tim Roth, and lots of pictures. Highlights are pictures of each film on which you may click to get a plot synopsis. There are also soundbites from his films, some of which contain (predictably) explicit language. Written by

a fan, there is the opportunity to join in the adoration in the chat room.

Virtual McGregor

http://www.enter.net/~cybernut/ewanmenu.htm

With a biography and filmography, the bulk of this site is made up of various articles and pictures of the Scottish actor, making it a central resource for fans. There are many sound links, taken from the dialogue and soundtracks of McGregor's films. The site warns, however, that some of the film dialogue contains explicit language.

Welcome to the Ultimate Cary Grant Pages

http://www.ifb.co.uk/~pingu/cg/c_grant.htm

Tribute to the urbane film star. A very detailed biography of Grant covers all the events of his life from his Bristol childhood to Hollywood stardom. There are profiles of his wives, his co-stars, and his friends, a very large collection of photographs, a quiz, and information about Cary Grant appreciation societies.

US Cinema Actors (Pre-war)

Arbucklemania

http://www.silent-movies.com/Arbucklemania/

Large site about the actor Fatty Arbuckle. Featured is a large gallery, biography, and a detailed filmography. Several essays, articles, and reviews are also available, as are a number of interesting facts about the actor.

Astor, Mary

http://www.mdle.com/ClassicFilms/FeaturedStar/perfor57.htm

Profile of the US film actress. It relates how her parents pushed her into films, her success in silent movies, and her successful transition to the 'talkies'. The sad events of the end of her life are also related. This site also includes links to information about those who worked with Astor, and plot, cast, and production details of her films.

Ball of Fire: For Barbara Stanwyck

http://www.moderntimes.com/bab/

Fan page for the Hollywood screen actress that includes specific pages for her films *Ball of Fire* and *Double Indemnity,* as well as a biography and filmography. The site also includes some audio clips and pictures divided into selections from the 1930s and 40s.

Bow, Clara

http://www.cs.monash.edu.au/~pringle/silent/ssotm/Jan96/

Profile of the career of the 'Jazz Baby'. There is a photo of the actress and summaries of all her films. Bow's troubled childhood and the public scandals that haunted her are described.

Carole Lombard – Comedy Genius

http://www.mdle.com/ClassicFilms/FeaturedStar/star68.htm

Tribute to the US comedy actress. A home page leads to a profile, filmography, and a series of photographs.

Charlie Chaplin Filmography

http://www.cs.monash.edu.au/~pringle/silent/chaplin/filmography.html

Concise filmography of all Charlie Chaplin's films, including plot summaries, cast lists, and information about their production.

Cooper, Gary

http://www.reelclassics.com/Actors/Cooper/cooper.htm

Tribute to actor Gary Cooper. You will find a filmography, numerous film stills and full-colour film posters. There is a special section of images, quotes, and interesting trivia about Cooper's 1942 film *The Pride of the Yankees.* Click on 'next page' to see three more pages of film stills and film posters. The last page includes a list of additional Gary Cooper links.

Crawford, Joan

http://www.reelclassics.com/Actresses/Crawford/crawford.htm

Tribute to actress Joan Crawford. You will find two pages of film stills and full-colour film posters. The brief text includes links to some of Crawford's co-stars, including Bette Davis and Clark Gable. The second page includes a list of additional Joan Crawford links.

Crosby, Bing

http://www.reelclassics.com/Actors/Bing/bing.htm

Tribute to US crooner Bing Crosby. The information is arranged over two pages. The first page includes the lyrics to 'Blue Skies' from the 1946 film of the same title, plus numerous film stills and full-colour film posters. Click on 'next page' to see the second page, which features lyrics and a sound clip of the song 'White Christmas', additional film stills and film posters, plus a list of additional Bing Crosby links.

Davis, Bette

http://www.reelclassics.com/Actresses/Bette/bette.htm

Tribute to US film star Bette Davis. You will find a biography, filmography, and numerous images of full-colour film posters and an article entitled 'Smokescreen: Bette Davis and the Cigarette'. The biography page includes hypertext links to information about such co-stars as Humphrey Bogart, Joan Crawford, and Henry Fonda. Click on 'next page' to see three more pages of film stills and film posters. The last page includes lists of famous quotes (some with audio clips) and related Bette Davis links.

Flynn, Errol

http://www.errolflynn.net/index.html

Lavish tribute to the swashbuckling star from a fan. There is a full biography of Flynn, details of all his films, and audio and video clips of the most memorable moments. The site is regularly updated with news of articles and new publications about the Tasmanian-born American. Flynn fans are also notified whenever his films are shown on American, Australian, or European TV.

Fonda, Henry

http://www.reelclassics.com/Actors/Fonda/fonda.htm

Tribute to US actor Henry Fonda. You will find a filmography, an audio clip from *The Grapes of Wrath,* numerous film stills, and a portrait. Click on 'next page' to see another page of film stills.

The second page includes a list of additional Henry Fonda links.

Gable, Clark

http://www.reelclassics.com/Actors/Gable/gable.htm

Tribute to US actor Clark Gable. You will find numerous film stills and full-colour film posters, an audio clip from *Mutiny on the Bounty,* plus a special section of images, quotes, and audio clips from *Gone With the Wind.* Click on 'next page' to see another page of film stills and film posters. The second page includes a list of additional Clark Gable links.

Gish, Lillian

http://www.mdle.com/ClassicFilms/FeaturedStar/star61a.htm

Profile of 'the first lady of the silent screen'. Her long Hollywood career is well described at this site. There are also details of the plots and co-stars of all her films.

Grable, Betty

http://www.geocities.com/Hollywood/Hills/2440/index-g.html

Biography of the shapely US actress, dancer, and celebrated pin-up girl. It traces the Grable's mother's role in propelling her into the entertainment business and her subsequent glittering Hollywood career. This site also contains details of all her films.

Groucho Zone

http://www.sirius.com/~rickc/groucho.htm

Very entertaining site devoted to comic Groucho Marx. Don't miss the extensive quotes section, which features dozens of his most famous caustic quips, plus brief excerpts from various biographies. You can listen to more than a dozen audio clips of the best Groucho Marx insults, as well as classic lines from Marx Brothers films. There is a photo gallery containing over 40 images of Groucho, a section featuring transcripts of some of his funniest routines, a bibliography of books and articles by and about Groucho, and links to related sites.

Hepburn, Katharine

http://www.reelclassics.com/Actresses/Katharine/katharine.htm

Tribute to US film star Katharine Hepburn. You will find information about Hepburn's career, a filmography, famous quotes, a newspaper article in praise of her talents, and numerous film stills and full-colour film posters, plus special sections on *The African Queen* and *The Philadelphia Story,* which include images, audio clips, and more. Click on 'next page' to see two more pages of information, film stills, and film posters. The last page includes lists of additional Katharine Hepburn links and sites devoted to her films.

Huston, Walter

http://schwinger.harvard.edu/~terning/bios/Huston.html

Summary of the life and achievements of the Canadian actor. His career as an engineer, vaudeville star, and Hollywood actor is recounted. There are details of a biography and a detailed filmography.

Lloyd, Harold

http://www.haroldlloyd.com/hhlhome.htm

Huge source of lovingly compiled information on the US film comedian. The contents include audio files of Lloyd speaking about himself, reviews of his films, articles assessing his place in cinema history, and a quiz for Lloyd fans. A biography of Lloyd (unhelpfully accessed at the bottom of the home page) hails him as an archetype of the 'American dream'.

Louise Brooks Society

http://www.pandorasbox.com/

Beyond the usual biography, adulation, and picture gallery of this silent film actress, this site distinguishes itself by including a wealth of interviews and articles from contemporary 1920s magazines, a trivia quiz, and background information on the 'jazz age'.

Loy, Myrna

http://members.aol.com/alisaahunt/myrna/myrna.htm

Good account of the life and career of the versatile US actress. Her main films are summarized and there is an account of her commitment to liberal causes. There is also a complete filmography.

Official Roy Rogers – Dale Evans Site

http://www.royrogers.com/

Lavish tribute to the 'king of the cowboys' and 'queen of the west'. There are full details of both Roy Rogers's and Dale Evans's lives and a complete filmography, as well as an interesting analysis of the reasons for the success of their films. This site also includes a large collection of thumbnails of golden onscreen moments, a guide to the Roy Rogers and Dale Evans Museum, and a message board for fans.

Official Site of Gloria Swanson

http://www.cmgww.com/stars/swanson/swanson.html

Good source of information on the star of the silent screen. A biography attests to her influence not only as an early film star but also as a fashion icon. This site also offers a complete listing of Swanson's films.

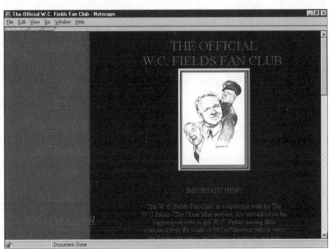

Official W C Fields Fan Club

http://www.webtrec.com/wcfields/

Large source of information on the talented performer. There are comprehensive details of Fields's career and news about the efforts of his fan club to preserve his memory. There are animations of Fields juggling and several audio clips. Details are also provided of attempts to get film studios to release unseen Fields footage from their vaults.

Rains, Claude

http://www.reelclassics.com/Actors/Rains/rains.htm

Tribute to actor Claude Rains. You will find numerous film stills and full-colour film posters, and special sections on *Casablanca, Lawrence of Arabia,* and *Mr Smith Goes to Washington,* which include images, sample dialogue, famous quotes, and audio and film clips. Look at the bottom of the main page for a list of additional Claude Rains links.

Rediscovering Rudolph Valentino

http://www.mdle.com/ClassicFilms/Guest/valntino.htm

Profile of the silent film star. The site contains biographical information on Valentino, a filmography, and a page with twelve photographs of Valentino mainly taken from his films.

Remick, Lee

http://205.186.189.2/cgi-win/AVG.exe?sql=2P_IDPI59559

Profile of the US actress once typecast as 'the US equivalent to Brigitte Bardot'. Remick's versatility and the range of her stage, screen, and television performances are set out. There are also plot, cast, and production details of all of her films.

Rogers, Ginger

http://www.geocities.com/Hollywood/Hills/2440/index-7.html

Photo and biography of the legendary multitalented US performer. It traces the childhood beginnings of her long career, her vaudeville career, and the Hollywood success she shared with Fred Astaire. It reveals her frustration that her association with Astaire forever overshadowed her achievements as an actress.

Rooney, Mickey

http://www.reelclassics.com/Actors/Rooney/rooney.htm

Tribute to US actor Mickey Rooney. You will find two pages of information about Rooney's career, numerous film stills, and full-colour film posters. The brief text includes links to many of Rooney's co-stars, including Elizabeth Taylor and Spencer Tracy. The last page includes a list of additional Mickey Rooney links.

Temple, Shirley

http://www.reelclassics.com/Actresses/Shirley/shirley.htm

Tribute to US actress Shirley Temple. You will find three pages of information about Temple's career, plus film stills and full-colour film posters, and a bibliography of books about Temple. The last page includes a list of additional Shirley Temple links.

Webworld of Bela Lugosi

http://www.auracom.com/~tournier/webworld.htm

Tribute to the horror actor from a fan. There are extensive biographical details and information on all his films. In addition, this site includes a large selection of photographs, articles about Lugosi, a trivia quiz for Lugosi fans, and poetry written by the actor.

West, Mae

http://www.sirius.com/~kims/maewest.html

Tribute to US actress and writer Mae West. In addition to biographical information, you will find West's complete filmography, including synopses, film stills, and original *Variety* reviews; a photo gallery from both the pre-Hollywood and Hollywood years, and a bibliography of West's plays. There is also information concerning issues of online censorship.

Bacall, Lauren

http://mrshowbiz.go.com/people/laurenbacall/content/Bio.html

Profile of the US actress. The contrast between Bacall's iconic status and her turbulent private life is brought out. There is also a photo of Bacall and a description of her ongoing career.

Brandoland

http://www.best.com/~wcleere/brandoland/streetcar.html

Tribute to US actor Marlon Brando. You will find a number of sections, including updates on the latest news about Brando, quotes by and about Brando covering a number of issues, including comments on his acting style and reflections on a number of his films and co-stars. Film stills and other images of Brando are dispersed throughout the site.

US Cinema Actors (Post-war)

Andrews, Dana

http://www.reelclassics.com/Actors/Dana/dana-bio.htm

Tribute to US actor Dana Andrews. You will find a filmography, a video clip of the original trailer for *Laura,* several famous quotes, numerous film stills and full-colour film posters. There is a special section of text and images concerning Andrews's 1946 film *The Best Years of Our Lives.*

Burt Reynolds Page

http://www.geocities.com/~macweb/burtreynolds/

Tribute to the US film actor. There is a good profile of his career, a filmography, and a number of photographs. Latest news of the actor and links to other Reynolds sites are also included.

Christopher Reeve Home Page

http://www.geocities.com/Hollywood/Studio/4071/

Tribute to the star of *Superman.* There is a biography of Reeve and reviews of all of his films. In the large number of interviews which are included, Reeve expresses his determination to overcome the constraints of his handicap.

Reeves's fundraising work on behalf of disabled peoples' organizations is included, together with latest medical reports on his condition and prospects for recovery.

Clint Eastwood – World Wide Web Page

http://www.man-with-no-name.com/

Guaranteed to make the day for Eastwood fans. This lavish tribute to Eastwood compiled by a fan looks back over fifty years of his career. There are full details of all Eastwood's films as well as sound, music, and video clips. A lively trivia section also reports some little-known facts about this actor.

Cruise, Tom

http://www.thezone.pair.com/cruise/

Comprehensive details of the career of the clean-cut US actor. There is a biography of Cruise, details of all of his films, and sound and video clips.

Dean, James

http://www.reelclassics.com/Actors/Dean/dean.htm

Tribute to US actor James Dean. It includes several film stills and three full-colour film posters from *Rebel Without a Cause, East of Eden,* and *Giant.* You will also find a brief list of famous quotes and a number of additional James Dean links.

De Niro, Robert

http://home.att.net/~vellinor/deniro.html

Tribute to the US actor. A biography traces his upbringing, commitment to method acting, and the importance of his relationship with Martin Scorsese. De Niro's major films are described, and there are several photos, alongside latest career news.

Dennis Hopper Unofficial Fan Page

http://www.geocities.com/Hollywood/Academy/8538/

Profile of the US actor and film director. A biography of Hopper includes an autobiographical sketch and details of awards he has won. There is an extensive collection of on- and off-screen photographs.

Discovering Doris Day

http://www.geocities.com/SunsetStrip/Amphitheatre/6146/dorisday-biography.htm

Extensive biographical information about the 1950s film star. This site also includes many images of the celebrity, and a full discography.

Douglas, Kirk

http://www.reelclassics.com/Actors/Kirk/kirk.htm

Tribute to US actor Kirk Douglas. The information is arranged over two pages. The first page features film stills and full-colour film posters. The second page includes a video clip of Douglas singing in the 1954 film *20,000 Leagues Under the Sea,* plus more film stills and posters and a list of additional Kirk Douglas links.

Dunaway, Faye

http://mrshowbiz.go.com/people/fayedunaway/content/Bio.html

Profile of the US actress. It traces the army officer's daughter's early success in the theatre, the rise to fame with *Bonnie and Clyde,* and the subsequent chequered career revived with a belated Oscar. There are links to co-stars and directors she worked with.

Dustin Hoffman – A Man of Many Faces

http://home.earthlink.net/~joepez/hoffman/

Fan's tribute to the US actor. The contents include a biography, detailed filmography, listing of Academy Award nominations, and a large gallery of photographs. The latest news of Hoffman's career is included.

Fonda, Jane

http://mrshowbiz.go.com/people/janefonda/

Profile of the life and career of the US actress. It traces aspects of her life as a sixties sex symbol, political activist, serious actress, fitness instructor, and wife of a media magnate. There is a photo of Fonda, and details of all her films and romantic entanglements.

Fontaine, Joan

http://www.reelclassics.com/Actresses/Fontaine/fontaine.htm

Tribute to actress Joan Fontaine. You will find three pages of information about Fontaine's career, plus film stills and full-colour film posters, a list of famous quotes, and her filmography. The brief text includes links to some of Fontaine's co-stars, including Orson Welles and Laurence Olivier. The last page includes a list of additional Joan Fontaine links.

Gardner, Ava

http://www.avagardner.org/

Large source of information on the sensuous US film actress, from the Ava Gardner Museum. There are extensive biographical details, a complete filmography, reminiscences from those who knew Gardner, and details of television screenings of her films. A large number of photographs are also included.

Grace Kelly – Princess Grace of Monaco Page

http://members.tripod.com/~gracepage/

Tribute to the US actress. Biographical sections examine her careers as actress, mother, and royal wife. There are a number of photos, a trivia quiz for Kelly fans, and links to a large number of other Kelly sites.

Griffith, Melanie

http://www.antoniobanderasfans.com/melanie_griffith.htm

Profile and photo of the US actress. A biography traces the transformation of the baby-faced girl into a Hollywood star. There is equal coverage of her turbulent private life. A listing of her films contains plot and casting details.

Hackman, Gene

http://www.pair.com/marilynn/hackman.htm

This tribute to US actor Gene Hackman features a biography taken from *Baseline's Encyclopedia of Film*. There is also a filmography of Hackman's extensive work, two photographs, and a list of his Academy Award honours.

Hanks, Tom

http://mrshowbiz.go.com/people/tomhanks/content/Bio.html

Biography of the likeable US actor. A biography attests to his quintessentially American 'Mr Everyman' appeal. There are full details of his film and television performances, and a revealing interview with Hanks which includes some sound clips.

Hayworth, Rita (Margarita Carmen Cansino)

http://www.mmje.demon.co.uk/hayworth.htm

Tribute to the talented US dancer and actress. The contents include a biography, details of her films, an extensive bibliography, and photos. There are details of the Rita Hayworth Fan Club and links to other Hayworth sites.

Heston, Charlton

http://www.reelclassics.com/Actors/Heston/heston.htm

Tribute to US actor Charlton Heston. You will find numerous film stills and full-colour film posters. Click on 'next page' to see one more page of film stills, film posters, and information about Heston's film *Ben-Hur*. The second page includes a list of additional Charlton Heston links.

Holden, William

http://www.geocities.com/Hollywood/Theater/6980/holden.htm

Good profile of the career of the US actor. It traces how he moved from stock 'boy-next-door' roles to leading man status and Oscar success. The site also includes a complete listing of his films and several photos.

Hope Enterprises

http://bobhope.com/

Web site of the wise-cracking comedian. A full biography of Hope's long career in the entertainment business is well supported by photographs. There are details of Hope's friendships with US presidents, a biography of his wife, and details of his films and records. An audio clip of Hope telling a characteristic joke is also included.

Jerry Lewis Web Site

http://users.aol.com/norky1995/index.html

Huge source of information for fans of the US comedian. A detailed biography traces his career from his debut aged five. Lewis's film, television, and stage performances are extensively described. There are photos, links to other Lewis sites, and all the latest news.

Jimmy Stewart Museum

http://www.jimmy.org/

Complete account of the life and career of Jimmy Stewart. The biography covers every detail of his long career and gives an intimate picture of the off-screen actor. There's a listing of all 80 of Stewart's films with plot synopses, cast, photos, and reviews of the best-known. There is a selection of the many tributes that poured in after his death.

Judy Garland Database

http://www.zianet.com/jjohnson/contents.htm

Comprehensive source of information about Judy Garland and her career. In addition to a biographical sketch of Garland, which includes a chronology of her MGM years, you will find a complete filmography with a page or two devoted to each film, information about Garland's music and her radio and television appearances, a bibliography, magazine articles about Garland, samples of her poetry, quotes by and about Garland, a photo gallery, plus trivia quizzes. There is also a word search.

Julie Andrews Resource Page

http://www.geocities.com/Hollywood/7308/news.htm

Tribute to entertainer Julie Andrews. Much of the information is arranged by the many show business categories in which Andrews has excelled: Broadway, musicals, comedies and drama, discography, and books. Most of these articles include photographs. You will also find an informative biography (with images), plus a bibliography containing numerous articles and books about Andrews.

Kaye, Danny

http://www.reelclassics.com/Actors/Kaye/kaye.htm

Tribute to actor and comedian Danny Kaye. You will find a filmography, numerous film stills and full-colour film posters, a section of dialogue from the 1956 film *The Court Jester,* which includes a brief audio clip, and a discussion forum. Click on 'next page' to see another page of film stills and film posters, and a list of additional Danny Kaye links.

Keitel, Harvey

http://mrshowbiz.go.com/people/harveykeitel/content/Bio.html

Profile of the US actor. It traces his difficult adolescence, his belated entry into cinema with the help of Martin Scorsese, and his typecasting as a thug. There are details of Keitel's private life, a photo, and comprehensive details of his films.

Lange, Jessica

http://mrshowbiz.go.com/people/jessicalange/content/Bio.html

Profile of the US actress. It traces her childhood, studies in France, the typecasting resulting from her success in *King Kong,* her subsequent Oscar successes, and her romantic entanglements. There is also a photo and details of all her films.

Lemmon, Jack

http://www.gigaplex.com/celebs/lemmon.htm

Revealing interview in which the veteran US actor looks back over his career. There are details of his personal life and additionally a short biography.

Marilyn Pages

http://www.ionet.net/~jellenc/marilyn.html

Online adulation of the Hollywood screen actress that includes a biography, filmography, library of images, and a list of memorabilia.

Michelle Pfeiffer Homepage by Milena

http://www.geocities.com/Hollywood/Set/4654/

Large site dedicated to the actress Michelle Pfeiffer, containing a biography, filmography, and a number of quotations. There are a number of photographs, as well as audio and video clips, and links to other sites about this Hollywood actress.

Minnelli, Liza

http://mrshowbiz.go.com/people/lizaminnelli/

Profile of the career of Judy Garland's celebrated daughter. It describes her lack of a conventional childhood, rapid rise to stardom, and complex personal life. There is a photo of Garland and links to other Garland sites. This site concludes that she exhibits her mother's twitchy vivacity but has a better sense of survival.

Mitchum, Robert

http://mrshowbiz.go.com/people/robertmitchum/
content/Bio.html

Profile of the rugged, laconic US film actor. It traces his rise through derided B-movie appearances to Hollywood stardom and anti-hero cult status. There are also some details of his private life and romantic liaisons.

Novak, Kim

http://members.aol.com/HarlowGold/kimnovak.html

Good profile of the enigmatic Hollywood sex symbol. It includes a filmography, links to articles about Novak on the Web, and other sites focused on her. Her main films are summarized, with particular focus on her role in Hitchcock's masterpiece *Vertigo*.

Official Julie Tango John Travolta Website

http://www.sonic.net/~mfortsch/menu.html

Tribute to the US actor from a fan. The contents include a biography, filmography, reviews, articles, a discussion of Travolta's interest in scientology, and a large selection of photographs. Frequently updated with news of Travolta and the activities of his fan club.

Official Site of Montgomery Clift

http://www.cmgww.com/stars/clift/clift.html

Good source of information about the US actor. A biography reveals Clift's great reluctance to move from theatrical success to Hollywood. There is a listing of his films, a number of photos, and quotes by and about Clift.

Pacino, Al

http://www76.pair.com/marilynn/al.htm

Good profile of the life and film career of the US actor. There is a list of his films including details of the most important ones. A large number of photographs of Pacino are included.

Peck, Gregory

http://www.reelclassics.com/Actors/Peck/peck.htm

Tribute to US actor Gregory Peck. You will find three pages of information about Peck's career, including numerous film stills and full-colour film posters. The brief text includes links to many of Peck's co-stars, including Audrey Hepburn,

Ingrid Bergman, and director Alfred Hitchcock. The last page includes a list of additional Gregory Peck links.

Phyliss's Kevin Costner Page

http://www.geocities.com/Hollywood/7555/

Tribute to the US actor from a fan. A good biography of Costner traces how the involvement of the young marketing student in amateur theatre led on to Hollywood success. There are a large number of photos, audio clips, and links to other Costner sites.

Poitier, Sidney

http://mrshowbiz.go.com/people/sidneypoitier/
content/Bio.html

Interesting profile of the trailblazing black US actor. It traces the tenacity with which he overcame infant illness, racial prejudice, and menial work in the Bahamas and New York to win success with *Guess Who's Coming to Dinner*. His modesty and efforts to preserve his privacy are highlighted.

Price, Vincent

http://www.reelclassics.com/Actors/Price/price.htm

Tribute to actor Vincent Price. You will find information about Price's career, numerous film stills and full-colour film posters, and a video clip of the original trailer from Price's 1944 film *Laura*. Click on 'next page' to see two more pages of film stills and film posters. The last page includes a list of additional Vincent Price links.

Schwarzenegger, Arnold

http://www.schwarzenegger.com/

Dedicated to the muscle-bound actor, this site contains details of Schwarzenegger's life and work. As well as a very detailed filmography, you can learn about Arnie the athlete (he was Mr Universe before becoming an actor) and Arnie the activist.

Shrine to Bruce Lee

http://www.ocf.berkeley.edu/~chenj/brucelee/bruce
lee.html

Dedicated to martial arts actor Bruce Lee, this site contains a biographical timeline, filmography, and an extensive gallery. Unusually for sites of this type, there is a section on the star in his more domestic guise.

Sigourney Weaver Pages

http://www.uni-c.dtu.dk/~unikcm/Sigourney/Sigourney.html

Profile of the life and career of the US actress. It traces her childhood, adoption of the name Sigourney, early theatrical work, and the stardom achieved through the sci-fi series of *Alien* films. There is a photo of Weaver and details of all her films.

Streep, Meryl

http://www.geocities.com/Hollywood/Hills/2844/meryl.html

Comprehensive tribute to US actress Meryl Streep. Here you will find Streep's filmography, a collection of film posters, quotes from various interviews, transcripts of chat show appearances, Streep's 1983 commencement speech at Vassar, an image gallery, a number of articles and interviews, the latest news on Streep's upcoming films, and more.

Sylvester Stallone Home Page

http://pubweb.nwu.edu/~mmp856/sly.htm

Tribute to US actor and director Sylvester Stallone. Despite a dubious introduction, this page features interesting transcripts of two interviews taken from *Parade* and *Esquire* magazines, film posters from *Rocky IV* and *Rambo: First Blood Part II,* several audio clips of music from the *Rocky* soundtrack, a video clip of the *Rambo* trailer, and a section called 'Stallone in the News' which links up to transcripts of recent newspaper articles and reviews.

Taylor, Elizabeth

http://www.reelclassics.com/Actresses/Liz_Taylor/liz.htm

Tribute to US actress Elizabeth Taylor. You will find three pages of information about Taylor's career, plus film stills and full-colour film posters, a list of famous quotes, and her filmography. The brief text includes links to some of Taylor's co-stars, including James Dean, Paul Newman, and Montgomery Clift. The last page includes a list of additional Elizabeth Taylor links.

Tracy, Spencer

http://www.reelclassics.com/Actors/Tracy/tracy.htm

Tribute to actor Spencer Tracy. You will find film stills and full-colour film posters. The brief text includes links to many of Tracy's co-stars, including Katharine Hepburn and Elizabeth Taylor. Look at the bottom of the page for a list of additional Spencer Tracy links.

Tribute to Humphrey Bogart

http://www.macconsult.com/bogart/

Done almost exclusively in black and white, this site offers a complete tribute to film noir hero Humphrey Bogart. You will find biographical information, photo stills and sound clips from his films (as well as a number of non-film images of Bogart), full-colour images of film posters, a filmography, bibliographies of both Bogart and Lauren Bacall, plus Bogie Trivia and several other games.

Unofficial Harrison Ford Stuff Home Page

http://home.onestop.net/lpc/ford/

Online tribute to one of Hollywood's most consistently successful current stars that includes everything from a biography and trivia, through stills from his films, to audio and video clips.

Wayne, John

http://www.geocities.com/~jhirsch/

Tribute to US actor John Wayne. Despite the occasionally jingoistic focus, you will find insightful articles about Wayne's many films, arranged by film title, each of which includes a number of film stills, and some of which feature audio clips. You will also find John Wayne trivia, quotes, 'bloopers', a filmography, audio clips, and special sections devoted to his war films and westerns.

Welcome to the Gene Scene – The Gene Kelly Home Page

http://members.aol.com/humorone/gene.htm

Large source of well presented information on the US entertainer. There is a good biography of Kelly, a detailed filmography with plots and cast details of all his films, and a huge number of photographs. This site also includes a section on

Kelly memorabilia, a quiz for Kelly fans, and a comprehensive bibliography.

Whoopi Goldberg Profile

http://www.achievement.org/autodoc/page/gol0pro-1

Description of the life and work of the US actress and charity activist Whoopi Goldberg. The Web site contains not only a profile and biographical information, but also a lengthy interview with Goldberg from 1994, accompanied by a large number of photographs, video sequences, and audio clips.

Miscellaneous Cinema Actors

Andress, Ursula

http://www.geocities.com/Hollywood/9766/andress.html

Profile of the Swiss actress. It traces how she was brought to the USA as 'the new Dietrich' and won fame for her bikini-clad role in *Dr No*. There are links to a whole host of information about this actress, including a filmography and multimedia section.

Bardot, Brigitte

http://www.xs4all.nl/~robinw/brigitte/index.htm

Good source of information on the French actress and animal rights campaigner. There is a biography, filmographies, a series of photographs, and links to other Bardot sites.

Blanchett, Cate

http://gingerblue.com/cate/

Dedicated to the Australian film actress. This site includes a biography of Blanchett, a filmography, film trailers from her recent films, and audio files of the actress.

Colbert, Claudette

http://us.imdb.com/AName?Colbert,+Claudette

Summary of the career and screen legacy of the French-born actress. It traces how her screen debut was in a flop which almost ended her career, and yet how she went on to become Hollywood's best-paid star. A filmography has plot and cast details of all of her films.

Complete Guide to Klaus Kinski

http://dantenet.com/er/Kinski/k2contents.html

Tribute to the German actor. Biographical notes, and extensive quotes from Kinski's frank autobiography and interviews paint a good picture of his tortured life. A filmography is accompanied by a series of reviews of his major films.

Davis, Judy

http://www.geocities.com/SoHo/Study/5680/home.html

Fan page for this Australian actress which contains production notes for her future projects as well as the usual filmography and picture/sound archive. There is also a bibliography of magazine articles and links to other similar Web sites.

Dietrich, Marlene

http://www.reelclassics.com/Actresses/Marlene/marlene.htm

Tribute to actress Marlene Dietrich. You will find two pages of film stills and full-colour film posters. The second page includes a long list of additional Marlene Dietrich links and sites devoted to her films.

Ford, Glenn

http://www.geocities.com/Hollywood/Hills/8628/ford.htm

Lavish tribute to the long career of the Canadian star, who says he has never played anybody but himself. In addition to a biography and many offscreen images of the actor, there are complete descriptions of all his films, each with large numbers of onscreen shots.

Ingrid Bergman Page

http://www.ingridbergman.com/

Comprehensive chronological list of the actress's films, with interesting additional information, such as reviews, other cast members, and several images.

Loren, Sophia

http://mrshowbiz.go.com/people/sophialoren/

Profile of the Italian actress. This site traces her rise from poverty, her success in low-budget Italian films, her move to Hollywood, and her relationship with Carlo Ponti. There is a photo of Loren and details of all of her films.

Lorre, Peter

http://www.reelclassics.com/Actors/Lorre/lorre.htm

Tribute to character actor Peter Lorre. You will find numerous film stills and full-colour film posters, plus a special section of images, quotes, and audio clips from *Casablanca*. Look at the bottom of the page for a list of additional Peter Lorre links.

Mel Gibson Page

http://www.geocities.com/Hollywood/Set/8173/home4b.html

Tribute to actor and director Mel Gibson. In addition to a brief biography, you will find an extensive photo gallery, a filmography which includes brief reviews (caveat: the reviewer is also the adoring Webmaster), a chat page, a section called 'daily scoop' which is apparently updated once or twice a month, and a page of links to related sites.

Pickford, Mary

http://schwinger.harvard.edu/~terning/bios/Pickford.html

Profile of the Canadian who became 'America's sweetheart'. There is a photo of Pickford and a summary of her career. There is also a detailed filmography.

Pidgeon, Walter

http://www.reelclassics.com/Actors/Pidgeon/pidgeon.htm

Tribute to Canadian actor Walter Pidgeon. You will find text from a *New York Times* article about Pidgeon, numerous film stills and full-colour film posters, and special sections on *How Green Was My Valley* and *Mrs Miniver*, which include images, information, and an audio clip. Click on 'next page' to see another page of film stills and film posters. The second page includes a list of additional Walter Pidgeon links.

Shearer, Norma

http://schwinger.harvard.edu/~terning/bios/NShearer.html

Profile of the Canadian actress. The main events of her life and career are set out. There is a detailed filmography and a screen photo of Shearer with Clark Gable.

Sutherland, Donald

http://schwinger.harvard.edu/~terning/bios/Sutherland.html

Profile of the Canadian actor. There is a photo of Sutherland and a summary of his career. There is also a detailed filmography.

Wray, Fay

http://schwinger.harvard.edu/~terning/bios/Wray.html

Profile of the Canadian-born actress made famous by *King Kong*. The main events of her life and career are set out. There is also a detailed filmography.

Cinema Directors & Producers

Burton, Tim

http://home.acadia.net/userpages/joel/timburton/

Tribute to director Tim Burton. A great source of information about Burton's films, which includes synopses, Burton's thoughts on his films, numerous images, and links to articles and reviews. The information is arranged by film title.

On this site you will find the full narration of *Vincent*, two textual interviews and several audio clips of interviews, a photo gallery, and biographical information about some of the stars of Burton's films, including Jack Nicholson and Winona Ryder.

Capra, Frank

http://www.reelclassics.com/Directors/Capra/capra.htm

Tribute to director Frank Capra. You will find two pages of information about Capra's career, plus numerous full-colour film posters, and special sections on *It's a Wonderful Life* and *Mr Smith Goes to Washington,* which include images, sample dialogue, famous quotes, and audio and video clips. The second page is devoted to Capra films that starred Jimmy Stewart, with a link to a page about Stewart, plus a list of additional links to Frank Capra sites.

Chuck Jones Profile

http://www.achievement.org/autodoc/page/jon1pro-1

Description of the life and work of the US film animator Chuck Jones, famous for his creation of characters such as Bugs Bunny, The Roadrunner, and Pepe le Pew. The Web site contains not only a profile and biographical information, but also a lengthy interview with Jones from 1993 accompanied by a large number of photographs, video sequences, and audio clips.

Cukor, George

http://www.reelclassics.com/Directors/Cukor/cukor.htm

Tribute to director George Cukor. You will find two pages of information about Cukor's career, plus numerous full-colour film posters, and special sections on *The Philadelphia Story* and *My Fair Lady,* which include images, sample dialogue, famous quotes, and audio clips. The second page includes a list of additional links to George Cukor sites.

De Mille, Cecil B

http://reelclassics.com/Directors/deMille/demille.htm

Tribute to director Cecil B De Mille. You will find two pages of information about De Mille's career

and his films, a list of famous quotes, plus numerous full-colour film posters. The text includes links to information about some of the stars of his films, including William Holden, Claudette Colbert, and Gary Cooper. Look at the bottom of the page for a list of additional links to Cecil B De Mille sites.

Disney, Walt

http://www.pathfinder.com/time/time100/builder/profile/disney.html

Part of a larger archive from *Time* exploring the most influential people of this century, this article highlights the life and work of US filmmaker and animator Walt Disney. The profile features a timeline and audio clips.

Dreyer, Carl

http://us.imdb.com/Name?Dreyer,+Carl+Theodor

Biography and filmography of the Danish film director. In addition to plot and casting details for all of his films, there is a bibliography and an interview with Dreyer.

Eisenstein, Sergei M

http://us.imdb.com/M/person-all?Eisenstein%2C+Sergei+M%2E

Profile of the life and films of the influential Soviet film director. The main events of his life are described together with a detailed filmography containing plot and casting details of his films.

Ford, John

http://www.reelclassics.com/Directors/Ford/ford.htm

Tribute to director John Ford. You will find two pages of information about Ford's career, plus numerous full-colour film posters, and a special section on Ford's 1941 film *How Green Was My Valley,* which includes images, audio, and information. The second page includes a list of additional links to John Ford sites.

Francis Ford Coppola Profile

http://www.achievement.org/autodoc/page/cop0pro-1

Description of the life and work of the US director, producer, and screenwriter Francis Ford Coppola. The Web site contains not only a profile and biographical information, but also a lengthy interview with Coppola accompanied by a large number of photographs, video sequences, and audio clips.

George Lucas Profile

http://www.achievement.org/autodoc/page/luc0pro-1

Description of the life and work of the film director and producer George Lucas. Most famous for his *Star Wars* trilogy and the Indiana Jones films, Lucas has moved on to become a successful film executive. This Web site contains not only a profile and biographical information, but also a lengthy interview with Lucas from 1995, accompanied by a large number of photographs, video sequences, and audio clips.

Hawks, Howard

http://www.reelclassics.com/Directors/Hawks/hawks.htm

Tribute to director Howard Hawks. You will find information about Hawks's films, plus a number of full-colour film posters. The text includes links to information about some of the stars of his films, including Humphrey Bogart, Katharine Hepburn, and Cary Grant. Look at the bottom of the page for a list of additional links to Howard Hawks sites.

Hitchcock Page

http://www.primenet.com/~mwc/

Fan page for Alfred Hitchcock, the classic suspense director. It includes a filmography, life story, film sequences (mainly stills), and links to other related sites.

Huston, John

http://www.reelclassics.com/Directors/Huston/huston.htm

Tribute to director John Huston. You will find several full-colour film posters and a special section on Huston's 1951 film *The African Queen* with Humphrey Bogart and Katharine Hepburn, which includes images, information, audio clips, and more. The text on the main page includes links to information about some of the stars of his films. Look at the bottom of the main page for a list of additional links to John Huston sites.

Krzysztof Kieslowski Home Page

http://www-personal.engin.umich.edu/~zbigniew/Kieslowski/kieslowski.html

Memorial page to the Polish film director which includes letters from fans, a biography of the man and some of the people who worked with him, images, reviews, and a filmography.

Kubrick Multimedia Film Guide

http://www.indelibleinc.com/kubrick

In-depth site on the US film director and producer who is known for demanding complete artistic control over his films. This site includes a wealth of images and commentary on many of his works, as well as some audio clips and rarely seen pictures.

Lupino, Ida

http://members.xoom.com/binkmeister/IdaLupino.htm

Large source of information on the actress and director. Many of her films are extensively analysed and there is a complete listing of her film and television work. A thoughtful review of Hollywood's first successful female director presents the views of famous actors and directors she worked with.

F A C T

HITCHCOCK, ALFRED (JOSEPH) (1899–1980)

English film director, a US citizen from 1955. A master of the suspense thriller, he was noted for his meticulously drawn storyboards that determined his camera angles and for his cameo walk-ons in his own films.

LynchNet: The David Lynch Resource

http://www.lynchnet.com/

Combined resource of information about the American director and his work. Highlights include a selection of personal quotes, a trivia section, and many audio and video clips. All the director's films are listed including his cameo, musical, and editing credits. Many of the film titles included on the page are also hypertext links to reviews. There is also a discussion board and sections on his works in television and other media.

Malle, Louis

http://mrshowbiz.go.com/people/louismalle/

Profile of the innovative French director. A biography traces how his family wealth helped start his career but delayed critical acclaim. His career in France and the USA is outlined and the themes of his films summarized. There is also a photo of Malle.

Mayer, Louis B

http://schwinger.harvard.edu/~terning/bios/Mayer.html

Profile of the Hollywood mogul. The main events of his entrepreneurial life are set out together with details of his major films. There is a bibliography and also some entertaining quotes by and about Mayer.

Scorsese, Martin

http://www2.trincoll.edu/~dstewart/

Profile of the US film director. It traces Scorsese's upbringing, his decision not to enter the priesthood, his early interest in writing, and the importance of his relationship with the actor Robert de Niro. There are plot and cast details of his major films, a number of photos, and latest news of Scorsese's career.

Scruffle's Steven Spielberg Directory

http://www.geocities.com/~scruffles/main.html

Tribute to the world's foremost mainstream film director. There is a biography and detailed filmography with details of his best-known films. Audio and video clips help illustrate Spielberg's extraordinary creativity.

Sennett, Mack

http://us.imdb.com/Bio?Sennett,+Mack

Profile of the 'king of comedy'. It traces Sennett's rise from his humble origins to establishing slapstick as a film genre. His methods of film-making are amusingly described.

Spike Lee Biography

http://timecast2.timecast.com/spikelee/theater/leebio_frm.html/

Tribute to US director and actor Spike Lee. Here you will find Lee's complete filmography, which includes his feature films, shorts, commercials, and music videos, and a comphrensive biography.

Stevens, George

http://www.reelclassics.com/Directors/Stevens/stevens.htm

Tribute to director George Stevens. You will find information about Stevens's films, plus a number of full-colour film posters. The text includes links to information about some of the stars of his films, including Elizabeth Taylor, James Dean, and Katharine Hepburn. Look at the bottom of the page for a list of additional links to George Stevens sites.

Tarantino Planet

http://www.nevada.edu/~hoppes/qt/new/index.html

Informative and well-designed site about the director Quentin Tarantino and his films. This site features a biography of Tarantino, information on the main actors in several of his films, a gallery of images, some of the scripts, and interesting facts about the films themselves.

Wes Craven's World

http://www.wescraven.com/test3.htm

Impressive site dedicated to the life and works of US director and writer Wes Craven. Included here is a biography, filmography, updates on recent projects, and the opportunity to e-mail your questions to Craven.

Wilder, Billy

http://www.reelclassics.com/Directors/Wilder/wilder.htm

Tribute to director Billy Wilder. You will find information about Wilder's films, plus a number of full-colour film posters. The text includes links to information about some of the stars of his films, including Audrey Hepburn, Gary Cooper, and Humphrey Bogart. Look at the bottom of the page for a list of additional links to Billy Wilder sites.

Woody Allen – Deconstructing Woody

http://www.idt.unit.no/~torp/woody/

Complete source of information on the US film maker. Contents include a full filmography, images, details of songs in his films, and a selection of audio samples. There is information on the casts, plots, and music of all of Allen's films, plus links to critical appreciations and Allen discussion groups.

Miscellaneous Cinema

Academy of Motion Picture Arts and Sciences

http://www.oscars.org/

Home page of the Oscar. This site contains information about the Oscar awards, as well as much useful information on the Academy itself and its other work in promoting the cinematic art as a whole.

American Variety Stage: Motion Pictures

http://lcweb2.loc.gov/ammem/vshtml/vsfilm.html

Part of the Variety Stage Collection of the US Library of Congress celebrating vaudeville and popular entertainment, this page features 61 rare motion pictures of variety acts dating from 1897 to 1920. Some of the acts pictured include burlesque, dance, comic sketches, and dramatic sketches. The films include brief notes. Should you not wish to download the films, each title includes several still-frame photographs. You can browse the collection by keyword, subject, title, or author.

Bill Douglas Centre for the History of Cinema and Popular Culture

http://www.ex.ac.uk/bill.douglas/

Collection based at the University of Exeter, England, of historical cinematic artefacts. The site contains a guided tour through various sections, with plenty of images, including some of 19th-century magic lanterns – the forerunners of cinema entertainment.

Centennial Salute to Cinema

http://photo2.si.edu/cinema/cinema.html

Visit the very early and less-known stages of the cinema, including presentations of the first magic lantern broadsides, the first frame-by-frame movement experiments, and early motion picture advertisements.

Disney Home Page

http://disney.go.com/home/homepage/today/html/index.html?

Official Disney site. The site is designed as a 'family entertainment' package, in line with the company's ethos. There is a lot of informative and entertaining material here, but don't look here for a critical overview of either the man or his legacy.

Horror News

http://www.horrornews.com/index.shtml

Central source of information on the horror genre. The latest developments in horror films, literature, cartoons, music, and the theatre are presented. There are profiles of horror films and biographies of leading past and present horror writers. A number of useful links to other horror sites are included.

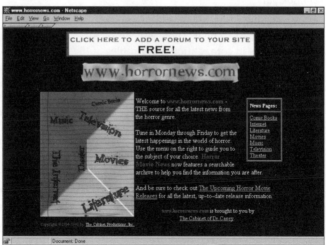

Internet Movie Database

http://www.uk.imdb.com/

Database of over 170,000 films. You can search for information about films, actors and actresses, or character names. This site contains details of almost every film ever produced, with links off-site to related Web pages, and many films have extra information such as quotes, trivia, or continuity errors.

Inventing Entertainment: The Early Motion Pictures of the Edison Company

http://lcweb2.loc.gov/ammem/edhtml/edhome.html

Part of the American Memory presentation of the US Library of Congress, this collection was designed in celebration of US inventor Thomas Edison's 150th birthday. It includes eight motion pictures produced by the Edison Manufacturing Company, including *The Great Train Robbery*. Each film has a brief description. This site includes a brief biography of Edison, plus information on the Edison Manufacturing Company and the advent of motion pictures. In addition, there is information on sound recordings and the invention of the phonograph. The site organizers plan to add samples of early sound recordings soon.

Le Festival – Official Selection

http://www.festival-cannes.fr/cannes98/va/index.html

Official site of Cannes, the world's foremost international film festival. There are complete details of films in competition and profiles of the jury. There is also an interesting history of the festival.

Medieval Films

http://www.fordham.edu/halsall/medfilms.html#celtic

Extensive and well-informed database of films with a medieval perspective. Visitors can search through the big hits as well as less well-known productions on such topics as the late Roman emperors, the Robin Hood myth, Joan of Arc, medieval France, and the Knights of the Round Table.

Movies, Race, and Ethnicity

http://www.lib.berkeley.edu/MRC/EthnicImagesVid.html

Bibliography, held at California University in the USA, of ethnic and racial representations in cinema. Including sections on African-Americans, Jews, and Latinos, the site contains articles discussing the ways in which different racial groups are represented in films.

Movieweb

http://movieweb.com/

US-based site dedicated to (mainly current) films. Links to all the major studios on the Web, plus previews and trailers of upcoming films (in QuickTime format – note that these clips can be large files which may take some time to download).

Science Web Goes to the Movies

http://scienceweb.dao.nrc.ca/movies/movies.html

Explains the real-life science behind the often dubious science depicted in films and suggests experiments to try at home. This site uses still-frames of specific films and dialogue or sound clips to assist with the scientific explanation. Also, you can e-mail your own questions about science in the cinema.

Special Effects

http://www.pbs.org/wgbh/nova/specialfx/sfxhome.html

Companion to the US Public Broadcasting Service (PBS) television programme *Nova,* this page explores the history and techniques of special effects in the film industry. Learn about the first use of special effects in film, which dates back to the 19th century, and follow the course of progress in the field up to the present. An interactive Java section reveals how films trick the eye. Film buffs can even test their knowledge with the special effects trivia quiz.

Westerns.com

http://www.westerns.com/home.htm

A must for lovers of westerns. Mosey on through this site for screen shots from classic westerns, sound clips, and much frequently-updated trivia about westerns. There are a huge number of links to sites either associated with the real history of the American West or Hollywood's version of it.

Comedy

Abbott and Costello Home Page

http://www.city-net.com/abbottandcostellofc/

Official site of the comedy duo Abbott and Costello. There is a biography, information about their films, animation, and audio and video clips. Also included in this site are news, fun facts, and details of the Abbott and Costello fan club and its quarterly magazine.

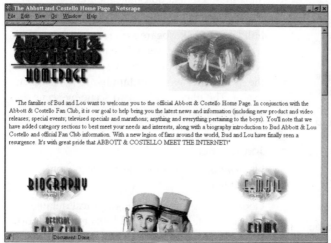

Connolly, Billy

http://www.btinternet.com/~sarsen/billy/billy.html

Self-titled the 'first and best fan website' dedicated to the Scottish actor, writer, comedian, and musician. This site is well-presented, with many biographical and career details, lists of his past and future projects, and a humour section, with jokes along Connolly's usual (adult) themes.

Cook, Peter

http://www.scream.demon.co.uk/pcook.html

Tribute to the English satirist. It traces his career as an entertainer: through public school, with the Cambridge Footlights Review and Beyond the Fringe, at *Private Eye* magazine, and his collaboration with Dudley Moore. There is a photo of Cook and information about the Peter Cook Appreciation Society.

Dame Edna Megapage

http://members.aol.com/dameedna2/

All there is to know of the life and interests of the 'housewife-megastar'. Sponsored by the 'Friends of the Prostate', the site offers a history of Dame Edna's glittering career, a large number of photographs, and a letter from the icon.

French, Dawn

http://dawnfrench.tripod.com

Biography and career details of the actress, writer, and comedian, written by a fan. There is also information on her work for the charity Comic Relief and on her clothes business for women with fuller figures. This site contains lots of pictures and links to other sites of interest, including a similar, informative site on her partner and fellow comedian Lenny Henry.

Harry Enfield's Television Programme

http://homes.arealcity.com/harry/

Dedicated to the characters of the TV show more than to the man himself, with typescripts and soundbites from the programme, as well as links to other Enfield sites and a mailing list.

Howerd, Frankie

http://www.carryonline.com/carry/howerd.html

Biography of Frankie Howerd. A complete filmography is included with audio clips and links to two of his most memorable *Carry On* films.

Humphries, (John) Barry

http://users.aol.com/raregems/biography.htm

Biography of the Australian actor and author. It traces his education, his early interest in repertory, and his creation of Dame Edna Everage and Sir Les Patterson. There are full details of Humphries's television career and the many books he has written. There are also several photos of the man himself.

Laurel and Hardy

http://www.laurel-and-hardy.com

Good graphics characterize this official site, which has a detailed 'Background' section, plus detailed notes on all the duo's feature film shorts and silent movies. There is also more recent news on the pair, including information on the restoration of their films. A feedback section allows you to join the mailing list.

Mayall, Rik

http://wesjen.simplenet.com/rik/

A fan's tribute to the British actor and writer, containing a detailed biography of his personal and career details, as well as a lovingly compiled archive of quotations from the man himself (which does contain some colourful language), and 'The Accident News Archive', a series of newspaper articles pertaining to his quad bike accident in 1998.

Monty Python's Flying Circus in Australia

http://www.stone-dead.asn.au/

Claims to be the world's largest site for Monty Python fans. There are audio and video clips of many Python sketches, songs, and films. The host of features includes Python quizzes, links to other Python sites, and even an opportunity to order cheese from Mr Wensleydale (though it is unlikely to be in stock).

Tony Hancock Home Page

http://www.achilles.net/~howardm/tony.html

Well-organized review of the life of the famous comedian. In addition to biographical details, you can listen to some of Hancock's most famous sketches. There are also links to other Hancock appreciation sites.

Two Ronnies

http://bennett.tvheaven.com/tworonnies.htm

A fan's account of the creation of *The Two Ronnies*, and a filmography for both Barker and Corbett. There are several good pictures, and links to sites by the same author on the subject of other British comedy programmes, including *Blackadder* and *Fawlty Towers*.

British Theatre

Complete Works of Shakespeare

http://the-tech.mit.edu/Shakespeare/works.html

Complete works of William Shakespeare. Text searching is available across all poems and plays, and plays are also accessible by act and scene. This site also contains an index of other Shakespeare sites on the Web.

Edinburgh Festival Online

http://www.go-edinburgh.co.uk/

The official Edinburgh Festival Web site with full details of all the contributing arts.

Hamlet

http://the-tech.mit.edu/Shakespeare/Tragedy/hamlet/hamlet.html

Full text of Shakespeare's tragedy, complete with a list of *dramatis personae*. The text is annotated with links to a comprehensive glossary explaining the meaning of words unfamiliar to the modern reader. The play may be read scene-by-scene or loaded as a single file.

Jonson, Ben

http://www.luminarium.org/sevenlit/jonson/index.html

Good-looking site with biographical details, famous quotes, essays, and links to many works by this famous playwright and poet. This site also includes some contemporary background music.

King Lear

http://the-tech.mit.edu/Shakespeare/Tragedy/kinglear/kinglear.html

Full text of Shakespeare's tragedy, complete with a list of *dramatis personae*. The text is annotated with links to a comprehensive glossary explaining the meaning of words unfamiliar to the modern reader. The play may be read scene by scene or loaded as a single file.

Macbeth

http://the-tech.mit.edu/Shakespeare/Tragedy/
macbeth/macbeth.html

Full text of Shakespeare's tragedy, complete with a list of *dramatis personae*. The text is annotated with links to a comprehensive glossary explaining the meaning of words unfamiliar to the modern reader. The play may be read scene by scene or loaded as a single file.

Major Barbara by Bernard Shaw

http://www.best.com/~hansen/
DrPseudocryptonym/Shaw_MajorBarbara.html

Text of Shaw's play published in 1907. Shaw prefaced *Major Barbara* with 'An essay as first aid to critics', which is also included on the site.

Middleton, Thomas

http://www.tech.org/~cleary/middhome.html

Attractive site devoted to the works of Thomas Middleton, with a portrait of the dramatist. Click on an image to access Middleton's plays – whether works of sole authorship, collaborations, or works of questionable attribution.

Midsummer Night's Dream

http://the-tech.mit.edu/Shakespeare/Comedy/
midsummernightsdream/amidsummernights
dream.html

Full text of Shakespeare's comedy, complete with a list of *dramatis personae*. The text is annotated with links to a comprehensive glossary explaining the meaning of words unfamiliar to the modern reader. The play may be read scene by scene or loaded as a single file.

Misalliance

http://tom.cs.cmu.edu/cgi-bin/book/lookup?num=943

Complete text of this play by George Bernard Shaw, which first appeared in 1910.

Olivier, Laurence

http://www.reelclassics.com/Actors/Olivier/
olivier.htm

Tribute to actor Laurence Olivier. You will find information about Olivier's venerable career, numerous film stills, and full-colour film posters. There is also a list of additional Laurence Olivier links at the bottom of the page.

Oscariana

http://www.jonno.com/oscariana/1.html

Using a selection of contemporary records, from newspapers to personal letters and poems, this site charts the downfall and subsequent trial of Oscar Wilde, which led to his eventual imprisonment. It is illustrated with a selection of photographs of the author and his friends and family.

Othello

http://the-tech.mit.edu/Shakespeare/Tragedy/
othello/othello.html

Full text of Shakespeare's tragedy, complete with a list of *dramatis personae*. The text is annotated with links to a comprehensive glossary explaining the meaning of words unfamiliar to the modern reader. The play may be read scene by scene or loaded as a single file.

Pygmalion

http://www.bartleby.com/138/index.html

Online edition of Bernard Shaw's play *Pygmalion* (1912).

Redgrave, Vanessa

http://www.geocities.com/Hollywood/9766/
redgrave.html

Huge source of information on the controversial English actress. There are links to a large number of articles on Redgrave, film reviews, and interviews. There are several biographies and detailed filmographies, in addition to photographs and details of awards she has won.

Revenger's Tragedy, The

http://etext.lib.virginia.edu/etcbin/browse-mixed-
new?id=TouReve&tag=public&images=images/
modeng&data=/texts/english/modeng/parsed

Complete text of Cyril Tourneur's play, as well as a selection of images from earlier print editions.

Riders to the Sea

http://etext.lib.virginia.edu/etcbin/browse-mixed-
new?id=SynRide&tag=public&images=images/
modeng&data=/texts/english/modeng/parsed

Complete text of this play by J M Synge. This site also features a number of illustrations from the print edition of the work.

Romeo and Juliet

http://the-tech.mit.edu/Shakespeare/Tragedy/
romeoandjuliet/romeoandjuliet.html

Full text of Shakespeare's romantic tragedy, complete with a list of *dramatis personae.* The text is annotated with links to a comprehensive glossary explaining the meaning of words unfamiliar to the modern reader. The play may be read scene by scene or loaded as a single file.

'Rosencrantz and Guildenstern Are Dead – Aspects of the Human Condition'

http://yosh.gimp.org/~saji/stoppard.html

Essay based around the play *Rosencrantz and Guilderstern are Dead* by Tom Stoppard.

Royal Academy of Dramatic Art

http://rada.drama.ac.uk/

Site of Britain's premier institution for the training of actors. There are details of the various courses offered by RADA.

Royal Court Theatre

http://www.royalcourttheatre.com/

Information on the work of the theatre noted for showcasing new productions and innovation in the British theatre. There are details of performances, summaries of new works, and news of educational activities. The Royal Court's online newsletter provides a behind-the-scenes glimpse of life in this busy institution.

Royal Shakespeare Company

http://www.stratford.co.uk/rsc/

Site of the prestigious British theatre company. In addition to full details of the RSC's current repertoire in London and Stratford, there is access to information about William Shakespeare.

Samuel Beckett End Page

http://humanitas.ucsb.edu/projects/beckett/
endpage.html

Features a biography, chronology, and bibliography of the Irish writer. This site also includes a list of Beckett's contemporaries, the home of the official Samuel Beckett Society and general information on the Theatre of the Absurd.

Shakespeare Illustrated

http://www.emory.edu/ENGLISH/classes/
Shakespeare_Illustrated/Shakespeare.html

Rich compilation of 19th-century paintings inspired by productions of Shakespeare's plays. The paintings are grouped by artist and play, and the site also offers a bibliography of related criticism, inviting the visitor to draw conclusions on the interdependence of text, performance, and painting.

Shakespeare's Globe

http://www.rdg.ac.uk/globe/Globe.html

Outstanding presentation of the Globe Theatre, with masses of information on both the original building and the rebuilt version. There is archaeological material, drawings, and an illuminating account of Shakespeare's London. These are followed by a detailed timeline of the long-winded reconstruction and a wealth of pictures from all stages of the process. The site also has a database of performances and a separate section on the Shakespeare programmes for all nationalities and all ages run by the Shakespeare Globe Trust.

Shavian Ideal: George Bernard Shaw's Man and Superman

http://www.fas.harvard.edu/~art/super1.html

Essay investigating the history and aesthetic of George Bernard Shaw's *Man and Superman.* This essay provides background information on Shaw and the play, including insight into Shaw's often vitriolic criticisms of other playwrights's work. This page includes several images.

Sir Derek Jacobi Home Page

http://www.dabbler.com/jacobi/home.html

Tribute to the English actor. There is a detailed biography, reviews of many of his performances, and a complete listing of articles about Jacobi. A large number of photos are included together with news of Jacobi's latest roles.

Trevor Nunn Profile

http://www.achievement.org/autodoc/page/
nun0pro-1

Description of the life and work of the theatre and television director Trevor Nunn. The Web site contains not only a profile and biographical information, but also a lengthy interview with Nunn from 1996 accompanied by a large number of photographs, video sequences, and audio clips.

work, and biographical and career details.

American Variety Stage: Houdini

http://lcweb2.loc.gov/ammem/vshtml/vshdini.html

Part of the American Memory presentation of the US Library of Congress, this page documents the career of legendary escape artist Harry Houdini, and includes numerous photographs and memorabilia dating from 1886 to the years following his death in 1926. There is also biographical information, and the images include brief notes. Click on the images to increase their size.

Background to Noh-Kyogen

http://www.iijnet.or.jp/NOH-KYOGEN/english/english.html

Clearly presented and comprehensive guide to the Japanese dramatic form. There is a history of the development of Nō, description of its stock characters, and analysis of the role of the chorus and musicians. There are examples of several masks and detailed notes on the Nō stage.

Bankhead, Tallulah

http://www.reelclassics.com/Actresses/Tallulah/tallulah.htm

Tribute to actress Tallulah Bankhead. You will find information about Bankhead's career, film stills and full-colour film posters, and a list of famous quotes. The brief text includes links to some of Bankhead's co-stars, including Cary Grant and director Alfred Hitchcock. Look at the bottom of the page for a list of additional Tallulah Bankhead links.

Barnum, P T

http://www.ucc.uconn.edu/~kap96001/

Good source of information on the legendary huckster and marketing genius. There are profiles of the 'freaks' and curiosities exhibited by Barnum. There is a bibliography and information about his role in the Ringling Brothers and Barnum and Bailey Circus.

Bertolt Brecht Home Page

http://www.geocities.com/Broadway/Stage/1052/brecht1.htm

Intimate profile of the German playwright. In addition to an account of his literary, dramatic, and political concerns, there is an intimate account of Brecht's turbulent personal life. There are also summaries of his major works.

Beyond the Horizon

http://www.bartleby.com/132/index.html

Online edition of O'Neill's play *Beyond the Horizon*.

David Belasco Page

http://www.angelfire.com/ny/davidbelasco/

Profile of the US writer. It traces his long involvement in the US theatre as actor, producer, manager, and playwright. There are details of the New York theatre which bears his name and a bibliography.

Dramatist Henrik Ibsen

http://home.sol.no/~abjerkho/grimstad/ibsentxt.htm

Extended guide to the life and works of the

Norwegian dramatist. It charts his years of exile, the long and hard struggle for success, and his searching analysis of passions hidden behind the apparent solidity of middle class values.

Jarry, Alfred

http://hamp.hampshire.edu/~ngzF92/jarrypub/jarry.html

Good account of the outrages, eccentricities, and literary achievements of the French Surrealist. There is a complete bibliography of articles by and about Jarry in English and French and a link to another site dedicated to the memory of the Madman of Laval.

Kabuki for Everyone

http://hotei.fix.co.jp/kabuki/kabuki.html

Introduction to the traditional form of Japanese theatre. As well as a wide range of articles, the site includes images, videos, and audio clips relating to kabuki performances.

Maffei, Marchese Francesco Scipione

http://www.knight.org/advent/cathen/16058b.htm

Biography of the Italian dramatist and archaeologist. It traces his contributions to academic life in France, Britain, and Italy. The many intellectual interests of a man who learnt Hebrew at the age of 80 are described.

Miller, Arthur

http://kennedy-center.org/honors/years/miller.html

Profile of the renowned US playwright. There is a biography of Miller, a photo, and a listing of his plays, novels, and books of reportage.

Miracle Mongers and Their Methods by Harry Houdini

http://etext.lib.virginia.edu/etcbin/browse-mixed-new?id=HouMirM&images=images/modeng&data=/texts/english/modeng/parsed&tag=public

Houdini's celebrated exposé of 'fire eaters, heat resisters, poison eaters, venomous reptile defiers, sword swallowers, human ostriches, strong men, etc.'. The famous escapologist condemns all forms of quackery and charlatanism.

Play is the Thing

http://www.pbs.org/newshour/bb/entertainment/july-dec97/fo_10-9.html

Comprehensive source of information on the work of the Nobel prizewinning Italian satirist Dario Fo. Interviews with Fo and with drama critics highlight his career, his influence on contemporary theatre, and his clashes with the US and Italian governments and the Vatican.

Play That Electrified Harlem

http://lcweb2.loc.gov/ammem/fedtp/ftsmth00.html

Part of a larger site on the Federal Theater Project, this page is an article concerning Orson Welles's all-black production of *Macbeth* in Harlem during the Great Depression. The original article appeared in the January/February 1996 edition of *Civilization* magazine. This site includes a number of photos and images of items from Welles's 1936 production.

Sam Shepard Web Site

http://www.departments.bucknell.edu/theatre_dance/Shepard/shepard.html

Thoughtful and entertaining profile of the life and achievements of the multi-talented US writer and actor. There is coverage of his life, acting, pop-culture references, music, published works, and a biographical timeline.

Teacher's Guide to *The Crucible*

http://www.sdcoe.k12.ca.us/score/cruc/cructg.html

Comprehensive description of Arthur Miller's play *The Crucible.* The information included is aimed at teachers, but is equally appropriate for those studying the play. There are also several structured activities to help undertstanding of this work.

Wild Duck, The

http://etext.lib.virginia.edu/cgibin/toccer?id=IbsWild&tag=public&images=images/modeng&data=/lv1/Archive/eng-parsed&part=0

Text of Ibsen's famous drama.

Miscellaneous Theatre

American Variety Stage: English Playscripts

http://lcweb2.loc.gov/ammem/vshtml/vseng.html

Part of the Rare Book and Special Collections Division of the US Library of Congress celebrating vaudeville and popular entertainment, this page features unpublished manuscripts, including vaudeville comedy sketches, monologues, musical revue, and scripts from other genres. The playscripts include brief notes. You can browse the collection by keyword, subject, title, or author.

American Variety Stage: Sound Recordings

http://lcweb2.loc.gov/ammem/vshtml/vssound.html

Sound recordings selected from vintage phonograph records released between 1913 and 1927. This page, celebrating vaudeville and popular entertainment, is part of the Rare Book and Special Collections Division of the US Library of Congress and includes recordings of comic skits, popular music and songs, and a dramatic monologue. The audio includes brief notes. You can browse the collection by keyword, subject, title, or author.

American Variety Stage: Theatre Playbills and Programmes

http://lcweb2.loc.gov/ammem/vshtml/vsprgbl.html

Theatre playbills, programmes, and other materials from a number of US theatre productions dating from 1870 to 1920, which include the names of performers, productions, the various acts that made up the playbill, and advertisements. This page, celebrating vaudeville and popular entertainment, is part of the Rare Book and Special Collections Division of the US Library of Congress. The images include brief notes. You can browse the collection by keyword, subject, title, or author.

American Variety Stage: Yiddish-Language Scripts

http://lcweb2.loc.gov/ammem/vshtml/vsyid.html

Part of the Hebraic Section of the African and Middle Eastern Division of the US Library of Congress, this page celebrates Yiddish theatre and the Jewish contribution to US vaudeville and popular entertainment. It features 77 unpublished manuscripts including light comedies and dramas. The playscripts include brief notes. You can browse the collection by keyword, subject, title, or author.

Didaskalia

http://didaskalia.berkeley.edu

Academic journal devoted to ancient theatre and modern productions of ancient plays. This site contains a brief introduction to ancient theatre and some articles on the issues surrounding ancient drama, covering everything from its role in the ancient world to the complexities of staging authentic productions today.

Medieval Drama

http://www.leeds.ac.uk/theatre/emd/links.htm

One individual's collection of important medieval dramatic texts, as well as critical articles and discussion groups related to this field. The site also has some good practical resources on producing medieval drama, with pages full of images and ideas to help with props, performance, make-up, and set design.

Playbill Online

http://www1.playbill.com/playbill/

Online edition of the US theatre magazine providing listings and seating plans for Broadway productions. Here too, among other things, are interviews, features, weekly columns, theatre news from around the world, production photos, audio clips, and information about the theatre industry.

Theatre Arts Library

http://www.perspicacity.com/elactheatre/index.html

Plays, papers, historical documents, and other theatre links useful for the study of all aspects of the theatre. This site includes overviews of the leading playwrights in theatre history.

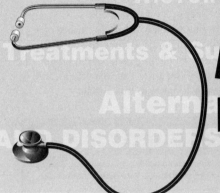

MEDICINE & HEALTH

Health

Aerobics!

http://www.turnstep.com/

Answers to 'Frequently Asked Questions' about aerobics, an illustrated guide to some basic step aerobic moves, and – for the more experienced – a library of exercises, from warm-ups to slides, plus an invitation to submit your own favourite exercise.

Air Pollution – Committee on the Medical Aspects of Air Pollutants

http://www.open.gov.uk/doh/hef/airpol/airpolh.htm

Comprehensive report on the state of Britain's air from the Ministry of Health. There is a large amount of textual and statistical information on all aspects of air pollution, description of improved warning and detection measures, and details of how the general public may access advice and information.

American Heart Association

http://www.americanheart.org/newhome.html

Home page of the American Heart Association offers a risk assessment test, information about healthy living, including the effects of diet, and access to resources for both patients and carers.

'Biodiversity Loss Threatens New Treatments'

http://www.bmj.com/cgi/content/full/316/7140/1261/l

Part of a collection of articles maintained by the *British Medical Journal*, this page features the full text of a news article originally published on 25 April 1998 that reports on how the loss of biodiversity will adversely affect the future of human health. You can also search the collections under which this article appears, search other articles written by the author of this article, and submit or read responses to this article.

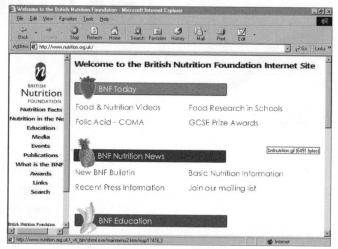

British Nutrition Society

http://www.nutrition.org.uk/

Offering educational resources for parents, schools and teachers, the British Nutrition Foundation Web site has a wide range of information about the nutritional value of your diet.

Children's Health

http://www.kidshealth.org/

In-depth coverage of children's health issues, including infections, behaviour and emotions, food, and fitness. The site also includes an interactive map of the human body, designed for children to explore, and you can e-mail any health questions that aren't answered online.

Eat Less, Live Longer

http://whyfiles.news.wisc.edu/057aging/index.html

Part of the Why Files project, published by the National Institute for Science Education (NISE) and funded by the National Science Foundation, this page provides insight into scientific research on increasing lifespans by reducing caloric intake. The highly readable text, laid out over six pages, includes information about 'undernutrition without malnutrition', a technique of caloric restriction that has significantly increased the lifespans of lab animals. Find out why and how this technique works and learn about the role of anti-oxidants in the ageing process. Numerous images and diagrams enhance the text throughout. You will find a comprehensive bibliography of sources for further research.

HEBSWeb

http://www.hebs.scot.nhs.uk/

Neatly designed information service run by the Health Education Board of Scotland. The site is devoted to the promotion of public health issues and includes factcards, posters, booklets, and statistics on smoking, mental and sexual health, dietary issues, accidents, and alcohol and drug misuse. The site also provides extensive accounts of campaigns, activities, support groups, leaflets, and other information especially geared for Scotland. There is also plenty of information for healthcare professionals.

FACT

PUBLIC HEALTH (community medicine)
science of preventing disease and promoting health at community level rather than on an individual basis. At its most basic it includes the provision of an adequate supply of clean water and the safe disposal of sewage.

Insomnia? Just go to Sleep and Forget It

http://www.well.com/user/mick/insomnia/insomnia.html

Tips and advice for insomniacs. The site does not purport to give professional medical aid, but it offers a collection of tried methods that have proved generally helpful. It leads the sufferers through the standard techniques and afterwards introduces them to some more radical methods, like sleeping with your head facing north or visualizing the unpleasant things often associated with getting up on a cold and miserable morning.

International Travel and Health

http://jupiter.who.ch/yellow/welcome.htm

World Health Organization database of vaccination requirements for every country in the world. The site contains a mass of practical advice for international travellers. Information is regularly updated.

MEdiC – Heath Explorer – Osteoporosis

http://medic.med.uth.tmc.edu/ptnt/00000767.htm

Fact sheet with basic information on osteoporosis. It includes risk factors and a catalogue of calcium food sources with exact nutritional information.

MedicineNet

http://www.medicinenet.com/

Immense US-based site dealing in plain language with all current aspects of medicine. There is a dictionary of diseases, cures, and medical terms. The site also includes an 'Ask the Experts' section, lots of current medical news, and last, but not least, some important first aid advice.

Menopause Information and Resources

http://www.pslgroup.com/MENOPAUSE.HTM

Guide to the menopause, hormone-replacement therapy, and some other women's health issues. This site offers a whole host of recent medical reports and news, as well as basic facts and advice.

Multimedia Medical Reference Library

http://www.med-library.com/medlibrary/

Huge medical reference work on the Web, with detailed text, diagrams, and explanations of a great range of ailments and other medical matters. A full search engine is available to help you locate your section of interest quickly.

National Health Service (NHS)

http://www.nhs50.nhs.uk/

Features a detailed history of the NHS, what health services were like before the NHS, and a glimpse into the future with 'Technology for tomorrow'.

NHS Story

http://www.nhs50.nhs.uk/nhsstory-index.htm

NHS (National Health Service)

F
A
C
T

one of the biggest public health organizations in the world, set up in 1948 to provide free health care for everybody in Britain. The hopes of its founders, that it would so improve public health that its cost could be easily contained, have proved in vain. Better and more expensive treatments have sent costs soaring, though it has succeeded in its basic aims.

Well-organized history of Britain's National Health Service. Written as part of the NHS's 50th birthday celebration, this account conveys the excitement generated in 1948 by the first ever provision of a free comprehensive health service. The evolution of the NHS is traced, decade by decade, with the help of lively text and photographs.

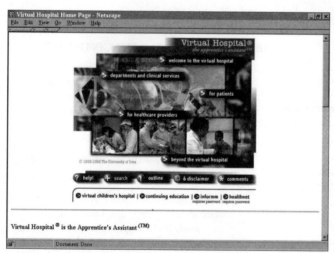

Virtual Hospital ® is the Apprentice's Assistant (TM)

Plainsense Men's Health

http://www.plainsense.com/Health/Mens/

Covers a wide range of issues specific to male physical and mental health, with practical advice on self-help and treatment options.

Plainsense Women's Health

http://www.plainsense.com/Health/Womens/index.htm

Covers a wide range of issues specific to female physical and mental health, with practical advice on self-help and treatment options.

Tobacco Alert

http://www.who.int/psa/psa6.htm

Special 1996 No Smoking Day edition of the World Health Organization's tobacco report. It is unabashedly dedicated to remedying a global health problem which accounts for 6% of all fatalities worldwide. As well as this detailed and well referenced report on contemporary tobacco use, the site also contains back issues of *Tobacco Alert* and other resources on tobacco and health.

Virtual Hospital

http://indy.radiology.uiowa.edu/VirtualHospital.html

Virtual Hospital with multimedia instructional tools, contents of a wide series of medical publications, simulations of patients, patient textbooks, peer-reviewed Web resources on common medical problems, and an online continuing education service for health care providers and patients.

Yoga Studio

http://www.timages.com/yoga.htm

Interactive yoga studio offering tips on preparation for beginners, a chat forum for the exchange of experiences and ideas with practitioners, and books, videos, tapes, and workshops listings. Visitors can even customize their own online yoga class with the help of the shockwave plug-in.

Your Body and Nutrition

http://www.ilcnet.com/~nutrition/body.htm

Information and pictures on the way the human body works. There are pages on different cell functions and the importance of free radicals. Each page is accompanied by a picture and a brief explanation. It is a commercially sponsored site, but there is a lot of good and free biological information here.

The Body

Anatomy and Function of the Ear

http://www.voice-center.com/ear_anatomy.html

Concise medical information on the anatomy and function of the ear. The site includes separate sections on the three sections of the ear, and describes various hearing problems.

Antibody Resource Page

http://www.antibodyresource.com/

Fascinating access site for all you could ever want to know about antibodies and some things you'd probably rather not know! This site contains several educational resources (aimed at university level), but also contains images, animations, and descriptions of research into many different types of antibodies.

Breaking the Code of Colour

http://www.hhmi.org/senses/b/b110.htm

As part of a much larger site called 'Seeing, Hearing, and Smelling the World', here is a set of pages examining the way we perceive the world through the sense of sight. It is divided into four sections called 'How do we see colours?', 'Red, green, and blue cones', 'Colour blindness: more prevalent among males', and 'Judging a colour'. This site makes good use of images and animations to help with the explanations, so it is best viewed with an up-to-date browser.

Famous Left-Handers

http://www.indiana.edu/~primate/left.html

Thorough listing of famous left-handers. Among this list are the last four US Presidents, Joan of Arc, Charlemagne and Queen Victoria. On a more serious note, there are accounts of ordinary people being stigmatized for left-handedness and a plea for greater understanding. There are links to many other left-handedness sites.

Heart: An Online Exploration

http://sln.fi.edu/biosci/heart.html

Explore the heart: discover its complexities, development, and structure; follow the blood on its journey through the blood vessels; learn how to maintain a healthy heart; and look back on the history of cardiology.

How We See Things That Move

http://www.hhmi.org/senses/b/b210.htm

As part of a much larger site called 'Seeing, Hearing, and Smelling the World', here is a set of pages examining the way we are able to see and understand movement. It is divided into three sections: 'The strange symptoms of blindness to motion', 'A hot spot in the brain's motion pathway', and 'Integrating information about movement'. This site makes good use of images and animations to help with the explanations, so it is best viewed with an up-to-date browser.

Human Anatomy Online

http://www.innerbody.com/htm/body.html

Fun, interactive, and educational site on the human body. The site is divided into many informative sections, including hundreds of images, and animations for Java-enabled browsers.

It's All in the Brain

http://www.hhmi.org/senses/a/a110.htm

As part of a much larger site called 'Seeing, Hearing, and Smelling the World', here is a set of pages introducing the way in which we perceive the world through our senses. It is divided into five sections: 'Illusions reveal the brain's assumptions', 'Sensing change in the environment', 'Vision, hearing, and smell: the best-known senses', 'A language the brain can understand', and 'More than the sum of its parts'. This site use images and animations extensively, so it is best viewed with an up-to-date browser.

Lifeblood

http://sln2.fi.edu/biosci/blood/blood.html

Introduction to blood, with graphics and links to other pages where you will find out everything you might ever think to ask about blood.

Locating a Mouse by its Sound

http://www.hhmi.org/senses/c/c210.htm

As part of a much larger site called 'Seeing, Hearing, and Smelling the World', here is a page examining the way we can locate objects through sound alone. It is divided into four sections called 'A brain map of auditory space', 'The value of having two ears', 'Bat sounds and human speech', and 'On the trail of a deafness gene'. This site makes good use of images and animations to help with the explanations, so it is best viewed with an up-to-date browser.

Mystery of Smell

http://www.hhmi.org/senses/d/d110.htm

As part of a much larger site called 'Seeing, Hearing, and Smelling the World', here is a page examining the way our sense of smell works. It is divided into four sections called 'The vivid world of odours', 'Finding the odourant receptors', 'How rats and mice – and probably humans – recognize odours', and 'The memory of smells'. This site makes good use of images and animations to help with the explanations, so it is best viewed with an up-to-date browser.

Neuroscience for Kids

http://faculty.washington.edu/chudler/neurok.html

Explore the nervous system – your brain, spinal cord, nerve cells, and senses – by means of this impressive site, designed for primary and secondary school students and teachers.

Odyssey of Life

http://www.pbs.org/wgbh/nova/odyssey/

Companion to the US Public Broadcasting Service (PBS) television programme *Nova*, this page examines the formation of embryos. It includes time-lapse video sequences of growing embryos. Two leading spokesmen of the evolution/creation debate state their opposing viewpoints regarding the age-old question 'How did we get here'? Their debate is carried out online through a series of letters in which they reply to the other's position and expand on their own. There is also an interview with the photographer of the programme in which he discusses the tricky techniques and technology required to film living embryos inside the womb.

Primate Handedness and Brain Lateralization

http://www.indiana.edu/~primate/index.html

Rather scholarly title for what is a very readable account of left- and right-handedness in humans and other primates.

Quivering Bundles That Let Us Hear

http://www.hhmi.org/senses/c/c110.htm

As part of a much larger site called 'Seeing, Hearing, and Smelling the World', here is a page examining the way our ears work. It is divided into four sections called 'Signals from a hair cell', 'The goal: extreme sensitivity and speed', 'Tip links pull up the gates', and 'On the trail of a deafness gene'. This site makes good use of images and animations to help with the explanations, so it is best viewed with an up-to-date browser.

Respiratory System

http://library.advanced.org/10348/find/content/respiratory.html

Detailed description of how respiration occurs in humans. The text is accompanied by useful graphics.

Science of Love

http://whyfiles.news.wisc.edu/033love/index.html

Part of the Why Files project, published by the National Institute for Science Education (NISE) and funded by the National Science Foundation, this page provides a scientific answer to the age-old query 'why do fools fall in love?'. The highly readable text, laid out over ten pages, provides 'intriguing evidence that humans communicate with unconscious chemical signals', called pheromones. Numerous images and diagrams enhance the text throughout. The more tricky terms are linked to a glossary, and you will find a comprehensive bibliography of sources for further research.

Secret Sense in the Human Nose?

http://www.hhmi.org/senses/d/d210.htm

As part of a much larger site called 'Seeing, Hearing, and Smelling the World', here is a page examining the way our sense of smell detects odours we are not aware of. It is divided into three sections called 'Sniffing out social and sexual signals', 'Triggers of innate behaviour', and 'Pheromones and mammals'. This site makes good use of images and animations to help with the explanations, so it is best viewed with an up-to-date browser.

Urgent Need to Use Both Eyes

http://www.hhmi.org/senses/b/b410.htm

Part of a much larger site called 'Seeing, Hearing, and Smelling the World', this page examines the reason why we have two eyes on the front of our head – binocular vision. This site makes good use of images and animations to help with the explanations, so it is best viewed with an up-to-date browser.

Virtual Body

http://www.medtropolis.com/vbody/

If ever something was worth taking the time to download the 'Shockwave' plug-in for, this is it. Authoritative and interactive anatomical animations complete with voice-overs guide you round the whole body, with sections on the brain, digestive system, heart, and skeleton.

Visible Embryo

http://www.visembryo.com/

Learn about the first four weeks of human development.

Visible Human Project

http://www.nlm.nih.gov/research/visible/visible_gallery.html

Sample images from a long-term US project to collect a complete set of anatomically detailed, three-dimensional representations of the human body.

Visual Pathway

http://www.hhmi.org/senses/b/b150.htm

As part of a much larger site called 'Seeing, Hearing, and Smelling the World', here is a page explaining the way light travels from the eye to the brain and how it is converted into images our brain can understand. This site makes good use of images and animations to help with the explanations, so it is best viewed with an up-to-date browser.

Diseases & Disorders

Acne Vulgaris (Pimples)

http://www.nsc.gov.sg/commskin/Acne/acne.html

Practical advice for acne sufferers. The causes of the condition and its diagnosis are explained with the aid of pictures, and there are tips on washing the face and treating acne.

AIDS and HIV Information

http://www.thebody.com/index.shtml

AIDS and HIV site offering safe-sex and AIDS prevention advice, information about treatments and testing, and health and nutritional guidance for those with the disease.

Allergy Facts

http://www.onlineallergycenter.com/about.htm

Extended fact sheet about allergies. It provides basic information about the causes, symptoms, and treatment of allergy attacks, and helps clarify typical misunderstandings about allergy sufferers. It also provides tips for the everyday life of an allergy sufferer and an extended list of allergy symptoms.

Amniocentesis

http://www.aomc.org/amnio.html#_wmh4_822004218

Comprehensive plain-English guide to amniocentesis. For a pregnant woman considering the procedure, this is an invaluable source of information. The advantages and the risks of sampling the amniotic fluid are clearly presented.

Anthrax

http://www.outbreak.org/cgi-unreg/dynaserve.exe/cb/anthrax.html

Basic medical details of the livestock disease and biological weapon anthrax. The Web site contains brief sections covering characteristics of the disease, the symptoms it causes, cautions and precautions, first aid therapy for victims of the disease, and a list of neutralization and decontamination methods.

Attention-Deficit Hyperactivity Disorders

http://www.mentalhealth.com/dis/p20-ch01.html

Part of Internet Mental Health, this is a section from a freely available encyclopaedia of 'Mental health information'. It contains information on attention-deficit disorder, its treatment, and links to other related sites.

Black Death

http://history.idbsu.edu/westciv/plague/

Part of a larger site on the history of western civilization maintained by Boise State University, this page provides an introduction to the Black Death. Information is organized into 22 brief articles, each concerning a specific aspect of the plague, such as its origins and arrival in the West, a description of the disease and the various forms of plague, medical measures to combat it, and its wide-reaching effects on the population, economy, culture, and so on. You can start at the beginning and work your way through the articles in chronological order or go directly to a page that interests you. There is also a list of references for further study.

Bovine Spongiform Encephalopathy (BSE)

http://cahpwww.nbc.upenn.edu/bse/bse1.html

Collection of informative articles chronicling the BSE (or 'mad cow') controversy in the UK, including background information and official reports.

Breast Cancer Awareness

http://avon.avon.com/showpage.asp?
thepage=crusade

Promotes awareness of this disease through a library of frequently asked questions about breast cancer and mammograms, as well as a glossary of common terms and access to support groups. There is also information about fundraising activities and recipients of awards for people and groups seen to be contributing the most to the fight against this disease. The Web site is sponsored by the make-up company Avon.

British Dyslexia Association

http://www.bda-dyslexia.org.uk/

Huge source of practical information on dyslexia for adult sufferers and parents and teachers of dyslexic children. All aspects of dyslexia, from identifying the condition in toddlers to computer software for dyslexics, are covered by this informative site. There is information about UK support groups and other resources.

Cancer: The Facts

http://www.icnet.uk/research/factsheet/index.html

Information on cancer from the Imperial Cancer Research Fund. There is a simple explanation of what cancer is, followed by links to other sites dealing with the different types of cancer – bowel, leukaemia, lung, pancreatic, skin, and multiple myeloma cancers, as well as cancers specific to either men or women, or prevalent within families. Cancer statistics are also given.

Candidiasis

http://www.projinf.org/fs/candida.html

Thorough source of information about thrush. Causes, symptoms, and both conventional and unorthodox treatments are described in medical, but generally understandable, language. There is also useful information on a variety of forms of prophylaxis. This is essential reading for anybody troubled by candidiasis.

Cerebral Palsy Tutorial

http://galen.med.virginia.edu/~smb4v/tutorials/cp/cp.htm

Multimedia tutorial on cerebral palsy for children and parents. It discusses the causes and different kinds of the disorder, describes a series of therapeutic interventions, and presents equipment of different kinds that can prove useful for children with this debilitating condition.

CF Web – Online Information About Cystic Fibrosis

http://cf-web.mit.edu/

Huge clearing house of information about cystic fibrosis compiled by the Massachusetts Institute of Technology. There is a three-hundred page listing of frequently asked questions, containing information on a wide range of treatments. There are also links to related sites around the world. This is an invaluable site for the medical profession, and for sufferers wanting advice or to share their experience (and grievances).

Childhood Infections – Appendicitis

http://kidshealth.org/parent/common/appendicitis.html

Facts and advice on appendicitis. This page gives a detailed description of the infection, its incubation period, and its duration. There are also notes on the prevention of appendicitis and details of what to do should the symptoms occur.

Childhood Infections – Common Cold

http://kidshealth.org/parent/common/cold.html

Useful information about the common cold. There is a detailed description of the infection, its symptoms, and its duration. There are also notes on possible ways to prevent the spreading of the infection and details of what to do should the symptoms occur.

Childhood Infections – Croup

http://kidshealth.org/parent/common/croup.html

Facts about croup part of a larger child health site. There is a detailed description of the infection, its symptoms, and its duration. A sound file is included to demonstrate the cough of croup sufferers. There are also notes on the prevention of croup and details of what to do should the symptoms occur.

Childhood Infections – Measles

http://kidshealth.org/parent/common/measles.html

Educational page on measles, providing information on the signs, symptoms and progress of the disease. It also addresses issues such as possible complications, vaccination, home treatment, and contagiousness.

Childhood Infections – Meningitis

http://kidshealth.org/parent/common/
meningitis.html

Essential information on the signs and symptoms, and appropriate treatment of meningitis in children. The site also discusses the incubation, duration, and contagiousness of the illness, as well as the preventive measures that can be taken in certain cases.

Childhood Infections – Mumps

http://kidshealth.org/parent/common/mumps.html

Useful information about mumps. There is a detailed description of the infection, its symptoms, and its duration. There are also notes on the prevention of the infection and details of what to do should the symptoms occur.

Childhood Infections – Pertussis (Whooping Cough)

http://kidshealth.org/parent/common/
whooping_cough.html

Information about whooping cough from a larger site on children's health. There is a detailed description of the infection, its symptoms, and its duration. There are also notes on the prevention of whooping cough, how it can be treated both at home and professionally, and what to do should the symptoms occur.

Childhood Infections – Pneumonia

http://kidshealth.org/parent/common/
pneumonia.html

Useful information about pneumonia. There is a detailed, illustrated description of the infection, its symptoms, and its duration. There are also notes on the prevention of the infection and details of what to do should the symptoms occur.

Childhood Infections – Rabies

http://kidshealth.org/parent/common/rabies.html

Facts about rabies from a larger resource on children's health. There is a detailed description of the infection, its symptoms, and its duration. The page also contains notes on the prevention of the infection and details of what to do should the symptoms occur.

Childhood Infections – Rubella

http://kidshealth.org/parent/common/
german_measles.html

Information on rubella, or German measles. This page provides a detailed description of the infection, its symptoms, and its duration. There are also notes on the prevention of the infection and details of what to do should the symptoms occur.

Childhood Infections – Scarlet Fever

http://kidshealth.org/parent/common/
scarlet_fever.html

Detailed information about scarlet fever. Part of a larger site, this page contains a detailed description of the infection, its symptoms, and its duration. There are also notes on the prevention of the fever, how the infection can be treated both at home and professionally, and what to do should the symptoms occur.

Childhood Infections – Sinusitis

http://kidshealth.org/parent/common/sinusitis.html

Facts and afvice on sinusitis. There is a detailed description of the infection, its symptoms, and its duration. There are also notes on the prevention of the infection, how it can be treated both at home and by a doctor, and what to do should the symptoms occur.

Childhood Infections – Tetanus

http://kidshealth.org/parent/infections/tetanus.html

Important information on the signs and symptoms of tetanus, the incubation, duration, and treatment of the illness. Specific reference is made to neonatal tetanus, which affects newborn infants as a result of inefficient surgical techniques during delivery.

Childhood Infections – Tonsillitis

http://kidshealth.org/parent/common/tonsillitis.html

Useful information about tonsillitis. There is a detailed description of the infection, its symptoms, and its duration. There are also notes on the prevention of the infection, how it can be treated both at home and professionally, and what to do should the symptoms occur.

Childhood Infections – Varicella (Chicken Pox)

http://kidshealth.org/parent/common/chicken_pox.html

Educational information sheet concerning chicken pox, featuring sections on signs and symptoms, prevention, incubation and duration, contagiousness, and home treatment of this common children's disease.

Chronic Fatigue Syndrome FAQ

http://www.cais.com/cfs-news/faq.htm

Extensive answer sheet shedding light on the hottest questions regarding chronic fatigue syndrome. The site deals with issues such as the relation to stress and depression, the possible causes and duration of the illness, and the onset and clinical symptoms of the disease. It also discusses a series of common misunderstandings related to the syndrome.

Creutzfeldt-Jakob Disease & Bovine Spongiform Encephalopathy

http://www.open.gov.uk/doh/cjd/cjd1.htm

Official presentation of research findings on CJD and BSE from Britain's Ministry of Health. These pages bring together a huge archive of material gathered from Britain and abroad.

Dengue and Dengue Haemorraghic Fever

http://www.who.int/ith/english/dengue.htm

World Health organization fact sheet on the tropical disease and its recent history. The fact sheet also details policy and resources required to bring about effective control of the disease.

Disability named ADD

http://www.chadd.org/facts/add_facts01.htm

Well-written fact sheet containing practical information on Attention Deficit Disorders for parents and teachers of diagnosed children. The condition, its diagnosis, and treatment are exhaustively discussed. There is also a comprehensive listing of resources and further sources of information.

Endometriosis

http://www.geocities.com/HotSprings/1712/whatis.htm

Information about endometriosis. The facts about this common and poorly-understood disease are well presented. Methods of treatment are explained and there is a link to a site with advice on pain management and to a newsgroup for endometriosis sufferers.

Flu is a Bummer

http://falcon.cc.ukans.edu/~jbrown/flu.html

Explains the basics of influenza and answers such as questions as why it can be caught more than once and why we cannot be immunized against it. The article also features links expanding on a number of issues raised during the discussion.

Gulf War Syndrome

http://www.cais.com/cfs-news/gulfwar.htm#TALK

Huge clearing house of latest information about Gulf War Syndrome. Information is targeted both at Gulf War veterans and the medical profession. In addition to a large range of medical reports, there are media articles and updates of the latest litigation on both sides of the Atlantic. The site includes a large number of links to veterans' organizations and medical researchers.

High Blood Pressure

http://www.americanheart.org/Heart_and_Stroke_A_Z_Guide/hbp.html

Page from the American Heart Foundation which explains what causes high blood pressure, and what can be done to prevent it.

Human Genetic Disease: A Laymans Approach

http://mcrcr2.med.nyu.edu/murphp01/lysosome/hgd.htm

Comprehensive manual of cell biology for the

family. It includes discussions of cell structure, DNA, chromosomes, and the detection of genetic defects. It also outlines the main goals of state-of-the-art genetic research.

Impetigo

http://www.nsc.gov.sg/commskin/Impetigo/impetigo.html

Well-presented information about impetigo from Singapore's National Skin Centre. A picture is included to help identify the condition.

Information about Deafblindness

http://www.s55wilma.demon.co.uk/info-db.html

Copious information on deafblindness written by James Gallager, who is himself deafblind. He explains how he communicates with other deafblind people and with the hearing-seeing world around him. There are links to UK deafblind organizations and groups, to the Deafblind Manual Alphabet, and to the Braille and Moon systems of embossed reading. The site also includes a biography of Dr William Moon.

Overview of this disease – its transmission, symptoms, treatment, and prevention. This text-only site makes grim reading, but has plenty of practical information to help you avoid catching this tick-borne disease and also what to do if you do catch it.

Malaria

http://www.malaria.org/WHAT.HTM

Page from the Malaria Foundation covering frequently asked questions on malaria. The Web site contains answers to a comprehensive list of questions regarding the disease, including thorough descriptions of the virus and its related diseases.

Ménière's Disease

http://www.zak.co.il/deaf-info/old/meniere.html

Information about symptoms, treatment, links to other contacts, and frequently asked questions about Ménière's Disease.

Narrow Tunnel of Light

http://www.hhmi.org/senses/b/b310.htm

As part of a much larger site called 'Seeing, Hearing, and Smelling the World', here is a page examining progress being made to combat the genetic sight disorder retinitis pigmentosa, which can leave people completely blind by the age of 40. This site makes good use of images and animations to help with the explanations, so it is best viewed with an up-to-date browser.

Oncolink Survivor Stories

http://cancer.med.upenn.edu/psychosocial/personal/survivors/

Site containing survivor stories from those who have gone through the experience of cancer. The patients go through the facts, describes their own feelings, and provide answers to many crucial questions.

OncoLink – The University of Pennsylvania Cancer Centre Resource

http://cancer.med.upenn.edu/

As the title of this site says, a broad resource of cancer-related information for sufferers and their families. It includes sections on 'Causes,

Jet Lag

http://www.outsidein.co.uk/nojetlag.htm

Advice for travellers on how to adapt to changes in time zones. Calculations on how to adjust internal clocks are suited to the separate needs of 'night owls' and 'larks'. The physiological consequences of jet lag are also well explained.

Lyme Disease

http://www2.lymenet.org/domino/file.nsf/UID/lymenetguide

screening, and prevention', 'Clinical trials', and 'Conferences and meetings'.

Outbreak – Ebola

http://www.outbreak.org/cgi-unreg/dynaserve.exe/Ebola/index.html

US-run site that chronicles the history of the Ebola virus. The scientific developments in treating the virus are also described, and there are quotes from the leading researchers in the field of fil-virus treatment. A 'Frequently Asked Questions' section should calm those worried about an Ebola pandemic.

Outbreak: Emerging Diseases

http://www.outbreak.org/cgi-unreg/dynaserve.exe/emergence.html

Comprehensive Web site that includes details of online information services addressing emerging diseases around the world.

F A C T

DISEASE

condition that disturbs or impairs the normal state of an organism. Diseases can occur in all life forms, and normally affect the functioning of cells, tissues, organs, or systems. Diseases are usually characterized by specific symptoms and signs, and can be mild and short-lasting – such as the common cold – or severe enough to decimate a whole species – such as Dutch elm disease.

Outbreak – Staphylococcus

http://www.outbreak.org/cgi-unreg/dynaserve.exe/staph.html

Thorough description of this bacterial infection from US-based site. The latest news on outbreaks and treatments, and the details of new strains which are resistant to antibiotics, are included.

People's Plague: Tuberculosis in America

http://www.pbs.org/ppol/

Companion to a US Public Broadcasting Service (PBS) television programme that was first shown in October 1995, this site investigates the history of tuberculosis in the USA and the ongoing fight against this deadly disease. It includes a 'Close-up' section with detailed information about Dr

Robert Koch, the doctor who discovered the tubercle bacilli in 1882; the Chiricahua Apache tribe that was virtually annihilated by tuberculosis; the sanitariums that housed the sick and dying; the USA's declaration of war against the disease; and the status of tuberculosis today. There are numerous photographs, plus audio and video clips taken from interviews with physicians and patients. Complete transcripts of the PBS programme can be downloaded in English or Spanish.

Plague

http://www.outbreak.org/cgi-unreg/dynaserve.exe /Plague/index.html

Basic medical details of the versions of plague bactertia and viruses that are used as biological weapons. This Web site contains brief sections covering characteristics of the diseases, including their toxicology, the symptoms they cause, cautions and precautions, first aid therapy for victims of the diseases, and a list of neutralization and decontamination methods.

Plaguescape

http://www.plaguescape.com/

Scientific analysis of the ten biblical plagues of Egypt, based upon modern epidemiological principles.

Psoriasis

http://www.nsc.gov.sg/commskin/Psoriasi/psoriasi.html

Well-presented practical information about psoriasis from Singapore's National Skin Centre. The condition is explained in simple language supported by a picture. There are details of various treatment regimes.

Repetitive Strain Injury

http://engr-www.unl.edu/ee/eeshop/rsi.html

Unofficial, but very informative and extensively-linked, site produced by a sufferer of RSI. It includes a section on the symptoms, as well as diagrams and photos of how to type without straining your back or hands. The site is largely focused upon prevention rather than cure.

Retinoblastoma

http://www.healthanswers.com/database/ami/converted/001030.html

Good source of basic information on the cancer of the retina. Symptoms, diagnosis, and treatment of this rare tumour are explained in readily understandable language.

Scabies

http://www.nsc.gov.sg/commskin/Scabies/scabies.html

Well-presented information about scabies from Singapore's National Skin Centre. There is a picture of the condition and information on its transmission and treatment.

Schizophrenia

http://www.pslgroup.com/SCHIZOPHR.HTM

Facts about schizophrenia – causes and symptoms, the different types of the disease, how it affects sufferers' family members, available treatments, and new developments. The site includes a list of available support resources.

Seasonal Light – SAD Home Page

http://www.geocities.com/HotSprings/7061/sadhome.html#SC

Thorough source of support for SAD (seasonal affective disorder) sufferers and those treating them. The site includes information about this form of depression as well as reference to books, and articles. There is information on seasonal light device manufacturers and contacts for self help – 'walkers in darkness' – groups in the UK.

Shingles

http://www.nsc.gov.sg/commskin/Shingles/shingles.html

Guide to diagnosing and treating herpes zoster from Singapore's National Skin Centre. There are pictures to illustrate the condition.

Sleep Disorders and Snoring

http://www.newtechpub.com/phantom/faq/osa_faq.htm

Basic answers to common queries on snoring and sleep apnoea. Visitors are offered reference information and opinions on the treatment of the above disorders. They are also advised to seek specialist help.

Smallpox

http://www.outbreak.org/cgi-unreg/dynaserve.exe/Smallpox.html

Story of the eradication of the smallpox virus. The Web site covers the eradication program from its earliest stages to the final destruction of the virus, described by the WHO as 'man's greatest achievement'. A photograph of the virus is included on the Web site via a hypertext link, and an interview with John Scott Porterfield, one of the workers responsible for the virus' destruction, is also available here.

Tendinitis and Bursitis

http://www.healthtouch.com/level1/leaflets/ACR/ACR035.htm

Well-written information on these soft-tissue rheumatisms from the American College of Rheumatology. The causes of the conditions are well explained, together with preventive advice. Diagnostic and curative procedures are explained in easy-to-understand language.

Tennis Elbow – Lateral Epicondylitis

http://www.scoi.com/teniselb.htm

Good explanation of the causes of tennis elbow and what can be done about it. There is a diagram of the tendons and muscles in the arm. Surgical and other forms of treatment are discussed.

Tinnitus

http://www.deafblind.com/tinnitus.html

Good source of practical information and advice for those with ringing in the ears. The causes of the condition are described and various coping mechanisms are set out.

Urticaria

http://www.nsc.gov.sg/commskin/Urticari/urticari.html

Practical information about hives from Singapore's National Skin Centre. Information about its causes includes advice about diet. There are three photos of the condition and advice about treatment.

Viral Warts

http://www.nsc.gov.sg/commskin/Warts/warts.html

Practical information about warts from Singapore's National Skin Centre. Various treatment methods, none of them foolproof, are described. There is advice for patients who have cryotherapy and reassurance to suffers that warts are not cancerous. There are three photos of various kinds of warts.

World of Multiple Sclerosis

http://www.ifmss.org.uk/

International cooperative effort utilizing experts in all areas of MS to offer current and useful information to all members of the MS community. The Web site includes answers to common questions, publications, current news, databases, services, and societies.

Yellow Fever

http://www.outbreak.org/cgi-unreg/dynaserve.exe/YellowFever/index.html

Outbreak page on yellow fever. The Web site contains a section on frequently asked questions about the disease, and a section on current and recent outbreaks. The outbreaks section is updated regularly, often giving numbers of casualties and descriptions of operations by the World Health Organization to curb the spread of any outbreak.

Bacteria & Viruses

Bacterial Evolution: Score one for Punk Eek

http://www.sciam.com/explorations/072196explorations.html

Part of a larger site maintained by *Scientific American,* this page reports on research conducted at Michigan State University in which scientists sped up the evolution of bacteria in order to study the theory of 'punctuated equilibrium', which seeks to explain why evolutionary changes sometimes take place with relative suddenness after aeons of general stasis. The text includes hypertext links to further information, and there is also a list of links to critical analysis of punctuated equilibrium and related sites on the Web.

Bad Bug Book – Hepatitis A Virus

http://vm.cfsan.fda.gov/~mow/chap31.html

Concise fact sheet about hepatitis A. The site includes basic information on the

nature and diagnosis of the disease, as well as brief discussions of its frequency and of foods associated with it.

Bad Bug Book – Salmonella

http://vm.cfsan.fda.gov/~mow/chap1.html

Fact sheet with basic information about salmonella. It offers details on the nature and the diagnostic procedures of the disease, susceptible groups, and the potential complications following the disease, as well as guidelines for cooking eggs, the food mainly associated with salmonella.

Bad Bug Book – Streptococcus

http://vm.cfsan.fda.gov/~mow/chap21.html

Brief fact sheet with background information on streptococcus. It includes discussions of the nature and diagnosis of the disease, the foods normally associated with it, its frequency, course, and complications.

Botulinal Toxins

http://www.outbreak.org/cgi- unreg/dynaserve.exe/cb/BotulinalToxin.html

Basic medical details of the biological weapon version of botulinal toxin. The Web site contains brief sections covering characteristics of the disease including its toxicology, the symptoms it causes, cautions and precautions, first aid therapy for victims of the disease, and a list of neutralization and decontamination methods.

Bugs in the News!

http://falcon.cc.ukans.edu/~jbrown/bugs.html

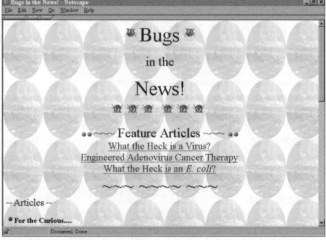

Lively articles fill you in not just on the micro-organisms in the news, but also on immunity, antibiotics, and molecular-biology issues in the 'real' world.

Home, Bacteria-Ridden Home

http://www.sciam.com/explorations/
072197bacteria/mirsky.html

Part of a larger site maintained by *Scientific American,* this page examines the increasing threat of bacteria that have become resistant to antibiotics and provides a warning from a medical researcher at Tufts University who suggests that a range of new kitchen and bathroom products designed to kill bacteria may instead be producing increasingly harmful strains. The text includes hypertext links to further information, and there is also a list of related links at the bottom of the page.

Microbe Zoo

http://commtechlab.msu.edu/sites/dlc-me/zoo/

Colourful and interactive zoo of some of the microbes that surround us. It includes sections on the 'domestic' microbes, the vampire ones that suck the life from other bacteria, the killers which destroy stone buildings, those in aquatic environments, and those that are to be found in beer, bread, chocolate, wine and other food.

Treatment & Support

Alzheimer's Disease Web Page

http://www.visn1.org/alzheimer

Although some of the pages on this site are aimed

at the local community, there is much to interest those further afield – with information for families, caregivers, and investigators.

National Aphasia Association

http://www.aphasia.org/

US-based site with a lot of straightforward information about aphasia; for example, there is a page of important facts and a true/false quiz. The site also contains information about current research and links to support groups for sufferers, their friends, and families.

Audio Description Home Page

http://www.artswire.org/ArtsWire/ad/index.html

Ingenious site that produces audio description files for blind people. These files, of which there are several samples here, describe exhibitions, museums, etc., so that they can be enjoyed by blind people just as much as by the sighted.

British Osteopathic Association

http://www.osteopathy.org/main/index.htm

Well-organized site that explains the basics behind the medical practice of osteopathy and gives details of related sites of interest and registered colleges and practitioners in the UK.

Bypass Ahead

http://whyfiles.news.wisc.edu/028heart/index.html

Part of the Why Files project, published by the National Institute for Science Education (NISE) and funded by the National Science Foundation, this page describes the process of coronary bypass surgery. The highly readable text, laid out over 15 pages, includes information on how the heart works, facts and figures about bypass surgery, and new techniques being developed to make the surgery easier and safer. Numerous images and diagrams enhance the text throughout. The more tricky terms are linked to a glossary, and you will find a comprehensive bibliography of sources for further research.

Caesarean Section – A Brief History

http://www.nlm.nih.gov/exhibition/
cesarean/cesarean_1.html

Despite the title, this is a fairly comprehensive history of the Caesarean

---

F
A
C
T

ALZHEIMER'S DISEASE

common manifestation of dementia, thought to afflict one in 20 people over 65. After heart disease, cancer, and strokes it is the most common cause of death in the Western world. Attacking the brain's 'grey matter', it is a disease of mental processes rather than physical function, characterized by memory loss and progressive intellectual impairment.

section operation. Starting with the early history of the operation, this Web site advances through to modern day medicine, charting progress with concise text and many diagrams. Also included are several text references for further reading. The material here is taken from a brochure issued to accompany an exhibition at the US National Library of Medicine in Bethesda, Maryland, USA.

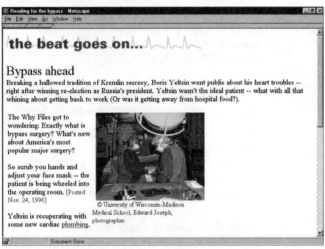

see p 267

Cancer Help UK

http://medweb.bham.ac.uk/cancerhelp/indexg.html

UK cancer information in the form of news, glossaries, treatments, research, help, and support.

Cryonics Frequently Asked Question List

http://www.cs.cmu.edu/afs/cs/user/tsf/
Public-Mail/cryonics/html/overview.html

Answers to all the questions you could possibly ask about the controversial practice of cryonics. If, after reading this, you are tempted to give it a go, be warned. Of the sixty people who have been suspended, forty have been thawed out and buried, as the cryonics companies they had paid went bankrupt.

Down's Syndrome Web Page

http://www.nas.com/downsyn/

Well-organized source of information about the syndrome – with articles, essays, lists of organizations worldwide, toy catalogues, the 'Brag Book' photo gallery, and links to other helpful Web sites.

Facing Huntington's Disease

http://neuro-chief-e.mgh.harvard.edu/
MCMENEMY/facinghd.html

Basic information about Huntingdon's Disease. Sympathetically presented by the British Huntington's Disease association, the guide covers how HD is passed on, how it is diagnosed, the risks to children conceived by couples at risk, and the course of this degenerative illness.

Facts About Inflammatory Bowel Disease

http://www.ccfc.ca/brochures/facts.html

Excellently presented information on inflammatory bowel disease (IBD) from the Crohn's and Colitis Foundation of Canada. The variety of conditions classified as Crohn's disease or ulcerative colitis are described. Symptoms and signs of the onset of IBD are explained by means of diagrams and text. Various treatment regimes are described with a plain-English guide to the medical jargon patients are likely to hear from doctors.

Facts About Tourette Syndrome

http://members.tripod.com/~tourette13/

Large source of sympathetically-written information for those suffering from the neurological disorder or those living with them. A history of the syndrome and earlier misunderstanding of its causes is included. Written by a Tourettes sufferer, there is a full description of its many forms of apparently bizarre behaviour and a good bibliography.

First Comprehensive Site on Tuberculosis

http://www.lupingroup.com/

Useful information about tuberculosis. The fact sheet includes presentations on the signs and tests for TB, an explanation of TB infection and the ways TB is spread, and an assessment of the importance of drugs for the cure of the disease. This site is interesting in that it presents information that is useful for both scientists working within the field and people with a more general interest.

Glaucoma Research Foundation

http://www.glaucoma.org/

Source of well-presented information on glaucoma. There is an informative list of 'Frequently Asked Questions' about the disease and the latest research findings. There are also links to a number of optometric and opthalmological organizations and to a search engine.

'Long Term Pharmacotherapy of Depression'

http://www.bmj.com/cgi/content/full/
316/7139/1180

Part of a collection of articles maintained by the *British Medical Journal*, this page features the full text of a 18 April 1998 editorial addressing the 'importance of long term psychological and pharmacological treatment'. In addition to the editorial, you will find a list of related articles from the extensive *PubMed* collection. You can also search the collections under which this article appears, search other articles written by the authors of this article, and submit or read responses to this article. A list of references is also included.

Melatonin Mania

http://www.sciam.com/explorations/
040196explorations.html

Part of a larger site maintained by *Scientific American*, this page cautions people against taking supplemental doses of melatonin in order to reduce insomnia, improve sex lives, and cure ailments. It includes the opinions of several medical researchers who are critical of 'melatonin mania' and the scientifically unsubstantiated claims of some. The text of the article includes hypertext links to further information, including articles and summaries of recent research on melatonin and its effects, as well as a chapter outline of the book *The Melatonin Miracle*. There is also a list of related links at the bottom of the page, including one to scientific articles on melatonin.

Parkinson's Disease: Hope through Research

http://www.ninds.nih.gov/patients/Disorder/
parkinso/pdhtr.htm

Extensive background information on Parkinson's disease. Amongst other issues, it discusses the causes and symptoms of the disorder, the diagnostic methods used and the treatments and medications that are available, the role of surgery in the treatment of the disease, and diet and exercise as ways of alleviating its symptoms.

Royal National Institute for the Blind United Kingdom

http://www.rnib.org.uk/

Well-organized site of Britain's leading organization for the visually impaired. The RNIB's work is clearly explained. This site provides advice and general information on loss of eyesight.

Short Visit to the Museum of Contraception

http://www.salon1999.com/07/features/contra.html

Bizarre history of contraception seen through the eyes of a journalist visiting the museum. Many of the 'devices' are odd to say the least, for example one of the exhibits in the museum is based around the adage 'If a woman were to take a weasel testicle and bones and strap it to her thigh, she would not fall pregnant.'. The article does not make it clear if any of the methods described have been tested.

Stroke Mini Fact Sheet

http://www.ninds.nih.gov/patients/disorder/stroke/
strkmini.HTM

Mini fact sheet and handy reference tool on strokes. It offers a brief description of the diagnostic symptoms, a list of the warning signs of the onset of the attack and suggested resources for further information on strokes, the brain, and the ways to prevent, and how to deal with, stroke attacks.

Welcome to the Home Page for Hernia Information

http://www.hernia.org/

Easy to understand information about the various kinds of hernia. The causes of hernia are described, together with different repair techniques and advice to sufferers.

Welcome to the UK Autism Web Site

http://www.autism-uk.ed.ac.uk/

Academic site with comprehensive practical information and advice on autism. Aimed at meeting the needs of carers of autistic children and professional neuro-psychologists. There is a section on treatments and therapies, contact addresses for support groups, and indicators of further sources of information.

Medical Techniques & Research

Animated Medical Graphics

http://www.animatedmedical.com/

Uses animations to explain medical terms and topics to those without a medical background. Non-medical analogies are used in the explanations, to make the topics as accessible as possible.

Approaching Death – Improving Care at the End of Life

http://www.nap.edu/readingroom/books/approaching/

Comprehensive US report on attitudes to death and standards of medical care for the elderly. A huge range of social, medical, and ethical issues confronting ageing societies in advanced industrial countries is sensitively addressed.

Centre for Narcolepsy Research

http://www.uic.edu:80/depts/cnr/

Comprehensive source of information on the disabling sleep disorder. There is practical advice for sufferers and more technical information for the medical profession and narcolepsy researchers. There is also a good 'Frequently Asked Questions' section and guide to other sources of information and support.

Coma

http://www.pbs.org/wgbh/nova/coma/

Companion to the US Public Broadcasting Service (PBS) television programme *Nova*, this page documents the revolution taking place in the medical industry regarding the treatment of coma patients. This site includes a detailed geography of the brain and an interview with renowned neurosurgeon Dr Jamshid Ghajar. You can also go 'On call' with Dr Ghajar at a New York City hospital and follow the case of a boy who has suffered head trauma. Read a transcript of the final scene from the hospital drama *Chicago Hope*, and click on the underlined words to learn what the technical jargon really means.

Cut to the Heart

http://www.pbs.org/wgbh/nova/heart/

Companion to the US Public Broadcasting Service (PBS) television programme *Nova*, this page provides an interesting look at the history and pioneers of heart surgery. Read an article written by Robert Soufer, MD, which originally appeared in the *Yale University School of Medicine Heart Book*. This article provides an overview of the heart's function, the causes of heart failure, who is likely to develop heart failure, and what can be done to treat it. There is a section of photographs of troubled hearts with brief descriptions of what is ailing them. You can also view a map of the heart, which features a labelled diagram and an animated GIF of the path of bloodflow through the heart with numbered descriptions. Below the diagram of the heart you will find a link to interesting facts about the human heart.

Dentistry Now

http://www.DentistryNow.com/Mainpage.htm

Canadian-based site that includes an index of dentists worldwide. There is also an index of university courses where dentistry can be studied. In addition, the site contains a section on common dental problems and a good site for kids called 'Tooth fairy' to introduce them to the importance of cleaning their teeth.

'Drug Treatment in Heart Failure'

http://www.bmj.com/cgi/content/full/316/7131/567

Part of a collection of articles maintained by the *British Medical Journal* (*BMJ*), this page features the full text of a 14 February 1998 editorial concerning the treatment of heart failure, in which the author advocates the need to implement 'the new evidence on preventing coronary heart disease effectively in general practice'. In addition to the editorial, you will find a list of related articles from the *BMJ*'s collection. You can also search the collections under which this article appears, search other *BMJ* articles written by the author of this article, and submit or read responses to this article. There is a list of references at the bottom of the article.

Everything You Ever Wanted To Know About Brain Surgery... Almost

http://www.brain-surgery.com/

Comprehensive Web site on brain surgery. The Web site features sections suitable for both surgeons and prospective patients, including an online gallery of operations, a history of brain surgery, and an offer of a free consultation. Several diseases which are treated with brain surgery are also described here, and a guide to the various stages of the operation may also be useful for patients.

HIV Research Lab

http://www.brown.edu/Research/TB-HIV_Lab/

Interesting window into a vital area of scientific research, courtesy of an American laboratory investigating HIV and tuberculosis. The page tries to place its work in a socioeconomic context and there is a lot here of interest to the general browser.

New Imaging Techniques Show Brain at Work

http://www.hhmi.org/senses/e/e210.htm

As part of a much larger site called 'Seeing, Hearing, and Smelling the World', here is a page examining the advances in brain scanning techniques that have helped scientists understand the difference between the senses. It is divided into three sections called 'The PET scan difference between seeing and hearing words', 'Giant magnet reveals the brain's activity', and 'What is this person hearing – music or just meaningless

clicks?'. This site makes good use of images and animations to help with the explanations, so it is best viewed with an up-to-date browser.

Obstetric Ultrasound

http://www.ob-ultrasound.net

Comprehensive, plain-English guide to obstetric ultrasound scanning. For any pregnant woman interested in knowing about the technique, this is an invaluable source of information. There is a clear explanation of what can be learnt about the foetus by the use of ultrasound. Further information on a variety of aspects of pregnancy and birth can be accessed.

'Preventing Recurrent Coronary Heart Disease'

http://www.bmj.com/cgi/content/full/316/7142/1400

Part of a collection of articles maintained by the *British Medical Journal*, this page features the full text of a 9 May 1998 editorial concerning coronary heart disease, in which the authors explain that lowering the heart rate may reduce mortality. In addition to the editorial, you will find a list of related articles from the *BMJ*'s collection and the extensive *PubMed* collection. You can also search the collections under which this article appears, search other articles written by the authors of this article, and submit or read responses to this article. There is also a list of references at the end of the article.

Prosthetic History Page

http://www.nupoc.nwu.edu/prosHistory.html

History of prosthetics from prehistory to modern times. The Web site describes artificial limbs in historical terms, citing many cases from classical texts. The Web site lacks the graphics which would make it much more interesting, but the text descriptions made are reasonably lengthy and complete.

'Putting the Rest Cure to Rest – Again'

http://www.bmj.com/cgi/content/full/316/7134/796

Part of a collection of articles maintained by the British Medical Journal, this page features the full text of a 14 March 1998 editorial concerning flawed advice that doctors are giving patients suffering from chronic fatigue syndrome. In addition to the editorial, you will find a list of related articles from the extensive PubMed collection. You can also search the collections under which this article appears, search other articles written by the authors of this article, and submit or read responses to this article. There is a list of references at the bottom of the article.

Question of Genes: Inherited Risks

http://www.pbs.org/gene/

Companion to a US Public Broadcasting Service (PBS) television programme, this page explores the controversial subject of genetic testing, emphasizing its social, ethical, and emotional consequences. It includes summaries of the seven case studies featured on the television programme, including video clips. There is also a section on the basics of genetic testing, which features the transcript of an interview with a genetic counsellor. You will also find a list of resources for further research and a forum for discussion.

'Recent Advances: Diabetes'

http://www.bmj.com/cgi/content/full/316/7139/1221

Part of a collection of articles maintained by the British Medical Journal, this page features the full text of an 18 April 1998 clinical review regarding the alarming rise in the number of patients with diabetes around the world. The text includes diagrams, and there is a list of references. In addition to the clinical review, you will find a list of related articles from the extensive PubMed collection. You can also search the collections under which this article appears, search other articles written by the author of this article, and submit or read responses to this article. There is a list of references at the bottom of the article.

'Science, Medicine, and the Future: Alzheimer's Disease'

http://www.bmj.com/cgi/content/full/316/7129/446

Part of a collection of articles maintained by the British Medical Journal, this page features the full text of a 7 February 1998 clinical review regarding the causes of Alzheimer's disease and recent advances in the understanding and care, as well as the future treatment, of the disease. The text includes diagrams. In addition to the clinical review, you will find a list of related articles from the extensive PubMed collection. You can also search the collections under which this article

appears, search other articles written by the authors of this article, and submit or read responses to this article. There is a list of references at the bottom of the article.

Telemedicine: A Guide to Assessing Telecommunications for Health Care

http://www.nap.edu/readingroom/books/telemed/summary.html

Overview of the development of telemedicine and summary of a US report into its future direction. The difficulties of evaluating telemedicine are set out.

Transplantation and Donation

http://www.transweb.org/index.htm

This site includes information about organ and tissue transplantation and donation, the latest research developments, and answers to commonly asked questions. It is supported by articles and reports from medical professionals.

Treating Eating Disorders

http://www.sciam.com/explorations/1998/030298eating/

Part of a larger site maintained by *Scientific American*, this page explores research concerning two new hormones that can modulate hunger and satiety. Learn the effects that this discovery may have on eating disorder prevention programs and medications to treat these disorders. You can find information about anorexia nervosa, bulimia nervosa, and binge eating. There are also links to other Web sources.

Understanding Gene Testing

http://www.gene.com/ae/AE/AEPC/NIH/index.html

Comprehensive US Department of Health overview of all the issues involved in gene testing. Basic information about genetics is accompanied by an explanation of the diseases which can be predicted by testing. There is also a glossary explaining the terminology in readily understandable language.

Virtual Anaesthesia Textbook

http://www.usyd.edu.au/su/anaes/VAT/VAT.html

Huge source of information on all aspects of anaesthesia. Though primarily designed for anaesthetists, a non-medical reader wishing to learn about the history and practice of modern anaesthesia would find a lot of interest on this massive site. A search engine facilitates navigation. There are also links to anaesthesia sites around the world.

Alternative Medicine

Acupuncture.com

http://acupuncture.com/

Thorough introduction to the alternative world of acupuncture with descriptions of the main notions and powers of herbology, yoga, Qi Gong, and Chinese nutrition. Consumers are given access to lists of practitioners and an extensive section on acupuncture research. Practitioners can browse through journal listings and the latest industry news and announcements.

Alternative and Complementary Medicine Centre

http://www.healthy.net/clinic/therapy/

Guide to a range of disciplines within the field of complementary medicine, which also considers their relationship to mainstream medical treatment.

Basic Principles of Chinese Medicine

http://www.healthy.net/library/books/modacu/mod1.htm

Comprehensive guide to Chinese medicine. The conceptual basis of Chinese medicine is fully explained, together with a description of how particular organs fit within the overall system of the body. The Chinese view of the causes of disease and identification of symptoms is also clearly set out here.

Grey Wings Herbal

http://www.geocities.com/Athens/4177/herbal.htm

Soothing music plays while you await the loading of a home page filled with information about herbal medicine.

Instructions are provided on preparing a great range of herbal medicines and using herbs in food. The site is part of the herb and herbal products Web ring. There is also a plain-English guide to the large number of horticultural and medical terms used by herbal medicine practitioners.

Homeopathy Home Page

http://www.homeopathyhome.com/

Jumping-off point for a huge range of information on homeopathy. This well-arranged site accesses information on the homeopathic treatment of a variety of ailments and results of research into its efficacy. The online edition (and back issues) of *Homeopathy Online* have interesting articles on the application of homeopathy.

Rolf Institute

http://www.rolf.org/wir/index.html

Comprehensive argument of the effectiveness of Rolfing structural integration – a theory about the importance of posture expounded by Dr Ida Rolf. There is information on training to be a Rolfer, addresses of 900 Certified Rolfers in 26 countries, and links to Rolfing sites.

Shiatsu – Japanese Massage

http://www.rianvisser.nl/shiatsu/e_index.htm

Well-written introduction to the theoretical underpinnings and the practice of shiatsu. The origins of this ancient Japanese pressure technique are explained with reference to the theory of yin and yang. Diagrams are used to explain techniques. There is a bibliography and a list of addresses of shiatsu therapists.

Sivananda Yoga – Proper Breathing

http://www.sivananda.org/breathin.htm

If you thought you knew how to breathe, this site may hold a few surprises for you.

F A C T

RESPIRATION
metabolic process in organisms in which food molecules are broken down to release energy. The cells of all living organisms need a continuous supply of energy, and in most plants and animals this is obtained by **aerobic** respiration. In this process, oxygen is used to break down the glucose molecules in food.

Drugs

Alcohol Concern

http://www.alcoholconcern.org.uk/

Huge resource addressing many of the problems surrounding alcohol abuse. Factsheets and information are available, as well as the latest news on alcohol abuse.

Antibiotics: How Do Antibiotics Work?

http://ericir.syr.edu/Projects/Newton/12/Lessons/antibiot.html

Introduction to the use and importance of antibiotics in easy-to-understand language. The site also includes a glossary of scientific and difficult terms, a further reading list, and an activities sheet.

Aspirin – Molecule of the Month

http://www.bris.ac.uk/Depts/Chemistry/MOTM/aspirin/aspirin.htm

Interactive presentation on aspirin with information on its properties and uses and a rotatable image of its molecule from the Department of Chemistry at Bristol University, UK, for those with Java-enabled browsers.

'Britain's New Strategy for Tackling Drugs Misuse'

http://www.bmj.com/cgi/content/full/316/7142/1399

Part of a collection of articles maintained by the British Medical Journal, this page features the full text of a 9 May 1998 editorial in praise of the UK government's new national drug strategy, which is 'more seriously committed to evidence than to rhetoric'. In addition to the editorial, you will find a list of related articles from the extensive PubMed collection. You can also search the collections under which this article appears, search other articles written by the authors of this article, and submit or read responses to this article. There is a list of references at the bottom of the article.

Closing in on Addiction

http://www.sciam.com/explorations/112497addiction/

Part of a larger site maintained by Scientific American, this page includes facts and figures on drug and alcohol addiction, information about the effects of drugs on the brain, new discoveries related to abuse and addiction, and two special sections on new methods for treating smoking and alcohol addicts. The text includes hypertext links to further information, and there is also a list of related links at the bottom of the page.

Cocaine Anonymous World Services

http://www.ca.org/

Details of the work of the global organization for recovering cocaine addicts. There is information about their work and practical advice on kicking the habit. There is also a self-test for those who think they might be addicted.

Discovery of Insulin

http://web.idirect.com/~discover/

Details the discovery of the protein hormone insulin. This site includes brief descriptions of the lives of the team that made the discovery. An overview of insulin and diabetes is also included here, describing the hormone and the disease, as well as current developments in the continuing research programmes around the world.

Ecstasy.org

http://www.ecstasy.org/

Huge clearing house for information on this popular recreational drug. This includes instructions for paramedics and hospital staff, how to get an ecstasy sample chemically assessed, how to recognize danger signs, notes on the dance-music scene, and what to do if arrested for possession. On the question of the dangers of the drug, the site is noncommittal, presenting a huge sample of contradictory scientific opinion.

Internet Drug Index

http://www.rxlist.com/

Online list of prescription and non-prescription drugs, with a search engine to help find specific types or products and access to information about indications and side effects too.

Kava in Vanuatu

http://www.vanuatutourism.com/kava.htm

Large source of information on the popular South Pacific recreational drug. Concentrating on kava rituals in Vanuatu, there is a description of the plant, preparation of the intoxicating beverage, the social context in which it is drunk, and its health effects. There are also several interesting photos and links to other kava sites around the Pacific and details of the spread in use of kava to Australia and North America.

LSD – My Problem Child

http://www.flashback.se/archive/my_problem_child/

Complete text of the book written by the discoverer of lysergic acid diethylamide. Hoffman describes in detail the chemical explorations which led to the discovery, the pharmacological properties of the drug, the history of its psychiatric and recreational use, and his relationships with Aldous Huxley and Timothy Leary. The spiritual insights and the dangers of the drug are also set out at this site.

Marijuana as a Medicine

http://www.calyx.com/~olsen/MEDICAL/

Campaigning site arguing for the legalization of cannabis for medical purposes. A wide range of research evidence is produced to show the effectiveness of cannabis in the treatment of everything from glaucoma to menstrual cramps. There is information on ongoing legal

controversies around the issue and links to a large number of similar sites.

Molecular Expressions: The Pharmaceutical Collection

http://micro.magnet.fsu.edu/pharmaceuticals/index.html

Fascinating collection of images showing what over 100 drugs look like when recrystallized and photographed through a microscope.

Opium Kings

http://www.pbs.org/wgbh/pages/frontline/shows/heroin/

Companion site to the PBS television programme *Frontline*, this page includes information about opium and heroin, their effects on the brain, and the strategies that law enforcement agencies have developed to fight opium production and heroin addiction. Articles describe the process of turning poppies into heroin and an outline the history of opium going back to its initial cultivation in 3400 BC. You can also find interviews with US 'drug czars', a US Drug Enforcement Agency official, and a former ambassador to Burma. There are maps and charts of areas where opium is cultivated and maps that detail the heroin trade routes.

Pharmaceutical Information Network

http://pharminfo.com/

Access information about analgesics from this US site, with its substantial drugs databases, related publications, and news.

United Nations International Drug Control Programme

http://www.undcp.org/

Informative source of information on the work of the UN agency charged with coordinating international efforts to control the narcotics trade. There are details of international treaties and projects to discourage the use, manufacture, and distribution of drugs.

History of Medicine

Ancient Medicine/Medicina Antiqua

http://web1.ea.pvt.k12.pa.us/medant/

Ancient Greek and Roman medicine. Containing hypertext editions of Greco-Roman medical texts, this multi-awardwinning site forms a starting point for those wishing to study this section of the classics.

Banting, Sir Frederick Grant

http://www.nobel.se/laureates/medicine-1923-1-bio.html

Profile of the life and career of the Nobel laureate. It traces his childhood, early interest in divinity, developing interest in diabetes, and his death in a plane crash. There is also a picture of Banting.

Biography of Emil Adolf Behring

http://nobel.sdsc.edu/laureates/medicine-1901-1-bio.html

Informative biography of the German physician from the Nobel Foundation. Included in the biography are details of his childhood and university education, as well as information on his scientific research. Throughout the text there are hypertext links to articles on related topics.

Biography of Girolamo Cardano

http://www.lib.virginia.edu/science/parshall/cardano.html

Interesting biography of the turbulent life of the Italian physician and mathematician. It traces his

miserable and brutal upbringing, the renown he won, and the disappointments that drove him to take his own life. There is also an image of Cardano.

Country Joe McDonald's Florence Nightingale Tribute

http://www.dnai.com/~borneo/nightingale/

Tribute to Florence Nightingale by a Vietnam War veteran, in the form of a chronology of her life, with notes on her fellow nurses, a short autobiographical piece, a large number of images, a recording of her voice, and links to related sites, including a collection of her letters.

F A C T

NIGHTINGALE, FLORENCE (1820–1910)

English nurse, the founder of nursing as a profession. She took a team of nurses to Scutari (now Üsküdar, Turkey) in 1854 and reduced the Crimean War hospital death rate from 42% to 2%.

From Quackery to Bacteriology: the Emergence of Modern Medicine to 19th-Century America

http://www.cl.utoledo.edu/canaday/quackery/quack-index.html

Online exhibit which traces the development of medicine through printed works: from heroic medicine at the beginning of the 19th century through to quackery movements, the experience of the Civil War, the improvements in medical education, and the formulation of the germ theory at the end of the 19th century. Other topics covered in the exhibit include women's health, mental health, public health, and preventative medicine as advocated through physical fitness and nutrition.

Gertrude B Elion Profile

http://www.achievement.org/autodoc/page/eli0pro-1

Description of the life and work of the winner of the Nobel Prize for Medicine Gertrude Elion. The Web site contains not only a profile and biographical information, but also holds a lengthy interview with Elion from 1991 accompanied by a large number of photographs, video sequences, and audio clips.

Influenza 1918

http://www.pbs.org/wgbh/pages/amex/influenza/

Companion site to the PBS television programme *The American Experience,* this page provides information about the influenza pandemic of 1918 that killed 20 million people worldwide. It provides a history of the epidemic and accounts of survivors, and broaches the subject of whether it could happen again. You can also download a transcript of the television programme and listen to audio clips.

Medicine of Egypt

http://www.teleport.com/~spindel/Egypt/ EgyptPAge.html

This page contains information about the history of medicine in Egypt. It describes the plants used in Egyptian medicine, as well as the tools and the historical sources available. It even has backing music with an appropriate Egyptian feel!

On the Natural Faculties

http://classics.mit.edu/Galen/natfac.html

Text of this work by the Greek physician Galen.

Plague and Public Health in Renaissance Europe

http://jefferson.village.virginia.edu/osheim/intro.html

Electronic text selection of government decrees, medical narratives, and religious writings about the plague epidemic that swept through Europe during the Renaissance.

Redi, Francesco

http://galileo.imss.firenze.it/multi/redi/index.html

Biographical Web site on the Italian physician and poet run by the Institute and Museum of the History of Science in Florence, Italy. The site includes a virtual visit video clip (in Quick Time format) to the room in the museum dedicated to Redi. Also included are details of Redi's scientific works, medicine, and poetry, along with portraits of the man himself.

Works by Hippocrates

http://classics.mit.edu/Browse/browse-Hippocrates.html

Translations of the works of Hippocrates by Francis Adams in downloadable form. Seventeen works by the father of medicine are to be found here, ranging from *On Ancient Medicine* (this was written in 400BC!) to *On The Surgery.* The site also includes the philosopher's best known work *The Oath.* The text files are very large (with some exceptions, notably *The Oath*), but the server is very fast so don't be put off downloading.

Psychology

Anomalist Site

http://www.anomalist.com/

Internet edition of a twice-yearly magazine exploring the mysteries of science, history, and nature. Created by writers, scientists, and investigators intrigued by 'that which departs from the common', the online presentation includes contributions on every neglected, unexplained, unexpected, and extraordinary aspect of the world, and invites contributions from visitors.

Classics In The History Of Psychology – *Laws of Organization in Perceptual Forms*

http://www.yorku.ca/dept/psych/classics/ Wertheimer/Forms/forms.htm

Transcript of Max Wertheimer's 1923 paper *Laws of Organization in Perceptual Forms.* This paper outlined the principles of Gestalt psychology, and therefore formed the basis for much of the development in the science in the early part of this century.

Classics in the History of Psychology – 'New Methods for the Diagnosis of the Intellectual Level of Subnormals'

http://www.yorku.ca/dept/psych/classics/Binet/ binet1.htm

Complete text of French psychologist Alfred Binet's 1905 essay. Also included here is an introduction to the text, as well as a commentary on it.

Classics In The History Of Psychology – *Psychology As The Behaviourist Views It*

http://www.yorku.ca/dept/psych/classics/Watson/ views.htm

Full transcript of John B Watson's 1913 paper *Psychology As The Behaviourist Views It*. This is Watson's most famous publication, and probably did more than anything else to turn psychology into a mainstream science and away from its introspective origins.

Classics in the History of Psychology – 'Stream of Consciousness'

http://www.yorku.ca/dept/psych/classics/James/jimmy11.htm

Transcript of James's 'Stream of Consciousness' theory as first published in *Psychology*, Chapter XI, (Cleveland & New York, World). The first sentence of the chapter sums up James's contribution to the science of psychology: 'The order of our study must be analytic.' James's belief in the value of scientific experimental method changed psychology forever.

Classics in the History of Psychology – *The Principles of Psychology*

http://www.yorku.ca/dept/psych/classics/James/Principles/index.htm

Text of William James's classic book.

Depression Central

http://www.psycom.net/depression.central.html

Jumping-off point for information on all types of depressive disorders and on their most effective treatment. This site is divided into many useful sections, including 'Bipolar disorder', 'Depression in the elderly', and 'Electroconvulsive therapy'.

Electroconvulsive Therapy

http://text.nlm.nih.gov/nih/cdc/www/51txt.html

Official US review of the most controversial of psychiatric treatments. The history of ECT is examined and studies of its effectiveness assessed. The risks and adverse side effects of the procedure and indications and contraindications are set out.

Experimental Psychology Lab

http://www.psych.unizh.ch/genpsy/Ulf/Lab/WebExpPsyLab.html

Take part in online psychology experiments carried out by the University of Tübingen's Psychology Institute. There are a variety of experiments here, some requiring Java and ActiveX, and some only in German.

Freud Web

http://landow.stg.brown.edu/victorian/science/freud/Freud_OV.html

Overview of Sigmund Freud's life and works. The pages include a biography, a chronology, cultural context, and an examination of Freud's theories and techniques. There is also a bibliography and a black-and-white photograph of Freud.

George Combe: Elements of Phrenology

http://www.plattsburgh.edu/faculty/friesep/combe01.htm

Hypertext version of George Combe's book of 1834 *Elements of Phrenology*. This wacky Victorian 'science' gave the English language expressions like, 'You need your head examining', and this Internet edition of the book helps explain how and why. Many graphics taken from the original text are included, and a sample case is also described, that of the famous novelist Charlotte Bronte.

Interpretation of Dreams (3rd edition) by Sigmund Freud

http://www.psychwww.com/books/interp/toc.htm

A A Brill's 1911 translation of Freud's classic analysis of dreams. The section on typically recurring dreams is particularly interesting.

Memory

http://ericir.syr.edu/Projects/Newton/11/memory.html

Illuminating information on the complicated processes of memory. The site also provides a glossary of terms, a list of activities for the testing or strengthening of the memory, and some suggested reading.

Mental Health

http://www.mentalhealth.com/

Aiming 'to improve understanding, diagnosis, and treatment of mental illness throughout the world', this well-designed encyclopedia of mental disorders offers comprehensive information on diagnosing and treating mental health problems, and includes an online magazine.

Museum of the History of Psychological Instrumentation

http://www.chss.montclair.edu/psychology/museum/museum.html

Museum of mad scientists' tools. If you expect to see pictures of couches and clipboards on this Web site you are going to be disappointed since a disturbingly high proportion of the tools listed have electrodes attached. The instruments described and pictured on these pages were the tools of a generation of psychology experimenters, and as with all historic science equipment look bizarre to the modern eye. So if you've ever wondered what a 'Wundt's tachistoscope' does and what it looks like, this is the place to find out.

Personality and IQ Tests

http://www.davideck.com/online-tests.html

Selection of personality and IQ tests for you to try. This site includes explanations and examples of an enneagram, colour test, Keirsey temperament test, personality profile, and love test. There is also an extentsive selection of IQ tests.

Sigmund Freud: The Father of Psychoanalysis

http://austria-info.at/personen/freud/index.html

Maintained in English by the Austrian National Tourist Office, the page provides a timeline of biographical information about Freud, plus analyses of his ideas and the impact of his theories on his most notable followers.

Varieties of Religious Experience by William James

http://www.psychwww.com/psyrelig/james/toc.htm

Online version of James' seminal work on the psychology of religion. A series of well-arranged notes accompany the text and show the ongoing relevance of his analysis.

'What Won't Go Away: *Waterland* and Traditional Psychotherapy'

http://www.student.gu.se/~jawi0004/grahams.html

Text-only essay about Graham Swift's critically acclaimed novel *Waterland.*

MUSIC & DANCE

British Composers

Andrew Lloyd Webber

http://www.geocities.com/Broadway/1586/alw.html

Come to this unofficial online magazine for information about Andrew Lloyd Webber productions, past and present, plus a brief biography, and details of the awards they have won.

Arnold Bax Web Site

http://www.musicweb.force9.co.uk/music/bax/Welcome.htm

Details about the English symphonist Sir Arnold Bax, as well as an numerous articles on topics such as Bax's symphonies, his relationship with Elgar, and his unpublished works. This site contains many photographs and audio clips from Bax's music.

Bantock Society

http://www.musicweb.force9.co.uk/music/bantock/index.htm

Site from Coventry University, UK, featuring an article about the composer Granville Bantock, as well as a recording of some of his work, and information about The Bantock Society.

Britten, Benjamin

http://www.geocities.com/Vienna/Strasse/1523/britten.htm

Comprehensive source of information on the British composer. In addition to a biography, there is a huge bibliography of books, articles, and dissertations about Britten, a complete discography, and a listing of recordings of Britten as conductor, pianist, and violist.

Elgar Society and Elgar Foundation

http://www.elgar.org/

Biography and chronology of Edward Elgar's life, complete with pen portraits, photographs, and manuscript scans. This site also features a character study, an illustrated tour of the houses in which he lived, and descriptions of his major works together with audio clips of the music.

Gustav Holst Site

http://wso.williams.edu/~ktaylor/gholst

Illustrated chronology and biography of the composer Gustav Holst. There is a detailed list of Holst's compositions which features brief descriptions and audio clips. This site also features the lyrics to 'In the Bleak Midwinter' and 'I Vow to Thee, My Country', plus background information about several of his compositions.

Howells, Herbert

http://www.gprep.pvt.k12.md.us/~gldaum/howells/howells1.html

Biography and photograph of the composer Herbert Howells, together with a selected discography, in which many recordings are described. There is also an essay about his music and a list of available recordings.

Malcolm Arnold Society

http://www.musicweb.force9.co.uk/music/arnold/ithink.htm

Essay written by the composer Malcolm Arnold on the subject of music – 'I think of music in terms of sound'. This site also features a biography, discography, and an essay on Arnold's collaboration with rock musician Jon Lord.

Nyman, Michael

http://www.december.org/nyman/index.htm

Stylish page about English musician Michael Nyman, with news of current projects and performances, a biography, lists of his compositions, sound clips, and links to related pages.

F A C T

NYMAN, MICHAEL (1944–)
English composer. His highly stylized music is characterized by processes of gradual modification by repetition of complex musical formulae (known as minimalism).

Purcell, Henry

http://portico.bl.uk/exhibitions/purcell/overview.html

Audio clip of funeral march composed by Purcell, and images of the manuscripts displayed by the British library on the 300th anniversary of his death, including a page from a newly discovered volume of Purcell's compositions.

Radio 3

http://www.bbc.co.uk/radio3/

For classical music lovers, the Radio 3 Web site includes details of current programmes, as well as feature articles, quizzes, and 'Composer of the week' and 'Artist of the week' sections.

Ralph Vaughan Williams Web Page

http://www.cs.qub.ac.uk/~J.Collis/RVW.html

Chronology of Ralph Vaughan Williams's life, analyses of his major works, anecdotes, and a listening guide for the uninitiated.

Royal Philharmonic Orchestra

http://www.rpo.co.uk/

Performance and education are the main themes of this site from the Royal Philharmonic Orchestra, with a full programme for adults and children.

Symth, Ethel

http://metalab.unc.edu/cheryb/women/dame-ethel.html

Full profile of the composer and feminist organizer. This page contains an account of her life, music, and political work.

Walton, William

http://www.geocities.com/Vienna/5827/ walton.htm

Comprehensive tribute to the English composer. There are details of his stage, orchestral, choral, chamber, and film music, a list of recordings, and a bibliography. A detailed biography of Walton assesses his place in 20th-century British music.

William Alwyn Society

http://www.musicweb.force9.co.uk/music/alwyn/index.htm

Biography, gallery, discography, and information on the films and documentaries in which Alwyn's music was used. This site also contains an article written by Alwyn himself, together with details of the William Alwyn Society.

European Composers

Bartók, Béla

http://www.ultranet.com/%7Ecwholl/bartok/bartok.html

Biography of the Hungarian composer. It describes his musical upbringing, the influence of Liszt, Brahms, and Richard Strauss, his interest in folk music, his career, and financial problems in later life. There are photos of Bartók and also an assessment of his place in modern music.

Beethoven, Ludwig

http://www.geocities.com/Paris/3486/beetfi.html

Extensive site on this famous composer. As well as detailed information about his life, this site also contains a complete listing of his works, and an extensive selection of audio clips.

Berlioz, Hector

http://w3.rz-berlin.mpg.de/cmp/berlioz.html

Detailed biography on the French Romantic composer. This site also includes a detailed description of Hector Berlioz's *Symphonie fantastique,* notes on his major works, and an informative bibliography.

Bizet, Georges

http://w3.rz-berlin.mpg.de/cmp/bizet.html

Portrait and biography of the French composer. It traces his musical career from his period as a child prodigy to the lukewarm reception originally given his masterpiece *Carmen,* which is said to have hastened his death.

Boulez, Pierre

http://www.u.arizona.edu/~jkandell/music/boulez.html

Thorough profile of the innovative French musician. The site contains a biography, portrait, and assessment of his contribution to contemporary music. There is a list of recommended recordings and audio and video clips of Boulez conducting and talking about music.

Dvořák, Antonín

http://www.hnh.com/composer/dvorak.htm

Biography and description of the work of this Czech composer. His influence in the development of Czech musical nationalism is related. There are also details of his orchestral, chamber, piano music, and operas, as well as recommended recordings.

Eternal Student – The Symphonies of Anton Josef Bruckner

http://www.classical.net/music/comp.lst/articles/bruckner/bruckner.html

Good guide to the life and achievements of the Austrian composer. It traces his rise from his impoverished peasant background, his teaching career, and the musical success which arrived late in life. This is an intimate portrait of a musician beset by self doubt.

Fauré, Gabriel

http://207.158.243.119/html/gabriel_faur_.html

Site devoted to a loving appreciation of the French composer, Fauré. There is a biography, timeline, bibliography, audio clips, and photo gallery.

George Frideric Handel Home Page

http://www.intr.net/bleissa/handel/home.html

Comprehensive site dedicated to the baroque composer Handel. This site features a chronology of his life, a detailed list of his compositions, details of Handel festivals, reviews of recent releases, and links to related Web sites.

Gustav Mahler WWW Pages

http://www.netaxs.com/~jgreshes/mahler/

Pages devoted to an appreciation of the life and works of Gustav Mahler, headed by a large black and white photograph of the composer. The site includes a lengthy account of the Mahlerfest XI in Colorado, USA, as well as information on scores and newly released CD recordings. In addition, there are links to reviews, forthcoming concerts and festivals, and conductors who had a special affinity for Mahler. There is also a link to a page containing audio clips of his music.

Igor Stravinsky Web Page

http://www.geocities.com/Vienna/1807/strav.html

Profile of the life and works of the Russian composer Igor Stravinsky. The page includes a black-and-white photograph of Stravinsky, an annotated compendium to his complete works, and a timeline of his life, as well as some more personal stories written by the author of this Web site.

Josquin Des Prez

http://www.classical.net/music/comp.lst/josquin.html

Life and legacy of the Flemish composer. The known biographical details of his life are related alongside an analysis of his influential role in the development of melody and harmony. There is a listing of his best-known masses and motets.

JS Bach Archive and Bibliography

http://www.let.rug.nl/Linguistics/diversen/bach/intro.html

Dedicated to the life and works of the composer, this page offers an illustrated biography, an extensive bibliography, portraits, and a guide for the 'Bach tourist'.

Kurt Weill Home Page

http://www.kwf.org/

Produced by the Kurt Weill Foundation, New York, USA, that provides information about Kurt Weill and his wife, Lotte Lenya. There are biographies, photographs, bibliographies, and details of their work, plus information about the foundation's activities.

Mozart, Wolfgang Amadeus

http://www.acronet.net/~kb9chf/WolfgangAmadeusMozart.html

Dedicated to one of the most renowned classical composers, this site includes

---

F A C T

MAHLER, GUSTAV (1860–1911)

Austrian composer and conductor. His epic symphonies express a world-weary Romanticism in visionary tableaux incorporating folk music and pastoral imagery.

several portraits of Mozart and his family, a biography, an explanation of the cataloguing system for Mozart's many works and a listing of them all, by Köchel number. This site also contains many audio clips of the composer's works.

Prokofiev
http://www.siue.edu/~aho/musov/sergei.html

Part of a larger site concerning composers of the Soviet Union, this page explores the relationship of composer Sergey Prokofiev to the Soviet state. This relationship is explored through three articles. You will also find a bibliography of his work, divided into two parts, beginning with his first piano sonata written at the age of 16.

Richard Strauss Biography
http://www.azopera.com/c_bios/rstrauss.php3

Detailed biography of Richard Strauss. Although the main focus of this biography is on Strauss's career as a composer and conductor, attention is also paid to his childhood and education, his relationship with the Nazis, and his legacy.

Richard Wagner Archive
http://www.utu.fi/~hansalmi/wagner.spml

Collection of all kinds of material relating to Wagner, prepared by a scholar of his life and work. This site includes sections on his life, his opera, later compositions, his writings, and writing about him.

Schubert Institute (UK)
http://dialspace.dial.pipex.com/ramorris/

Information about the life and works of composer Franz Schubert. There is a bibliography, a number of articles, and details of Schubert-related events. The site also contains details of requests for information and research papers.

Shostakovichiana
http://www.siue.edu/~aho/musov/dmitri.html

Wealth of information and images concerning Russian composer Dmitry Shostakovich. This site includes a number of recollections and reminiscences of Shostakovich, a chronology of his life and times, letters he wrote to his friend Isaak Glikman, information about his alleged

interrogation by the NKVD in 1937, Russian and Soviet reviews of and commentary on his symphonies, reviews of books about Shostakovich, and the latest CD recordings of his work.

Sibelius, Jean
http://w3.rz-berlin.mpg.de/cmp/sibelius.html

Appreciation of the works of the Finnish composer Sibelius. This site includes detailed information about his symphonies, numerous audio clips, and a bibliography.

Smetana, Bedrich
http://www.hnh.com/composer/smetana.htm

Biography and description of the work of the Bohemian composer and Czech nationalist. His operas, orchestral, and chamber music are described. There is also a list of recommended recordings of his work.

Toscanini, Arturo
http://www.bmgclassics.com/bmg/bmg/biography/toscanin.html

Well-presented overview of the man and his work. The article examines his impact on the musical world and a list of recommended listening is included at the end.

Webern, Anton von
http://w3.rz-berlin.mpg.de/cmp/webern.html

Assessment of the life and career of the Austrian composer. It traces his interest in atonality, his conducting career, and the almost geometrical perfection of his music. There is a listing of his principal works, photos of von Webern, and a bibliography.

Welcome to the Johannes Brahms WebSource
http://www.mjq.net/brahms/

Substantial source of information on the German musician. The site includes a good biography, a list of compositions, a guide to Brahms festivals, and details of Brahms societies and scholars around the world.

Zoltán Kodály Home Page
http://www.music.indiana.edu/kodaly/kodaly.htm

Tribute to the Hungarian composer and educator. This site includes a list of his compositions, an appreciation of his contribution to musical education, a bibliography, and links to Kodály organizations. There are also several audio clips.

US Composers

Barber, Samuel

http://www.classical.net/music/comp.lst/barber.html

Profile of the US composer. There is a photo, detailed biography, listing of the major works in his repertoire, and details of his recordings.

Bernstein, Leonard

http://www.leonardbernstein.com

Celebration of Bernstein's legacy. This is a very comprehensive guide to the US composer and conductor that includes images, audio and video clips, full scores of some of his works, a biography, and plentiful articles about the man and his musical career.

Cage, John

http://newalbion.com/artists/cagej/

Annotated discography of the works of John Cage, with an autobiographical statement. It includes a forum for the discussion of the philosophy, writings, art, life, and influence of the composer.

George and Ira Gershwin Archive

http://www.sju.edu/~bs065903/gershwin/homepage.htm

Celebration of the talents of George and Ira Gershwin, with answers to 'Frequently Asked Questions', a complete chronological list of their works, analysis of George's compositions, quotations from Ira's lyrics, and pages on the Gershwins on stage, on film, and in print.

John Philip Sousa Home Page

http://plato.digiweb.com/~dlovrien/sousa/

Biographical timeline, a listing of all his compositions, a hundred or so sound clips, and information about the some of the more famous soloists who played with Sousa's Band.

Philip Glass on the Web

http://www.lsi.upc.es/~jpetit/pg/glass.html

Multimedia Web site that explores the work of US composer Philip Glass. In addition to images and audio clips, the site includes Glass discographies, articles, scores, lyrics, and further links to relevant sites.

Scott Joplin Home Page

http://www.geocities.com/BourbonStreet/2783/

Short biography of the 'King of Ragtime' and a near-complete sound library of his compositions.

Operas & Operettas

Art of Maria Callas

http://welcome.to/Maria_Callas

Celebration in sight and sound of Maria Callas's greatest roles. There is very little biographical information here, instead each section aims to bring to life one of the roles Callas performed. There is information on the opera and the composer, why Callas was attracted to the role, critical response, and WAV format sound clips.

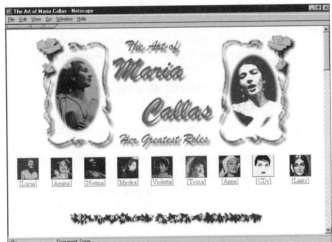

Domingo, Placido

http://www.placidodomingo.com/

Comprehensive information on the life of the celebrated Spanish tenor makes this an essential site for Domingo devotees. In addition to biographical details and information about Domingo's current performance schedule, there are a large number of photographs, reviews of performances, and profiles of the singer. This site also includes details of recordings and links to his fan club and other Domingo sites.

D'Oyly Carte Family

http://math.idbsu.edu/gas/html/carte.html

Biography of the Richard D'Oyly Carte, the driving force behind the Gilbert and Sullivan collaboration. There are also links to Carte's wife Helen Lenoir, to his children Rupert and Bridget, who took control of their father's affairs after he died, and to the Savoy Hotel which contributed so much wealth to the family fortunes. There are also several portraits of members of the D'Oyly Carte family.

English National Opera

http://www.eno.org/

Details of the company, its current productions, and the low-price ticket scheme 'Enjoy opera for schools'.

Gilbert and Sullivan Home Page

http://math.idbsu.edu/gas/GaS.html

Devoted to the operas and other works of W S Gilbert and Arthur Sullivan, and including biographies, plot summaries, librettos, song scores, lyrics, audio files, and articles.

OperaGlass Database

http://rick.stanford.edu/opera/main.html

Comprehensive reference material on opera, including individual operas, composers, performance histories, synopses, and librettists.

Pavarotti, Luciano

http://www.pavarottiinconcert.com/

Huge source of information on the Italian tenor. A detailed biography describes Pavarotti's rise to fame from his humble origins. There are audio clips of the man in concert, photos, and details of his current performance and recording schedules.

F A C T

OPERA

dramatic musical work in which singing takes the place of speech. In opera the music accompanying the action has paramount importance, although dancing and spectacular staging may also play their parts.

Royal Opera House

http://www.royalopera.org/

Web site of Britain's leading opera house. There

are sections providing practical information on current performances and bookings and a history of the Royal Opera. In addition, an education section has a host of practical activities designed to interest young people in opera and ballet.

Sydney Opera House Home Page

http://www.soh.nsw.gov.au/

Comprehensive information about Sydney's sail-shaped landmark. There is a history of the building, profile of Opera House facilities, and frequently updated details of performances.

Teatro alla Scala

http://lascala.milano.it/

Bilingual site of Italy's foremost opera house. There is a listing of performances and ticketing information. There is also a virtual visit behind the scenes.

Pop Music

ABBAnatic

http://www.sirius.com/~funnyguy/abba.html

Dedicated to the Swedish pop group Abba, this site contains information about bootlegs, post-Abba projects by all members of the group, and many photographs of both album covers and the band.

Art Garfunkel Website

http://www.artgarfunkel.com/

Large site devoted to Art Garfunkel. It features a biography, photo gallery, and even a list of every book he has read since June 1968. There are a number of song clips, lyrics, and also the transcripts of numerous interviews.

Bagism

http://www.bagism.com/

All the covers, and most of the lyrics from John Lennon's albums. The site also has a library of letters, articles, and several chronologies, as well as space for fans to communicate and send in artwork and poems.

Beach Boys Web Sounds

http://www.personal.u-net.com/~pcworld5/index.htm

Beach Boys site featuring a vast number of audio clips available for downloading, including some rare files not normally available. There is an extensive gallery, a chat room, and also links to other Beach Boys sites.

Beastie Shrine

http://beastieshrine.isontheweb.com/

Little is left out in this well-designed homage to the rap group the Beastie Boys. Not only are there lyrics, sound files, and a discography, there is also Beastie Boys software, articles, and recent news.

Beautiful South

http://www.beautifulsouth.co.uk/

Official site of the pop band the Beautiful South. Featured here are a profile of all the members of the band, a photo gallery, and an extensive discography with lyrics of many of their songs.

Bee Gees Official Web Experience

http://www.beegees.net/

Featured in this official site of the pop band the Bee Gees are numerous sound and video files, as well as a brief biography of the Gibb brothers, a list of 'Frequently Asked Questions', and information about their upcoming live dates.

Björk – Web Sense

http://www.bjork.co.uk/bjork/

Wealth of information about this highly individual singer, including news, a timeline, music samples, lyrics, quotes, photos, video clips, and even the star's own 'extrasensory' guide to the Web.

Blurspace

http://www.parlophone.co.uk/blur/

Official Blur site focusing largely on the band's albums, with release information, lyrics, and sound samples. As well as including information on their albums, the site also has a news section to keep fans up to date.

Bob Dylan Music Lounge

http://www.geocities.com/SunsetStrip/Alley/8361/index.html

Comprehensive tribute to Dylan. This site includes a full biography, Dylan and his links with Arlo Guthrie, a listing of all of his albums, album covers, and latest tour and recording news. Part of the Bob Dylan Web ring, onward travel from here to other Dylan appreciation sites is painless.

Byrds Home Page

http://www.lyon.edu/webdata/users/kadler/public_html/rmcguinn/index.html

Brings together material contributed by fans and by former Byrds member Roger McGuinn. It includes answers to 'Frequently Asked Questions', audio clips, guitar tablatures, and memories and reflections about the group.

Cemetery Gates

http://moz.pair.com/

Tribute to Morrissey and the Smiths, with biographies, interviews, discographies, lyrics, audio clips, contact addresses for fanzines, and even a roll call of all the people who have graced the covers of their albums and singles.

Charles, Ray

http://www.raycharles.com/toc.htm

Featuring both a biography and an autobiography, this site contains more information about the singer than even the most ardent fan could require. The site also lists a discography, awards and achievements the singer has received, and details of how to join the fan club.

Cher's Official Web Site

http://www.cher.com

Features an illustrated biography of Cher, together with an extensive photo gallery and numerous sound clips. There is also information about her films, as well as video clips, details of upcoming live appearances, and a chat area for fans.

Cliff Richard Home Page

http://www.dds.nl/~cliff/

Fulsome tribute to Harry Webb. The contents include a discography, biography, bibliography, lyrics, pictures, audio and video clips, and contact addresses for fan clubs in the 'International Cliff Richard Movement'. This frequently updated site has all the latest news of this perennial popstar.

Cohen, Leonard

http://www.music.sony.com/Music/ArtistInfo/LeonardCohen/index.html

This official Leonard Cohen site from Sony Music offers audio clips from all his best-known songs, a bibliography, links to other Cohen sites, and latest tour and recording details. It also has a full biography and discography.

Cole Porter Wide Web

http://www.coleporter.org/

Homage to this popular-music lyricist that includes biographical articles, recommended albums, quotations, lyrics, and a catalogue of all his songs, sorted by title, musical, and year.

Crow, Sheryl

http://www.sherylcrow.com/

Official site of the singer Sheryl Crow that features profiles and photographs of the band, a tour diary, and information about upcoming live appearances. There are also sound and video clips from all of her records.

Cure, The

http://www.prayersforrain.com/

Must for fans of The Cure. There are complete details of the history of the band, list of songs with lyrics, recent news of the band, and links to the large number of other Cure sites.

Dave Clark Five, the

http://www2.rpa.net/~theboltons/DC5main.htm

Features a discography, complete with album covers and reviews. There is also a list of 'Frequently Asked Questions'.

David Bowie: Teenage Wildlife

http://www.etete.com/Bowie/

Well-designed site which is changed weekly and offers an extensive library of information about Bowie and his work. It includes details of songs and lyrics, films and videos, a large collection of images, and current news. Readers are encouraged to write in with their opinions in weekly polls on questions such as 'Should Bowie revive the Ziggy Stardust character?'

Depeche Mode

http://www.depechemode.com/

Official Web site that includes recent news, a photo gallery, and a detailed discography. There are also audio and video samples, song lyrics, and numerous magazine articles.

Diana Ross Fan Club

http://www.geocities.com/Broadway/Alley/4138/

International Diana Ross fan club Web site, which includes sound clips of unreleased material, latest information about the singer and her recent projects, and an extensive discography.

Eddie Cochran Story

http://home.wanadoo.nl/rock_and_roll/eddie.htm

Includes an informative biography and photo gallery of the singer Eddie Cochran. There is also a UK and US discography, as well as the lyrics to over a hundred songs.

Elvis Costello Home Page

http://www.elvis-costello.com/

Information about Elvis Costello's albums and live performances, plus answers to 'Frequently Asked Questions', and lots of interview transcripts and articles.

Elvis Presley Home Page

http://sunsite.unc.edu/elvis/elvishom.html

Unofficial page that mixes factual information – a pictorial tour of Graceland, for example – and conjecture about continued sightings of Elvis. There are also links to related literature and a list of lyrics.

Eurythmistan

http://www.vibber.dk/eurythmistan/

Features a detailed biography of the Eurythmics, together with an illustrated discography and photo gallery. There are also numerous lyrics, news pages, and links to related sites.

Everly Brothers International Info Circle

http://www.xs4all.nl/~ebi/

Features regular news updates and information on upcoming tours, as well as a detailed discography, biography, and photo gallery. Also included are a number of sound clips and an archive of press articles.

Fairport Convention Home Page

http://www.fairportconvention.co.uk/welcome.htm

Official Web site of Fairport Convention that includes a history of the band, a discography, and concert photos and reviews. There are also several feature articles, as well as information on upcoming live appearances.

Gaffaweb

http://www.gaffa.org/

Massive tribute to Kate Bush, featuring in-depth reviews of many of her songs and video releases. This site contains a list of 'Frequently Asked Questions', numerous press articles, and a photo gallery of several hundred images.

Gaia – The Olivia Newton-John Home Page

http://www.onlyolivia.com/onj.html

Features an informative and illustrated biography of Olivia Newton-John, as well as a detailed discography, and a list of her television and film appearances. There is also a photo gallery and recent news.

Glastonbury Festival of Contemporary Performing Arts

http://www.glastonbury-festival.co.uk/

Official site of the Glastonbury Festival, including photographs and reviews from several recent festivals. There's also practical advice on how to get to the festival, what to bring, and ways to avoid the 'horror' of the toilets.

Grateful Dead

http://www.dead.net/

Astronomically-themed home page that allows access to a huge amount of frequently updated information lovingly compiled by fans. There are comprehensive biographies of Jerry Garcia and other band members and full details of all their music.

Illustrated Elton John Discography

http://ej.kylz.com/

Complete listing of Elton John's albums, singles, and lyrics, plus links to related sites, and even a puzzle to play. Their is also a 'tour' section that gives a complete and illustrated discography.

International Lyrics Server

http://www.lyrics.ch

Can you remember the artist and not the words, or vice versa? If so, try this huge, non-profit database with flexible searching facilities, located in Switzerland and providing the lyrics, artists, and albums of 59,000 songs across an extended range of music genres. Additions and requests are welcome.

Internet Beatles Album

http://www.getback.org/

Extensive collection of Beatles information, photos, and sound clips. Biographical sections are provided on the four members and on Stuart Sutcliffe, Brian Epstein, George Martin, and Pete Best. Other information includes a library of related newsgroup articles, exhaustive discographies, and a 'Today in Beatles History' feature.

Jamiroquai – The Funkin' Site

http://www.funkin.net/jamiroquai/

Includes a profile of the English band Jamiroquai, together with information on their album and single releases. There is also an archive of magazine articles and interviews, as well as screensavers, sound files, and guitar tablatures.

Michael Jackson Internet Fan Club

http://www.MJIFC.com/

Pages that claim to be the largest Michael Jackson information site on the Internet. Click on the main menu for links to news (updated almost daily), the 1997 world tour, lists of lyrics and videos, awards, interviews and speeches, the fan club, and much more.

Morissette, Alanis

http://www.alanismorissette.com/

Aesthetically-pleasing site that includes audio and video clips, as well as several poems written by Morissette herself. Also featured is an art gallery and details of upcoming live appearances.

Morrissey Solo

http://www.morrissey-solo.com/

Includes all the latest news and tour dates for the singer Morrissey. There is also a large archive of newspaper and magazine articles and interviews, as well as sound and video clips.

NME (*New Musical Express*)

http://www.nme.com

Weekly guide to the UK rock and pop scene, with sections on 'News', 'Reviews', 'Charts', and a searchable gig database.

Official Céline Dion Website

http://www.celineonline.com/

Features an illustrated biography, as well as a photo gallery, a detailed discography, and numerous sound clips. Also included are a list of 'Frequently Asked Questions', a news archive, and details of forthcoming live appearances.

Orbison, Roy

http://www.orbison.com/

Loving tribute to the balladeer from his widow. This site includes a detailed biography, photos, audio clips of Orbison talking and singing, interviews, messages from fans, and latest news of re-releases.

Pet Shop Boys Digitally

http://www.parlophone.co.uk/psb/

Official site, featuring a profile of the Pet Shop Boys, together with recent news and a photo gallery. There is also a discography and a list of frequently asked questions.

Prodigy.org

http://www.theprodigy.org/

Features a biography of the band, as well as a profile of the band members, a discography, and a photo gallery. Also included is a list of the equipment that the Prodigy use during their live sets.

Pulp World

http://come.to/pulpworld/

Features a brief biography of the band and its members, together with a detailed discography, lyrics archive, and a large photo gallery. There is also the opportunity to listen to several audio clips from one of their concerts.

F A C T

PULP

Sheffield band formed 1978, notable for the witty, humorous lyrics of singer Jarvis Cocker (1963–), often dealing with the themes of sex and class.

Punk Page

http://www.thepunkpage.com/

Access to punk music lyrics, pictures, sounds, magazines, and record labels, as well as hyperlinks to other relevant sites.

Quincy Jones Profile

http://www.achievement.org/autodoc/page/jon0bio-1

Description of the life and work of the US music impresario Quincy Jones. The Web site contains not only contains a profile and biographical information, but also has a lengthy interview with Jones accompanied by a large number of photographs, and video and audio clips.

Radio 1

http://www.bbc.co.uk/radio1/reception/reception.html

Radio 1's official Web site, which contains news, reviews, programmes, and coming attractions on air and around the UK.

Rave On

http://www.visuallink.net/kdwilt/index.html

Fulsome unofficial tribute to Buddy Holly. This site includes a biography, discography, photos, lyrics, and a morbidly full account of the fateful plane crash on the 'Day that Music Died'.

REM Home Page

http://www.svs.com/rem/

Brings together contributions from users of the REM newsgroup, with news and tour information, sound and video clips, a discography, and links to a complete database of REM lyrics.

Seventies Dance Music

http://izan.simplenet.com/70.htm

Lava lamps and glitter balls decorate this site dedicated to disco music from the 1970s. Included here is a hit parade, featuring not only a list of the best 172 disco songs from the decade, but also numerous sound files, lyrics, and images.

Sinatra, Frank

http://members.aol.com/jillywest/

Profile of the legendary US entertainer. A biography traces the crooner's transformation into a respected actor. There are full cast, plot, and production details of his films and listings of his television appearances and music recordings.

Stephen Sondheim Stage

http://www.sondheim.com/

Polished site including biographical information, frequently updated news, interviews with Sondheim and with people who have worked closely with him, a complete discography, details of past and current productions, a library of sound clips, and articles from *The Sondheim Review* magazine.

Spice Shack

http://www.musicfanclubs.org/spiceshack/home.htm

Includes a profile and photo gallery of all members of the Spice Girls. There are also numerous magazine articles and sound clips, as well as videos of live performances and interviews.

(The Artist Formally Known As) Prince

http://www.geocities.com/SunsetStrip/1131/index.htm

Must for fans of (the artist formerly known as) Prince. The site includes a biography, audio clips, discography, photos, interviews, and articles on the multitalented performer. There are links to a number of other Prince sites.

Tom Waits Miscellania

http://www.front.net/gtausch/waits.html

Extensive source of information on the gravel-voiced singer, songwriter, and actor. There is a biography and a 'Frequently Asked Questions' section. A complete discography and filmography traces Waits career. There are also a host of magazine and newspaper articles on Waits', audio clips of Waits singing and talking, and latest news of his career. This site is quite plainly designed, but is packed with information.

U2 Zone

http://www.theu2zone.com/

Well-designed tribute to U2 that features a discography, complete with numerous sound clips and lyrics for many of their songs. There are also several video clips and screensavers, as well as an illustrated history of the band.

Unofficial Eurovision Song Contest Home Page

http://www.geocities.com/TelevisionCity/1812/eschome.htm

Great resource for anyone intrigued by the annual European pop festival. As well as an illustrated table of every winner since 1956, when the contest was first staged, there is a history of the event, quizzes, and photos.

Unofficial Paul Simon Web Site

http://members.xoom.com/_XOOM/pspages/index.htm

Loving tribute to Paul Simon and his music. There are details of every Simon album, album cover, and lyrics. Links to other Simon appreciation sites provide a comprehensive biography and connection to the Paul Simon newsgroup.

Van Morrison Home Page

http://www.harbour.sfu.ca/~hayward/van/

Lots of information about Van Morrison and his music. There's even a glossary of terms and references, from barmbrack to Wagon Wheel biscuits, found in his lyrics.

Verve, the

http://the-raft.com/theverve/

Includes an illustrated biography of the band the Verve, as well as a detailed discography, reviews of their live appearances, and the latest news.

Virtual Voyager – In Search of Elvis

http://www1.chron.com/voyager/elvis/

Reporter David Galloway's day-by-day account of his visit to the First Annual International Conference on Elvis Presley ('Six days of intensive Elvisia') makes this a cut above the usual run of fan sites.

Whitney Worship Web Page

http://www.whitney-fan.com/

Fulsome tribute to pop star Whitney Houston. Everything there is to know about Houston, her life, her music and film career, song lyrics, photos, concert schedules, and chat from fans is contained here. There are also links to the large number of other Houston sites.

Blues

Blues Access Online

http://www.he.net/~blues/

Online version of Blues Access magazine, with sample features, festival listings, and lists of other blues-related sites. In addition to all this and the current edition of the magazine, this site also contains a useful 'Essential blues' section listing a number of 'essential' purchases in several sub-genres of blues music, from harmonicas to classic Chicago blues.

FACT

BLUES

African-American music that originated in the work songs and Negro spirituals of the rural American South in the late 19th century. It is characterized by a 12-bar, or occasionally 16-bar, construction and melancholy lyrics which relate tales of woe or unhappy love.

Hooker, John Lee

http://www.virginrecords.com/hooker/

Virgin Records site on the blues guitarist. A biography of Hooker has links to many of the artists he has teamed up with during his long career. There is information on his major albums, audio clips, and an interview conducted by his daughter.

Howlin' Wolf

http://www.blueflamecafe.com/Howlin_Wolf.html

Interesting profile of the bluesman. It traces the life of Chester Arthur Burnett and how only in middle age did he shoot to fame and escape from working as a farmer. There is an audio clip from 'Back Door Man' and links to other famous musicians with whom he worked.

King of the Blues

http://www.worldblues.com/bbking/default.asp

Detailed biography of the blues guitarist B B King, plus photos, and sound clips. This site includes sections such as 'Young bluesman', 'Rise to stardom', and a complete discography.

Leadbelly

http://www.blueflamecafe.com/Leadbelly.html

Interesting profile of the life of Huddie Ledbetter. It relates how the resourceful blues player obtained a pardon from serving a life sentence for murder by singing for the Texan governor. There is an audio clip from 'Forth Worth and Dallas Blues', links to other famous musicians he worked with, and to further biographical information from the Rock'n'Roll Hall of Fame.

Muddy Waters

http://www.blueflamecafe.com/Muddy_Waters.html

Interesting biography of the rhythm-and-blues player. This account of his life has links to the great number of musicians he influenced. There is also an audio clip of him in action.

Professor Longhair

http://www.wolfrec.com/playlist/longhair.HTM

Selection of recordings to download by Professor Longhair, including 'Tipatina' and 'Got My Mojo Working'.

Rush, Otis

http://www.cstone.net/users/rickd/jukejoint/ori.htm

Features a photo gallery, illustrated discography, and a selection of sound files. There are links to lyrics and related sites.

Country

Cash, Johnny

http://www.johnnycash.com

Full profile of the 'Man in Black' from his official Web site. Include a full biography, complete discography, photo gallery, latest news, and tour schedules.

Haggard, Merle

http://imusic.com/showcase/country/merleh.html

Profile of the life and music of the country artist. There is a full discography, audio clips, and a bulletin board for Haggard fans.

Harris, Emmylou

http://www.nashville.net/~kate/

Huge source of information on this country singer. Compiled by a fan, this site includes a biography, discography, notes on every album, audio clips, photos, and regularly updated news of Harris's concerts and her campaign against landmines. There are links to other sites and to the Harris newsgroup.

Parton, Dolly

http://imusic.com/showcase/country/dolly.html

Profile of the 'first lady of country music'. The site includes photos, a biography, a complete discography, and an audio clip from her most recent album. There's also a bulletin board for Dolly's fans.

Roughstock's History of Country Music

http://www.roughstock.com/history/

Look at some of the most influential artists and songs of country music from the 1930s through to the present day, with photos, and sound and video clips.

Welcome to the Randy Newman Home Page

http://randynewman.com/

Detailed biography of this musician, reflecting on the formative influences in his career. This comprehensive site also includes a complete discography, lyrics, sound clips, bibliography, and links to other related sites.

Williams, Hank

http://www.geocities.com/Nashville/3439/index.html

Profile of the life and music of Hank Williams, from childhood poverty to his premature death from alcohol and drugs. There are pictures of Williams, an assessment of his musical legacy, lyrics, quotes, 'Quick facts', pictures, and audio clips.

Willie Nelson

http://imusic.com/showcase/country/willienelson.html

Profile of this enduring country and western outlaw. There is an interesting biography, complete discography, photos, and a sound clip from his latest album.

Folk & Roots

Bajan Calypso Barn

http://www.iere.com/thebarn/

Focuses largely on the form of calypso found in
Barbados, although there is some coverage, too, of
calypso on Trinidad and Tobago, the islands of its
birth. You can expect a wealth of song samples
and information about key artists.

Bhangra Network

http://www.bhangra.co.uk/index.htm

Aims to bring you the best in bhangra music,
with news of new releases, music and video clips,
the UK top ten, and an interactive poll.

Bluegrass Connection

http://www.gotech.com/homepg.htm

Bluegrass music home page. The site features
details of musicians, festivals, supplies, links, and
a discography. It also includes details of the 1997
bluegrass music awards, with several
photographs of the awards ceremony and concert.

F A C T

BLUEGRASS

US country music of the Appalachian Mountain
states, characterized by high harmony singing
and virtuoso banjo or mandolin playing.
Singer and mandolin player Bill Monroe
(1911–96) is the founder of the genre with his
band the Blue Grass Boys (formed 1938).

BM's Bob Marley Pages

http://www.livemarley.com/

Biography and discography of the reggae singer,
as well as the lyrics from many of his albums.
There is a chronological index detailing his
concerts, and you can even download songs from
these performances, including several songs from
his last-ever concert.

California Gold: Northern Californian Folk Music from the Thirties

http://lcweb2.loc.gov/ammem/afccchtml/
cowhome.html

Part of the American Memory presentation of the
US Library of Congress, this comprehensive
collection comprises 35 hours of folk music
recorded in 12 languages, plus photos, drawings,
and written documents from a variety of ethnic
communities in Northern California during the
1930s. Recordings can be browsed by subject,
ethnic group, performer, musical instrument, or
title.

Folk Music Home Page

http://www.jg.org/folk/

There is an explosion of information about folk
music on the Internet and this site tries to cover
the depth and breadth of it. It primarily provides
an organized set of pointers to other pages, but
also includes some original material of its own.

Guthrie, Woody

http://xroads.virginia.edu/~1930s/RADIO/c_w/
guthrie.html

Must for fans of the radical folk singer. This site
includes a biography, sound clips, photos,
discography, lyrics, assessment of Guthrie's
influence on other musicians, and links to other
sites and the Guthrie newsgroup. Everything
there is to know about Woody and his legacy is to
be found here.

Joan Baez Web Pages

http://baez.woz.org/

Official site of the US folk singer and
political activist. There is a detailed
biography of Baez, a large number of
photos, a discography, and latest tour
news. The lyrics of all of her songs may
also be accessed at this site.

Joni Mitchell Home Page

http://www.JoniMitchell.com

Celebration of the music, art, and life of Joni
Mitchell, with articles and essays, lyrics and
sound clips, a gallery of Joni Mitchell's paintings
and drawings, and a discussion forum for fans.

Pancultural Journey with Ry Cooder

http://atn.addict.com/ATN/issues/1.01/Features/Ry
_Cooder/

Intimate interview with the legendary guitarist. In
addition to details of his musical and personal
life, there are audio clips, photos, and news of his
latest projects.

Real Jamaica Ska

http://www.slip.net/~skajam/

Comprehensive source of information on ska. There is an history of the music form and its importance to Jamaican culture. There is a listing of ska albums, photos of artists, and latest record-release news.

Reggae Update

http://www.earthchannel.com/reggaesupersite/

Ultimate reggae site. All the latest news from the reggae scene is presented, together with biographies of Bob Marley, Peter Tosh, and other Wailers.

RootsWorld

http://www.rootsworld.com/rw/

Online magazine of world music, roots, and folk, with a wealth of feature articles, reviews, and sound clips.

Traditional World Music Recordings

http://www.medieval.org/music/world.html

Extensive index of resources relating to world traditional music, including Hindustani, Iranian, and Javanese. Each page includes an introduction to the specific musical style and recommended titles. Unfortunately, as yet, there are no audio clips.

F A C T

WORLD MUSIC (roots music)
popular music which has its roots in folk music, especially non-European folk music. It is usually performed by artists from the country it comes from, and has a distinct regional character.

Jazz

Basie, Count

http://www.kcstar.com/showtime/music/basie.htm

Full profile of the legendary bandleader. There is a biography, complete with reminiscences of those who knew him. There are also several photos.

Bix Beiderbecke Resources

http://ms.cc.sunysb.edu/~alhaim/index.html

Large resource for fans of the jazz musician Bix Beiderbecke. Included here are a detailed and illustrated biography, sound files, and a massive bibliography covering biographies, articles, and essays.

Coleman 'Hawk' Hawkins

http://www.technoir.net/jazz/hawkins.html

Profile of the US tenor saxophonist and his role in the development of modern jazz. There is a photo of the 'Hawk' and links to biographies of his contemporaries.

Coleman, Ornette

http://www.eyeneer.com/Jazz/Ornette/index.html

Biographical essay on the importance of Ornette Coleman's introduction of 'free jazz' in the 1950s. This site also contains a link to a page about his concept of the 'harmolodic'.

Cole, Nat 'King'

http://downbeatjazz.tunes.com/sections/artists/text/bio.asp?from=go&id1=7132

Features a biography of the US jazz singer and musician Nat 'King' Cole, together with a discography and photo gallery. There is also a message board and a selection of newspaper articles.

Ella Fitzgerald Memorial Page

http://www.users.bigpond.com/paultassone/EFINDEX.HTM

Loving tribute to Ella Fitzgerald in the form of a number of essays about her life and music, an interview with her biographer, fans' reminiscences, a discography, and a number of sound clips of her voice.

Holiday, Billie

http://www.gibbs-smith.com/books/billie.html

Biography of the legendary singer who asked in vain not to be talked about after she was gone. This account of the troubled life of 'Lady Day' has pictures of the singer and an audio clip.

Jazz Central Station

http://jazzcentralstation.com/jcs/station/

Stylish and busy jazz site in the style of a train journey. 'Trains' depart regularly for jazz festivals all over the globe. Alternatively, passengers can enter a listening car with recommended choices, or they can take the musicians' express where they will meet the artists, find out about their instruments, and get details on jazz education. There are also audio clips of jazz and interviews with the stars.

Jazz Photography of Ray Avery

http://www.book.uci.edu/Jazz/JPRA1.html

Extensive gallery of classic jazz photographs from the 1950s. The exhibition presents snapshots from the recording studios of Los Angeles, the happenings in night-clubs of the area, and festivals all over the world. A documentary on the rise of the legendary West Coast jazz scene through the lens of the jazz photographer, Roy Avery, the site also provides biographical and discographical details of some of the most important artists of the time, and a special exhibition store with books and CDs.

Louis Armstrong: Oh, You Dog!

http://www.foppejohnson.com/armstrong/

Well designed site containing a brief tribute to the US jazz cornet and trumpet player and singer, as well as a very detailed discography. Although this is the focus of the site, there are also other features, such as a table showing the development of the All-Stars and a number of links to related sites.

Love Supreme

http://jazz.route66.net/aLoveSupreme/index.html

John Coltrane, one of the pioneers of modern jazz, gets a fulsome Web treatment with copious information on every aspect of his life and music, including a year-by-year chronology, recommendations for new listeners, recent releases, discography, bibliography, a sound clip directory, and links to many other related sites.

Milestones: A Miles Davis World Wide Web Site

http://www.tune-up.net/

Tribute to Miles Davis prepared by a fan. This frequently updated site contains a biography of Davis, a complete discography, latest news of bootleg albums and official re-releases, audio and

video clips, and album covers. There are also links to other Davis sites and a bibliography.

Miller, Glenn

http://downbeatjazz.tunes.com/sections/artists/text/bio.asp?from=go&id1=7116

Dedicated to the US trombonist and bandleader, this site includes a extensive biography, as well as articles, a photo gallery, and a detailed discography.

Neville Brothers' Web Site

http://www.nevilles.com/

Official site that is a colourful introduction to the brothers' work, both inside and outside the rhythm-and-blues group that brought them their fame. The site also includes a discography, current tour information and an opportunity to 'chat' with the four brothers.

Reinhardt, Django

http://ourworld.compuserve.com/homepages/SRoyall/history.htm

Profile of the legendary Belgian gypsy and his contribution to modern jazz. A good account of his short life is accompanied by photographs.

Rude Interlude

http://www.ilinks.net/~holmesr/duke.htm

Duke Ellington's home page, dedicated to his memory and musical legacy, which consists of an illustrated appreciation of his work, a listening list, and links to related sites.

Thelonious Monk Web Site

http://www.achilles.net/~howardm/tsmonk.html

Short biography, quotations by and about the man and his music, concert reviews, links to related sites, lots of pictures, and even an opportunity to download some Thelonious Monk wallpaper for your computer.

Tribute to Charlie 'Yardbird' Parker

http://www.geocities.com/BourbonStreet/5066/

Features a selection of the alto saxophonist's work available to download. Also included here are a photograph, and a list of Parker's music recommended by the site's creator.

Wynton Marsalis Profile

http://www.achievement.org/autodoc/page/mar0pro-1

Description of the life and work of the jazz trumpet player Wynton Marsalis. The Web site contains not only a profile and biographical information, but also holds a lengthy interview with Marsalis from 1991 accompanied by a large number of photographs, and video and audio clips.

Rock

Band Home Page

http://theband.hiof.no/

Tribute to Bob Dylan's one-time backing group, with accounts of the Band's history, an index of Band-related material in the printed media and on the Internet, audio and video clips, photos, concert dates, and links to related artists.

Behind Blue Eyes – A Life of Pete Townshend

http://www.thewho.net/Chris/Who20.html

Critical review of a biography of the legendary rock musician. The mixture of arrogance, self-loathing, bad temper, and self-aggrandizement that has characterized Townshend's career is brought out. The reviewer finds no answer to the question of why Townshend in his prime was able to articulate the concerns of other hapless adolescents.

Bo Diddley Backstage

http://www.inergy.com/Originator/

Comprehensive site about 'Big Bad Bo'. In addition to tracing his long musical career, Diddley's influence on a generation of rock musicians is highlighted. There is also a full discography, details of his rarer recordings, and a list of related sites.

Chuck Berry Home Page

http://shell.ihug.co.nz/~mauricef/frames9.htm

Biography of the singer and guitarist, as well as several articles about him. There is a large discography here, along with

guitar music and lyrics. As well as this, there is a large gallery and, of course, the opportunity to listen to several audio clips.

Electric Magic

http://www.led-zeppelin.com/

Online edition of the Led Zeppelin fanzine, with rare photographs, audio and video clips, articles, news, reviews, biographies, lyrics, and a discography.

Fleetwood Mac Legacy

http://www.fmlegacy.com/

Includes a comprehensive discography of Fleetwood Mac, complete with lyrics, images, and several audio and video clips. There are also a number of articles on the band, as well as an informative biography.

Glory Days!

http://www.springsteen.de/

Loving Swedish tribute to 'The Boss'. There are details of all the bands Springsteen has played with, comprehensive details of all albums (with lyrics, chords, and explanations of songs), pictures, sound clips, and a variety of links to other Springsteen sites.

Haley, Bill

http://www.athenet.net/~genevinc/BillHaley.html

Comprehensive portrait of the seminal rocker from the Rockabilly Hall of Fame. A biography of the singing cowboy who popularized rock and roll is accompanied by many on and off-stage pictures of Haley and the musicians who teamed up with him.

Hendrix, Jimi

http://www.geocities.com/SunsetStrip/1384/

Wealth of information about Jimi Hendrix, with guitar tabulatures and chords, lyrics, photos,

---

F A C T

HENDRIX, JIMI (JAMES MARSHALL) (1942–1970)

US rock guitarist, songwriter, and singer. He was legendary for his virtuoso experimental technique and flamboyance, and remains one of the most influential guitarists.

sound clips, newspaper and other articles, and links to related sites.

HyperRust Never Sleeps – The Unofficial Neil Young Pages

http://HyperRust.org/

Huge source of information on the long career of Neil Young. Lovingly compiled by a fan, the contents of this much visited site include a full biography, comprehensive discography, song lyrics, latest release and concert news, articles, books about Young, and links to other related sites.

Hypertext Who

http://www.thewho.net/hyper/

Brief history of the band, plus reviews, lyrics, photos, articles, and news items. As well as this, the site contains a discography, biographies of all four members, and tour dates.

Iggy Pop

http://virginrecords.com/iggy_pop/

Managed by the singer's record label, this site features a large amount of news, articles, and multimedia content about Iggy Pop. There is a large photo gallery, organized as a timeline; a detailed discography; and the opportunity to download recordings of interviews and videos of trailers and concerts too.

Kurt Cobain Internet Shrine

http://kurt-cobain.com/

As its title suggests, this site pays tribute to Kurt Cobain, the late singer from Nirvana. It includes a detailed biography of Cobain, a discography, and the lyrics to many of his songs. There are also numerous sound clips, photographs, and an account of Cobain's suicide.

Lou Reed and the Velvet Underground

http://www.poiHQ.com/loureed/

Interviews with the band members, plus a gallery of album covers and photos, archives of fan material, and discographies. There is also an opportunity to send comments about the reforming of the band and even an explanation of why the offensive language has been removed from the site.

Manic Street Preachers Home Page

http://www.manics.co.uk/

Biographies of band members, a discography, lyrics, guitar music, a collection of past interviews and reviews, and recent band and tour news. For those who wish to understand the lyrics in depth there is also a guide to the people, organizations, and movements mentioned in the songs.

Nirvana Web Archive

http://www.ludd.luth.se/misc/nirvana/

Site contains discographies, lyrics, pictures, guitar chords, and sound clips. It also includes special sections devoted to Kurt Cobain's suicide and to *Nirvana Unplugged,* the band's last official recording.

Official Oasis Home Page

http://www.oasisinet.com/

Official site that offers a discography, lyrics, press clippings (features, reviews, and press releases), photos, audio and video clips, and a list of online Oasis-related events.

Official Rolling Stones Web Site

http://www.stones.com/retro/

Dedicated to The Rolling Stones and including photos, a guide to the band, a discography, sound clips, band news, and links to other sites.

Pink Floyd – Set the Controls

http://www.mtnlake.com/~robp/floyd1.html

Well-designed site, with each of its main subsections named after a member of

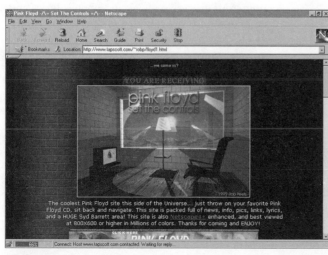

the group – hence 'Roger's photo gallery' and 'David's Pink Floyd links'. As well as the usual interviews and album details, there are animations, a readers' poll, and a chance to find out about a one-time Pink Floyd project called 'The giant slug'.

Queen Home Page

http://queen-fip.com/

Slickly-presented official site that opens with a futuristic cityscape – click on the opera house and you'll find sound clips and a discography of the group, move on to the communications tower and you'll find a forum for fans, and so on.

Rock and Roll

http://www.pbs.org/wgbh/pages/rocknroll/

Companion to a US Public Broadcasting Service (PBS) television programme, this site documents the history of rock and roll, from the time of its controversial spawning all the way through to its modern incarnations, with information and images from all ten episodes of the documentary that was first shown in 1996. The site also includes audio clips of backstage interviews, a special audio tribute to the electric guitar, plus information about the series and a discography featuring a number of top ten lists.

Rockmine Archives

http://www.rockmine.music.co.uk/Rockmn.html

Masses of information on the world of rock music. The site claims to be 'The Internet's largest music archive' and offers a huge interactive encyclopedia with over 13,000 entries, 400 photos, rock timelines, trivia lists, a chat zone, and a graffiti area. Rock fans can also find special appendices on classic rock singers, bands, and obituaries for famous musicians whose lives were cut short. Quizzes for Java-enabled browsers, audio interviews, as well as downloadable screensavers and fonts are amongst the extra bonuses of the site.

Shrine to Eric Clapton

http://bvsd.k12.co.us/~dewitt/clapton/pc/

Tribute to blues and rock guitarist and singer Eric Clapton. In addition to biographical information, you will find an extensive discography and videography, news (including tour information), a photo gallery, a bibliography of the numerous

books about Clapton, plus a MIDI library that features over three dozen audio clips.

Shrine to the Sex Pistols

http://pcstraining.uts.ohio-state.edu/consult/decarlo.7/pistols.htm

Homage to the notorious punk group. This site includes many photos of the band, reviews of concerts, audio clips, and links to other Pistols site. This site is scathing in its condemnation of Sid Vicious. However, there is a link from here to a shrine to Johnny Rotten.

Smith, Patti

http://imusic.com/showcase/rock/pattismith.html

Profile of the singer-songwriter. There is a biography, discography, photo, audio clips of her most recently-released work, and bulletin board for exchange of news and opinions with other Smith fans.

Smokey Robinson and the Miracles Fan Club

http://www3.edgenet.net/smokey_miracles/

Authorised fan club with frequently updated news of Smokey and the other Miracles. There are photos of the band, details of concerts, current releases, and how to subscribe to the quarterly magazine for fans.

Talking Heads Net

http://talking-heads.net/

Complete source of information on Talking Heads and their individual members. There is a history of the band and its members' solo projects, numerous articles, reviews and photos, lyrics and chords, sound clips, and latest news of the band.

Turner, Tina

http://imusic.com/showcase/contemporary/tinaturner.html

Profile of the rock star. There is a good account of her career, a complete discography, audio clips from her latest recording, and a bulletin board for fans.

Woodstock

http://www.woodstock.com/

Official site of the Woodstock festival that contains information on the festival itself, as well as extensive coverage of the artists. There are feature articles, biographies, and sound and video files, dating back to the first festival in 1969.

Zappa.com

http://www.zappa.com/

This site includes a 'Frankzappedia' (with discography, photos of every album cover, and song lists) a two-hour audio biography, and latest re-release information. There are even details about the ZappaFrank comet named in his honour.

Soul

Brown, James

http://www.rockhall.com/induct/browjame.html

From the Rock and Roll Hall of Fame, a short biography of the 'Godfather of Soul' and a few sound clips. The biographical content is fairly brief, but the sound clips are available in several formats.

Franklin, Aretha

http://imusic.com/showcase/urban/
arethafranklin.html

Good profile of the career of the 'Queen of Soul'. Contents include a biography, discography, audio samples, latest news, and a bulletin board for Franklin fans. There are links to other related sites.

Marvin Gaye Biography

http://www.sdf.se/~simon/marvin/biography.html

Fascinating biography of the Motown star. This detailed account of his troubled life and violent death also has photos and information on all of his albums.

Motown

http://www.motown.com/

Introduction to the Motown record label. Each month three artists are featured – click on the link for access. The site also includes a history of Motown's first 25 years and a link to trivia

---

F
A
C
T

SOUL MUSIC

emotionally intense style of rhythm and blues sung by, among others, Sam Cooke, Aretha Franklin, and Al Green (1946–   ). A synthesis of blues, gospel music, and jazz, it emerged in the 1950s.

---

questions such as 'What is Stevie Wonder's real name?' and 'which Nobel Peace prizewinner released an album on Motown?'

Otis Redding Story

http://www.otisredding.com/page2.html

Ultimate site for Redding fans that includes a biography, a full discography, details of some of his most famous songs, details of the Redding Memorial Fund, and links to related sites.

Supremes, the

http://www.motown40.com/history/archives/s/
supremes/1.html

Official site from Motown records that includes an illustrated biography of the Supremes, as well as a discography, several sound files, and a trivia quiz.

Unofficial Stevie Wonder Internet Archive

http://student-www.uchicago.edu/users/
jrgenzen/stevie-intro.html

Biography of Stevie Wonder, plus a discography, lyrics, trivia, multimedia clips, and news.

Dance

American Ballet Theater

http://www.abt.org/

Site of the prestigious US ballet company. This site contains full details of current performances, profiles of dancers and choreographers, photographs, and a history of the company. Its educational work to popularize ballet is explained and a very helpful online dictionary of ballet terms is included.

see p 303

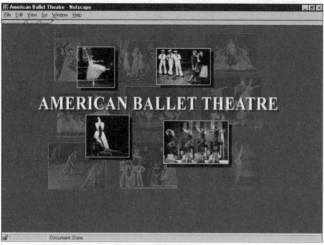

Astaire, Fred

http://www.reelclassics.com/Actors/Astaire/astaire.htm

Tribute to the singer, dancer, and actor Fred Astaire. You will find a filmography, audio clips of Astaire singing 'Puttin' on the Ritz' from the 1946 film *Blue Skies,* numerous film stills, magazine covers, and full-colour film posters. There is a special section devoted to Audrey Hepburn and Astaire's 1957 musical *Funny Face.* Click on 'next page' to see another page of film stills. The site also includes lists of famous quotes and of additional Fred Astaire links.

Australian Ballet

http://www.realmech.com.au/ballet/

Site of Australia's national ballet company. There is a history of the ballet and details of its administrative structures and office holders. There is also a guide to current performances.

BalletWeb

http://www.novia.net/~jlw/index.html

Site devoted to classical ballet, with commentary on dance issues, photo-essays, and the Electronic Ballerina – a computer animation illustrating ballet steps.

Baryshnikov, Mikhail

http://mrshowbiz.go.com/people/mikhailbaryshnikov/

Profile and photo of the diminutive classical dancer. This site traces the professional and romantic success he won following his defection to the USA. He describes work of his modern dance companyand provides details of Baryshnikov's stage, film, and television performances.

Bolshoi in History

http://www.bolshoi.ru/eng/frame.html

History of the Bolshoi Theatre in Moscow, Russia, from its inception in 1776, through many trials and tribulations, up to the present day. The site is illustrated with pictures of the theatre and its ballet company at different times in its history. There is also a portrait of the architect A Cavos, who rebuilt the theatre after the disastrous fire of 1853.

Davis, Sammy

http://www.sammydavis-jr.com/Pages/hmpage.htm

Official tribute to entertainer Sammy Davis, Jr. The 'Read' section of the site contains transcripts of interviews with the celebrity and a comphrensive biography. This site also contains an extensive photo gallery of pictures of Davis from the fifties through to the eighties.

Doris Humphrey Society

http://homepage.interaccess.com/~jprost/dhs/

Profile of the life and legacy of the innovative US choreographer. Her role as a pioneer of the American Modern Dance movement is set out. There is also a photo of Humphrey dancing.

English National Ballet

http://www.ballet.org.uk/ballet/cgi-bin/index.cgi

The National Ballet's Web site includes a 'Tour schedule' and 'Company news', as well as an opportunity to contribute to the 'Online think tank' and 'Performance reviews'. There is also a 'Ballet school' for aspiring dancers.

English National Ballet

http://www.ballet.org.uk/ballet/cgi-bin/index.cgi

Home page of the English National Ballet, with information on tours and performances, reviews, a complete list of their dancers, a history, a gallery of photos, a further-reading list, and a discussion forum.

History of the Kirov Ballet

http://www.webcom.com/shownet/kirov/kirov3.html

History of the development of ballet in Russia and the growth of the Kirov-Mariinsky Ballet company. The text has numerous links to significant places such as St Petersburg, influential patrons such as Empress Catherine II, and famous ballerinas and choreographers such as Pavlova and Diaghilev.

Liondance

http://elektron.et.tudelft.nl/~wingchun/Lion.html

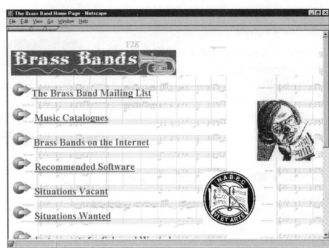

Chinese liondance Web site describing the traditional Chinese New Year celebration from its origins up to modern day liondancers. The site includes many pictures of the colourful costumes as well as hyperlinks to other liondance Web sites.

Twyla Tharp Profile

http://www.achievement.org/autodoc/page/tha0pro-1

Description of the life and work of the dancer and choreographer Twyla Tharp. The Web site contains not only a profile and biographical information, but also holds a lengthy interview with Tharp from 1993, accompanied by a large number of photographs, and video and audio clips.

Instruments

Bagpipes of the World

http://www.rootsworld.com/rw/feature/gaida.html

Bagpipe music from around the world. This illustrated site includes features about artists and audio clips of bagpipe music from Sweden, Hungary, Ireland, Northumbria, and Galicia. There are also links to a guest book and reviews of recent recordings.

Brass Bands – The Official Brass Band Site

http://www.smsltd.demon.co.uk/

Clearing house of information for the British brass band movement. There are details of a brass band mailing list and brass band RealAudio concerts. There are samples from all the best-known pieces in the brass band repertoire and latest news of bands.

Brief History of Electronic Music Instruments

http://www.ief.u-psud.fr/~thierry/history/history.html

Stylish history of a series of electronic musical instruments. The site deals with three main categories, the electromagnetic, triode lamp, and transistor instruments. It offers concise accounts of their development as well as photographs of some of them.

F A C T

ELECTRONIC MUSIC

music composed mainly of electronically generated and modified sounds. The term was first used in 1954 to describe music made up of synthesized sounds recorded on tape, to distinguish it from so-called *musique concrète* (concrete music).

Description of the Hurdy-Gurdy

http://www.midcoast.com/~beechhil/vielle/descript.html

Detailed description of the hurdy-gurdy with a numbered diagram showing 20 key features – click on each number for an explanation. There is also a link to three sound clips, and to the home page created by hurdy-gurdy player Matthew Szostak of Maine, USA.

5-String Banjo

http://www.trussel.com/f_banj.htm

Featuring a banjo tune index, a banjo book list, banjo history, advertisements for used banjos, and a short banjo story. The site loads with a Java MIDI player that plays banjo tunes while you browse, with a selection jukebox in a separate frame.

For Those Who Like the Didgeridoo

http://www.pacificnet.net/~mtemple/didghome.htm

Find out about the history of the didgeridoo, or didjeridu. This site also includes lessons on how to play one as well as music reviews, how to make your own, and how they work.

Guide to Medieval and Renaissance Instruments

http://www.s-hamilton.k12.ia.us/antiqua/instrumt.html

Well-designed site which contains detailed information about a variety of medieval and renaissance musical instruments, including information about how each was made and played. Most are accompanied by images and downloadable sounds.

Harmonica World

http://www.bekkoame.ne.jp/~mshige/

Harmonica site aspiring to connect harmonica players and fans all over the world. It includes help for beginners and more advanced players with a useful 'Frequently Asked Questions' section, keys for harmonica songs, an extensive CD list, as well as details of new releases, profiles of harmonica players, several audio clips of harmonicas, and a photo catalogue of a series of harmonica types.

Instrument Jokes

http://www.mit.edu/people/jcb/jokes/

Vast compilation of jokes about musical instruments, musicians, and conductors. It also features a collection of humorous musical quotations and amusing explanations of classical music definitions.

International Saxophone Home Page

http://www.saxophone.org/

Popular instrument site with masses of information about the world of the saxophone. The site hosts advice from major saxophone dealers, a saxophone buyer's guide, CD reviews, links to a vast number of saxophonists, saxophone ensembles, bands featuring saxophones, and a picture gallery with free photos for downloading. There is also a recommended resource which particularly welcomes reader-submitted materials.

Internet Piano Page

http://www.geocities.com/Paris/3486/

Lots of sound samples from the classical piano repertoire from Bach to Rachmaninov. All of the files are in the most common and easy-to-use MIDI format and are arranged by composer.

Locksley's E-Z Harp Method

http://www.geocities.com/Athens/Forum/5387/ezharp.htm

Thorough introduction to the Celtic harp. After a short historical presentation, the site offers extended descriptions of the harp and its parts, as well as elaborate definitions of tunes, modes, main chords and faked chords, shakes, rattles, and graces. The tutorial also includes useful advice for potential buyers of the instrument, some suggestions for further reading and listening, college-level courses, and a glossary of musical terms.

Mountain Dulcimer Home Page

http://www.santarosa.edu/~csherman/dulcimer.html

Home page of the Appalachian mountain dulcimer. This site includes instructions on how to play the mountain dulcimer, details of its origins, listings of mountain dulcimer festivals and workshops, and some audio clips. It also features recent musical releases on CD and tape.

National Flute Association Online

http://kristin.newdream.net/flute/

Information on new flute music, composers, performers, competitions, and music clubs. There are a few audio clips of flautists and information about worldwide flute summerclasses.

Piano Page

http://www.ptg.org/

Essential reference on the world of the piano. This site offers tips about the piano industry, technical information, specialist guidance on buying a piano, excerpts from a spectacular picture book on the history of the piano, a virtual piano museum, and details on a series of relevant Usenet groups and mailing lists.

Renaissance Consort

http://www.hike.te.chiba-u.ac.jp/cons1/

Exhibition of Renaissance instruments that offers a range of photos and an audio clip for each one, as well as further audio clips of music played by typical Renaissance ensembles.

Tzara's Tabla Home Page

http://www.tabla.com/

Vast amount of information about the tabla. There is an introduction to the tabla itself, as well as details of its history, and a glossary of words related to this instrument. This site also features a selection of articles about the instrument, information about its acoustic properties, and a list of strokes and sounds of the tabla.

Veil and Drum

http://www.al-mustarib.org/

Hands-on site dedicated to 'Arabic culture and people between the time of Harun al-Rashid and the comming of the Mongols'. This includes images of dances, clips of drum rhythms to practise, as well as practical information about costumes, art, and food.

Violin Making by Hans Johannsson

http://www.centrum.is/hansi/

Slightly different from the average home page – this one is produced by an Icelandic violin maker. There are illustrated sections on all aspects of his trade, including 'Construction', 'Care and maintenance', and 'The bow'. There are also a few sound clips of violins he has made.

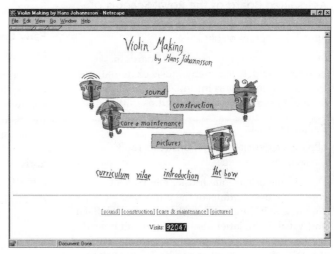

Wheatstone English Concertina – Neil Wayne

http://www.d-and-d.com/contributions/tina-history.html

Comprehensive information about the history, development, and structure of the English concertina. The history of the instrument is closely bound up with the history of the Wheatstone family, and in particular with the life of Charles Wheatstone, its inventor. The site includes extensive biographical details and information about Wheatstone's musical research, as well as black and white photographs of concertina prototypes. There are also notes on concertina sales in the 19th century and material from the Wheatstone Factory archives.

Miscellaneous Music

A Cappella Central

http://www.casa.org/web_directory.html

Contains a number of 'Frequently Asked Questions' on different a cappella topics. These include information on the various a cappella organizations; a guide to arranging, performing, and recording a cappella music; and also details of a cappella albums, arrangements, workshops, and competitions. This site also includes a number of links to a cappella sites around the world.

Associated Board of the Royal Schools of Music

http://www.abrsm.ac.uk/

Official site from the Associated Board, the institution which sets many music examinations. Included in this site is information about the different exams, and advice for those sitting them.

Baroque Music

http://www.geocities.com/Paris/Rue/1663/music.html

Description of baroque music. The Web site consists of descriptions of the important composers of the period, including Handel, Bach, and Vivaldi; the latter also has a portrait posted on the site. Perhaps the most important feature of this Web site is its well researched links section which draws together the scattered sites dealing with this subject.

Byzantine Chant

http://www.0wned.org/~pavlos/

Concise introduction to all aspects of Byzantine music, for those who 'practise it, study it, are

interested in it, and those who just happened by'. It offers sections on the history of the genre, its famous eight modes, and a series of sound clips from individual artists and choir performances.

Ceolas Celtic Music Archive

http://www.ceolas.org/ceolas.html

Database including an introduction to Celtic music, radio programmes with Celtic music from around the world, recommended albums and new releases, profiles and discographies of the more popular Celtic soloists and groups organized geographically, material on the most popular instruments played by the artists, and transcriptions of several hundred traditional tunes.

Chamber Music Conferences

http://www.ultranet.com/~cwholl/cmc/cmc.html

This page offers details of a variety of chamber-music conferences and master classes around the world, for both amateur, professional, and student musicians.

Chord Archive

http://www.guitar.net/cotw/index.html

Marvellous teach-yourself tool for all guitar enthusiasts. The site offers a tutorial on guitar chords with explanatory notes and helpful drawings. The tutees can even hear each chord if they have the appropriate plug-in.

Early Child Ballads

http://www.pbm.com/~lindahl/ballads/early_child/

Description of the early ballads of Francis James Child, the 19th-century US composer and songwriter. The site also includes a description of the historical background of the ballad form and its 'modern' rediscovery.

Early Music by Women Composers

http://150.252.8.92/www/iawm/pages/

Carefully prepared presentation of medieval, Renaissance, and baroque women composers. It includes a chronology, a CD discography, MIDI soundfiles, reference sources, and illustrations by early women artists.

Glossary of Musical Terms

http://www.hnh.com/mgloss.htm

Online A–Z glossary of musical terms, with links to articles on composers, including a list of recommended works.

GramoFile Home Page

http://www.gramofile.co.uk

Over 20,000 reviews of classical music releases are available at this site. They are searchable by a wide variety of criteria, including month of release, composer, title, orchestra, and record label. There are plans to make this a subscription-based site, but at the moment access to the reviews is free.

Gregorian Chants

http://www.music.princeton.edu/chant_html/

Site dedicated to early Christian music that includes a lot of contextual information through its linked pages: audio clips, history, and manuscripts, in addition to pages about the music and theory of chants.

Indian Classical Music

http://www.aoe.vt.edu/~boppe/MUSIC/music.html

Several essays on Indian, North Indian, South Indian, and Karnatic music. There is also a list of both Karnatic and Hindustani ragas, a bibliography, and details about several of the great masters of Indian music.

> **F A C T**
>
> **INDIAN MUSIC**
>
> an oral culture of great antiquity, allied to Muslim traditions of the Middle East and Central Asia, it resembles the medieval European troubadour tradition of composer-performer, being an art of skilful extemporization in a given mood (rasa), selecting from a range of melody prototypes (ragas) and rhythmic formulae (talas).

King's Singers

http://www.kingssingers.com/

Overview of the career, performance, and recordings of the King's Singers, the six Englishmen who form one of the world's most highly acclaimed vocal ensembles. This site also has details about their latest tour itinerary.

> **F A C T**
>
> **CLASSICAL MUSIC**
>
> term used specifically to refer to the period between approximately 1750 and 1830, in which composers' concerns for form and symmetry were analogous to those of the ideals of classical Greek and Roman art and philosophy.

Little Russia Music Page

http://russia.uthscsa.edu/Music/

Site devoted to Russian opera, folk, and pop, with audio clips and visuals of numerous Russian artists.

Musica Research Notes

http://musica.uci.edu/mrn/acumidx960718.html

Music research magazine crammed with many articles on such topics as the connection between music and memory, child development, human mood, adolescent behaviour, ageing, and language recovery after brain damage.

Musicianship Basics

http://www.dragnet.com.au/~donovan/mb/music.html

Theory tutorial designed by music teachers for use in schools and private studios with 50 graded activities which cover basic music skills for students of all ages. The skills taught include basic starting steps such as reading notes in the treble and bass clefs, aural recognition of scales and common intervals, recognition of common chords in manuscript or on a keyboard, and aural recognition of major and minor tonality.

Salzburg Festival

http://www.salzb-fest.co.at/salzb-fest/index_e.html

Well-presented guide to the famous music festival. There are details of all plays, concerts, and operas performed, together with booking and ticket information for festival-goers.

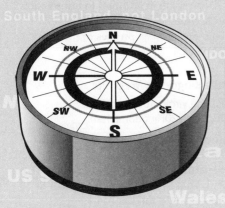

PEOPLES AND PLACES

Europe, Ancient Sites

About Delphi

http://www.vacation.net.gr/p/delphi.html

Good source of information on this ancient Greek city. The mythology of the oracle and its place in Greek culture is explained. There is a also a guide to the archaeological discoveries made here and some practical information for visitors.

Ancient City of Athens

http://www.indiana.edu/~kglowack/athens/

Photographic archive of the archaeological and architectural remains of ancient Athens, Greece. As the site says, 'It is intended primarily as a resource for students of classical art and archaeology, civilization, languages, and history'. However, there is much here of interest for the general browser.

Ancient Sites: Rome

http://www.ancientsites.com/as/rome/

Lively meeting point for all those interested in ancient Rome. The site offers atmospheric tours through ancient routes and landmarks, as well as images of the ancient city. The visitor may also enter a discussion forum, play online games, and try to answer trivia questions, all related to the city of Rome. Dedicated visitors can even practise their Latin.

F A C T ROME, ANCIENT

Ancient Rome was a civilization based on the city of Rome. It lasted for about 800 years. Traditionally founded as a kingdom in 753 BC, Rome became a republic in 510 BC following the expulsion of its last king, Tarquinius Superbus. From then, its history is one of almost continual expansion until the murder of Julius Caesar and the foundation of the empire in 27 BC under Augustus and his successors.

Discover Laconia

http://www.apel.ee.upatras.gr/www/pub/
peloponnese/laconia.html

Guide to this Greek district. There are descriptions of the rich history and cultural heritage of the region in addition to information on Byzantine churches and other places of interest. This site also has profiles of the main towns in Laconia.

Early British Kingdoms Web Site

http://freespace.virgin.net/david.ford2/
Early%20British%20Kingdoms.html

Ample information about celebrated as well as less well known kingdoms that existed in Britain after the departure of Romans and until the 11th century, with links and frequent references to Celtic mythology and folklore.

Pamukkale

http://www.exploreturkey.com/pamukkal.htm

Good guide to the history of Turkey's 'Holy City' and the current attractions of Pamukkale. Information on recent archaeological discoveries is presented here and there are also good pictures of the ruins and the spectacular geological formations in the area.

Pompeii Forum Project

http://jefferson.village.virginia.edu/pompeii/
forummap.html

Clickable map of the Forum at Pompeii provides the interface to this virtual reconstruction of the Roman town, analysing the archaeological evidence and materials found on the site of Pompeii. The project aims not just to look at how Pompeii was in the Roman world, but also to fit this picture into a broader context of urban development, drawing parallels with modern urban studies.

Santorini

http://www.dilos.com/region/cyclad/
santorin.html

This page provides historical and tourist information about the Greek island of Santorini, or Thera, the volcanic island whose eruption in 1500 BC buried the village of Akrotiri and may have resulted in the demise of the Minoan civilization on Crete. You will also find links to tourist information about other Greek islands.

Who Were the Celts?

http://sunsite.unc.edu/gaelic/celts.html

Concise and informative overview of Celtic culture, language, and early history.

Asia & Middle East, Ancient Sites

Bangladesh

http://www.ranainside.com/bangladesh/menu.html

Online guide to Bangladesh. The site includes information on all aspects of life and culture in Bangladesh, including the architecture and history of the country.

Cambodia Mega Attraction – Angkor

http://www.asiatour.com/cambodia/e-04angk/ec-ang10.htm

Guide to Cambodia's most impressive attraction. Good photographs accompany a history of the vast complex and details of Angkor Thom, Angkor Wat, and other sites.

Garden of Gethsemane

http://198.62.75.1/www1/jsc/TVCgeths2.html

Comprehensive guide to the garden and the Kidron valley. The churches on the site are fully described. There are also a series of high resolution photos at this site.

Jerusalem in Old Maps and Views

http://www.israel-mfa.gov.il/mfa/maps.html

Selection of old maps of Jerusalem, produced by the Israeli Ministry of Foreign Affairs. Maps and views dating as far back as 564 AD offer visitors a bird's-eye view of the history of the city and of the uncomfortable mix of Judaism, Christianity, and Islam within its much disputed boundaries.

Phrygia

http://www.focusmm.com/civcty/phyr_00.htm

Outline of the ancient kingdom. The history of the migration of the Balkan people, the foundation of the kingdom by King Midas, and the cultural absorption of Phrygians into Anatolian culture is traced. There are also some examples of Phrygian objects at this site.

Virtual Tour of Jerusalem

http://www.md.huji.ac.il/vjt/

Virtual tour of the city of Jerusalem. The text is brief but refreshingly non-partisan in dealing with the diversity of cultures and faiths which have shaped the city. There are images of sites significant for Jews, Christians, and Moslems.

Walk Round Harappa

http://www.harappa.com/walk/index.html

Virtual tour around the ancient ruins of the city of Harappa. The site provides background information about the city and a small map showing its location. There are links to 29 views of the ruins, including granaries, walls, ringstones, bathing areas, and huts. There are also some audio clips of local sounds, Qaqaali music, and a Harappa folk tale – all accompanied by photographs and explanations.

Walk Through Mohenjodaro

http://www.harappa.com/har/moen0.html

Virtual tour round the ancient ruins of the city of Mohenjodaro. Click through the links to view colour photographs of the Buddhist stupa, the city bath, a street, a well, a street drain, and an overview of the city.

Northern England

Barnsley Online

http://www.barnsley.gov.uk/

Well-presented guide to Barnsley prepared by the local council. In addition to details of government services, the local economy, and investment opportunities, there is a great amount of practical information for visitors to Barnsley and the rest of south Yorkshire.

Bolton

http://www.bolton.gov.uk/

Official source of information on Bolton. This site includes local government services, business information, a history of the city, and general information for visitors. There is also a useful map to help locate local attractions.

Borough of Blackburn

http://irisi.works.co.uk/GRAPHICS/CSITES/blckburn/

Official guide to Blackburn. There is information on local government services and a guide to the local economy. Information sections for visitors and residents on local history, attractions, and amenities are brief.

City of Bradford

http://www.bradford.gov.uk/

Comprehensive and well-organized official guide to Bradford. The needs of residents, investors, and visitors are well catered for. The civic pride of the city shines through in a good account of the history of the former wool capital of the world and its evolution into a modern multicultural city. There is also a good guide to local government services.

City of Leeds

http://www.leeds.gov.uk/

Colourful presentation of the main aspects of life in Leeds. Valuable community and benefit services information is offered with separate sections on legal, financial, employment, and other related issues. It also provides comprehensive information on museums, galleries, theatres, sports, and shopping in the area. The city's history is covered with a large number of photos which can also be sent as 'postcards' across the Web.

> **F A C T**
>
> **LEEDS**
>
> industrial city and metropolitan borough in West Yorkshire, England, 40 km/25 miles southwest of York, on the River Aire; population (1991) 424,200 (city), 680,700 (district).

County of Cheshire

http://www.u-net.com/cheshire/

Well-organized official guide to Cheshire. Information for tourists (available in six

languages), residents, and investors is comprehensive. A clickable map of the county allows access to information on all the schools in the county. There is information on sixty tourist attractions in the county. There are details of walking routes and public rights of way in Cheshire.

Crewe and Nantwich – A Guide for Visitors and Business

http://www.crewe-nantwich.gov.uk/

Official guide to Crewe and Nantwich. There are full details of local government services, investment opportunities, community organizations, recreation facilities, and places of interest. There is also a history of Crewe and some useful links.

Cumbria County Council

http://www.cumbria.gov.uk/

Well-organized official guide to the services and facilities in Cumbria for local people, business, and visitors. Information on local government services and the work of the council is extensive. The travel section has links to the many tourist attractions in the county and to sources of transport information.

Darlington Borough Council

http://www.darlington.org.uk/council/

Official guide to the borough of Darlington. There is extensive information on local government services and the workings of local democracy. News of local government events is regularly updated. However, sparse information on local history and amenities makes this site less attractive for non-residents.

Durham City

http://www.durhamcity.gov.uk/

Official information on Durham. There is comprehensive coverage of local government services, the work of the city council, and local business. Information for visitors can be found at the Tour of Durham Cathedral and Castle site.

Durham County Council

http://www.durham.gov.uk/

Official information on the county. There is full coverage of local government functions and investment opportunities, as well as maps, images of the area, and details of local tourist attractions.

Ellesmere Port and Neston Borough Council

http://irisi.works.co.uk/GRAPHICS/CSITES/ellesmer/

Official guide to the southern Wirral. This site includes information on local government services, local industry, and a brief history. The section on tourism, however, does not have a great deal of practical information.

Harrogate Borough Council

http://www.harrogate.gov.uk/frames.htm

Comprehensive guide to the Yorkshire district. There are profiles of all the communities in the area and a wealth of practical information for visitors and residents. In addition, there are details of local government services, maps, and information on business activities.

Historic Lancaster

http://www.lancs.ac.uk/users/history/lanchistory/index.htm

Good locally prepared guide to the heritage of Lancaster. The history of the city is told in conjunction with information for visitors to Lancaster's historical sites. The text accompanying J M W Turner landscapes provides further information on Lancaster's long history.

Kingston upon Hull City Council

http://www.hullcc.gov.uk/index.html

Official guide to the city. The needs of residents and visitors are well served. Contents include information about local government services, community groups, and businesses. The section for visitors includes information on local attractions, history, famous residents, and forthcoming events.

Lake District National Park Authority

http://www.lake-district.gov.uk/index.htm

Official guide to the attractions of Britain's largest national park. There are sections on geology, history, conservation activities, and exhibitions in the Park's visitors' centre. There is a daily weather report for keen walkers, as well as also some fabulous photographs of Lakeland beauty spots.

Lancashire

http://www.lancashire.com/regionf.htm

Information on the 'Red Rose County'. Lancashire is stereotypically an area associated with dark mills and industrial gloom and this Web site aims to dispel some of those myths. It also includes descriptions of the county's history, politics, and geography, as well as descriptions of the region's tourist attractions.

Morecambe Bay – Places to Go, Things to Do

http://theboard.newsquest.co.uk/llt/lancaster/morecambe.html

Fulsome guide promoting the attractions of Morecambe Bay. With a little persistence, information on every attraction in Morecambe and around the bay can be accessed. For further information the tourist office can be e-mailed.

Preston, Lancashire

http://www.compulink.co.uk/~rmo/preston.htm

In-depth information about Preston, Lancashire, by a local. This well-designed site provides you with everything you would want to know about the town, including its history, a map, a list of little-known facts, and a photo gallery.

Tour of Durham Cathedral and Castle

http://www.dur.ac.uk/~dla0www/c_tour/tour1.html

Introduction to the architecture and history of Durham Cathedral, including an interactive tour guide of this imposing structure.

Virtual Chester

http://www.woodbank.com/cityguide/chester/

Complete guide to this English city for visitor and resident alike. This site covers a large number of areas, including accommodation in Chester, a guide to eating out, and also a feature about the city's many tourist attractions. It also features details of forthcoming events in the city.

Virtual Manchester

http://www.manchester.com/home.html

Lively and comprehensive guide to the city of Manchester, with information on nightlife, education, events, enterprise, accommodation, maps, organizations, property, shopping, sport, and travel.

Wakefield on the Web

http://www.wakefield.gov.uk/

Good official guide to this Yorkshire city. There is an outline of government services, and business and employment opportunities in Wakefield. There are also guides to local historical sites and a good history of the now defunct mining industry.

Welcome – This is Chester City Council Web Site

http://www.chestercc.gov.uk/

Good official guide to Chester. Investment opportunities are clearly explained. The needs of visitors also are well catered for, with clearly accessible information on transport services, history, leisure amenities, and tourist attractions. The information on accommodation is conveniently arranged by price category.

Welcome to Blackpool – Entertainment Capital of the North

http://www.blackpool.gov.uk/

Thorough official guide to the night life, accommodation, and leisure facilities of this seaside resort. In addition, there is a history of the town, a profile of the local economy, and information on local government services.

Welcome to Burnley

http://www.burnley.gov.uk/

Well-organized official guide to the Lancashire town. Burnley's civic pride shines through sections on the history of the town and a profile of its newly-reintroduced town cryer. There are links to the online edition of the local paper, the tourist office, and a number of other useful Burnley sites.

Welcome to Bury Metro

http://www.bury.gov.uk/Index.htm

Official guide to Bury that includes a full description of the structure and services provided by the borough. Clicking 'Welcome' on the home page accesses general information on Bury and its history as well as practical information required by visitors.

Welcome to Oldham

http://www.oldham.gov.uk/

Good official guide to the northwestern English town. There is information on local government

services, business, events, community news, shopping, and sports amenities.

Welcome to the Yorkshire Dales

http://www.yorkshirenet.co.uk/ydales/index.html

Well-organized guide to the Dales. There is easily accessible information on the habitat, landscape, and history of the area. All kinds of information required by tourists are provided. There are also links to a host of other tourist attractions in the Dales.

Welcome to York

http://www.britain.co.uk/tourism/wel2york.html

Complete guide to the English city of York. There is a guide to the many hotels of the city, featuring contact details as well as photographs of the places themselves. There are also notes on the many tourist attractions and places to eat out. A number of detailed maps complete this informative guide.

Wigan Metropolitan Borough

http://www.wiganmbc.gov.uk/

Well-presented official guide to Britain's twelfth largest metropolitan district. The contents include local government services, business opportunities, local attractions, cultural events, and community news. There is also a section on amenities in the nearby countryside.

Eastern England

Bury St Edmunds

http://bury.finder.co.uk/

Guide to this English town for tourists, residents, and businesses. There are details of the local museums, schools, and leisure facilities, as well as notes on eating out and evening entertainment. A history of the town is also included, as is a guide to health in the area, providing details of local hospitals and doctors. A soundtrack accompanies this site, although you are invited to 'kill' the sound, should you so wish.

Cambridgeshire County Council

http://www.camcnty.gov.uk/

Well-presented official guide to this county. There is comprehensive information on local government services and the proceedings of the county council. There is a wealth of statistical information to be accessed. The needs of visitors are catered for by provision of a large number of links to local attractions and tourist information services.

Cambridge-UK

http://www.e-cambridge.co.uk/

Complete guide to this city. The areas covered here include details of travel to, from, and in Cambridge by either train, bus, or car; churches and museums in the city; and also information about the university. There are even details of walks, suited for people with only a short time to stay, those with more time, and those who wish to visit a particular area of the city.

Great Yarmouth Borough Council

http://www.great-yarmouth.gov.uk/

Well-presented guide to the Norfolk resort. This site includes a history, as well as details of local amenities, local government services, transport, business opportunities, accommodation guide, history, and local events. A search engine helps navigation around this site.

Ipswich Borough Council

http://www.ipswich.gov.uk/

Official guide to the Suffolk county town. This well-presented site has information on local government services, local business, history, and amenities. There are pictures of attractions in the town and a search engine.

King's College Chapel

http://www.kings.cam.ac.uk/chapel/index.html

Pictorial guided tour of the historic chapel of King's College, Cambridge. The site includes a brief history, a selection of general photographs of the chapel, and an in-depth look at the stained glass windows for which the chapel is renowned.

Newmarket Home Page

http://www.newmarketracecourses.co.uk/

Official site of the unofficial headquarters of English horse racing. There are full details of fixtures and runners and a list of previous winners. Well-organized practical information for punters visiting Newmarket is also available.

Welcome to King's Lynn and West Norfolk Borough Council

http://www.west-norfolk.gov.uk/

Comprehensive official guide to King's Lynn and adjacent areas of West Norfolk. This site includes a guide to local government, the work of the borough council, business life, local attractions, and a history. A pull-down menu allows access to information on a number of communities within the borough.

Welcome to North Lincolnshire

http://www.northlincs.gov.uk/

Good source of information on the English unitary authority. There is a description of the area and its communities. Information is provided on local government services, industry and employment, education, leisure, and tourist attractions.

Southern England, not London

Bedford Borough Council

http://www.bedford.gov.uk/

Well-presented official guide to Bedford. Information on local government services, local institutions, businesses, and amenities is extensive. The needs of visitors are well catered for with a history of the town and practical information. Should you need them, further details can be obtained by e-mail.

Borough of Basingstoke and Deane

http://www.basingstoke.gov.uk/index.html

Official guide to Basingstoke and the Hampshire Borders. In addition to details of government services, local councillors, the local economy, and investment opportunities, there is a great amount of practical information for visitors to the area.

Canterbury Tour

http://www.hillside.co.uk/tour/tour.html

Interactive tour of Canterbury, Kent. The tour features paired photographs of monuments and features, so you can see the view behind you as well as in front, and this site also features a history of the city.

Chichester – A Little Piece of Heaven in a Corner of Sussex

http://www.chichester.gov.uk/

Well-organized guide from Chichester District Council. There is an accommodation listing and updated news of local events. A business section provides a good profile of the local economy and the residents of Chichester.

Christchurch Borough Council – Where Time is Pleasant

http://www.christchurch.gov.uk/

Official profile of the Dorset seaside town. Clearly proud of its heritage, the borough council presents a good account of the town's history and includes some photos of local landmarks. Thorough practical details for visitors are provided via a link to a tourist office.

Coventry City Council

http://www.coventry.gov.uk/

Well-organized official guide to Coventry for residents, investors, and visitors. There is comprehensive coverage of local government services, the work of the local council, and local business. There are a large number of links to local institutions and community groups.

Croydon Online

http://www.croydon.gov.uk/

Well-organized and searchable official guide to the outer London borough. The section on local government services and the work of local councillors is very good. This site also includes a history of the borough, a guide to recreation facilities, a full list of accommodation, and attractions for tourists.

Dartmoor National Park Authority

http://www.dartmoor-npa.gov.uk/

Official guide to the moors and valleys of Dartmoor. There are sections on geology, history, and conservation activities and additional educational materials for those wishing to learn

more. Practical information on accommodation, guided walks, and other attractions in the area is provided for visitors and there are links to other Dartmoor sites.

Deal

http://www.doveruk.com/ddc/deal.htm

Profile of the Kent resort. A history of the town is accompanied by an image of Walmer Castle and details of local attractions.

Dorchester

http://www.dorset-cc.gov.uk/dorch.htm

Description of Dorset's county town. There are details of local attractions in the town made famous by Thomas Hardy as 'Casterbridge'. There are also some images of the town and a good street map.

Dover District Council

http://www.doveruk.com/ddc/

Thorough guide to the work of Dover District Council. Comprehensive, detailed information on local government services and the structure of the local council, outweighs the available information for visitors, though this site does contain some brief practical details.

East Sussex County Council Home Page

http://www.eastsussexcc.gov.uk/

Official information on East Sussex. This site includes descriptions of the main towns, demographic and economic profiles, comprehensive reports on local government

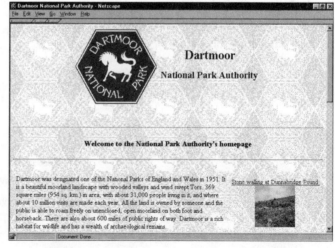

services, and the work of the council. The lack of practical information for visitors (or links to it) is a drawback of this otherwise well-arranged site.

England's Isle of Wight

http://www.isleofwight.gov.uk/

Colourful home page that introduces this thorough guide to the island. Local government services and the workings of local democracy are fully described. The tourism section includes a full listing of attractions and other practical information.

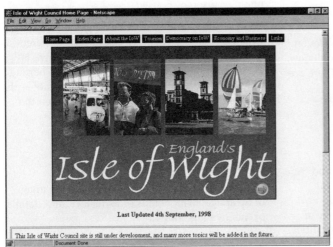

Epsom and Ewell On The Internet

http://www.epsom.townpage.co.uk/

Well-organized unofficial guide to Epsom and Ewell. Contents include local history, local government services, details of community organizations, transport information, and some photos.

Essex County Council Web Site

http://www.essexcc.gov.uk/

Well-arranged and searchable official guide to Essex. Contents include local government services, education, tourism, history, and travel information.

Glosnet

http://www.gloscc.gov.uk/

Official and searchable information about Gloucestershire from the local council. This well-organized site includes a map and description of the county, comprehensive detail of local government services, business life, information

about local community organizations, recreation amenities, and tourist attractions.

Gosport – The Millennium Town

http://www.gosport.gov.uk/

Well-arranged official guide to Gosport. The long history of the town and the naval dockyard is presented with informative text and photographs. There is a full listing of local attractions, government services, and investment opportunities.

Guide to the New Forest

http://www.aard-vark.com/forest/

Automated guide to the flora, fauna, rivers, and walks of the New Forest in Hampshire. In a neat feature, the text and numerous photographs change automatically as you read.

Guildford Borough

http://www.guildfordborough.co.uk/

Official guide to the Surrey borough. This site includes a map, details of amenities and tourist attractions, an alphabetical list of local government services, and an accommodation guide.

Hampshire County Council

http://www.hants.gov.uk/hcc/index.html

Comprehensive and well-presented official guide to the county. There is a full listing of local government functions, the structure of the council, and local community organizations. The section on attractions and amenities has updated information on a wide range of cultural, recreational, and entertainment events. A search engine (called the Hants Ferret) allows access to everything on this large site.

Historical Cornwall

http://www.cranstar.co.uk/History.htm

Collection of pages devoted to Cornwall, its history, culture, and industry. Topics include Cornish saints, Cornish firsts, Cornish folklore, and even Cornish eccentrics.

It's Better in Bournemouth

http://www.bournemouth.gov.uk/

Thorough official information from the local council on business opportunities, convention facilities, and tourist amenities. A search engine facilitates navigation around this well-arranged site.

Lewes District Council

http://www.lewes.gov.uk/

Well-arranged official guide to the Sussex town and the surrounding area. There is a listing of local attractions with some good photographs. There is a full description of local government services, economic opportunities, and accommodation.

Lyme Regis

http://www.dorset-cc.gov.uk/lyme.htm

Information about the port on the Dorset–Devon border. There is a map of the town, an aerial view, and information for visiting yachtsmen. There are also several photos of the town and the surrounding area.

Official Tunbridge Wells Online

http://www.twells.com/twol_new/index.html

Guide to this town for tourists, residents, and businesses. For tourists, there is much useful information on topics such as accommodation, travel, and eating out. There is also a history of the town and details of sport and leisure facilities. For businesses, there is a searchable database of the companies in the area, as well as notes on employment in Tunbridge Wells.

Oxfordshire County Council

http://www.oxfordshire.gov.uk/

Official guide to the central England county. This site contains information on local government services and elections, tourist attractions, towns, parishes, and district councils. There is also a large searchable database of local enterprises.

Portland

http://www.dorset-cc.gov.uk/isleport.htm

Profile of the Dorset island that has provided stone for both St Paul's Cathedral and the UN headquarters. There is information for sailors and an account of lighthouses protecting mariners along the treacherous Portland coast.

Romsey Villages – Romsey

http://www.hants.gov.uk/localpages/south_west/romsey/romsey_town/about.html

Official guide to Romsey and surrounding villages from Hampshire County Council. There is a history of the town, full listing of local attractions, leisure amenities, and events.

Sandwich

http://www.doveruk.com/ddc/sandwich.htm

Profile of the history and attractions of the small Kent port from Dover District Council. Additionally, there is information about the town's golf courses.

States of Jersey

http://www.jersey.gov.uk/

Official information about the largest of the Channel Islands. This well organized site caters for the needs of residents and visitors. There is good coverage of the history and cultural heritage of Jersey. Information for visitors is first-rate with details of local attractions, events, and even the weather.

Swanage

http://www.dorset-cc.gov.uk/swanage.htm

Description of the Dorset town. There are images of Swanage, brief details of its history, and details of the Swanage railway.

Thanet District Council

http://www.thanet.gov.uk/

Comprehensive municipal guide to the Kent district. Council services, business life, training and investment opportunities, and assistance to investors, are extensively described. This site also offers an overview of life in Thanet and information on history, culture, and leisure pursuits.

Tolpuddle

http://www.dorset-cc.gov.uk/tolpudd.htm

Report on the most famous sons of Tolpuddle. This account of the six men who laid the foundations of trade unionism in Britain has a link to the local museum commemorating their endeavours.

Torbay Live!

http://www.torbay.gov.uk/

Official guide to Torbay and the English Riviera. Organized by Torbay Council, the contents include information on the town, its council, and local business. The visitors' guide has a wealth of practical information. Frequently updated with news of events, this site also has a daily weather report for the area.

Virtual Brighton and Hove

http://www.brighton.co.uk/

Searchable guide to the attractions of Brighton. The needs of convention organizers, holiday-makers, day-trippers, shoppers, and students are all catered for. There is also a section on the gay scene in the town. For residents there is comprehensive information on local government services and community organizations.

Virtual Hastings

http://www.astec-comp.co.uk/hastings/

Official guide to the Sussex resort. This site includes good listings of local attractions, schools, places to eat and drink, and an accommodation guide.

Virtual River Thames

http://www.riverthames.org/

Well-designed site that allows you to explore the River Thames. There is a description of virtually every part of the river from Cricklade, Wiltshire, all the way to London, and all the text is accompanied by photographs. The site also includes a 'River Thames calculator', which allows you to find out the distance between any two locks on the river.

Welcome to Colchester

http://www.colchester.gov.uk/

Official guide to Britain's oldest city. A well-organized 'Slide show' introduces the history and culture of Colchester. Local government services, the workings of local democracy, and local sites and amenities are clearly presented.

Welcome to Fareham

http://www.fareham.gov.uk/homepage.htm

Well-organized official guide to the Hampshire town. Drop-down menus on the home page access information on local government services, the workings of local democracy, business, local events, and leisure amenities. There is also a search engine and links to other Hampshire sites.

Welcome to the Ancient Town of Rye

http://www.rye-sussex.co.uk/

Thorough and well-presented official guide to Rye. The needs of tourists, shoppers, and business people are fully catered for. There is an entertaining history of the town, full listing of local accommodation, and frequently updated information on local events.

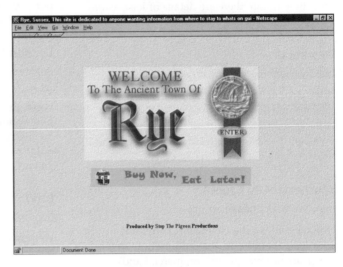

Welcome to the English County of Dorset

http://www.dorset-cc.gov.uk/dorset2.htm

Official guide to Dorset. A multilingual home page leads to a wealth of information on the functions of local government in the county, an interactive map which provides interesting information on several Dorset towns, a diary of local events, and a good guide for business people. Links also provide access to practical information required by visitors.

Welcome to the Plymouth Pages

http://www.plymouth.gov.uk/

Official source of information on the city of Plymouth. In addition to details of services offered by the city's council and businesses, there is a visitor's guide to the city and its attractions. There is also a good history and details of local events.

Welcome to WWW Page of Chelmsford Borough Council

http://www.chelmsfordbc.gov.uk/

Official guide to Chelmsford. This site includes a full description of local government services, plans for economic development, amenities, and cultural events. There is a good general history of the town and the borough.

West Berkshire County Council

http://www.westberks.gov.uk/

This site provides full coverage of local government services and information about councillors for Newbury and the surrounding area. In addition, there are details of leisure and recreation facilities in the area.

Weymouth

http://www.dorset-cc.gov.uk/weyport.htm

Brief account of the Dorset port. It charts the fame which came upon it when George III came to bathe here and its important role in the D-Day invasion. The site includes some images of the town.

Winchester City Council

http://www.winchester.gov.uk/

Official guide to the Hampshire cathedral city. In addition to comprehensive information on local government services and commercial and community organizations, there is a thorough and informative tourist guide. There is a good history, map, suggested walking tour, shopping and accommodation guide, and information on activities of interest to children.

London

Greenwich Council

http://www.greenwich.gov.uk/

Official information about the 'home of time'. This site includes a comprehensive guide to local government services, community groups, local events and amenities. This site is frequently updated with local news.

Havering Council – Information and Services

http://www.lattimore.co.uk/havering/index.html

Comprehensive official guide to this outer London borough. Government services, local business, and community organizations are fully described, together with information on local

amenities, places of interest, and accommodation. There is also a map of Romford.

Lewisham People's Web

http://www.lewisham.gov.uk/

Well-presented official introduction to the inner London borough. There is an interesting local history of the various distinctive areas of the borough. The needs of residents, business people, and visitors are also catered for.

London Borough of Harrow

http://www.harrowlb.demon.co.uk/

Well-arranged official guide to this outer London borough. This site includes a good introductory description of the borough, a full listing of local businesses, details of local government services, a guide to events, and information on local amenities.

London Borough of Hillingdon

http://www.hillingdon.gov.uk/index.pl5

Well-organized guide to this outer London borough. There are full details of local government services, local business, and community groups. The guide to tourism and leisure facilities is comprehensive. There is also a good history of the borough.

LondonNet – The Net Magazine Guide to London

http://www.londonnet.co.uk/

Informative guide to London, suitable for both tourists and residents alike. There are notes on accommodation in London, covering hotels, apartments, and even places for the 'cost conscious'. Other areas covered here include the museums to visit, the best ways to travel, and the pick of the London nightlife. In addition, there are also notes on the places to shop and eat.

Royal Borough of Kingston upon Thames

http://www.kingston.gov.uk/

Comprehensive source of official information on this outer London borough. The workings of local democracy are described in detail. There is an outline of government services, listing of local attractions, services available to tourists, and a good history of the oldest of the four Royal Boroughs of England and Wales.

Royal Parks of London

http://www.open.gov.uk/rp/rphome.htm

Locations and descriptions of London's nine royal parks. The history of each park is briefly described on this Web site, and a list of the amenities available in each park is also provided. There is even an 'active' map showing the locations of the parks: clicking on a name calls up details of that park.

Tyburn Convent

http://www.tyburnconvent.org.uk/

Beautifully-designed site maintained by Tyburn convent in London. Included here are details of the history of the Tyburn gallows, where many Catholic martyrs died. You can also take a virtual tour around the convent as it is today.

Welcome to Brent

http://www2.brent.gov.uk

Well-presented official guide to this London borough. There is a wealth of information on government services, community organizations, local business, and amenities. There are extensive lists to other London sites and a search engine.

Welcome to Hackney Council Online

http://www.hackney.gov.uk/

Official information about this inner London borough. In addition to complete details of local government services and the workings of local democracy, there are pictures of sites in Hackney, a listing of local events, and links to further information.

Welcome to the London Borough of Ealing

http://www.ealing.gov.uk/

Good official guide to Ealing. This visitor-friendly municipal site contains a lot of information on the historical and other attractions of the borough, including a tour of pubs, clubs, and discos. There is also a frequently updated guide to local events.

Welcome to the London Borough of Enfield

http://www.enfield.gov.uk/

Well-organized official guide to this outer London borough filled with information for residents and visitors. This site includes local government functions, local amenities, an accommodation guide, advice to young people, business opportunities, and Enfield's links with Europe.

Welcome to the London Borough of Hounslow

http://www.hounslow.gov.uk/

Official guide to this west London borough. There is full information on local government services and the working of the borough council. There are details of local amenities and information on the culture and a long history of the villages that make up the borough.

Welcome to the London Borough of Tower Hamlets

http://www.towerhamlets.gov.uk/

Thorough official guide to this inner London borough. There is a good presentation of local government services and amenities, in addition to information on the difficulties faced by the local economy. The site also provides a history of the borough and photographs of the Tower of London, Canary Wharf, and other attractions.

Welcome to the Royal Borough of Kensington and Chelsea

http://www.rbkc.gov.uk/

Good official guide to this historic inner London borough. Historical information is accompanied by an alphabetic listing of the many famous former local residents commemorated by blue plaques placed outside their homes. The site contains information on the many parks, museums, and cultural centres in the borough. Local government services are described, there is also a business section, and an accommodation guide.

Welcome to Waltham Forest

http://www.lbwf.gov.uk/

Municipal guide to this outer London borough. There is information on the council and local democracy, a socio-economic profile of the population, an outline of education services, and guides to community organizations and employment opportunities. Leisure and cultural amenities in the borough are also described here.

Western England

Bristol City Council

http://www.bristol-city.gov.uk/

Huge official source of information on the city of
Bristol. In addition to details of services offered
by the city's council, there is a comprehensive
visitor's guide to the city and its attractions. There
is a good history, profiles of some prominent
Bristolians, and frequently updated details of
local events.

Hereford City Council

http://www.worcestershire.gov.uk/pages/
hcc/hfd_cit.htm

Official guide to this cathedral city. In addition to
information on local government and community
services, there is a map of Hereford and
information for visitors. There is a good history of
the cathedral and its famous Mappa Mundi as well
as a comprehensive guide to local attractions.

Malvern Hills District Council

http://www.worcestershire.gov.uk/infoweb/mh_dc/
mhdchome.htm

Official guide to the spa town and the Malvern
Hills. There is information on local community
care services and conference facilities. The tourist
guide lists the main attractions to be found in and
around Malvern and has some pictures of the area.

Midlands

Birmingham

http://birmingham.gov.uk/

Full details on the city of Birmingham,
England, for both visitors and residents.
This official, illustrated site contains
sections such as 'Tourism and leisure',
'Education and employment', 'Business'
and 'Birmingham press cuttings'.

Chesterfield

http://www.chesterfieldbc.gov.uk/

Official guide from Chesterfield
Borough Council. There is a good

outline of local government and its services and
business opportunities. The needs of visitors are
less well catered for: the tourism page simply
invites you to write off for an information pack
and there is currently no information on the
town's history.

Derby Tourist Information Web Site

http://www.derby-city-council.gov.uk/

Official guide to Derby. This site includes basic
information about local attractions, restaurants
and accommodation, sports and leisure, travel
information and facilities for the disabled.

HighPeakNet

http://www.highpeaknet.com/

Unofficial guide to Britain's longest-established
national park (putting to shame the official site to
which it is linked). Click on 'OPEAK' on the
home page for a comprehensive guide to the
geology, geography, and history of the Peaks.
There is a host of practical information for visitors
and links to all the tourist sites in the area.

Leicestershire at the Heart of the Shires

http://www.leics.gov.uk/lcc/index.html

Good official source of information for visitors,
residents, and investors in Leicestershire. There
are profiles and photos of the main towns in the
county. Information is also provided on
attractions, accommodation, entertainment, and
recreational amenities.

Lichfield, Staffordshire

http://www.lichfield.gov.uk/

Good official introduction to Lichfield. There is
information about Samuel Johnson's birthplace,

Lichfield Cathedral, and other attractions. A good history has information about Johnson and other prominent Lichfield residents. Local government services and amenities are also described here.

Luton Borough Council

http://www.luton.gov.uk/

Thorough official source of information about the city of Luton in Hertfordshire. A profile of the local community includes a history and details of economic life. Local government services are set out and local events listed.

Shakespeare's Stratford

http://www.stratford.co.uk/

Information about both this English town and one of its more famous inhabitants, William Shakespeare. There are details of local attractions and theatres, as well as a guide to eating out and accommodation in the town. The section of Shakespeare covers his life and times and also notes on 'performing Shakespeare', focusing on the work of the Royal Shakespeare Company and the Shakespeare Institute.

Stafford Borough Council

http://www.staffordbc.gov.uk/

Guide to the central English city and surrounding area. There is information on council services, commercial and business opportunities, and events.

Virtual Nottingham

http://www.ukcity.com/nottingham/

Complete guide to Nottingham for both visitors and residents alike. This site contains information about accommodation, eating out, and entertainment in the city of Nottingham. The site also features details of the many businesses in Nottingham, broken down into categories such as banks, solicitors, and builders.

Virtual Wolverhampton

http://wolverhampton.broadnet.co.uk/

Provides not only a virtual tour of this English town, but also a large amount of information for both residents and tourists. For the tourist, there

are notes on the various ways of getting to Wolverhampton, as well as on the places to stay during your visit. There are a number of maps, which allow you to pinpoint the places of interest mentioned throughout the site. For both residents and visitors there are details of entertainment and leisure facilities and local sporting events.

Walsall Metropolitan Borough Council

http://www.walsall.gov.uk/

Well-presented municipal guide to the Midlands city. There is information on local government services, the local council, business life, markets, cultural events, and leisure services. Through an interactive map, you can access information on the history of various communities in the borough.

Warrington Borough Council

http://www.warrington.gov.uk/town_home.htm

Official municipal guide to the north western English city. There is a history of Warrington, an outline of its industry, commerce, and council services, and information on transport, local amenities, and shopping. There are useful maps and a number of photographs of the city and its attractions.

Welcome to Dudley Metropolitan Borough

http://www.dudley.gov.uk/

Good official guide to Dudley. The borough is well-described with sections on the local economy, environment, population statistics, history, and geology. There is a thorough outline of local government services and the structure of the council. There is a good set of links to other public services in the region and information on local business opportunities.

Welcome to Worcestershire

http://www.worcestershire.gov.uk

Official guide to the county. The long history of the county is traced, there is a description of local cultural attractions, information on waterways and renting canal boats, and links to further sources of information for both visitors and residents.

Northern Ireland

City of Derry

http://www.interknowledge.com/northern-ireland/ukider00.htm

Official Web site of the Northern Ireland tourist office on the city of Derry. The Web site briefly describes the history and major attractions of the city; photographs of several of these attractions are included on the page. The surrounding area is also described on this Web site, including the Sperrin Mountains and County Londonderry.

County Antrim

http://www.interknowledge.com/northern-ireland/ukiant00.htm

Official Web site of the Northern Ireland tourist office on County Antrim. The Web site describes the history and major attractions of this Northern Irish county; photographs of several of these attractions are illustrated on this page.

County Armagh

http://www.interknowledge.com/northern-ireland/ukiarm00.htm

Official Web site of the Northern Ireland tourist office on County Armagh. The Web site briefly describes the history and major attractions of the county, and photographs of several of these attractions are included on the page.

> **F A C T**
>
> **ARMAGH (Irish *Ard Mhacha* 'the height of Mhacha', a legendary queen)**
>
> smallest county of Northern Ireland; flat in the north, with many bogs and mounds formed from glacial deposits; low hills in the south, the highest of which is Slieve Gullion (577 m/1,893 ft); principal rivers are the Bann, the Blackwater and its tributary, the Callan. The county town is Armagh.

County Down

http://www.interknowledge.com/northern-ireland/ukidwn00.htm

Official Web site of the Northern Ireland tourist office on County Down. The Web site briefly describes the history and major attractions of the county, and photographs of several of these attractions are included on the page. The Web site also features further pages of information on the county, such as descriptions of St Patrick's Grave and the Mountains of Mourne.

County Tyrone

http://www.interknowledge.com/northern-ireland/ukityr00.htm

Official Web site of the Northern Ireland tourist office on County Tyrone. The Web site briefly describes the history and major attractions of the county, and photographs of several of these attractions are included on the page.

Down District Council

http://www.downdc.gov.uk/

Official guide to County Down. Services provided by local government, the functioning of local democracy, and business opportunities are well described. There is a list of tourist attractions in the county and a brief history. However, visitors will look here in vain for a great deal of practical information.

Fermanagh District Council

http://www.fermanagh.gov.uk/

Official guide to the county. A useful and expandable map is offered on the home page. There are also some details of Fermanagh's history, amenities, local government functions, and business opportunities.

Northern Ireland Assembly

http://www.ni-assembly.gov.uk/index.htm

Information about the Assembly, its publications and committees, and a 'Register of members' interests'.

Northern Ireland Tourist Board

http://www.ni-tourism.com/index.asp

This site covers the needs of anyone planning to visit Northern Ireland, from accommodation to events and attractions. It also features a virtual tour covering history, activities, food and drink, and places to stay.

Scotland

Argyll and Bute Council

http://www.argyll-bute.gov.uk/

Official guide to Argyll and Bute. In addition to full information on the services of the local council, there are details of accommodation for visitors, and a 'What's on' guide to local events. There is also a good bibliography of publications concerning Argyll and Bute.

Comhairle nan Eilean Siar

http://www.w-isles.gov.uk/

Well-presented bilingual guide to the isolated islands of the Outer Hebrides. In addition to information on government services, there are interesting sections on the local environment, climate, the Gaelic language, transport, and the future of crofting. There is also a useful series of links.

Dundee City Council

http://www.dundeecity.gov.uk/

Official and searchable guide to Dundee. The home page clearly sets out details of the site's material on local government services, business opportunities, and education. Information on the city, its history and facilities has to be accessed by clicking on 'Dundee City of Discovery'.

Edinburgh

http://www.city.net/countries/united_kingdom/scotland/edinburgh/

Comprehensive guide to the Scottish capital, updated daily and including information on accommodation, food and drink, parks and gardens, and shopping.

Falkirk Online

http://www.falkirk.net/

Well-organized and searchable official source of information on Falkirk and the surrounding area. There are sections on local government services, business, local events, tourism, history, sport and leisure, and community organizations.

Gathering of the Clans Home Page

http://www.tartans.com/

Online guide to all Scottish clans with a searchable database of surnames and their related clans, as well as images and information about each one. There are also extensive pages on other aspects of Scottish culture, including music, literature, and history.

Glasgow

http://www.city.net/countries/united_kingdom/scotland/glasgow/

Concise guide to the city – for visitors and residents alike, including information on accommodation, museums, food, and entertainment.

Online Guide to Orkney

http://www.orknet.co.uk/tourism/ork_map.htm

Well-illustrated and informative trip around the numerous islands that make up the Orkneys, off the north coast of Scotland. There are a wide selection of pictures and details of historical sites in the area.

Places of Interest in Harris

http://www.witb.co.uk/islands/places_harris.htm

Good introduction to the second-largest island of Scotland's Outer Hebrides. There is well-presented information on the history, culture, and attractions of Harris. The site also includes a series of photographs and suggestions for hill walks in the local area.

Places of Interest in Lewis

http://www.witb.co.uk/islands/places_lewis.htm

Good introduction to the largest island of Scotland's Outer Hebrides. An interactive map leads to well-presented information on the history, culture, and attractions of all parts of the island. This site also includes a series of photographs.

Uists, Benbecula, and Barra

http://www.witb.co.uk/islands/isl_uis.htm

Good introduction to the smallest of the islands of the Outer Hebrides. There is well-presented information on archaeology, history, wildlife, birdwatching, and other local attractions. There is also a series of good photographs.

Virtual Hebrides – Trusadh nan Eilean

http://www.hebrides.com/

Huge source of information on all aspects of life in the isolated islands of northwest Scotland. The site has a wealth of public and community information in a region where distance and lack of transport has made the Internet an important source of communication. There is accommodation information, photographs, audio and video clips of Gaelic music, maps, and island and clan histories.

Welcome to Angus

http://www.angus.gov.uk/

Comprehensive source of information on Angus. Prepared by the local authority, this site includes information on local government services, businesses, and a history of the region. Visitors are well provided for, with links to a large number of local attractions.

Welcome to the City of Aberdeen

http://www.efr.hw.ac.uk/Aberdeen/

Information about Aberdeen prepared by the city's council. There are sections on Aberdeen's history, economy, and the oil industry. However, there isn't very much in the way of practical information for visitors.

Welcome to West Dunbartonshire Council's Web Site

http://www.west-dunbarton.gov.uk/

Official Web site of the recently-created Scottish unitary authority. There is information on council services, amenities, natural history, and cultural heritage of the area. There is a guide to local business life, and investment and employment opportunities, as well as a map of West Dunbartonshire and other new Scottish authorities.

Wales

Cardiff, Capital City of Wales

http://www.cardiff.gov.uk/

Official guide to the Welsh capital. Local government functions are fully explained and investment opportunities outlined. There are many photos of the city and a listing of local amenities and historic sites.

Carmarthenshire County Council – Croeso – Welcome

http://www.carmarthenshire.gov.uk/

Official guide to the county. There is information on local government services, activities to promote the Welsh language, and associations with the European Union. The tourist information section is comprehensive, with a complete listing of accommodation, tourist attractions, and local amenities.

Croeso I Gyngor Gwynedd

http://www.gwynedd.gov.uk/

Official guide to the Welsh authority. Primarily of interest to residents, it contains a comprehensive listing of local government functions, the workings of local democracy, and local recreation amenities.

Llanfair P G

http://www.nwi.co.uk/llanfair/index.htm

Site about the village with the longest name in Britain, including a history that dates back to the Neolithic period, an audio clip of how to say it properly, along with a tutorial on its pronunciation, and a tourist guide to the surrounding area.

Pembrokeshire Coast National Park

http://www.pembrokeshirecoast.org.uk/

Official guide to Britain's only coastal national park. The shimmering sunset of a stunning home page leads to information on the coastline, beaches, and the area's Celtic and Norman heritage. All information required by visitors and schoolchildren studying the area is provided. There is also updated news of local events and reports from the park authority.

Welcome to the Caerphilly County Borough Web site

http://www.caerphilly.gov.uk/

Good official guide to the town and borough. This site includes local government services, local business, and a history of the area. A clickable map allows access to information on a large number of villages. There are full details of the amenities and tourist attractions in the area, together with a useful note on Welsh place names.

Austria

Burgenland

http://www.tourist-net.co.at/burgl1e.htm

Enthusiastic promotion of the attractions of the Austrian state. The leisure opportunities, hospitality, folk heritage, cuisine, and wine of Burgenland are described. There is an outline of the history and a description of the character of Burgenlanders.

City of Graz

http://www.gcongress.com/graz.htm

Informative guide to Austria's second city. An aerial photo on the home page leads to comprehensive information on history, museums, business, and the city's universities. There is also practical information on hotels, restaurants, and transport.

City of Salzburg – The Stage of the World

http://www.salzburginfo.or.at/desk/frame_trailer.htm

Helpful guide to the Austrian city. There is information on hotels, restaurants, museums, galleries, and other attractions, as well as cultural events. The site also has a number of good photographs.

Innsbruck, Austria

http://cityguide.lycos.com/europe/austriahungary/
AUTInnsbruck.html

Guide to the Tirolean capital. There is a good description of this city and its attractions. There are also links to a number of local institutions and the media.

Kitzbühel, Austria

http://www.ski-europe.com/factsheets/
kitzbuhel.html

Comprehensive guide to the world-renowned ski resort. There is information on all the facilities and ski runs of the Tirolean resort. There is also a map of the town and a regularly updated report on current ski conditions.

Servus in Linz

http://tourist.linz.at/index_e.htm

Guide to the Upper Austrian capital. The industrial and trading basis of the city's

prosperity is described. A well-presented tour of the attractions of the old city has a large number of photographs and well-written text. There is practical information for visitors on accommodation, local attractions, and Danube River cruises.

Vienna

http://www.info-austria.net

Guide to Vienna. Aimed at the tourist, this site details what to do before you go, and what to do when you get there. History, geography, and travel information, as well as features on festivals, make up the majority of the remaining information on this site, but there are also details of local transport and a list of useful telephone numbers.

Benelux Countries

Amsterdam Channel Home Page

http://www.channels.nl/adam.html

Provides an innovative 'tour' of Amsterdam through a wealth of images of the city – select the direction you wish to follow next and a view of that area is called up. There are links to details of some sites and a street map is also available.

Directorate IJsselmeer Region

http://www.waterland.net/rdij/indexen.html

Well-presented official information from the Dutch Ministry of Works on 'the wet heart of the Netherlands'. There is a good history of the IJsselmeer polders and the scheme to tame the Zuider Zee. The operation of the complex water management scheme is fully explained. Several environmental aspects of the scheme are also covered.

Finding Out Everything About Charleroi

http://www.charleroi.be/edecou_1.htm

Well-arranged guide to this Belgian city. Charleroi, its inhabitants, their culture, and heritage are interestingly described with the help of photos. There are also maps and information about walks, museums, and events in Wallonia.

Ghent Digital City

http://people.orbitone.com/olivier/ghent/

The site provides a digital tour of the Belgian city. You can take a walk through the city and view the historic landmarks, as well as reading about local hotels and restaurants.

Leiden

http://www.visitholland.com/cities/more/leiden/main.html

Good introduction to this Dutch city. A description of Leiden provides details of museums, churches, educational institutions, and other attractions. For visitors there is practical information on eating, accommodation, and transport. This site also includes suggestions on places to visit in the vicinity of Leiden.

Mechelen

http://trabel.com/mechhistory.htm

Good source of information on this Belgian industrial city. There is a good summary of the city's history and a guide to its historic buildings and other attractions.

Province of Vlams Brabant

http://www.vl-brabant.be/website/

Good official guide to the Belgian province of Brabant. There are well presented data on demography and the economy. Other sections include details of the provincial administration, profiles of Leuven and other towns, and comprehensive tourist information on attractions, cuisine, and accommodation. There are also a number of photographs.

'S-Hertogenbosch

http://stuwww.kub.nl/~s339881/sbos.html

Enthusiastic guide to this Dutch city from a proud resident. There are photos, statistics, a history of Den Bosch, information on historic buildings, and a guide to the best bars. There are also links to a large number of other Den Bosch sites.

Staad Brugge

http://www.brugge.be/toerisme/en/index.htm

Well-arranged and fast-loading source of information on this Belgian city. A virtual walk through Bruges describes many buildings and the city's heritage, with the help of photographs. For actual visitors, there is practical information that includes details of local transport, opening hours of attractions, accommodation, and car parking.

Things to see in Brussels

http://pespmc1.vub.ac.be/BRUSSEL.html

Guide to places of interest to visit in this city, from medieval houses to futuristic buildings, provided by the Free University of Brussels.

Tourist Office for Flanders

http://www.toervl.be/en/intra_0_en.shtml

Good official source of information on the history, geography, and culture of the Dutch-speaking region of Belgium. There are sections on gastronomy, accommodation, attractions, festivals and celebrations, in addition to profiles of the main cities and towns of Flanders.

Tournai

http://www.tournai.be/

Good source of official information on the Belgian city. There is a summary of its long history and descriptions of local traditions, cuisine, churches, museums, and other places of interest.

Utrecht, Netherlands

http://cityguide.lycos.com/europe/northwest/NLDUtrecht.html

Good source of information on this Dutch city. There is coverage of history, culture, accommodation, and transportation. Links provide access to further tourist information, educational institutions, local media, and a weather report.

Welcome to the Province of Flevoland

http://www.flevoland.nl/uk/info/index.html

Good official introduction to the northern Dutch province created from land reclaimed as a result of the massive Zuider Zee project. There is a history of the province, economic profile, outline of government services, and contact addresses for the provincial government and other institutions.

Eastern Europe

Bucharest Online – Your Complete Guide to the Capital of Romania

http://bucharest.com/bol/

Well-presented guide to the Romanian capital. Descriptions of the city and its history are accompanied by photographs. There is also transport and commercial information. This site also includes a search engine.

Budapest: A Little Tour

http://www.fsz.bme.hu/hungary/budapest/budapest.html

Comprehensive guide to the city, including its history, detailed information on places of interest, transport, and entertainment. The site contains a gallery of maps and pictures, and some audio clips of Hungarian music.

Buryatia

http://www.buryatia.ru/index_e.html

Illustrated page devoted to the Republic of Buryatia. A general introduction is followed by links to its coat of arms, history, natural environment, culture, education, science, and economy.

Celebrating 17 Centuries of the City of Split

http://www.st.carnet.hr/split/

Good source of information on this Croatian port. There are many photos of the city and descriptions of Diocletian's palace and other noted buildings. This site was prepared to mark the 1,700th anniversary of the founding of the city.

Chelyabinsk – Capital of the Southern Ural

http://www.chelyabinsk.ru/eng/

Guide to the Russian industrial city. There is information on business, arts and entertainment, events, science and education, and local government. In addition the site includes maps, tourist advice, and links to local media.

Chişinău, Moldova

http://cityguide.lycos.com/europe/blacksea/MDAChisinau.html

Good introduction to the Moldovan capital. There is a description of the city, its economy, and history. Among the useful links are those to the Moldovan government site and one describing the revival of the Jewish community in Chişinău.

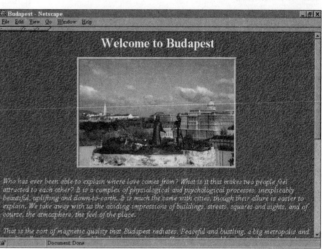

Cluj-Napoca

http://cityguide.lycos.com/europe/blacksea/ROMCluj-Napoca.html

Good guide to the Transylvanian capital. There is a description and history of the city in addition to information on museums, accommodation, and entertainment. There are a large number of pictures and useful links to other sources of information.

Cracow

http://www.kraków.pl/WK/EN/index.html

Official guide to the Polish World Heritage city. There are sections on the government structure, local economy, cultural life, and local attractions. There is practical information for visitors.

Debrecen

http://www.lib.klte.hu/debrecen/index.english.html

Well-organized guide to Hungary's second-largest city. A guided tour, with good photographs, highlights the historical, literary and cultural heritage of Debrecen. There is also a map and transport information.

Exploring Moscow

http://www.interknowledge.com/russia/
moscow01.htm

Walk about Moscow with stops at the Kremlin, Red Square, Lenin's Mausoleum, St Basil's cathedral, old Moscow, and other highlights of the Russian capital. The site also offers separate sections on fine art and theatrical life in the city, a calendar of events, and advice on accommodation.

Györ

http://www.arrabonet.gyor.hu/gyor/index-eng.html

Good guide to the Hungarian city. A guided tour of the town is accompanied by a series of photographs. There is a description of the sensitive and extensive post-1945 restoration of the city centre.

In Your Pocket Home Page

http://www.inyourpocket.com/

Root page of a handy and interactive site providing everything you could ever want to know about several Eastern European and Baltic cities. The electronic form of a previously published guide book, the site includes sections on such topics as language, media, what to see, getting there, where to stay, what to buy, transportation, entertainment, and sports.

Kalingrad in Your Pocket Home Page

http://www.inyourpocket.com/Kaliningrad/
index.htm

Guide to everything you ever wanted to know about this Russian exclave. This is an electronic form of a published guide book and includes sections on such topics as language, media, what to see, getting there, and where to stay.

Karelia

http://www.karelia.ru/start_e.html

Well-presented guide to Russia's Karelian Republic. The site provides good outline of Karelian history and culture and many photographs of the region. There is also practical information for visitors to both Finnish and Russian Karelia.

Kaunas in Your Pocket Home Page

http://www.inyourpocket.com/Lithuania/Kaunas_in
dex.htm

Guide to everything you ever wanted to know

about Lithuania's second city. This is the electronic version of a published guide book and includes sections on such topics as language, media, what to see, getting there, and where to stay.

Kiev, Ukraine

http://cityguide.lycos.com/europe/blacksea/
UKRKiev.html

Large source of information on the Ukrainian capital. There are descriptions of the city, its history, attractions, entertainment, and cultural events. There are also links to a number of sources of information on Ukraine.

Klaipeda in Your Pocket Home Page

http://www.inyourpocket.com/Lithuania/
Klaipeda_index.htm

Everything you ever wanted to know about this Lithuanian city, from the electronic version of a published guidebook and includes sections on such topics as language, media, what to see, getting there, and where to stay.

Ljubljana

http://www.ijs.si/slo/ljubljana/

Well-presented guide to the Slovenian capital. A clickable map highlights points of interest in the city. There is history and a large number of photographs in addition to practical information for visitors.

Minsk in Your Pocket Home Page

http://www.inyourpocket.com/Belarus/
Minsk_index.htm

Guide to everything you ever wanted to know about this Belarusian capital city. This is the electronic version of a published guide book and includes sections on such topics as language, media, what to see, getting there, and where to stay.

Natural World Heritage Properties – Lake Baikal

http://www.wcmc.org.uk/protected_areas/data/wh/
baikal.htm

Good source of information on the world's deepest lake. There are descriptions of physical features, conservation activities, climate, flora and fauna, cultural heritage, and facilities for visitors. Scientific research and constraints on environmental management are well summarized.

Nyíregyháza

http://www.bgytf.hu/nyiregy/docs/nyiregy.html

Well-presented official guide to the Hungarian city. A welcome from the mayor leads to information on the history, economy, and attractions of Nyíregyháza. There is also a series of photographs of the highlights.

Odessa Web

http://www.odessit.com/tours/tours/english/overview.htm

Guide to this Ukrainian seaport. Dealing with Odessa's past and present, this site has sections on the history and cultural traditions and also the night life. There are also a number of photographs of notable buildings.

Prague Info at SunSITE – Czech Republic

http://sunsite.ms.mff.cuni.cz/prague/

Guide to the city of Prague. This ancient European city is one of the most beautiful in the world, but to look at the front end of this Web site you'd never guess that. It clearly falls into the high on content, low on style category, but if plain straightforward information is what you're after then this is the place to visit. Including all the usual tourist information on hotels, restaurants and travel, the Web site also gives information on local transport fares, the history of Prague and the Czech Republic, and everyday life in the city.

Riga in Your Pocket Home Page

http://www.inyourpocket.com/Latvia/Riga_index.htm

Guide to everything you ever wanted to know about this Baltic capital city. This is an electronic form of a published guide book and includes sections on such topics as language, media, what to see, getting there, and where to stay.

Romania & Constitutional Monarchy

http://www.geocities.com/CapitolHill/Lobby/8957/

Historical information, facts, and stories about Romania. The history of the Romanian Monarchy and, in particular, His Majesty, King Michael I, are described here. The Web site features interviews with the king and many photographs of members of the Romanian royal family.

Russian Backcountry

http://www.glasnet.ru/glasweb/asebrant/test3.html

Personal eulogy by a native of Russia's beautiful countryside. There are plenty of images and introductions to the major sites on this page, including Lake Baikal and the Altai mountain system.

Russia Phototrack

http://www.cs.toronto.edu/~mes/russia/photo.html

Impressive image gallery from, and illustrated narratives about, Russia. The pictures are divided by regions and focus on people's everyday lives, hopes, and fears, as well as landscapes and astonishing monuments.

Saint Petersburg, Russia

http://www.geocities.com/TheTropics/Shores/6751/

Introduction to the city of St Petersburg, including a walking tour and a map, a guide to the city's museums, a history, and a regularly updated 'What's new' section.

Skopje, Republic of Macedonia

http://www.skopje.com.mk/english/index.html

Guide to the Macedonian capital. The economic basis, cultural life, and academic institutions of Skopje are described prior to a summary of the city's long history. There are also a number of photographs.

Szczecin Information Service

http://www.szczecin.pl/szczecin.eng.html

Front page for a number of sites describing various aspects of this Polish city. The topics covered include the history of the city, the local economy, tourist information, and details of the local universities. Some sections of the site are awaiting translation from Polish, but there is quite a lot of information here in English.

Tallinn in Your Pocket Home Page

http://www.inyourpocket.com/Estonia/Tallinn_index.htm

Everything you ever wanted to know about the Estonian capital. This is an electronic form of a published guide book and includes sections on such topics as language, media, what to see, getting there, and where to stay.

Tatarstan on the Internet

http://www.kcn.ru/tat_en/index.htm

Page devoted to Tatarstan, an autonomous republic within the Russian Federation. Click on the links to find out about its politics, economics, history, culture, science, education, and religion. The site also provides information about its capital Kazan.

Tbilisi – The Warm Heart of Georgia

http://www.parliament.ge/~nino/tbilis/tbilisi.html

Good introduction to the Georgian capital. The history and cultural traditions of the city are presented with the help of good photographs. This site also contains information on cultural and educational institutions in the city.

Timişoara Home Page

http://www.webcom.com/~timis/timisoara/timisoara.html

Good guide to the western Romanian city. A detailed history concludes with the city's role in the overthrow of the Ceausescu regime. Information on the city's architecture is complemented by good photos. The multicultural harmony of this ethnically diverse city close to Serbia is also highlighted.

Tirana

http://www.albania.co.uk/cityguide/tirana.html

Good introduction to the Albanian capital. There are descriptions of the city, its history, public buildings, and cultural and artistic institutions. There are a number of photographs to accompany the descriptions.

Ulan-Ude, Buryatia

http://www.travel2russia.com/city11.htm

Detailed chronology of major events in the history of the Ulan-Ude, capital of the Buryat Republic, from 1666 when Cossack troops camped at the River Uda up to 1996, the 300th anniversary of the city's foundation.

Vilnius in Your Pocket Home Page

http://www.inyourpocket.com/Lithuania/Vilnius_index.htm

Guide to the capital city of Lithuania. This is an electronic form of a published guide book and includes sections on such topics as language, media, what to see, getting there, and where to stay.

Virtual Livonia

http://www.goodnet.com/~vanags/livonia.html

Latvian site dedicated to the preservation of the Livonian language and culture. There is information and maps about the wider historical region of Livonia and the northwestern part of Latvia where the language is on the verge of extinction. The site also includes a bibliography of resources on Livonian language and culture.

Welcome to Lviv

http://www.lviv.ua/

Large source of information on this western Ukrainian city. Nationalist pride is apparent in the guide to the attractions of this most Ukrainian of the cities of the Ukraine. The site includes practical information on transportation, museums, restaurants, shopping, and accommodation.

Welcome to Plovdiv!

http://www.plovdiv.org/

Guide to the second-largest Bulgarian city. A good history of the city and guide to its attractions are illustrated with photographs. There is also information on famous residents, as well as cultural and commercial events.

Welcome to Sofia

http://www.sofia.com:8080/realindex.html

Large source of information on past and present life in the Bulgarian capital. The contents include shopping, sightseeing, a good history, a guide to cultural events, accommodation, restaurants, media, and sports. There is also a map and many photographs of the city.

Welcome to the City of Kharkov

http://home.vicnet.net.au/~ruscom/other/cities/kharkov/

Profile of the Ukrainian city from a proud Kharkovite. There is a good illustrated history of Kharkov and there is a link to a bilingual Russian-English site for exchange of information about the city and its residents.

Welcome to Toruń

http://www.man.torun.pl/

Guide to the home town of Copernicus. There is a history of the ancient city, an introduction to the economy and government of modern Toruń, a listing of events, a guided walk through the old city, and many photographs of this city, classified as a World Heritage site.

Welcome to Warsaw

http://www.ovpm.org/ovpm/sites/avarso.html

General guide to the city of Warsaw, its university, its weather, and additional information about other sights and attractions in Poland.

Welcome to Zagreb

http://www.tel.fer.hr/hrvatska/HRgradovi/Zagreb/Zagreb.html

Guide to the Croatian capital that includes a description and outline of Zagreb's history. This site also includes maps, photos, a webcam trained on the city centre, and a restaurant guide.

WWW Irkutsk

http://www.icc.ru/fed/title_eng.html

Proudly-presented and well-arranged guide to this Siberian city. Irkutsk's history, cultural heritage, economy, and the artistic and scientific achievements of its inhabitants are set out. There is also a wealth of practical information for visitors and investors and a number of useful links.

France

Ajaccio

http://www.internetcom.fr/corsica/uk/regAjac/Ajaccio/

Opening with an evocation of the history and conquest of Ajaccio, here is a pictorial guide to Corsica's capital and its two harbours. The site also includes details of the city's museums, including the Bonaparte House; festivals, excursions and sports; and links to the other highlights of the Corsican region.

Amiens Cathedral

http://www.arch.columbia.edu/DDL/projects/amiens/

Virtual tour of Amiens Cathedral with video clips, images, music, and architectural details. The next best thing to being there! Users with slow links should be aware that the site is heavily illustrated so may be slow to load.

Avignon

http://www.avignon-et-provence.com/avi/gb/pres/p1.htm

Guide to the French 'city of the popes'. There is a detailed history of Avignon and profiles of its most famous inhabitants. The site also includes information on hotels, entertainment, museums, and cultural events.

Bordeaux, France

http://cityguide.lycos.com/europe/france/FRABordeaux.html

Large source of information on the capital of Aquitaine. There is a good description of the city and the wine trade. The site offers guides to local attractions, bars, restaurants, hotels, a weather report, and links to local media.

Bretagne – History and Tradition

http://www.bretagne.com/english/doc/firsthis.htm

Huge source of information on the history, culture, and heritage of Brittany. There is a history of the region from Neolithic times to the modern day. In addition, this site has information on Brittany's maritime heritage and profiles of famous Bretons.

Burgundy – Land of Great Art and Good Living

http://www.crt-bourgogne.fr/anglais/

Good official guide to the French region. There is information on regional history and culture and Burgundy's renowned food and wines. There is also comprehensive information on accommodation.

Cannes Pages

http://www.micronet.fr/~fgarreau/

Good guide to France's playground of the rich and famous. A Picasso sketch of the Bay of Cannes on the home page leads to detailed information on cultural events, entertainment, accommodation, restaurants, and transport.

Discovering Lyon

http://www.ec-lyon.fr/tourisme/Lyon/index.html.en

Well-arranged guide to France's third-largest city.

An aerial photograph on the home page leads to comprehensive information on Lyon's many attractions. A guide to Lyonnais cuisine, included on this site, contains several recipes.

Grenoble-Isére

http://www.grenoble-isere.com/sommaire_a.htm

Comprehensive source of information on the French alpine city from the local enterprise board. There is extensive coverage of the research institutes, traditional, and high-tech industries contributing to Grenoble's prosperity. The needs of visitors are also well catered for with information on accommodation, a history, suggested walks, and guides to museums and nearby ski resorts.

Lille, France

http://cityguide.lycos.com/europe/france/
FRALille.html

Good source of information on the history, culture, and amenities of the former capital of Flanders. There is information on the city's underground and Eurostar services through this important rail junction. This site also offers a guide for shoppers and a listing of accommodation.

Marseille

http://www.mairie-marseille.fr/

Official Web site of France's second-largest city. The 2,600-year-old history of the city is proudly presented. There are sections on the arts, business life, local government, and tourism.

Paris Pages

http://www.paris.org/

Essential reference tool for every wanderer around Paris, as it is crammed with information on every aspect of Parisian life. Among its many attractions, the site has features on the culture of the city as well as masses of tourist information.

Rennes, France

http://cityguide.lycos.com/europe/france/
FRARennes.html

Good guide to the ancient capital of Brittany. There is information on the culture, history, educational facilities, and economy of the city.

There is also a guide to accommodation, attractions, and leisure facilities and links to local media.

Rouen, France

http://cityguide.lycos.com/europe/france/
FRARouen.html

Guide to the 'city of a thousand spires'. There is a description of Rouen – its history, culture, and attractions. This site also has a weather forecast for the area and links to the media and other local sources of information.

Strasbourg Online

http://www.strasbourg.com/index.html

Well-presented guide to the seat of the European parliament. There are sections on art, history, culture, business, Alsatian wine and cuisine, and famous residents. This site includes a map of the city, practical information for visitors, and a large number of links to sources of further information in both English and French.

Touring Guide of Provence

http://www.provenceweb.fr/e/provpil.htm

Comprehensive guide to the six départements comprising the region of Provence. There are details of the history and attractions of all the cities in the region. The site also includes maps and information on accommodation and restaurants.

Tours, France

http://cityguide.lycos.com/europe/france/
FRADijon.html

Information on Touraine, the Loire Valley, and the city of Tours. There are details of local attractions, cuisine, education and culture, and accommodation. There are also links to local news providers and information on local events.

Welcome to Aix-en-Provence

http://www-eleves.int-evry.fr/~galland/Aix/Eng/

Guide to Aix-en-Provence, home town of Paul Cézanne, with a chronological history, general information, a clickable map giving a virtual tour of the city, student and travel information, and links to other Provençal sites.

Welcome to Nice French Riviera

http://www.nice-coteazur.org/americain/index.html

Good source of information on France's fifth-largest city from the Nice municipal Web site. It includes sections on local history and culture, the economy, municipal services, museums, and other attractions. There is a map, photographs of the city, and news of events.

Welcome to Normandy

http://normandy-tourism.org/gb/index.html

Guide to the northwestern region of France. The history, culture, economy, climate, and government structure of Normandy are comprehensively presented. There is a series of maps, as well as practical information for tourists, gastronomes and those interested in D-Day.

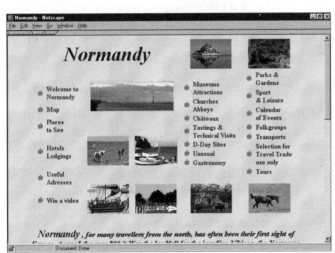

Welcome to Toulouse

http://www.cict.fr/toulouse/EBienvenue.html

Basic history and tour of Toulouse. It includes details of the main monuments and interesting places to visit in the surrounding area, as well as cultural information, leisure facilities, and art galleries in the city itself. This site provides easy-to-follow information, with the main access points to the city clearly indicated and a map with details of the subway. There is also a small section on the economy, education, and research facilities.

Germany

Aachen

http://www-i5.informatik.rwth-aachen.de/mjf/stadt-aachen.html

Guide to Aachen, the German city and spa, its history and culture, with maps and pictures of its cathedral and museums, and links to related sites.

Bavaria Online

http://www.bavaria.com/

Multilingual site on this area of Germany that includes sections on culture, travel, business, entertainment, and shopping. The site is filled with images and short essays on related subjects like architecture and the Oktoberfest.

Berlin

http://userpage.chemie.fu-berlin.de/adressen/berlin.html

City guide to Berlin. Aimed at the tourist, this site details what to do before you go and what to do when you get there. History, geography, and travel information, as well as features on festivals, make up the majority of the remaining information on this site, as well as details of local transport and a list of useful telephone numbers. There are also some images of Berlin, and maps of the city area.

Bonn, Germany

http://cityguide.lycos.com/europe/germany/DEUBonn.html

Guide to the former German capital. There is a description of the city and its history and information about transport, entertainment, and culture. The site also includes links to local educational and cultural sites.

Cologne

http://travel.roughguides.com/content/1969/index.htm

Good source of historical and practical information on Germany's fourth-largest city. The city's main monuments and attractions are described and there is information on accommodation, transport, and entertainment.

Dortmund

http://www.dortmund.de/indexeng.htm

Official information on the German city. It stresses the strategic location and investment opportunities in this Rhine-Westphalian city. However, there is also information on sport, culture, and museums, as well as links to local scientific and academic institutions.

Frankfurt Main

http://city-info.nacamar.de/city/frankfurt/ e_frankfurt.html

Good source of information on German's financial capital. There are sections providing an overview of the city's history, culture, tourist attractions, and economic base. There are also a number of photographs.

Hannover – City of Fairs

http://www.expo.hannover.de/english/start/ tourist.htm

Guide to the history, culture, and attractions of the German city. There are listings of accommodation and restaurants, as well as some useful transport information. A good interactive map of the Hannover region allows access to information on a large number of nearby communities.

Hansestadt Lübeck

http://www.luebeck.de/en/

Comprehensive information on the Hanseatic port, its history, and its heritage. There are details of attractions and local events and there are links to sources of further information.

Internet City Guide Trier

http://www.uni-trier.de/trier/trier_eng.html

Guide to Germany's oldest city. There are sections on history, culture, wine-making, and tourist attractions. This site also includes a number of useful maps.

Lutherstadt Wittenberg

http://www.wittenberg.de/e/

Well-arranged official guide to 'the city of the Reformation' A interesting tour of the city highlights Wittenberg's history, prominent monuments, notable citizens, and musical heritage. There is also information on education, science, business life, investment opportunities, transport system, and leisure opportunities.

Munich

http://www.city.net/countries/germany/munich/

Overview of the city of Munich, including arts and entertainment facilities, news, weather, places of interest to visit, and travel information.

Nuremberg

http://cityguide.lycos.com/europe/germany/ DEUNuremberg.html

Well-illustrated guide to the German city. There is a good tour of the city and its attractions. A history of the town includes dramatic before and after photos of the damage inflicted by bombing during World War II.

Rostock – Hanseatic City and a Lot More

http://www.uni-rostock.de/rostock/e11.htm

Thorough and well-presented guide to the German city. Accompanied by a large number of photographs, there is information on sightseeing attractions, the seaside, history, museums, art galleries, theatres, and transport.

Stuttgart City Guide

http://www.stgt.com/stuttgart/homee.htm

Good guide to the German city. There is a history, map, transport information, weather report, and commercial directory. This site also includes a large number of photographs of historic buildings.

Welcome to Hamburg

http://www.rrz.uni-hamburg.de/Hamburg/ HH_homepage_english.html

Thorough guide to the north German city from Hamburg University. An extensive sightseeing tour explains the attractions of the city with the assistance of photographs. There is detailed information on the local economy, higher education, cultural events, popular entertainment, and transport.

Greece

About Aegina Island

http://www.vacation.net.gr/p/aegina.html

Good source of information on the Greek island. There is a map, and a description and guides to history, beaches, nightlife, and archaeological sites. There are also profiles of the main towns, information on transport services from Piraeus, and some good photographs.

About Delos Island

http://www.vacation.net.gr/p/delos.html

Profile of the small Greek island. The importance of Delos in Greek mythology and history is set out and the archaeological discoveries that have been made here are summarized. A suggested walking tour of Delos is accompanied by good photographs.

About Epirus

http://www.vacation.net.gr/p/epirus.html

Good guide to the mountainous northwestern region of Greece. There is information on the landscape, flora and fauna, and history. The site also includes profiles of the four prefectures in the region and their main towns.

About Ithaca Island

http://www.vacation.net.gr/p/ithaki.html

Guide to the birthplace of Odysseus. There is a map, a description of the island, a historical summary, and information on archaeological and other attractions. The site also offers profiles of the towns of Ithaca and Starves.

About Kefalonia Island

http://www.odysseas.com/kefalon.html

Guide to the largest of Greece's Ionian Islands. There is a map of the island, a description of the landscape, and a guide to beaches. The character of the people is described along with their traditional agricultural way of life. There is also a good history and a tour of Cephalonia supported by photographs.

About Naxos Island

http://www.odysseas.com/naxos.html

Guide to the largest and most fertile of Greece's Cyclades islands. There is a map of the island, an outline of its history, and a guide to beaches, museums, and nightlife. This site also includes a profile of the town of Naxos and a number of photos of the island.

About Patmos Island

http://www.vacation.net.gr/p/patmos.html

Guide to the Greek Dodecanese island. There is a good account of the island's turbulent history. This site also offers a map, a guide to the capital, and suggestions of places to visit.

About Peloponnese – Introduction

http://www.vacation.net.gr/p/pelopon.html

Comprehensive guide to Greece's Peloponnese region. Landscape, history, and attractions are described for all parts of this mountainous peninsula. There is also a map of the region.

About Skyros (Skiros) Island

http://www.vacation.net.gr/p/skiros.html

Good guide to the island of Greece's Sporades. There is a description of local arts and crafts, Byzantine and Venetian monuments, museums, and beaches. This site also includes transport information and suggested excursions.

Corfu, Greece

http://cityguide.lycos.com/europe/greece/GRCCorfuIsland.html

Large source of information on the northernmost of Greece's Ionian Islands. All aspects of the island's history, archaeology, and culture are covered here. There is a map and details of accommodation, places of interest, and local transport.

Crete

http://www.areianet.gr/infoxenios/english/crete/crete.html

Well-presented guide to the largest Greek island. There is information on geography, landscape, history, archaeology and architecture, the character of the people, and local traditions. The site also includes profiles of the leading towns on the island and a number of photographs.

Cultural Map of Hellas

http://www.culture.gr/2/21/maps/hellas.html

'Clickable' map allowing you to browse around contemporary Greece and discover detailed information about the different museums, archaeological sites, and monuments in each region.

Discover Arcadia

http://www.apel.ee.upatras.gr/www/pub/ peloponnese/arcadia.html

Guide to the heritage and attractions of this Greek region. There is a history and a description of the towns and monasteries in the prefecture of Arcadia.

Discover Corinthia

http://www.apel.ee.upatras.gr/www/pub/ peloponnese/corinthia.html

Guide to the Peloponnesian city and its district. There is a description of the landscape and the modern town, in addition to a guide to the ancient site, information on the Corinth canal, a summary of the region's complex history, and guide to places of interest to tourists.

Discover the Town of Patras

http://www.apel.ee.upatras.gr/www/pub/patras/ patras.html

Guide to the largest city of Greece's Peloponnese region. Presented by the local university, there is information about Greece's third-largest city and its cultural heritage. There are guides to places of historical and cultural interest, details of accommodation, and photographs of Patras.

Evia Island

http://www.vacation.net.gr/p/evia1.html

Well-presented guide to Greece's second-largest island. Places of interest ranging from beaches to churches are described. There are also illustrated profiles of Chalcis and other towns on the island.

Ionian Islands

http://www.areianet.gr/infoxenios/english/ionian/ ionian.html

Good introduction to this Greek island group. Profiles of each of the seven main islands describe history, cultural heritage, and places of interest. There is also practical information on accommodation and transport.

Island Of Kos

http://www.helios.gr/dodecanese/kos/

Good source of information on the Dodecanese island. An interactive map of Kos accesses profiles of all parts of the island. There is practical information on transport and accommodation and a good history of the island.

Lemnos

http://www.duth.gr/NEAegean/Lemnos/

Well-presented guide to the Greek island. There is a good map of Lemnos, a geographical description, an account of Lemnos in Greek mythology, a modern history, and a tour of the attractions of the island. There is also a series of photographs to enhance the text.

Lesvos – More Than Just Another Greek Island

http://www.lesvos.com/

Impressive guide to the lush Greek island. There is a wealth of detailed practical information for visitors on everything from local beaches to local businesses. The site also includes a detailed explanation of local mythology and history.

Lesvos: Mytilini (the Capital)

http://www.vacation.net.gr/p/lesvos3.html

Profile of the capital of the Greek island of Lesvos. There is a good atmospheric description of life in Mytilini and information about historic buildings in the town. There are also some good photographs.

Mount Athos

http://www-media.dbnet.ece.ntua.gr/athos/uk/ general/top.htm

Virtual tour of Mount Athos, offering background information on the geography, history, and political status of the community, as well as an extensive photographic gallery covering all 20 monasteries of the Holy Mount.

Rhodes

http://www.areianet.gr/infoxenios/english/ dodecanese/rhodes/rhodes.html

Guide to the largest of Greece's Dodecanese islands. There is a good overall description. Details of the history and attractions of the towns on the island are supported by photographs. There is a wealth of practical information on transport, accommodation, and wining and dining.

Samos

http://cityguide.lycos.com/europe/greece/
GRCSamosIsland.html

Large source of information on the Greek 'island of the blessed'. The history and heritage, as well as the natural and cultural attractions of Samos are presented. There is also practical information on transport and accommodation.

Thessalia (Thessaly)

http://www.vacation.net.gr/p/thesali1.html

Good guide to the fertile central Greek region. The mythological and historical importance of Thessaly is summarized. There are profiles of all the prefectures in the region and their main towns. Places of interest for visitors are also pointed out.

Thessaloniki

http://philippos.mpa.gr/other/thessaloniki/
index.html

Illustrated official guide to Greece's second city that includes sections on the history, monuments, tourism, transportation, shopping, and entertainments which can be found there.

Thrace

http://www.vacation.net.gr/p/thrace.html

Good introduction to the Greek region of Thrace. There are guides to the attractions of the three mainland Thracian prefectures and to the island of Samothrace. There are good photographs, transport information, and a guide to places of interest.

Welcome to Athens

http://agn.hol.gr/hellas/attica/athens.htm

Virtual guide to the city, including maps and lists of places to stay, museums and galleries, and details of regular cultural events.

Zakynthos, Greece

http://www.zante.com/~gkallas/

Guide to the southernmost Ionian island. There are good descriptions of the island's geography, heritage, history, ethnic traditions, and modern attractions. A tour of the island is supported by photographs. There is also

a copy of Edgar Allan Poe's *Sonnet to Zante*, which was written in praise of the island.

Ireland (Eire)

Complete Guide to Galway

http://www.wombat.ie/galwayguide/

Thorough and well-arranged source of information on this western Irish county. The needs of residents, tourists, and investors are fully met with sections on attractions, transport, entertainment, accommodation, things to do with children, community groups, and local government services. In addition to a good summary of Galway's history, there are online versions of several detailed history books of the county.

Connemara, Ireland

http://www.connemara-ireland.com/

Large source of well-presented information on this western Irish region. The site includes information on landscape, history, accommodation, restaurants, tourist attractions, business information, and genealogy. There is also a map and descriptions of a large number of towns.

Cork Guide Online

http://www.cork-guide.ie/corkcity.htm

Good source of information on Ireland's third-largest city. A description of the city, its heritage,

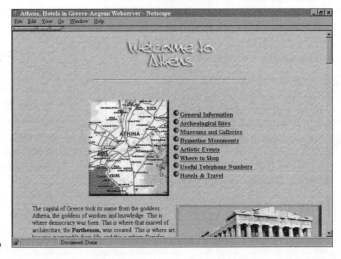

and attractions is accompanied by some fine photographs. There is also information on accommodation, entertainment, transport, and restaurants

County Kildare, Ireland

http://cityguide.lycos.com/uk/ireland/
IRLCountyKildare.html

Large source of information on the Irish county. There are guides to the main towns and attractions in Kildare, a description of the county and its economy, and a map. Information on accommodation and links to local media and institutions are also included.

History of Magh Eó (Mayo Abbey) in County Mayo in the West of Ireland

http://www.mayo-ireland.ie/Mayo/Towns/
MayAbbey/HistMAbb/HistMAbb.htm

History of the abbey from which the county of Mayo in the Republic of Ireland takes its name. The abbey was founded in the 7th century, and this Web site explains the motives for its slightly unusual location in the centre of a plain miles from anywhere. The Web site also features a wealth of historical details about the abbey and the surrounding area from the time of its founding right up to the present day.

Kerry Insight

http://ireland.iol.ie/kerry-insight/

Guide to the Irish county. This site includes sections on fishing, sports, entertainment, accommodation, places of historical interest, events and festivals, an extensive commercial directory, community organizations, guides to towns in the county, maps, and a weather report.

Killarney Online

http://www.killarneyonline.ie/

Good source of information on Killarney and its famous lakes. There is a profile of the city, its history, and economy. This site offers comprehensive information on accommodation, local places of interest, and a wide range of leisure activities.

Limerick Online

http://www.limerickonline.com/

Large source of information on the Irish county. There are descriptions of the county, Limerick, and other towns. Other sections include details of

accommodation, entertainment, a weather report, and an online version of a local newspaper.

Waterford City

http://goireland.miningco.com/library/weekly/
aa092297.htm

Guide to the Irish city. There is a description of the prosperous modern town and an outline of its history. Details are provided about monuments and other sites in the town, together with practical information on food, accommodation, and entertainment.

Waterford, Ireland

http://www.cs.ncl.ac.uk/genuki/irl/Waterford/

Good source of information on the southeastern Irish county. Profiles of the main communities may be accessed through the interactive map on the home page. There is a good description of Waterford's distinctive geology and landscape, and a summary of the county's rich history.

Welcome to County Wicklow – The Garden of Ireland

http://www.wicklow.ie/

Well-arranged guide to this eastern Irish county from the local Enterprise Board. An interesting virtual tour of the county can be accessed via a clickable map. In addition to details of the county's history and heritage, there is a wealth of practical information for both visitors and residents alike.

Italy

Abruzzo

http://www.mi.cnr.it/WOI/deagosti/regions/
abruzzo.html#Pescara

Good overview of Italy's mountainous Abruzzo region. There are sections on geography, landscape, flora and fauna, population, and economy. There is also a regional map, and information for tourists, as well as notes on the main cities.

Amalfi

http://www.starnet.it/italy/amalfi/ingamwel.htm

Introduction to the Italian coastal town. Notable local buildings are described with the support of photographs. There is a history of the town, map of the area, and information on hotels and restaurants in Amalfi.

Assisi

http://listserv.american.edu/catholic/franciscan/ tour/tour.html

Walking tour around the home town of St Francis. There are photos of the churches in the town and information about them. The needs of visitors are met with information about the town, as well as details of transport and accommodation.

Basilicata

http://www.mi.cnr.it/WOI/deagosti/regions/basilict.html

Good overview of the southern Italian region. There are sections on geography, landscape, flora and fauna, population, and economy. The site includes a map and information for tourists, as well as descriptions of the sights and history of the cities of Potenza and Matera.

Be Our Guest in Bergamo

http://www.uninetcom.it/guest/

Good guide to Italy's 'gateway to the Alps'. There is a good history and guide to the old town. The character of the people is lovingly described. The site also has a good map of the city and advice on cuisine, entertainment, and shopping.

Cagliari, Italy

http://cityguide.lycos.com/europe/italy/ITACagliari.html

Source of information on the Sardinian capital. There is a guide to the city's history, monuments, and museums. There is an aerial photograph, other photos of Cagliari, a guide for foreigners wishing to settle in the city, and a link to an online magazine about Sardinia.

Calabria

http://www.mi.cnr.it/WOI/deagosti/regions/calabria.html#Calabria

Well-arranged profile of the region at the tip of the Italian peninsula. There is information on geography, landscape, flora and fauna, population, Calabrian dialects and non-Italian

languages, cultural heritage, and the economy. This site includes a map of Calabria and suggestions for tourists. There are also descriptions of the sights and history of the cities of Catanzaro, Cosenza, and Reggio di Calabria.

Campania

http://www.mi.cnr.it/WOI/deagosti/regions/campania.html#Campania

Good overview of Italy's Campania region. There are sections on geography, landscape, flora and fauna, population, local dialects, and the economy. There is information on the history of Naples, Salerno, and the other main cities, as well as a map, and information for tourists.

City of Bari

http://www.csata.it/Bari_info/Bari_intro_en.html

Guide to the capital of Italy's Puglia region. There is a photo of the city and an outline of Bari's history, culture, climate, and main attractions. There is also a listing of local hotels.

Como Lake

http://www.traveleurope.it/como.htm

Good guide to the Italian resort city and its famous lake. There is information on Como and other lakeside towns, transport on the lake, the island of Comacina, and the regional silk industry. There is also a guide to local cuisine and information on accommodation.

Cosenza

http://www.sirfin.it/aptd/inglese/apt_graf.htm

Well-arranged guide to the Calabrian city. The history and architecture of this city are described alongside good photographs. There is information about accommodation and transport and links to other Cosenza and Calabrian sites in both English and Italian.

Cremona

http://www.traveleurope.it/cremona.htm

Guide to the city in Lombardy. A section on the artisan crafts of Cremona focuses on the continuing importance of violin, viola, and cello manufacture. There is also a list of accommodation.

Discover Vicenza

http://vicenza.org/vicenza/homeus.html

Guide to the Italian World Heritage city. There is an outline of the history of the town, the economy, a description of its sites, and a guide to its gastronomy and wine. Itineraries are suggested for visitors and further sources of information are indicated.

Emilia-Romagna

http://www.mi.cnr.it/WOI/deagosti/regions/emilia.html

Good overview of the prosperous northern Italian region. There is information on geography, landscape, flora and fauna, population, local dialects, and the economy. This site also includes a map and information for tourists, including descriptions of the sights and history of the main cities of the region.

Ferrara and Delta of Po River

http://www.traveleurope.it/ferrara.htm

Profile of the historic Italian city. There is a description of Ferrara, its history, and the nearby Po delta. There are also photos of notable buildings.

Florence and Tuscany

http://es.rice.edu/ES/humsoc/Galileo/Student_Work/Florence96/

Web site run by Rice University on Renaissance Florence and Tuscany. The site includes a tour of Florence, details of Florentine music, the Medici family, Florentine architecture, and details of modern life in the city and region.

Friuli-Venezia Giulia

http://www.mi.cnr.it/WOI/deagosti/regions/friuli.html

Good overview of the northeastern Italian region. There is information on geography, landscape, flora and fauna, population, local dialects, and the economy. This site also includes a map of the

region and information for tourists, including descriptions of the sights and history of the main cities.

History of Sardinia

http://www.crs4.it/~luigi/SARDEGNA/sardegna.html

Illustrated history of Sardinia from prehistoric times to the modern age. There are many pictures of historical artefacts and their locations, as well as explanatory maps of the island.

History of Venice

http://www.doge.it/storia/storiai.htm

From the first inhabitants to the present day, this is a look at the origins and historical development of the Italian city of Venice. It includes numerous pictures and photographs of the city, and a map of the surrounding area.

Lazio

http://www.mi.cnr.it/WOI/deagosti/regions/lazio.html#Lazio

Well-arranged overview of the central Italian region. There is information on geography, landscape, flora and fauna, population, local dialects, architecture, heritage, and the economy. This site includes a map of Lazio and suggestions for tourists. There are also descriptions of the sights and history of Rome and other cities in the region.

Liguria

http://www.mi.cnr.it/WOI/deagosti/regions/liguria.html

Good overview of the northwestern region of Italy. There is information on geography, landscape, flora and fauna, population, local dialects, and the thriving economy. This site also includes a map of Liguria and suggestions of places to visit for tourists.

Living Venice

http://www.webcom.com/~italys/

Short 'virtual tour' through the city, complete with photographs.

Lodi and the Lodigiano

http://www.traveleurope.it/lodi.htm

Guide to the Italian town and its fertile hinterland. There is a good history of the town and guide to local attractions, architecture, and festivals. There are also photos of the historic buildings.

Marche

http://www.mi.cnr.it/WOI/deagosti/regions/
marche.html#Marche

Well-arranged overview of the central Italian region. There are details of the main cities such as Ancona. There is information on geography, landscape, flora and fauna, population, local dialects, architecture, heritage, and the economy. This site includes a map of the Marches and suggestions for tourists. Alongside a map of the whole region, there are descriptions of what makes this region unique.

Milan, Italy

http://www.smau.it/magellano/english/ciaomi99/

Good source of information on Italy's second-largest city. There is extensive coverage of history, attractions, accommodation, culture, entertainment, and commercial services. There are links to the latest financial information, the weather, an entertainment guide, and the trilingual site of the local football team, A C Milan.

Modena

http://www.traveleurope.it/modena.htm

Profile of the Italian city. There is a good description of the medieval heart of the city, as well as a guide to local cuisine, nightlife, entertainment, and hotels.

Molise

http://www.mi.cnr.it/WOI/deagosti/regions/
molise.html#Molise

Well-arranged overview of Italy's most recently created region. There is information on geography, landscape, flora and fauna, population, the Molise dialect, and the economy. This site also includes a map of the region and suggestions for tourists. (There are descriptions of the sights and history of the cities of Campobasso and Isernia.)

Napoli Virtuale

http://www.napolivirtuale.com/english/rubriche.htm

Multimedia guide to Naples, in English, Italian, and German. There is a virtual tour of the attractions of the city, phots and video clips, and details about the various monuments and cuisine available here.

Palermo, Italy

http://cityguide.lycos.com/europe/italy/
ITAPalermo.html

Source of information on the Sicilian capital. The complex history, multicultural influences, customs, and festivals of Palermo are well presented. There is a weather report, links to local media, and information on local entertainment.

Parma, Italy

http://cityguide.lycos.com/europe/italy/
ITAParma.html

Comprehensive source of information on the northern Italian city. There is a good guide to the history, museums, churches, galleries, and other cultural institutions. There is an interactive map, weather report, and links to the local university and media.

Perugia

http://cmtrasimeno.net/en/comuni/perugia/

Guide to the history, culture, and attractions of the Italian borough. All sections are well illustrated, and include 'History', 'Local crafts', 'Environment', 'Food and drink', and 'Exhibitions and events'.

Piemonte

http://www.mi.cnr.it/WOI/deagosti/regions/
piemonte.html#Piemonte

Good profile of the largest region of mainland Italy. There is information on geography, landscape, flora and fauna, population, local dialects, and the thriving economy. This site also includes a map of Piedmont and key places to visit, including descriptions of the sights and history of Turin and the other main cities.

Puglia

http://www.mi.cnr.it/WOI/deagosti/regions/
puglia.html#Puglia

Overview of the region at the heel of Italy. As well as a history of many important places in the area, this site includes a map of the region and information for tourists, as well as descriptions of the sights and histories of the main cities of Puglia.

Rimini, Italy

http://cityguide.lycos.com/europe/italy/
ITARimini.html

Good source of information on the lively Italian resort city. There is a detailed history of the city and neighbouring towns in Romagna. There is also an accommodation guide, weather report, and links to sources of local news.

Rome, Italy

http://www.geocities.com/Athens/Forum/2680/

Huge source of information on 'the eternal city'. An offbeat introduction to the 'home of popes and pickpockets' leads to detailed information on the history, monuments, and modern attractions of the Italian capital. There is a weather report, links to local media, and access to a large number of guides to Rome.

Sardegna

http://www.mi.cnr.it/WOI/deagosti/regions/
sardegna.html#Sardegna

Well-arranged profile of the second-largest Mediterranean island. There is information on geography, landscape, flora and fauna, population, Sardinian dialects, the island's autonomous status, and the economy. This site includes a map of the island and suggestions for tourists. There are also descriptions of the sights and history of Cagliari and other Sardinian cities.

Sicilia

http://www.mi.cnr.it/WOI/deagosti/regions/
sicilia.html#Sicilia

Well-arranged profile of the largest Mediterranean island. There is information on geography, landscape, flora and fauna, population, Sicilian dialects, the island's autonomous status, cultural heritage, and the economy. This site includes a map of the island and suggestions for tourists. There are also descriptions of the sights and history of Palermo, Catania, and other Sicilian cities.

Siena Online

http://www.sienaol.it/

Good guide to the Tuscan city. Siena's long history is well explained and there are a series of good photographs.

Sites of Lombardy

http://www.initaly.com/~initaly/regions/lombardy/
sites.htm

Introduction to the region of Lombardy in northern Italy. Its most attractive features are described, including the cities of Sabbioneta, Mantova, Cremona, Pavia, Milan, Brescia, Bergamo, and Castiglione Olona. Click to the next page to find out about local festivals and fairs, and to the previoius page to read about pilgrimage chapels, markets, wines, and gold clubs.

Stromboli Online

http://educeth.ethz.ch/stromboli/

This very large Web site includes geological and historical information on the Italian volcano, and also includes many multimedia clips including a virtual climb of the volcano, some 3D stereoscopic images, and downloadable video clips. Maps of the area are also included.

Toscana

http://www.mi.cnr.it/WOI/deagosti/regions/
toscana.html#Toscana

Well-arranged overview of Italy's fifth-largest region. There is information on geography, landscape, flora and fauna, population, local dialects, architecture, heritage, and the economy. This site includes a map of Tuscany and suggestions for tourists. The site also includes descriptions of the sights and history of Florence, Pisa, Siena, and other Tuscan cities.

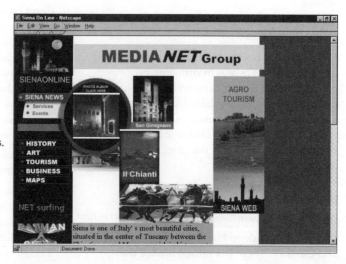

Town of Aosta

http://cityguide.lycos.com/europe/italy/
ITAAosta.html

Good guide to the northern Italian city. There are sections on art, folklore, nature, and opportunities for skiing and hiking. This is on top of extensive coverage of the city's rich history.

Town of Sorrento, Italy

http://italiaonweb.com/sorrento/en/frame.htm

Good guide to the Neapolitan resort town from the Sorrento municipality. There is a history of the town and a guide to its attractions. This site also includes an interactive map of the area, a commercial directory, transport information, and a guide to local government services.

Trentino-Alto Adige

http://www.mi.cnr.it/WOI/deagosti/regions/
trentino.html#Trentino

Well-arranged overview of Italy's most northerly region. There is information on the region's autonomous status, geography, landscape, flora and fauna, population, local Italian, Ladino, and German dialects, and the economy. The site includes a map of Trentino-Alto Adige and suggestions for tourists. There are also descriptions of the sights and history of the cities of Trento and Bolzano.

Trieste, Italy

http://cityguide.lycos.com/europe/italy/
ITATrieste.html

Good guide to the northeastern Italian port. The history and mixed Italo-Slavic culture of the city are well presented. There are a large number of photos and useful information for visitors. This site even includes a weather report and links to sources of local news.

Turin, Italy

http://cityguide.lycos.com/europe/italy/ITATurin.html

Large source of information on the Italian industrial city. The main attractions and history of the city are presented together with practical information required by visitors. There is a weather report, map, and links to local media.

Udine, Italy

http://cityguide.lycos.com/europe/italy/
ITAUdine.html

Thorough source of information on this north Italian city. The history and attractions of Udine and its environs are set out. There is a section on the local cuisine, other practical information for tourists, and a series of useful maps.

Umbria

http://www.mi.cnr.it/WOI/deagosti/regions/
umbria.html#Umbria

Well-arranged overview of the mountainous, landlocked central Italian region. There is information on geography, landscape, flora and fauna, population, local dialects, architecture, heritage, and the economy. This site includes a map of Umbria and suggestions for tourists. There are also descriptions of the sights and history of the cities of Perugia and Terni.

Valle d'Aosta

http://www.mi.cnr.it/WOI/deagosti/regions/
valaosta.html#Valled'Aosta

Well-arranged overview of the region in the extreme northwest of Italy. There is information on geography, landscape, flora and fauna, population, local Italian, French, and German dialects, and the economy. This site includes a map of Valle d'Aosta and suggestions for tourists. There are also descriptions of the sights and history of the city of Aosta.

Veneto

http://www.mi.cnr.it/WOI/deagosti/regions/
veneto.html#Veneto

Well-organized overview of the northeastern Italian region. There is information on geography, landscape, flora and fauna, population, local dialects, architecture, heritage, and the economy. The site includes a map of Venetia and suggestions for tourists, as well as descriptions of the sights and history of Venice, Padua, Verona, and other Venetian cities.

Villa d'Este – Tivoli

http://www.arts.monash.edu.au/visarts/diva/
d'este.html

Photographic shots of the famous Villa d'Este in Tivoli, just outside Rome, one of the most typical examples of Renaissance garden architecture and design. All photographs are presented in thumbnail form; click on the ones you want to download at full size.

Welcome to the City of Bologna

http://www.comune.bologna.it/TouringBologna/

Official guide to this north Italian city. Bologna's history and cultural achievements are well-presented. Guides to the university, cathedral, palaces, and parks are informative and supported by good photographs. There are also links to other sources of online information.

Welcome to the City of Treviso

http://www.traveleurope.net/treviso.htm

Well-arranged guide to this north Italian city. There is a good history of the city and information about restaurants, accommodation, and attractions in Treviso and nearby towns. There are also maps and a number of photos.

Portugal

Coimbra, Portugal

http://cityguide.lycos.com/europe/portugal/
PRTCoimbra.html

Guide to the history, culture, and attractions of the former Portuguese capital. Practical information on accommodation, restaurants, transport, and attractions is presented here. There are links to the city's famous university and to local media, as well as a section on Coimbra's celebrated Fado music.

Lisbon

http://www.EUnet.pt/Lisboa/i/lisboa.html

Bilingual site with information about the 'city of the seven hills' including its history, a town map, and information on museums, restaurants, bars, and hotels. It also includes plenty of pictures and some audio clips from Portuguese artists.

Madeira Web

http://www.madeira-web.com/PagesUK/index.html

Guide to the Portuguese island group. There are sections on history, culture, food, and government services, in addition to practical information for visitors to Madeira and Porto Santo. There is also a bibliography giving links to further sources of information.

Porto, Portugal

http://cityguide.lycos.com/europe/portugal/
PRTPorto.html

Good source of practical, historical, and cultural information on Portugal's second city. The attractions of the city are well-presented. There is also information on the celebrated 'vinho do Porto' – port – which takes it name from the city.

Welcome to the Algarve

http://www.nexus-pt.com/algarve.htm

Comprehensive source of information on the region of southern Portugal. A clickable map gives access to information on the history, culture, and facilities of all the communities of the Algarve. There is a weather report and links to local newspapers, as well as more practical information for tourists and residents.

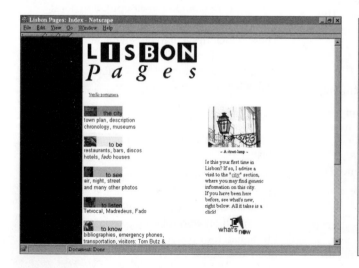

F A C T

ALGARVE (Arabic al-gharb 'the west')

ancient kingdom in southern Portugal, bordered on the east by Spain, and on the west and south by the Atlantic Ocean; it is co-extensive with the modern district of Faro; area 5,071 sq km/ 1,958 sq mi; population (1991) 341,400.

Scandinavia, Iceland & Greenland

Aarhus Webben

http://www.aarhuswebben.dk/index.uk.html

Guide to the Danish city of Aarhus. There is information on the city's culture, entertainment, restaurants, and hotels. A street map is also provided and there are links to local Web sites.

Ålborg

http://www.tourist-aal.dk/

Complete guide to the Danish port of Ålborg, from general information, tourist services, major attractions – including museums and the zoo – sports, food, accommodation, activities, touring and holiday suggestions. All sections are accompanied by many maps and pictures.

City of Oulu

http://www.ouka.fi/oulu_ee.html

Large and well-presented trilingual source of information on the largest city in the north of Finland. This site includes history, cultural heritage, local government services and local democracy, local community news, the environment, economy, and employment and investment opportunities. There are a number of photos and an impressive series of links to local institutions and companies.

Excite Travel: Copenhagen, Denmark

http://www.city.net/countries/denmark/copenhagen/

Comprehensive guide around Copenhagen that offers all the essential facts plus useful directions concerning hotels, eating out, transportation, and sightseeing. Its travel tools include searchable maps, message boards and a 'Yellow pages' section on things to see and do. The site also features selected links to useful pages on all aspects of life in Copenhagen.

Faroe Islands – A Brief Introduction

http://www.sleipnir.fo/faroe/faroe.htm

Comprehensive official source of information on the Faroe Islands. There are sections on the Faroese language, geography, history, economy,

tourism, and current political controversies in this autonomous region of Norway. The Faroese also reply to those who criticize their traditional hunting of pilot whales.

Göteborg Tourist Information

http://centralen.gp.se/tourist/

Good guide to the Swedish port city. This site includes a description, and detailed guides to attractions, history, restaurants, and accommodation. There is also a useful search engine.

Greenland Guide

http://www.greenland-guide.dk/

Official guide to Greenland. The site is highly informative about all regions of the country and is filled with practical information. There are also links to several other sites on Greenland.

Helsinki

http://www.city.net/countries/finland/helsinki/

Visitor's guide to the city that includes information about hotels, shopping, weather, transport, culture, museums, and food. There is also information on newspapers, the underground system, and a host of other sections packed with practical travel information.

Official Trondheim Website

http://www.trondheim.com/english/

Thorough and well-presented information on the Norwegian city. This site includes profiles of business life, local government services, tourism, transportation, cultural activities, and academic institutions. There are also a large number of photos on this practical site.

Reykjavík – Next Door to Nature

http://www.rvk.is/vefur/owa/disp.birta?pk=542

Well-arranged bilingual source of information on the Icelandic capital. The needs of tourists and investors are well provided for, including sections on the history, accommodation, transport, cultural events, and entertainment. There are also a number of photographs.

Saami Country and Its People

http://www.sametinget.se/english/sapmi/index.html

Colourful and well designed site with information about the history, culture, religion, and reindeer farming of the Saami, or Lapp, people. The site also contains traditional Saami music and lots of pictures, as well as information about how to visit Saami country.

Stavanger

http://home.sol.no/~kmeyer/sg01.htm

Good introduction to the Norwegian seaport. On the home page there is an aerial photo of the city. The site also provides a practical description of the modern town and a competent account of Stavanger's long history.

Stockholm

http://www.city.net/countries/sweden/stockholm/

Guide to the city of Stockholm. This site includes local news and weather, as well as details of places to visit, hotels, transportation, and maps of the area.

Turku – Åbo – Typky

http://www.turku.fi/welcomee.html

Comprehensive guide to this Finnish port. There is an outline of the city, its history, and its culture as well as sections on government services, environmental issues, restaurants, accommodation, and events. This site also offers a large number of photos and maps.

Uppsala

http://www.uppsala.se/english/index.htm

Thorough, bilingual (English and Swedish) guide to Sweden's fourth-largest city. There is a good description of the city, its history, attractions, and amenities. The site also offers sections on industry, commerce, the environment, and municipal services.

Visby – World Heritage City

http://www.ovpm.org/ovpm/sites/avisby.html

Information about the capital of Gotland and World Heritage site. There is a history of the Hanseatic League city and a description of its sights. There is also a link to information about UNESCO's criteria for World Heritage status.

Welcome to Bergen – The Gateway to the Fjords of Norway

http://www.uib.no/Bergen/reiseliv/tourist/index.html

Well-arranged guide to the Norwegian city. This site includes a history, a guide to local attractions, and information about cultural life. There are also details of how to visit nearby fjords.

Welcome to Kalmar

http://www.kalmar.se/english/

Well-arranged guide to the southern Swedish city and its hinterland. A description and history are supported by a large number of photographs. There is comprehensive information on the environment, local government, entertainment, transport, accommodation, and local attractions.

Welcome to Linköping

http://www.linkoping.se/international/Engelska/

Profile of Sweden's fifth-largest city. There are outlines of Linköping's history, economic base, and educational institutions. The cathedral and other attractions are also described.

Welcome to Malmö

http://www.malmo.com/

Well-arranged guide to this Swedish port. There is information on tourist attractions, business, shopping, transport, festivals, culture, food, and sports amenities.

Welcome to Tampere

http://www.tampere.fi/elke/mato/english/

Information on this Finnish city which is Scandinavia's largest inland community. There is a history of Tampere, description of places of interest, guide to museums, and information on restaurants and accommodation. A number of photos of Tampere are included, which can be sent as electronic 'postcards' across the Internet.

Spain

Balearic Islands, Spain

http://cityguide.lycos.com/europe/spain/
ESPBalearicIslands.html

Source of information on all of the Balearic Islands. The history, culture, and political status of this Mediterranean island chain are well-presented and there is a wealth of practical information for visitors and residents. This site also includes a weather report and links to local media and other sources of local information.

Barcelona, Spain

http://cityguide.lycos.com/europe/spain/
ESPBarcelona.html

Guide to the Catalan capital. Information on the history, culture, traditions, churches, museums, architectural sites, cafes, transport system, and restaurants of Barcelona is well-presented. There is also a weather report, maps, and links to local media.

Bilbao, Spain

http://www.bizkaia.net/bizkaia/English/General_
information/Routes_and_places/I1VILLA.HTM

Good source of information on the northern Spanish city. This site includes a history of Bilbao, an introduction to Basque culture, details of local attractions, and information on transport and other government services. There is also practical information for visitors, a map, a weather report, and links to local newspapers.

Cantabria – Informacion Turistica

http://turismo.cantabria.org/siting/derecho.htm?
tema=geo&loc=01

Well-presented information on the Spanish autonomous region. A 'clickable' map allows access to descriptions of all parts of Cantabria. This site includes sections on accommodation, beaches, and cultural events. There are also a number of video clips highlighting the attractions of the area.

Community of Castille and Leon

http://www.DocuWeb.ca/SiSpain/english/politics/
autonomo/leon/index.html

Official information on this Spanish autonomous region. There is a history of the region, a description of the capital city Valladolid, and an explanation of the political process leading to the establishment of autonomy in 1982. There is also listing of other Castilla-León Web sites.

Córdoba, Spain

http://cityguide.lycos.com/europe/spain/
ESPCordoba.html

Source of information on the Spanish city. The Judaic, Islamic, and Christian heritage of Córdoba

is well presented, with interesting text and a large selection of photographs. This site also includes comprehensive information on accommodation, local attractions, and restaurants.

Costa del Sol, Spain

http://cityguide.lycos.com/europe/spain/
ESPCostadelSol.html

Comprehensive source of information on the 300 km-long Spanish coastal region. There is information on all the main resorts as well as the history and culture of the region. The needs of tourists, residents, and investors are all catered for. This site also includes a weather report and links to local media.

Extremadura

http://www.DocuWeb.ca/SiSpain/english/politics/
autonomo/extramad/index.html

Official information on the autonomous Spanish region. There is a history of the region, a description of the capital city Merida, and an explanation of the political process leading to the restoration of autonomy in 1982. There is also a listing of other Extremaduran Web sites.

Gibraltar Home Page

http://www.gibraltar.gi/home.html

Official page for Gibraltar, created in December 1995. Ample travel, health, currency, and shopping information are provided and there are also sections on the facilities for people with special needs. The site offers a choice of places worth visiting and it also has a link to the Gibraltar Tourist Board.

Granada, Spain

http://cityguide.lycos.com/europe/spain/
ESPGranada.html

Substantial source of information on the historic Andalusian city. The heritage of Granada is well presented, with interesting text and a large selection of photographs. There is comprehensive information on accommodation, the Alhambra and other local attractions, and restaurants.

Malaga, Spain

http://cityguide.lycos.com/europe/spain/
ESPMalaga.html

Substantial site of information on the capital of the Costa del Sol. Details of Malaguenan heritage, customs, and cuisine are all well-presented. The site includes a wealth of practical information about accommodation, restaurants, local attractions, and entertainment. There is also a weather report and link to sources of local news.

Mallorca Online

http://www.mallorcaonline.com/malhomu.htm

Huge source of information on the largest of Spain's Balearic Islands. The needs of tourists, residents, and investors are all taken care of. A number of interesting articles on local history and culture attest to the charms of the island, which boasts a three-thousand-year tradition of tourism. The site also includes maps, a weather report, and a guide to local businesses.

Murcia

http://www.DocuWeb.ca/SiSpain/english/politics/autonomo/murcia/index.html

Official Spanish government information on the autonomous region. There is a history of the region of Murcia, a description of the capital city, an explanation of the political process leading to the establishment of autonomy in 1982, and details of the regional government. There is also a listing of other Murcian Web sites.

Pamplona, Spain

http://cityguide.lycos.com/europe/spain/ESPPamplona.html

Substantial source of information on the capital of the Spanish province of Navarre. The history, culture, and cuisine of Pamplona is well-presented. There is a wealth of practical information about accommodation, restaurants, the Alcazar and other local attractions, the famous fiesta, and cultural events. The site also includes a weather report.

Principality of Asturias

http://www.DocuWeb.ca/SiSpain/english/politics/autonomo/asturias/index.html

Official Spanish government information on this autonomous principality. There is a history of Asturias, a description of the capital city, Oviedo, an explanation of the political process leading to the establishment of autonomy in 1982, and details of the regional government. There are also links to other Asturias Web sites.

Rioja, La

http://www.DocuWeb.ca/SiSpain/english/politics/autonomo/rioja/index.html

Official information on the small Spanish autonomous region noted for its wine. There is a history of La Rioja, a description of the capital city Logrono, and an explanation of the political process leading to the restoration of autonomy in 1982. There is also a list of other Web sites on La Rioja.

Santander

http://turismo.cantabria.org/siting/derecho.htm

Information on the capital of Spain's Cantabria region. There is a map, photographs, and a description of Santander and its history. Three videos highlighting the attractions of the city may be downloaded.

Segovia Aqueduct

http://www.cyberspain.com/ciudades-patrimonio/fotos/segacui.htm

Photos and descriptions of the Roman aqueduct and the Alcázar – the symbols of this central Spanish city. The history of Segovia is related through its best-known monuments.

Seville, Spain

http://www.sol.com/

Substantial source of information on the Andalusian capital. The history, culture, and cuisine of Seville are well-presented. There is a wealth of practical information about accommodation, restaurants, the Alcázar and other local attractions, the famous fiesta, and cultural events.

Valencia, Spain

http://www.red2000.com/spain/valencia/index.html

Thorough source of information on Spain's third-largest city. There is a good history and introduction to local cultural life. This site also includes a guide to local cuisine and restaurants, and a good section on local attractions and suggested excursions.

Welcome to the Torremolinos Page

http://www.andalucia.com/torremolinos/home.htm

Introduction to the Andalusian resort. Local efforts to throw off the resorts negative image are related. There is a description of the natural and modern attractions of the town and the traditional fishing industry, as well as a listing of local hotels.

Switzerland

Basel Online

http://www.bsonline.ch/english/index.cfm

Large source of information on the Swiss city. There are sections on the history, culture, traditions, museums, nightlife, transport system, accommodation, and cuisine of the city. There are also a number of photos and links to regularly updated information on local events.

Davos

http://www.davos.ch/index_e.html

Comprehensive guide to the Swiss mountain resort. There are details of both winter and summer recreational and convention facilities. The site also offers maps of ski runs, a weather report, and information about transport and accommodation.

Geneva

http://www.city.net/countries/switzerland/geneva/

Everything for the visitor to Geneva, including guides to accommodation, maps, news, and weather reports. The site also contains some general information about this Swiss city.

Guide of Lausanne Welcomes You

http://cityguide.lycos.com/europe/switzerland/CHELausanne.html

Large source of information on the Swiss city. There are sections on culture, accommodation, nightlife, leisure activities, museums, and educational institutions. An interesting tour of each part of the city is accompanied by good photographs.

Lake Geneva Region Web Site

http://www.lake-geneva-region.ch/gb/index_f.html

Large source of information on Lake Geneva and its communities. There are guides to the cities and mountain areas of the region. This site also includes extensive details of opportunities for both summer and winter sports, and hiking.

Montreux

http://www.montreux.ch/

Large source of information on the Swiss resort town. The attractions of the town and region are well described. There are also guides to the city's celebrated jazz and television festivals.

St Moritz – Top of the World

http://www.stmoritz.ch/

Thorough guide to 'probably the most famous resort in the world'. There are sections on climate, events, nightlife, transport, and accommodation.

Welcome to Berne

http://www.berntourismus.ch/

Large source of well-arranged official information on the Swiss federal capital. There are sections on the city's history, attractions, accommodation, as well as some lesser known facts. This site also offers maps, a guide to the local cuisine, and a listing of restaurants.

Zermatt Welcomes You

http://www.zermatt.ch/index.e.html

Well-organized official guide to this Swiss ski resort. There is a wealth of information on ski conditions, ski runs, facilities, ski hire, accommodation, and the history of the resort. A number of photos of the resort are also included.

Africa

Africa – Documents on Fourth World Affairs

http://www.cwis.org/africa.html

Interesting text archive on several groups of indigenous people of Africa, maintained by the Fourth World Documentation Project. Their aim is to increase knowledge about, and understanding of, the problems that these largely unrecognized national populations face within their states.

Cape Town

http://www.toptentravel.com/capetown.html

City guide to Cape Town, South Africa. Aimed at the tourist, this site details what to do before you go, and what to do when you get there. History, geography, and travel information, as well as features on festivals, make up the majority of the remaining information on this site, but there are also details of local transport and a list of useful telephone numbers. It also includes images of Cape Town, and maps of the city area.

Casablanca

http://gcd3.ugr.es/~yassir/casablanca.html

Fine collection of photographs from Casablanca that are well worth a look even though the minimal text introducing them is in Spanish. Visitors need only select and click on the individual photographs and they get larger versions, expertly capturing the everyday life, the history, the monuments, and the landscape both in and around the city.

Letter from Melilla

http://www.forward.com/BACK/97.03.21/letter.html

Well written journalistic article on Spain's Moroccan enclave. The ethnic diversity and cultural harmony of the mixture of Spanish, Judaic, and Muslim culture is well described.

Marrakech

http://gcd3.ugr.es/~yassir/marrakech.html

Fine collection of photographs from Marrakech, thoroughly enjoyable even though the minimal text introducing them is in Spanish, expertly capturing the everyday life, the history, the monuments, and the landscape in and around the city.

Mauritania – Overview

http://www.arab.net/mauritania/overview/mauritania_overview.html

Comprehensive introduction to Mauritania. The site includes historical presentations, details of topography and climate, overviews of the language and traditions of the country, and sections on the economy and transport.

Mayotte

http://www.umsl.edu/services/govdocs/wofact96/167.htm

Profile of this French island claimed by the neighbouring state of Comoros. There is information (from the CIA's World Fact Book) on geography and population, and a brief overview of the economy.

Namib: Africa's Burning Shore

http://www.pbs.org/edens/namib/

Companion to the US Public Broadcasting Service (PBS) television programme *The Living Edens*, this page concerns the inhospitable land of the Namib Desert along the southwestern coast of Africa and the animals that dwell there. Information about the various animals that populate Namib are arranged by time of day; clicking on afternoon, for example, will let you examine the sturdiest animals of Namib. Read about the Benguela Current of the South Atlantic Ocean and other geographical features that provide for the very existence of life here. You can also read about the producer's journey through the fiery sand dunes. Once you have browsed the various sections, test your knowledge with the trivia quiz. There is also a list of resources and links for further research.

Oromia Support Group

http://www.hslib.washington.edu/clinical/ ethnomed/oromocp.html#oromocultprof

Huge source of information on Ethiopia's largest ethnic group. The culture, history, traditions, and language of the Oromo are extensively described. There are a large selection of newspaper articles and human rights reports on the plight of 'Africa's forgotten people'. The site also offers details of Oromo political organizations and the movement for the independence of Oromia.

Tristan da Cunha – South Atlantic Ocean

http://www.rothley.demon.co.uk/tristan.htm

Detailed history of this remote island. There's a map and a full account of the history of the local population during the 19th century. Information on the lives of the two hundred Tristans still living on the island is however sparse.

Walvis Bay

http://www.azania.co.za/namibia/walvis_bay/ default.htm

Profile of Namibia's chief port. The history of the former South African enclave is presented. There is information on accommodation, local businesses, news, and events, as well as details of plans to develop the port's infrastructure.

Western Sahara Page

http://www.sas.upenn.edu/ African_Studies/Country_Specific/ W_Sahara.html

Country map, world factbook entry, and other online resources related to the Western Sahara.

Zanzibar – Stone Town

http://zanzibar.net/stonetow.html

Illustrated pages, mainly aimed at tourists, describing the old city and cultural heart of Zanzibar, now designated a World Heritage site. Highlights of this city include: the Old

Dispensary, the Market, Livingstone's House, the Peace Memorial Museum, the Palace Museum, and the Arab Fort.

Middle East

Abadan

http://www.abadan.com/

Enthusiastic homage to, and colourful tour of, Abadan in Iran. The site includes many pictures, stories, poems and the latest news – there is even an Abadani dictionary – and links to other Iranian sites.

Abu Dhabi

http://www.uaeforever.com/AbuDhabi/

Well-presented guide to the largest and richest of the United Arab Emirates. There is a good description of the history, cultural heritage, attractions, and local economy. There are a number of good photos of Abu Dhabi and its ruler, the UAE president.

Ajman

http://www.uaeforever.com/Ajman/

Guide to the smallest of the United Arab Emirates. There is a good description of the history and attractions of Ajman as well as photos of the emirate and its ruler.

Alexandria, Egypt

http://ce.eng.usf.edu/pharos/alexandria/

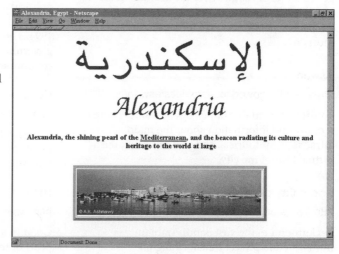

Information about the Egyptian city of Alexandria including an historical guide, a visitor guide, a picture gallery, maps, and links to related Web sites.

Ankara

http://www.focusmm.com/ank_02.htm

Outline of the Turkish capital. The history of the city is summarized and its public buildings, institutions, and attractions described. There are also photos and a guide to cultural events.

Applied Resource Institute – Jerusalem

http://www.arij.org/

Comprehensive Palestinian source of up-to-date information on geography, climate, water, agriculture, land use, and settlement activities in the West Bank. This site is indispensable for understanding the Israeli-Palestinian conflict over natural resources.

Ashkelon – Gateway to the Mediterranean

http://www.ashkelon.gov.il/

Official site of Ashkelon municipality. There is information on archaeology, history, tourist facilities, and local industry. There are plenty of images to support the text and even a video clip. The site also includes several tours around the city with maps and hyperlinks to details of the sites along the way.

Asiut

http://www.idsc.gov.eg/govern/ASU.htm

Official Egyptian government site on the governorate of Asiut. There is information on geography, population, industry, agriculture, education, public services, infrastructure, and tourism.

Aswan

http://its-idsc.gov.eg/tourism/docs/aswan/

Tourist guide to this upper Egypt resort. There is a photo and information about the main attractions for tourists, and you can also take a virtual tour of the city.

Boom City of Yanbu

http://www.arab.net/saudi/business/sa_yanbu.html

Background to the vast Saudi Arabian infrastructure project transforming an insignificant Red Sea fishing village into a major industrial city. There is a comprehensive history of the Yanbu scheme and a description of the port and petrochemical industries established there.

Cairo, the Jewel of the Orient

http://ce.eng.usf.edu/pharos/cairo/

Comprehensive guide to the city's history with a gallery of maps and pictures. It includes detailed information for visitors – places to visit (both ancient and modern), where to stay, where to eat, and details of transportation.

Dubai

http://www.uaeforever.com/Dubai/

Well-presented guide to the second-largest of the United Arab Emirates. There is a good description of the history of the trading entrepot, the role of the Makhtoum family, as well as details of it's cultural heritage, attractions, and the local economy. There are a number of good photos of Dubai and its ruler.

Fujairah

http://www.uaeforever.com/Fujairah/

Well-presented guide to the compact non-oil emirate of the United Arab Emirates. There is a good description of the history, cultural heritage, and local attractions. The text is supported by a number of good photos.

Gaza Strip

http://www.umsl.edu/services/govdocs/wofact96/97.htm

Source of basic information on the Gaza Strip provided by the CIA. The site has an overview of political and economic developments since the handover of Gaza to the Palestinian Authority in 1994. There is information on population, government, transport infrastructure, and communications. A map of Gaza is also included.

Haifa

http://www.haifa.gov.il/

Official site of Haifa Municipality. There is information on history, the local economy, culture, tourism, and investment opportunities.

Izmir

http://www.turkey.org/turkey/tourism/izmir/izmir.htm

Good guide to Turkey's third biggest city – 'the pearl of the Aegean'. There is an outline of the city's history and heritage, and a guide to hotels, museums, and other places of interest. Information on nearby recreational areas is supported by photographs.

Jewish Community of Hebron

http://www.virtual.co.il/communities/israel/

Site of the controversial Jewish settlement in Hebron. It provides an illuminating insight into the mentality of the militant settlers at the heart of the Middle Eastern flashpoint.

Jubail New Industrial City and Saudi Arabia's Economic Development

http://pw2.netcom.com/~interdev/jubail.htm

Overview of the importance of the creation of Jubail for the long-term future of the Saudi economy. Written by an engineer closely associated with the project from the outset, it describes the vast infrastructure project to transform a fishing village into a major Saudi city. There are a number of photos of Jubail and projections of its future growth.

Makkah (Mecca)

http://darkwing.uoregon.edu/~kbatarfi/makkah.html

Brief history of the holy city of Mecca that gives a general introduction to the place's importance to Muslims and also includes a gallery of several images in and around the Gran Mosque.

Nazareth – The Flower of Galilee

http://198.62.75.1/www1/ofm/san/TSnzmain.html

Christian guide to Nazareth. This site includes information about the town, archaeological findings, and a good history. There are also many stunning high-resolution photos.

Peace with the Golan – Tourism on the Golan Heights

http://www.golan.org.il/tourism3.html

Israeli guide to the attractions of the disputed Golan Heights. Confined to describing Israeli settlements, this guide makes no mention of the Druse inhabitants of this annexed Syrian territory.

Philae

http://www.horus.demon.co.uk/Nile/Philae.html

Guide to this ancient edifice rescued from the rising waters of the Aswan Dam. There is a photo, description of the site, and a history.

Port Said

http://www.idsc.gov.eg/govern/PSD.htm

Official Egyptian government site on the governorate of Port Said. There is information on geography, population, industry, agriculture, education, public services, infrastructure, and tourism.

Ramallah Online Travel Guide

http://www.birzeit.edu/ramallah/

Well-presented guide to the Palestinian city. There is a comprehensive history of Ramallah and guide to its current attractions. A number of colourful photos attest to the optimism of a community now attempting to recover from the difficulties of Israeli occupation.

Ras al Khaimah

http://www.uaeforever.com/RasAlKhaimah/

Guide to the most traditional of the United Arab Emirates. There is a good description of the history and attractions of the small strategically placed emirate. There are also good photos of Ras el Khaimah and its leader.

Salalah

http://www.msdg.com/oman/salafr.htm

Description of the capital of Oman's Dhofar region. The history of the city and its development is sketched. There is also a photo and a description of local economic activities.

Sharjah

http://www.uaeforever.com/Sharjah/

Guide to the third-largest of the United Arab Emirates. There is a good description of the history, cultural heritage, and attractions, accompanied by some photos of the highlights.

Umm al Quwain

http://www.uaeforever.com/UmmAlQuwain/

Guide to the second-smallest of the United Arab Emirates. Alongside an illustrated description of the local attractions, there are descriptions of the emirate's history and cultural heritage. There are a number of photos of Umm al Qaiwain and its ruler.

Water Disputes in the Tigris–Euphrates Basin

http://www.access.ch/tuerkei/GRUPF/water/chapter1/chap1c.htm

Good analysis of the tensions between Turkey,

Syria, and Iraq over use of the waters of the rivers of Mesopotamia. The political and environmental consequences of Turkish damming of the rivers are objectively examined.

Welcome to Antalya

http://www.antalya-ws.com/

Good guide for visitors to the Turkish Mediterranean port. An interactive map allows access to information on Antalya and nearby towns. This site also includes information on hotels, real estate, car hire agencies, and entertainment. There is also a good guide, and some photographs, of the several sites of historic interest in the vicinity.

China

Beijing Pages

http://www.flashpaper.com/beijing/

Everything about the Chinese capital, from its location and population to its culture, economy, and government. The site also includes detailed tourism links as well as information about industrial development in the city.

Brief Introduction to Anhui Province

http://www.wtci.org/mdsisters/province_of_anhui.htm

Information about the eastern Chinese province of Anhui, covering topography, climate, rivers and lakes, agriculture, industry, communications, and main cities. There is also a longer section devoted to the province's economic development.

Brief Introduction to Shandong Province, China

http://www.shandong-china.com/intro.htm

Profile of Shandong province, with basic information about its location, population, and climate; its importance in history and historical figures; its agriculture and fishing industry; and the general character of its people. The site also includes a map and a photograph of a local Confucian ceremony.

Changchun City

http://china.muzi.net/travel/city/changchun.htm

All about the capital of the Jilin province, Changchun. This site includes information about industrial and agricultural development, traffic and communications, financial institutions and markets, science and education, and tourism.

Dalian

http://www.chinapages.com/liaoning/dalian/dalian.htm

Page dedicated to the attractions of the city of Dalian. The text has numerous links to photographs of the city's major sites, including the city centre, the harbour, Jinshi beach, and geological formations. There are also photographs of the annual Dalian International Fashion Festival.

Hong Kong

http://zero.com.hk/z.html

Jumping-off point for sources of political, social, and cultural news about Hong Kong. This site is directed at the tourist and includes practical information on such topics as sightseeing, shopping, transportation, where to stay, and local culture, as well as a more practical hotel and restaurant guide.

Outline of Jilin Province of China

http://www.chinarainbow.com/english/intro.htm

Page devoted to basic facts and figures about the Chinese province of Jilin, including location, topography, boundary, area, climate, and population. A map of the province has links to major cities. There are also links to the provincial governor and to the Provincial Communist Party secretary.

Shanghai

http://www.sh.com/attracti/attracti.htm

Guide to Shanghai. History, geography, and travel information as well as features on festivals make up the majority of the tourist-oriented information on this site, in addition to local transport information and a list of useful telephone numbers.

Forbidden City

http://china-window.com/beijing/tour/city/zijincheng.html

Colourful pages devoted to the architectural wonders of Beijing's Forbidden City, once the palace of the Chinese emperors. There is a brief introduction to the main aspects of the palace, and links to numerous colour photographs displaying the palace's most interesting features.

Tianjin Home Page

http://gao.fsn.net/

Personal guide to this northern Chinese city. As well as a history and many photographs of the city's sights, there is also a town map, several audio clips of the city and its inhabitants, and details of the tourist attractions, weather, and food.

Xi'an

http://www.chinapages.com/shaanxi/xian/xian.html

Concise overview of the ancient Chinese city and its history.

Yangtze River Three Gorges Tour

http://www.chinavista.com/travel/yangtze/main.html

Virtual tour down the Chang Jiang River, including the famous Three Gorges. These extensive pages include maps of the Three Gorges area and a chart showing distances between the main towns and cities along the river. The numerous colour photographs include views of the river's source on the Qinghai–Tibetan Plateau, and the Three Gorges, as well as many of the historical sites along its banks.

India

AgraOnline

http://www.agraonline.com/

Complete guide to the Indian city of Agra aimed at both tourists and residents alike. For the tourist, there is detailed information about the ways to travel to Agra and also where to stay once you get there. There are also notes on the places to visit, where to go shopping, and the best places to eat out. In a developing section for the resident, there are details of handicrafts and emporiums and also other trade information.

Andhra Pradesh

http://www.andhrapradesh.com/

Official guide to the Indian state of Andhra Pradesh. There is a welcome from the region's chief minister, a profile of the local economy and government, and a guide to tourist attractions and places of pilgrimages. There are also a number of photographs.

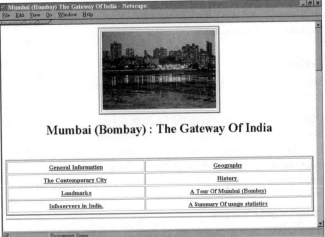

Bombay: The Gateway of India

http://www.bchs.uh.edu/~mdoshi/Bombay/Bombay.html

General outline of the city of Bombay, including a detailed history section, facts on its geography and weather, important institutions, and pictures of landmarks.

Calcutta

http://ezinfo.ucs.indiana.edu/~mduttara/wb/calintro.html

Detailed tour of the city of Calcutta, including its people, architecture, economy, and history. There is also an overview of the museums, libraries, and other cultural institutions that can be found in this city.

Destination Karnataka

http://www.lonelyplanet.com/dest/ind/kar.htm

Traveller's guide to the southwestern Indian province. The guide incorporates all the usual travel information, but also includes many pictures of the region and unofficial reports from travellers to the area. A section on attractions 'Off the beaten track' contains details of towns and cities the majority of tourists never visit, and visitors to this Web site are given the option to view a 'Slide show' of the area.

Goa

http://www.goa-interactive.com/goa/gazette.htm

Comprehensive information on Goa for tourists, residents, business people, and expatriate Goans. Organized by Government of Goa, the site is easy to navigate and has a useful search engine as well as links to a large number of other Goan sites.

Gujjars

http://ourworld.compuserve.com/homepages/MABrandon/

Illustrated introduction to the Gujjars, a semi-nomadic people inhabiting areas of India and Pakistan. There is a section on their origin and a map showing their current location, along with some photos.

India's Caste System

http://www.csuchico.edu/~cheinz/syllabi/asst001/spring98/india.htm

Detailed essay explaining the caste system, which was the basis for Indian society, and is still significant. The essay is accompanied by relevant photographs showing members of each caste.

Lakshadweep

http://india.indiagov.org/states/lak/lak.htm

Official Indian Government source of information on the Lakshadweep archipelago. There is a brief outline of the history, culture, economy, and tourist attractions of these islands.

Rajasthan

http://www.bayarea.net/~emerald/raja1.html

Rajasthani traditions and spirit are captured at this site, with pictures and information on each of its major cities – Jaipur, Jodhpur, Udaipur, and Jaisalmer. You can also find out about cuisine, travel, accommodation, and historical landmarks.

Miscellaneous Asia

Bali

http://werple.mira.net.au/~wreid/bali_p1a.html

Guide to the Indonesian holiday destination of Bali. Aimed at the tourist, this site details what to do before you go, and what to do when you get there. There are also details of the area's history and geography, as well as features on festivals, and some useful travel information. The site also includes many images of Bali, and maps of the area.

Bangkok

http://www.bu.ac.th/thailand/bangkok.html

Aspects of life in this thriving Thai city, described by some as the Venice of the East. This site, run by Bangkok University, is equally appropriate for the business traveller and the tourist, with maps, photographs, accommodation and embassy details, in addition to cultural background and culinary information.

Brief History of the Ainu People

http://bioc09.uthscsa.edu/natnet/archive/nl/9304/0031.html

Sympathetically written account of the history of Japan's indigenous people. It traces the process of military and cultural subjugation of the Ainu. This site also includes details of the ongoing tensions between the Japanese and a people still not officially recognized and in danger of losing their language.

British Indian Ocean Territory

http://www.umsl.edu/services/govdocs/wofact96/45.htm

Geographical details of the British Indian Ocean Territory provided by the CIA. The details are fairly extensive and cover almost every aspect of life in the region.

Fukuyama City

http://hiroshima.topica.ne.jp/guidemap/fukuyama-c/fukuyama-c.html

Profile of Fukuyama City in Hiroshima Prefecture, Japan. A brief introduction to the history of the city is followed by information about the main places of interest as well as festivals, local events, and tourist information. The pages are illustrated with photographs of the city's attractions.

Hafa Adai and Welcome to the Commonwealth of the Northern Mariana Islands

http://www.saipan.com/

Illustrated guide to the Northern Mariana Islands. Click on the links to find out about the islands' history, geography, government, tourism, business, news, weather reports, and education.

Himalayas: Where Earth Meets Sky

http://library.advanced.org/10131/ javascriptmenu_final.html

Explores numerous aspects of the Himalayas, including its geography, biodiversity, and geologic past, as well as the culture and history of the region, and the environmental problems facing the area. Visitors will find a variety of maps, three different quizzes, travellers' comments, plus audio clips and numerous photos.

Inland Sea

http://www.pbs.org/inlandsea/

Companion to a US Public Broadcasting Service (PBS) television programme, this page explores the beauty of Japan's landlocked Inland Sea through maps, images, and brief descriptions, and honours the traditional lifestyles of the native islanders. This site includes four audio clips of music composed by renowned Japanese composer Toru Takemitsu and an interview with Donald Richie, author of the book *The Inland Sea*.

Inner Mongolia Overview

http://www.bupt.edu.cn/regnet/inmon.html

All about Inner Mongolia – its population, climate, education, economy, agriculture, industry, transportation, and cities. The page is illustrated with a few colour photographs, and there are links to others showing features and national customs.

Kyoto Information

http://www.joho-kyoto.or.jp/Joho-KyotoHome/Infor/ Infor/INFOR.html

Good guide to the Japanese port. An overview of Kyoto's 1,200-year history is supported with ample photos. In addition to a guide to the city's traditional crafts and industries, there is information on the contemporary business scene. Details of local attractions are also given at this site.

Lhasa Archive Project

http://www.asianart.com/lhasa_restoration/ index.html

Fascinating pages describing Tibet's capital, Lhasa, and the rapid urban development that has destroyed so much of its ancient heritage. The site introduces the conservation project planned by the Tibet Heritage Fund and the aims of this organization. There are a number of photographs of the city, and links to maps showing its growth over the last 50 years.

Macau

http://www.cityguide.gov.mo/

General information about Macau, with short articles on its government, language, population, currency, and religions. There is also an index with links to travel information, entry procedures, tours, sightseeing, entertainment, dining out, events, and public holidays. The site is illustrated with photographs of the territory.

Nagoya

http://www.city.nagoya.jp/indexe.html

Official guide to the central Japanese city. This site includes a history, comprehensive listing of places of interest, information on traditional crafts, and a guide to shopping, entertainment, and dining.

Novgorod the Great

http://www.novgorod.ru/heritage/eng/

Good guide to the culture and history of the Russian World Heritage city. There are descriptions and photos of the many historical buildings in Novgorod. This site includes sections on Novgorodian artistic and musical traditions.

Shan People of Burma

http://pw2.netcom.com/~burma/tai/pride.html

Pages devoted to the history, language, culture, and present situation of the Shan, or Tai, people of Burma. There is also a link to the Panglong Agreement that led to Burma's independence in 1948.

Singapore – The People

http://www.sg/flavour/people.html

Comprehensive page devoted to the people of Singapore, their origins, religion, and customs. Scroll through the information, or click on headings, to find out about early immigration; birth, marriage and death; language and literacy; religions; and numerous local festivals.

Time Out Guide to Istanbul

http://www.ddg.com/ISTANBUL/

Virtual tour of Istanbul including a description of all the important sites, a library of pictures, and both 2D and 3D maps of the city.

Tokyo

http://www.tokyo-now.com/index.asp?lang=e

City guide to the Japanese capital Tokyo. There are also details of the city's history, geography, and features on festivals. The section on tourist information is supplemented with maps and photographs and contains a list of useful phone numbers.

Tundra Nenets

http://www.helsinki.fi/~tasalmin/tn.html

Guide to the culture and language of the Nenets, the most numerous of the Samoyed people. The structure of the language is set out in great detail. The cultural and economic factors leading to the Russification of Nenets culture are also described at this site.

Welcome to Pusan

http://pusanweb.com/

Comprehensive guide to Korea's main port. There is useful information on Pusan's history, culture, cuisine, transport, and facilities for visitors.

Australia

Ashmore and Cartier Islands

http://www.umsl.edu/services/govdocs/wofact96/23.htm

CIA resource of details about the Australian dependency that is only seasonally inhabited. A brief map is provided, along with some political background.

Australian Aborigine

http://aboriginalart.com.au/

Well-organized site run by the Arrernte indigenous community in the Northern Territory, Australia. It includes information about the history, land, and culture of the community, with many historical photographs, some audio clips of greetings, and traditional didgeridoo music.

Australian Capital Territory

http://www.act.gov.au/

Official guide to Australia's federal territory. There is information on government services, business life, local amenities, and the environment. This site also includes a guide to tourist attractions in Canberra and elsewhere in the territory.

Ballarat Tourism and Accommodation Directory

http://www.ballarat.com/

Well-presented guide to Victoria's historic gold-rush town. There is a thorough listing of local accommodation and attractions, and a guide to nearby national parks. There is also a history of this, Victoria's largest inland city.

Barossa Valley

http://www.southaustralia.com/tourism/barossa.htm

Informative and non-commercial site highlighting the attractions of Australia's premier wine-growing region. A history of the valley covers aboriginal life, European discovery, and settlement by the persecuted German Lutherans who planted the first vines. There is practical information on accommodation and visits to vineyards and other attractions.

Bathurst Home Page

http://cww.octec.org.au/bathurst/bathurst.htm

Good source of information on Australia's oldest inland city. There is a history of the town, photographs, and a map. There is also a comprehensive listing of local businesses.

Brisbane City Life

http://www.maxlink.com.au/bcl/

Huge source of information on Queensland's capital. There are details of the city's history, climate, transport, accommodation, education, community groups, tourist attractions, and cultural events. There is also a good search engine.

Broken Hill

http://www.brokenhill.nsw.gov.au/

Tribute to the Australian outback city from a resident. The history and heritage of the town are presented through a series of photos and accompanying text. There is a listing of tourist attractions.

Canberra's Top Secret Tour

http://www.topsecret.canberra.net.au/

Interactive tour of Australia's national capital. The main attraction of this site is the 'Top secret' tour around sites of scandal and intrigue, and the Web site also includes a detailed map of the city.

City of Orange

http://cww.octec.org.au/orange/ ogewelc.htm

Guide to this city in New South Wales. This site includes history, business, entertainment, employment and investment opportunities, and local attractions. There is also good coverage of local government services and community news.

Destination Perth

http://www.lonelyplanet.com/dest/aust/perth.htm

Online Lonely Planet guide to Perth, the capital of Western Australia. This site includes details of the city's history, environment, and tourist attractions. This site also features a map of the local area.

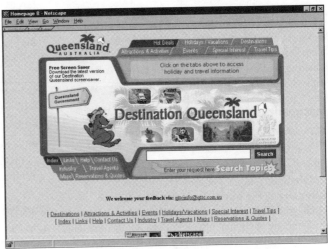

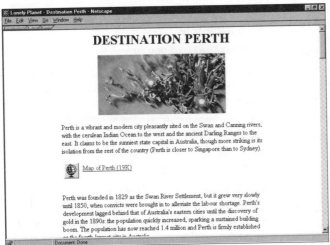

Destination Queensland

http://www.qttc.com.au/

Large source of well-organized official tourist information on Australia's fastest growing state. The attractions of all regions of the vast state are described and easily accessible. Practical information is provided together with links to

further sources. There is extensive information on the state's commitment to ecotourism and environmental protection.

Gippsland Tourism

http://www.gippslandtourism.com.au/

Good guide to the attractions and scenic beauty of Australia's largest network of inland waterways. The major tourist locations are described with the help of good photographs. There are also suggested touring itineraries and a list of accommodation.

Gold Coast City Council

http://www.goldcoast.qld.gov.au/

Official guide to Australia's fastest growing region. Local government and business activities are summarized and there is information for visitors to Gold Coast resorts. A regularly updated image of the beach allows you to check out local surfing conditions.

Great Barrier Reef Marine Park Authority

http://www.gbrmpa.gov.au/

Comprehensive official information on all aspects of the Great Barrier Reef and efforts to preserve this World Heritage Area. The online edition of the authority's quarterly *Reef Research* gives detail of current related scientific work.

Interactive Tour of Tasmania

http://www.tased.edu.au/tot/index.html

Interactive tour of this Australian island state. The

site includes some spectacular photographs of the various parts of the island and a description of the flora and fauna indigenous to the area. The maps of the island on the site are interactive – clicking on the name of a town or region calls up a photograph and description of that area.

Macquarie Island – Report on a Short Visit

http://www.anbg.gov.au/projects/macquarie/macq-report.html

Description of a brief botanical expedition to this uninhabited island. The report contains a summary of the purposes of the expedition, background information about the topography and history of the island, as well as an account of the expedition itself, and the plants that were collected and brought back to the Australian National Botanical Gardens.

Maryborough City Life

http://www.aia.net.au/kdk/mbh

Colourful guide to this southeast Queensland city. This site includes a guide to local history, local government functions, community groups, and information on local events and tourist attractions. There are also a number of photos.

Melbourne City Search

http://www.melbourne.vic.gov.au//

Searchable source of information on Australia's second city. Primarily designed for residents, this site is updated on a daily basis with news of local events, community groups, local government, cultural life, sport, and weather. For visitors there is information on accommodation and tourist attractions.

Norfolk Island on the Net

http://www.nf/

Web site organized by the 1,500 inhabitants containing a wealth of information on the island, its unique culture, and attractions for visitors. These pages even include a guide to the local language, Norfolk, an amalgam of 18th-century English and Tahitian. The local phone book is included – the only one in the world to include nicknames (the reason being that there are so few surnames in this close-knit community).

Nullarbor Plain

http://atn.com.au/wa/desert/null-b.htm

Guide for motorists crossing the arid wastes of

the Australian plateau. The main towns and facilities along the Eyre Highway are described. There is also advice as well as warnings for tourists to the region.

Port Augusta – Crossroads of Australia, Gateway to the Outback

http://pacomms.mtx.net/

Official guide to this South Australian port. There is a history of the town, details of local government services, and information for visitors.

Port Pirie

http://www.stmarks.pp.catholic.edu.au/icon/pirie/portpiri.html

History and guide to this South Australian port. There is information about local tourist attractions and this site also includes a good map of the city and the surrounding region.

Riverina Regional Development Board

http://www.wagga.net.au/~rrdb/

Good official guide to the Riverina region of New South Wales. There is information on the local economy, investment opportunities, and attractions. There is also a map, a local newsletter, and news of current events.

Rockhampton

http://www.rcc.qld.gov.au

Guide to the attractions of this Queensland port. There is a history of the region, a map, and practical information for visitors.

Simpson Desert

http://198.142.19.2/Travel/Australia/NT_info/NTTC/simpson.html

Guide to the Simpson Desert from the Northern Territory tourism department. There is a description of the terrain and vegetation as well as advice (and warnings) for tourists heading off the beaten track in this wilderness area.

South Australian Tourist Commission

http://www.tourism.sa.gov.au/

Well-presented official guide to this Australian state. There is information on all the regions and a guide to the food and wine for which South Australia is noted. There are suggested touring itineraries and listing of tour operators, accommodation, and further sources of information.

Sunshine Coasting

http://www.sunzine.net/suncoast/welcome.html

Guide to Queensland's Sunshine Coast. Natural and other attractions of the area are well described. There are photos, maps, and details of accommodation, real estate, and business opportunities.

Sydney Interactive Visitors Guide

http://www.visitorsguide.aust.com/~tourism/sydney/index.html

Interactive guide to Sydney, Australia. The guide features the 'museums, art galleries, history, maps, attractions, tours, festivals, hotels, and fine dining for both visitors and residents of Sydney.'

F A C T

SYDNEY

principal port of Australia and capital of the state of New South Wales; population (1996) 3,276,500. Founded in 1788, Sydney is situated on Port Jackson inlet on the southeast coast of Australia, and is built around a number of bays and inlets that form an impressive natural harbour.

Taree

http://www.finalword.com/ubd_www/Taree.htm

Profile of this New South Wales river town. There is a history of Taree and the Manning River and a description of the attractions of the district.

Tasmania – Discover Your Natural State

http://www.tourism.tas.gov.au/nu_index.html

Official guide to Australia's island state. The quiet charms of 'Tassie' and local pride in its heritage, culture, and cuisine are evoked by informative text and a series of photographs. The history of the state is presented by means of quotes from famous visitors. All the regions of the state are covered.

Thursday Island

http://www.walkabout.fairfax.com.au/smh/locations/QLDThursdayIsland.shtml

Profile of the island in Queensland's Torres Strait.

This site provides a history of settlement on the island and the pearl industry. There is practical information for visitors and a comic poem highlighting the former perils of existence on this remote island.

Toowoomba Net

http://www.toowoomba.net.au/

Comprehensive information on Queensland's 'garden city' and the surrounding Darling Downs. There is extensive coverage of local business, cultural, and community life. The needs of visitors are also well catered for.

Townsville Magazine

http://ultra.ultra.net.au/~tsvmag/cont.html

Guide to Australia's largest tropical city. There are descriptions of the city, nearby rainforest, and Barrier Reef attractions with practical information for visitors. An offbeat article on the glories of mangoes, cane toads, and prawns conveys the varied attractions of life in Townsville.

Warrnambool – Centre of Victoria's Shipwreck Coast

http://www.warrnambool.org/wbool.html

Good official guide to this Victorian resort city. There is information on the history, economy, local government, tourist attractions, and sporting amenities. There is also a calendar of local events and guide to the surrounding area.

Warrumbungle National Park

http://www.anypoint.net/apa000/000927.htm

Guide to this spectacular national park. There is a description of geology, flora, and fauna, and the importance of the mountain range in Aboriginal culture. There is also some practical information for visitors.

Welcome to Australia's Northern Territory

http://www.nt.gov.au/welcome.shtml

Good official introduction to the 'top end' of Australian. There is information on the landscape, economy, and government structure.

Welcome to Cairns Online – Your Gateway to the Tropical North

http://www.cairns.aust.com/

Comprehensive guide to this tropical Queensland city. There is information on tourist attractions, environmental issues, business life, and accommodation. There is also a useful search engine.

Wollongong – City of Diversity

http://www.wollongong.nsw.gov.au/

Well-presented official guide to this New South Wales coastal city. There is comprehensive information on local community, business, and cultural activities, as well as local government services. This site also includes a history of the area and guide to local attractions for visitors.

Worldwide Wagga Wagga

http://www.wagga.net.au/

Comprehensive guide to the largest provincial city in New South Wales. There is a well-arranged history of the area, local government services, and community organizations. The site also includes information on local attractions, sporting amenities, and business opportunities.

Miscellaneous Oceania

Australs Islands

http://www.tahiti-tekuratravel.com/islands/eaus.html

Guide to the major Austral islands of Tubuai and Rurutu. There are descriptions, histories, photos of both islands, and details of accommodation.

Bay of Plenty

http://www.bayofplenty.co.nz/

Guide to the towns, beaches, and other natural attractions of the New Zealand region. There is practical information for visitors and a suggested itinerary. There are also a number of links to other sites around the inlet.

Bisita Guam

http://bisitaguam.com/

Interesting guide to the US Pacific territory. Presented from the viewpoint of the native

Chamorro people, it recounts the impact of Western culture on the lifestyle, language, and faith of the inhabitants. A detailed history covers the period from Magellan, through US colonization and Japanese occupation, to the present day. This impressive site is organized by a former US congressman.

Come Meet the Banabans

http://www.ion.com.au/~banaban/

Poignant campaigning site highlighting the plight of the inhabitants of the Kiribati island of Banaba. There is a detailed history of the island, the cultural disruption caused by Christianity, the ecological vandalism of the phosphate industry, and the forced relocation of the Banaban people. Efforts to rehabilitate the island are described.

Hamilton – Heart of the Mighty Waikato

http://www.chemistry.co.nz/waikato.htm

Well-arranged guide to the city of Hamilton and the Waikato region. The attractions, economy, and lifestyle of New Zealand's productive agricultural region are set out. There is also a history and practical information for visitors.

New Caledonia Tourism

http://www.newcaledonia.org/

Guide to the French Pacific territory. There is a good introduction to local history and Melanesian culture. Visitors are provided with practical information about attractions, transport, and accommodation.

Palmerston North – Knowledge City

http://www.pncc.govt.nz/

Good official source of information on the New Zealand city. This site includes details of the history, local commerce, educational institutions, and community news. There are also a number of good photographs and a map of the city.

Pitcairn Island Web Site

http://www.wavefront.com/~pjlareau/pitc1.html

Web site organized by the 50 descendants of the *Bounty* mutineers still living on Pitcairn Island. There is a map, a history of the mutiny, a full list of Pitcairners and how they are interrelated, and a virtual shopping centre. There are ham radio and satphone contacts for the island, which only receives mail every three months. This site is an extraordinary achievement for a small and clearly proud community.

Port-Vila, Vanuatu

http://cityguide.lycos.com/oceania/west_pacific/
VUTPortVila.html

Guide to the capital of Vanuatu. There is coverage
of local attractions, culture, and history. The site
also has practical information for visitors and
those planning to reside in the city, and the text is
improved by the inclusion of several photographs
of Port-Vila.

Secrets of Easter Island

http://www.pbs.org/wgbh/nova/easter/

Companion site to the PBS television programme
Nova, this page seeks to answer the many
mysteries surrounding the inhabitants of this
remote island and the giant statues they
produced. Archaeologist Jo Anne Van Tilburg
attempts to reconstruct the statues based on her
theories of how they might have been built.

Stewart Island

http://nz.com/tour/StewartIsland/

Good source of information on the smallest of
New Zealand's three main islands. The rich flora
and fauna of the island are described, together
with its history. There is also information on how
to get to Stewart Island, what to do, and where to
stay.

Tahiti

http://tahiti.com/directories/tahiti-guide.htm

Huge source of well-presented information on
Tahiti and other islands in French Polynesia.
Polynesian history and culture are
sympathetically explained. There is also a host of
practical information and suggestions for visitors.

Taupo, New Zealand – a New Zealand destination for Fishing, Hunting, Whitewater Rafting, Skiing

http://www.taupo.com/expindex.html

Guide to New Zealand's dramatic caldera lake.
Attractions for visitors are described and
accompanied by photos. There is also extensive
practical information for trout fishermen, and a
section of 'Taupo Trout Recipes'.

Visit Niue

http://www.nunames.nu/visitniue/views.htm

Guide to the Polynesian coral atoll. There is
information on history, culture, flora and fauna,
and local cuisine. The needs of divers and
fishermen are catered for and there is information
on transport and accommodation.

Welcome to Paradise – the Cook Islands

http://www.ck/index.html

Very thorough guide to the Cook Islands in
English and French. The many pages are packed
with information on the geography, culture,
economy, and government of the fifteen far-flung
islands. The differing needs of tourists and
investors are both met by this well-organized site.

Welcome to Wanganui

http://www.wanganui.govt.nz/

Well-presented official guide to this New Zealand
port and the surrounding area. There is
information on the local economy, government,
and tourist attractions. To encourage visitors to
the site to explore all its pages, there is a quiz on
the contents of the site.

US Cities & Towns

Absolutely Albany

http://www.albany.org/index.html

Good official guide to the capital of New York
state. The needs of business people and tourists
are catered for with comprehensive information
on history, local attractions, and accommodation.
There are also maps and links to the many
museums and historical sites in the area.

Anchorage, Alaska

http://www.ci.anchorage.ak.us/Anchorage/
index.html

Guide to Alaska's largest city. There is
comprehensive information on the history of the

city, a guide to points of interest in the city, a calendar of local events, and advice on planning a visit. Comprehensive details on winter sports, ranging from dog mushing to skijoring, encourage visitors to think of Anchorage as a year-round vacation destination.

Austin

http://austin.citysearch.com/

Comprehensive and searchable guide to Austin. The needs of visitors are comprehensively met with information on local attractions, cultural activities, local events, accommodation, and night life. Residents are also catered for with full details of local government functions, community groups, and local businesses.

Berkeley Convention and Visitors Bureau

http://www.berkeleycvb.com/

Official guide to Berkeley. The plain home page does not do justice to a site that has a wealth of information on accommodation, transport, sites of interest, local events, community groups, and local government services.

Birmingham

http://www.bcvb.org/

Official guide to Alabama's largest city from the local Convention and Visitors Bureau. There is a history of this city, photos, a list of attractions and accommodation, and other practical information for visitors. Links include one to the civil-rights museum, highlighting the role played by local residents and Martin Luther King in ending segregation.

Bloomington, Illinois

http://cityguide.lycos.com/greatlakes/ BloomingtonIL.html

Good source of information on the Illinois city associated with Abraham Lincoln, Pullman coaches, and the famous Route 66. There is a good history of the city and profiles of its famous residents. The site also includes links to local universities, government, and information on local attractions and events.

Boston Online

http://www.boston-online.com/

Complete guide to the city of Boston. The site is

filled with practical information for travellers, including several suggested walking tours. There are lots of images of the city and a number of useful links to local media and companies.

Champaign-Urbana Convention and Visitor's Bureau

http://mri.beckman.uiuc.edu/c-u.html

Large source of information on this central Illinois city. There is information on history, local attractions, sporting facilities, entertainment, and the University of Illinois, in addition to reports on the weather and local news.

Charleston

http://www.charleston.net/visitor/index-t.html

City guide to Charleston, South Carolina. Aimed at the tourist, this site has information on history and geography, as well as features on festivals, and a wide range of travel information.

Charlotte's Web

http://www.charlottecvb.org/

Well-organized site of the Charlotte (North Carolina) Convention and Visitors' Bureau. There's a comprehensive listing of local attractions, hotels, restaurants, and events. The maps provided are also very useful. The pride of the city in its heritage and achievements is clear.

Chattanooga – Come See For Yourself!

http://www.chattanooga.net/cvb

Official guide to Chattanooga from the Convention and Visitors Bureau. There are sections on what to do, wining and dining, accommodation, and local events.

City of Anaheim

http://www.anaheim.net/

Official guide to Anaheim and the surrounding area. This site includes practical information for business people, local residents, and visitors. There is comprehensive coverage of local government services, and a description of local attractions stresses that the area has many other attractions in addition to Disneyland.

Dearborn Online

http://www.dearborn-mi.com/

Good guide to Dearborn. Primarily intended for residents, it has sections on local government services, community groups, job opportunities, and local events. There is also a guide for tourists with comprehensive information on local attractions, accommodation, and restaurants.

Decatur Area Convention and Visitors Bureau

http://www.decaturcvb.com/

Large source of information on this central Illinois city. The needs of business people and tourists are well catered for. There is information on history, local attractions, sporting facilities, entertainment, and the University of Illinois, in addition to reports on the weather and local news.

Denver Online

http://www.denveronline.com/

Information about the city of Denver for visitor and resident alike – with community services, maps, weather reports, and an entertainment guide.

DiveIn Chicago

http://www6.interaccess.com/chicago/

Comprehensive source of current information on life in the 'windy city'. There is an exhaustive list of everything going on in Chicago and lots of practical information. There is even a 'virtual ride' that takes you on a tour of Chicago after dark.

Duluth, Minnesota

http://www.visitduluth.com/

Official guide from the local Convention and Visitors Bureau. This site includes a video and audio clip with a welcome message from the mayor, pictures of Duluth, details of local attractions and accommodation, shipping news, updated local news stories, and a daily weather report.

El Paso, Texas

http://cs.utep.edu/elpaso/main.html

Guide to this quintessential 'cowboy' town. This site contains pictures, maps, and information gathered under such headings as 'History', 'Sites', and 'Events'.

Erie, Pennsylvania

http://www.erie.net/~chamber

Well-organized official guide to Erie from the local chamber of commerce. The needs of visitors, residents, and business people are catered for with comprehensive information. There is an interesting history of the city, a thorough guide to government services, and regularly updated news of local events.

Fairbanks Convention and Visitors Bureau Guide

http://www.explorefairbanks.com/

Official guide from the Fairbanks Convention and Visitor's Bureau. There is comprehensive information on the history of Fairbanks, local wildlife, events, and wilderness tours. All possible needs of winter and summer visitors are catered for on this attractive and well-organized site. During the months of winter darkness there is even a daily Aurora Borealis forecast for this town close to the Arctic Circle.

Fayetteville, North Carolina

http://www.foto.com/fayettevillenc/

Official guide from the Fayetteville Convention and Visitor's Bureau. Information on local attractions and amenities is well-presented. There are number of links, including to nearby Fort Bragg, the USA's largest military installation.

Fort Worth – West and Rest

http://www.fortworth.com/

Well-arranged guide to 'Cowtown' from the Fort Worth Convention and Visitors Bureau. There is a wealth of practical information for business and leisure visitors, as well as sections on local attractions, history, accommodation, shopping, and entertainment, and a good selection of photographs.

Fresno City and County Convention and Visitors Bureau

http://fresno-online.com/cvb/

Well-arranged official guide to Fresno. The needs of vacationers and business people are catered for with information on the history of the city and comprehensive information on local attractions, accommodation, restaurants, transport, and recreation facilities. There are a huge number of links to local institutions, community organizations, and businesses.

Grand Rapids/Kent County Convention and Visitors Bureau

http://www.grcvb.org/

Good official guide to Grand Rapids and the surrounding area. There is a comprehensive listing of attractions and local events, together with a guide to accommodation and eating out.

Greater Buffalo Convention and Visitors Bureau

http://www.buffalocvb.org/

Well-arranged official guide to Buffalo, New York. This site includes details of regional attractions and local events, as well as entertainment, shopping, and accommodation guides.

Greater Columbus Convention and Visitors Bureau

http://columbuscvb.org/

Official guide to the 16th-largest US city. It contains the sort of practical information required by tourists and business travellers and is a comprehensive source of information on local attractions. However, there is no general description of this Ohio city or its history.

Greater Hartford Convention and Visitors Bureau

http://www.grhartfordcvb.com/

Official guide to the Greater Hartford area in Connecticut, from the local convention and visitor's bureau. This well-arranged site has information on local attractions, history, accommodation, and transport. There are also useful links to Yale University and other local institutions.

Greensboro, North Carolina

http://www.greensboronc.org/

Comprehensive official guide from the Greensboro Convention and Visitor's Bureau. Visitors are provided with comprehensive information on local attractions, accommodation, shopping, and transport. There is also a daily weather report and an updated 'What's on' listing.

Houston

http://www.houston-guide.com/

Official guide to the city of Houston, Texas. Clickable points on the city's lone star symbol lead to comprehensive information on facilities and attractions in the city. There is also a host of useful links to other Web sites in Houston.

Johnstown Pennsylvania Historical Information

http://www.johnstownpa.com/history.html

Comprehensive history of Johnstown, Pennsylvania. This Web site begins with the time of the earliest explorers to travel through the area, and follows the city's history right through to the 1990s. The 20 main pages of this Web site are listed in chronological order, each containing a fairly lengthy description of a particular period in the city's history.

Juneau, Alaska – The Capital City Home Page

http://www.juneau.lib.ak.us/juneau.htm

Official information about the Alaskan capital from the local council. This well-organized site caters for the needs of both residents and visitors. There are full details of the work of government departments, the state legislature, and local community organizations. There are also a great number of articles on the history of Juneau. The information for visitors includes a full listing of local attractions, accommodation, local events, and wilderness excursions.

Key West Paradise

http://www.keywestparadise.com/

Tourist-oriented information on the southernmost town in the USA. Surely one of the most multimedia-aware locations on the Internet, the front page features a MIDI file of steel band music and many of the island's main attractions have a 360 degree virtual visit available. The sensation of being able to look in any direction from a static viewpoint alone is worth visiting this site for, and of course there is plenty of other tourist information about the island here too.

Land of Legends – Albuquerque, New Mexico

http://www.abqcvb.org/

Well-presented official guide to Albuquerque. There are informative sections on local history,

Native American culture, cultural events, and accommodation. There is also some advice on correct etiquette when visiting Native American pueblos.

Laramie, Wyoming

http://www.Laramie.org/

Comprehensive guide to the famous Wyoming town. This site includes a good history, a map of the area, business information, and a full listing of recreation and tourist facilities in Laramie and Albany County.

Las Vegas

http://www.klas-tv.com/

Largest source of information on life in the 'entertainment capital of the world'. A search engine gives access to all you could possibly need to know about Vegas – from sites of wedding parlours to the rules of blackjack. There are a host of links, including the Las Vegas Tourist Bureau. This is a good one-stop site for visitors to Vegas.

Lexington Fayette Urban County Government

http://www.lfucg.com/

Good guide to Kentucky's second city. This site includes full details of local government services, community and business information, recreation amenities, and tourist attractions. A virtual tour of Lexington offers a number of thumbnail images and links to many places of interest.

Life of a City: Early Films of New York City, 1898–1906

http://lcweb2.loc.gov/ammem/papr/nychome.html

Part of the American Memory presentation of the US Library of Congress, this collection includes 45 motion pictures of big-city life at the turn of the 20th century, many of which were produced by the Edison Company. Some of the films' subject matter includes immigrants landing at Ellis Island, early views of Broadway and Union Square, a parade of cars, Buffalo Bill and his Wild West show, and the excavation of the Pennsylvania Tunnel. Should you not wish to download the entire film, each title contains sample still-frames. This site also includes an article on New York City at the turn of the century and the collection can be browsed by keyword, subject, or title.

Little Rock

http://www.littlerock.com/lrcvb/

Official guide from this city's Convention and Visitors Bureau. This site is a comprehensive source of information for visitors. Local attractions, events, accommodation, and transport are fully described. Naturally, the city also makes much of its links with Bill Clinton.

Long Beach Convention and Visitors Bureau

http://www.golongbeach.org/mainmenu.htm

Good official guide to those planning to visit or do business in California's fifth-largest city. Information is comprehensive and well-arranged. This site includes details of all local attractions, accommodation, where to eat and drink, events, and night life.

Metropolitan Detroit

http://209.238.191.172/

Official guide to Detroit from the Convention and Visitors Bureau. The needs of both conventioneers and tourists are fully met. A 'What's on' guide is updated each day. There is also a good history of Detroit plus some quirky facts (Detroit had the world's first traffic-lights and has the world's only floating post office).

Miami Information Access

http://miami.info-access.com/

Good starting point for information on Miami. It includes details of activities and attractions, businesses, and hotels in the area, as well as a more locally aimed community notice board and information on local libraries and schools.

Mobile

http://www.mobile.org/home.phtml

Official guide to the Alabaman port from the Convention and Visitors Bureau. A welcome message from the black female mayor highlights the cultural diversity which is the theme of the extensive and fascinating history section. An events list, accommodation and transport guide, and listing of local attractions also help to make this an informative site.

Monterey Guest Life

http://www.guestlife.com/monterey/index.html

Guide to the former Californian capital and the

attractions of the Monterey Peninsula. In addition to a map and practical information for visitors, there is an interesting section on Monterey's artistic heritage and the considerable number of noted authors who have lived and worked in Monterey.

Montgomery

http://www.montgomery.al.us/

Official guide to the Alabaman capital from the Municipality of Montgomery. In addition to information on local government services and community organizations, there is a guide for visitors and links to a number of other local sites.

Mr Miami Beach

http://www.pbs.org/wgbh/pages/amex/miami/

Companion to the US Public Broadcasting Service (PBS) television programme *The American Experience*, this page tells the enthralling story of Carl Graham Fisher, the millionaire who turned a thousand acres of Florida swampland into trendy Miami Beach. There are special illustrated sections on Miami Beach today, which include images and information about the Art Deco District of South Beach, a celebration of the early days of car travel. Send an electronic 'postcard' to a friend by clicking on one of six colourful reproductions of vintage Miami Beach postcards.

Napa Valley Convention and Visitors Bureau

http://www.napavalley.com/napavalley/cvb/nvcvb.html

Official guide to the attractions of California's Napa Valley. In addition to comprehensive information on the history of wine making and local wineries, there is information about other attractions, accommodation, and wining and dining. There is also a daily weather forecast and a full listing of local business and community organizations.

Nashville

http://nashville.musiccityusa.com

Official guide to the mecca of country music from the Nashville Convention and Visitors Bureau. This frequently updated and well-arranged site includes a huge listing of local attractions, information on wining, dining, and

accommodation, as well as news of local events. There is also a good map and a search engine.

New Haven

http://www.newhavencvb.org/

Good guide to New Haven, Connecticut, with comprehensive information for both residents and visitors. Frequently updated with news of local events, local news stories, sports results, and weather reports, this site also has a good history and a virtual tour of Yale University.

New York

http://www.metrobeat.com/

Impressive, user-friendly guide to New York City, filled with practical information. There are interesting feature articles and constant updates on what's on in the Big Apple. If the pace of life gets too hectic, the search engine can even provide a comprehensive listing of mind and body healing centres.

Official St Louis Visitors Guide

http://www.st-louis-cvc.com/

Official guide to St Louis. The needs of visitors are well catered for with maps, transport information, a list of local attractions, accommodation lists, a guide to local nightlife, and suggestions for day trips.

Oklahoma City

http://www.okccvb.org/

Well-organized official guide to Oklahoma City from the local convention and visitor's bureau. A tour of the city presents Oklahoma's rich history while highlighting it's current attractions. There is a useful map of the city, comprehensive accommodation details, and regularly updated news of local events.

Online Guide to Greater Louisville

http://www.louisville-visitors.com/

Good official guide to Louisville from the Convention and Visitors Bureau. The site offers comprehensive information on local attractions, events, accommodation, transport, and business services. There is a good history of Louisville and a listing of famous residents (topped by Muhammad Ali).

Pasadena

http://pasadena.citysearch.com/entry/start.html

Comprehensive and searchable guide to Pasadena. The needs of visitors are comprehensively met with information on local attractions, cultural activities, local events, accommodation, and nightlife. Residents are catered for with full details of local government functions and community groups.

Passporte! Your Complete Travel Guide to San Francisco

http://bayarea.citysearch.com/San_Francisco/Hotels_and_Tourism/

Thorough guide to San Francisco, California. There is a comprehensive list of all the attractions, accommodation, and events happening in this US city. A helpful price guide, for those unused to the value of the US dollar, converts prices into a currency of your choice. There is a good search engine and a vast number of links to other sites in this vibrant city guide.

Philadelphia Official Internet Visitors Guide

http://libertynet.org/phila-visitor/

Official guide to the 'city of brotherly love' in the USA. This site provides comprehensive details of the city's past in addition to the more practical information required by visitors.

Phoenix and Valley of the Sun

http://www.arizonaguide.com/index.html

Official guide to the USA's seventh-largest city from the convention and visitors bureau. This well-arranged site caters for the needs of newly-arrived residents and visitors. Information not immediately accessible from the home page can be reached through the good search engine.

Portland

http://katu.citysearch.com/

Professional and comprehensive guide to Portland, Oregon. The needs of visitors are comprehensively met with information on local attractions, cultural activities, local events, accommodation, and night life. Residents are served with full details of local government functions, community groups and local businesses. Updated on a daily basis with local news stories, this site also has a search engine.

Refreshingly Different Modesto

http://www.ainet.com/mcvb

Good guide to the city which boasts the world's largest winery. Organized by the convention and visitors bureau, the site provides information on the history of the city, accommodation, places to eat and drink, and local attractions.

Reno

http://www.playreno.com/

Comprehensive guide to the north Nevadan town and nearby Lake Tahoe. In addition to a large amount of information on gaming, there are sections on dining, shopping, transport, golf, skiing, and other recreation activities.

Saginaw Overview

http://www.saginawpartners.org/body_saginaw.htm

Profile of Saginaw from the local Chamber of Commerce. There is a description of the local industrial base, agriculture, recreation facilities, cultural events, and nature reserves.

Saint John, New Brunswick

http://www.city.saint-john.nb.ca/

Official guide to St John. This site includes details of local business life, local government, recreation activities, transportation, and accommodation. A link to the local tourist department lists nearby attractions and outlines the history of the city founded by displaced American loyalists.

Salt Lake City

http://www.saltlake.org

Good official guide to those planning to visit or do business in Utah's capital. The home page looks crowded but allows access to a vast amount of well arranged information. Accommodation is searchable by category and by location. An interactive map leads to information on local attractions. There is regularly updated news of local events and skiing conditions.

San Diego

http://www.city.net/countries/united_states/california/san_diego/

Exhaustive guide to the city of San Diego, including detailed outlines of places of interest to visit, a guide to where to eat, where to stay, sports and recreational facilities, and travel information.

Santa Cruz

http://www.guestlife.com/monterey/areas/areassanta.html

General introduction to Santa Cruz county. This site includes descriptions of the local landscape, local attractions, and information about the local branch of the University of California.

Santa Fe

http://www.santafe.org/

Visitors are offered climate and geographical information, brief expositions of the Native American, Hispanic, and European traditions that blend within the boundaries of the city, tours to historic downtown sites, and listings of art events in the city. There is a well-presented introduction to the culture and the city of Santa Fe in New Mexico, on lodging, restaurants, and the cuisine. They can also avail themselves of maps of the area, a calendar of local events, and a 'Fast facts' sheet.

Saratoga County Travel Guide

http://www.saratoga.org/

Official chamber of commerce guide to Saratoga. There is a good history of the region and brief information about horse-racing, cultural events, and local attractions.

Seattle

http://www.ci.seattle.wa.us/

Large collection of information on the city of Seattle, Washington. It includes details about the environment, recreational activities, places of interest to visit, musical venues, theatres, and transportation, as well as traffic-flow reports and maps.

Seven Tours of Philadelphia

http://www.ushistory.org/districts/historicdistrict/index.html

Prepared by the Independence Hall Association of Philadelphia, this impressive site offers seven detailed virtual tours through Philadelphia, including the Historic District, North of Market Street, Benjamin Franklin Parkway, Washington Square, and Society Hill. For each tour, the screen is divided into sections that permit easy navigation. Each tour includes an interactive map and text with numerous images. The Historic District tour takes you through many of the most important buildings and sites of Revolution-era US history, such as Independence Hall and the Liberty Bell.

Sioux City

http://www.siouxlan.com/ccat

Well-arranged official guide to Sioux City. Information is provided on local events, business, shopping, accommodation, wining and dining, and tourist attractions. There is also a daily weather report.

Springfield Convention and Visitor's Bureau

http://www.springfield.il.us/visit/

Official guide to Springfield. This site (entered by clicking the nose of the city's most famous son, Abraham Lincoln) provides a wide range of information on history, local attractions, and accommodation.

Step into the Real Texas – Amarillo

http://www.amarillo-cvb.org

Well-organized official guide to Amarillo and the Texas Panhandle. The needs of both tourists and business people are well catered for. There is a complete list of local attractions and events, information on accommodation, and links to a number of sites in Amarillo. Navigation is helped by a pair of Stetsons which invite you to mosey on back to the home page.

Visit Tucson – Arizona's Other Natural Wonder

http://www.arizonaguide.com/cities/tucson/index.html

Official guide to Tucson. This site includes a history of the city, a guide to local business, and a comprehensive listing of tourist attractions. Current events are listed and there is even advice to travel writers on interesting aspects of the city and its heritage they might choose to write about.

Washington DC

http://www.washington.org/

Site of the Washington DC Convention and Visitors' Association. This is a helpful guide filled with practical information for tourists and details of the attractions in the Washington area. There is also a useful set of maps.

Welcome to Dayton, Ohio

http://dayton.bettertown.net/

Comprehensive guide to the US city that styles itself as the 'birthplace of aviation'. This site includes community, government, and business information, local news stories, and a regular weather report.

Welcome to Destination Long Island, NY

http://www.licvb.com/

Good official guide to Long Island from the local convention and visitors bureau. All needs of visitors are well catered for on this easily navigable site. There are details of the attractions, restaurants, places to stay, exhibitions, sports facilities, and guided tours.

F A C T

LONG ISLAND

island east of Manhattan and southeast of Connecticut, USA, separated from the mainland by Long Island Sound and the East River; population (1990) 6,861,500. It is mainly a residential district with farming in the east.

Welcome to Lansing, Michigan

http://www.lansing.org/

Official guide to the Michigan capital from the local convention and visitors bureau. The needs of business people and visitors are well catered for on this easily navigable site.

Welcome to New Orleans

http://www.nawlins.com/

Thorough official source of information on New Orleans. The site is indispensable for visitors to the city and has a comprehensive search engine.

Welcome to the Official Site of Broward County, Florida

http://www.co.broward.fl.us/

Clearly-presented information about Fort Lauderdale and the surrounding area. In addition to information on local government services and local community organizations, there is a good guide for visitors filled with practical information on local attractions, accommodation, and wining and dining. There is also a map, a history of the area, a daily weather report, and a huge number of links to related sites.

Welcome to the Web Site for Ann Arbor, Michigan

http://www.annarbor.org

Official guide to Ann Arbor from the convention and visitors bureau. The regularly updated contents of this site include a local events listing, sports news, weather report, and history. There is also a live image from downtown Ann Arbor that is updated every two minutes throughout the day and night.

Williamsburg Online

http://www.williamsburg.com/

Home page of the reconstructed colonial town in Virginia, with a guide on where to eat, sleep, shop, and play golf. The site contains plenty of information and detailed historical maps of the town as it was in colonial times.

Woonsocket – My Home Town – History and Culture of Woonsocket

http://www.geocities.com/Athens/Parthenon/9105/

Woonsocket, Rhode Island, culture and history page. In addition to describing the past of the city, this Web site includes many photographs of the present city. Visitors can take a virtual trip down the Main Street or around the local museum, or just take a look at Woonsocket's new downtown area.

You're Something Special in Winston-Salem

http://www.winstonsalem.com/

Good official guide to North Carolina's fourth-largest city. There is a history, several maps, a list of local attractions, an events guide, and details of accommodation to assist visitors. The business information section includes a good guide to the city's technology sector.

US States

Alabama History Page

http://www.mindspring.com/~rjones/

Ample audio-visual and other archive material about Old Alabama Town collected by a proud Alabaman (and obviously a Web devotee). The site features an Alabama Heritage Calendar, photos of lithographs from the early 1900s, excerpts from Governors' inaugural speeches, and an audio clip of the state song.

Alaska OnLine

http://www.alaskanet.com/index.html

Among the attractions of this site on the 50th state are the pages on the marine ecosystem of Alaska and those on Iditasport – the ultimate winter race through the vast terrain of Alaska. The site also provides ample material on the cultural, tourist, and historical attractions of the area.

Best of Hawaii

http://www.bestofhawaii.com/

Jumping-off point for visitors seeking information about the best of Hawaii. This site includes a wealth of information aimed at the tourist – including maps, food, weather, accommodation, and even an online version of the Hawaiian phone directory.

In the Beginning Was the Word

http://www.loc.gov/exhibits/russian/s1a.html

Exhibition on the relations between Russians and Alaskans from the time of the Alaskan discovery instigated by Peter the Great up to the beginning of this century. The exhibits, including letters, decrees, maps, lithographic reprints, and other visual material, chart the different stages in the confrontation of Alaskans and Russians, the role of the Russian church in Alaskan trade and government, and its importance in the preservation of Alaskan language and culture.

Inupiat of Arctic Alaska

http://www.lib.uconn.edu/ArcticCircle/HistoryCulture/Inupiat/

Historical, cultural, and social information about the indigenous people of Arctic Alaska, including a discussion of the many natural impediments facing the Inupiat and how they have applied ingenuity to survive. This site includes many images of Inupiat life, an Inupiat aboriginal calendar, and a link to information on the Land Claims Settlement Act of 1971.

Kodiak Island

http://www.alaskaone.com/kodiak/

Official guide to Kodiak Island, Alaska. There are comprehensive details of the range of wilderness activities available in the area and practical information for visitors. There is also a map and daily weather forecast.

Virtual Field Trip

http://hawaii.ivv.nasa.gov/space/hawaii/virtual.field.trips.html

Virtual field trips around the islands of Hawaii for educators, geologists, or simply potential tourists, funded by NASA's 'Infrastructure and Technology' programme. These trips take you on different tours around the islands. Visitors are shown parts of Hawaii from space and the air, as well as ground photos of points of interest.

Mississippi Village Home Page: Towns and Villages

http://www.greatriver.com/maps/mrpc.htm

Extensive and detailed itinerary of attractions in towns and villages along the entire Mississippi River, from Minnesota, Wisconsin, Iowa, Illinois, Missouri, Kentucky, Tennessee, Arkansas, Mississippi, and Louisiana.

North Carolina Encyclopedia

http://statelibrary.dcr.state.nc.us/NC/COVER.HTM

Web site run by the State Library of North Carolina that provides details on many aspects of the state. The site includes, among the general and geographical data, historical information from the time of Raleigh's settlement of Roanoke Island, USA. Curious facts also abound here, including a section on the state vegetable of North Carolina.

Pennsylvania History

http://www.ushistory.org/pennsylvania/index.html

This page concerns the early history of the area that would become the US state of Pennsylvania from 1630 to 1776. It includes several articles regarding the earliest Dutch settlers, William Penn's charter, and the formation of the Commonwealth of Pennsylvania.

Prehistory of Alaska

http://www.nps.gov/akso/akarc/

Alaska's prehistory divided into five sections: 'early prehistory', 'tundra and Arctic Alaska', 'southeast Alaska', 'southwest Alaska and Pacific coast', and 'interior Alaska'. there are also links to Alaska's 15 national parks and preserves – click on the acronym to access a general description of each park's cultural resources.

Welcome to Arkansas USA

http://www.arkansasUSA.com/

Lots of useful information about Arkansas state with community and property pages and sections on business, arts, sports, outdoor activities, and shopping. Due to the well known political connections of the state, the site also offers accounts of vital issues of the US administration.

West Virginia

http://wvweb.com/

Concise guide to the state of West Virginia. This site includes details of its cities, places of interest to visit, government organizations, and where to go shopping.

US Significant Sites & Landmarks

Alaska's Cold Desert

http://www.blm.gov/education/arctic/arctic.html

Sponsored by the US Bureau of Land Management, this site explores Alaska's unique arctic ecosystem, with a special focus on the adaptations required of plants and animals to survive the stressful climate. This site also investigates conservation issues, such as the challenges facing public and private land managers who must conserve this ecosystem while accommodating growing demands for development. There are also classroom activities.

Ellis Island Home Page

http://www.ellisisland.org/

Ellis Island Immigration Museum Web site. The site includes a description of the museum and a 'wall of honour' of family names that have passed through the immigration centre there. More practical visitor information is also available should you require it.

Explore the Hudson Valley's Rich History

http://www.hudsonriver.com/history.htm

Extensive and engaging account of the rich history of Hudson valley and river in New York State, USA. The article includes details on the life, society, and resources of the region from as early as 1609, when the Englishman Henry Hudson sailed along the river, thinking that he was just discovering a quick passage to China.

Ghost Towns of Arizona

http://www.swlink.net/~pjcat/ghost.html

Small but gripping tour through the ruins of the dead towns of Arizona, which were created in the late 19th century and abandoned by the 1920s. This site offers photos from the deserted buildings and brief accounts of their short lives. Promising to bring in more evidence soon, the site is important for everyone interested in the everyday aspects of American history.

Grand Canyon

http://www.kaibab.org/

Visitors to this site will find an outline of the geological and human history tracing the gradual conquest of the Canyon, and a spectacular photo gallery with close-ups and panoramas. There are also details of recommended hikes and trails, and you can discover valuable tips on hiking and backpacking.

Grand Canyon Flood

http://www.pbs.org/kuat/grandcanyonflood/

Companion to a US Public Broadcasting Service (PBS) television programme, this site documents a scientific experiment to restore a more natural balance to the ecosystem of the Grand Canyon by opening up Glen Canyon Dam and flooding the Colorado River. Click on the interactive map of the Colorado River to tour research sites and learn about some of the anticipated, as well as the unanticipated, outcomes. You can also learn about possible future implications of the Grand Canyon flood. You will find information on why the experiment was conducted, profiles of the scientists involved, and more. This site includes video clips of the flood in progress and a section on classroom activities.

Grand Teton National Park

http://www.nps.gov/grte/

Good guide to the Tetons from the US National Park Service. This site includes geology, flora and fauna, a map of the park, guide to popular hikes, and detailed information on a wide range of outdoor activities. There is a good bibliography and link to the Grand Teton Natural History Association.

High Plains: Land of Extremes

http://www.blm.gov/education/
high_plains/high_plains.html

Sponsored by the US Bureau of Land Management, this site investigates the grasslands of the High Plains east of the Rocky Mountains of the USA. This site explores how plants and animals have adapted to the harsh conditions and looks at the unique characteristics of the High Plains ecosystem, primarily the northern portion, and methods of improving and sustaining the health and productivity of this vast grassland.

Interactive Sante Fe Trail

http://raven.cc.ukans.edu/heritage/research/sft/

Comprehensive guide to the Sante Fe Trail from the University of Kansas. In addition to a full history of the trail (and useful resources for history teachers), there is a host of practical information for those wishing to re-tread the pioneers' footsteps. There are many images of places along the trail and a huge number of links to other online information.

Johnston Atoll National Wildlife Refuge

http://bluegoose.arw.r9.fws.gov/NWRSFiles/Refug
eSystemLeaflets/R1/IP/Johnston/Johnston.html

US Fish and Wildlife Service guide to the geology, ecology, flora, and fauna of this island still contaminated by nuclear fall-out and now maintained as a storage site for chemical munitions. There is a history of the island and information on its endangered species and migratory birds.

Lake Champlain and Lake George Historical Site

http://www.geocities.com/~jmillard/

Dedicated to the history of the two lakes in Vermont, that played a key role in the Anglo-French conflicts in the region in the early part of the 18th century. The Web site is divided into several subpages, each containing a different type of information. For example there is a page offering a tour of the historical islands of Lake George, and another offers a geographical map of the area. Perhaps the best starting point for visitors is the site map, which lists all the

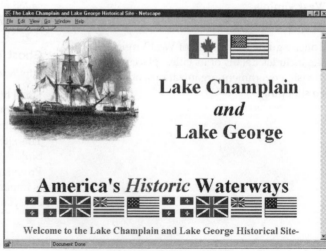

resources available on this Web site and offers hyperlinks to them.

Mesa Verde National Park

http://www.nps.gov/meve/mvnp/pages/mvnp.htm

Complete guide to this World Heritage Site – the first US National Park set up to preserve prehistoric culture. This large and well-organized site has a very full account of geological research, archaeological findings about Pueblo culture, and a comprehensive history of the area. The needs of visitors are catered for with a wealth of practical information.

Niagara Falls Convention and Visitors Bureau

http://www.nfcvb.com/

Official guide to the Niagara area in the state of New York. In addition to interesting facts about the falls, there is extensive information on local tours, transport, accommodation, places to eat, local festivals, and events.

Oregon Trail: The Trail West

http://www.ukans.edu/kansas/seneca/oregon/index.html

Comprehensive Web site dealing with the settlers' trail to the West. The trail is followed through all the states on its route, each state presented as a different page on this Web site. The history of the state of Oregon is also described here, as are various other related settler trails.

Pike's Peak Country – A Mountain of Good Times

http://www.pikes-peak.com/

Comprehensive guide to the many tourist facilities and attractions in this part of Colorado. It includes sections on shopping, maps, eating, transportation, and even a history of the famous eponymous peak at the heart of this region.

Rocky Mountains National Park

http://www.csn.net/~arthurvb/rmnp/rmnp.html

Unofficial guide to the large Coloradan national park compiled from visitors' reports. There is comprehensive coverage of all the facilities in the park and guides to history, wildlife, and all park trails. There is also a series of detailed maps and a daily weather report.

Saratoga National Historical Park

http://www.nps.gov:80/sara/f-sara.htm

Well-arranged official guide to the famous battle site. There is a good history of the events leading up to the battle with biographies of the leading protagonists. A clickable map of the battle site facilitates understanding of the events that led to the historic British defeat. In addition, there is practical information for visitors to the historical park and details of educational activities.

Total Yellowstone Page

http://www.yellowstone-natl-park.com/

Guide to the world's longest established national park. This site includes a history of the park, information about hiking, wildlife, accommodation, fishing and driving, daily weather reports, and a guide to the geysers. There are also regular updates of a project to reintroduce wolves into the park.

Welcome to the Adirondack Region

http://www.adirondacks.org/

Comprehensive official guide to the Adirondacks. There is a good overview of the region and its history. All possible needs of visitors –whether motorists, canoeists, cyclists, snowmobilers, or hikers – are covered and an interactive map facilitates navigation around this well-presented site.

Welcome to the Official Web Site of the Golden Gate Bridge

http://www.goldengate.org/

Full source of information on the bridge. A history section deals with construction and subsequent improvements to San Francisco's famous landmark. There are technical details, many photographs, and practical information for tourists.

Canada

Acadian Cultural Society Page de la Maison

http://www.angelfire.com/ma/1755/

Run by the Acadian Cultural Society, this page describes Acadian history. The site features a section on Acadian genealogical research specifically aimed at those of Acadian descent, and links to other Acadian resources on the Web are also listed.

Cape Breton Island, Atlantic Canada's Masterpiece

http://www.cbisland.com/core.html

Good official guide to the island. An interactive map gives access to information from all districts on attractions, accommodation, cultural heritage, and a range of recreational activities.

Fredericton

http://www.city.fredericton.nb.ca/welcome.html

Official guide to Fredericton. There is information about local government services, business life, community organizations, and local attractions. Maps, a weather report, and accommodation and events listings are other useful features of this site.

Montreal

http://www.montreal-live.com/

Both historical and contemporary information on Montreal. Visitors can choose from a general presentation of the city and its development, tourist information, specialized overviews of arts, architecture, and business in the city, and a review of the history of the Olympic Games.

Ottawa History

http://www.dickshovel.com/otta.html

Large Web site on the history of the Ottawa people. The comprehensive information contained in the site is all on one page, and is in the format of a very large text file. The topics covered on the Web site include lists of village names, culture, history of the tribes, population, sub-nations, and the geographical distribution of the Ottawa people.

Québec City and Area

http://www.quebec-region.cuq.qc.ca/eng/otc1e.html

Comprehensive guide to the history, culture, and attractions of the only fortified city in North America. The practical needs of visitors are fully met with information on accommodation, restaurants, local events, and sites of interest.

Québec History at a Glance

http://www.tourisme.gouv.qc.ca/anglais/tourisme_a/histoire_a.html

Introduction to the history, culture, and economy of Québec. It is accompanied by photos of the province and a video. This is part of the official site of the Québec government which contains a wealth of information on the provincial government, economic opportunities, tourist information, and local news stories.

Saskatoon – City of Bridges

http://duke.usask.ca/~lowey/Saskatoon/index.html

Official guide to Saskatoon. There is a good history of the evolution into the largest city of the former temperance colony of Saskatchewan. Local amenities, attractions, and events are listed, together with local government services. The pride of the city in its achievements shines through in this well-arranged site.

Thousand Islands Virtual Travel Guide

http://www.visit1000islands.com/index.htm

Official Canadian-American guide to the Thousand Islands. There is comprehensive information for visitors on a range of leisure pursuits including fishing, hunting, hiking, golf, boating, and bungee jumping. Information on these topics can be accessed via an interactive map.

Toronto Star City Search

http://www.starcitysearch.com/

Huge source of information on Canada's largest city. Primarily designed for residents, this site is constantly updated with news of local events, community groups, local government, cultural life, sport, and weather. For visitors there is information on accommodation and tourist attractions. There is also a good search engine.

TourOttawa

http://www.tourottawa.org/index.html-ssi

Official guide to Canada's fourth-largest city and national capital. Information provided for visitors includes transport, accommodation, local events, and things to do.

Vancouver – Spectacular by Nature

http://www.tourism-vancouver.org/

Official guide to Vancouver, from the convention and visitors bureau. There are 'Frequently Asked Questions' about the city, listings of accommodation, restaurants, and local attractions as well as some useful transport information. Navigation around this site can be difficult, but there is a search engine to help find what you want.

Welcome to the Bay of Fundy

http://www.tourismnbcanada.com/web/english/pla nit!/driveit!.asp?drive=fundy

Colourful guide to the bay and its natural and man-made attractions. There is a good explanation of the reasons why it has the world's most dramatic tides. There is also a well-organized virtual tour around the Bay, accompanied by good photographs.

Welcome to the City of Victoria

http://www.City.Victoria.BC.CA/

Thorough official guide to western Canada's oldest city. There is an illustrated history, as well as a wealth of practical information for tourists, and sections on local government and business services.

Welcome to the Sault St Marie Convention and Visitors Bureau

http://www.saultstemarie.com/

Thorough official guide to Sault St Marie. This site includes a good history of the city, accommodation and events listings, gambling information, restaurant guide, and sports news.

Welcome to Whitehorse Online

http://www.city.whitehorse.yk.ca/

Official guide to Canada's most westerly city. There are details of local government services, business activities, and community groups. Information for visitors includes local attractions, suggested drives and hikes, and a guide to the Klondike Bathtub Race and other events.

Winnipeg

http://www.Tourism.Winnipeg.MB.CA/

Comprehensive official guide to the Manitoban capital. There is a full account of how the former fur-trading centre has evolved into a modern entrepreneurial city. Practical information for visitors includes maps, listings of events and attractions, and tour advice.

Yellowknife – Capital City of the Northwest Territories

http://www.ssimicro.com/ftpages/yellok.html

Information about the history, society, and attractions of Yellowknife. Among the local pursuits described are log sawing, ice sculpting, dog sled racing, and a midnight golf competition.

Central & Latin America, Caribbean & West Indies

Acapulco Today

http://accessmexico.com/acapulco/

Cornucopia of images, maps, news, and general information on this Mexican seaside resort – its culture, nightlife, food, and events. This site also includes details of local archaeological digs and an exploration of the Mayan world, with many links to other Mexican sites.

Anguilla

http://www.umsl.edu/services/govdocs/wofact96/ 16.htm

Geographical, economic, and population information about Anguilla held by the CIA on their World Fact Book Web site. The information contained here is both extensive and comprehensive, from life expectancy to military manpower, and all points between.

Aruba

http://www.umsl.edu/services/govdocs/wofact96/ 22.htm

CIA-run Web site cataloguing the state of current affairs on the Caribbean Dutch dependency. The information provided includes that on population, politics, and geographical areas among others. Maps and images of the national flag are also available to download.

Bon Bini – Welcome to Aruba

http://www.interknowledge.com/aruba/anscripts/
default.asp?

Aruba Tourism Authority guide to the Caribbean island which is an autonomous part of the Netherlands. This easily navigable site has lots of information on the culture and history of Aruba and a wealth of practical information required by visitors. In the unlikely event that you can't find what you are looking for, a useful facility allows you to e-mail a question to the tourism authority.

British Virgin Islands

http://www.umsl.edu/services/govdocs/wofact96/
46.htm

CIA-run Web site providing in-depth information on the British Caribbean islands. The site also includes some downloadable images of the national flag and a brief map of the islands.

Cayman Islands

http://www.umsl.edu/services/govdocs/wofact96/
56.htm

Political and economic details of the Caribbean islands famous for their low taxes. This site run by the CIA contains information on almost every aspect of life on the island, and also contains some downloadable files with maps and images of the national flag.

Copán Ruins Home Page

http://www.honduras.net/copan/index.html

Home Page of the Copán ruins in western Honduras. The site includes photographs, historical details, and general tourist information about the ruined city. The site also includes a photographic and audio tour of the ruins, their associated museum, and visitor centre.

Turks and Caicos Gateway

http://www.turksandcaicos.tc/

Well-organized site promoting tourism and investment opportunities in the British Caribbean colony. There is a map of the archipelago and information on transportation, accommodation, education, and local attractions. There are also some good photographs to accompany the text.

Welcome to the Panama Canal

http://www.mrtc.org/~twright/panama/pan004.htm

Good source of information on the organization, operation, and history of the Panama Canal from its operating authority. Photographs and diagrams help explain the workings of the canal and its system of locks.

South America, not Brazil

Amazon Interactive

http://www.eduweb.com/amazon.html

Interactive guide to the Amazon River, specifically focusing on the part that runs through Ecuador but covering all aspects of the river. There are many photographs and illustrations, text on different aspects and questions designed to test your knowledge on such areas as climate, geography, and inhabitants, as well as an 'Ecotourism simulation game' which puts you in control of an ecotourism project in the region.

F A C T

RIVER
a river originates at a point called its source, and enters a sea or lake at its mouth. Along its length it may be joined by smaller rivers called tributaries. The point at which two rivers join is called the confluence.

Andean History

http://www.ddg.com/LIS/aurelia/andhis.htm

History of the Andes, from aboriginal societies to the fast-growing nations of the present day, with links to the countries and from there to Andean geography, geology, climate, flora, and fauna.

Arequipa, Peru

http://cityguide.lycos.com/southamerica/nw_sam/
PERArequipa.html

Profile of the 'white city' of Arequipa in southern Peru. There is a general introduction to the city's main features, and four sections – 'visitors' guide', 'culture and history', 'news and weather', and 'entertainment' – each with links to further useful information in English and Spanish about both the city and the country.

Asunción, Paraguay

http://cityguide.lycos.com/southamerica/east_sam/
PRYAsuncion.html

Profile of Asunción, capital of Paraguay. There is a general introduction to its main features, and four sections – 'visitors' guide', 'culture and history', 'news and weather', and 'entertainment' – with links to photographs, and to further useful information in English and Spanish about the city and the country.

Bermuda

http://www.umsl.edu/services/govdocs/wofact96/
38.htm

CIA-run Web site giving details of this island's economy, politics, and geography. The facts presented here are very in-depth and provide the user with a clear picture of the island. An image of the national flag is also available for downloading, as are some brief maps of the island.

Bogotá, Colombia

http://cityguide.lycos.com/southamerica/
north_sam/COLBogota.html

Page devoted to Colombia's largest city, Bogotá. There is a general introduction to the city's attractions, and four sections – 'visitor's guide', 'culture and history', 'news and weather', and 'entertainment' – each with links to further useful information in both English and Spanish about both the city and the country.

Buenos Aires, Argentina

http://cityguide.lycos.com/southamerica/
south_sam/ARGBuenosAires.html

Profile of Argentina's multi-ethnic capital, Buenos Aires. There is a general introduction to the city's main features, and four sections – 'visitors' guide', 'culture and history', 'news and weather', and 'entertainment' – with links to photographs, and to further useful information in English and Spanish about the city and the country.

Cali, Colombia

http://cityguide.lycos.com/southamerica/
north_sam/COLCali.html

Page devoted to the Colombian city of Cali. There is a general introduction to the city's attractions and mention of its association with the drug

trade, as well as four sections – 'visitors' guide', 'culture and history', 'news and weather', and 'entertainment' – each with links to further useful information in English and Spanish about both the city and the country.

Caracas, Venezuela

http://cityguide.lycos.com/southamerica/
north_sam/VENCaracas.html

Profile of Venezuela's cosmopolitan capital, Caracas. There is a general introduction to the city's main features, and four sections – 'visitors' guide', 'culture and history', 'news and weather', and 'entertainment' – each with links to further information in English and Spanish about both the city and the country.

Cartagena, Colombia

http://www.liat.com/cartagena.htm

Page devoted to the ancient Colombian city of Cartagena. There is a general introduction to the city's attractions, and four sections – 'visitors' guide', 'culture and history', 'news and weather', and 'entertainment' – each with links to further useful information in English and Spanish about both the city and the country.

Cayenne, French Guiana

http://cityguide.lycos.com/southamerica/
north_sam/GUFCayenne.html

Profile of Cayenne, capital of French Guiana. There is a general introduction to the city's attractions, and four sections – 'visitors' guide', 'culture and history', 'news and weather', and 'entertainment' – each with links to further useful information about both the city and the country.

Culture of the Andes

http://www.andes.org

Photographs, music, poems, and stories from the Andean people of Bolivia, Peru, Ecuador, Argentina, and Chile, plus a lesson in the Quechua language and some Quechuan jokes.

Cuzco, Peru

http://cityguide.lycos.com/southamerica/nw_sam/
PERCuzco.html

Page devoted to the ancient Peruvian city of Cuzco. There is a general introduction to the city's main features, and four sections – 'visitors' guide', 'culture and history', 'news and weather', and 'entertainment' – each with links to further useful information in English and Spanish about both the city and the country.

Falkland Islands Showcase

http://www.vni.net/~kwelch/penguins/showcase/showcase_Falklands.shtml

Well-illustrated site showing off the various aspects of life on the Falkland Islands. Information on history, wildlife, vegetation, and people is supplemented by a number of colour photographs.

Fernando De Noronha

http://www.noronha.com.br/indexe.htm

Examination of the unique ecosystem of the isolated archipelago of Fernando de Noronha, off the northeastern coast of Brazil. With dozens of colourful photographs, this site provides an informative insight into the islands and their history and includes a photo gallery of some of the flora and fauna. There are also details on how to get there and where to stay.

Georgetown, Guyana

http://cityguide.lycos.com/southamerica/north_sam/GUYGeorgetown.html

Profile of Guyana's attractive capital, Georgetown. There is a general introduction to the city's main features, and four sections – 'visitors' guide', 'culture and history', 'news and weather', and 'entertainment' – each with links to further useful information about both the city and the country.

Guayaquil, Ecuador

http://cityguide.lycos.com/southamerica/nw_sam/ECUGuayaquil.html

Profile of the city of Guayaquil, Ecuador's busiest port. There is a general introduction to the city's main features, and four sections – 'visitors' guide', 'culture and history', 'news and weather', and 'entertainment' – each with links to photographs, and further information in English and Spanish about both the city and the country.

Iguaçu Falls – Great Water

http://darkwing.uoregon.edu/~sergiok/brasil/iguacu.html

Stunning photography and description of the Brazilian falls which in Guarani mean 'great water'. There is also information on the vegetation and the Guarani.

Kingdom of Araucania and Patagonia

http://www.geocities.com/Athens/Crete/2954/index.html

History of the kingdom founded in 1860 by Mapuche Indians. The page includes links to the Mapuche nation, a royal portrait gallery, maps, and essays, as well as details about the Royal House of Araucania in exile. The site is maintained by the North American Araucanian Royalist Society.

La Paz, Bolivia

http://cityguide.lycos.com/southamerica/east_sam/BOLLaPaz.html

Profile of La Paz, Bolivia, the highest capital city in the world. There is a general introduction to the city's main features, and four sections – 'visitors' guide', 'culture and history', 'news and weather', and 'entertainment and photos' – with links to photographs, and to useful information in English and Spanish about both the city and the country.

Lima, Peru

http://cityguide.lycos.com/southamerica/nw_sam/PERLima.html

Profile of the historic city of Lima, capital of Peru. There is a general introduction to the city's main features, and four sections – 'visitors' guide', 'culture and history', 'news and weather', and 'entertainment' – each with links to further useful information in English and Spanish about both the city and the country.

Manu: Peru's Hidden Rainforest

http://www.pbs.org/edens/manu/

Companion to the US Public Broadcasting Service (PBS) television programme *The Living Edens*, this page investigates the flora and fauna of the Manu Rainforest of Peru. Click on images of the plants and animals to read brief descriptions of them. You can also learn about conservation issues, explore the cultures of native tribes who inhabit this remote area, and find out about the medicinal plants that heal their people. You can also read the producer's journal, which documents his explorations and research into the secluded Yura tribe. Once you have browsed the various sections, test your knowledge with the trivia quiz. There is also a list of resources and links for further research.

Medellín, Colombia

http://cityguide.lycos.com/southamerica/north_sam/COLMedellin.html

Page devoted to the Colombian city of Medellín, a busy industrial and commercial centre. There is a general introduction to the city's attractions, and four sections – 'visitors' guide', 'culture and history', 'news and weather', and 'entertainment' – each with links to further useful information in English and Spanish about both the city and the country.

Mendoza, Argentina

http://cityguide.lycos.com/southamerica/south_sam/ARGMendoza.html

Profile of the city of Mendoza, centre of Argentina's wine-producing area. There is a general introduction to the city's main features, and four sections – 'visitors' guide', 'culture and history', 'news and weather', and 'entertainment' – with links to photographs, and to further useful information in English and Spanish about the city and the country.

Paramaribo, Suriname

http://cityguide.lycos.com/southamerica/north_sam/SURParamaribo.html

Profile of Surinam's historic capital, Paramaribo. There is a general introduction to the city's main features, and four sections – 'visitors' guide', 'culture and history', 'news and weather', and 'entertainment' – each with links to further information in English and Dutch about both the city and the country.

Patagonia: Life at the End of the Earth

http://www.pbs.org/edens/patagonia/

Companion to the US Public Broadcasting Service (PBS) television programme *The Living Edens,* this page explores the natural history of Patagonia, including the Ephemeral Lakes, Punta Tombo, and the National Parks of Los Glaciares and Torres del Paine. Read what the experts have to say about conservation issues in Patagonia and the migration of the Megellanic penguins. Learn about the human inhabitants of this challenging

environment. Once you have browsed the various sections, test your knowledge with the trivia quiz. There is also a list of resources and links for further research.

Potosí, Bolivia

http://cityguide.lycos.com/southamerica/east_sam/BOLPotosi.html

Profile of Potosí, Bolivia, once one of South America's wealthiest cities. There is a general introduction to its main features, and four sections – 'visitors' guide', 'culture and history', 'news and weather', and 'entertainment and photos' – with links to photographs, and to further useful information in English and Spanish about both the city and the country.

Quito, Ecuador

http://cityguide.lycos.com/southamerica/nw_sam/ECUQuito.html

Profile of the Ecuadorian capital, the beautiful city of Quito. There is a general introduction to the city's attractions, and four sections – 'visitors' guide', 'culture and history', 'news and weather', and 'entertainment' – each with links to further useful information in English and Spanish about both the city and the country.

Santa Cruz, Bolivia

http://cityguide.lycos.com/southamerica/east_sam/BOLSantaCruz.html

Profile of the tropical city of Santa Cruz in Bolivia. There is a general introduction to its main features, and four sections – 'visitors' guide', 'culture and history', 'news and weather', and 'entertainment and photos' – with links to photographs, and to further useful information in English and Spanish about both the city and the country.

Santiago

http://sunsite.dcc.uchile.cl/chile/turismo/santiago.html

Comprehensive introduction to Chile's capital city, Santiago. The page includes information about historical landmarks, cultural and artistic life, its natural environment, shopping, restaurants, conference centres, and its suburbs, as well as general information about population, climate, language, and transport. There is also a list of useful addresses in the city.

Sentinel of Stone – Mountaineering on the Aconcagua

http://www.aconcagua.com.ar/intro_e.html

Climber's guide to the highest mountain in the Americas. There is a description of the mountain and both conventional and high-risk routes to the summit are well described with the assistance of photographs.

South Georgia and the South Sandwich Islands

http://www.intergo.com/Library/ref/atlas/samerica/sx.htm

Information about South Georgia and the South Sandwich Islands, dependent territory of the UK. Click on links for details of geography, people, government, economy, transportation, communications, and defence.

Tierra del Fuego, Argentina

http://cityguide.lycos.com/southamerica/south_sam/ARGTierradelFuego.html

General introduction to the 'land of fire', Tierra del Fuego, and its capital Ushuaia. The site also includes four sections – 'visitors' guide', 'culture and history', 'news and weather', and 'entertainment' – with links to photographs, and to useful information in English and Spanish.

Trip to the End of the World

http://www.cco.caltech.edu/~salmon/argentina1.html

Personal and entertaining travel diary of a couple's trip around the south of Argentina – the site contains a few images and plenty of insight into what it is really like to travel in far-flung places.

Valencia, Venezuela

http://cityguide.lycos.com/southamerica/north_sam/VENValencia.html

Profile of Valencia, capital of Carabobo State, Venezuela. There is a general introduction to the city's main features, and four sections – 'visitors' guide', 'culture and history', 'news and weather', and 'entertainment' – each with links to further information in English and Spanish about both the city and the country.

Valparaiso

http://www.chileweb.net/valparaiso/

Bilingual (English and Spanish) pages devoted to the Chilean city of Valparaiso. Links in the text direct you to information about its history, location, attractions, and its position as port and legislative centre. There are a number of photographs.

Brazil

Belém, Brazil

http://www.belem.com/

Profile of Brazil's port city of Belém. There is a general introduction to its main features, and four sections – 'visitors' guide', 'culture and history', 'news and weather', and 'entertainment and photos' – with links to photographs, and to further useful information in English and Portuguese about both the city and the country.

Belo Horizonte, Brazil

http://cityguide.lycos.com/southamerica/east_sam/BRABeloHorizonte.html

Guide to Belo Horizonte. This site provides a general introduction to its main features, and four sections – 'visitors' guide', 'culture and history', 'news and weather', and 'entertainment' – with links to photographs, and to further useful information in English and Portuguese about both the city and the state of Minas Gerais, of which it is the capital.

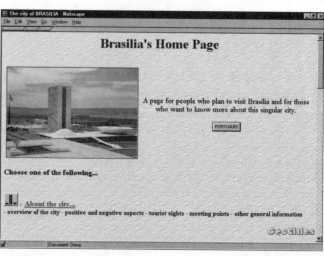

Brasilia's Home Page

http://www.geocities.com/TheTropics/3416/

Good introduction to the Brazilian capital. There is a history of the construction of the city, a description of its attractions, and a frank listing of its problems. There are a large number of photos.

Curitiba – 'Land of Abundant Pine Cones'

http://darkwing.uoregon.edu/~sergiok/brasil/curitiba.html#start

Information on the city and the state of Paraná, of which it is the capital. There are also links to other sources of information on Curitiba.

Manaus, Brazil

http://cityguide.lycos.com/southamerica/east_sam/BRAManaus.html

Profile of Manaus, capital of Amazonas, Brazil. There is a general introduction to the city's main features, and four sections – 'visitors' guide', 'culture and history', 'news and weather', and 'entertainment' – with links to photographs, and to further useful information in English and Portuguese about both the city and the Amazon region.

Recife, Brazil

http://www.recife.com/

Profile of the city of Recife, sometimes known as the 'Venice of Brazil'. There is a general introduction to its main features, and four sections – 'visitors' guide', 'culture and history', 'news and weather', and 'entertainment' – with links to photographs, and to further useful information in English and Portuguese about both the city and the country.

Rio de Janeiro, Brazil

http://www.if.ufrj.br/general/tourist.html

Profile of the colourful Brazilian city of Rio de Janeiro. There is a general introduction to the its main features, and four sections – 'visitors' guide', 'culture and history', 'news and weather', and 'entertainment' – with links to photographs, and to further useful information in English and Portuguese about both the city and the country.

Salvador, Brazil

http://cityguide.lycos.com/southamerica/east_sam/BRASalvador.html

Profile of the Brazilian port of Salvador. There is a general introduction to the city's main features, and four sections – 'visitors' guide', 'culture and history', 'news and weather', and 'entertainment' – with links to photographs, and to further useful information in English and Portuguese about the city and the Bahia state.

Salvador – World Heritage City

http://www.ovpm.org/ovpm/sites/asalva.html

Information on the capital of Bahia. There is a history and description of the city. The reasons why UNESCO classified Salvador as a World Heritage city are also set out.

São Paolo, Brazil

http://cityguide.lycos.com/southamerica/east_sam/BRASaoPaulo.html

Profile of São Paolo, Brazil's largest city. There is a general introduction to the its main features, and four sections – 'visitors' guide', 'culture and history', 'news and weather', and 'entertainment' – with links to photographs, and to further useful information in English and Portuguese.

Warriors of the Amazon

http://www.pbs.org/wgbh/nova/shaman/

Companion to the US Public Broadcasting Service (PBS) television programme *Nova*, this page explores the shamanistic traditions of the Huaorani people who live deep inside the Amazon. Learn about the plants that for centuries local shamans have been turning into medicines. There is also a list of resources for further reference.

Peoples from the Americas

Algonkin History

http://www.dickshovel.com/alg.html

Detailed account of the history of the Algonkin people. The site includes information on their location, language, population, and culture, as well as links to related groups.

American Documents on Fourth World Affairs

http://www.cwis.org/americas.html

Extensive text archive on the indigenous peoples of the Americas, maintained by the Fourth World Documentation Project in an attempt to increase knowledge about, and understanding of, the problems that these largely unrecognized national populations face within their states.

Cherokee Nation

http://www.powersource.com/cherokee/

Cherokee nation home page. This Web site features the seal of the Cherokee nation, details of the modern day tribal council, a timeline of Cherokee history, and links to both the Cherokee National Historical Society and the Cherokee Cultural Society.

Chickasaw History

http://www.dickshovel.com/chick.html

Very large Web site on the history of the Chickasaw Native American people. The comprehensive information contained in the site is all on one page, and is in the format of a very large text file. The topics covered on the Web site include lists of village names, culture, history of the tribes, population, sub-nations, and the geographical distribution of the Chickasaw people. The Web site author includes the following colourful passage describing the valiant nature of the people: 'Variously described as the Unconquered and Unconquerable or the Spartans of the lower Mississippi Valley, the Chickasaw were the most formidable warriors of the American Southeast, and anyone who messed with them came to regret it, if they survived!'

Comanche History

http://dickshovel.com/ComancheOne.html

Detailed history of the Comanche including information on their population, language, and culture. It also includes links to related groups.

Delaware Tribe of Indians

http://www.delawaretribeofindians.nsn.us

All you could want to know about the Delaware tribe including information about their history, clothing, language, music treaties, and culture.

Erie History

http://www.dickshovel.com/erie.html

Detailed history of this extinct Native American people; it also includes information on their location, language and culture. In addition, there are some links to related groups.

First Nations Histories

http://www.dickshovel.com/Compacts.html

Expanding list giving compact histories, origins, and traditions of more than two dozen Native American tribes (the organizers plan to eventually cover 240). The site also includes a detailed bibliography of its various sources.

> **F**
> **A**
> **C**
> **T**
>
> **AMERICAN INDIAN (Native American),** member of one of the aboriginal peoples of the Americas. The first American Indians arrived during the last ice age, approximately 20,000–30,000 years ago, passing from northeastern Siberia into Alaska over a land-bridge across the Bering Strait.

Huron History

http://www.dickshovel.com/hur.html

This site provides a detailed history of the Hurons plus information about their population, location, language, and culture. It also includes links to related groups.

Illinois History

http://www.dickshovel.com/ill.html

Very large Web site on the history of the Illinois Native American people. The comprehensive information contained in the site is all on one page, and is in the format of a very large text file. The topics covered on the Web site include lists of village names, culture, history of the tribes, population, sub-nations, and the geographical distribution of the Illinois people.

Indian Pueblo Cultural Centre

http://hanksville.phast.umass.edu/defs/
independent/PCC/PCC.html

Broad source of information regarding the numerous pueblo populations that inhabited the

Southwest of America, centuries before the first European explorers came to the Americas. This site provides information on 19 pueblos and their peoples and cultures, including the Taos and Zuni pueblos. You can also view 12 wall murals painted by pueblo artists, find out directions to the pueblos, learn about scheduled events, and discover the proper etiquette when visiting the pueblos.

Iroquois History

http://www.dickshovel.com/iro.html

Large Web site dedicated to the history of the Iroquois people. The comprehensive information contained in the site is all on one page, and is in exclusively text format. The topics covered on the Web site include lists of village names, culture, history of the tribes, population, sub-nations, and the geographical distribution of the Iroquois.

Mahican History

http://www.dickshovel.com/Mahican.html

Large Web site on the history of the Mahican, or Mohican, Native American people. The comprehensive information contained in the site is all on one page, and is in the format of a very large text file. As an interesting aside the author states 'When James Fenimore Cooper wrote *Last of the Mohicans* in 1826 he made the Mahican famous. Unfortunately, he also made them extinct in many minds and confused their name and history with the Mohegan from eastern Connecticut. This error has persisted, and most Americans today would be surprised to learn that the Mahican are very much alive and living in Wisconsin under an assumed name, Stockbridge Indians.'

Menominee History

http://www.dickshovel.com/men.html

Very large Web site on the history of the Menominee Native American people. The comprehensive information contained in the site is all on one page, and is in the format of a very large text file. The topics covered on the Web site include lists of village names, culture, history of the tribes, population, sub-nations, and the geographical distribution of the Menominee people.

Miami History

http://www.dickshovel.com/mia.html

Very large Web site on the history of the Miami Native American people. The comprehensive

information contained in the site is all on one page, and is in the format of a very large text file. The topics covered on the Web site include lists of village names, culture, history of the tribes, population, sub-nations, and the geographical distribution of the Miami people.

Micmac History

http://www.dickshovel.com/mic.html

Large Web site dedicated to the history of the Micmac people. The comprehensive information contained in the site is all on one page, and is in the format of a very large text file. The topics covered on the Web site include lists of village names, culture, history of the tribes, population, sub-nations, and the geographical distribution of the Micmac people.

Offering From Crow Country

http://www.dickshovel.com/crow.html

Lyrical descriptions of the home of the Crow tribe of Native American Indians. The descriptions of the country are taken from Oration by Chief Arapooish of the Crow, and make the place sound more than a little attractive to live in. There are some advertisements on this Web site for products made by the tribe to supplement their income.

Ojibwa History

http://www.dickshovel.com/ojib.html

Large Web site on the history of the Ojibwa Native American people. The comprehensive information contained in the site is all on one page, and is in the format of a very large text file. As an interesting aside the author states 'The Ojibwe and Chippewa are not only the same tribe, but the same word pronounced a little differently due to accent. If an 'O' is placed in front of Chippewa (O'chippewa), the relationship becomes apparent.'

Sauk and Fox history

http://www.dickshovel.com/sf.html

Very large Web site on the history of the Sauk and Fox Native American people. The comprehensive information contained in the site is all on one page, and is in the format of a very large text file. The topics covered on the Web site include lists of village names, culture, history of the tribes, population, sub-nations, and the geographical distribution of both the Sauk and the Fox people.

Shawnee History

http://www.dickshovel.com/shaw.html

Very large Web site on the history of the Shawnee Native American people. The comprehensive information contained in the site is all on one page, and is in the format of a very large text file. The topics covered on the Web site include lists of village names, culture, history of the tribes, population, sub-nations, and the geographical distribution of the Shawnee people.

South Dakota – A Guide to the Great Sioux Nation

http://www.state.sd.us/state/executive/tourism/sioux/sioux.htm

Comprehensive and sympathetically written guide to the history and culture of the Sioux. There is background information on all of the tribes making up the Sioux Nation. This site describes the natural landmarks and legends associated with the tribe. Tourists are advised how to respect Sioux culture. If you want to know the etiquette when attending a powwow this is the site to go to.

Arctic & Antarctic

Antarctica

http://www.umsl.edu/services/govdocs/wofact96/17.htm

Geographical and political information on the southern continent. This CIA-run Web site answers virtually every question one could think of asking about modern Antarctica.

Arctic Circle

http://arcticcircle.uconn.edu/

Well written site with information about all aspects of life in the Arctic. There are sections on history, natural resources, the rights of indigenous peoples, and issues of environmental concern.

Arctic Ocean

http://www.umsl.edu/services/govdocs/wofact96/19.htm

Geographical information on the world's northernmost ocean. This CIA-run site also includes information on the politics of the region, and provides the user with a summary map to download.

Bouvet Island

http://www.umsl.edu/services/govdocs/wofact96/43.htm

Information on the Southern Atlantic dependency of Norway. Only the CIA, who run this site, could find five pages to write about an island that is uninhabited and covered with glacial ice most of the year.

British Antarctic Survey Home Page

http://www.nbs.ac.uk/

Information about the British Antarctic Survey's activities – its press releases, scientific groups, and research programmes.

Information Documents about the Antarctic

http://www.icair.iac.org.nz/education/resource/informat/informat.htm

Set of resources about the Antarctic that includes information about geology, marine life, conservation of the continent, and how life there has adapted to the cold. It can be slow to load, but it contains plenty of pictures and hyperlinks, so is worth the wait.

Language & Linguistics

Acronyms and Abbreviations

http://www.ucc.ie/acronyms/

Immense database of abbreviations, acronyms, and their expanded forms, fully searchable by abbreviation or keyword. It is possible to submit new additions for consideration.

Akkadian Language

http://saturn.sron.ruu.nl/~jheise/akkadian/index.html

Source of information on the Akkadians and their language. Extensive details on Akkadian phonetics, morphology, paradigms, and dialects (of interest mainly to professional linguists) are accompanied by a good general introduction to Mesopotamia and Assyriology.

Alliterations

http://www.iron.k12.ut.us/schools/cms/ resource/ ALLIT.HTM

Clear and concise introduction to alliterations for children. A definition is included here, and there are also a number of examples provided by both the author of the site and by children too.

Anagram Insanity

http://anagram.avatartech.com/pages/ anagram.html

Anagram-producing page that is basic but effective. Simply key in a string of characters and the server will return an exhaustive list of possible permutations of letters. The site also includes a set of variables to sort and display your search.

Arabic

http://philae.sas.upenn.edu/Arabic/arabic.html

Twelve dialogue lessons from which to learn Arabic. This site also has a library of Arabic images.

Arabic Writing

http://www.islam.org/Mosque/ihame/Ref3.htm

Informative pages on the history of the Arabic script. There are examples of Arabic writing and colour photographs of various calligraphic styles found in ancient texts. In addition, there are links to aspects of Islam and Islamic and Middle Eastern history.

Bird's Eye View of the Syriac Language and Literature

http://www.geocities.com/Athens/Parthenon/ 5157/51edip.htm

Profile of this ancient Semitic language spoken over the course of history by Zoroastrians, Buddhists, Jews, Christians, and Muslims. This history of the language and its literature continues up to the present with details of the Syriac dialects still spoken by Christians in various parts of the Middle East.

F A C T

BRAILLE

system of writing for the blind. Letters are represented by a combination of raised dots on paper or other materials, which are then read by touch. It was invented in 1829 by **Louis Braille** (1809–1852), who became blind at the age of three.

Braille and Moon

http://www.rnib.org.uk/braille/welc.htm

Comprehensive information about Braille and Moon from Britain's Royal National Institute for the Blind. You can see how Braille works by typing text and seeing it translated. There is also a good biography of Louis Braille and downloadable Braille and Moon true-type fonts.

Brief History of the English Language

http://www.m-w.com/about/look.htm

Part of a site maintained by Merriam-Webster, this page features a brief history of the English language, showing its evolution through the three periods of Old, Middle, and Modern English. You will also find links to other information provided by Merriam-Webster, such as a collection of brief biographies and the process by which words are selected for inclusion in the dictionary.

Chinese Characters

http://zhongwen.com/

Extensive Web site covering the genealogy of Chinese characters. This Web-based etymological dictionary for learning Chinese characters covers over 4,000 characters, including several types of pronunciation for each and a 'family tree' diagram to demonstrate the characters' genealogy. The site also includes a Chinese-English dictionary containing many thousands of entries.

Cuneiform Writing System

http://saturn.sron.ruu.nl/~jheise/akkadian/akkadian .html

Scholarly account of the origin and development of Babylonian and Assyrian cuneiform. There are sections on the origin of this early writing style, as well as detailed examinations of the order, physical appearance, and value of cuneiform signs.

Elements of Style

http://www.bartleby.com/141/index.html

William Strunk's guide provides a succinct and effective insight into the elementary rules and principles of English grammar. It includes such topics as 'Words commonly misspelled' and 'Elementary principles of composition'.

Esperanto – The International Language

http://esperanto.org/angle/

Thorough official source of information (in many languages) on the international language spoken by two million people. The structure of Esperanto and the history of its development are clearly set out. There is information on national societies and details of Esperanto language courses.

Etymological Dictionary of the Gaelic Language

http://www.smo.uhi.ac.uk/gaidhlig/faclair/macbain

E-text of an etymology of Gaelic compiled by Alexander MacBain and published by Gairm Publications, Glasgow.

Euskara – Language of the Basques

http://students.washington.edu/buber/Basque/Euskara/

Thorough introduction to the language of the Basques (a language so complex that a Basque tale relates how the Devil spent seven years trying to learn it, only to give up). There are Basque lessons, an online dictionary, information on software, advice for those learning the language, and a guide to Euskara media.

Finnish–English Dictionary

http://dictionaries.travlang.com/EnglishFinnish/

Useful dictionary for anyone interested in the Finnish language. Just type in an English or Finnish word, and the equivalent word in the other language will be displayed. The service is provided by the Finnish company Mofile Place.

Finno-Ugrian Languages

http://www.helsinki.fi/hum/sugl/fgrlang.html

Guide to the Finno-Ugric (Uralian) language group. There is information on Hungarian, Finnish, and Estonian, and many of the more minor languages in danger of extinction. Lexical and morphological similarities between the languages are examined. This Finnish site also provides a variety of links for further information.

Foundation for Endangered Languages

http://www.bris.ac.uk/Depts/Philosophy/CTLL/FEL/

Bristol University site bringing together the latest information and research on the world's endangered languages. There are online editions of the foundation's newsletter and a large number of contact addresses for scholars and indigenous peoples struggling to preserve their language.

Frequently Asked Questions About Japanese

http://theory.kek.jp/~ben/alternative_faq.html#grammar

Good source of information on the Japanese language. The Japanese writing system and its origins as well as various systems of romanization are explained in detail. This site also includes the background on word origins, together with advice on learning Japanese, and links to other sources of related information.

Gaelic and Gaelic Culture

http://sunsite.unc.edu/gaelic/gaelic.html

Dedicated to the Gaelic and Celtic culture and language. This site includes information on the three Gaelic languages; Irish, Manx, and Scottish, along with audioclips giving examples of each.

Glossary of Rhetorical Terms With Examples

http://www.uky.edu/ArtsSciences/Classics/rhetoric.html

If you are ever confused about how to distinguish synecdoche, litotes, and prolepsis, then this is the site for you. There are also links to other rhetoric and classicist sites.

Hindi Language and Literature

http://www.cs.colostate.edu/~malaiya/hindiint.html

Exploration of Hindi language and culture providing links to information about Hindi-speaking regions, dialects, traditional songs, authors, and poets. There are additional links to relevant Hindi resources on the Web.

Journal of Pidgin and Creole Languages

http://www.siu.edu/departments/cola/ling/

Results of current research into the theory and description of these languages, supported by an interactive glossary of pidgin and Creole terms and audio samples.

Learn Chinese

http://pasture.ecn.purdue.edu/~agenhtml/agenmc/china/ctutor.html

Audio tutorial of basic Mandarin Chinese. Whether you are travelling to China or just going to the local takeaway, this site has a few quick phrases for you to learn. The phrases are presented in both written and audio form and there are over two hundred to choose from.

Linguaweb

http://www.linguaweb.ndirect.co.uk/

Language site aimed at students who are studying French, German, and Spanish. The site includes reading, writing, and oral exercises for each language.

Little Venture's Latin Pages

http://www.compassnet.com/mrex/index.html

Online aid to learning or brushing up Latin. Operated by an experienced teacher of the language, this site answers e-mailed grammar and vocabulary inquiries. There is a full list of 'Frequently Asked Questions' about grammar, a Latin quiz, a fun etymology section, an explanation of the Roman calendar system, and useful links for students or teachers of classics.

Mercator Project

http://www.troc.es/mercator/

Site of the European Union initiative to preserve minority languages and cultures within the EU. There is general information on a wide variety of languages with links to further specialist resources. This site also includes details of the activities of a number of language promotion organizations and academic institutions throughout Europe.

Modern English to Old English Vocabulary

http://www.mun.ca/Ansaxdat/vocab/wordlist.html

Comprehensive online dictionary of modern English words paired with their Old English counterparts.

Mongol Script and Language

http://members.aol.com/yikhmongol/monls.htm

Description of the history of the Mongol script and language. The site includes illustrations of classical Mongolian handwritten script and classical Mongolian printed script. There are also links to other sites about Mongolian writing.

Noam Chomsky Archive

http://www.worldmedia.com/archive/

Substantial collection of the political work and thought of the US academic and philosopher Noam Chomsky, with online books, articles, a long archive of his correspondence, an extended list of interviews given by him, and more than seven hours of audio clips.

Peter J Keegan's Maori Language Web Pages

http://webpages.netlink.co.nz/~pkeegan/rauemi/index.html

Good introduction to the Maori language. A 'Frequently Asked Questions' section provides information on the origin and structure of the language, its modern use, and contemporary Maori literature. There is also a good guide to Maori dictionaries and to online Maori language resources.

Punctuation Made Simple

http://www.cas.usf.edu/JAC/pms/

Handbook aimed at writers and editors, but could help anyone to improve their punctuation. It includes clear information on the correct use of brackets, semicolons, and so on.

Pun Page

http://punpunpun.com/

Page of puns in every shape and form, many of them extremely corny. The site features sections such as 'Pun of the day', 'Longer puns', 'Legal puns', and 'Past puns'.

Roget's Thesaurus

http://humanities.uchicago.edu/forms_unrest/ROGET.html

Online, public domain version of *Roget's Thesaurus* (last updated in 1991).

Runes, Alphabet of Mystery

http://members.aol.com/cbsunny/index.html

Introduction to the ancient Germanic alphabet, with information on both the alphabet and the stones the letters were traditionally carved upon.

Sapir, Edward

http://kroeber.anthro.mankato.msus.edu/
information/biography/pqrst/sapir_edward.html

Profile of the German linguist and anthropologist
and his pioneering research into Native American
languages and the insights derived from it.

Semaphore

http://155.187.10.12/flags/semaphore.html

Diagrams and instructions of how to
communicate using this flag signalling system. It
includes diagrams of all the letters and numbers
and a link to a companion page for the
international maritime signal flag system.

Sign Writing Site

http://www.signwriting.org/

Information about sign language with lessons,
dictionaries, stories, and computer programs in
sign language. The site includes sections on 'Basic
introduction', 'Questions and answers', and 'Sign
language history'.

Steganography

http://members.tripod.com/steganography/
stego.html

Thorough guide to the technique of camouflaging
messages. The contents include the history of
steganography, description of various techniques,
a guide to available software, and discussions of
the implications of steganographic technology.

Translating Dictionaries

http://dictionaries.travlang.com/

Comprehensive resource for anyone needing to
translate words or phrases. Included here are
dictionaries translating to English from German,
Dutch, French, Spanish, Portuguese, Italian,
Danish, Swedish, Finnish, Norwegian, Afrikaans,
and Latin, among others.

Traveller's Japanese With Voice

http://www.ntt.co.jp/japan/japanese/

Introduction to Japanese at a level
suitable for the business traveller or the
occasional visitor to the country. The Web
site is broken down into six subsections,
the first deals with pronunciation, the
second with essential expressions, and the

remaining four with real life scenarios and the
language commonly used in them.

Wacky Words

http://www.harperchildrens.com/games/
wackywrd.htm

Interactive word game to help improve your
grasp of grammar. You are invited to fill in a
variety of words under the headings of nouns,
adjectives, and so on, with help available. A
personalized story is then created from your
words so that you can see how the words are
used.

Welcome to the Walloon Language Page

http://www.wallonie.com/wallang/index.htm

Guide to the history, culture, and language of the
Walloons. Presented by a society promoting
Walloon culture, the assertion that Walloon is no
more than a dialect of French is strongly
disputed. In addition to a description of the
language, the cultural dangers facing its existence
are set out. There is also a map of Wallonia.

Welsh Course

http://www.cs.brown.edu/fun/welsh/home.html

Course on the Welsh language that contains a
lexicon and glossary as well as a set of graded
lessons. It also includes other related cultural and
linguistic resources.

Wordbot

http://www.cs.washington.edu/homes/kgolden/
wordbot.html

Linguistic site that allows you to load pages from
the Internet and run them through a variety of
filters. These filters can translate foreign language
pages into your own language, link words to
dictionary definitions, or look up synonyms and
antonyms. It's a complicated process, but the

F A C T

LANGUAGE

There are about 6,000 languages spoken
worldwide, but 90% of these are in some
danger of falling into disuse. More than half
the world's population speaks one of just five
languages – Chinese, English, Hindi, Russian,
and Spanish.

results are worth the effort now that more languages are making it onto the Web.

Word Page

http://users.aol.com/jomnet/words.html

This page offers ten different English words per week. All the words are followed by lucid definitions, their origins, words of similar/opposite meaning, and examples of each one in use.

World Wide Words

http://www.quinion.demon.co.uk/words/index.htm

Interesting site listing the latest neologisms (new words) in the English language. Topical words, turns of phrase, and weird words too new to be found in dictionaries are listed and defined. There are also a large number of articles on latest developments of the language.

Anthropology

Amazons

http://www.net4you.co.at/users/poellauerg/Amazons/index.html

Firmly asserting the existence of the mythical ancient Amazons, this site aims to function as a forum for debate on all aspects of the life of this ancient matriarchal tribe. The site offers visual representations, including the earliest accepted one, archaeological suggestions on the possible first location of the Amazons, and evidence of some primitive writing signs related to them and to other famous, and allegedly contemporary, matriarchal groups in the wider Mediterranean region.

Benedict Register – Table of Contents

http://iberia.vassar.edu/vcl/information/special-collections/benedict/benedict_register.html

Substantial amount of information on the US anthropologist from Vassar College. There is an informative biographical essay on Benedict's role in the establishment of US anthropology. Virtually everything she ever wrote, from academic works to private letters, may also be accessed at this site.

Evans-Pritchard, E E

http://kroeber.anthro.mankato.msus.edu/information/biography/abcde/evanspritchard_ee.html

Profile of the pioneering English social anthropologist. It focuses on his fieldwork in Sudan, his ability to popularize anthropology for a wider audience, and his influence as a teacher at Oxford.

Franz Boas and Early Camera Study of Behaviour

http://www.temple.edu/anthro/ruby/boas.html

Tribute to the German-born founder of US academic anthropology. It concentrates on Boas' enthusiasm for photography of dance and movement as part of his belief that the anthropologist had a mandate to study all aspects of human behaviour. Boas' vigorous opposition to doctrines of racial superiority is highlighted.

Kroeber, Alfred Louis

http://kroeber.anthro.mankato.msus.edu/information/biography/klmno/kroeber_alfred.htmlm

Good assessment of the career of the US anthropologist. It traces his pioneering role in establishing the discipline of archaeology and forging links with anthropology. There is a photo of Kroeber, and a summary of his main work.

Leakey, Louis

http://kroeber.anthro.mankato.msus.edu/information/biography/klmno/leakey_louis.htmlm

Account of the life and career of the missionary's son who did much to establish the African origins of human life. It traces his upbringing among the Kikuyu, his early interest in anthropology, his financial and academic struggles, and his work with his second wife, Mary, in Olduvai Gorge.

Malinowski, Bronislaw

http://kroeber.anthro.mankato.msus.edu/information/biography/klmno/malinowski_bronislaw.html

Profile of the pioneering Polish-born social anthropologist. It traces his education in science, the beginnings of his interest in anthropology, and the period in the Trobriand Islands which established his commitment to painstaking fieldwork. There is a summary of his academic career, a listing of his major books, a bibliography, and a photo.

Mary Leakey: Unearthing History

http://www.sciam.com/explorations/
121696explorations.html

Part of a larger site maintained by
Scientific American, this page honours the
life of Mary Leakey and her
contributions to anthropology. It features
an interview from 1994, in which Leakey
discusses, among other things, her
discoveries at the Olduvai Gorge and the
footprints of Laetoli. The text includes
hyperlinks to further information, and
there is also a list of related links.

Morgan, Lewis Henry

http://kroeber.anthro.mankato.msus.edu/
information/biography/klmno/
morgan_louishenry.html

Profile of the early US anthropologist. It traces his
commitment to protection of Native Americans
and his role in establishing kinship studies. A
discussion of his beliefs in unilinear evolution
judges Morgan to be Eurocentric, but, in the
context of his times, a pioneer humanitarian.
There is also a photo of Morgan and a
bibliography.

Thor Heyerdahl – A Living Legend

http://www.heureka.fi/en/x/nxjohansen.html

Description of the works of Thor Heyerdahl, the

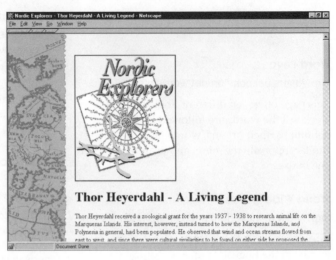

Norwegian archaeologist, anthropologist and
explorer. This site describes Heyerdahl's best-
known expeditions and also describes his more
recent works.

Tylor, Edward

http://kroeber.anthro.mankato.msus.edu/informatio
n/biography/pqrst/tylor_edward.html

Portrait and biography of the English
anthropologist. The site at Mankato State
University, Minnesota, includes a timeline of the
life and works of Tylor and also a reference
bibliography for sources of further information.

POLITICS, ECONOMICS & LAW

UK Government

British Immigration and Visa Requirements

http://193.114.50.10/travel/visa.asp

Clear explanation of UK entry requirements provided by the Foreign and Commonwealth Office. Addresses of all British consular offices are provided and it is possible to download application forms and a variety of explanatory leaflets.

Cabinet Office Home Page

http://www.cabinet-office.gov.uk/

Site of the UK cabinet which includes the latest news from Whitehall, access to reports and papers from different departments, and statistics and information about government policy. There is also a full explanation of the 'Government Machine', with links to related sites.

Citizen's Charter Unit

http://www.open.gov.uk/charter/ccuhome.htm

Open government at work. This official explanation of the work of the unit charged with realizing the UK's Citizen's Charter explains the various charters, provides discussion documents, explains how to complain about government services, and invites public feedback.

Department of the Environment, Transport, and the Regions

http://www.detr.gov.uk/

Information and statistics about a wide range of issues relevant to transport and the environment in the UK.

FCO Online

http://www.fco.gov.uk/news/

Official statements of British foreign policy. Updated several times daily, this is an invaluable source of information on British policy on a wide range of issues concerning the international community.

Hansard – House of Commons Debates

http://www.parliament.the-stationery-office.co.uk/pa/cm/cmhansrd.htm

The complete proceedings of the House of Commons, posted each day at 12.30 p.m. You can also search archived proceedings going back to 1996.

Her Majesty's Customs and Excise

http://www.hmce.gov.uk/

Information for businesses and the public about UK Customs regulations and allowances. There is also comprehensive advice for travellers.

HM Land Registry

http://www.landreg.gov.uk

Explanation of the role of the land registration agency for England and Wales. There are reports on property prices, links to regional offices, and details of how to obtain online access to registry documents (this service is not free).

House of Commons – Members, Ministers, and Committees

http://www.parliament.uk/commons/lib/lists.htm

Regularly updated list of members of the British lower house, provided by the House of Commons. MPs are easy to locate as they are listed by their name, by constituency, and by county.

Houses of Parliament Home Page

http://www.parliament.uk/

Site of the UK's House of Commons and House of Lords. There is a guide to visiting, and access to the many government publications and committees.

HSE – Health and Safety Executive

http://www.open.gov.uk/hse/hsehome.htm

Explanation of HSE's role in protecting the health of the British workforce. There are reports on particular dangers in the workplace and ways of minimizing occupational risks. There is also a full list of leaflets and videos produced by the Commission.

Millennium Commission

http://www.millennium.gov.uk/

Established to assist communities in the UK mark the millennium, the Millennium Commission's Web site includes details of how you can apply for a grant, and highlights many of the events taking place in the UK to commemorate the millennium.

Ministry of Agriculture, Food, and Fisheries

http://www.maff.gov.uk/maffhome.htm

Official site for this government ministry includes extensive information on farming, fisheries, and food as well as a news section. It also contains a wealth of related official statistics, on such topics as 'Land use' and 'Household food consumption', which it is possible to download and view in Excel or Lotus.

National Assembly for Wales

http://www.assembly.wales.gov.uk/index_e.html

Describes the structure and business of the Welsh Assembly, with 'Press notices', 'Who's who in the Assembly', and a 'Record of proceedings'.

NIO Online

http://www.nio.gov.uk/index.htm

Comprehensive information on the administration of criminal justice, security, and the police in Northern Ireland. Frequently updated, this site charts the latest developments in the search for peace and also provides a good introduction to the economy and culture of Ulster.

Office of Fair Trading

http://www.oft.gov.uk/

Site of the agency charged with protecting consumers and enforcing UK competition policy. The mandate, structure, and history are set out, together with advice to consumers, information on publications, and a large number of news items dealing with current investigations and matters of concern. There is also a good source of impartial advice for anybody considering buying a car.

OFSTED Reports Database

http://www.ofsted.gov.uk/reports/index.htm

OFSTED Reports Database with the full text of reports from OFSTED inspections. Visitors may search by school name, education authority, or postcode. The reports are in PDF format, so you may need to download the Adobe Acrobat Reader – a link to the download site is included.

Oftel

http://www.oftel.gov.uk/

Comprehensive details of the watchdog agency overseeing Britain's telecommunications industry. Its work is well described – there is advice to consumers, industry guidelines, and a list of publications.

OFWAT – Office of Water Services

http://www.open.gov.uk/ofwat/index.htm

Description of the role of the agency charged with monitoring and regulating the supply of water in the UK. There are full reports on the efficiency of water and sewerage services, the role of this organization, and mechanisms for assisting aggrieved customers of water companies.

Parliamentary Glossary

http://www.ukpol.co.uk/hou.shtml

Useful page which explains the terminology used in the UK's Houses of Parliament, from 'Act of parliament' to 'Whip'.

Patent Office – Home Page

http://www.patent.gov.uk/

Guide around the confusing notions surrounding rights and intellectual property. The site takes the visitors through such things as patents, trade marks, designs, and copyright. It also informs them of a series of relevant services offered by the Patent Office, and gives advice on the topic of intellectual property rights on the Internet.

Royal Mail

http://www.royalmail.co.uk

Official and comprehensive coverage of postal services in the UK, including a 'Postal rates calculator' and 'Postal services guide'.

Scottish Parliament

http://www.scottish.parliament.uk/

Information about the Scottish Parliament and its activities, including 'The Parliament buildings', 'What's happening', 'Agenda and decisions', and information about the members of the Scottish Parliament.

Select Committees

http://www.parliament.uk/commons/selcom/cmsel.htm

Complete guide to the many select committees of the UK's House of Commons. There is regularly updated news of the sittings of each committee, transcripts of their deliberations, press releases, and details of their members.

Source, The

http://www.statistics.gov.uk/

UK government service Web site that provides easy access to statistics, including demographics and the most popular girls' and boys' names in the UK.

10 Downing Street

http://www.number-10.gov.uk/index.html

Official Web site of the British prime minister's residence includes a virtual tour, biographies of recent prime ministers, press releases, and copies of speeches and interviews.

UK Passport Agency

http://www.open.gov.uk/ukpass/ukpass.htm

Information about the operations of the agency which issues British passports. There is comprehensive information on who is eligible to get one, how to obtain or renew a passport, and a regularly updated indication of how long you might have to wait for them to issue one.

Welcome to CNT

http://www.cnt.org.uk/

Site of the UK Commission for New Towns charged with the management of assets of the UK's new towns. The commission's role to promote relocation of enterprises is well described with a wealth of information and case studies. There are also profiles of the infrastructure, workforce, and advantages of each new town.

Work of the Audit Commission

http://www.audit-commission.gov.uk/

Explanation of the functions of the body charged with ensuring the financial accountability of the British government. There is a history of the external checking of public finances in Britain, an executive summary of the commission reports, and a full description of services offered.

US Government

Federal Bureau of Investigation Home Page

http://www.fbi.gov/homepage.htm

Visit the FBI home page for information about – amongst other things – its 'Ten most wanted fugitives', the FBI Academy, key cases, the investigation of computer crime, and reports about surveillance issues and international concerns.

House of Representatives

http://www.house.gov/

Official source of information on the US lower house. The contents of this well arranged site include a listing of the offices of all members, information on House committees and commissions, voting records, House schedules, and matters currently under discussion.

National Security Agency

http://www.nsa.gov:8080/

The newly transparent NSA sets out its intelligence mission. This site includes a biography and message from the director, structures of the agency, and coordination with other organizations in the US intelligence community.

Reno, Janet

http://www.wic.org/bio/jreno.htm

Profile of the first female US Attorney General from a site saluting women leaders. It traces her Miami upbringing, Harvard education, overcoming of obstacles as a female lawyer, her reform of the juvenile justice system in Florida, and the priorities she has set herself as Attorney General.

US Capitol

http://www.aoc.gov/

Official guide to the building symbolizing the USA and its people. There is a history of the construction of the Capitol, as well as information on its art collection, the US Botanic Garden, and Congressional office buildings. There are also a large number of photos of the Capitol, inside and out.

US Coast Guard – Always Ready

http://www.uscg.mil/

Comprehensive official information on the US Coast Guard. An informative history is supported by photographs. There are also details of Coast Guard services and information for recruits.

US Senate

http://www.senate.gov/

Official guide to the workings of the US upper house. There is a history of the Senate and clear explanation of its procedures and terminology. Information is provided on all senators and details of all recent legislative actions and deliberations of Senate committees. The site incorporates a useful search engine.

Vice President

http://www.whitehouse.gov/WH/EOP/OVP/index.html

Personalised home page of the US vice president. This section of the official White House site gives a full account of Al Gore's role in formulating policy on a wide range of issues. There are biographies of Al and his wife Tipper. Audio and video clips allow you to experience the highlights of Gore's political career and there are many thumbnail pictures to expand and view.

Weekly Compilation of Presidential Documents

http://www.access.gpo.gov/nara/nara003.html

Published every Monday, this site includes all presidential statements, messages, and other materials released by the White House during the preceding week. Documents are available, and searchable, from 1996 to the present.

Welcome to the White House

http://www.whitehouse.gov/WH/Welcome.html

Official guided tour of the White House with details of the president's and vice president's accomplishments and reviews of the lives and families of past presidents with accompanying photographs. Visitors are also given access to

presidential speeches, press releases, and other White House documents, and they can take a virtual tour of the White House. The site also features the First Lady's weekly column and her reports on life in the White House.

White House

http://www.whitehouse.gov

Valuable source of official speeches, US government documents, and biographical information about President Clinton, as well as a history of the White House and its past presidents.

White House for Kids

http://www.whitehouse.gov/WH/kids/html/kidshome.html

Guided tour of the White House specially designed for kids and hosted by Socks, the feline member of the Clinton family. It includes a walk around the house, brief historical overviews, details about the current President and his family, and specific sections on the White House kids and pets that have lived at various times in the presidential residence.

William J Clinton Forty-Second President 1993–

http://www.whitehouse.gov/WH/glimpse/presidents/html/bc42.html

Biography and presidential record of the 42nd, and current, president of the USA. The Web site contains a brief biography and portrait of both Clinton and the First Lady. This site also includes a transcript of president Clinton's inaugural address.

Miscellaneous Government Organizations

Current Leaders Worldwide

http://personales.jet.es/ziaorarr/00now.htm

This site offers a regularly updated resource on current heads of state and government for every country. Other features include 'Political leaders 1945–99', 'Women world leaders 1945–99', 'European governments 1990–99', 'First African rulers', and 'Political obituary 1990–99'. There is also an excellent selection of links to related sites and educational resources.

Government of Ireland

http://www.irlgov.ie/gov.htm

Complete guide to all the departments of the Irish government, including contact details. The 'Department of the taoiseach' includes a virtual tour of the parliament building, complete with the history of the position of taoiseach, or prime minister.

Israel Ministry of Foreign Affairs

http://www.mfa.gov.il/mfa/home.asp/

Created by the Israeli Ministry of Foreign Affairs, these detailed pages provide information about the ministry, recent developments in Israel including the peace process, and an introduction to aspects of Israeli government and life.

Political Parties

African National Congress

http://www.anc.org.za/

Official site for the majority party (and the best known outside the country) of South Africa's parliament. There is some political bias here, but it contains a lot of information about contemporary South Africa, including access to

news resources and current political issues facing the fledgling democracy.

Australian Labor Party

http://www.alp.org.au/

Large site of the Australian Labor Party. There is extensive coverage of their policies and profiles of party leaders. A well presented and frequently-updated summary of opinion polls shows the mood of the Australian electorate.

Conservative Party

http://www.conservative-party.org.uk/

Official UK Conservative Party Web site, including an archive of press releases written by major party figures. There are also links to all the local constituency associations and a list of Conservative MPs sorted by various criteria.

Democrat Party Online

http://www.democrats.org/

Latest in news and features from the US Democrat Party, as well as background historical information and current grass-roots campaigns.

European Politics

http://www.agora.stm.it:80/politic/europe.htm

As well as giving a country-by-country breakdown of the major political parties in Europe, this network of pages also gives very up-to-date information about election results and political candidates. There is also information on the differing styles of government and country-specific political news.

Green Party of England and Wales

http://www.greenparty.org.uk/

Home page of the Green Party in Britain. Options offered include a statement of principles, information on current campaigns, and election results. An extensive list of links makes it easy to contact party branches throughout the UK. This site is also useful as a source of addresses for a host of green and environmental organizations around the globe.

History and Profile of the Inkatha Freedom Party

http://www.ifp.org.za/

Information about the Inkatha Freedom Party of South Africa. The site discusses the party's origins, its philosophy, the meaning and symbolism of the word 'Inkatha', its flag, and its policies. There is also information on recent events, press releases, and speeches.

Kurdistan Democratic Party

http://www.kdp.pp.se/

Official site of the longest established Iraqi Kurdish party. There is a history of the party in addition to its current structures and policies. Frequently updated, this provides a good introduction to Kurdish culture and the tangled politics of internal conflict within the Kurdish Autonomous Region in northern Iraq.

Labour Party

http://www.labour.org.uk

Home page of the British Labour Party. A brief glimpse of Tony Blair is followed by a menu offering a range of options. Search engines make it easy to identify and communicate with Labour parliamentarians and party representatives, and to find potted biographies. It is easy to access party policy by inputting key words.

Liberal Democrats

http://www.libdems.org.uk

Home page of the Liberal Democrat Party in Britain. Their policy and principles are clearly set out. A search engine makes it easy to locate local and national party representatives and policy statements. There is also a brief history of the party.

Likud Party

http://www.likud.org.il/english/index.html

Official site of the right-wing Israeli party. There is a history of Likud, profile of its leaders, and description of its party structures. Likud attempts to justify its controversial policies of opposition to a Palestinian state or return of Palestinian exiles.

National Party of Australia – Queensland

http://www.npa.org.au

Official site of Australia's third-largest political party. Party policies and structures at state and federal level are set out, together with information about their parliamentarians and achievements as the junior partner in Australia's coalition government. The site also provides full details of the party's constitution, latest conferences, and an opportunity to cast your vote in a selection of 'Current issues'.

Patriotic Union of Kurdistan

http://www.puk.org/

Official site of the Iraqi Kurdish political party currently in power in the southern half of the Kurdish Autonomous Region. There is a description of the history, structure, and policies of the party. This site provides one perspective on the turbulent politics of northern Iraq.

Plaid Cymru, the Party of Wales

http://www.plaidcymru.org/

Welsh nationalists set out their vision for a free Wales. The home page leads to a nationalist perspective on the *pobl* (people) and how Plaid Cymru's *polisiau* (policies) meet their needs. The structure of the party is fully explained. The site examines, from a Welsh nationalist perspective, many of the problems associated with the fact that Wales is governed from Westminster.

Scottish National Party

http://www.snp.org.uk/

Well-organized site of Scotland's nationalist party. There are full details of their structure, policies, and representatives. The home page has a constantly incrementing account of the amount of Scottish tax revenue they claim is being purloined by Westminster. Click on the picture of Alex Salmond which appears on many pages and you are given the opportunity to send him an e-mail.

Sinn Féin

http://sinnfein.ie/index.html

Against a background of a green and united Ireland, the oldest political party in Ireland presents its case. There are extensive links to sites supporting the republican cause in Northern Ireland. The online edition of the *An Phoblacht* newspaper provides a republican outlook on the search for a lasting peace in Northern Ireland.

Ulster Unionist Party

http://www.uup.org/

Union Jack-filled site of Ulster's main political party. This well-organized site has comprehensive information on the party, its officers and party conferences. Befitting a party with a commitment to preserve the past, there is a detailed history of the party. The constantly updated current affairs section presents a detailed exposition of mainstream Unionist views on the difficult search for a lasting peace.

Welcome to Front National

http://www.front-nat.fr/anglais/indexc.htm

Web site of the extremist right wing party founded by Jean-Marie le Pen. The alleged 'decadence' of modern France is denounced and controversial solutions put forward by a party convinced of its destiny to 'purify' French life. An uncritical biography of le Pen hails him as a 'a pupil of the nation, fervent patriot, man of action, and statesman '.

Welcome to Republican Mainstreet

http://www.rnc.org/

Official site of the 'grand old party' of the USA. A home page, depicting images of a collection of inner-city businesses, offers access to information on Republican policies, party structure, representatives, press releases, and trivia quizzes.

Political Figures

Albright, Madeleine

http://secretary.state.gov/www/albright/albright.html

Biography of the US Secretary of State Madeleine Albright, currently the highest-ranking woman in the US government.

Banda, Hastings

http://www.africanews.org/south/malawi/stories/19971201_feat2.html

Profile of the Malawi politician, written shortly after his death in 1997. It traces his humble origins, his work as a clerk in a mine, his medical studies, his work in Ghana, and his friendship with Kwame Nkrumah. Banda's long political career in Malawi, from leading the nation to independence to the humiliating end of his autocratic rule, is traced.

Bhutto, Benazir

http://www.wic.org/bio/bbhutto.htm

Biography of Pakistan's former prime minister from the Women's International Center Web site. It describes her education, election as first non-British president of the Oxford Union, shock at the execution of her father, struggle for democracy, and periods as Pakistan's leader. This partisan site complains about the alleged intrigues which drove Bhutto from office.

George Bush Presidential Library

http://csdl.tamu.edu/bushlib/library/museum/museum.html

Official presidential archive chronicling Bush's long career of public service. There are comprehensive biographies of George and his wife Barbara, an extensive photo collection, and a mass of official papers. There is a virtual tour and details of past, current, and future exhibits.

Heath Under Attack

http://www.stanford.edu/~cjacoby/heath.html

Perceptive (if somewhat academic) article on the political career of Ted Heath. A long account of Heath's period as prime minister is followed by an analysis of his troubled relationship with Margaret Thatcher and his ideological disagreements with Thatcherism. There is also a good bibliography.

How One Woman Became the Voice of Her People

http://www.amnesty-usa.org/amnesty/feats/aungsan.html

Well-written biography of the world's most prominent political prisoner, Aung San Suu Kyi. Her childhood, academic career, and family life in Britain is traced before a description of her non-violent struggle against the junta in Myanmar (Buma). There is a picture of her and extracts from speeches and interviews.

Keating, Paul

http://www.virtualaustralia.com.au/people/prime_ministers/paul_keating.htm

Profile of the career of the Labor prime minister noted for his efforts to reshape Australia's identity in Asia. This is a good profile of 'the Placido Domingo of Australian politics'.

Machiavelli, Nicolò

http://www.utm.edu/research/iep/m/machiave.htm

Profile of the life and legacy of the first great political philosopher of the Renaissance. The influence of that turbulent political events he witnessed had on his political philosophy is described. There is also a summary of his most famous work, *The Prince.*

Mandela, Nelson

http://www.anc.org.za/people/mandela.html

Detailed profile of the former South African president Nelson Mandela. This site includes

> | APARTHEID (Afrikaans 'apartness')
> F
> A
> C
> T
>
> racial-segregation policy of the government of South Africa from 1948 to 1994. Under the apartheid system, nonwhites – classified as Bantu (black), coloured (mixed), or Indian – did not share full rights of citizenship with the white minority. For example, black people could not vote in parliamentary elections, and until 1990 many public facilities and institutions were restricted to the use of one race only.

information on many aspects of his personal as well as political life.

Netanyahu, Binyamin

http://www.abcnews.com/reference/bios/netanyahu.html

Profile of the first Israeli prime minister to be directly elected. The combative politician's career in the USA and Israel is traced, together with the details of the effect of his administration on the Israeli–Palestinian peace process.

Peres, Shimon

http://nobel.sdsc.edu/laureates/peace-1994-2-bio.html

Profile of the career of the veteran Israeli politician. Prepared by the Nobel Committee when he was jointly awarded the 1994 Peace Prize, it outlines the main details of his life. There is also a photograph of the former Labour leader.

Prime Minister of Australia – the Honourable John Howard

http://www.effect.net.au/cuddlyk/myworld/history/howard.html

Profile of the career of the politician who restored the Liberal Party to power in Australia in 1996. There is a good analysis of how the self-styled 'Lazarus with a triple by-pass' played on popular fears to oust Labor from power.

Quayle Quote List

http://www.cs.ncl.ac.uk/people/chris.holt/home.informal/bar/corsair.afdq/quayle.quotes/

Official Quayle Quote List gives access to a wide range of comments made by Dan Quayle on issues such as national defence, women, and the environment.

Rebel With a Cause: Laurent Kabila

http://www.abcnews.com/sections/world/kabilabio507/index.html

Profile of the veteran Congolese politician. Written after the culmination of his thirty year campaign to oust Mobutu Sese Seko, it examines Kabila's Marxist past and the circumstances that led to his military takeover of Zaire, now known as the Democratic Republic of the Congo.

Sanchez, Oscar Arias

http://www.nobel.se/laureates/peace-1987-1-bio.html

Profile of the winner of the Nobel Peace Prize. Arias's career as a lawyer, Costa Rican politician, and member of the Socialist International is traced. His efforts to bring peace to central America are described.

Serbian Nationalism, Slobodan Milosevic, and the Origins of the Yugoslav War

http://www.suc.org/politics/papers/history/vujacic.html

Long analysis of the career of the Serbian president. It examines his rise to power within the Yugoslav Communist Party before a meticulous examination of his pivotal role in the conflict in the former Yugoslavia. Doubts are expressed as to whether the charisma and populist appeal of this politician can be maintained.

Shamir, Yitzhak

http://www.israel-mfa.gov.il/facts/state/shamir.html

Uncritical official biography of the right-wing Israeli politician. It traces his Polish origins, his discontent with mainstream Zionism, his leadership of the Stern Gang terrorist movement, and his period as prime minister.

Stresemann, Gustav

http://www.nobel.se/laureates/peace-1926-2-bio.html

Profile of the German chancellor and foreign minister. It traces his earliest involvement in economic and political life and how his support for German military might have been tempered by a growing realization that national strength could not be achieved by force. His role in the

Weimar republic is traced, together with an examination of the work with the British and French foreign ministers which led to his sharing of the 1926 Nobel Peace Prize.

Who Killed Petra Kelly?

http://bsd.mojones.com/mother_jones/JF93/hertsgaard.html

Speculation about the mysterious death of the prominent German environmentalist. An examination of various theories leads to the conclusion that Kelly was probably murdered by her partner. The background to her relationship with Gert Bastian is examined in detail.

Yeltsin, Boris

http://www.cs.indiana.edu/hyplan/dmiguse/Russian/bybio.html

Biographical material about Boris Yeltsin, including sections on his family background, early education, engineering career, and gradual political involvement which culminated with his central role in the days of the 1991 coup and his election to the presidency of Russia. Though focusing on Yeltsin, the presentation offers ample background material on the old regime and on Russia today and its political leaders.

Political History

'A Case for Gun Control'

http://www.asahi-net.or.jp/~zj5j-gttl/guns.htm

Detailed essay written by Jason Gottlieb on the arguments for greater gun control in the USA.

Chris De Witt's Berlin Wall Website

http://www.appropriatesoftware.com/BerlinWall/welcome.html

Useful resources relating to the Berlin Wall. This site contains several photo galleries, as well as some personal articles. A number of links are also featured, including articles on the history the wall.

Founding Fathers

http://www.nara.gov/exhall/charters/constitution/confath.html

Designed by the National Archives and Records Administration, this site provides information on the delegates to the US Constitutional Convention of 1787. Delegates are listed by the states that sent them to the Convention. Click on the state or delegate to read biographies. Each biography also includes an image.

Letter Accompanying the US Constitution

http://odur.let.rug.nl/~usa/D/1776-1800/constitution/const_l.htm

Part of a larger site on historical documents, this page is the text of a letter written by the President of the Federal Convention to the President of Congress which introduce the US Constitution for consideration.

Modern History Sourcebook: The Brezhnev Doctrine, 1968

http://www.fordham.edu/halsall/mod/1968brezhnev.html

Brief introduction to the Brezhnev Doctrine, as well as a number of extracts from the doctrine itself.

South African Constitution

http://www.constitution.org.za/drafts/wdrafts/sacon96.htm

Dedicated to the new Constitutional Assembly in South Africa, and includes the new constitution in full.

Tiananmen – 1989

http://www.christusrex.org/www1/sdc/tiananmen.html

Photographic history of the demonstrations and massacre in Tiananmen Square, Beijing in 1989. This site holds over 250 photographs divided into five subcategories covering all aspects of events leading up to, during, and after the massacre.

Truman Doctrine

http://www.yale.edu/lawweb/avalon/trudoc.htm

Part of the Avalon Project at the Yale Law School, this page is the text of US President Harry S Truman's address before a joint session of Congress on 12 March 1947, during which he expounds the principles that would become known as the Truman Doctrine.

What Shaped South Africa

http://www.sapolitics.co.za/hist1.htm

Four-page essay on South Africa's political and economic history from 1910 to the collapse of apartheid, by South African political commentator and analyst Daniel Silke. The site is prepared by the South African Political Information Exchange. There are also links to other articles on South African issues.

Political Theory

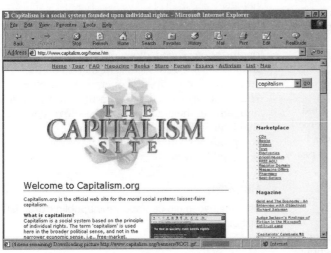

Capitalism.org

http://www.capitalism.org/home.htm

Philosophical, economic, and political examination of capitalism. This site includes a 'Capitalism tour', a multimedia introduction to capitalism, and an online version of *Capitalism Magazine*.

Liberalism

http://plato.stanford.edu/entries/liberalism/

Detailed history and analysis of the political and philosophical tradition of liberalism. The role of John Stewart Mill and other seminal liberals is traced prior to an examination of the ongoing debates within the liberal tradition. The site also includes a comprehensive bibliography.

Principles of Communism

http://csf.colorado.edu/psn/marx/Archive/1847-Prin/

Translation of the text of Friedrich Engel's *The Principles of Communism,* a first draft of a declarative, defining document for the communist movement.

Propaganda

http://carmen.artsci.washington.edu/propaganda/contents.htm

This site presents a broad examination of the art of propaganda. Articles cover the seven basic methods of propaganda and explore the logical fallacies involved. There are special sections on wartime and political propaganda. In addition to reading articles, you can watch video clips of propagandist films dealing with issues such as demonizing the enemy, the Cold War, and the Red Scare, including Leni Reifenstahl's documentary deifying the Nazis at the Nürnberg rallies, *Triumph of the Will.*

Voting Systems

http://ourworld.compuserve.com/homepages/votelaw/voting.htm

Extensively-linked site on different voting styles across the world. Although this site is not elaborate, it does contain a lot of information on the varying forms elections can take. It also includes access to data from recent elections around the world.

> **F A C T**
>
> **POLITICAL THEORY**
> the philosophical questioning of the assumptions underlying political life; for example, the grounds on which an individual is obliged to obey the state.

Political Organizations (Non-governmental) & Labour Unions

AFL-CIO – Today's Unions

http://www.aflcio.org/

Headquarters of the federation of US trade unions. This large site has comprehensive information on the workers' federation and its concerns about worker's rights, executive pay, civil rights, and globalization. There are a large number of links to US unions and related progressive organizations.

AnarchaFeminism (Anarchist Feminism)

http://www.geocities.com/Paris/2159/anrfem.html

Irish feminist site with anarchist analyses of women's plight. Contents include profiles of Emma Goldman and women who fought for the anarchist cause in the Spanish Civil War, a bibliography, and links to other anarchist feminist sites.

Campaign for Nuclear Disarmament

http://www.cnduk.org/welcome.htm

Information about Britain's longest established antinuclear campaign. This site would be helped by the addition of a search engine. However, among its highlights are a list of contacts to peace campaigners throughout the UK.

Confederation of British Industry

http://www.cbi.org.uk/home.shtml

Representing over 250,000 public and private sector companies, the CBI Web site has sections on 'News', 'CBI at work', and 'Business services'.

Constitution and Laws of the Knights of the Ku Klux Klan

http://www.lib.msu.edu/spc/digital/radicalism/hs2330.k6a51921.htm

Facsimile version of an early 20th-century manuscript of the Ku Klux Klan constitution from the Radicalism Collection of the Michigan State University Libraries, USA. Click on each number to view any of the 101 pages in turn.

Electoral Reform Society

http://www.gn.apc.org/ers/

Details of the organization campaigning to replace Britain's 'first past the post' electoral system with a form of proportional representation. Clicking the STV option on the home page tells you everything there is to know about the single transferable vote. The site also has interesting data on British and European parliamentary organizations and links to other electoral reform sites around the world.

European Monetary Union – The Legal Framework

http://www.cliffordchance.com/library/publications/emu_legal/section1.html

Good objective analysis of the background to the introduction of a single European currency. The history of the European Monetary System is examined and its progress on implementation of the Maastricht Treaty. There is also a timetable of the stages towards full monetary union.

Hamas

http://oicj.acsp.uic.edu/spearmint/public/extremist/hamas/

Unflattering profile of the Harakat al-Muqawama al Islamiya (Hamas), from a US anti-terrorist organization. The ideology of Hamas and its foundation are described. Information on the structure, leadership, and operational activities of Hamas is part factual, part speculation. For all its antipathy to the organization, the site recognizes that Hamas has indicated a willingness to compromise should Israel withdraw from the occupied West Bank.

Hizbollah

http://oicj.acsp.uic.edu/spearmint/public/extremist/hizbollah/index.cfm

Unflattering profile of 'the party of God' from a US anti-terrorist organization. The ideology of the party and its foundation are described. Information on the structure, leadership, and operational activities of Hezbollah is part factual, part speculation.

Ideology of the Black Panther Party

http://douglass.speech.nwu.edu/hill_a15.htm

This page is the text of an article written by David Hilliard, chief of staff of the Black Panther Party, on 8 November 1969, during the trial of Bobby Seale, chairman of the Black Panthers. It is a statement clarifying Black Panther ideology that originally appeared in the *Black Panther* newspaper.

Industrial Workers of the World

http://fletcher.iww.org/

Extensive information on the ongoing struggles of the labour movement in the USA and Australia. There is a history of the organization, details of its current structures and campaigns, and fervent appeals for working-class solidarity.

Institute of Global Communications Internet

http://www.igc.apc.org

Subtitled 'Connecting the people who are changing the world', this site offers a wide range of up-to-date news and information on political and campaign issues. It is grouped by area and subject – and includes such topics as 'Health', 'Indigenous peoples', and 'Ecojustice network'.

National Rifle Association of America

http://www.nra.org/

Large, well-organised site of the leading US gun lobby. The case for the right to bear arms is forcefully presented. There is detailed information on gun laws in each state and NRA lobbying activities in addition to news of NRA marksmanship events.

National Union of Students

http://www.nus.org.uk/

As well as information about the UK NUS and its current executive, this site features 'Student News', the magazine *NUS Network,* and articles about student welfare, entertainment, money, media, and the latest on the NUS' fees campaign.

NUT Online

http://www.teachers.org.uk

Official site of the UK National Union of Teachers (NUT). The site contains help for student teachers, discussions of pay and conditions, health and safety articles, and details of NUT policies on important issues.

Peace Pledge Union

http://www.gn.apc.org/peacepledge/

Well organized site of Britain's Peace Pledge Union. There is information of the agency's work for peace and disarmament, resources for teachers, history of the union, and frequently updated news of current pacifist campaigns.

Sendero Luminoso – A Study in Paradox

http://vub.mcgill.ca/journals/latitudes/1sendero.htm

Long and thoughtful analysis of modern Peruvian society and the socio-economic conditions that spawned the secretive terrorist movement also known as the 'Shining Path'. The success of Sendero is ascribed to the underlying racial and economic inequality in Peru and the movement's refined Maoist propaganda skills.

Trades Union Congress

http://www.tuc.org.uk/

Site of the organization which (despite falling

membership) still represents 6.7 million British workers. There are details of the 72 affiliated unions, a history of the TUC and, in keeping of the times, some very commercial special offers for trade unionists.

International Political Organizations

Baltic Assembly, Baltic Council of Ministers, and Nordic Council

http://www.lrs.lt/baltasm/indexa.htm

Official guide to the regional coordination mechanisms for the Baltic States. The history and structure of the Baltic Council, and its role in increasing cooperation between Latvia, Lithuania, and Estonia, are set out. Wider regional dialogue with the Scandinavian states through the Nordic Council is described.

Commonwealth Institute

http://www.commonwealth.org.uk/

Full outline of the role of the Commonwealth Institute. In addition to general information about the Commonwealth and its institutions, there are details of current exhibitions at the Institute. There are also extensive links to embassies, tourist offices, and other institutions in Commonwealth states.

Council of Europe

http://www.coe.fr/index.asp

Home page of the 50-year-old Strasbourg-based organization charged with strengthening democracy, human rights, and the rule of law among the 40 member states. There is a large documentary archive.

European and Asian Documents on Fourth World Affairs

http://www.cwis.org/eurasia.html

Extensive text archive on the indigenous people of Europe and Asia maintained by the Fourth World Documentation Project and intended to educate the international community about the problems that these largely unrecognized national populations face within their states.

European Union

http://europa.eu.int/

Official, multilingual site for the European Union. It contains a lot of well presented information about all areas of the union, including policy, the various institutions, up-to-date news, and answers to the most common questions.

NATO

http://www.nato.int/

Official site of the North Atlantic Treaty Organization. This site includes a guide to NATO's structure, its members and partners, and staff vacancies; a complete archive of all official documents and both general and specific NATO publications; sub-sites presenting specific areas of the alliance's activities; and a multimedia section with photos (including a special section on NATO's 50th anniversary), videos, and virtual visits.

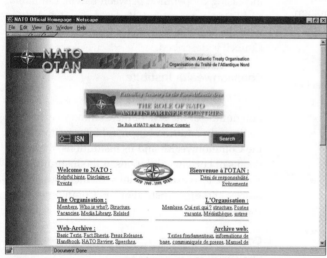

Oceania – Documents on Fourth World Affairs

http://www.cwis.org/melpac.html

Extensive text archive on the indigenous people of Oceania. This database aims to increase knowledge and understanding of the problems that these largely unrecognized national populations face within their states. It is maintained by the Fourth World Documentation Project.

Organization for Security and Cooperation in Europe

http://www.osceprag.cz/

Site of the UN organization charged with keeping the peace in Europe. It contains regularly updated information on the work being done around such issues as arms control, election monitoring, and conflict prevention. The structure of the organization and its parts is well explained and there is a comprehensive archive.

Organization of African Unity

http://www.oau-oua.org/

Site of the organization aiming to improve economic, cultural, and political cooperation in Africa. The organization's charter, history, and structures are comprehensively explained. There is frequently updated information on summits, commissions, and job vacancies, in addition to recent press releases.

Organization of American States

http://www.oas.org/

Home page of the alliance of states working towards social and economic development in Latin America. There is an explanation of the organization's structure and its work on issues such as drugs, corruption, poverty, environment, trade, education, democracy, and human rights. Its online magazine (in English and Spanish) may also be accessed.

Treaty Establishing the European Community

http://europa.eu.int/abc/obj/treaties/ en/entoc05.htm

Complete text of the founding document of the European Economic Community. This is provided by the European Union and includes all associated protocols and documents of ratification.

**F
A
C
T**

UNITED NATIONS (UN)

association of states for international peace, security, and cooperation, with its headquarters in New York. The UN was established in 1945 by 51 states as a successor to the League of Nations, and has played a role in many areas, such as refugees, development assistance, disaster relief, cultural cooperation, and peacekeeping.

United Nations Home Page

http://www.un.org/

Official site providing a general overview of the United Nations with news, photographs, key documents, and links to UN departments and information resources.

Humanitarian Aid, Charities & Human Rights

ActionAid Home Page

http://www.actionaid.org/

Home page of one of the UK's leading development agencies that includes good resources for teachers. The online version of ActionAid's magazine is full of well-written accounts of development projects around the world.

F
A
C
T

AMNESTY INTERNATIONAL

human-rights organization established in the UK in 1961 to campaign for the release of prisoners of conscience worldwide; fair trials for all political prisoners; an end to the death penalty, torture, and other inhuman treatment of all prisoners; and the cessation of extrajudicial executions and 'disappearances'. It is politically and economically unaligned.

Amnesty International Online

http://www.amnesty.org/

Home page of the world's foremost human rights organization, with easily accessible information on its structure, current campaigns, and how you can help. There is a library of documents on human rights for every corner of the world.

Campaign Against Arms Trade

http://www.caat.demon.co.uk/

Work of the British organization campaigning to end the international arms trade and Britain's role in it. A huge amount of information on the international arms trade, new defence

technologies, and abuses of human rights can be accessed. There are also a large number of links to other peace and disarmament organizations.

CARE International

http://www.care.org/

Home page of the UK office of CARE International, a confederation of agencies that delivers relief assistance to people in need. The page provides links to all the CARE members, including those in the UK, and offers development news, related publications and articles, information on regional needs, and regional CARE programmes, as well as world development statistics on hunger, poverty, AIDS, the abuse of the environment, children's malnutrition, and illiteracy.

Charity Commission for England and Wales

http://www.charity-commission.gov.uk/

Functions of the body charged with supervising the 160,000 registered charities in England and Wales are fully explained. A search engine allows particular charities to be identified and offers a brief profile of their activities.

Charter 88

http://www.charter88.org.uk/home.html

Site of the British human rights organization campaigning for a written constitution. There is a description of the work of the organization, frequently-updated details of its campaigns, links to local groups around Britain, and to sites listing virtually all the world's written constitutions.

Clara Barton in Dansville

http://dansville.lib.ny.us/clara.html

Profile of the energetic life of the founder of the US Red Cross. This site traces her active engagement in humanitarian activities during the US Civil War, her work in Switzerland, and her long tenure as US Red Cross leader.

Disaster Relief

http://www.disasterrelief.org/

Comprehensive site run partly by the American Red Cross, giving information on both natural and man-made disaster stories from around the world. There is a forum for discussion on disaster relief with opportunities to get involved, as well as plenty of detailed and well-presented information, including pictures and maps of affected areas.

East Timor Human Rights Centre

http://law.murdoch.edu.au/minihub/ethrc/

Australian centre for the promotion of human rights in Indonesian-controlled East Timor. Human rights violations, extra-judicial executions, and disappearances, are factually chronicled. Please note that this site does include some pictures of tortured Timorese.

54 Ways to Help The Homeless

http://earthsystems.org/ways/

Very good introduction to this complex social issue, which begins by debunking many myths about who the homeless actually are, before moving on to a series of wide-ranging pragmatic approaches to this problem. The list of resources at the end is exclusively US-based, but there is a great deal of useful thought-, and it is hoped by the author, action-provoking information here.

Gay and Lesbian Pride Trust

http://www.pride.org.uk/

Home page of the UK-based gay rights group. The site has extensive details of the annual gay pride parade in London, including images and video clips from previous years. It also contains information about the Trust's activities throughout the rest of the year.

Human Rights Caravan

http://rights.amnesty.org/

Comprehensive review of the effect of the Universal Declaration on Human Rights fifty years after its inception. This report from Amnesty International has the full text of the Declaration, details of 50th anniversary celebrations, and information for those wishing to help this charity to make its provisions more enforceable.

Human Rights Web Home Page

http://www.hrweb.org/

Information on human rights issues. The site provides beginners with an introduction to the main human rights concepts. It also offers a short

history of the human rights movement; those who would like to play a role in it should consult the primer for new human rights activists. It also features documents from the United Nations and other sources, as well as short biographies and links to pages about individual prisoners of conscience.

Intermediate Technology Development Group

http://www.oneworld.org/itdg/

Full account of the work of the British aid organization working with rural poor to develop relevant and sustainable technologies. Reports of the low-tech projects supported by this charity make fascinating reading. Of equal interest is work with other British aid agencies to develop approaches to project monitoring and evaluation which involve local people.

International Committee of the Red Cross

http://www.icrc.org/

Home page of the Red Cross Movement, with frequently updated reports on the charity's operations in more than 50 countries. There is extensive coverage of issues surrounding international humanitarian law, as well as of current Red Cross campaigning issues.

International Fund for Agricultural Development

http://www.unicc.org/ifad/home.html

Site of the UN agency charged with tackling rural poverty and hunger. Its work and structures are explained, there are details of international conferences, and an overview of the agency's first twenty years. Press releases are available together with a number of photos.

National Lottery Charities Board

http://www.nlcb.org.uk/

Full details of how Britain's official lottery assists charities in Britain and abroad. The structure and function of NLCB is fully explained. There is an easy-to-follow guide to submitting a funding application and details of all grants made to date.

OneWorld

http://www.oneworld.org/index.html

OneWorld is an Internet community of 260 organizations working for human rights and sustainable development worldwide. This well-organized site offers news, commentary, and analysis of global issues and has extensive links. News from around the world not picked up by the conventional media is well presented and accessible through a search engine. All the member agencies of the network can be easily contacted.

Orphan Trains

http://www.pbs.org/wgbh/pages/amex/orphan/index.html

Companion to the US Public Broadcasting Service (PBS) television programme *The American Experience,* this page tells the story of the controversial Children's Aid Society, an organization that between 1854 and 1929 rounded up some 100,000 poor and homeless children from the streets of New York City and relocated them to rural areas of the USA. The programme transcript is available for reading and there is a list of sources.

Peace Corps – The Toughest Job You'll Ever Love!

http://www.peacecorps.gov/

Promotional site to encourage US youth to participate in the work of the Peace Corps. Peace Corps programmes around the world are described together with an overview of host countries. The work of individual volunteers is highlighted. There is also information on Peace Corps educational projects targeted at school teachers.

Project Hope

http://www.projhope.org/

Home page of HOPE, a humanitarian organization providing health policy research and assistance in more than 70 countries all over the world. The site offers a wide range of development news and HOPE events, information about international health education programs, and a brief overview of the challenges it has faced since 1958.

Save the Children Fund

http://www.oneworld.org/scf/

Home page of the UK's leading children's charity, with extensive information on its work nationally and in more than 50 other countries. Key topics in international development are presented in a lively manner.

UNICEF United Nations Children's Fund

http://www.unicef.org/

This is a comprehensive guide to the work of the agency and the tasks it has set itself. As well as providing excellent statistical data and narrative information, there is a section on 'Voices of Youth', with quizzes, discussion forums, and educational activities. UNICEF's annual 'State of the World's Children' report can also be accessed here.

United Nations Development Programme

http://www.undp.org/

Full account of the work of the UN agency that works to foster sustainable development in less-developed countries. This is a good source of information on global development issues.

United Nations Documents and Submissions on Fourth World Affairs

http://www.cwis.org/

Extensive database of digitised texts maintained by the Fourth World Documentation Project, testifying to the involvement of the United Nations in Fourth World affairs. It includes draft declarations, position papers, session documents, and other statements and submissions dealing with problems that indigenous peoples all over the world face within their states.

United Nations High Commissioner for Human Rights

http://www.unhchr.ch/

This site from the UN includes the full text of the Universal Declaration of Human Rights in 270 languages.

United Nations High Commissioner for Refugees

http://www.unicc.org/unhcrcdr/

Access to databases of the United Nations High Commissioner for Refugees, including an overview of the organization's activities and many images.

Vanished Gallery

http://www.yendor.com/vanished/index.html

Chronicle of the thousands of Argentine civilians and alleged 'subversives' who were tortured or disappeared during the years of military dictatorship. It includes details on numbers, photographs and information on the main perpetrators and first-hand accounts of torture and abduction.

Welcome to Oxfam UK and Ireland

http://www.oxfam.org/

Web site of the UK's foremost nongovernmental development and relief agency, giving comprehensive information on Oxfam's work around the world and regular updates on its current campaigns.

Welcome to the Rotary International Web Site

http://www.rotary.org./

Central source of information on the worldwide Rotary movement. There are details of Rotary activities in 158 countries. The site also includes a history of the philanthropic society, an exposition of its guiding principles, and an outline of its administrative structure.

Welcome to the Samaritans Online

http://www.samaritans.org.uk/

Well organized site of the UK voluntary organization providing support to the suicidal and despairing. There is a 'Frequently Asked Questions' section about depression and details of the services provided by the Samaritans. There are statistics on suicide in the UK and an interesting analysis of trends.

World Food Programme

http://www.unicc.org/wfp/

Information on the work of the UN agency charged with addressing the needs of the one out of seven people on Earth who are starving. This is a good source of frequently-updated information on international efforts to assist the victims of man-made and natural disasters, and of disaster mitigation initiatives.

World Health Organization

http://www.who.ch/

Overview of the World Health Organization, including its major programmes, and recent world health reports.

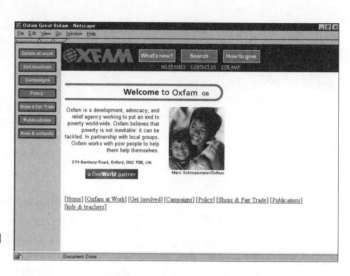

Law & Lawyers

Beccaria, Cesare

http://www.utm.edu/research/iep/b/beccaria.htm

Profile of the Italian criminal justice reformer. It describes his campaign against the use of torture and capital punishment and the acclaim he won despite his chronic shyness. There is a long summary of his best-known work *On Crimes and Punishments*.

Bentham Archive of British Law

http://www.ndirect.co.uk/~law/bentham.htm

Law resource for research and guidance 'produced to appeal to a wide range of people – from laymen with legal problems or interests, to

killers', and 'Terrorists, spies, and assassins'.

<table>
<tr><td rowspan="6" style="vertical-align:top">F
A
C
T</td><td>

BENTHAM, JEREMY (1748–1832)

English philosopher, legal and social reformer, and founder of utilitarianism. The essence of his moral philosophy is found in the pronouncement of his *Principles of Morals and Legislation* (written in 1780, published in 1789): that the object of all legislation should be 'the greatest happiness for the greatest number'.

</td></tr>
</table>

students, right up to practitioners'. The site is intended to provide background information and not as a substitute for professional consultation. It includes introductions to Roman, property, European, media, and computer law; the full text of recent Acts of Parliament and of the European Union courts; legal contacts and addresses; and a link to the page of the group which campaigns against miscarriages of justice, 'Scandals in Justice'.

Bill of Rights

http://earlyamerica.com/earlyamerica/freedom/bill/index.html

Full text of the US Bill of Rights. This site also contains a short background introduction to this significant document.

Code of Hammurabi

http://www.lawresearch.com/v2/codeham.htm

Translation of, and commentary on, the *Law Code of Hammurabi*, one of the earliest recognized lawcodes of the ancient world.

Court of Justice of the European Communities

http://europa.eu.int/cj/en/index.htm

Official guide to the history and structure of Europe's highest court. Full texts of judgements and lists of cases pending can be accessed. This site gives an indication of the enormous range of issues involved in the interpretation and application of the treaties of the European Union.

Crime Library

http://crimelibrary.com/index.html

Collection of stories and essays about infamous criminals and crimes, divided into 'Classic crime stories', 'Gangsters, outlaws and G-men', 'Serial

killers', and 'Terrorists, spies, and assassins'.

Crime Prevention Initiatives

http://www.crime-prevention.org.uk/home_office/guide/

Practical advice on protecting yourself, your family, home, and personal possessions against crime, reproduced from the Home Office publication, *Your Practical Guide to Crime Prevention*.

Crown Prosecution Service – Working in the Interests of Justice

http://www.cps.gov.uk/

Official site of the body responsible for criminal prosecutions in Britain and Wales (data also provided in Welsh). This is a good introduction to the work of this organization with practical information for defendants, victims, and witnesses. There is also a downloadable video highlighting the work of the Crown Prosecution Service.

Death Penalty Information

http://sun.soci.niu.edu/%7Ecritcrim/dp/dp.html

Treats a very emotive subject in a factual way, and is notable in that it comes from the USA, where capital punishment still operates. More information is provided for the case against capital punishment, but an attempt is made to give space to both sides of the argument.

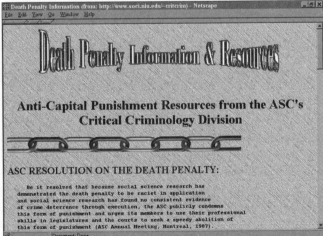

Events of the Sacco and Vanzetti Case

http://flag.blackened.net/daver/anarchism/saccvanz.html

Details of the famous US political trial. The events leading to the controversial execution of the two Italian immigrants are retold. This anarchist site has no doubts concerning the innocence of the two men.

Future of Legal Aid in England and Wales

http://www.lovellwhitedurrant.com/NewSite/pr/lit.htm

Detailed examination of Lord Mackay's July 1996 white paper on proposed reforms of the legal aid system.

General Council of the Bar

http://www.barcouncil.org.uk/

Professional body for barristers in England and Wales. The site outlines the role of barristers within the UK legal system, and their education and training, and provides a 'Bar council directory'.

Interpol

http://193.123.144.14/interpol-pr/

International Criminal Police Organization Web site. This well-designed site contains a wealth of information about the organization, including a detailed explanation of its structure and history, and also includes exhibitions on the work of Interpol.

Law Commission – Working for Better Law

http://www.gtnet.gov.uk/lawcomm/misc/about.htm#consolidation

Comprehensive information on the role of the Law Commission in England and Wales. There are full details on all the laws currently under review. Recent judgements of the commission can also be easily accessed.

Medieval Law and Politics

http://www.millersv.edu/~english/homepage/duncan/medfem/law.html

Information on the legal position of medieval women. The issues treated include 'Gender equality', 'Women in the Magna Carta', 'Women and English medieval common law', 'Casting spells', and even 'Kissing cousins'.

Right of Way

http://www.ramblers.org.uk/rowfaq.html

Practical information about rights of way in Britain from Britain's Rambler's Association. The legal status of a right of way, how paths can become rights of way, and the duties and responsibilities of walkers, farmers, and public authorities are clearly spelt out.

Roman Law

http://www.jura.uni-sb.de/Rechtsgeschichte/Ius.Romanum/english.html

Dedicated to collating information on Roman law, including key Latin texts and hyperlinks to other Web sites on the classics.

Salmon Portland Chase

http://odur.let.rug.nl/~usa/B/spchase/chasexx.htm

Part of a larger site on historical documents, this page is devoted to the life and death of Chief Justice of the US Supreme Court Salmon Portland Chase. Divided into six sections, this site includes information on his years as a US senator and chief justice, including his role as chief justice during the impeachment trial of US President Andrew Johnson.

Supreme Court Decisions, 1937–1975

http://www.access.gpo.gov/su_docs/supcrt/index.html

Full text of more than 7,000 US Supreme Court decisions handed down between 1937 and 1975. Cases are accessible by case name, case number, or a keyword search.

Supreme Court Opinion, 1993–1998

http://fedbbs.access.gpo.gov/court01.htm

Decisions and related documents of the Supreme Court handed down since 1993. This page is updated as decisions are made.

United Nations Crime and Justice Information Network

http://www.ifs.univie.ac.at/~uncjin/uncjin.html

Global crime prevention and criminal justice information network on the Web. It provides access to United Nations documents, links to other UN organizations, and country-specific information including a whole range of area maps.

World Intellectual Property Organization

http://www.wipo.org/eng/index.htm

Home page of the UN agency charged with protecting intellectual property. The text is legalistic in tone but is essential for those wanting comprehensive information on such topics as international copyright treaties, trademarks, and Internet domains.

Economic Organizations

European Free Trade Association

http://www.imf.org/external/np/sec/decdo/efta.htm

Introduction to the group of European states that are not levying import duties on each other. There is a history of the organization, an explanation of its structure, a description of its relationship with the European Union, and contact addresses.

G8 Information Center

http://www.g7.utoronto.ca/

Run by the University of Toronto, this site details the economic summits and meetings of the Group of Seven and Group of Eight, and provides copies of relevant documents.

International Monetary Fund

http://www.imf.org/external/index.htm

Explanation of this organization's role in promoting international monetary cooperation and assisting states with balance-of-payments difficulties. This is a well organized and informative site with a good search engine and

quick access to thousands of documents and press releases dealing with global economic issues.

OECD – Organization for Economic Cooperation and Development

http://www.oecd.org

Regularly updated site with information on the role, structure, and history of this organization. A large number of documents can be accessed and there is a search engine that aims to explain the work of the 29 member nations. It is a superb source of statistical information for anybody interested in the workings of the global economy.

OPEC Online

http://www.opec.org/

Site of the oil producers' association that attempts to regulate price and production. There are profiles of the oil industry in the 11 member states, a good history of the organization, press releases, and information on publications. This is an important site for an understanding of the contemporary world oil market

World Trade Organization

http://www.wto.org/wto/index.htm

Extensive information on the functions of the UN agency charged with administering international trade agreements. The contents are in English, French, and Spanish and the full text of many international agreements are included. There is also a useful search facility and list of 'Frequently Asked Questions'.

Banks

Bank for International Settlements

http://www.bis.org/

Full source of official information on this international bank and its role to promote cooperation among central banks. The history and structure is well explained, and reviews, press releases, and publications may be accessed. There is also a listing of all the world's central banks which have Web sites.

European Bank for Reconstruction and Development

http://www.ebrd.com/

**F
A
C
T**

ECONOMIC ACTIVITY

the production and distribution of goods and services to satisfy the wants and needs of consumers and other businesses. It produces a wide range of commodities, usually classified under three headings: consumer goods, producer goods, and services.

Explanation of the role and structure of the London-based group that finances 'the economic transition in central and eastern Europe and the CIS'. The text is heavy-going and aimed at economists interested in developments in central Europe and the former Soviet Union, or countries wishing to find about the mechanisms of obtaining economic support.

Grameen Bank

http://www.citechco.net/grameen/bank/

Information about the pioneering work of the Grameen Bank, which extends credit without collateral to the poor of Bangladesh. The site includes sections on 'Statistical updates', 'Balance sheets', 'Micro credit', and a bibliography.

Reserve Bank of Australia

http://www.rba.gov.au/about/ab_ind.html

Home page of Australia's central bank. The history and structure of the RBA is explained. There are press releases, texts of speeches, and the bank's quarterly reviews. This is an essential site for anybody interested in monitoring the state of Australia's economy.

World Bank Home Page

http://www.worldbank.org/

Easy-to-use site that explains the workings of the organization. It includes sections on current events, press releases and bank news, country information, publications, and research studies.

Money, Finance & Fiscal Policy

Bank of England – Banknote Printing

http://www.bankofengland.co.uk/banknotes/index.htm

This easily navigable site is well linked and contains details of the origins of money and the complex printing process involved in the manufacture of new notes. The site also contains information about the Bank of England's other work.

Budget

http://www.hm-treasury.gov.uk/pub/html/budget.html

Frequently updated information on the UK's budget from the Treasury. There is an index of official press releases relating to the budget. Accompanying documents provide a picture of the state of Britain's public finances.

Dow Jones Indexes

http://indexes.dowjones.com/

Latest readings from the Dow Jones Index, 'the Markets' Measure'. The various indexes are backed up with explanations of the methodology used to compile them, and archives of previous readings.

Federal Budget of the USA

http://www.access.gpo.gov/omb/index.html

Download entire federal budget documents or search for individual sections. This site includes a citizens' guide with information about the budget and budget process for the general public, as well as the 'Economic Report of the President' for the years 1995–1998.

Federal Reserve Board

http://www.bog.frb.fed.us

Description of the complex functioning of the US central banking system. As well as explaining its structure, a large selection of press releases, speeches, surveys, and economic statistics make this an invaluable source of information for those interested in the state of the US economy.

History of Money from Ancient Times to the Present Day

http://www.ex.ac.uk/~RDavies/arian/llyfr.html

Online version of a book about the history of money. It begins with a 'Comparative history of money' and ends with 'Third world money and debt in the 20th century'. The text also contains links to sources of related data.

FISCAL POLICY

that part of government policy concerning taxation and other revenues, public spending, and government borrowing (the public sector borrowing requirement).

London Stock Exchange

http://www.londonstockexchange.co.uk/

London Stock Exchange Web site that tells you how the exchange and its markets work. The site includes details on what the LSE does, how the exchange is organized, a brief history, and planned future developments. The site also holds information on how the stock market is regulated.

164 Currency Converter

http://www.oanda.com/cgi-bin/ncc

Simple to use and effective site allowing you to do automatic conversions to and from a wide range of currencies, from the Afghani to the zloty. You can select the amount to convert and also the date of the exchange rate you want to use.

Secrets of Making Money

http://www.pbs.org/wgbh/nova/moolah/

Companion to a US Public Broadcasting Service (PBS) television programme, this page investigates the science and art of minting money. Click on any feature of an interactive US $100 bill to learn more about it. Much of the information concerns techniques designed to confound counterfeiters. There is a fun section that lets you try your hand at identifying bogus bills. You can also read about the history of money, which stretches all the way back to the days of bartering, and find out about tomorrow's digital cash. Watch out for a cheeky, winking Benjamin Franklin on the home page's $100 bill. There is also a list of resources for further reference.

Stockmarket – the UK's Personal Finance Web Site

http://www.moneyworld.co.uk/stocks/index.html

Constantly updated financial information from the leading stock exchanges. You can follow the fortunes of the FTSE and the Dow and the latest currency fluctuations. If your investments plummet there are links to a number of financial advisors. The site also includes a selection of financial articles from the British press.

UK PAYE Tax Calculator

http://listen.to/taxman

A quick, unofficial calculator to work out your personal tax liability. Based on gross income per annum, it includes tax allowances and National Insurance contributions, and provides a breakdown by year, month, and week.

US Securities and Exchange Commission

http://www.sec.gov/

Information on the US agency charged with the regulation of securities and financial markets. The quasijudicial regulatory functions are described in detail. Information is provided about enforcement actions with descriptions of selected criminal proceedings, and there is also advice for small businesses.

Economic Theory

Adam Smith: Excerpt from *The Wealth of Nations:* Regarding the Cost of Empire

http://odur.let.rug.nl/~usa/D/1776-1800/adamsmith/wealth02.htm

Part of a larger site on historical documents, this page is a section of text from political economist Adam Smith's book *The Wealth of Nations.* This passage is a plea to the English rulers to reconsider their policy of empire building. A brief introduction provides historical context.

Benedetto Croce: 'Historical Materialism and the Economics of Karl Marx'

http://socserv2.socsci.mcmaster.ca/~econ/ugcm/3ll3/marx/croce.htm

Part of the Archive for the History of Economic Thought at McMaster University, this page provides the text of several of Croce's essays, in which he attempts 'to make clear by philosophical criticism the real purpose and value of Marx's work'. Each of the essays include notes. At the bottom of the page, you will find the text of two letters to Vilfredo Pareto. There is also an introduction by A D Lindsay.

Business Ethics Magazine Online

http://condor.depaul.edu/ethics/bizethics.html

Online version of a print magazine which combines two aspects often thought not to sit well together: business and ethics. This site, predominantly text-based, proves that there is plenty of mileage in the topic and plenty of room for improvement.

Cooperative Principles and History

http://www.wisc.edu/uwcc/prin.html

Clear exposition of the definition, values, principles, identity, and history of the cooperative movement, by the University of Wisconsin Center for Cooperatives.

Economic Consequences of the Peace, The

http://socserv2.socsci.mcmaster.ca/~econ/ugcm/
3ll3/keynes/peace

Complete text of John Maynard Keynes's famous work published in 1919.

Friedrich Hayek Scholars Page

http://www.hayekcenter.org/friedrichhayek/
hayek.html

Text-only site which nevertheless contains an extensive bibliography relating to the economist Friedrich Hayek. This is a large resource for further research, which also contains a number of quotations.

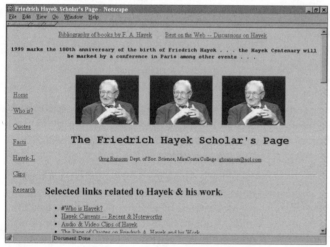

Irving Fisher Essays

http://socserv2.socsci.mcmaster.ca/~econ/ugcm/
3ll3/fisher/index.html

Two essays written by economist Irving Fisher: 'Precedents for Defining Capital', which was originally published in the *Quarterly Journal of Economics*, and 'Is 'Utility' the Most Suitable Term for the Concept It is Used to Denote?', which was originally published in 1918 in the *American Economic Review*.

John Atkinson Hobson: 'Work and Wealth: A Human Valuation'

http://socserv2.socsci.mcmaster.ca/~econ/ugcm/
3ll3/hobson/index.html

John Hobson's essay 'Work and Wealth: A Human Valuation', in which he investigates the effects of economic processes on human welfare and seeks 'some intelligible and consistent method of human valuation for economic goods and processes'.

John Law: 'Money and Trade Considered'

http://socserv2.socsci.mcmaster.ca/~econ/ugcm/
3ll3/law/index.html

Text of a 1705 article written by John Law, in which he investigates various proposals 'to remedy the difficulties the nation is under from the scarcity of money'. Law examines the nature of money and the effects of money on trade.

John Selden: 'A Briefe Discourse Concerning the Powers of the Peeres'

http://socserv2.socsci.mcmaster.ca/
~econ/ugcm/3ll3/selden/index.html

Selden's essay of 1640, 'A Briefe Discourse Concerning the Powers of the Peeres and Comons of Parliament, in Point of Judicature', which includes a brief history of the formation of the English state.

Joseph A Schumpeter: 'On the Concept of Social Value'

http://socserv2.socsci.mcmaster.ca/
~econ/ugcm/3ll3/schumpeter/index.html

Joseph Schumpeter's essay 'On the Concept of Social Value', in which he undertakes a careful study of the meaning and significance of 'social value' in relation to contemporary economics. This essay originally appeared in the 1908–1909 edition of the *Quarterly Journal of Economics*.

Malthus' 'Essay on the Principle of Population'

http://www.ac.wwu.edu/~stephan/malthus/
malthus.0.html

Site devoted to the text of Thomas Robert Malthus's projection of population growth. There is also a portrait of the famous English economist.

Marshall, Alfred

http://socserv2.socsci.mcmaster.ca/~econ/ugcm/
3ll3/marshall/index.html

Books one to five of Alfred Marshall's *The Principles of Economics*. You will also find the text of his essay 'On Rent', as well as four reviews of various editions of *The Principles of Economics*.

Principles of Political Economy

http://socserv2.socsci.mcmaster.ca/~econ/ugcm/
3ll3/ricardo/prin/index.html

Complete text by English economist David Ricardo.

Strategy and Conflict: An Introductory Sketch of Game Theory

http://www.coba.drexel.edu/economics/
mccain/game/game.html

Full guide to the history and practice of game theory. This site contains all there is to know about zero-sum games and a variety of dilemmas and conundrums. Game theory is applied to all aspects of human life from marriage vows to companies on the verge of bankruptcy.

Tinbergen, Jan

http://www-history.mcs.st-and.ac.uk/history/
Mathematicians/Tinbergen.html

Biography of the Nobel prizewinning economist. The site contains a description of his working relationships with his contemporaries, and also features a photograph of Tinbergen. Several literature references for further reading are also listed.

Towards a Better Future – The Works of Manfred Davidmann

http://www.solbaram.org/

Collection of works by this scholar on the problems facing the contemporary world. They are on a wide range of topics from economics, through public policy and religion, to sociology. The works are organized thematically and the full texts are available, as well as a brief description for those pressed for time.

Vilfredo Pareto: 'New Theories of Economics'

http://socserv2.socsci.mcmaster.ca/~econ/ugcm/
3ll3/pareto/index.html

Vilfredo Pareto's essay 'New Theories of Economics', in which he attempts to clarify certain points he had made in a previous work on economics. This essay originally appeared in the *Journal of Political Economy* during the 1890s.

Walter Bagehot: 'A New Standard of Value'

http://socserv2.socsci.mcmaster.ca/~econ/ugcm/
3ll3/jevons/bagehot.htm

Article by Walter Bagehot that originally appeared in the 20 November 1875 edition of *The Economist*. In this article, Bagehot rejects the notion, put forth by William Stanley Jevons, that economic science will produce a better standard of value than gold or silver.

'Wealth' by Andrew Carnegie

http://www.furman.edu/~benson/docs/carnegie.htm

This page features the text of an essay written by the industrialist Andrew Carnegie, in which he discusses the ethics and social obligations associated with great individual wealth. This essay, in which he pens the famous line 'the man who dies thus rich dies disgraced', was originally published in the *North American Review* in June 1889.

'Wealth of Nations, The'

http://english-www.hss.cmu.edu/18th/
wealth-of-nations.txt

Contains the text of this work by the Scottish economist Adam Smith.

William Stanley Jevons: 'Account of a General Mathematical Theory of Political Economy'

http://socserv2.socsci.mcmaster.ca/~econ/ugcm/
3ll3/jevons/index.html

William Stanley Jevon's essay 'Account of a General Mathematical Theory of Political Economy', which appeared in the June 1866 edition of *Journal of the Royal Statistical Society*. You will also find an article by Walter Bagehot which was written in response to an essay of Jevon's concerning a theoretical standard of value other than gold or silver.

Armed Forces & Services

British Army

http://www.army.mod.uk/

Home page of the British Army. There is extensive information on the structure of the army, weapons systems, current deployments, and career opportunities. An 'Army World Challenge' game asks what you would do if faced with five challenging scenarios developed from actual current operational missions.

General Colin L Powell Profile

http://www.achievement.org/autodoc/page/pow0pro-1

Description of the life and military career of the US General Colin L Powell. The Web site contains not only a profile and biographical information, but also a lengthy interview with General Powell from 1992 accompanied by a large number of photographs, and video and audio clips from various stages in his career.

General H Norman Schwarzkopf Profile

http://www.achievement.org/autodoc/page/sch0pro-1

Description of the life and career of the US general 'Stormin' Norman Schwarzkopf in which the Gulf War features prominently. The Web site contains not only a profile and biographical information, but also a lengthy interview with Schwarzkopf from 1992 accompanied by a large number of photographs, and video and audio clips.

Helmuth von Moltke, the Elder – 'On the Nature of War'

http://h-net2.msu.edu/~german/gtext/kaiserreich/moltke.html

Brief introduction to the life of the Prussian general, Helmuth Johannes Ludwig von Moltke, as well as the text of this letter in which he puts forth his views on the necessity of war.

History of the Russian Navy

http://www.neva.ru/EXPO96/book/book-cont.html

Illustrated and comprehensive look at the Russian navy from its beginnings in the 9th century (with Kievan Grand Prince Oleg's attack on Constantinople) through its many engagements on many seas, and culminating with its service in World War I. There are 11 sections to investigate and numerous colourful images of Russian sea vessels.

HMS Warrior

http://www.wtj.com/artdocs/warrior.htm

This site pays homage to the *HMS Warrior,* the world's first ironclad warship. This site reveals the design features that made the *HMS Warrior* the pinnacle of naval technology at the time of its delivery. The text is complimented by numerous colour photographs of the fully restored ship, which is currently moored at the Portsmouth Navy Yard in southern England.

Life of Francis Marion, The

http://tom.cs.cmu.edu/cgi-bin/book/lookup?num=843

Complete text of William Gilmore Simms's biography of the US military leader Francis Marion.

Marshall, George Catlett

http://www.nobel.se/laureates/peace-1953-bio.html

Biography of the diplomat and general who led the biggest army ever assembled. Marshall's military career from his distinguished service in World War I to his appointment as US chief of staff is traced. His role in the reconstruction of Europe after 1945, for which he won the Nobel Peace Prize, is described.

Military Activities: Panoramic Photographs

http://lcweb2.loc.gov/cgi-bin/query/r?ammem/pan:@field(SUBJ+@band(Military.+))

Part of the Panoramic Photo Collection of the US Library of Congress, this page features some 500 panoramic photographs of US military activities, most of which are from around the time of World War I. To find a specific image, click on 'New Search' and try a word search. Many of the photos include brief notes.

National Guard – Always Ready, Always There

http://www.ngb.dtic.mil/

Official information on the US militia force. There is a history of the National Guard and recruitment information, and this site describes National Guard activities in all the US states and overseas. The National Guard's song can also be played.

National Reconnaissance Office – Freedom's Sentinel in Space

http://www.nro.odci.gov/

Public face of the US military's spy satellite programme. The newly transparent organization offers information on its administrative structure, declassified images, and news of satellite launches.

Naval Activities: Panoramic Photographs

http://lcweb2.loc.gov/cgi-bin/query/r?
ammem/pan:@and(+fleet+battleship.+)

Part of the Panoramic Photo Collection of the US Library of Congress, this page features 30 panoramic photographs of US naval activities, most of which are pre-World War I, including a panorama of the wreck of the *USS Maine* in 1911. To find a specific image, click on 'New Search' and try a word search. Many of the photos include brief notes.

Naval Dockyards Society

http://www.canterbury.u-net.com/Dockyards/

Home page of the Naval Dockyards Society. The society 'provides a forum for all those who have an interest in naval dockyards and associated organizations, including hospitals, victualling yards and Ordnance Board establishments. It is concerned with any aspects of naval dockyards: construction, history, workforce as well as the surrounding communities.' This Web site holds a lengthy article on 'The Royal Dockyards' by Dr Philip MacDougall, and publishes a copy of the society's newsletter containing various dockyard-related articles.

Royal Air Force

http://www.raf.mod.uk/

Well-organized and informative site of the UK's air force. In addition to information for would-be recruits, there is extensive information on the role of the RAF and profiles of all RAF aircraft, weapons systems, and bases. The PR-savvy RAF also puts its case for the need for continued low-flying operations.

Royal British Legion

http://www.britishlegion.org.uk/

Site of Britain's leading war veterans' organization. There is comprehensive information about the history of the British Legion, its current activities, and its annual Poppy Appeal. A 'Lost trails' section helps reunite ex-servicemen.

Royal Navy

http://www.royal-navy.mod.uk/

Official guide to the Royal Navy that includes information about the latest training, deployments worldwide, and career opportunities, a history of the navy from its humble beginnings, as well as a 'future' section for each of the four arms of the service.

Special Air Service (SAS)

http://www.ability.org.uk/intro.html

Unofficial information on the elite British Army regiment. Known facts about the SAS are presented, together with information gleaned from the press on their counterinsurgency and anti-terrorist operations. There is also a long listing of books about the SAS.

Top Gun Over Moscow

http://www.pbs.org/wgbh/nova/topgun/

Companion to a US Public Broadcasting Service (PBS) television programme, this page features an inside look at the Russian air force. Two essays offer insight into the current state of the force, which has lost much of its budget since the fall of the Soviet Union, and offer slightly differing conclusions as to whether it remains a viable defensive force. You will also find a fun section explaining the science behind centripetal force and 'pulling Gs' in the cockpit. Watch video clips of harrowing manoeuvres, the crash of a MIG-29 at a Paris airshow, and the effects that G-forces have on the face. You can also read the full text of the programme.

United States Marine Corps

http://www.usmc.mil/

This official site explains how it has been 'making Marines and winning battles since 1775'. There is a history of the Corps, information for recruits, an online magazine, and information on current assignments.

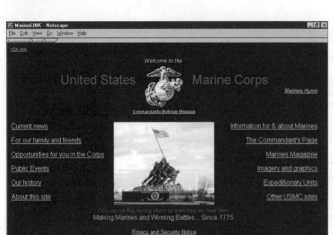

expanding on a number of issues raised in the essay, such as the space race and the USA's relations with Cuba and Vietnam.

Chemical and Biological Warfare Chronicle

http://www.stimson.org/cwc/index.html

Features on difficult biological- and chemical-warfare issues, where policy, technology, and politics intersect. It includes information on current treaties as well as maps of biological- and chemical-weapons sites.

US Army Home Page

http://www.army.mil/

All there is to know about the 'Mission' and 'Vision' of the US Army. The soldier-filled home page offers access to a mass of information. At the top of the list of 'Frequently Asked Questions' is an assurance that the army is tackling sexual harassment. A section called 'Posture statement' does not advise soldiers how to stand up straight but is an analysis of the army's readiness capacity.

US Military Academy West Point

http://www.usma.edu/

PR-savvy site of this military academy. There is extensive information on all aspects of life in the academy including academic and sports news, exhortations on Duty, Honor and Country, the academy's Mission Statement, letters from cadets, and news of how cadets help out in local emergencies. Information on initiation rituals is not to be found.

Methods & Means of Warfare

Arms Race – How Technology Defined Our Identity

http://icdweb.cc.purdue.edu/~phealy/arms.html

Illustrated account of the arms race as part of the Cold War. It contains links

Nuclear Test Ban Treaty

http://www.ctbt.rnd.doe.gov/ctbt/index.html

US Department of Energy site that explains the efforts to ensure that the signatories remain faithful to the letter of the comprehensive nuclear test ban treaty. There are sections on the various monitoring methods including hydroacoustic, seismic, radio nuclides, and infrasound, as well as onsite inspections.

Patriot Air Defence System

http://www.army-technology.com/projects/patriot/index.html

Comprehensive source of information on the US missile system. It traces the research and development that led to the manufacture and deployment of the system during the Gulf War. There is also a detailed explanation of how Patriots work.

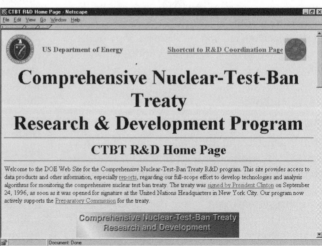

VX Nerve Gas

http://www.outbreak.org/cgi-unreg/dynaserve.exe/cb/vx.html

Basic medical details on the chemical weapon VX gas, possibly the deadliest weapon in existence.

The Web site contains brief sections covering characteristics of the weapon, including its toxicology, the symptoms it causes, cautions and precautions, first aid therapy for victims of the gas, and a list of neutralization and decontamination methods.

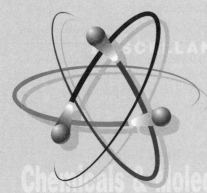

SCIENCE

Astronomy

AJ's Cosmic Thing

http://www.mindentimes.on.ca/CosmicThing/
Main.html

Set any time, date, longitude, latitude, and
position in the setting window, and this
impressive plotter applet will display stationary
or moving full-sky images of objects in the sky.
Clicking on plotted objects reveals information
about the object. There is a technical page for
those wishing additional information.

Astrolabe – An Instrument with a Past and a Future

http://www.astrolabes.org/

Good guide to this ancient astronomical computer.
The long history of the instrument, and its
importance in the history of astrology and
astronomy, is explained with the help of good
photographs. A section on the parts of the astrolabe
explains how the instrument works and its uses.

Bad Astronomy

http://www.badastronomy.com/

Pages designed and maintained by Phil Plait, an
astronomer and teacher, that are dedicated to
exposing misinformation and myths about
astronomy. As well as keeping you up-to-date on
astronomical events, this site also has a section
called 'Bite-sized astronomy' which contains an
essay explaining one concept about the science,
which is changed on a weekly basis.

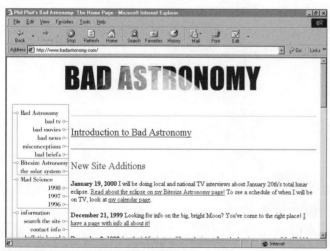

Brief History of Cosmology

http://www-history.mcs.st-and.ac.uk/~history/
HistTopics/Cosmology.html

Based at St Andrews University, Scotland, a site
chronicling the history of cosmology from the
time of the Babylonians to the Hubble Space
Telescope. It includes links to the biographies of
the key historical figures responsible for the
advancement of the subject and a brief list of
references for further reading.

Face of Venus Home Page

http://www.eps.mcgill.ca/~bud/craters/
FaceOfVenus.html

Overview and description of the surface of the
planet Venus. It includes interactive databases of
coronas and craters, and many images.

FAQ on Telescope Buying and Usage

http://www.xmission.com/~dnash/astrodir/saafaq/
faq.html

Extensive and plain-English guide to buying a
telescope. For anybody interested in astronomy
and contemplating buying a telescope or setting
up an observatory, this is an indispensable source
of non-commercial advice. There is a full
explanation of jargon used in astronomy and
guides to help the amateur astronomer.

Inquirer's Guide to the Universe

http://sln.fi.edu/planets/planets.html

Web site designed for teachers and students, with
pages on 'Space science fact' – the universe as
humans know it today – and 'Space science
fiction' – the universe as humans
imagine it might be. Features include
planetary fact sheets, information about
planets outside the Solar System, virtual
trips to black holes and neutron stars,
space quotes, and a course in spaceship
design.

J-Track Satellite Tracker

http://liftoff.msfc.nasa.gov/RealTime/
JTrack/Spacecraft.html

Real-time tracking system that displays
on a world map the current position and
orbit information for the space shuttle,
Mir space station, Hubble Space
Telescope, and the UARS and COBE

satellites. Pressing the shift button on your keyboard while clicking on a craft will take you to a page with information about that craft.

Learning Centre for Young Astronomers

http://heasarc.gsfc.nasa.gov/docs/StarChild/StarChild.html

Introduction to our universe for young astronomers. The presentation covers a wide range of issues with discussions of quasars, comets, meteoroids, the Milky Way, black holes, the Hubble Space Telescope, space wardrobes, and space probes. The tutorial is offered at two levels – one basic and one more advanced – and also includes online activities, visual material, and an illuminating glossary of space terms.

Lunar Eclipse Computer

http://aa.usno.navy.mil/AA/data/docs/LunarEclipse.html

Part of a larger site on astronomical data maintained by the US Naval Observatory, this site provides data on recent and upcoming lunar eclipses for any location around the world. The data available includes the local time of each eclipse 'event'; the altitude and azimuth of the Moon at each of the events; plus the time of moonrise immediately preceding, and the time of moonset immediately following, the eclipse. Sections of 'Frequently Asked Questions' and research information are also included.

Phases of the Moon 1999–2005

http://www.stormfax.com/moon.htm

Invaluable site for those interested in observing the phases of the moon. Presented in calendar format, this site lists extremely precise times and dates for the phases of the moon day by day up to the year 2005. There is also a list of definitions to explain the terminology used to describe the phases.

Practical Guide to Astronomy

http://www.aardvark.on.ca/space/

Well-illustrated guide to astronomy that contains explanations of many aspects of the subject, including the 'Big Bang' theories of English physicist Stephen Hawking, a list of early astronomers and their key discoveries, and an in-depth look at all the main elements of our Solar System.

Ptolemy's Geography

http://sunsite.unc.edu/expo/vatican.exhibit/exhibit/d-mathematics/Ptolemy_geo.html

Door into the ancient world – particularly the way the ancient Greek astronomer Ptolemy envisioned the earth. It includes expandable images of various texts and diagrams written by, or about, Ptolemy.

Scientific Revolution in Astronomy

http://history.idbsu.edu/westciv/science/

Part of a larger site on the history of western civilization maintained by Boise State University, this page provides an introduction to the scientific revolution in astronomy during the 16th and 17th centuries. Information is organized into 17 brief articles on astronomy and early astronomers, including a look at the trial of Galileo, the problem of the planets, acceptance of Newton, the problem of the Copernican Theory, and so on. You can start at the beginning and work your way through the articles in chronological order or go directly to a page that interests you. There is also a list of references for further study.

Shapley-Curtis Debate in 1920

http://antwrp.gsfc.nasa.gov/diamond_jubilee/debate20.html

Description of the debate that led to the scale of our galaxy being greatly modified. This Web site describes the history of the argument, and also covers Cepheid variables – the phenomenon that led to the discovery of the universe outside our spiral galaxy. To spoil the plot it turns out that both astronomers were actually wrong, but Shapley more so than Curtis.

Sky and Telescope

http://www.skypub.com/sights/sights.shtml

Online edition of the astronomy magazine *Sky and Telescope*. Information is included about daily astronomical events, and tips are provided on how to get the best view.

Solar System

http://www.hawastsoc.org/solar/eng/homepage.htm

Educational tour of the Solar System. It contains information and statistics about the Sun, Earth, planets, moons, asteroids, comets, and meteorites found within the Solar System, supported by images.

Solar System Live

http://www.fourmilab.ch/solar/solar.html

Take a look at the entire Solar System as it might be seen at different times and dates or from different viewpoints.

Stars and Constellations

http://www.astro.wisc.edu/~dolan/constellations/constellations.html

Hugely informative site on stars and constellations. It includes star charts of all major stars and constellations, details of the origins of the various names, photographs of the galaxy and the milky way, and details on what stars can be seen at any given time.

Sun and Moon Data for One Day

http://aa.usno.navy.mil/AA/data/docs/RS_OneDay.html

Part of a larger site on astronomical data maintained by the US Naval Observatory, this site includes the times of sunrise, sunset, moonrise, moonset, transits of the Sun and Moon, and the beginning and end of civil twilight, along with information on the Moon's phase. Information can be accessed by filling out one of two forms, depending on whether you live in or outside of the USA. For US cities and towns, there are links to US Census Bureau maps of the area for which astronomical data has been given. There are also sections of 'Frequently Asked Questions' and research information.

Virtual Reality Moon Phase Pictures

http://tycho.usno.navy.mil/vphase.html

GIF image display of the current phase of the moon, updated every four hours. You can also find the moon phase for any date and time between 1800 and 2199 AD.

Windows to the Universe

http://www.windows.umich.edu/

NASA-funded project providing detailed information about both Earth and space sciences. The information is divided into three levels: beginner, intermediate, and advanced, and covers such topics as the planets in our solar system, the Earth and its atmosphere, and also links to sites with information on earthquakes and

---

**F
A
C
T**

ASTRONOMY

science of the celestial bodies: the Sun, the Moon, and the planets; the stars and galaxies; and all other objects in the universe. It is concerned with their positions, motions, distances, and physical conditions and with their origins and evolution.

volcanoes, precipitation and sea ice, and storms and hurricanes.

Astronauts & Space Exploration

About Goddard Space Flight Centre

http://pao.gsfc.nasa.gov/gsfc/welcome/history/history.htm

Primarily composed of a biography and achievement history of the American rocket pioneer Robert Goddard, the Web site also describes the Goddard Space Flight Centre at Greenbelt, Maryland, and details the type of mission they are responsible for undertaking. As part of NASA's huge Internet resources there are many links to related topics.

Alan Shepard Profile

http://www.achievement.org/autodoc/page/she0pro-1

Description of the life and career of the first American in space, Alan Shepard. The Web site contains not only a profile and biographical information, but also holds a lengthy interview with Shepard from 1991 accompanied by a large number of photographs, video sequences, and audio clips.

Armstrong, Neil

http://www.3d-interact.com/ SpaceMuseum/armstrong.html

Biography of the first man on the moon from the

Neil A Armstrong Museum. It traces Armstrong's childhood interest in flying, his first flying lessons aged 15, his military service, his epic mission, and his post-NASA career as academic, farmer, and businessman.

Ask An Astronaut

http://www.nss.org/askastro/

Multimedia archive of the 1972 *Apollo 17* mission to the moon, with video and audio files, plus mission details and astronaut biographies. Sponsored by the National Space Society, this site includes numerous images, a list of questions and answers, and links to related sites.

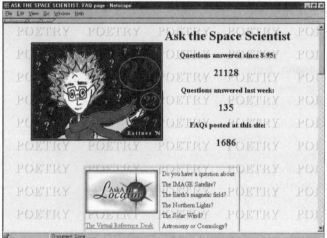

Ask the Space Scientist

http://image.gsfc.nasa.gov/poetry//ask/askmag.html

Well-organized NASA site with answers to any question about astronomy and space. The site endeavours to send a reply to any question about space and astronomy within three days. There are useful links to question archives, general files, and other space-related Web sites.

Astro Weight

http://members.tripod.com/scifitimes/astrowt/astrowt.htm

Enter your weight and click on 'Calculate', and this site gives your weight on all nine planets of the Solar System plus the largest five moons of Jupiter. It also includes a link to a page where you can calculate your age in all nine planetary years.

Cassini Mission to Saturn

http://www.jpl.nasa.gov/cassini/

Well-presented information on the purposes of the Cassini space probe, launched in 1997 to the planet Saturn. The complexities of designing the probe and its instruments and navigating it to the distant planet are explained in easy-to-understand language with the aid of good graphics. There are also interesting details of what is already known about Saturn's moons.

Europa

http://www.hawastsoc.org/solar/eng/europa.htm

Comprehensive latest information on Jupiter's moon. There is a full discussion of evidence that Europa may have running water on its surface. There are also a number of false and natural colour images of Europa.

Gagarin, Yuri

http://www.allstar.fiu.edu/
aerojava/gagarin.htm

Biography of the peasant's son who became 'the Columbus of the cosmos'. It traces Gagarin's education and training as a pilot prior to describing the courage with which he piloted *Vostok 1*. There is also a picture of the intrepid cosmonaut.

history of rocketry and chronologies of exploration by the USA, Russia, Japan, and Europe.

Kagoshimaken

http://sv1.Internet.pref.kagoshima.jp/pref/english/6space/6a.html

Kagoshima is one of Japan's rocket launching sites and part of the Institute of Space and Astronautical Science at the Ministry of Education. This site includes details of the facilities, plus a 'Young astronauts' club' and information about future plans.

Kennedy Space Centre

http://www.ksc.nasa.gov/

NASA's well-presented guide to the history and current operations of the USA's gateway to the universe. There is an enormous quantity of textual and multimedia information of interest for the general reader and for those who are technically minded.

Korolev, Sergei P

http://www.hq.nasa.gov/office/pao/
History/sputnik/korolev.html

Biography of the Soviet rocket designer from NASA, the institution he spent his career attempting to outdo. There is a photo of Korolev, an account of his technical achievements, and details of the imprisonment he suffered at the hands of Stalin.

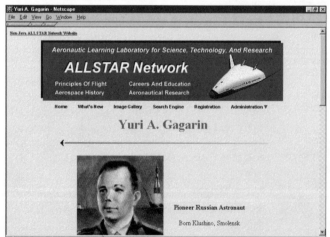

History of Space Exploration

http://www.hawastsoc.org/solar/eng/ history.htm

Who was the first woman astronaut? Find out at this site, which also contains information on the

Kourou – Europe's Spaceport

http://www.ifs.univie.ac.at/~jstb/esn07-1.html

Information about the European Space Agency's launch site at the Guiana Space Centre in Kourou. The page describes the history of the centre from the development of the first Ariane launch complex in the 1970s, to its subsequent expansion and present-day capacity and function. The text is illustrated with a colour photograph of the launch site.

Magellan Mission to Venus

http://www.jpl.nasa.gov/magellan/

Details of the NASA Magellan project that sent a probe to Venus. It includes a full mission overview, technical details about the planet, many images, and an animated view of Venus.

Mission Mars

http://library.advanced.org/10274/

View of what a colony on Mars might look like in 2050. Navigate around the fictional Martian colony, Koinae, learning about daily life, the climate, terrain, and research projects on Mars.

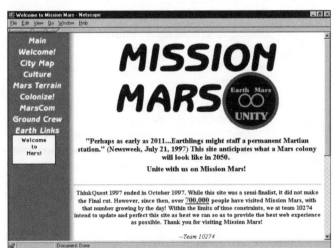

Moon: Home, Sweet Home

http://www.sciam.com/explorations/1998/
0316moon/sweet.html

Part of a larger site maintained by *Scientific American*, this page explores the discovery of ice on the moon and how it may speed plans to build lunar bases and colonies. You will find images and hypertext links to further

information. Find out about NASA proposals for moon bases, learn about the Moon Treaty that would regulate development on the moon, and read differing opinions on whether commercial interests should be permitted to exploit the moon's resources.

NASA Home Page

http://www.nasa.gov/

Latest news from NASA, plus the most recent images from the Hubble Space Telescope. This site also contains answers to questions about NASA resources and the space programme, and a gallery of video, audio clips, and still images.

NASA Shuttle Web

http://spaceflight.nasa.gov/shuttle/index.html

Official NASA site for all shuttle missions. There is extensive technical and non-technical information, both textual and graphic. Questions can be sent to shuttle crew members during missions. There is an extensive list of frequently asked questions. There are helpful links to related sites and even a plain-English explanation of NASA's bewildering jargon and acronyms.

Online Rocketry

http://www.rocketryonline.com/

Searchable site with reference materials, organizations, clubs, upcoming launches, products, books, and clubs devoted to rocketry.

Picture Gallery

http://southport.jpl.nasa.gov/pic.html

Small but spectacular collection of radar images taken from onboard space shuttle *Endeavour* in 1994 and offered by NASA. The collection also includes 3D images, videos, and animations. The high technology enthusiast will also find ample details on the imaging radar system used for the project.

Project *Galileo* – Bringing Jupiter to Earth

http://www.jpl.nasa.gov/galileo/

Full details of the groundbreaking mission to the Solar System's largest planet. There are regularly updated reports on instructions being given to the probe by the Jet Propulsion Laboratory, Pasadena, California, and of data being received from *Galileo*. There are numerous images of Jupiter and its moons and an animation showing fluctuations in the Great Red Spot. If you cannot find an answer to your query in the frequently asked questions you may e-mail the project.

Project Gemini

http://www.ksc.nasa.gov/history/gemini/gemini.html

Official NASA archive of the Gemini space programme. There are comprehensive details (technical and of general interest) on all the missions included in the project. There is also a comprehensive photo library, a video of a launch, and a search engine.

Project Mercury

http://www.ksc.nasa.gov/history/mercury/mercury.html

Official NASA archive of the programme that led to the first crewed US space flight in 1961. There are comprehensive details (technical and of general interest) on all the manned and unmanned flights included in the project. There is a comprehensive photo library and a search engine.

Project Skylab

http://www.ksc.nasa.gov/history/skylab/skylab.html

Official NASA archive of the project that launched the USA's first experimental space station in 1973. There are comprehensive details (technical and of general interest) on all the experiments included in the project. There is also a selection of photos and videos and a search engine.

Report of the Presidential Commission on the Space Shuttle Challenger Accident

http://www.ksc.nasa.gov/shuttle/missions/51-l/docs/rogers-commission/table-of-contents.html

Report of the independent commission which reviewed the circumstances surrounding the *Challenger* disaster for President Reagan.

Shuttle-Mir

http://spaceflight.nasa.gov/history/shuttle-mir/

Official Web site of the Shuttle-Mir joint operations. There is extensive information ranging from the technical to human interest stories from crew members. The site also includes some low- and high-resolution images of the spacecraft, the crew at work, and the Earth.

Space Trivia Page

http://neurolab.jsc.nasa.gov/trivia_pers.htm

NASA Web site that answers all the questions you could ask about the history of space exploration, including a section on 'Firsts'.

Sputnik: The Beep Heard Round the World

http://www.sciam.com/explorations/100697sputnik/hall_1.html

Part of a larger site maintained by *Scientific American*, this page recalls the launching of Sputnik 1 and the dawn of the 'Space Race' between the USA and USSR. You will find information on the subsequent race to the moon, the legacy of *Sputnik 1* (in the form of the thousands of satellites that currently orbit the Earth), and more. The text includes hypertext links to further information, and there is also a list of related links.

United Space Alliance: Shuttle Tracking Monitor

http://www.unitedspacealliance.com/live/tracker.htm

Displays real-time animated space shuttle positioning based on a live telemetry feed from Mission Control in Houston. A display tells you the current mission and name of the space shuttle in orbit. There is a link to a diagram of the space shuttle; click on a particular element to learn about its various components. You can also take a virtual tour of the space shuttle facilities at Kennedy and Johnson centres.

Voyager Project Home Page

http://vraptor.jpl.nasa.gov/voyager/voyager.html

Comprehensive information on the *Voyager* probes and what they have told us about the further reaches of the Solar System. There are details of the organization of the *Voyager* mission, the systems that are still functioning, and the data they are sending back. The 'Gee-Whiz' section offers a host of amazing facts.

Welcome to the Mars Missions, Year 2000 and Beyond!

http://marsweb.jpl.nasa.gov/

Well presented NASA site with comprehensive information on current and future missions to Mars. There are fascinating and well written accounts of Pathfinder and Global Surveyor, and large numbers of images of the red planet.

Welcome to the Mars Missions, Year 2000 and Beyond!

Mars Pathfinder

Mars Global Surveyor

MARS SURVEYOR 98

Mars Surveyor 98

Mars Surveyor 2001

WITS Simulation of the Mars Pathfinder Sojourner Rover

http://mars.graham.com/wits/

Developed by NASA's Jet Propulsion Laboratory, Pasadena, California, this site allows you to interact with a simulated rover, telling it where to go and what to do. The images you see are the actual images *Pathfinder* beamed back to Earth from Mars. Other features include an online tutorial and documentation.

Observatories & Telescopes

Armagh Observatory Home Page

http://star.arm.ac.uk/home.html

Historical astronomical observatory in Armagh, Northern Ireland. Founded in 1790, the observatory was at the forefront of astronomy for

over a hundred years, and still remains a highly active educational institution today.

European Southern Observatory

http://www.eso.org/

Reports from the inter-governmental European observatory. Contents include description of ESO observing facilities, the structure of ESO, press releases, scientific reports, lists of ESO publications, and images of space.

Jodrell Bank Home Page

http://www.jb.man.ac.uk/index.html

Comprehensive Web site describing the Nuffield Radio Astronomy Laboratories at Jodrell Bank, Cheshire, UK. The radio telescope has been used for astronomy for many years. This Web site describes some of the important discoveries it has led to and also hints at future developments.

Kitt Peak National Observatory

http://www.noao.edu/kpno/kpno.html

Comprehensive information on the range of research carried out at Kitt Peak, near Tucson, Arizona. In addition to scientific information of interest mainly to professional astronomers, there are details of current weather conditions at Kitt Peak and information for visitors. Visible and infrared images from satellites in geostationary orbits can be accessed.

Mauna Kea Observatories

http://www.ifa.hawaii.edu/mko/mko.html

Official site of the renowned observatories. A clickable photo on the home page accesses information on the functions and findings of the group of telescopes atop Hawaii's highest peak. In addition to scientific data, there is information on access for visitors.

Mount Stromlo and Siding Spring Observatories

http://msowww.anu.edu.au/

Searchable site of Australia's leading observatories. In addition to scientific data of interest only to astronomers, there is general information on current research, downloadable images of space, and information about the observatories.

National Astronomy and Ionosphere Centre

http://www.naic.edu/

Reports from the world's largest radio telescope, at Arecibo, Puerto Rico. There is readily understandable information on the work of NAIC and facilities for visitors. There is a wealth of data for professional radio astronomers, a newsletter reporting latest research, a gallery of photos, and links to a number of related sites.

Nuffield Radio Astronomy Laboratories

http://www.jb.man.ac.uk/

Information about the work of Britain's premier radio telescope facility at Jodrell Bank, Cheshire. There is a full description of current research, listing of astronomers, and details for visitors. An intimate feel of the world of radio astronomy is provided by the link to the JB (Jodrell Bank) Alternative Page on which students report on their work and post their favourite images of space.

Robotic Telescope

http://www.telescope.org:80/rti/

How about a robot-controlled telescope high on the Yorkshire Moors, England, from which you can request a picture of anything in the northern sky? This site contains that, as well as a library of images to download, details of current academic research (and an opportunity to get involved), and a resource of school projects and teaching ideas.

Royal Greenwich Observatory

http://www.ast.cam.ac.uk/RGO/

Official and searchable site of the world's most famous observatory. In addition to a history and guide for visitors to the observatory's museum, there are comprehensive details of current RGO research (no longer carried out in Greenwich).

This is an important site both for students of astronomy and for those seeking information on the latest research.

Space Telescope Electronic Information Service

http://www.stsci.edu/

Home page of the Hubble Space Telescope. The site includes an archive of past observations, a description of the instruments aboard, and a section for educators, students, and the general public – with pictures, audio clips, and press releases.

Stanford Solar Centre

http://solar-center.stanford.edu/

Introduction to the Sun and its effect on the Earth, designed with school children in mind. The site contains information about the Sun's part in global-warming, as well as a quiz, solar art, and various folklore tales about the Sun.

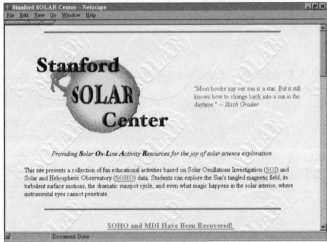

Stratospheric Observatory for Infrared Astronomy

http://sofia.arc.nasa.gov/

General information on the California-based Stratospheric Observatory For Infrared Astronomy (SOFIA) project, run by the German space agency DARA and NASA.

Space Phenomena

Asteroid Introduction

http://www.hawastsoc.org/solar/eng/asteroid.htm

What is the difference between an asteroid and a meteorite? Find out at this site which contains a table of statistics about asteroids, a chronology of asteroid exploration, and images of selected asteroids.

Astrophotography

http://www-personal.umich.edu/~jstys/

Enthusiastic site on astrophotography that contains many images, including some of the Andromeda galaxy and comets and moons, together with general information on how to take your own pictures of the night sky.

Comet Hale-Bopp Home Page

http://www.jpl.nasa.gov/comet/

Nearly 5,000 images of the comet, which was visible to the naked eye when it came within 190 million km/118 million m of the Earth in 1997, information on its discovery and position, and details of current research findings.

Comet Introduction

http://www.hawastsoc.org/solar/eng/comet.htm

Learn how to make a comet nucleus at this site, which also contains a diagram and explanation of their orbits, a chronology of comet exploration, plus information and photographs of selected comets.

Comet Shoemaker-Levy Home Page

http://www.jpl.nasa.gov/sl9/

Description of the comet's collision with Jupiter in 1994, the first collision of two Solar System bodies ever to be observed. There is background information, latest theories about the effects of the collision, and even some animations of Jupiter and the impact.

Constellations and Their Stars

http://www.vol.it/mirror/constellations/

Notes on the constellations (listed alphabetically, by month, and by popularity), plus lists of the 25 brightest stars and the 32 nearest stars, and photographs of the Milky Way.

Doomsday Asteroid

http://www.pbs.org/wgbh/nova/spacewatch/

Companion to the US Public Broadcasting Service (PBS) television programme *Nova*, this page provides information on comets: what they are made of, where they come from, and why they are important to us. It includes images and information about the Hale-Bopp and Hyakutake comets, including a number of images from the Hubble Space Telescope. You can also view images of Venus. There is a recipe for making your own comet, courtesy of the Jet Propulsion Laboratory, and a list of resources for further research.

Earth and Moon Viewer

http://www.fourmilab.ch/earthview/vplanet.html

View a map of the Earth showing the day and night regions at this moment, or view the Earth from the Sun, the Moon, or any number of other locations. Alternatively, take a look at the Moon from the Earth or the Sun, or from above various formations on the lunar surface.

Halley's Comet

http://nautilus.fis.uc.pt/astronomy/solar/eng/halley.htm

Attractive site devoted to the comet – with facts and statistics, images, and information about the spacecraft that have visited it.

Jupiter

http://www.hawastsoc.org/solar/eng/jupiter.htm

Full details of the planet and its moons including a chronology of exploration, various views of the planet and its moons, and links to other planets.

Little Green Men, White Dwarfs, or Pulsars?

http://www.bigear.org/vol1no1/burnell.htm

Entertaining first-hand history of the discovery of pulsars. This is the text of an after-dinner speech given by Bell Burnell. It gives an intimate account of the excitement and challenges of gamma and X-ray astronomy. There is also a brief biography of the pioneering astronomer.

Mars

http://www.hawastsoc.org/solar/eng/mars.htm

Detailed description of the planet Mars, commonly referred to as the Red Planet. It includes statistics and information about the surface, volcanoes, satellites, and clouds of the planet, supported by a good selection of images.

Mars Meteorites

http://www.jpl.nasa.gov/snc/

Information and images of the 12 Mars meteorites that have been discovered on Earth, including the latest news on research that debunks NASA's initial claim that a meteorite contained evidence of Martian life. You can research the news archives, and there is information on future missions to Mars.

Mercury

http://www.hawastsoc.org/solar/eng/mercury.htm

Detailed description of the planet Mercury. It includes statistics and information about the planet, along with a chronology of its exploration supported by a good selection of images.

Moon

http://www.hawastsoc.org/solar/eng/moon.htm

Detailed description of the Moon. It includes statistics and information about the surface, eclipses, and phases of the Moon, along with details of the Apollo landing missions. The site is supported by a good selection of images.

Neptune

http://www.hawastsoc.org/solar/eng/neptune.htm

Detailed description of the planet Neptune. It includes a chronology of the exploration of the planet, along with statistics and information on its rings, moons, and satellites. This site is supported by a good selection of images.

Nine Planets

http://seds.lpl.arizona.edu/nineplanets/nineplanets/nineplanets.html

Multimedia tour of the Solar System, with descriptions of each of the planets and major moons, and appendices on such topics as astronomical names and how they're assigned, the origin of the Solar System, and hypothetical planets.

Pluto

http://www.hawastsoc.org/solar/eng/pluto.htm

Detailed description of the planet Pluto. It includes a chronology of the exploration of the planet, along with statistics and information on its rings, moons, and satellites. There is also a good selection of images.

Rivers of Fire on the Sun

http://www.sciam.com/explorations/091597sun/powell.html

Part of a larger site maintained by *Scientific American,* this page reports on the findings of a team of scientists from Stanford University who identified 'rivers' of white-hot plasma flowing on the sun. Colour diagrams depict solar flows and labelled cutaway views of the sun's interior. Click on the images to increase their size. The text includes hypertext links to further information, and there is also a list of related links.

Saturn

http://www.hawastsoc.org/solar/eng/saturn.htm

How many rings does Saturn have? How many satellites? Find out this and more at this site, which also features a video of a storm in the planet's atmosphere, and information on the international Cassini mission to Saturn and Titan.

Solar Eclipse Information

http://www.eclipse.org.uk/default_hi.htm

Pages dedicated to the eclipse that was visible over the UK on 11 August 1999. This site contains detailed information about the science of eclipses, and contains images of the event.

Sun

http://www.hawastsoc.org/solar/eng/sun.htm

All you every wanted to know about our closest star, including cross sections, photographs, a history of exploration, animations of eclipses, and much more. You can also take a multimedia tour of the Sun or find out what today's weather is like on the Sun.

Uranus

http://www.hawastsoc.org/solar/eng/uranus.htm

Did you know that Uranus is tipped on its side? Find out more about Uranus, its rings, and its moons at this site. Also included are a table of statistics about the planet, photographs, and animations of its rotation.

Venus Introduction

http://www.hawastsoc.org/solar/eng/venus.htm

All you ever wanted to know about Venus can be found at this site, which includes a table of statistics, photographs of the planet, animations, information about its volcanic features and impact craters, plus a chronology of exploration.

Virtual Mars

http://members.aol.com/edhobbs/applets/vmars/

View a 3D image of Mars. Clicking on a land feature centres your view at that spot and allows you to rotate the planet. Click on the button below the image to toggle the names of surface features and landing sites, including the *Pathfinder* and *Viking 2* sites. Night and day areas are recalculated every five minutes to adjust to rotation.

Web Nebulae

http://www.rog.nmm.ac.uk/astroweb/twn/intro.html

Images of nebulae, plus a short account of the different types of nebulae and a glossary of related terms.

Astronomers

Adams, John Couch

http://www-history.mcs.st-and.ac.uk/history/ Mathematicians/Adams.html

Biography and portrait of the famous 19th-century British mathematician. Details of Adam's work leading to the discovery of Neptune and other work on orbits and gravitation are also available at this site. It also features reference sources in the form of books and journals that contain Adam's work and biographical details.

Al-Battani, Abu Allah Mohammad ibn Jabir

http://www-history.mcs.st-and.ac.uk/history/ Mathematicians/Al'Battani.html

Biography of the 9th-century Arab astronomer and mathematician. Al-Battani's works are also described and there is a short list of publications for further reference.

Barnard, Edward Emerson

http://astro.uchicago.edu/yerkes/virtualmuseum/ Barnardfull.html

Extensive biography of the pioneering US astronomer. This interesting and lively account of Barnard's life is supported by a large number of pictures of the astronomer, the telescopes he used, and the comet named after him.

Bessel, Friedrich Wilhelm

http://www-history.mcs.st-and.ac.uk/history/ Mathematicians/Bessel.html

Extensive biography of the German astronaut and mathematician. The Web site contains a clear description of the work of Bessel, and also describes his working relationships with his contemporaries. Also included are several literature references for further reading on the mathematician and a portrait of Bessel.

Brahe, Tycho

http://es.rice.edu/ES/humsoc/Galileo/People/tycho _brahe.html

Full account of the life and work of the Danish astronomer. There are pictures of Brahe, instruments he used, and the observatory he founded. There is an explanation of the Tychonic world view, whereby the Earth was held to be the centre of the universe while planets revolved around the Sun.

Brown, Ernest William

http://www-groups.dcs.st-and.ac.uk/history/
Mathematicians/Brown.html

Devoted to the life and work of Ernest Brown. In addition to biographical information, you will find a list of references about Brown and links to essays that discuss his contribution to mathematics. The text of this essay includes hypertext links to the essays of those mathematicians and thinkers who influenced Brown. You will also find an image of him, which you can click on to enlarge, and a map of his birthplace.

Callipus of Cyzicus

http://www-groups.dcs.st-and.ac.uk/history/
Mathematicians/Callippus.html

Dedicated to the life and contributions of astronomer Callipus, this site provides biographical information and a list of references to articles and other websites that refer to Callipus. The text of this essay includes hypertext links to the essays of those mathematicians and thinkers who influenced Callipus. You will also find a map of his birthplace.

Cassini, Giovanni Domenico

http://www-groups.dcs.st-and.ac.uk/history/
Mathematicians/Cassini.html

Profile of the life and career of the astronomer Giovanni Cassin. As well as biographical information, the site contains a reading list and links page. The text of this essay includes hypertext links to the essays of those mathematicians and thinkers who influenced Cassini. You will also find an image of him, which you can click on to enlarge, and a map of his birthplace.

Celsius, Anders (1701–1744)

http://www.astro.uu.se/history/Celsius_eng.html

Biography of Swedish astronomer Anders Celsius. Famous for his creation of the Celsius temperature scale, the astronomer was also the first to realize that the aurora phenomenon was magnetic in nature. A portrait of Celsius is also available from this page.

Chandrasekhar, Subrahmanyan

http://www-groups.dcs.st-and.ac.uk/history/
Mathematicians/Chandrasekhar.html

Web site on the life and contributions of Indian-born US astronomer Subrahmanyan Chandrasekhar. As well as a biography, this site contains a list of references about Chandrasekhar, and links to essays that reference him. The text of this essay includes hypertext links to the essays of those mathematicians and thinkers who influenced Chandrasekhar. You will also find an image of him, which you can click on to enlarge, and a map of his birthplace, Lahore (now in Pakistan).

Dr Clyde Tombaugh Profile

http://www.achievement.org/autodoc/page/
tom0pro-1

Description of the life and work of the discoverer of Pluto, astronomer Dr Clyde Tombaugh. The Web site contains not only a profile and biographical information, but also holds a lengthy interview with Tombaugh from 1991 accompanied by a large number of photographs, video sequences, and audio clips.

Eddington, Arthur Stanley

http://www-groups.dcs.st-and.ac.uk/history/
Mathematicians/Eddington.html

Devoted to the life and contributions of astrophysicist Arthur Eddington. In addition to biographical information, you will find a list of references about Eddington and links to essays that reference him. The text of this essay includes hypertext links to the essays of those mathematicians and thinkers who influenced Eddington. You will also find an image of him, which you can click on to enlarge, and a map of his birthplace.

Flamsteed, John

http://www-history.mcs.st-and.ac.uk/history/
Mathematicians/Flamsteed.html

Biography of the English astronomer. Aside from his methodical astronomical observations, Flamsteed is most noted for having the Royal Observatory at Greenwich built for him during his period as Astronomer Royal. Several literature sources for further reading on the life and works of Flamsteed are listed here, and his portrait is also shown at this Web site.

Halley, Edmond

http://es.rice.edu/ES/humsoc/Galileo/Catalog/Files/halley.html

Detailed notes on the life of English astronomer Edmond Halley. The information here covers his life dates, family, and education. There are also descriptions of his religion, scientific disciplines, patronage, and his role in the development of technology.

Herschel, Caroline

http://www.agnesscott.edu/lriddle/women/herschel.htm

Profile of the German-born astronomer. It traces her triumph over physical affliction, her interest in music, and her achievements in astronomy. Her role in the discovery of Neptune and comets is also described.

Kepler, Johannes

http://es.rice.edu/ES/humsoc/Galileo/People/kepler.html

Profile of the life and work of the German astronomer. Kepler's life is traced through his early conversion to Copernican theory, his work with Tycho Brahe, and the support he gave to Galileo. The traumas of his personal life, the accusations of witchcraft levelled against his mother, and the turmoil caused to his career by the Thirty Years War, are all set out here. This account has pictures of Kepler and a high-resolution image of the model he used to demonstrate the relative distances of the planets from the Sun.

Laplace, Pierre Simon

http://www-history.mcs.st-and.ac.uk/history/Mathematicians/Laplace.html

Biographical details of French 18th-century mathematician Pierre Simon Laplace. The site has a picture of Laplace and describes how his work has influenced mathematicians and physicists from later centuries, including Einstein. Over 40 references to Laplace's work are available via a hypertext link.

Leverrier, Urbain Jean Joseph

http://www-groups.dcs.st-and.ac.uk/history/Mathematicians/Le_Verrier.html

Devoted to the life and contributions of astronomer Urbain Leverrier. In addition to biographical information, you will find a list of references about Leverrier and links to essays that reference him. The text of this essay includes hypertext links to the essays of those mathematicians and thinkers who influenced Leverrier. You will also find an image of him, which you can click on to enlarge, and a map of his birthplace.

Maskelyne, Nevil

http://www-groups.dcs.st-and.ac.uk/history/Mathematicians/Maskelyne.html

Dedicated to the life and work of Nevil Maskelyne. In addition to biographical information, this site lists references about Maskelyne and links to essays that reference him. The text of this essay includes hypertext links to the essays of those mathematicians and thinkers who influenced Maskelyne. You will also find an image of him, which you can click on to enlarge, and a map of his birthplace.

Newcomb, Simon

http://www-groups.dcs.st-and.ac.uk/history/Mathematicians/Newcomb.html

Web site devoted to the life and contributions of Simon Newcomb. In addition to biographical information, you will find a list of references about Newcomb and links to essays that reference him. The text of this essay includes hypertext links to the essays of those mathematicians and thinkers who influenced Newcomb. You will also find an image of him, which you can click on to enlarge, and a map of his birthplace.

Picard, Jean

http://www-groups.dcs.st-and.ac.uk/history/Mathematicians/Picard_Jean.html

Devoted to the life and contributions of astronomer Jean Picard. In addition to biographical information, you will find a list of references about Picard and links to essays that reference him. The text of this essay includes hypertext links to the essays of those mathematicians and thinkers who influenced Picard. You will also find a map of his birthplace.

Ptolemy, The Man

http://seds.lpl.arizona.edu/billa/psc/theman.html

Profile of the astronomer, mathematician, and geographer. The few known biographical facts are related, together with summaries of his achievements. The text is supported by a number of diagrams and a map. There are links to a number of other Ptolemy, astronomy, and Greek geography sites.

Regiomontanus, Johann Müller

http://www-groups.dcs.st-and.ac.uk/history/Mathematicians/Regiomontanus.html

Biography and discussion of the work of the astronomer Regiomontanus. In addition to a profile, you will find a list of references about Regiomontanus and links to essays that reference him. The text of this essay includes hypertext links to the essays of those mathematicians and thinkers who influenced Regiomontanus. You will also find an image of him, which you can click on to enlarge, and a map of his birthplace.

Sagan, Carl

http://www.sciam.com/explorations/010697sagan/010697explorations.html

Part of a larger site maintained by *Scientific American,* this page honours the life of Carl Sagan and his commitment and contributions to science. The text includes numerous hypertext links to further information, and you can read several papers Carl Sagan wrote for *Scientific American.* There is also a list of related links, including two interviews with Sagan and an obituary.

Schwarzschild, Karl

http://www-groups.dcs.st-and.ac.uk/history/Mathematicians/Schwarzschild.html

Devoted to the life and contributions of Karl Schwarzschild. In addition to biographical information, you will find a list of references about Schwarzschild and links to essays that reference him. The text of this essay includes hypertext links to the essays of those mathematicians and thinkers who influenced Schwarzschild. You will also find an image of

him, which you can click on to enlarge, and a map of his birthplace.

Ulugh Beg

http://www-groups.dcs.st-and.ac.uk/history/Mathematicians/Ulugh_Beg.html

Devoted to the life and contributions of Ulugh Beg. In addition to biographical information, you will find a list of references about Ulugh Beg and links to essays that reference him. The text of this essay includes hypertext links to the essays of those mathematicians and thinkers who influenced Ulugh Beg. You will also find a map of his birthplace.

Genetics

Biotechnology

http://www.foodfuture.org.uk/bio6.htm

Part of the 'Food for our future' Web site, which aims to inform consumers about the benefits and concerns over biotechnology. This presentation focuses on the positive side of genetically modified foods.

Breaking The Genetic Code

http://www.nih.gov/od/museum/neir1.htm

Museum exhibit Web site describing the Nobel prizewinning work of Nirenberg on genetics. The site is broken down into three small pages with links to descriptions of the instruments used in Nirenberg's work. Along with the brief text description of the discovery, several photographs and other images are also featured.

Darwin, Charles

http://www.literature.org/Works/Charles-Darwin

Complete text of Darwin's seminal works *On the Origin of Species.*

Dr Frankenstein, I presume?

http://www.salonmagazine.com/feb97/news/news2970224.html

Interview with the man who made the first cloned mammal, Dolly. Embryologist Dr Ian Wilmut speaks to Andrew Ross about his worries and his future projects, about the distinction between science fiction and human cloning, and about what could go wrong with researching this delicate area.

Hello Dolly

http://whyfiles.news.wisc.edu/034clone/

Imaginative and humorous look at the issue of cloning, presented by the *Why Files*, an online magazine on the science behind the news. Genes, chromosomes, DNA, ethical considerations, and the 'lucky lamb' itself are all covered here. The magazine also features a series of interviews with specialists on genetics, bioethics, and other fields related to the experiment.

Human Genome Project Information

http://www.ornl.gov/TechResources/
Human_Genome/home.html

US-based site devoted to this mammoth project – with news, progress reports, a molecular genetics primer, and links to other relevant sites.

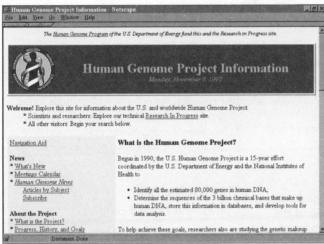

Natural History of Genetics

http://raven.umnh.utah.edu/

Through a combination of scientific experts and teachers, this site offers an accessible and well designed introduction to genetics. It includes several guided projects with experiments and explanations aimed initially at young teenage children. However, this site also includes 'Intermediate' and 'Expert' sections allowing this page to be used by a wide variety of ages and levels of

expertise. In addition to the experiments, the site also includes sections on such topics as 'Core genetics', 'Teacher workshops' and 'Fun stuff'.

Peeking and Poking at DNA

http://www.sciam.com/explorations/033197aps/
033197gibbs.html

Part of a larger site maintained by *Scientific American*, this page reports on new microscopes that are allowing molecular biologists and other scientists to study ever smaller subjects. Find out how these instruments work and what exciting new things scientists are discovering as a result. The text includes hypertext links to further information, and there is also a list of related links at the bottom of the page, including one to a video clip of DNA.

Turning Back the Strands of Time

http://www.sciam.com/explorations/1998/
020298telomere/

Part of a larger site maintained by *Scientific American*, this page reports on the discovery of an enzyme that slows down the ageing process in cells. Find out how this enzyme works and learn what the applications of this discovery may be on degenerative diseases and human ageing. Will wrinkles soon be a thing of the past? Find out here. The text includes hypertext links to further information, and there is also a list of related links at the bottom of the page.

'What is Genetic Engineering'

http://online.sfsu.edu/~rone/
GE%20Essays/WhatisGE.html

Essay by Dr Ricarda Steinbrecher which explains the concepts behind the controversial science of genetic engineering. The basic biology is clearly explained, although it should be pointed

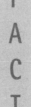

GENETICS

branch of biology concerned with the study of heredity and variation; it attempts to explain how characteristics of living organisms are passed on from one generation to the next.

out that the author is opposed to the unregulated growth of biotechnology.

Your Genes, Your Choices: Exploring the Issues Raised by Genetic Research

http://www.ornl.gov/hgmis/publicat/genechoice/index.html

Illustrated, electronic book that describes the science of genetic research, as well as the ethical, legal, and social issues that it raises. Detailed and informative in itself, the site also contains an extensive bibliography.

Evolution

Darwin Buffet

http://eve.chem.wesleyan.edu/Chem350/Buffet/default.html

Attempt to place Darwin's ideas – scientific, sociological, and theological – in the the context of his time. The site includes pages on key figures who influenced his thinking, like Jean Baptiste de Lamarck, Charles Lyell, and Thomas Malthus, as well as essays on his impact and links to related sites.

F A C T

EVOLUTION

the slow, gradual process of change from one form to another, as in the evolution of the universe from its formation to its present state, or in the evolution of life on Earth.

Darwin, Charles

http://userwww.sfsu.edu/~rsauzier/Darwin.html

Informative biography of Charles Darwin, which takes into account his upbringing and education, as well as details of his work on evolution. There is also information on related figures, such as his cousin Sir Francis Galton, and the naturalist Alfred Russel Wallace.

Evolutionist, The

http://cpnss.lse.ac.uk/darwin/evo/

Online magazine devoted to evolutionary ideas which includes features, interviews, and comment. It currently includes an article on the recent political interest in Darwinism and a column on the limits of evolutionary theory.

Life in Extreme Environments

http://www.reston.com/astro/extreme.html

Fully searchable database of information on the scientific research into plants and animals living in extreme conditions. The site includes sections on organisms that can survive extremes of darkness, cold, radiation, and heat.

Live A Life Page

http://alife.fusebox.com/

Fascinating page that brings together interactive programs to simulate ecological and evolutionary processes. Included is an adaptation of Richard Dawkins's Biomorphs program, described in *The Blind Watchmaker*, which enables the user to select 'morphs' for certain qualities and watch as their offspring evolve.

Rambling Road to Humanity

http://www.sciam.com/explorations/evolution/gibbs.html

Part of a larger site maintained by *Scientific American*, this page investigates research suggesting that human evolution has not experienced the kind of steady improvement of the species that has often been accepted. There are several pictures and a number of links, including links to an abstract of the researchers' results that appeared in *Nature* magazine.

Tree of Life

http://phylogeny.arizona.edu/tree/phylogeny.html

Project designed to present information about the phylogenetic relationships and characteristics of organisms, illustrating the diversity and unity of living things.

Biologists

Crick, Francis Harry Compton

http://kroeber.anthro.mankato.msus.edu/ information/biography/abcde/ crick_francis.htmlm

Profile of the life and achievements of the pioneer molecular biologist. It traces his upbringing and education and how he brought his knowledge of X-ray diffraction to his work with James Watson in unravelling the structure of DNA. There is a photo, a listing of Crick's major books and articles, and a bibliography.

Dawkins, Richard

http://www.world-of-dawkins.com/

Biographical information about Richard Dawkins, plus quotes, interviews,

papers, articles, and excerpts from his books. This is an unofficial site gathering together a whole host of regularly updated information from a wide variety of sources.

Dobzhansky, Theodosius

http://kroeber.anthro.mankato.msus.edu/ information/biography/abcde/ dobzhansky_theodosius.html

Profile of the pioneering geneticist. It traces his childhood interest in insects, the frustration of his ambitions in the Soviet Union, and his subsequent research in the USA. There are photos of Dobzhansky and a bibliography.

Dr James D Watson Profile

http://www.achievement.org/autodoc/ page/wat0pro-1

Description of the life and works of the discoverer of the DNA molecule, Dr James Watson. Watson won the Nobel prize for his most famous discovery in 1962. The Web site contains not only a profile and biographical information, but also holds a lengthy interview with Watson from 1991 accompanied by a large number of photographs, video sequences, and audio clips.

Fleming, Alexander

http://www.pbs.org/wgbh/aso/databank/entries/ bmflem.html

Biography of the Scottish bacteriologist, accompanied by an explanation of his discovery of penicillin.

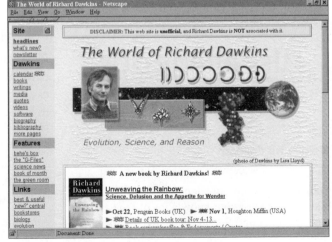

Fossey, Dian

http://kroeber.anthro.mankato.msus.edu/
information/biography/fghij/
fossey_dian.html

Profile of the life and death of the US zoologist. It traces how the young occupational therapist developed an interest in gorillas, taught herself biology, was the first to live intimately with gorillas, went on to establish academic credentials, and was able to highlight the plight of gorillas.

Hopkins, Sir Frederick Gowland

http://web.calstatela.edu/faculty/nthomas/
hopkins.htm

Maintained by Nigel Thomas, PhD, at California State University, Los Angeles, this page is devoted to the life and scientific work of Frederick Hopkins. Biographical information includes text and a timeline of important moments in Hopkins' life. You will also find a bibliography of books by and about Hopkins. A special 'science section' provides information on essential amino acids and vitamins. There is also a bibliography of texts about vitamins.

Leeuwenhoek, Antony van

http://www.ucmp.berkeley.edu/history/
leeuwenhoek.html

Profile of the self-taught 'janitor of Delft'. It traces how his business success allowed him to pursue his scientific passions and win fame for his pioneering work in microscopy. There is a portrait of Leeuwenhoek and picture and a description of one of his best-known lenses.

Miscellaneous Biology

Biology for Children

http://www.kapili.com/biology4kids/index.html

Fun, interactive introduction to biology. You can take a quiz to test your knowledge of the basics, take a tour around the site, or search for specific information.

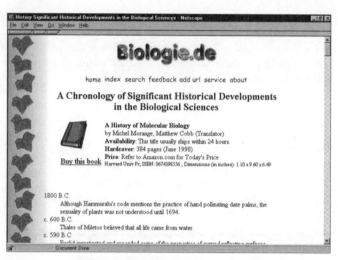

Biology Timeline

http://www.zoologie.biologie.de/history.html

Chronology of important developments in the biological sciences. It includes items from the mentioning of hand pollination of date palms in 1800 BC to the Nobel Prize award for the discovery of site-directed mutagenesis in 1993. The site also includes a list of sources.

Cells Alive

http://www.cellsalive.com/

Lively and attractive collection of microscopic and computer-generated images of living cells and micro-organisms. It includes sections on HIV infection, penicillin, and how antibodies are made.

Colour Matters

http://www.lava.net/~colorcom/
entercolormatters.html

Examination of the interaction between colour and the disciplines of physiology, psychology, philosophy, architecture, and optics.

Dictionary of Cell Biology

http://www.mblab.gla.ac.uk/dictionary/

Searchable database of more than 5,000 terms frequently encountered in reading modern biology literature. The dictionary can be searched as a whole or in sections, such as 'Disease', 'Cytoskeleton', and 'Nucleus, genes, and DNA'.

Dinosaur Controversies

http://www.mov.vic.gov.au/dinosaurs/dinoscontr.stm

Aimed at schoolchildren, this site examines several of the controversies still baffling palaeontologists around the world. Several of the theories about why dinosaurs became extinct are explored here, as well as such questions as 'Did dinosaur parents care for their young?'. This page is part of a larger site full of dinosaur-related activities and features.

Dinosaur Extinction – The Volcano–Greenhouse Theory

http://www.vt.edu:10021/artsci/geology/mclean/ Dinosaur_Volcano_Extinction/

One theory about the reason why the dinosaurs became extinct in such a short space of time. In addition to arguing the case well,, this site also offers some links to related dinosaur sites.

Forensic Science Web Page

http://users.aol.com/murrk/index.htm

Aimed at the layperson, this site explains the basics of forensic science. It is broken up into a series of articles, each explaining a different discipline. Topics covered include firearms and toolmark identification, forensic psychiatry, and crime-scene processing. Each article includes a number of diagrams in order to make the science more easily understandable.

MendelWeb

http://www-hpcc.astro.washington.edu/mirrors/ MendelWeb/

Hefty resource for anyone interested in Gregor Mendel, the origins of classical genetics, and the history and literature of science. View or download Mendel's original paper, with hypertext links to glossaries, biographical information, and exercises, or look up the essays, timeline, bibliography, and statistical tools.

Molecular Expressions: The DNA Collection

http://micro.magnet.fsu. edu/micro/gallery/ dna/dna4.html

Spectacular gallery of DNA photographic representations in the laboratory as well as *in vivo*. This site also has links to several other sites offering photographs through a microscope of various substances, including computer chips and various pharmaceutical substances.

Protein Data Bank WWW Home Page

http://www.rcsb.org/pdb/

Expanding scientific site that contains a fully searchable database of molecules, including several images. This is useful for students as well as more in-depth researchers.

Use of Visual Information in Art

http://psych.hanover.edu/Krantz/art/

Online tutorial in the way various aspects of human perception are used by artists to create more realistic images. The tutorial contains examples from many famous artists and includes sections on shadow, interposition, relative size, and aerial perspective.

Chemicals & Molecules

Chlorine

http://c3.org/

Designed to promote better understanding of the science of chlorine chemistry, examining how it contributes to an enhancement of our standard of living and quality of life.

Davy Discovers Sodium and Potassium

http://dbhs.wvusd.k12.ca.us/Chem-History/ Davy-NaK-1808.html

Davy's paper to the Royal Society in 1808, entitled

On Some New Phenomena of Chemical Changes Produced by Electricity, Particularly the Decomposition of Fixed Alkalies, and the Exhibition of the New Substances which Constitute their Bases: and on the General Nature of Alkaline Bodies. Quite apart from it being the longest title ever, it seems astounding that only 190 years ago mankind did not know that common salt was sodium chloride, this paper marking the leap in knowledge which created a century of chemical discoveries.

Molecular Expressions: The Amino Acid Collection

http://micro.magnet.fsu.edu/aminoacids/index.html

Fascinating collection of images showing what all the known amino acids look like when photographed through a microscope. There is also a detailed article about the different amino acids.

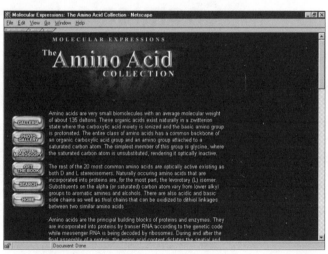

Molecular Expressions: The Pesticide Collection

http://micro.magnet.fsu.edu/pesticides/index.html

Fascinating collection of images showing what pesticides look like when recrystallized and photographed through a microscope. There is also an informative article about pesticides.

Molecular Expressions: The Vitamin Collection

http://micro.magnet.fsu.edu/vitamins/index.html

Fascinating collection of images showing what all the known vitamins look like when recrystallized and photographed through a microscope. There is also a brief article about vitamins.

Molecule of the Month

http://www.bris.ac.uk/Depts/Chemistry/MOTM/motm.htm

Pages on interesting – and sometimes hypothetical – molecules, contributed by university chemistry departments throughout the world.

Chemists

Alfred Nobel – His Life and Work

http://www.nobel.se/alfred/biography.html

Presentation of the life and work of Alfred Nobel. The site includes references to Nobel's life in Paris, as well as his frequent travels; his industrial occupations; his scientific discoveries; and especially his work on explosives, which led to the patenting of dynamite. Also covered are his numerous chemical inventions, which included materials such as synthetic leather and artificial silk, his interest in literature and in social and peace-related issues, and of course the Nobel Prizes which came as a natural extension of his lifelong interests.

Dr Linus Pauling Profile

http://www.achievement.org/autodoc/page/pau0pro-1

Description of the life and works of the multiple Nobel Prize winner Dr Linus Pauling. Dr Pauling is one of the very few people to have won more than one Nobel prize, having won the prize for chemistry in 1954, followed by the prize for peace in 1962. The Web site contains not only a

F A C T

MOLECULE
molecules are the smallest particles of an element or compound that can exist independently. Hydrogen atoms, at room temperature, do not exist independently. They are bonded in pairs to form hydrogen molecules. A molecule of a compound consists of two or more different atoms bonded together.

profile and biographical information, but also holds a lengthy interview with Dr Pauling from 1990 accompanied by a large number of photographs, video sequences, and audio clips.

Gibbs, Josiah

http://www-history.mcs.st-and.ac.uk/history/ Mathematicians/Gibbs.html

Photograph and biography of the 19th-century US mathematician and chemist. This site, run by St Andrews University, also provides information on Gibbs' Constant, along with literature references for further study.

G N Lewis and the Covalent Bond

http://dbhs.wvusd.k12.ca.us/Chem-History/ Lewis-1916/Lewis-1916.html

Transcript of one of the most important papers in the history of chemistry. In the paper G N Lewis forwards his ideas on the shared electron bond, later to become known as the covalent bond. This led to the deeper understanding of the principles of chemical reaction, and also provided science with a mechanism for the production of many compounds.

**F
A
C
T**

BOND

in chemistry, the result of the forces of attraction that hold together atoms of an element or elements to form a molecule. The principal types of bonding are ionic, covalent, metallic, and intermolecular (such as hydrogen bonding).

Lavoisier, Antoine Laurent

http://www.knight.org/advent/cathen/09052a.htm

Account of the life and achievements of the French chemist, philosopher, and economist. It traces his education and growing disillusionment with the theory of phlogiston. There is an account of how in order to pay for his scientific experiments he was forced to enter into government service, a fateful move leading, despite his many successes, to his violent death.

Libby, Willard Frank

http://kroeber.anthro.mankato.msus.edu/ information/biography/klmno/libby_willard.html

Profile of the Nobel prizewinning US chemist. It traces his academic career and official appointments and the process which led to his discovery of the technique of radiocarbon dating.

Miscellaneous Chemistry

Analytical Chemistry Basics

http://www.scimedia.com/chem-ed/analytic/ ac-basic.htm

Detailed online course, designed for those at undergraduate level, that provides the user with an introduction to some of the fundamental concepts and methods of analytical chemistry. Some of the sections included are gravimetric analysis, titration, and spectroscopy.

Avogadro's Hypothesis of 1811

http://dbhs.wvusd.k12.ca.us/Chem-History/ Avogadro.html

Avogadro's hypothesis was contained in the *Essay on a Manner of Determining the Relative Masses of the Elementary Molecules of Bodies, and the Proportions in which They Enter into These Compounds* from the *Journal de physique*, 73: 58-76 (1811). This Web site is a transcript of a translation of that essay taken from Alembic Club Reprints, No. 4, *Foundations of the Molecular Theory: Comprising Papers and Extracts by John Dalton, Joseph Louis Gay-Lussac, and Amadeo Avogadro, (1808–1811)*.

Bronsted on Acids and Bases

http://dbhs.wvusd.k12.ca.us/Chem-History/Bronsted-Article.html

Transcript of an article by Bronsted on the properties of acids and bases. The transcript as featured here is not complete, but does cover the essential points in which Bronsted defines the acid and the base. Several examples of his ideal reactions are shown, as well as a brief summary of the properties of the substances.

Chemistry for Children

http://www.chem4kids.com/

Fun introduction to chemistry. You can take a quiz to test your knowledge of the basics, take a tour around the site, or search for specific information.

Chemistry of Carbon

http://cwis.nyu.edu/pages/mathmol/modules/carbon/carbon1.html

Introduction to carbon, the element at the heart of life as we know it. This site is illustrated throughout and explains the main basic forms of carbon and the importance of the way scientists choose to represent these various structures.

**F
A
C
T**

ORGANIC CHEMISTRY
branch of chemistry that deals with carbon compounds. Organic compounds form the chemical basis of life and are more abundant than inorganic compounds.

Chemistry of the Ozone Layer

http://pooh.chem.wm.edu/chemWWW/courses/chem105/projects/group2/page1.html

Interesting step-by-step introduction to the ozone layer for those wishing to understand the chemistry of ozone depletion, the role of chlorofluorocarbons, the consequences of increased radiation for life on Earth, and actions to tackle the problem. The information may be readily understood by those with a basic knowledge of chemistry.

Chromatography

http://www.eng.rpi.edu/dept/chem-eng/Biotech-Environ/CHROMO/chromintro.html

Explanation of the theory and practice of chromatography. Designed for school students (and introduced by a Biotech Bunny), the contents include equipment, analysing a chromatogram, and details of the various kinds of chromatography.

Crystallography and Mineralogy

http://www.iumsc.indiana.edu/docs/crystmin.htm

Understand the shapes and symmetries of crystallography, with these interactive

drawings of cubic, tetrahedral, octahedral, and dodecahedral solids (just drag your mouse over the figures to rotate them).

Dennis Kunkel's Microscopy

http://www.pbrc.hawaii.edu/~kunkel/

This site is a photomicographer's dream – full of pictures taken with both light and electron microscopes. As well as several differing galleries of images, there is also information about microscopy and how the pictures were taken.

'Dissociation of Substances Dissolved in Water' by Svante Arrhenius

http://dbhs.wvusd.k12.ca.us/Chem-History/Arrhenius-dissociation.html

Extract from the above paper which appeared in *Zeitschrift fur physikalische Chemie*, I, 631, in 1887. In the paper Arrhenius discusses the dissociation of certain substances in water, an observation which led to deductions on electrolysis and his Nobel Prize in 1903.

Electrical Decomposition by Michael Faraday

http://dbhs.wvusd.k12.ca.us/Chem-History/Faraday-electrochem.html

Transcript of Faraday's paper in *Philosophical Transactions of the Royal Society*, 1834, in which Faraday describes for the first time the phenomena of electrolysis. The lengthy text is complete with simple diagrams of Faraday's own equipment.

Elementistory

http://smallfry.dmu.ac.uk/chem/periodic/elementi.html

Periodic table of elements showing historical rather than scientific information. The contents under the chemical links in the table are mainly

---

**F
A
C
T**

ELEMENT
substance that cannot be split chemically into simpler substances. The atoms of a particular element all have the same number of protons in their nuclei (their atomic number). Elements are classified in the periodic table of the elements.

---

brief in nature, providing primarily names and dates of discovery.

Gold Prospecting

http://www.klws.com/gold/gold.html

Everything you ever wanted to know about gold prospecting. Scrolling down past the advertisements on the home page accesses a good question and answers page, plus information on the chemistry of gold, the history of man's relationship with the metal, geology, information on prospecting sites, and advice on technique and equipment.

Hydrology Primer

http://wwwdutslc.wr.usgs.gov/infores/hydrology.primer.html

Information from the US Geological Survey about all aspects of hydrology. The clickable chapters include facts about surface water and ground water, the work of hydrologists, and careers in hydrology. For answers to further questions click on 'ask a hydrologist', which provides links to other US national and regional sources.

International Global Atmospheric Chemistry

http://web.mit.edu/afs/athena.mit.edu/org/i/igac/www/

Examination of the complex chemistry of the atmosphere and how it is being affected by human development. It includes a good introduction with diagrams, as well as other more academically-inclined information for those wishing to make a serious study of this topic.

Introduction to Proteins

http://biotech.icmb.utexas.edu/pages/science/protein_intro.html

Introduction to the world of proteins with discussions of their structures and sequences, as well as descriptions of some major kinds of proteins. The site also includes a useful glossary and offers a variety of photographic shots.

Nobel Prize in Chemistry 1998

http://www.nobel.se/announcement-98/chemistry98.html

Description of the scientific advances that led to the award of the 1998 Nobel Prize. The description on this page covers all the basic aspects of their 'theoretical studies of the properties of molecules and the chemical processes in which they are involved'.

Photosynthesis Directory

http://esg-www.mit.edu:8001/esgbio/ps/psdir.html

Wealth of scientific information concerning photosynthesis, its stages and its importance from MIT in Boston, USA. The site discusses issues such as the evolution and discovery of photosynthesis, the chloroplast, and the chlorophyll, and all steps of the light and dark reactions that take place during photosynthesis. The site also offers detailed diagrams of the procedures discussed.

> **F A C T**
>
> ### PHOTOSYNTHESIS
>
> process by which green plants trap light energy from the Sun. This energy is used to drive a series of chemical reactions which lead to the formation of carbohydrates. For photosynthesis to occur, the plant must possess chlorophyll and must have a supply of carbon dioxide and water.

Polymers and Liquid Crystals

http://plc.cwru.edu/

Online tutorial about two modern physical wonders. The site is divided into a 'Virtual textbook' and a 'Virtual laboratory', with corresponding explanations and experiments.

Royal Society of Chemistry

http://www.rsc.org/

Work of the UK society to promote understanding of chemistry and assist its advancement. There are full details of the society's research work, online and print publications, and comprehensive educational programme. All the resources of the largest UK chemistry library can be searched.

Sea Ice

http://www.antcrc.utas.edu.au/aspect/seaiceglossary.html

Information about sea ice. Satellite and photographic images are used to help explain the differences between pancake ice, shuga, and ice floes and between sea ice and icebergs.

Sören Sörenson and pH

http://dbhs.wvusd.k12.ca.us/Chem-History/Sorenson-article.html

Excerpt from a paper on enzymatic processes in which Sörenson defined pH as the relative concentration of hydrogen ions in a solution. This extract from the paper not only explains the origin of the term but also demonstrates its meaning.

Virtual Experiments

http://neon.chem.ox.ac.uk/vrchemistry/labintro/newdefault.html

Series of interactive chemistry experiments for A-level and university-level students hosted by this site from Oxford University, UK. As well as clear instructions and safety information, the site contains photos of key stages of each experiment. Please note that most of the experiments require specialist equipment and are not suitable for the home. However, the site does contain introductions to various subject areas, such as superconductors and simple inorganic solids.

Web Elements

http://www.shef.ac.uk/~chem/web-elements/web-elements-home.html

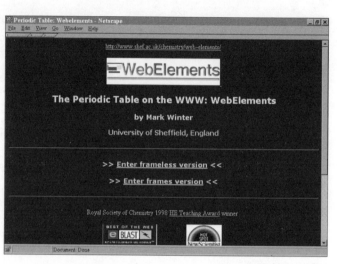

Periodic table on the Web, with 12 different categories of information available for each element – from its physical and chemical characteristics to its electronic configuration.

History of Mathematics

Arabic Numerals

http://www.islam.org/Mosque/ihame/Ref6.htm

Account of how numbers developed from their ancient Indian origins to the Modern Arabic numerals that are generally used today. There is a brief description of numbering systems used by the ancient Egyptians, Greeks, and Romans, and some of the problems these systems presented. The page also includes links to aspects of Islamic and Middle Eastern history.

F A C T

NUMBER
symbol used in counting or measuring. In mathematics, there are various kinds of numbers, but the main distinction is between **rational** numbers (integers, or whole numbers, and fractions) and **irrational** numbers (those not expressible as fractions and requiring symbols, such as $\sqrt{2}$, π, and e, to represent them).

Babylonian and Egyptian Mathematics

http://www-history.mcs.st-and.ac.uk/~history/
HistTopics/Babylonian_and_Egyptian.html

Description of the mathematics of these two early civilizations. The site includes maps of the area at the time, images of tablets and scrolls dating back to that era, and also a list of publications for further reference. A short description of a scribe, Ahmes, who is credited with producing the Rhine scroll is also included.

Development of Group Theory

http://www-history.mcs.st-and.ac.uk/history/
HistTopics/Development_group_theory.html

History of the development of group theory in mathematics according to St Andrews University, Scotland. Biographical information on the mathematicians responsible and a description of the topic are also included on this site, along with links to many other sources on the history of mathematics.

History of Mathematics

http://www-groups.dcs.st-andrews.ac.uk/history/
HistTopics/History_overview.html

Overview of the history of mathematics with numerous links to important mathematicians from ancient times to the present day. The site includes sections on the problems of notation and communication, and on brilliant discoveries. There is also an extensive bibliography.

Hypatia of Alexandria

http://www-groups.dcs.st-and.ac.uk/history/
Mathematicians/Hypatia.html

Part of an archive containing the biographies of the world's greatest mathematicians, this site is devoted to the life and contributions of Hypatia of Alexandria. In addition to biographical information, you will find a list of references about Hypatia and links to other essays in the archive that refer to her. The text of this essay includes hypertext links to the essays of those mathematicians and thinkers who influenced Hypatia. You will also find an image of her, which you can click on to enlarge, and a map of her birthplace.

Origin of the Celsius Temperature Scale

http://users.bart.nl/~sante/engtemp.html

Brief but comprehensive description of how Swedish astronomer Anders Celsius devised his temperature scale. The Web site is available in three languages, English, Swedish and Dutch, and the Swedish cover of Celsius's paper on his temperature scale is also shown here.

Pi Through The Ages

http://www-history.mcs.st-and.ac.uk/history/
HistTopics/Pi_through_the_ages.html

History of the calculation of the number pi. This site gives the figure that mathematicians from the time of Ptolemy to the present day have used for pi, and describes exactly how they calculated their figure. Also included are many historical asides, such as how calculation of pi led to a racial attack on an eminent professor in pre-war Germany. Reference publications for further reading are listed here, and there are also links to other pi-related Web sites.

Ptolemy's Table Of Chords

http://hypertextbook.com/eworld/chords.shtml

Demonstration of how trigonometry tables were constructed prior to the invention of infinite series. Ptolemy's methods are deciphered into modern notation, and the standard is such that secondary school students will find it challenging, but not unreadable.

Rise of Calculus

http://www-history.mcs.st-and.ac.uk/history/
HistTopics/The_rise_of_calculus.html

History of the development of calculus, from the time of the Greeks to the works of Cauchy in the 19th century. The site includes links to the biographical details of the mathematicians responsible for the rise of calculus, and also a brief list of reference publications for further information. Also included are several mathematical demonstrations on the use of calculus.

Mathematics

Abacus: The Art of Calculating with Beads

http://tqd.advanced.org/3711/

Clear explanation of how the abacus works – with demonstrations of how to add and subtract. This site requires a Java-enabled Web browser or Netscape 2.0+.

Beginnings of Set Theory

http://www-history.mcs.st-and.ac.uk/history/HistTopics/Beginnings_of_set_theory.html

Run by St Andrews University, Scotland, this site details the beginnings of set theory in mathematics. It includes biographical details of the mathematicians involved and gives a brief description of the topic with a few examples.

Chaos Club

http://www.chaosclub.com/

Introduction to chaos theory, for those with an underdeveloped mathematical background! The site includes a selection of games to illustrate the theory.

Cycloid

http://www-groups.dcs.st-andrews.ac.uk/history/Curves/Cycloid.html

Introduction to cycloids and links to associated curves. If you have a Java-enabled browser you can experiment interactively with this curve and its associates. There are also links to mathematicians who have studied the cycloid, including Galileo, who named the curve, and Cusa, who first studied it.

Dance of Chance

http://polymer.bu.edu/museum/

Examination of fractal patterns in nature, including those of bacterial growth, erosion, metal deposition, and termite trails. Are they dominated by chance or are other factors involved?

Ellipse

http://www-groups.dcs.st-andrews.ac.uk/history/Curves/Ellipse.html

Introduction to ellipses and links to associated curves. If you have a Java-enabled browser you can experiment interactively with this curve and its associates. There are also links to mathematicians who have studied the ellipse, to the ellipse's particular attributes, and to related Web sites.

Eric's Treasure Trove of Mathematics

http://www.astro.virginia.edu/~eww6n/math/math.html

Alphabetized and fully-searchable guide to a great many mathematical theories and concepts. The site is full of diagrams, equations, and usually clear explanations. The text is also extensively hyperlinked to take you easily between related entries.

Fermat's Last Theorem

http://www-groups.dcs.st-and.ac.uk/history/HistTopics/Fermat's_last_theorem.html

Account of Fermat's last theorem and of the many attempts made to prove it. It is extensively hyperlinked to related mathematicians and also includes a list of 17 references for further reading.

First Use of Zero and Negative Numbers

http://www.maxmon.com/300bc.htm

Page that describes how the concept of negative numbers became part of mathematical theory.

Frequently Asked Questions in Mathematics

http://www.cs.unb.ca/~alopez-o/math-faq/mathtext/math-faq.html

Expert answers to frequently asked questions, from 'Why is there no Nobel prize in mathematics?' to 'What is the current status of Fermat's last theorem?'

Fundamental Theorem of Algebra

http://www-history.mcs.st-and.ac.uk/~history/HistTopics/Fund_theorem_of_algebra.html

Web site run by St Andrews University, Scotland, chronicling the history of the theorem of algebra. The site also provides biographical details on many of the main characters involved in its development.

Googolplex

http://www.uni-frankfurt.de/~fp/Tools/Googool.html

Devoted to very large numbers, starting with a 'googol' (ten to the power of 100). This is a slightly quirky mathematics site, attempting to explain numbers that are so large as to defy comprehension. There is also a program for printing out one of these numbers, should you wish.

Great Internet Mersenne Prime Search

http://www.mersenne.org/prime.htm

In January 1996 the 'Great Internet Mersenne Prime Search' was launched by George Woltman, a programmer in Florida, to enlist the help of volunteers in tracking down the largest prime number. Software can be downloaded that will search for primes while your computer is idle.

Hyperbola

http://www-groups.dcs.st-andrews.ac.uk/history/Curves/Hyperbola.html

Introduction to the hyperbola and links to associated curves. If you have a Java-enabled browser you can experiment interactively with this curve and its associates. There are also links to mathematicians who have studied the hyperbola, to the hyperbola's particular attributes, and to related Web sites.

Maths Problem of the Month

http://www.mav.vic.edu.au/PSTC/

Australian site, updated monthly, containing not just one, but several problems each month. They are each designed for different levels of understanding. The main problems are divided into lower/middle primary, upper primary/lower secondary, and upper secondary levels. The site also includes a database of previous problems and a 'Challenging problem of the month'. In other words, there is something to tease every level of mathematical brain.

F A C T

MATHEMATICS

science of relationships between numbers, between spatial configurations, and abstract structures. The main divisions of **pure mathematics** include geometry, arithmetic, algebra, calculus, and trigonometry.

Matrices and Determinants

http://www-history.mcs.st-and.ac.uk/history/HistTopics/Matrices_and_determinants.html

History of the development and usage of matrices and determinants. This site also provides

biographical background on the mathematicians responsible for the advancement of the topic, along with a description of the subject, and some examples.

Online Maths Club

http://nrich.maths.org.uk/

Online maths club developed jointly by the Royal Institution and the University of Cambridge. There are questions (ranked by Key Stage), problems, puzzles and articles, and students are encouraged to send in solutions.

Parabola

http://www-groups.dcs.st-andrews.ac.uk/history/Curves/Parabola.html

Introduction to parabolas and links to associated curves. If you have a Java-enabled browser you can experiment interactively with this curve and its associates. There are also links to mathematicians who have studied the parabola, to the parabola's particular attributes, and to related Web sites.

Pavilion of Polyhedreality

http://www.georgehart.com/pavilion.html

Collection of images and instructions on how to make various polyhedrals, some from quite surprising materials.

Pythagoras' Theorem

http://www-groups.dcs.st-and.ac.uk/~history/Diagrams/PythagorasTheorem.gif

Simple site giving visual proof of Pythagoras's famous theorem.

Quadratic, Cubic, and Quartic Equations

http://www-history.mcs.st-and.ac.uk/history/HistTopics/Quadratic_etc_equations.html

History and usage of quadratic equations in mathematics. The site chronicles the discovery and development of this area of mathematics, and also provides biographical background information on those mathematicians responsible.

Random Number Generator

http://www.fourmilab.ch/hotbits/

Internet resource that delivers genuine random numbers, generated by radioactive decay.

Topology in Mathematics

http://www-history.mcs.st-and.ac.uk/~history/HistTopics/Topology_in_mathematics.html

History of topology in mathematical situations. Starting from the earliest application of the four colour theorem in mathematics, this Web site chronicles both the developments and the developers through to the formulation of the complete 1912 topology theory of Brouwer. Also included are several references for further reading and links to the biographies of those involved in the subject.

Trigonometric Functions

http://www-history.mcs.st-and.ac.uk/history/HistTopics/Trigonometric_functions.html

History of the development of the trigonometric functions in mathematics. The site also explains the basic principles of the use of these functions and details the role they have played in the advancement of other branches of mathematics. Biographical details of the mathematicians chiefly responsible for the discovery of trigonometry are also available here.

FACT

TRIGONOMETRY
branch of mathematics that solves problems relating to plane and spherical triangles. Its principles are based on the fixed proportions of sides for a particular angle in a right-angled triangle, the simplest of which are known as the sine, cosine, and tangent (so-called trigonometrical ratios).

What's New in Mathematics?

http://www.ams.org/new-in-math/

Section of the American Mathematical Society's Web site aimed at the general public, with features on latest developments and buzz words.

Mathematicians

Abel, Niels

http://www.shu.edu/academic/arts_sci/Undergraduate/math_cs/sites/math/reals/history/abel.html

Interesting account of the life of the pioneer in the field of elliptic functions. His desperate craving for knowledge, the chance to travel, and academic recognition are chronicled together with his early death from tuberculosis. There is also an assessment of his contribution to modern mathematics.

Agnesi, Maria Gaetana

http://www-history.mcs.st-and.ac.uk/%7Ehistory/Mathematicians/Agnesi.html

Biography and portrait of the first recognized woman mathematician. Agnesi's most famous curve, known as the witch of Agnesi, is shown on this site. Thirteen literature references containing further details of her works and biography are also listed.

Alan Turing Home Page

http://www.turing.org.uk/turing/

Authoritative illustrated biography of the computer pioneer, plus links to related sites. This site contains information on his origins and his code-breaking work during World War II, as well as several works written by Turing himself.

Aleksandrov, Pavel

http://www-history.mcs.st-and.ac.uk/history/Mathematicians/Aleksandrov.html

Biography and photograph of the Russian mathematician. This Web site also has links to the biographies of Aleksandrov's colleagues and contemporaries, as well as a short reference list of his publications.

Apollonius of Perga

http://www-history.mcs.st-and.ac.uk/history/Mathematicians/Apollonius.html

Biography of the Greek philosopher and mathematician Apollonius of Perga. Excerpts from an early 18th-century translation of Apollonius' greatest work, *Conics*, are included on this Web site, as are links to other important works. A list of publication references for further reading is also shown.

Archimedes Home Page

http://www.mcs.drexel.edu/~crorres/Archimedes/contents.html

Extensive material on the ancient Greek philosopher and mathematician Archimedes. The site includes sections on his life and travels, as well as extracts from ancient sources about his inventions and some famous problems associated with Archimedes.

Bernays, Paul Isaak

http://www-groups.dcs.st-and.ac.uk/history/Mathematicians/Bernays.html

Devoted to the life and contributions of Paul Bernays. In addition to biographical information, you will find a list of references about Bernays and links to essays that reference him. The text of this essay includes hypertext links to the essays of those mathematicians and thinkers who influenced Bernays. You will also find an image of him, which you can click on to enlarge, and a map of his birthplace.

Bernoulli, Johann

http://www.shu.edu/html/teaching/math/reals/history/bernoull.html

Page devoted to the life and ideas of mathematician Johann Bernoulli. In addition to biographical information, you will find links to the equations known as 'Bernoulli's inequality', which includes an explanation. You will also find a brief bibliography at the bottom of the page.

Birkhoff, George David

http://www-groups.dcs.st-and.ac.uk/history/Mathematicians/Birkhoff.html

Devoted to the life and work of George Birkhoff. In addition to biographical information, you will find a list of references about Birkhoff and links to essays that reference him. The text of this essay includes hypertext links to the essays of those mathematicians and thinkers who influenced Birkhoff. You will also find an image of him, which you can click on to enlarge, and a map of his birthplace.

Bolzano, Bernard

http://www.shu.edu/html/teaching/math/reals/history/bolzano.html

This page investigates the contributions of mathematician and philosopher Bernard Bolzano to the study of mathematics. It highlights Bolzano's three main areas of interest: logic, geometry, and the theory of real numbers. The text itself contains hypertext links to additional information. At the bottom of the page, you will find links to related information, such as the Bolzano and Bolzano-Weierstrass theorems, followed by a brief list of sources.

Boole, George

http://www-history.mcs.st-and.ac.uk/history/Mathematicians/Boole.html

Extensive biography of the mathematician. The site contains a clear description of his working relationship with his contemporaries, and also includes the title page of his famous book *Investigation of the Laws of Thought*. Several literature references for further reading on the mathematician are also listed, and the Web site also features a portrait of Boole.

Burnside, William

http://www-groups.dcs.st-and.ac.uk/history/Mathematicians/Burnside.html

Devoted to the life and contributions of William Burnside. In addition to biographical information, you will find a list of references about Burnside and links to essays that reference him. The text of this essay includes hypertext links to the essays of those mathematicians and thinkers who influenced Burnside. You will also find an image of him, which you can click on to enlarge, and a map of his birthplace.

Cantor, Georg Ferdinand Ludwig Philipp

http://www-groups.dcs.st-andrews.ac.uk/history/Mathematicians/Cantor.html

Site devoted to the life and work of the German mathematician Georg Cantor. There are links to people who influenced him, including Weierstrass, Kummer and Kronecker. Click to find out about his work on set theory and topology, and to view reference material.

Carathéodory, Constantin

http://www-groups.dcs.st-and.ac.uk/history/Mathematicians/Caratheodory.html

Devoted to the life and contributions of Constantin Carathéodory. In addition to biographical information, you will find a list of references about Carathéodory and links to essays that reference him. The text of this essay includes hypertext links to the essays of those mathematicians and thinkers who influenced Carathéodory. You will also find an image of him, which you can click on to enlarge, and a map of his birthplace.

Clifford, William Kingdom

http://www-groups.dcs.st-and.ac.uk/history/Mathematicians/Clifford.html

Interesting account of the life and work of the English mathematician. His work in developing non-Euclidean geometry is set in context with the work of other 19th-century mathematicians. A portrait emerges of an eccentric intellectual of vast physical strength who overworked, and drove himself to an early grave.

Condorcet, Marie Jean Antoine Nicolas de Caritat

http://www-history.mcs.st-and.ac.uk/history/Mathematicians/Condorcet.html

Biography of the French mathematician. The site contains a lengthy description of his working relationship with his contemporaries. Several literature references for further reading on the mathematician are also listed, and the Web site also features a portrait of Condorcet.

Dedekind, Wilhelm

http://www-history.mcs.st-and.ac.uk/history/Mathematicians/Dedekind.html

Brief biography and photograph of the German mathematician. This Web site also describes his works and offers links to descriptions of some of his theories and proofs. Dedekind's contemporaries and colleagues are also listed on this site.

De Morgan, Augustus

http://www-history.mcs.st-and.ac.uk/history/Mathematicians/De_Morgan.html

Biography and portrait of the British 19th-century mathematician Augustus de Morgan. De Morgan's works are also described. In particular, his four colour theorem is examined in some depth.

Descartes, René

http://www.knight.org/advent/cathen/04744b.htm

Extensive treatment of the life and philosophical, scientific, and mathematical achievements of Renatus Cartesius. The restless travels of the young savant are described before a detailed discussion of his contribution to learning.

F A C T

DESCARTES, RENÉ (1596–1650)

French philosopher and mathematician. He believed that commonly accepted knowledge was doubtful because of the subjective nature of the senses, and attempted to rebuild human knowledge using as his foundation the dictum *cogito ergo sum* ('I think, therefore I am').

Diophantus of Alexandria

http://www-groups.dcs.st-and.ac.uk/history/Mathematicians/Diophantus.html

Devoted to the life and contributions of Diophantus of Alexandria. In addition to biographical information, you will find a list of references about Diophantus and links to essays that reference him. The text of this essay includes hypertext links to the essays of those mathematicians and thinkers who influenced Diophantus. You will also find a map of his birthplace.

Eisenhart, Luther Pfahler

http://www-groups.dcs.st-and.ac.uk/history/Mathematicians/Eisenhart.html

Profile of the US geometrist. There is a summary of his work on the deformations of surfaces, his development of non-Riemannian geometry, and his Princeton career. This site also includes a photo of Eisenhart and a bibliography.

Fermat, Pierre de

http://www-history.mcs.st-and.ac.uk/history/Mathematicians/Fermat.html

Extensive biography of the French mathematical genius Pierre de Fermat. The site contains a description of his contributions to mathematics, including his last theorem and also much of his other works which were of more direct value to mathematics. Also included are the first page of his book *Ad Locos Planos et Solidos Isagoge* and an extract from his book *Maxima et Minima* (1679). Several references for further reading are also listed, and the Web site also features several portraits of Fermat.

Germain, Sophie

http://www-history.mcs.st-and.ac.uk/history/Mathematicians/Germain.html

Web site run by St Andrews University chronicling the life and works of the French mathematician. The site details her battle against the sexism inherent in her subject at the time, and while she did not fully triumph over the adversity she suffered, she achieved much that was thought impossible at the time for a woman; also included are examples of her work and links to the biographical details of her contemporaries. A list of literature references is also provided for further study of Germain.

Hamilton, Sir William Rowan

http://www-history.mcs.st-and.ac.uk/history/Mathematicians/Hamilton.html

Extensive biography of the Irish mathematician. The site contains a description of his contribution to mathematics, and in particular his discovery of quaternions. The Web site includes a page from his notebook on which there are several examples of the multiplication of quaternions. Several literature references for further reading are also listed, and the Web site also features a portrait of Hamilton.

Hilbert, David

http://www-history.mcs.st-and.ac.uk/history/Mathematicians/Hilbert.html

Extensive biography of the German physicist, philosopher, and mathematician. The site contains a description of his contributions to physics and mathematics, and in particular describes the fact that he is considered to have had the greatest influence in geometry after Euclid. Several references for further reading are also listed, and the Web site also features a photograph of Hilbert.

Introduction to the Works of Euclid

http://www.obkb.com/dcljr/euclid.html

Thorough introduction to the principles of Euclidean geometry. There is an emphasis on the Elements, but other works associated with, or attributed to, Euclid are discussed. The little that is known of the life of the mathematician is presented. There are a number of sources of further information.

**F
A
C
T**

GEOMETRY

branch of mathematics concerned with the properties of space, usually in terms of plane (two-dimensional) and solid (three-dimensional) figures.

Jacobi, Carl Gustav Jacob

http://www-groups.dcs.st-and.ac.uk/history/Mathematicians/Jacobi.html

Devoted to the life and contributions of Carl Jacobi. In addition to biographical information, you will find a list of references about Jacobi and links to essays that reference him. The text of this essay includes hypertext links to the essays of those mathematicians and thinkers who influenced Jacobi. You will also find an image of him, which you can click on to enlarge, and a map of his birthplace.

D'Alembert, Jean Le Rond

http://www-history.mcs.st-and.ac.uk/history/Mathematicians/D'Alembert.html

Biography and portrait of the French physicist and mathematician famous for his works on the use of differential equations in physics. In addition to a brief history of d'Alembert's work there are links to lengthy descriptions of his fields of expertise, and also a short publications list for use as a reference.

Kummer, Ernst

http://www-history.mcs.st-and.ac.uk/history/Mathematicians/Kummer.html

Extensive biography of the German mathematician. The site contains a description of his contribution to mathematics, in particular his work on Fermat's last theorem. Several literature references for further reading are also listed, and the Web site also features a photograph of Kummer.

Legendre, Adrien-Marie

http://www-groups.dcs.st-and.ac.uk/history/Mathematicians/Legendre.html

Devoted to the life and contributions of Adrien-Marie Legendre. In addition to biographical information, you will find a list of references about Legendre and links to essays that reference him. The text of this essay includes hypertext links to the essays of those mathematicians and thinkers who influenced Legendre. You will also find an image of him, which you can click on to enlarge, and a map of his birthplace.

Lindemann, Carl Louis Ferdinand von

http://www-groups.dcs.st-and.ac.uk/history/Mathematicians/Lindemann.html

Devoted to the life and contributions of Ferdinand Lindemann. In addition to biographical information, you will find a list of references about Lindemann and links to essays that reference him. The text of this essay includes hypertext links to the essays of those mathematicians and thinkers who influenced Lindemann. You will also find an image of him, which you can click on to enlarge, and a map of his birthplace.

Mandelbrot, Benoit

http://www-groups.dcs.st-and.ac.uk/history/Mathematicians/Mandelbrot.html

Web site dedicated to the life and work of Benoit Mandelbrot. In addition to biographical information, you will find a list of references about Mandelbrot and links to other essays that reference him. The text of this essay includes hypertext links to the essays of those mathematicians and thinkers who influenced Mandelbrot. You will also find an image of him, which you can click on to enlarge, and a map of his birthplace.

Markov, Andrei Andreyevich

http://www-groups.dcs.st-and.ac.uk/history/Mathematicians/Markov.html

Web site devoted to Andrei Markov. In addition to a biography, you will find a list of references about Markov and links to essays that reference him. The text of this essay includes hypertext links to the essays of those mathematicians and thinkers who influenced Markov. You will also find a map of his birthplace.

Mersenne, Marin

http://www-groups.dcs.st-andrews.ac.uk/history/Mathematicians/Mersenne.html

Site devoted to the life and works of the philosopher and mathematician Marin Mersenne with links to people that influenced him including Galileo and Descartes, as well as links to scientists who met with him in Paris, France. Also click to find out about Mersenne and Number Theory.

Möbius, August Ferdinand

http://www-history.mcs.st-and.ac.uk/history/Mathematicians/Mobius.html

Extensive biography of the mathematician. The site contains a description of his contribution to mathematics, especially for his conception of the Möbius strip, a two-dimensional surface with only one side. Several literature references for further reading are also listed, and the Web site also features a photograph of Möbius.

Napier, John

http://www-groups.dcs.st-and.ac.uk/history/Mathematicians/Napier.html

Devoted to the life and contributions of John Napier. In addition to biographical information, you will find a list of references about Napier and links to other essays in the archive that reference him. The text of this essay includes hypertext links to the essays of those mathematicians and thinkers who influenced Napier. You will also find an image of him, which you can click on to enlarge, and a map of his birthplace.

Oughtred, William

http://www-history.mcs.st-and.ac.uk/history/Mathematicians/Oughtred.html

Biography of the English mathematician. The site contains a description of his works, and includes a page from *Clavis Mathematicae* (1652) showing + and - and the notation for decimal fractions, all of which Oughtred is credited with inventing. Several literature references for further reading on the life and works of Oughtred are listed, and his portrait is also shown.

Pappus of Alexandria

http://www-groups.dcs.st-and.ac.uk/history/Mathematicians/Pappus.html

Website on the life and contributions of Pappus of Alexandria. In addition to biographical information, you will find a list of references about Pappus and links to essays that reference him. The text of this essay includes hypertext links to the essays of those mathematicians and thinkers who influenced Pappus. You will also find a map of his birthplace.

Poincaré, Jules Henry

http://www-history.mcs.st-and.ac.uk/history/Mathematicians/Poincare.html

Biography of the French mathematician. The site contains a description of his working relationships with his contemporaries, and also features a photograph of Poincaré. Several literature references for further reading on the works of Poincaré are also listed.

Pythagoras

http://www.utm.edu/research/iep/p/pythagor.htm

Profile of the legendary mathematician, scientist, and philosopher. An attempt is made to disentangle the known facts of his life from the mass of legends about him. His theories of the tripartite soul, transmigration, and the cosmological limit are summarized, alongside his interest in geometry.

Tartaglia, Nicolo Fontana

http://www-groups.dcs.st-and.ac.uk/history/Mathematicians/Tartaglia.html

Devoted to the life and contributions of Tartaglia. In addition to biographical information, you will find a list of references about Tartaglia and links to essays that reference him. The text of this essay includes hypertext links to the essays of those mathematicians and thinkers who influenced Tartaglia. You will also find an image of him, which you can click on to enlarge, and a map of his birthplace.

Venn, John

http://www-groups.dcs.st-and.ac.uk/history/Mathematicians/Venn.html

Web site dedicated to the logician John Venn. In addition to biographical information, you will find a list of references about Venn and links to essays that reference him. The text of this essay includes hypertext links to the essays of those mathematicians and thinkers who influenced Venn. You will also find an image of him, which you can click on to enlarge, and a map of his birthplace.

Atomic Structure

Aston Isotopes and Atomic Weights

http://dbhs.wvusd.k12.ca.us/Chem-History/Aston-MassSpec.html

Transcript of part of Aston's paper from 1920 outlining his ideas on atomic weights and isotopes. The paper led directly to the production of the first mass spectrometer, and thus led to the separation of many isotopic elements.

Beam Me Up: Photons and Teleportation

http://www.sciam.com/explorations/122297teleport/

Part of a larger site maintained by *Scientific American*, this page reports on the amazing research conducted by physicists at the University of Innsbruck who have turned science fiction into reality by teleporting the properties of one photon particle to another. Learn how quantum teleportation was accomplished and find out what the likelihood is that you will soon be teleporting yourself to those distant vacation spots around the world. The text includes hypertext links to further information, and there is also a list of related links at the bottom of the page.

Guided Tour of Fermilab Exhibit

http://www.fnal.gov/pub/tour.html

Guided tour of the particle physics laboratory Fermilab in Illinois, USA. It includes an explanation of the principles of particle physics, a guide to particle accelerators, and an insight into the experiments currently being conducted at the lab.

Hunting of the Quark

http://researchmag.asu.edu/stories/quark.html

Commentary on the research carried out at Arizona State University, USA, into sub-atomic particles. There is also a subsidiary page on the complexities of the subatomic world.

Leaping Leptoquarks

http://www.sciam.com/explorations/032497lepto/032497horgan.html

Part of a larger site maintained by *Scientific American*, this page follows the trail of two

German physicists in search of the elusive leptoquark. Find out about events that led them to believe they were witnessing a new phenomenon: a particle that combined aspects of the two elementary particles that make up atoms, leptons and quarks. The text includes hypertext links to further information, and there is also a list of related links at the bottom of the page.

Look Inside the Atom

http://www.aip.org/history/electron/jjhome.htm

Part of the American Institute of Physics site, this page examines J J Thomson's 1897 experiments that led to the discovery of a fundamental building block of matter, the electron. The site includes images and quotes and a section on the legacy of his discovery. Also included is a section on suggested readings and related links.

Particle Adventure

http://ParticleAdventure.org/

Introduction to the theory of fundamental particles and forces, called the Standard Model. It explores the experimental evidence and the reasons physicists want to go beyond this theory. In addition, it provides information on particle decay and a brief history section. A preview video is available to download, and you can choose from three ways to enter the tour. Classroom activities are provided, and for those in a hurry there is also a one-page summary of the key concepts.

F A C T.

NUCLEUS

the core of an atom is the **nucleus,** a dense body only one ten-thousandth the diameter of the atom itself. The simplest nucleus, that of hydrogen, comprises a single stable positively charged particle, the **proton.** Nuclei of other elements contain more protons and additional particles, called **neutrons,** of about the same mass as the proton but with no electrical charge.

Quantum Age Begins

http://www-history.mcs.st-and.ac.uk/history/HistTopics/The_Quantum_age_begins.html

St Andrews University-run Web site chronicling the discovery of quantum theory. Biographical

details of the mathematicians and physicists involved also is provided. The site also includes links to many other history of mathematics-related Web resources.

Schrödinger's Cation

http://www.sciam.com/explorations/061796explorations.html

Part of a larger site maintained by *Scientific American,* this page features an explanation of the quantum mechanics paradox known as 'Schrödinger's Cat', an experiment devised by Erwin Schrödinger to illustrate the difference between the quantum and macroscopic worlds. You will also find information about another experiment that showed an atom actually existing in two states at one time. The text includes hypertext links to further information about quantum mechanics, and there is also a list of related links at the bottom of the page.

Nuclear Energy & Radiation

Advanced Reactors

http://www.uic.com.au/nip16.htm

Overview of the features of the next generation of nuclear reactors currently being developed around the world. This 'Nuclear issues briefing paper', from Australia, focuses on the reactors currently being developed in USA, Japan, France, Germany, and Canada.

Essay about Marie and Pierre Curie

http://www.nobel.se/essays/curie/index.html

Extended essay on the life and deeds of Pierre and Marie Curie. The site spans the entirety of the couple's astonishing career and their contribution to the promotion of the understanding of radioactivity. It includes sections on Pierre's and Marie's joint research on radiation phenomena as well as Marie's own work after Pierre's untimely death in 1906: her discovery of the elements radium and polonium, her second Nobel Prize in Chemistry, her difficulties with the press, and her family life.

Fusion

http://www.pppl.gov/~rfheeter/

All-text site packed with information about fusion research and its applications. It is quite well organized and includes a glossary of commonly used terms to aid the uninitiated.

JET World Wide Web Page

http://www.jet.uk/

Web site of the Joint European Torus (JET) at Culham, UK, which includes an introduction to some aspects of nuclear fusion and an online tour of the project.

Nuclear Energy: Frequently Asked Questions

http://www-formal.stanford.edu/jmc/ progress/nuclear-faq.html

Answers to the most commonly asked questions about nuclear energy, particularly with a view to sustaining human progress. It contains many links to related pages and is a personal opinion that openly asks for comment from visitors.

Nuclear Physics

http://www.scri.fsu.edu/~jac/Nuclear/

'Hyper-textbook' of nuclear physics, with an introduction that includes a graphical description of the size and shape of nuclei and their other properties. The site also includes information about the work of nuclear physicists, and the uses and applications of nuclear physics from medicine, through energy, to smoke detectors.

Oak Ridge National Laboratory

http://www.ornl.gov/.index.html/

Main supplier of plutonium for US nuclear weapons sets out its post-Cold War efforts to beat swords into ploughshares. In addition to a good history and tour of the facility, there is access to a range of information on projects to achieve more efficient and environmentally friendly uses of US energy resources.

Radiation Reassessed

http://whyfiles.news.wisc.edu/020radiation/ index.html

Part of the Why Files project published by the National Institute for Science Education (NISE)

and funded by the National Science Foundation, this page provides insight into the controversy concerning the health effects of ionizing radiation. The highly readable text, laid out over 12 pages, includes information about what radiation studies from Hiroshima, Nagasaki, and Chernobyl have taught us, and what scientists are saying about exposure to small amounts of radiation. Is it always harmful? Numerous images and diagrams enhance the text throughout. The more tricky terms are linked to a glossary, and you will find a comprehensive bibliography of sources for further research.

Radioactivity in Nature

http://www.physics.isu.edu/radinf/natural.htm

Detailed explanation of the different types of radiation found naturally on Earth and in its atmosphere, as well as those produced by humans. It includes tables of the breakdown of nuclides commonly found in soil, the oceans, the air, and even the human body.

F A C T

RADIOACTIVITY

spontaneous alteration of the nuclei of radioactive atoms, accompanied by the emission of radiation. It is the property exhibited by the radioactive isotopes of stable elements and all isotopes of radioactive elements, and can be either natural or induced.

Rutherford on the Discovery of Alpha and Beta Radiation

http://dbhs.wvusd.k12.ca.us/Chem-History/ Rutherford-Alpha&Beta.html

Transcript of Rutherford's paper *Uranium Radiation and the Electrical Conduction Produced by It* which first appeared in the *Philosophical Magazine* in January 1899. The full paper with diagrams is reproduced here, and in it Rutherford describes the nature of the two types of radiation he discovered to be emitted from Uranium as it decays.

Rutherford's Discovery of Half-Life

http://dbhs.wvusd.k12.ca.us/Chem-History/ Rutherford-half-life.html

Transcript of Ernest Rutherford's paper describing his discovery of the half life of radioactive materials. The paper entitled *A Radioactive Substance emitted from Thorium Compounds* first appeared in the *Philosophical Magazine* in January 1900. The reproduction of it on this Web site is complete with several diagrams and all the relevant equations.

What is Uranium?

http://www.uic.com.au/uran.htm

Comprehensive and informative page on uranium, its properties and uses, mainly in nuclear reactors and weapons, provided by the Uranium Information Council.

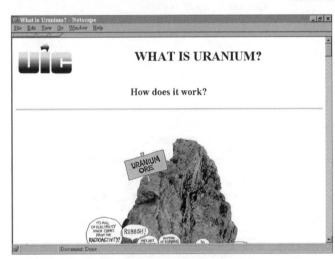

World Atom – International Atomic Energy Agency

http://www.iaea.org/

Public information source of the UN agency charged with monitoring and assisting the peaceful uses of nuclear energy. This well organized and easily navigable site is highly informative about the work of the IAEA and the many uses to which nuclear energy is put. The site is regularly updated and has many useful links.

Physicists

Abu Ali Hasan, Ibn Al-Haitham

http://www.mala.bc.ca/~mcneil/haithamt.htm

Good biography of the eminent Arab physicist. It traces the main events of his life and his contribution to optics, mathematics, physics, medicine, and the development of scientific method.

Ampère, André

http://www-history.mcs.st-and.ac.uk/history/ Mathematicians/Ampere.html

Biography and portrait of the famous French physicist and mathematician. This Web site also contains a brief history of Ampère's work and a list of 24 publications that may be used as a reference source.

Bernoulli, Daniel

http://www-history.mcs.st-and.ac.uk/ history/Mathematicians/ Bernoulli_Daniel.html

Biography of the Dutch physicist famous for his work on fluid flows. Along with a picture of Bernoulli, there is a family tree detailing the achievements of the remarkable Bernoulli family of scientists and mathematicians. The site also includes links to many of Bernoulli's colleagues and contemporaries.

Biography of A H Becquerel

http://www.nobel.se/laureates/ physics-1903-1-bio.html

Presentation of the life and discoveries of A H Becquerel, a distinguished scientist who was awarded the Nobel Prize in Physics jointly with Pierre and Marie Curie. This essay mainly focuses on Becquerel's contribution to the understanding of spontaneous radioactivity.

Born, Max

http://www-history.mcs.st-and.ac.uk/history/ Mathematicians/Born.html

Biography of the German-born British physicist. The Web site details the work of Born, and his relationships with his contemporaries and colleagues. Also included are several literature references for further reading on the physicist, and a portrait photograph of Born.

Boyle, Robert

http://www-groups.dcs.st-and.ac.uk/history/ Mathematicians/Boyle.html

Part of an archive containing the biographies of

the world's greatest mathematicians, this site is devoted to the life and contributions of chemist and physicist Robert Boyle. In addition to biographical information, you will find a list of references about Boyle and links to other essays in the archive that reference him. The text of this essay includes hypertext links to the essays of those mathematicians and thinkers who influenced Boyle. You will also find an image of him, which you can click on to enlarge, and a map of his birthplace.

Doppler, Johann Andreas

http://www-groups.dcs.st-and.ac.uk/history/
Mathematicians/Doppler.html

Part of an archive containing the biographies of the world's greatest mathematicians, this site is devoted to the life and contributions of physicist Christian Doppler. In addition to biographical information, you will find a list of references about Doppler and links to other essays in the archive that reference him. The text of this essay includes hypertext links to the essays of those mathematicians and thinkers who influenced Doppler. You will also find an image of him, which you can click on to enlarge, and a map of his birthplace.

Feyerabend, Paul

http://plato.stanford.edu/entries/feyerabend/#Crit

Detailed critical appraisal of the life and legacy of the Austrian philosopher of science. The main events and formative influences on his work are described together with his role in the shaping of 20th-century philosophy. There is an extensive bibliography of books by and about Feyerabend and guide to other Internet resources.

Feynman, Richard Phillips

http://www-groups.dcs.st-and.ac.uk/history/
Mathematicians/Feynman.html

Devoted to the life and contributions of physicist Richard Feynman. In addition to biographical information, you will find a list of references about Feynman and links to essays that reference him. The text of this essay includes hypertext links to the essays of those mathematicians and thinkers who influenced Feynman. You will also find an image of him, which you can click on to enlarge, and a map of his birthplace.

Hawking, Stephen

http://www.norfacad.pvt.k12.va.us/project/
hawking/hawking.htm

Stephen Hawking's own home page, with a brief biography, disability advice, and a selection of his lectures, including 'The beginning of time' and a series debating the nature of space and time.

Huygens, Christiaan

http://www-history.mcs.st-and.ac.uk/history/
Mathematicians/Huygens.html

Extensive biography of the Dutch astronomer, physicist, and mathematician. The site contains a description of his contributions to astronomy, physics, and mathematics. Also included are the title page of his book *Horologium Oscillatorium* (1673) and the first page of his book *De Ratiociniis in Ludo Aleae* (1657). Several references for further reading are also listed, and the Web site also features a portrait of Huygens.

Leo Szilard Home Page

http://www.dannen.com//szilard.html

Home page for the Hungarian-born physicist who was one of the first to realize the significance of splitting the atom. This site includes an illustrated biography, audio clips of people who worked with him, and documentation relating to the USA's decision to develop and then use the A-bomb.

Life and Theories of Albert Einstein

http://www.pbs.org/wgbh/nova/einstein/index.html

Heavily illustrated site on the life and theories of Einstein. There is an illustrated biographical chart, including a summary of his major achievements and their importance to science. The theory of relativity is, understandably, covered in more depth, along with photos and illustrations. The pages on his theories on light and time include illustrated explanations and an interactive test. There is also a 'Time-traveller' game demonstrating these theories.

Lorentz, Hendrik Antoon

http://www-history.mcs.st-and.ac.uk/history/
Mathematicians/Lorentz.html

Biography of the Dutch physicist. The Web site contains a description of his contribution to physics, and in particular in furthering Maxwell's electromagnetic theory. Several literature references for further reading on the life and works of Lorentz are listed, and his photograph is also shown.

Maxwell, James Clerk

http://www-history.mcs.st-and.ac.uk/history/ Mathematicians/Maxwell.html

Extensive biography of the Scottish physicist and mathematician. The site contains a description of his contribution to physics, in particular his work on electricity and magnetism. Several literature references for further reading are also listed, and the Web site also features a photograph of Maxwell.

Newton's birthplace: Woolsthorpe Manor, Lincolnshire

http://www.newtonia.freeserve.co.uk/W/index.html

Tour of Isaac Newton's birthplace, with biographical detail and pictures of the interior of the house. There are also plenty of hyperlinks within the text to information about his scientific achievements, and to the rest of his life in sections entitled 'Newtonia', 'Places', 'Bibliography', 'Chronology', and 'Biographies'.

Niels Bohr Institute History

http://www.nbi.dk/nbi-history.html

Short survey of the development of the Niels Bohr Institute, so intimately connected with Bohr's life work as a physicist. There are sections on the Institute today, a history from 1929–65, and a picture gallery.

Planck, Max Karl Ernst Ludwig

http://www-history.mcs.st-and.ac.uk/history/ Mathematicians/Planck.html

Biography of the eminent German physicist Max Planck. Planck is thought of by many to have been more influential than any other in the foundation of quantum physics, and partly as a consequence has a fundamental constant named after him. This Web site contains a description of his working relationships with his

contemporaries, and also features a photograph of Planck. Several literature references for further reading on the works of Planck are also listed.

Röntgen, Wilhelm Conrad

http://www.nobel.se/laureates/ physics-1901-1-bio.html

Biography of Wilhelm Conrad Röntgen, the German physicist who first realized the huge potential of the electromagnetic field of X-rays. The presentation includes sections on Röntgen's early years and education, his academic career and scientific experiments, and the miraculous coincidences that led him to his great discovery of X-rays.

Sakharov, Andrei

http://www.nobel.se/laureates/peace-1975-1- autobio.html

Brief autobiography written by the physicist and human rights campaigner for the Nobel Committee after he won the 1975 Peace Prize. Sakharov describes how his upbringing inculcated a love of literature, science, and music. He relates his pioneering work in Soviet nuclear physics and the deepening moral doubts this aroused. He movingly describes how it was his conscience that propelled him into an unwilling engagement with politics.

Schrödinger, Erwin

http://www-groups.dcs.st-and.ac.uk/history/ Mathematicians/Schrodinger.html

Part of an archive containing the biographies of the world's greatest mathematicians, this site is devoted to the life and contributions of physicist Erwin Schrödinger. In addition to biographical information, you will find a list of references about Schrödinger and links to other essays in the archive that reference him. The text of this essay includes hypertext links to the essays of those mathematicians and thinkers who influenced Schrödinger. You will also find an image of him, which you can click on to enlarge, and a map of his birthplace.

Miscellaneous Physics

About Rainbows

http://www.unidata.ucar.edu/staff/blynds/rnbw.html

Wealth of information on rainbows with fact sheets and diagrams, answers to a series of standard questions, an experiment section, and extensive bibliographies.

Accelerator Physics Group

http://wwwslap.cern.ch/

Virtual library dedicated to accelerator physics, with pages on design and components, as well as direct links to laboratories throughout the world.

Acoustic Illusions

http://cips02.physik.uni-bonn.de/~scheller/acoustic-illusions/main.html

Dedicated to the Shepard effect: a scale that gives the listener the impression of an endlessly rising melody, when in fact the pitch of the tones does not rise. Sound files illustrate this, and accompany an account of an experiment in which the Shepard effect was applied to J S Bach's *Das Musikalische Opfer/Musical Offering*.

F A C T

MELODY (Greek *melos* 'song')

in music, a recognizable series of notes played or sung one after the other, a tune. Melody is one of the three main elements of music, the others being rhythm and harmony.

Batteries Not Included

http://whyfiles.news.wisc.edu/shorties/fuel_cell.html

Part of the Why Files project published by the National Institute for Science Education (NISE) and funded by the National Science Foundation, this page touts the benefits of the fuel cell over the battery. Find out what makes the fuel cell a better, longer-lasting power source, and learn what the future may hold in store for the fuel cell.

Brownian Motion

http://dbhs.wvusd.k12.ca.us/Chem-History/Brown-1829.html

Transcript of 'Remarks on Active Molecules' by Robert Brown from *Additional Remarks on Active Molecules* (1829). The text describes Robert Brown's observations of the random motion of particles, which in turn led to the placement of the subject on millions of school exam papers.

Cryogenics

http://www-csa.fnal.gov/

Information site of the Cryogenic Society of America (CSA), a nonprofit technical society serving all those interested in any phase of cryogenics. This site provides online access to publications, supported by details of meetings and events.

Doppler Effect

http://www.lifeintheuniverse.com/doppler.html

Explanation of the Doppler effect and links to other related sites.

Einstein's Legacy

http://www.ncsa.uiuc.edu/Cyberia/NumRel/EinsteinLegacy.html

Illustrated introduction to the man and his greatest legacy – relativity and the concept of space-time. There is a video- and audio-clip version of the page courtesy of a US scientist and details about how current research is linked to Einstein's revolutionary ideas.

European Laboratory for Particle Physics

http://www.cern.ch/

Information about CERN, the world-class physics laboratory in Geneva. As well as presenting committees, groups, and associations hosted by the Laboratory, this official site offers important scientific material and visual evidence on the current activities and projects. Visitors will also find postings about colloquia, schools, meetings, and other services offered there. A special section is devoted to the history of the World Wide Web and the pioneering contribution of CERN in its conception and expansion.

Explanation of Temperature Related Theories

http://www.unidata.ucar.edu/staff/blynds/tmp.html

Detailed explanatory site on the laws and theories of temperature. It explains what temperature actually is, what a thermometer is, and the development of both, complete with illustrations and links to pioneers in the field. There is a temperature conversion facility and explanations of associated topics such as kinetic theory and thermal radiation.

How Things Work

http://howthingswork.virginia.edu/

Well organized site providing answers to any question relating to physics. There is a large database of previously asked questions which may be readily accessed. Run by the Professor of Physics at the University of Virginia, USA, the site is an essential point of reference for school science teachers and anybody with an interest in physics.

Internet Plasma Physics Education Experience

http://ippex.pppl.gov/ippex/

Aimed at teenagers, this site introduces some physics concepts through interactive pages on the topics of matter, electricity and magnetism, fusion, and energy. The site also contains a virtual fusion reactor and a page where you can send questions to scientists in the field.

Introduction to Mass Spectrometry

http://www.scimedia.com/chem-ed/ms/ms-intro.htm

Good introduction to the mass spectrometer and how it works. Different mass analyser designs are described, together with sections on ionization and ion detectors.

Introduction to Waves

http://id.mind.net/~zona/mstm/physics/waves/waves.html

Interactive site that begins with the basics – explaining and allowing you to manipulate

F A C T

WAVE

in physics, waves are oscillations that are propagated from a source. Mechanical waves require a medium through which to travel. Electromagnetic waves do not; they can travel through a vacuum. Waves carry energy but they do not transfer matter.

wavelength, amplitude, and phase shift of a simple wave. Further into the site there are more complex examinations of such things as Huygen's principle, interference, and wave propagation. You will need to have a Java-enabled browser to get the most out of this site.

LightForest

http://web.mit.edu/museum/lightforest/holograms.html

This site is centred around an artist's exhibition of superimposed holographic images of leaves. Whether the exhibition is to your taste or not, the pages explaining how the holograms were created is both well designed and informative.

Particle Physics

http://www.pparc.ac.uk/

Particle Physics and Astronomy Research Council Web site that includes information about its extensive research programmes in the fields of astronomy, planetary science and particle physics, as well as more general information on stars and the origins of the universe.

Physics 2000

http://www.colorado.edu/physics/2000/

Fun place to learn about 20th-century physics and familiar high-tech devices. This site is designed to make physics more accessible to people of all ages. The site is divided into three sections: 'What is Physics 2000?', 'Einstein's Legacy', and 'The Atomic Lab'.

Professor Bubbles' Official Bubble Home Page

http://bubbles.org/

Lively information about how to blow the best bubbles, and answers to frequently asked questions about bubbles – such as 'Why are bubbles always round?' and 'Why do bubbles have colour?'

Static Electricity

http://www.waterw.com/~science/january.html

Excellent site, explaining the theory simply, but thoroughly. It also includes several easy-to-do experiments to demonstrate the theory behind static electricity.

Unit Converter

http://www.webcom.com/legacysy/convert2/convert2.html

Simple, but very effective site that allows conversion from values in any of an astonishingly wide variety of units to any other relevant unit. The units available are listed together in groups from 'Acceleration', through 'Luminance' and 'Specific heat', to 'Weight (mass)'. All you have to do is select the category, the units you want to convert from and into, and type in the value you want to convert to get a fairly immediate answer. Please note: you will need a Java-enabled browser for this site to work.

Usenet Relativity FAQ

http://math.ucr.edu/home/baez/physics/relativity.html

Concise answers to some of the most common questions about relativity. The speed of light and its relation to mass, dark matter, black holes, time travel, and the Big Bang are some of the things covered by this illuminating series of articles based both on Usenet discussions and good reference sources. The site also directs the visitors to appropriate discussion groups where they can pose more questions, and also solicits more articles on themes not yet covered by the 'Frequently Asked Questions'.

Walk Through Time: The Evolution of Time Measurement

http://physics.nist.gov/GenInt/Time/time.html

Designed by the National Institute of Standards and Technology (NIST) Physics Laboratory to provide an historic understanding of the evolution of time measurement. There are sections on 'Ancient calendars', 'Early clocks',

'World time scales', the 'Atomic age', and 'The revolution in timekeeping'. The site also explains Greenwich Mean Time and world time zones. Visitors can synchronize their clocks to NIST time.

Miscellaneous Science

Access Excellence

http://www.gene.com/ae/

This US-based site for biology teachers, sponsored by a biotechnology company, has plenty to interest the casual browser as well – particularly. Highlights include its 'What's new?' section, with weekly science reports and interviews with scientists making the news, and 'About biotech', an in-depth look at the field of biotechnology.

Arthur C Clarke Foundation

http://www.cequel.co.uk/acclarke/

'Dedicated to the major scientific themes of Arthur C Clarke's life and work.' There are sections on futures, space, communications, and oceans. Also featured are sections archiving the works of Clarke and a timeline-style biography featuring many pictures and drawings.

Bad Science

http://www.ems.psu.edu/~fraser/BadScience.html

Unusual and thought-provoking site set up to

make teachers and pupils aware of examples of bad science teaching. It opens with a display of some major preconceptions behind incorrect presentation of science in the classroom, and also provides links to a number of bad science sites with a specific focus.

Bizarre Stuff you Can Make in your Kitchen

http://freeweb.pdq.net/headstrong/

Instructions on how to make or build many scientific projects from things you can find in the home. It includes how to make an electric lemon, a home-made hurricane, and even dancing mothballs. The experiments are graded for difficulty and organized by category so there is something for every age group here. Take note of the safety warning on the front page, though, as some of these experiments do use dangerous chemicals, electricity, etc, and younger children will need supervision.

Elementary Science

http://www.lme.mankato.msus.edu/ci/elem.sci.html

Brief biographies of famous scientists, some experiments to do in the home, a featured animal of the month, information on the night sky, and a 'Tell me why' feature. Updating appears to be irregular, but there are plenty of back issues still available.

Explore Science

http://www.explorescience.com/

Interactive explanations of some basic scientific concepts that have been elevated above the ordinary by the judicious use of 'Shockwave' animations. The sections covered on this site include mechanics, life sciences, optics, and astrophysics.

Family Explorer

http://www.webcom.com/safezone/FE/index.htm

Samples of activities and projects from 'Family Explorer', a monthly printed newsletter of science and nature activities for use by parents with their children.

Golden Opportunity for Science

http://www.blm.gov/education/going_4_the_gold/gold_poster.html

Sponsored by the US Bureau of Land Management, this site explores the origins of gold, and the history, science, and legends of gold mining in the American West. There are also suggestions for classroom activities.

Greenwich and the Millennium

http://www.nmm.ac.uk/ei/fact/millen.htm

Fact file produced by the National Maritime Museum on the role of the Royal Greenwich Observatory in the millennial procedures. This site also provides a history of the observatory.

Helios Science News

http://www.helios.org

Science and technology news site bringing you the latest stories day by day. There are also categorized and star-rated links to other sites.

History of the Royal Society

http://www-history.mcs.st-and.ac.uk/~history/Societies/RShistory.html

Web site run by St Andrews University detailing the history of the Royal Society. Biographical details of the founding members are provided, as is information on the main prizes the society awards for scientific achievement.

IMSS – History of Science Multimedia Catalogue Galileo Galilei

http://galileo.imss.firenze.it/museo/4/index.html

Room IV of the Institute and Museum of the History of Science, which is dedicated to Galileo. This Web site in Florence, Italy, includes a virtual visit (Quick Time format) to this room in the museum along with a multimedia catalogue that includes a descriptive text of the artefacts on display, accompanied by still, video, or animated images. There is an extensive list of objects to choose from, including, rather bizarrely, the middle finger of Galileo's right hand.

Mad Scientist Network

http://www.madsci.org/

Indispensable resource for school science teachers and children in need of answers to scientific questions. The Mad Scientist network is a group of scientists prepared to field queries on a vast range of subjects. There is an online archive of previous questions and answers, and helpful guides to accessing other general interest Web science sites.

New Scientist

http://www.newscientist.com/

Online, searchable version of the prestigious science journal.

Reeko's Mad Scientist Lab

http://www.flash.net/~spartech/ReekoScience/ReekoIndex.htm

Free, fun, and educational science experiments for kids and adults. Designed so you can to learn about basic science principles painlessly. The experiments can be sorted by category or skill level. Most of them can be done in the home and each of them contains detailed instructions and an explanation of the scientific principle demonstrated.

Royal Institution of Great Britain

http://www.ri.ac.uk/

Profile of the history and role of the world's longest established independent research organization. There is information on the structure of the RI, ongoing scientific research, and its extensive programme of activities to educate the public about science.

Scientific Misconduct

http://www.chem.vt.edu/ethics/vinny/www_ethx.html

Anatomy of a serious problem confronted by the scientific community, that of scientific misconduct. The site offers celebrated cases, reports, retaliations, articles on ethics in science, thoughts, and other material on plagiarism.

Strange Science

http://www.turnpike.net/~mscott/index.htm

Subtitled 'The Rocky Road to Modern Palaeontology and Biology', this site examines some of the medieval discoveries that led to the growth of interest in modern-day science. The site is illustrated with images that clearly show how people's perception of the world differed, and how people made up for gaps in their knowledge with a little imagination!

Vertebrate Flight Exhibit

http://www.ucmp.berkeley.edu/vertebrates/flight/enter.html

Examination of airborne animals and the human fascination with flight. This site is divided into five sections dealing with the physics, evolution, and origin of flight, plus a look at animals that are gliders and parachuters, and an insight into the three solutions to flight.

Wacky Patent of the Month

http://colitz.com/site/wacky.htm

This site is 'devoted to recognizing selected inventors and their remarkable and unconventional patented inventions.' Recently included patents have been bizarre to say the least, with a pat on the back device, a sanitary device for birds and a saluting device being fairly high in the order of 'merit'. This US-based site publicizes some inventions that just have to be seen to be believed.

Why Files

http://whyfiles.news.wisc.edu/index.html

Well designed and topical science site tackling a couple of recent issues in each bimonthly update. As well as having a lively presentation, it also includes a lot of useful background information, much of it aimed at the junior school level. This site also retains many of its previous entries, which are fully searchable.

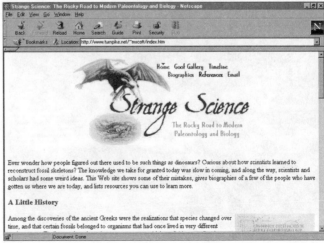

Wizard's Lab

http://library.advanced.org/11924/

Lots of fun, accessible science with spoken commentary for all those who love the Internet style of learning. A friendly 'wizard' leads surfers through the various corners of the virtual lab, so that they can learn about such topics as electricity, sound, light, energy, and magnetism. Each presentation concludes with useful summaries, particularly entertaining when given in the wizard's own voice. There is also a quiz section and a glossary of useful terms.

Unproved Theories

Alchemy Virtual Library

http://www.levity.com/alchemy/home.html

Virtual library dedicated to alchemy in all its facets. There are 600 sections, more than 130 graphics, and – for subscribers – an e-mail discussion forum.

Bigfoot – Fact or Fantasy?

http://www.netcomuk.co.uk/~rfthomas/ bigfoot.html

Details of the creatures known variously as bigfoot, yeti, and abominable snowman. On this site there is a page describing every type of bigfoot creature from around the world, and also examinations of the evidence supporting their existence.

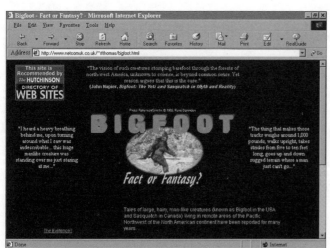

Bufora Online

http://www.bufora.org.uk/

British UFO Research Organization home page. Featuring news, selected articles, and events lists, as well as a research and investigation section, this site is ideal for anyone waiting for a close encounter.

Cryptozoology

http://www.ncf.carleton.ca/~bz050/ HomePage.cryptoz.html

Fascinating page, with an introduction to cryptozoology, sections on personalities in the field, and the latest news. This site also contains a list of many cryptozoological publications.

Kidnapped by UFOs?

http://www.pbs.org/wgbh/nova/aliens/ alienhome.html

Companion to the US Public Broadcasting Service (PBS) television programme *Nova*, this page takes a serious approach to alien abduction. It is divided into two sections: the believers and the sceptics. The debate includes renowned scientists, as well as abductees, who weigh in with their opinions on alien kidnappings. An interview with an artist abductee includes sketches of the aliens he claims to have come into contact with. The late astronomer Carl Sagan also states his position and there is a special feature on the physical evidence. Is there any? Find out here.

Sceptic's Dictionary

http://skepdic.com

Fully searchable database of information which turns a critical eye on many unusual phenomena. There are essays, mostly written by the producer of the page, on such topics as UFOs, the paranormal, frauds, and cryptozoology. Although the tone of this page is unabashedly sceptical, there are plenty of links to pages written with a more sympathetic viewpoint.

Unsolved Mysteries

http://www.pbs.org/wnet/hawking/ mysteries/html/myst.html

Part of a larger site on cosmology provided by PBS Online, this page features seven articles that address the most difficult questions regarding the mysteries of our universe. Some of the articles include 'Where does matter come from?', 'Is time travel possible?', 'Where is the missing matter?', 'An inhabited universe?', and 'Is there a theory for everything?' You can follow the link to the main site to explore other aspects of the cosmos.

SOCIETY

Schools

Eton College Unofficial Web Site

http://wtin.simplenet.com/eton.html

Comprehensive guide to the history, traditions, and famous old-boys of the prestigious school. Everything you want to know about Eton – from the 'wallgame', to the words of the boating song – can be found here. If you want to put your son down for Eton there are full enrolment and scholarship details.

Harrow School Ezine

http://www.harrowschool.org.uk/

Internet magazine run by Harrow school. The features on this largely self-promotional Web site depict many aspects of life at the English public school – past, present, and future. It includes a list of current pupils, old Harrovians, famous old boys, sports, and a 'What's on' section.

Independent Schools Information Service

http://www.isis.org.uk/

Official site of the organization that represents all of the UK's independent schools. As well as a fully-searchable list of the schools, there is advice on how to choose one for your child, information for non-UK residents and recent press releases of the organization.

Montessori Education

http://www.lfpm.com/montess.html#phil

Introduction to the main principles and practices of Montessori education. The site also offers an annotated bibliography, a list of public Montessori schools, and summaries of relevant published research.

F A C T

MONTESSORI, MARIA (1870–1952)

Italian educationist. Working with mentally disabled children, she developed the **Montessori method,** an educational system for all children based on an informal approach, incorporating instructive play and allowing children to develop at their own pace.

Nothing Matters

http://www.serve.com/Nowhere/

Provocative site that begins with the assumption that teaching and learning are both equally useless pastimes. Through an imaginary conversation, the point and the process of teaching and learning are examined with a whole host of links to related pages.

Schools on the Internet

http://schools.sys.uea.ac.uk/schools/schools.html

Developed from a project run by the School of Information Services, this site provides links to the Web sites of schools, searchable by area.

Straight Talk About School

http://www.lifesplaybook.com/

US-based site is not so much about school, but how to deal with the fact that you have to leave. There is a plenty of advice and information on how to decide which job would be best, and how to go about getting it. Sections include an interactive quiz to try to narrow down the options, a regularly changing careers 'expert', and a page where students share their own advice.

Higher Education

Amy and Jon's Oxford University Tour

http://users.ox.ac.uk/~kebl0613/oxford.html

Offers either a short 'Best of' or a full-length photographic tour of Oxford University, its many colleges, and associated buildings.

British Council Virtual Education Campus

http://www.britcoun.org/eis/index.htm

User-friendly guide to British education provided by the British Council. This easily-navigable site is an essential source of information for those wishing to study in Britain or to learn more about the British educational system. There are comprehensive profiles on just about every higher education or English language teaching institution in Britain.

Julliard School Gateway

http://www.julliard.edu/

Site of the celebrated New York performing arts college. There is a good history and a description of facilities at the Lincoln Center. Various courses offered by the college are also described with enrollment details.

Open University

http://www.open.ac.uk/

Well-designed page from Britain's largest teaching institution (in terms of student numbers). There are examples of the university's distance-learning programmes, an online prospectus, and details of the current crop of BBC weekend programmes, used extensively as part of many of the courses.

UCAS Home Page

http://www.ucas.ac.uk/

Official site for the organization that handles admissions to universities and colleges in the UK. This site is divided into four sections: a comprehensive search facility for all 'universities, colleges, and courses'; an 'advice centre' with information for both prospective students and parents, as well as details of how to apply for university electronically; information for 'for higher education staff'; and 'studentUK' which includes news, views, and advice for students.

UK Sensitive Map – Universities

http://www.scit.wlv.ac.uk/ukinfo/uk.map.html

Clickable map produced by the University of Wolverhampton that allows you to browse around all of the UK's universities and colleges. Click on the university you want to view to be taken straight to the institution's official site. This site also includes a clickable map of many UK research sites.

Yale University

http://www.yale.edu/

Well-designed guide to the Ivy League university. A home page of leather-bound books offers information for visitors, academics, prospective students, and alumni. All departments of this prestigious university can be accessed with ease through a search engine. There is also a section on various research projects, student life, and online magazines published by the university.

Miscellaneous Education

BBC Education Home Page

http://www.bbc.co.uk/education/

Regularly-updated page containing resources for teachers and schoolchildren. As well as Web pages on a variety of issues related to current BBC programmes, the 'learning station' section of this site has age- and key stage-related games and exercises for both primary and secondary schoolchildren. This site also contains resources for teachers and parents. There is quite a lot of promotion of the BBC's products here, but there are also plenty of freely available educational resources.

Commonwealth of Independent States (CIS)

http://www.rochester.k12.mn.us/kellogg/rodgers/1cis/thecis.htm

Educational site featuring maps and regional guides for the CIS, as well as homework exercises. The history of the area is also analysed in some depth.

Cultural Exchange

http://www.oceanintl.org/newsletter.htm

Bimonthly magazine produced by a non-profit US organization dedicated to promoting cultural exchange between students of different countries. The countries they exchange to and from is currently limited. However, this magazine has interesting and regularly changed features on different world areas, as well as geographical and cultural information.

Department for Education and Employment

http://www.dfee.gov.uk/

Official government site which includes contact details of Local Education Authorities in the UK, school and college performance tables, and recent news from the department.

Destination Kyrgyzstan

http://www.peacecorps.gov/wws/guides/kyrgyzstan/

Peace Corps guide, for schoolchildren, to this tiny Central Asian state. There are classroom activities divided by age group and teachers' notes, as well as plentiful maps, illustrations, and guides to other Internet resources.

Electronic School Online

http://www.electronic-school.com/

US-based online magazine targeted at comprehensive school children. It contains news and features relating to how technology is used by schools and children.

Global Show-and-Tell

http://www.telenaut.com/gst/

Represents a US school tradition dragged into the 1990s with the help of the Internet. It is essentially a gallery of children's art from around the globe, with the interesting addition that children can submit their own work to the expanding network of galleries.

Helping your Child Learn to Read

http://www.ed.gov/pubs/parents/Reading/index.html

Useful online leaflet with tips and advice for parents on how to help their children grow to like reading from an early age, with activities for children from infancy up to age 10.

Home Education Advisory Service

http://www.heas.org.uk

The Home Education Advisory Service is a charity set up by home educators to publicize education options for parents. Their Web site provides useful information for parents interested in educating their children at home, including 'Frequently Asked Questions' and information about the legal obligations of the parents.

International Kids Space

http://www.kids-space.org/

Interactive and colourful space for children's activities. You can pick an image and create a story, or pick up a story and create an image. You can also contribute your own music or listen to a live concert, if you are patient enough to wait for the sound files to be fully downloaded. Alternatively, you can simply make friends from all over the world.

Learn2.com: The Ability Utility

http://www.learn2.com/

Easy-to-follow tutorials in a broad range of subject areas. Within the 'Arts & crafts' section you can learn how to wrap the perfect present or make candles, while the 'Technology' pages guide you through such tasks as changing your browser's settings and cleaning you computer.

Learning Through Play

http://www.topmarks.co.uk/parents/words.htm

Contains advice and activities for parents wanting to give their children a head start at school. The pages have details of activities you can work through with your child at home.

Literacy

http://www.literacytrust.org.uk/Database/index.html

Maintained by the Literacy Trust, this site contains interesting pages of UK literacy statistics, details of government initiatives, and advice for parents on how to help their children learn to read.

Mighty Media

http://www.mightymedia.com/

Collaborative site set up by teachers, students and technology advocates. Their aim is to encourage 'the use of interactive communication technologies'. In essence, they offer support and advice for organizations or groups wanting to make use of the Internet, design their own Web page, etc.

National Curriculum

http://www.nc.uk.net/

Well-designed official site of the UK National Curriculum, with information about what attainment levels are required in each of the subject areas.

National Year of Reading

http://www.yearofreading.org.uk/

Information about the national year of reading from the UK National Literacy Trust. The Web site includes a teacher resource centre with practical tips to encourage reading, a searchable index of events, and a database of reviews and comments, to which you are invited to contribute.

New Tools For Teaching

http://ccat.sas.upenn.edu/jod/teachdemo/teachdemo.html

Introduction to the potential of new media for teaching (mainly humanities subjects) written by a classicist with a lot of knowledge and enthusiasm for the information age. The presentation offers useful tips on media such as the World Wide Web, the gophers, the newsgroups, and the Moos. This site also covers practicalities such as the cost of setting up computer suitable systems, and provides concrete advice and useful links to resources for the newly converted, as well as for teachers who are more technologically advanced.

Vidkids Media Literacy Program

http://cmp1.ucr.edu/exhibitions/cmp_ed_prog.html

Online project initiated by the California Museum of Photography, USA, setting out to give primary schoolchildren an opportunity to learn the technical and creative aspects of video and related media.

W E B Du Bois Virtual University

http://members.tripod.com/~DuBois/bibl.html

Wealth of information by and about the US educator of Dutch, African, and French ancestry. As well as access to works by Du Bois, the biography section of this site relates how be became the first Afro-American to earn a PhD from Harvard but was then barred from employment in US universities. His legacy as an inspiration to future generations of African-Americans is recounted.

News Sources

BBC News

http://news.bbc.co.uk/

Online news service from the BBC. Constantly updated, this is one of the best sources of news on the Internet. The long traditions of BBC news gathering are maintained at this site.

Central Europe Online

http://www.centraleurope.com/

Extensive general information magazine on central Europe, covering the Czech Republic, Slovakia, Poland, Hungary, and Slovenia. On the Web since 1995, it now offers daily news, articles from the local press, weekly regional round-ups, detailed travel and culture accounts, basic information about each of the countries covered, political background, and business and economics sections.

CNN Interactive

http://www.cnn.com/

Constantly updated news from the pioneering round-the-clock news service. An audio link allows CNN television news to be heard live. There is also a quiz to test your knowledge of current affairs.

Create Your Own Newspaper

http://crayon.net/

Innovative site allowing you to make a selection from a huge list of news sources so you can read the news, views, entertainment stories, and even cartoons you want to each day. Most of the local news and weather is US-based, but there is also a large selection of world news. Please note, you need to have an e-mail account so that once you have selected your newspaper, it can be delivered.

Economist

http://www.economist.com

Includes the complete text of *The Economist* every week, as well as a searchable archive of back issues since 1995. Software downloads are also included, as is an online shop where Economist products can be bought.

Electronic Telegraph

http://www.telegraph.co.uk/

Online edition of *The Daily Telegraph*.

Eurasia Research Centre Home Page

http://eurasianews.com/erc/homepage.htm

One of the principal resources offered by the Eurasia Research Centre, this Web site includes articles, papers, and commentaries on the politics, culture, history, and social, economic, and human rights conditions of the region. There are also links to further relevant sites on the Web.

Independent, The

http://www.independent.co.uk/

Online edition of *The Independent*, including full UCAS listings of UK university places.

Melbourne Online

http://www.theage.com.au/

Online edition of the long-established Australian newspaper. This is a good source of information on news about Victoria and Australian financial markets in general.

Moreover.com

http://www.moreover.com/

Very comprehensive news resource which collates over 1,500 news sources in over 170 categories.

Nature

http://www.nature.com/

Nature's site features recent and archive news articles from this well-established science magazine. Although there is a strong encouragement to subscribe to the magazine, there are several full articles freely available online, as well as a full sample issue of the magazine, and regularly updated 'Breaking news' and 'Nature science update' sections.

News Unlimited

http://www.newsunlimited.co.uk/

Online news service from *The Guardian* which is regularly updated throughout the day and contains a documentaries section, as well as web links related to the top stories. Although this site is free to use, you do have to register before you have full access.

Newswise

http://www.newswise.com/

Searchable database of recent news events in the fields of science, medicine, and business. The searching is easy to accomplish and can be used by anybody. An optional, free registration allows access to further journalistic information and services.

Private Eye

http://privateeye.uk.msn.com/nogo1.htm

Online version of Britain's foremost satirical magazine. Cartoons, sound clips, and articles present an alternative view of contemporary political life in Britain.

PR Newswire

http://www.prnewswire.com/

Regularly updated collection of international financial information. The site includes the latest news stories, investment profiles, and features broken down into industry groups; everything, in fact, to let you keep an eye on your investment, no matter how large or small.

Sydney Morning Herald Online

http://www.smh.com.au/

Online edition of Australia's longest established newspaper. This is a source of information on Australian news stories and events happening in Sydney.

Times, The

http://www.the-times.co.uk/

Online edition of *The Times*.

UK National Readership Survey

http://www.nrs.co.uk/contents.cfm

Invaluable guide to which newspapers and consumer magazines currently share the best readership figures in the UK. Currently the survey publishes data covering some 245 different publications, providing a reliable source of information for both publishers and other interested parties alike.

Undercurrents

http://www.undercurrents.org/

Alternative news magazine from this Oxford-based group. Exponents of 'video activism', the group provide news from the protest-line, covering issues such as hunting, vivisection, and the opening of the Newbury bypass. All the reports are accompanied by video stills and they tend to approach the stories from a different direction than the mainstream media.

Varsity Online

http://www.varsity.cam.ac.uk/

Online edition of Cambridge University's lively student newspaper. As well as indicating the current social, political, and sporting concerns of students in this prestigious university, the site provides an extensive 'What's on' guide to Cambridge.

Washington Post

http://www.washingtonpost.com

Online version of the US newspaper that includes the latest international news and sports coverage, as well as information about films, music, and food. There are also some of the cartoon strips from the paper and a section for classified adverts.

Community & Local Information

Scoot, the UK Business Directory

http://www.scoot.co.uk/

Useful information service for the UK. Scoot allows you to specify the service you need, and the city or town in which you need it, and then provides you with a full list of business information matching that description, along with their distance in miles from the specified location, and provides a street map of the area in most cases as well. The site also includes a hotel booking service, and a cinema listing directory.

UpMyStreet.com

http://www.upmystreet.com/

Compare the property value, council tax, crime rates, and education levels of your postal area with either the national average or another post code. This site also provides a wealth of information about your local area, and a range of detailed maps of the UK.

World Population Estimates

http://www.popin.org/pop1998/

Online edition of the United Nations' '1998 Revision of the World Population Estimates and Projections', which outlines the standard set of population figures used throughout the UN system. The site includes a projected estimate of the world population in 2050, and an assessment of the global demographic impact of HIV/AIDS.

Fashion

Chanel, Coco

http://www.pathfinder.com/time/time100/artists/profile/chanel.html

Part of a larger archive from *Time* exploring the most influential people of this century, this article highlights the life and work of French fashion designer Coco Chanel. The profile features a timeline and audio clips.

Clothing and Appearance of the Early Christian Anglo-Saxons

http://www.geocities.com/Athens/2471/dress2.html

Concise presentation of the development of Christian Anglo-Saxon dress, as it gradually differentiated itself from the pagan style of clothing. The page examines the possible influences behind this new type of dress and its significance in the growing attachment of Anglo-Saxons to the Frankish Empire, the Mediterranean world, and the Byzantine Empire.

Clothing and Appearance of the Pagan Anglo-Saxons

http://www.geocities.com/Athens/2471/dress.html

Extended essay that attempts to reconstruct the appearance and clothing of early (pagan) Anglo-Saxons, supplementing the lack of direct evidence from this country with the late Roman pictorial and literary representations of the continental Germanic people. The page takes us through the main garments, artefacts, and footwear traditionally connected with the appearance of early Anglo-Saxon men and women.

Dior, Christian

http://www.firstview.com/designerlist/ChristianDior.html

Features a biography of the fashion designer, as well as a number of images from several recent collections.

History of Costume

http://www.siue.edu/COSTUMES/history.html

Illustrated hypertext edition of Braun and Scheider's *History of Costume/Zur Geschichte der Kostüme,* a collection of plates originally published in the German magazine *Münchener Bilderbogen* between 1861 and 1880.

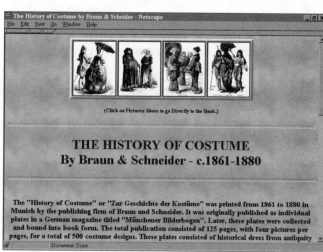

History of Kimono

http://web.mit.edu/jpnet/kimono/index.html

Comprehensive and illustrated history of the traditional Japanese costume. There is detailed information on male, female, and children's kimonos and how social, climatic, and legal factors, together with evolving skills in weaving and dyeing, have transformed the kimono.

History of the Scottish Kilt

http://www.mhc.edu/users/jet/kilthist.htm

Illustrated history of the kilt which explores the 19th-century contributions made by English and Scottish noblemen to a previously Highland Scots cultural tradition.

Karan, Donna

http://www.moda.italynet.com/
www.modaonline.IT/STILISTI/
donnakaran/eng/ECS9798.HTM

Descriptions and details of the fashion designer Donna Karan's latest collections. Although a largely text-based site, several photographs are used as examples of her designs.

Klein, Calvin

http://www.firstview.com/designerlist/
CalvinKlein.html

Brief biography of the fashion designer, as well as numerous images from his recent collections.

Regency Fashion Page

http://locutus.ucr.edu/~cathy/reg3.html

Very large Web site containing information on real clothing, fashion publications and plates, portraits, and scholarship on the period 1790–1822. The site houses over 350 images (mostly JPEG format) of period dress. The Web site is divided up into several sub-pages, for example there is a separate section on men's clothing, an Austen page, and an outerwear page.

Valentino

http://www.made-in-italy.com/fashion/
fashion/vale/vale.htm

Profile of the fashion designer, as well as descriptions of many of his latest fashion collections. A number of photographs from both the studio and the catwalk are used to illustrate these descriptions.

Versace, Gianni

http://www.geocities.com/FashionAvenue/1122/
versace/

Features a brief biography of the fashion designer Gianni Versace, a history of his rise to fame, and details of his final collection.

Westwood, Vivienne

http://interfashion.net/Designers/Westwood.html

Includes a brief biography of the fashion designer, as well as a small selection of her designs.

WESTWOOD, VIVIENNE (1941–)

English fashion designer of international renown. She first attracted attention in the mid-1970s as co-owner of a shop with the rock-music entrepreneur Malcolm McLaren (1946–), which became a focus for the punk movement in London.

Television & Radio

BBC Online

http://www.bbc.co.uk

Includes the latest news and weather, as well as television and radio listings. There is a Web guide and also links to sites dedicated to programmes on the BBC.

Channel Four

http://www.channel4.com/

Well-organized public information site of Channel Four. In addition to comprehensive details of current and upcoming television programmes, there is a range of information services. Teachers are assisted by a searchable online archive of educational materials. Material on a wide range of issues of public concern can be easily accessed. There are also contact details for a large number of organizations related to Channel Four's programmes.

Dr Who

http://www.dwguide.demon.co.uk/listjava.htm

Homage to the popular British television series. There are photographs and biographies of all the actors who played the time traveller. This site also has information on the Doctor's companions, Time Lords, the Tardis and Daleks. There are even a few audio clips and links to other sites for Dr Who fans.

Independent Television Commission

http://www.itc.org.uk/

Comprehensive details on the monitoring and regulation of Britain's independent television companies. The work of the Commission and its staff is explained and contacts supplied. There is a full explanation of Digital Terrestrial Television and the issues involved in its introduction.

Radio Broadcasts of Edward R Murrow

http://www.otr.com/murrow.html

Part of a larger site paying homage to the glory days of radio, this page features audio of three Edward R Murrow news broadcasts, including one live report from a London rooftop during the blitz, and one broadcast from the hearings on US Senator Joseph McCarthy and the House Un-American Activities Committee. In addition to the audio clips, you will find biographical information on Murrow and a photograph of the newsman.

Radio Days: Dramas

http://www.otr.com/drama.html

Part of a larger site that pays homage to the glory days of radio, this page features a number of audio clips from some of the most celebrated comedies, mysteries, private eye, and sci-fi radio programmes of the era. The programmes are arranged by genre, and each programme includes, in addition to the audio clips, a brief textual introduction and photograph.

Sci-Fi Channel: the Dominion

http://www.scifi.com/

Weekly online treasure-trove for lovers of science-fiction. The site offers an abundance of graphics, video and audio clips available for downloading, and a link to *Science-Fiction Weekly* featuring reviews, soundbites, and video clips from classic scientific fiction titles, cinema productions, and TV releases. Ample attention is also given to the latest sci-fi developments and new productions.

75 Years of the BBC

http://www.bbc.co.uk/info/75years.htm

Exhibition of the development and achievements of the BBC during the 75 years of its life, replete with rare and valuable archive material. For example, the site features audio clips from Edward VIII's abdication announcement in 1936, Chamberlain's announcement of the declaration of War in 1939, and VE Day celebrations in 1945. The site also offers rare photos, key dates, technological advances, behind-the-scenes accounts, and a wealth of challenging quizzes for each decade of the BBC's life.

Simpson, Bart

http://www.pathfinder.com/time/time100/artists/profile/simpson.html

Part of a larger archive from *Time* exploring the most influential people of this century, this article highlights Bart Simpson, the cartoon creation of Matt Groening, and an icon for many. The profile features a timeline and audio and video clips.

Welcome to ITV Online

http://www.itv.co.uk

Features details of programmes on ITV, as well as information about Children's ITV.

World of Cilla Black

http://www.geocities.com/SunsetStrip/Amphitheatre/6370/

Very extensive site featuring a wide range of material about Cilla Black, the popular television presenter and former singer. The site features a detailed biography, a discography, and a variety of multimedia elements.

Awards

BAFTA Awards

http://www.bafta.org/

Home page of the British Academy of Film and Television Arts. As well as details of the annual awards, this site also includes a history of the organization, recent press releases, and details of various BAFTA events.

Booker Prize Winners and Shortlisted Title Page

http://www.utc.edu/~engldept/booker/booker.htm

Chronological listing of Booker Prize winning and shortlisted authors, from 1969. There are links to selected authors with information about their

works, biographical details, reviews, and bibliographies.

History of the Pulitzer Prizes

http://www.pulitzer.org/history/

History of the Pulitzer Prizes from the award committee. There is a biography and photo of Joseph Pulitzer and information about the Columbia University School of Journalism he endowed.

Nobel Prize Internet Archive

http://www.nobelprizes.com/

Beautifully-designed archive with a wealth of information on all the Nobel prizewinners with biographies and bibliographies of each laureate. Alongside the mainstream information, there are other features such as why there is no prize in mathematics.

Pulitzer Prizes

http://www.pulitzer.org/navigation/index.html

Brief history of the Pulitzer Prize, along with brief biographies of the winners, and descriptions of their winning pieces of work. An interactive timeline lists all winners since 1917, and an archive of all Pulitzer prizewinning works from the past three years includes photos, editorial cartoons, music clips, and the full text of all winning articles. You can search by year, category, author, or explanatory text.

Topping Shakespeare?

http://www.nobel.se/essays/sture/index.html

Interesting thoughts about the selection of the

candidates and the criteria behind the awards of the Nobel Prizes in Literature by a member of the Swedish Academy. The essay offers ample historical details and other information related to Alfred Nobel's will regarding the awards, and the reception of, and reaction to, the goals of the prize through the years.

Celebrations

Chinese New Year

http://www.indiana.edu/~chasso/newyear.html

Traditions and origins of the Chinese new year celebrations are described on this Web site. The Chinese twenty-four-term calendar is also explained, and in addition, there is a Chinese to Western calendar converter program.

Easter Eggs

http://ns2.carib-link.net/eggs.html

Essay describing the history of the Easter egg, from its pagan origins to its role in Christian belief. This site also includes the background to the custom of giving painted and chocolate eggs at Easter.

Hallowe'en on the Net

http://www.holidays.net/halloween/

Spooky, creepy, and fun presentation of the celebrations during Hallowe'en. The site abounds in ghosts, goblins, dancing skeletons and virtual jack-o-lanterns for those with Java-enabled browsers, Hallowe'en stories, and holiday photos for the kids to print and colour. Please bring a friend.

New Year's Day

http://www.geocities.com/Heartland/Plains/7214/newyear.htm

Interesting essay on the history and traditions of New Year. This page covers the celebrations which occur in many different cultures, includes recipes for traditional food from around the world, and is accompanied by 'Auld Lang Syne'.

Origins of Hallowe'en

http://www.geocities.com/Athens/Forum/5452/hallorig.html

Good account of Hallowe'en organized by an improbably named witch, Rowan Moonstone. Articles trace the origins of the festival, refute the anti-Halloween arguments of Christian fundamentalists and provide a cross-cultural perspective by looking at parallels with the Mexican Day of the Dead.

Story of Mother's Day

http://www.holidays.net/mother/story.htm

History of how the Greek festival honouring Rhea evolved into Mothering Sunday. The US revival of the ancient festival is described. There are details of how the day is celebrated in various countries.

Thanksgiving on the Net – Welcome

http://www.holidays.net/thanksgiving/

Introduction to the US feast of Thanksgiving. It includes a synopsis of the thanksgiving rituals of ancient Greeks, Romans, Hebrews, Chinese, and Egyptians, and then moves on with the history of Thanksgiving with details on the first steps of the pilgrims and their relations with the Indians.

Valentine's Day

http://www.holidays.net/amore/story.html

Thorough history of how the pagan rites of Lupercalia evolved into the feast day of St Valentine. There are interesting details of how the modern festival is celebrated around Europe.

Welcome to Father's Day on the Net

http://www.holidays.net/father/

Father's Day and how to celebrate it. A history of the festival recounts the role of Sonora Dodd in proposing a national holiday, which was signed into US law 50 years later by President Lyndon Johnson. This site also includes suggestions on how to make gifts for your Dad and a selection of father-related poems.

Popular Culture

Alt.Culture: an A–Z of the 90s

http://www.altculture.com/cgi-bin/home.cgi

'Lively encyclopaedia of 1990s youth culture that spans grunge and gangsta, indie rock and indie film, cyberpunk and street fashion, extreme sports and political correctness, infomercials and zines'.

The venue is constantly updated and claims to receive five new entries each week.

Greatest Show on Earth

http://www.ringling.com/home.jtmpl

Site of the celebrated US circus founded by Charles Ringling. There are details of online and traditional circus entertainment offered by the company. This site also includes a biography of Ringling and his brothers, and account of the family's part in creating the modern circus spectacle.

Mardi Gras

http://www.mardigrasday.com/

Lively guide to the New Orleans Mardi Gras festival. You can almost feel the excitement of Bourbon Street through video and audio clips. In addition to practical information required by revellers, there are sections on the history of the festival, Cajun cuisine, and advice on how to organize a Mardi Gras party of your own.

Notting Hill Carnival

http://www.nottinghillcarnival.net.uk

Official Notting Hill Carnival Web site. This large and highly-rated Web site contains comprehensive information on the annual Afro-Caribbean festival in London. The site is updated roughly halfway between the yearly festivals, so you may have just missed last year's or be looking forward to the next one depending when you visit, and the site content varies accordingly.

Sociology

Auguste Comte in a Nutshell

http://www.hgx-hypersoft.com/clotilde/acprecur.htm

Insight into Auguste Comte's contributions to science and this site also touches on his ideas concerning politics, feminism, and religion. This page can be read in English and French. However, the additional information accessed through the numerous hyperlinks is currently only available in French.

Durkheim Pages

http://www.hewett.norfolk.sch.uk./curric/soc/durk.htm

Wealth of information regarding the French philosopher and sociologist Emile Durkheim. In addition to a biography, you will find critical summaries of Durkheim's four major works, an abstract of his philosophy lectures, a timeline of important events in his life and during the Third French Republic, the full texts of some of Durkheim's works, a complete bibliography of his works and one of works about Durkheim, and a glossary of important terms and concepts.

FACT

SOCIOLOGY

systematic study of the origin and constitution of human society, in particular of social order and social change, social conflict and social problems. It studies institutions such as the family, law, and the church, as well as concepts such as norm, role, and culture.

George's Page

http://paradigm.soci.brocku.ca/~lward/

Dedicated to the US psychologist and philosopher George Herbert Mead. The site has resources to support research on his contribution to social psychology.

Georg Simmel Essays

http://socserv2.socsci.mcmaster.ca/~econ/ugcm/3ll3/simmel/index.html

Part of the Archive for the History of Economic Thought at McMaster University, this page features the text of two essays by George Simmel: 'The Philosophy of Value', which appeared in the *American Journal of Sociology* in 1900, and 'How Is Society Possible?', which appeared in the *American Journal of Sociology* in 1910–11.

Kearl's Guide to the Sociology of the Family

http://www.trinity.edu/~mkearl/family.html

Very comprehensive and easy-to-use online resource for studying the sociological concept of family. Descriptions of the key ideas are supported by quotes and evidence from other sources.

Pink Swastika: Homosexuality in the Nazi Party

http://home.earthlink.net/~lively/pinkswastika/

Online text of a book examining homoeroticism in German militarism and fascism. The controversial argument put forward is that, although gays were persecuted under the Nazis, their experience cannot be compared with the suffering of the Jews. The author argues that throughout history deviant warmongering regimes have been led by pederasts and sadomasochists. His argument is controversial, but it is worth examining and is supported by a wealth of historical evidence.

Thomas Carlyle: An Overview

http://www.stg.brown.edu/projects/hypertext/landow/victorian/carlyle/carlyleov.html

Access point to the Victorian writer and critic, with links to political and social context, works, science, visual arts, literary relations, themes, symbolism, religion, and philosophy.

Thorstein Veblen Essays

http://socserv2.socsci.mcmaster.ca/~econ/ugcm/3ll3/veblen/index.html

Part of the Archive for the History of Economic Thought at McMaster University, this page features the text of over 15 essays by Thorstein Veblen, including 'Why is Economics Not an Evolutionary Science?', 'Theory of Business Enterprise', 'The Theory of the Leisure Class', 'The Barbarian Status of Women', 'The Beginnings of Ownership', 'The Irksomeness of Labor', three essays on 'The Preconceptions of Economic Science', and two essays on 'The Socialist Economics of Karl Marx'.

Food & Drink

Antique Roman Dishes

http://www.cs.cmu.edu/~mjw/recipes/

Online cookery book based on ancient Roman recipes. A guide to native Roman ingredients such as liquamen and silphium is also offered, as is a measurement conversion table.

Australian Wines

http://www.australianwines.com/

Glossary of wine terms, suggestions for storing and serving wine, and information on the Australian wine-producing regions and vintages, as well as reports on new wines.

Balti Page

http://www.ibmpcug.co.uk/~owls/balti.html

This site covers the history of the Balti curry, how to make a good Balti, and, if you can't manage that, where to buy one in the UK and Ireland. The site also boasts many hypertext links to other online Indian and curry resources.

Basics of Making Cheese

http://www.efr.hw.ac.uk/SDA/cheese2.html

Basic information on the art of cheese-making. The site offers ample material on the nutritional qualities of the milk, a step-by-step guide through the basic stages of cheese making, plus details on the basic components of cheese, and separate sections on farmhouse cheeses.

Beer from Germany

http://www.bier.de/b-000e.html

Well-designed and comprehensive guide to German beer in both English and German. A detailed history of beer provides a wealth of interesting historical trivia, for example, the Romans detested beer as a 'horrible Barbarian drink'. Other sections are included on different types of beer, a dictionary of beer terms, a top ten of German beers, a guide to breweries, and tips on home brewing.

Bread Chemistry

http://ericir.syr.edu/Projects/Newton/12/Lessons/bread.html

Exploration of the science behind bread making. The site also includes a glossary of difficult terms, further reading, and suggestion for activities related to bread and bread-making.

Bread Recipe Bin

http://countrylife.net/bread/recipes.html

Vast numbers of delicious bread recipes. Examples include cinnamon rolls, banana bread, sage bread, lemon loaf, honey bagel knots, beer biscuits, macadamia and pineapple loaf, vanilla nut bread and much more. As well as enjoying the expertise of others, visitors can share their own favourite recipe by posting it to the bakery recipe board.

Chaucerian Cookery

http://www.labs.net/dmccormick/ccookery.htm

Geoffrey Chaucer, poet and author of *The Canterbury Tales,* used food as a literary device to enrich the personalities of his characters. This Web site examines the references to food and medieval dishes in Chaucer's writings, studies the dietary habits of his characters, and gives a complete list of all foods Chaucer refers to. Included is 'A Chaucerian Feast', which presents an authentic Medieval feast based on the writings of Chaucer and other corresponding 14th-century recipes.

CheeseNet

http://www.wgx.com/cheesenet/

Well-designed and comprehensive guide to cheeses throughout the world. It includes an index of cheeses and a bizarre collection of cheese-related poems and stories.

Chilli!

http://www.tpoint.net/~wallen/chili.html

Online adulation of the hottest food in the world with personal recommendations on the many varieties and recipes, as well as advice on how to prepare the chillies themselves.

Cradle of Coffee

http://www.gpc.org.ye/Culture4.htm

Yemeni account of the origins of the habit of coffee-drinking. Supposedly, the beverage became known to Europeans when served by a local saint who was visiting Portuguese sailors. There is also

a brief history of the development of the international coffee trade through the Yemeni port of Al Mukha.

Curry House

http://www.curryhouse.co.uk/index.htm

Large number of recipes for curries, chutneys, pickles, and other spicy foods. This site also has a guide to curry restaurants in the UK, with a brief review entry for almost every town in the country. Users have the option to nominate their own favourite restaurant for inclusion in the list.

Food and Wines from France

http://www.frenchwinesfood.com/

Guide to the wines and foods of France, with a pronunciation database and information on wine terms, regions, and grapes. There is even a section to help you select the right wine and food when you are faced with preparing for that all important dinner party.

French Cheese: History, Variety, Taste, Tips

http://www.franceway.com/cheese/intro.htm

Contains a wealth of information about over 400 sorts of French cheese. The detailed presentation includes a brief account of the origins of cheese making, clues about pasteurized and non-pasteurized types, tips for shopping for cheese in France, advice on displaying and conserving it, and information on hygiene in farms and factories.

Frequently Asked Questions About Caffeine

http://www.cs.unb.ca/~alopez-o/caffaq.html

Source of information on caffeine and coffee. The chemistry of caffeine and its effects are clearly presented. For devotees of good coffee there is advice on various kinds of coffee and how to make the perfect brew. Studies on the side effects of excessive caffeine consumption are also summarized.

From Reactor to Refrigerator

http://whyfiles.news.wisc.edu/054irradfood/index.html

Part of the Why Files project, published by the

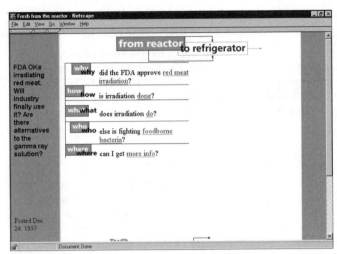

National Institute for Science Education (NISE) and funded by the National Science Foundation, this page explains the how, why, and what of food irradiation. The highly readable text, laid out over five pages, includes information about other techniques being offered as means to protect food. Numerous images and diagrams enhance the text throughout. You will also find a comprehensive bibliography of sources for further research.

Margarine on the Web

http://www.margarine.org/

Everything you could think of asking about margarine on one Web site. Besides the obvious recipes, nutrition, and product information, this site has a wealth of other facts on this butter substitute. The trivia section has answers to questions surely no one would need to know the answer to, like how many sticks (US eqivalent of tubs) of margarine stacked lengthways would it take to reach the moon, or how many pounds of margarine Americans eat each year.

Molecular Expressions: Ice Cream Collection

http://micro.magnet.fsu.edu/micro/gallery/
benandjerry/icecream.html

Spectacular collection of photographs of ice cream molecules. This unusual site puts under the microscope desserts as exotic as coffee almond fudge crunch, banana strawberry yoghurt, and toffee crunch.

Scotch Whisky Association

http://www.scotch-whisky.org.uk/frame.htm

Comprehensive site that covers everything you ever wanted to know about the world's 'leading noble spirit', including details of its history, production, and even a map of distillers.

Soda Bread Wisdom

http://www.ibmpcug.co.uk/~owls/
sodabred.htm

Soda bread recipes and history. If you've ever thought of making this Irish bread variety, this would be a good place to find out how. If you haven't, then it's a good place to find out why maybe you should.

Talking about Turkey

http://www.hoptechno.com/book15.htm

Dedicated to the game bird, this site contains information on buying, storing, thawing, stuffing, and preparing a turkey. The information here guides you through such questions as whether your turkey should be fresh or frozen, how it should be roasted, and how you test it for 'doneness'. There is also a guide to carving, how to make gravy, and how to store leftovers.

Thai Food

http://www.bu.ac.th/thailand/food.html

Translation from Thai to English of Thai food names. The site is run by Bangkok University and includes brief descriptions of many Thai dishes.

Types of Diet

http://www.healthy.net/library/books/haas/kitchen/
types.htm

Examines the various types of nutrition, what they are and what they mean in nutritional terms. These range from 'Omnivorous' to 'Industrialized'.

Welcome to Teatime.com

http://www.teatime.com/

Useful resource for tea lovers with nutrition information, flavours, a glossary of tea terms, and a wealth of features on tea-related issues, such as tea and health, tea and caffeine, the origins of tea tradition, and tea vendor lists. Visitors can also take part in chats, learn about tea books, and read tea quotes.

F
A
C
T

ESCHERICHIA COLI

rod-shaped Gram-negative bacterium that lives, usually harmlessly, in the colon of most warm-blooded animals. It is the commonest cause of urinary tract infections in humans.

What the Heck is an *E. coli* ?

http://falcon.cc.ukans.edu/~jbrown/ecoli.html

Explains the basics behind this bacterium which can cause food poisoning, including information on the dangerous strain of the bacterium and how it developed. It contains guidelines on reducing the risk of infection. There are a number of links throughout the article to sites expanding on issues raised.

Wild Mushroom

http://www.matkurja.com/slo/country/food/gobe/

Description of all the types of wild mushrooms to be found in Slovenia, with details of how to cook them.

Museums & Libraries

Ashmolean Museum

http://www.ashmol.ox.ac.uk/

Guide to the museum in Oxford, England, founded by Elias Ashmole. There are full details of permanent collections, exhibitions, and talks, together with other practical information for visitors.

Australian Museum Online

http://www.austmus.gov.au/index.htm

Well-organized site of the prestigious Australian museum. There is comprehensive information on the collections and research into anthropology, mineralogy, ornithology, and palaeontology. The site also offers some practical information for visitors.

Bodleian Library, University of Oxford

http://www.bodley.ox.ac.uk/

Web site of the Bodleian Library in Oxford, England. There is practical information for visitors and readers, and information on a range of online services offered by the library.

British Library

http://www.bl.uk/

Home page of the British Library. There is extensive information for users of the library's many services. The information provided is comprehensive and includes the capability to search through all the 9.5 million books catalogued since 1977.

British Museum

http://www.british-museum.ac.uk/

Comprehensive guide to the British Museum. The site has regularly updated information about current exhibitions. Maps of each floor of the museum allow a visit to be planned in advance.

Exploratorium

http://www.exploratorium.edu/index.html

Very well-designed site based on the hands-on science museum in San Francisco. Several of the museum's exhibits are recreated here, including a page on the science of ice hockey and a virtual dissection of a cow's eye. There is practical information about the museum and help for teachers, but most of the pages are interactive: full of images and audio clips to augment the text.

Fineart Forum Online WWW Resources Directory

http://www.msstate.edu/Fineart_Online/ art-resources/museums.html

Alphabetical index of art museums from the African American Museums Association to the Yale Centre for British Art, including a brief outline for each entry with hyperlinks to further information.

Franklin Institute Science Museum

http://sln.fi.edu/

Virtual museum of science with exhibits especially designed for online presentation. The topics include 'The circle of life', 'A robot zoo', 'The wind', 'The heart', 'Life in nature', and 'Man-made life'. An open-all-hours interactive museum which is rich in material, well-designed, and proof that learning can be fun and win over barriers of distance and nationality.

From Smithson to Smithsonian – Birth of an Institution

http://www.sil.si.edu/newstart.html

History of the US academic institution. A detailed biography of the British chemist, James Smithson, is accompanied by a series of photographs. There are details of Smithson's bequest, the foundation of the institution, profiles of early directors, and the acquisitions and expansions that have forged the modern Smithsonian.

Guggenheim Museum Bilbao

http://www.bm30.es/homegug_uk.html

Includes the background to the building of the Guggenheim Museum, which opened in 1997, as well as gallery plans and details of exhibitions.

History of Madame Tussauds

http://www.illumin.co.uk/illumin/interac/tuss.html

Well-presented information on Marie Grosholtz and the famous London wax museum she founded. The process of creating models is explained with informative text and good photos.

Imperial War Museum

http://www.iwm.org.uk/

Well-arranged guide to the Imperial War Museum, the Cabinet War Rooms, and the historic ship *HMS Belfast*. Attractions are described with the help of good photographs. Practical information for visitors is provided.

Ironbridge Gorge Museum Trust

http://www.vtel.co.uk/igmt/

Guide to the World Heritage Site and the museums of industrial archaeology to be found in 'the Silicon Valley of the 18th century'. There is a large map of the extensive site and practical information for visitors.

Library of Alexandria

http://www.perseus.tufts.edu/GreekScience/

Students/Ellen/Museum.html

History of the Library of Alexandria in Egypt, with sections on such topics as its foundation and development, the first librarians, and the work of scholars affiliated with Alexandria and the library.

Museum of Science and Industry in Manchester

http://www.msim.org.uk/

Complete guide to this museum, including details of current events and exhibitions, and a 'hands on' area with interactive content. You will need to download the 'Shockwave' plug-in to fully enjoy this site.

National Air and Space Museum, Smithsonian Institute

http://www.nasm.si.edu/

Museum in Washington DC, USA. This site includes sections on 'Visitor information', 'Students & teachers', 'Collections & research', and 'New exhibitions', among others.

National Museum of Photography, Film, and Television

http://www.nmsi.ac.uk/nmpft/

Details of collections, events, and forthcoming exhibits at the National Museum of Photography, Film, and Television, in Bradford, England. The educational section of this Web site includes resources based around the exhibitions which are sorted by Key Stage.

Natural History Home Page, Smithsonian Institute

http://www.mnh.si.edu/nmnhweb.html

Broad-ranging Web site with information on anthropology, botany, entomology, invertebrate zoology, mineral sciences, palaeobiology and vertebrate zoology, all taken from the Museum's collection of over 120 million scientific specimens and cultural artefacts.

Natural History Museum

http://www.nhm.ac.uk/

Written features about all the museum's major areas, with many pictures. The site also includes practical information about the museum's opening times. One further section is dedicated to developing and displaying 3-D virtual reality models of exhibits.

Russian Culture Pages

http://aie.riis.ru/english/culture/menu.html

Overview of Russian culture covering art, architecture, traditions, and cuisine. This site includes sections on dance, folk songs, sculpture, and painting, but it begins with a useful section entitled 'General characteristics of Russian art'.

Science Museum – Online Features

http://www.nmsi.ac.uk/on-line/

Online exhibitions from the Science Museum in London with well-designed and lively pages celebrating major scientific issues and projects, such as the fight against infections by the Public Health Laboratory Service, the revolutionary uses of the electron in human lives, and the history of flight. Impressive or rare photos, alongside illustrations and virtual experiments are some of the tools used in these online galleries. The site also features an online selection of some of the museum's most impressive exhibits.

Singapore's Online Museum

http://www.museum.org.sg/shm/shm.html

Nationally-run site to preserve Singapore's culture that includes sections on history and art. It has a regularly-updated selection of changing exhibitions and an archive of all previous ones. The art museum is separated into a Southeast Asian gallery and one that is more specific to Singapore.

Sir John Soane's Museum

http://www.soane.org/

Guide to the museum founded by the English architect. There is a profile of the life and legacy of Soane supported by photographs of his designs. Practical information is provided for visitors to this London museum.

University of Oxford Museums

http://www.ox.ac.uk/museums.html

Online guide to the museums run by Oxford University. This page includes details of the Ashmolean Museum of Art

and Archaeology, The Bate Collection of Musical Instruments, Museum of the History of Science, Oxford University Museum of Natural History, and The Pitt Rivers Museum.

Vatican Exhibition

http://sunsite.unc.edu/expo/vatican.exhibit/exhibit/Main_Hall.html

Online version of the Vatican museum allowing you to explore at leisure the wealth of artefacts. They are organized in various sections including archaeology, humanism, mathematics, and music. The site includes plenty of explanatory text and thumbnail images to expand views.

Victoria and Albert Museum

http://www.vam.ac.uk/

Guide to the world's largest museum of the decorative arts. There is information on permanent displays, exhibitions, public events, publications, and talks. Other museums operated by the V&A are described and there are good summaries of the museum's main collections.

Wilanow Palace Museum

http://sunsite.icm.edu.pl/art/wilanow/wilanow1a.htm

Online and bilingual exhibition based at the Polish palace near Warsaw that includes images and descriptions of historical objects on display there. There are also practical details about the museum's opening hours and information about the surrounding park and orangery.

Tourism

Foreign Languages for Travellers

http://www.travlang.com/languages/

Extensive site to help you out if you are travelling abroad. After selecting a language you can speak from the initial menu, you can then gain access to various pages which will help you learn the basics of a surprising variety of languages from Bengali to Esperanto.

Green Travel Network

http://www.greentravel.com/

Promoting environmentally responsible tourism for the more adventurous traveller. The Web site feature articles, 'Trip ideas', 'Trip planner', and more.

London Transport

http://www.londontransport.co.uk/

Latest travel news, as well as bus and tube maps and timetables, and a guide to visiting London. Latest news on the transport systems is also included.

Michelin Route Planner

http://www.michelin-travel.com/

Pan-European route planner – just enter your starting point, destination, and desired stop-over points, and this site can provide you with all the information you need.

Tourism Concern

http://www.gn.apc.org/tourismconcern/

Details of international campaigns to make the tourist industry more responsive to the needs of local people. There are reports from around the world of the environmental and social consequences of unplanned development of tourism. This site, and the educational resources it offers, are useful for teachers and of interest to students. Reading these accounts of indigenous people evicted from their land, or deprived of their livelihood by tourist resorts, may make you want to stay at home.

UK Travel Guide

http://www.uktravel.com/index.html

Essential resource for anyone planning to travel in the UK. It includes an A–Z of practical information from accommodation to the weather. The site also includes a 'clickable' map with features on towns and cities as well as several images.

Visit Britain – British Tourist Authority

http://www.visitbritain.com/frameset.htm

Comprehensive information on tourism in the British Isles, provided by the official tourist promotion agency. An interactive map and a good search engine make this a first-stop site for anyone contemplating a visit to Britain.

F A C T

TOURISM

travel and visiting places for pleasure, often involving sightseeing and staying in overnight accommodation. Regarded as an industry, tourism can increase the wealth and job opportunities in an area, although the work is often seasonal and low paid.

SPORT

American Football

Official Site of Johnny Unitas

http://www.cmgww.com/football/unitas/unitas.html

All there is to know about the legendary quarterback and his glittering US football career. The contents include a summary of his career, a biography of 'the golden arm', and a photo gallery.

Rockne, Knute

http://www.cmgww.com/football/rockne/rockne.html

Tribute to the memory of the charismatic American football coach, maintained by his grandchild. The main events of his life from his birth, through his extraordinary successes with Notre Dame, to his death in an air crash are set out. There are photographs of Rockne and a summary of his career achievements.

Super Bowl

http://www.superbowl.com/

Official guide to the highlight of the American football season. It contains a complete history of the Super Bowl, a list of the teams in contention, loads of gossip, news from fans, and video clips of plays. For any fan of American football this site is a must.

Team NFL

http://www.nfl.com/index.html

Official site of the US National Football League, with up-to-the-minute news and locker-room gossip.

F A C T

AMERICAN FOOTBALL

contact sport similar to the English game of rugby, played between two teams of 11 players, with an inflated oval ball. Players are well padded for protection and wear protective helmets.

Athletics

Bannister, Roger

http://cgi.cnnsi.com/features/1998/sportsman/1954/

Profile of English runner Roger Bannister, the first human being to run a four-minute mile. The Web site reprints the cover of *Sports Illustrated* celebrating Bannister's elevation to Sportsman of the Year in 1954, and provides a brief account of an athletics milestone.

British Athletics Federation

http://www.british-athletics.co.uk/

Useful, if basic site from the British Athletics Federation. The Web site includes a UK athletics club directory, tips on training and coaching, and links to athletics sites worldwide.

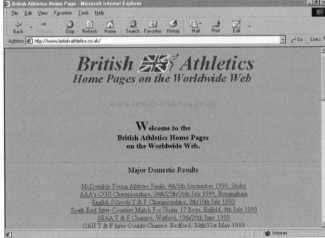

Hammer Throw

http://www.geocities.com/Colosseum/8682/ham.htm

Enthusiasts' guide to the sport of hammer throwing that includes a list of competitors with world rankings, photos, video clips, and links to some related sites.

Heptathlon

http://www.iaaf.org/TrainingTips/Sport/Hep/intro.html

Guide to the women's seven-event athletic competition. Stages in the development of the discipline leading to its Olympic debut in 1984 are set out. There is also some advice for those thinking of taking up competition.

High Jump

http://www.iaaf.org/TrainingTips/Sport/HJ/intro.html

History of the high jump. The Celtic origins of the sport are described, together with subsequent innovations leading to the modern discipline. Key landmarks such as development of the 'Fosbury flop' are described, together with profiles of modern high-jump stars.

International Amateur Athletics Federation

http://www.iaaf.org/

Wealth of authoritative information about athletics, with pages on each of the events from the 100m sprint to the triple jump – their histories, landmarks for men and women, and a breakdown of the qualities needed to compete successfully in that event. Here, too, are brief biographies of athletics legends such as Jessie Owens and the top athletes of today, video interviews and training tips from the likes of Jonathan Edwards, news and press releases, and extracts from *New Studies in Athletics*, the IAAF's quarterly magazine.

Javelin Throw

http://www.u.arizona.edu/~banken/javelin.html

The history of javelin throwing, from its earliest legendary associations with Hercules, through its modern revival in Scandinavia, and acceptance as a modern Olympic discipline, are traced. This site also includes details about some current world-class javelin throwers, details of world records, and some related articles, including one on 'The physics behind the throw'.

Long Jump

http://www.iaaf.org/TrainingTips/Sport/LJ/intro.html

Guide to the long jump. The Greek origins of the sport are described, together with moves towards establishment of the modern discipline. Key developments in long-jump techniques are described, together with profiles of modern long-jump stars.

Marathon

http://www.iaaf.org/TrainingTips/Sport/Mar/intro.html

International Amateur Athletic Federation guide to the athletics endurance race. The modern revival of the race and bizarre events in early modern Olympic marathons are described. Highlights in modern marathon history are set out, together with advice for those thinking of taking up competition.

Mike Buncic Discus Throw

http://www.powerlean.com/discusweb/discusindex.htm

Home page of the US discus athlete, Mike Buncic that, as well as some images of him in action, contains a detailed and clear set of help pages for training discus throwers.

Owens, Jesse

http://www.cmgww.com/sports/owens/

Biography and photographs of Jesse Owens, the legendary African-American athlete of the 1930s. The site also contains a list of quotes from Owens, who won four gold medals at the 1936 Berlin Olympics.

Shot Put

http://www.geocities.com/Colosseum/8682/shot.htm

Enthusiasts' guide to putting the shot, that includes a list of competitors with world rankings, images, video clips and some links to related sites.

Triathlete's Web

http://w3.one.net/~triweb/triweb.html

The 'Essentials' section contains answers to frequently asked questions, and this site also includes articles on such topics as safe cycling, the triathlete's lifestyle and relationships, and links to related sites around the world.

Triple Jump

http://www.iaaf.org/TrainingTips/Sport/TJ/intro.html

Guide to the triple jump. The Greek origins of the sport are described, together with subsequent Celtic and American innovations leading to the modern discipline. Key landmarks and stars of the modern triple jump are described.

UK:Athletics

http://www.ukathletics.org/

Latest athletics news, fixtures and results, plus

athletes' biographies, from the governing body of athletics in the United Kingdom. An informative results, records, and rankings section is another feature.

Viren, Lasse

http://www.uiah.fi/~kberg/index.html

Tribute to the Finnish runner Lasse Viren from a fan. There are several photos of Viren in action on the track and dressed in his policeman's uniform. There are also quotes from a book about Viren in which the great runner describes his approach to athletics.

Zatopek, Emil

http://www.sas.upenn.edu/~kovalsky/idol.htm

Profile of the carpenter's son who became the 'Iron Man' of distance running. His outstanding success on the track is lovingly chronicled together with the sporting philosophy to which he owed his success. There is an account of how his support for Dubček led to him becoming a virtual nonperson in Czechoslovakia.

Baseball

Aaron, Hank

http://cwws.com/~schubert/aaron.htm

Provides details and statistics on Hank Aaron's baseball playing. There is an audio clip of the announcer commentating on his 715th home run, together with photographs of the event, and even a video. There is information on each of his home runs, as well as a photograph album, a list of notable quotations about Aaron, and audio file of a speech given by the man himself.

Baseball Cards: 1887–1914

http://lcweb2.loc.gov/ammem/bbhtml/bbhome.html

Part of the American Memory presentation of the US Library of Congress, this page features early baseball cards of such legends as Ty Cobb, Tris Speaker, Christy Mathewson, and Cy Young. Click on any of the thumbnail images to increase its size.

Cal Ripken Jr

http://cbs.sportsline.com/u/fans/celebrity/ripken/

Profile of the 'Iron Man' of US baseball. This site includes a biography, latest statistics of his phenomenal career, photos, interviews, and audio and video clips.

Cobb, Ty

http://wso.williams.edu/~jkossuth/cobb/

This site focusses on selected areas of Ty Cobb's life, such as his early life, his baseball playing skills, and his relationships with other players, fans, and the sports media.

Dean, Dizzy

http://www.aparker.org/shoeless/dizzy.html

Good profile of the legendary baseball pitcher. There are pictures of Dean in action and a year-by-year account of his career. A selection of quotes illustrate Dean's offbeat sense of humour.

Early Baseball Photographs

http://lcweb2.loc.gov/ammem/jrhtml/jrgmabt.html

Part of the American Memory presentation of the US Library of Congress, this page features 34 images of early baseball, arranged into five sections: 'Baseball beginnings', 'Game day in the majors', 'Players', 'Non-major league baseball', and 'Major league teams and games'. There are photographs of some of baseball's most legendary players, including Ty Cobb, Cy Young, and Shoeless Joe, and a team photograph of the 1926 Yankees that includes Babe Ruth and Lou Gehrig. Brief notes accompany the images.

Jackie Robinson Foundation

http://www.jackierobinson.org

Site of the educational organization honouring the memory of the legendary African-American baseball player and civil-rights advocate. Robinson's career on and off the baseball field is described. The continuing activities of the Jackie Robinson Foundation are also set out.

Major League Baseball

http://www.majorleaguebaseball.com/

Official site of the US Major League baseball

organization. Every aspect of the sport is covered here, including fan forums, league schedules, game reviews, team gossip, and live scoreboards in the season. The site also features a wealth of regularly updated photographs and multimedia clips of the stars in action, and virtual tours of many stadiums are available through hypertext links.

Mickey Mantle – The American Dream Comes to Life

http://www.themick.com/

Comprehensive source of information on the life and career of the fabled baseball player. Every achievement of 'the Mick' is covered. There are also several photos of Mantle in action.

Musial, Stan

http://www.mosportshalloffame.com/smusial.htm

Biography of the baseball star. It traces Musial's long playing career and his post-retirement involvement in athletics. There is also a picture of 'Stan the Man'.

National Baseball Hall of Fame and Museum

http://www.baseballhalloffame.org/

Hall of Fame members' gallery with brief player profiles, statistics, photos, and links to official player Web sites. You can also view special online exhibits, take a peek at the Hall of Fame's monthly newsletter, and learn about the Hall of Fame's extensive collection of baseball memorabilia. Additionally, fans can get their toughest baseball-related questions answered by the Hall of Fame library's research services department. Visitor information is also available.

Official Babe Ruth League, Inc

http://www.baberuthleague.org/bindex.html

Full career of the legendary baseball player. There are many photos of the man and video clips of him in action. In one section of the site, you can experience what it was like to pitch to the great man.

Official Site of Christy Mathewson

http://www.cmgww.com/baseball/mathew/mathew.html

Profile of the US baseball pitcher. A biography provides an intimate portrait of the competitive sportsman whose clean-living private life made him a role model. There are pictures of 'Matty' and quotes that throw light on his approach to sport.

Shadowball: The Story of the Negro Leagues

http://www.negro-league.columbus.oh.us/

Comprehensive site that puts Negro League baseball into its historical and cultural context. An important site for the baseball fan seeking to understand the full picture of baseball in the USA, it includes information on the teams of the Negro Leagues, biographies and photographs of the major players, humorous quotes, and 'tall tales', plus a links page and an extensive bibliography of books, films, and documentaries on African-American baseball. There is even a 'Pagefinder' tool to ease your search.

USA Softball Online

http://www.softball.org/

Official site of the US Amateur Softball Association, providing a complete run-down of this baseball-related sport. The difference between the fast-pitch and slow-pitch version of the game is explained and a good section of 'Frequently Asked Questions' explains how the game differs from baseball. There is also regularly updated news of competitions in the USA and around the world.

Willie Mays Profile

http://www.achievement.org/autodoc/page/may0pro-1

Description of the life and achievements of Willie Mays, the man many describe as the best baseball player ever. This Web site contains not only a profile and biographical information, but also a lengthy interview with the player accompanied by a large number of photographs, and video and audio clips.

Basketball

Abdul-Jabbar, Kareem

http://www.unc.edu/~lbrooks2/jabbar.html

Describes Kareem Abdul-Jabbar's life and, of course, his career as a basketball player. There are both statistics and several photographs, as well as information about how to contact Abdul-Jabbar himself.

Bird, Larry

http://www.nba.com/pacers/bios/coach.html#top

Detailed biography of the basketball player. It traces his career from its earliest beginnings to his continued involvement with the game as a coach. There are also some off-court details about Bird.

British Basketball

http://www.eurobasket.com/eng/eng.htm

Results from the Budweiser League, news of the English national basketball team, a list of imported players with the teams they play for, and links to other English basketball sites, are all included at this Web site.

[Screenshot of British Basketball web page in Microsoft Internet Explorer, address http://www.eurobasket.com/eng/eng.htm]

Johnson, Magic

http://www.unc.edu/~lbrooks2/magic.html

Biography and career details of the basketball player. This site also contains some on- and off-court photos and links to related sites, including the '50 greatest NBA players of all time', in which he figures.

Jordan, Michael

http://jordan.sportsline.com

Official Web site of the basketball player. Contained here are details of his career, complete with statistics, game recaps, feature stories, and the opportunity to e-mail the man himself. In addition, there is a selection of photographs, and sound and video clips.

Naismith, James

http://schwinger.harvard.edu/~terning/bios/Naismith.html

Profile of the man who invented basketball and netball. The main events of Naismith's life are set out, and there is also a photo.

Official Site of the National Basketball Association

http://www.nba.com

Basketball Web site run by the sports governing body in the USA. Daily updated video clips, a fantasy league, and live commentary are just some of this site's features.

Women's National Basketball Association

http://www.wnba.com/

Official site of the Women's National Basketball Association. Here you will find a wealth of information on the WNBA, including player and team profiles that include photographs, audio, and video clips. You can also check out scores and statistics, look at a schedule of the season, and learn about the latest news affecting the league. There is an interesting interactive section that provides audio clips of player interviews and the answers to fans' e-mail questions. You can watch the top ten plays of the season. The WNBA rulebook is available to browse, and you can also read a timeline of women's involvement in basketball which goes back to 1892 and runs up to the inaugural season of the WNBA in 1997.

Boxing

Ali – A Brief History

http://www.webgalleria.com/alibio.html

Chronology of the career of Muhammad Ali in and out of the ring. The history describes all the boxer's main fights, and describes how joining the Nation of Islam affected his career.

International Boxing Hall of Fame

http://www.ibhof.com

As well as describing the Hall of Fame's activities and listing its members, there is comprehensive coverage of current boxing news, including fight schedules, world rankings, and title-holders. Additionally, there is a chronological record of every major world title fight, a list of all Olympic boxing medallists, sound clips, and pictures.

Lennox Lewis Official Web Site

http://www.lennox-lewis.com/

Heavyweight boxing champion Lennox Lewis's official presence on the Web. The site contains personal information, fight details, press articles and interviews, and details of how to join Lewis's fan club.

Prince Naseem Official Web Site

http://www.princenaseem.com/

News, pictures, and statistics for fans of English boxer Prince Naseem Hamed. The Web site includes daily updates on the flamboyant boxer's career, as well as details of how to join his fan club.

Robinson, Sugar Ray

http://worldboxing.com/classics/sugarray.htm

Outline of the long career of the US boxer. In addition to biographical details, this tribute to Ray has a statistical summary of his career, and there is also a description of how he acquired the nickname 'Sugar Ray'.

Rocky Marciano's Home Page

http://www.rockymarciano.com/

Sympathetic account of 'The Rock' presented by the historical society honouring the most famous son of the town of Brockton. Verging on the eulogistic, and filled with images of Marciano as fighter and family man, this is a fulsome tribute to the boxer.

Sky Sports Online Boxing

http://www.skysports.co.uk/skysports/boxing/

News and information on the UK and international boxing scene, from Sky Sports. The site includes breaking news, match reports, and TV boxing schedules.

Tyson, Mike

http://home.echo-on.net/~amanek/tyson/tyson.htm

Complete biography of 'Iron' Mike Tyson and his controversial career in and out of the ring. There are photos and regularly updated news of his latest fights and escapades. The author of this site makes no attempt to hide the fact that he remains a fan of this troubled boxer, but does include interesting sections on such topics as the 'Don King saga', a 'Tyson Web poll', and one called the 'Rumours section'.

Cricket

Brian Lara – World's Greatest Batsman

http://www.infochan.com/carib_sport/lara2.htm

Tribute to the great Trinidadian. This site contains a comprehensive account of his career and a thorough biography.

Charlton, Bobby

http://dnausers.d-n-a.net/dnetmQXk/legends/bobbycharlton.htm

Profile of English football legend Bobby Charlton. The Web page gives an account, backed up by statistics, of Charlton's career with Manchester United, from his survival of the infamous Munich air disaster to his spectacular success under Matt Busby in the 1960s.

CricInfo: The Home of Cricket on the Internet

http://www-uk.cricket.org/

Comprehensive online coverage of cricket. The site includes reports on recent and live test

CRICKET

bat-and-ball game between two teams of 11 players each. It is played with a small solid ball and long flat-sided wooden bats, on a round or oval field, at the centre of which is a finely mown pitch, 20 m/22 yd long. At each end of the pitch is a wicket made up of three upright wooden sticks (stumps), surmounted by two smaller sticks (bails). The object of the game is to score more runs than the opposing team.

matches, an interactive magazine, images, details of the domestic seasons throughout the cricket-playing world, an explanation of the laws of cricket, archival information, and statistics.

Cricket at the Australian Institute of Sport

http://www.ausport.gov.au/aiscri.html

History of the Australian cricket training academy. As well as including a history of the sport and an explanation of the current rules, this site also contains details of the intensive training programme followed by members of the institute.

Dispersing the Mists of Time

http://www.mhoerch.demon.co.uk/sabr13.html

Interesting account of the origins of cricket and basketball. Historical evidence concerning stoolball and other ancient English ball games is presented. The site examines a claim that stoolball is the precursor of the modern game of cricket.

Gooch, Graham

http://www-usa11.cricket.org/link_to_database/ PLAYERS/ENG/G/GOOCH_GA_01001446/

Biographical details of England cricketer Graham Gooch, with statistics on his playing career. The page contains links to press articles about Gooch, photographs, and a detailed match-by-match analysis of his performance.

Ian Botham – the Legend

http://www.sporting-life.com/botham/legend.html

Profile of Ian Botham, concentrating on the legendary England all-rounder's cricket career and his charity work. The site provides details of

Botham's record-breaking scores, and repeats some of his more outspoken comments. It contains a feedback page and step-by-step accounts of the marathon walks he has undertaken to raise money for leukaemia charities.

Kapil Dev's Home Page

http://www.cstp.umkc.edu/personal/ rganesh/kapildev/kapildev.html

Enthusiastically compiled site celebrating the life and career of Indian cricket all-rounder Kapil Dev, who is known as the 'Haryana Express'.

Lord's – The Home of Cricket

http://www.lords.org/

Official site of the world's foremost cricket ground. In addition to information about the ground, there is constantly updated cricket news. There are also hyperlinks which take you to just about every cricket club in the world.

Owen, Michael

http://www.isfa.com/server/web/uf/owen.htm

Unofficial home page devoted to Michael Owen, Liverpool player and darling of English football in the late 1990s. The site contains background information and links to other Owen-related sites.

Sky Sports Online Cricket

http://www.skysports.co.uk/skysports/cricket/

Authoritative and regularly updated information for followers of English cricket. Sky Sports's online cricket resource is a forum for news, analysis, photographs, and statistics on test series and county cricket. Highlights include an archive of World Cup 99 coverage and a 'Cricketcall' feature, allowing fans to have their say.

Tendulkar, Sachin

http://www.geocities.com/MotorCity/Speedway/48 61/ist.htm

Profile of the developing career of the Indian cricketer. There is a photo of the outstanding batsman, a description of his talents, and a prediction that he is on course to become the most successful Test batsman of all time.

Viv Richards

http://www-usa4.cricket.org/link_to_database/
NATIONAL/WI/PLAYERS/R/
RICHARDS_IVA_04001435/

Well-written tribute to the legendary Antiguan cricketer. Richard's charisma, physical prowess and his domination of the game of cricket at the height of his powers is assessed. There is a large selection of additional e-mailed tributes and an opportunity to add to them.

Women's Cricket

http://users.ox.ac.uk/~beth/wca.htm

Informative, but slightly uninteresting to look at, this site provided by the Women's Cricket Association contains many useful pages on the women's game. It offers news and information on club and international competitions, and links to other women's cricket sites.

Equestrian Sports

Aintree Racecourse

http://www.aintree.co.uk/

Latest news from the Aintree Racecourse, as well as maps of the course and information about past Martell Grand National events, including results, a commentary, and articles. There is also a history of the horse Red Rum.

Fact, Fiction, and Fables of the Melbourne Cup

http://www.billythepigs.com.au/
melbournecup/index.html

Information and obscure facts about Australia's foremost horse racing event. As race time approaches, the site publishes profiles of the leading contenders.

Goodwood Experience

http://www.goodwood.co.uk/

Well-organized guide to the Goodwood Estate, the famous Glorious Goodwood racecourse, and Goodwood House. There is a history of the now-disused racing track. The needs of punters are taken care of with a regularly updated fixture list and admission details.

Jockey Club

http://www.jockeyclub.com/

Official site of the governing body of English thoroughbred horse racing. The contents include the rules and structure of the Jockey Club, a complete list of English thoroughbreds, handicapping rules, and the American Stud Book. There are links to other racing bodies around the world.

Mining Co. Guide to Horse Racing

http://horseracing.miningco.com/

Huge source of constantly updated information on all aspects of horse racing. There are details of all UK race events with tips and latest betting information. There are articles on the sport, foreign racing news, a large number of links, and help for those new to the world of the turf.

Welcome to the Curragh Racecourse

http://www.curragh.ie/

Site of Ireland's premier racecourse. There is a good history of the Curragh and descriptions of facilities for punters. This site also includes information on the Irish Derby and other events, and a link to the Irish National Stud.

What is Dressage?

http://www.usdf.org/what.html

Two articles from the US Dressage Federation on the importance of dressage as a method of basic training and as a competitive sport.

Extreme Sports

AMA Superbike

http://www.amasuperbike.com/

Unofficial site about news and information relating to the teams, riders, and events in the Superbike World Championship and Grand Prix seasons. This site also provides feature articles on the riders, plus a 'Frequently Asked Questions' section.

Chainsmoke

http://www.chainsmoke.com/

International mountain biking resource that

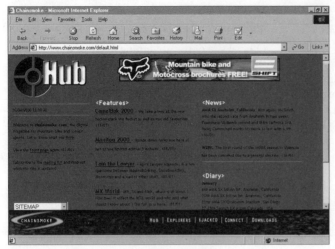

well explained with links to a number of sites for further information. For anybody contemplating taking up hang-gliding this is an essential first stop.

Skateboarding.com

http://www.skateboarding.com/

Lots of articles and features about skateboarding. This site includes features on recent events in the world of the sport and an archive of tricks that you can learn, as well as a photo gallery of famous skaters and a classified section.

includes a guide to some of the best alpine and cross-country routes, and racing and riding fixtures. Other features include news, advice and travel information for mountain-bikers, online shopping, and photographs.

GearHead Mountain Bike Cyberzine

http://www.gearhead.com/

Regularly updated product reviews, articles, interviews, stories, trail information, race results, and shop guides for the mountain-bike enthusiast.

Skydive!

http://www.afn.org/skydive/

Complete low down on skydiving. Everything a would-be skydiver needs to know can be found on this large and well-organized site. Text, pictures, and diagrams explain the joys, techniques, and dangers of the sport. A number of accounts from first-time jumpers are included, together with contact addresses for those persuaded to take a leap. There is a history of the sport, jokes about skydiving, and a number of links to other skydiving sites.

Snowmobile

http://www.off-road.com/snowmobile/

Site for snowmobile buffs. There is news of snowmobiling events, accounts from snowmobilers of journeys, technical details of new machines, photos, letters, weather reports, and links to dealers and rental agencies. Although clearly prepared for snowmobile fanatics, the site gives space to environmentalists concerned about the spread of the sport in North America.

UK Karting

http://www.karting.co.uk/

Comprehensive source of information about the karting scene in the UK, with news and results, a directory of indoor and outdoor tracks, a beginner's guide, tips, and factsheets.

Hang-Para Gliding FAQ

http://www.sky-adventures.com/hang/HGfaq.html

Comprehensive guide to hang- and para-gliding. Techniques and the basics of aerodynamics are

Football

Beckenbauer, Franz

http://www.geocities.com/Colosseum/Sideline/
8601/beckbaur.html

Profile of the legendary German football player. It traces the career of 'the Kaiser' from his recruitment by Bayern Munich at the age of 13, his debut for the German national team at the age of 19, his extraordinary success in the Bundesliga, and his World Cup successes both as a player and manager.

Best, George

http://dnausers.d-n-a.net/dnetmQXk/legends/
georgebest.htm

Sixties English soccer legend George Best celebrated in words and pictures. Lavishly decorated with photographs of Best in his footballing glory, this Web site contains facts and statistics about his Manchester United career and a detailed essay on his turbulent life.

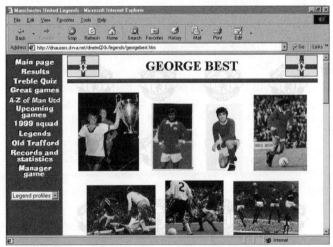

Border, Allan

http://www.q-net.net.au/~gihan/border/index.html

Profile of record-smashing Australian cricket legend Allan Border, who took the Ashes for his national side on successive tours in the 1980s. The Web site contains Border's Test statistics and examines his captaincy in detail. It also contains a page of tributes from fellow cricketers.

Charlton, Jack

http://www.baggies.com/profiles/jac_char.html

History of Jack Charlton's 21 years with Leeds United, and his later career as manager of the most successful national side in the Republic of Ireland's history.

David Beckham Profile

http://mufc.simplenet.com/mufc/beckfact.htm

Detailed profile of English footballer David Beckham, compiled by a fan. The site contains footballing facts and statistics, such as a table of goals scored and appearances for Manchester United, as well as screen wallpaper emblazoned with Beckham's image, a picture gallery, and collected articles and interviews with the England soccer idol.

England 2006

http://www.fa2006.org/

England's bid to host the 2006 World Cup. The reasons why the Football Association believes the cup should be held in Britain are forcefully presented, and the latest news of the campaign is also reported here.

Fédération Internationale de Football Association (FIFA)

http://www.fifa.com/index.html

Official site of FIFA, the world governing body of football. In addition to full details of the World Cup, there is an extremely detailed and well-presented history of the championship with results of every match ever played.

Football 365

http://www.football365.co.uk/

Football daily that contains breaking news, comment, and analysis. The site covers forthcoming fixtures and league tables, and provides a mailbox, fantasy game, and football-related fun.

Football Unlimited

http://www.footballunlimited.co.uk/

Football database from *The Guardian*. This site contains the breaking football stories from all divisions, and also includes the 'Statland' page which contains statistics from all divisions in the current season, as well as full statistics for each club. There is also a 'FUN' (Football Unlimited Network) page which has links to fan sites for a growing number of clubs.

Major League Soccer

http://www.mlsnet.com/index.html

Official site of US Major League Soccer. Read game summaries, check out the weekly standings, and get informed about news, statistics, the season's schedule, teams and players. You can also watch video clips of the week's highlights, and view clips from the video archive including the goals of the year from past seasons.

Moore, Bobby

http://www.geocities.com/Colosseum/Field/3163/moore.html

Biography of the late Bobby Moore, who captained England's World Cup side to victory in 1966. Footballing facts and figures are presented alongside photographs of the player at the height of his career. Created by a fan, this page has links to an archive of World Cup statistics.

Pelé

http://www.math.swt.edu/~ec33032/index.html

Profile of the Brazilian footballer featuring a biography, video clips, and a photo gallery of over 150 pictures. The site also has a text-only version for those with slower browsers.

Sky Sports Online Football

http://www.skysports.co.uk/skysports/football/

News, views, video footage, and information on football in the UK and beyond. Highlights of a comprehensive package include in-depth reportage on individual Premier League teams, a video vault of interviews with top players, as well as results, fixtures, and analysis in the run-up to the Euro 2000 competition.

Soccernet

http://soccernet.com/

Efficient source of information, with sections on English and Scottish football – bringing you news stories and comment, results, and profiles of the premier and national teams – and on European and global news and tournaments.

Van Basten, Marco

http://home.wxs.nl/~cpd/MARCO.htm

Tribute to the Dutch football player. The contents include a gallery of photos, a summary of the achievements of his career, and an interview with van Basten.

Games, Hobbies & Lotteries

Alekhine, Alexander Alexandrowitsch

http://icewall.vianet.on.ca/pages/knott/alekbio.html

Good biography of the Russian chess champion. It traces his privileged background in Tsarist Russia, the World War I injuries that honed his skills in blindfold chess, his victory in the first USSR chess championship, his years of exile, and the enforced collaboration with the Nazis that clouded his final years.

American Cribbage Congress

http://www.cribbage.org/

All there is to know about this card game including a full description of the rules. It is possible to download a program from this site so you can play against your computer. There is also news of competitions, latest rankings of cribbage stars, photos, cribbage poetry, and links to a large number of other cribbage sites.

Antarctic Philately: The Stamps

http://www.south-pole.com/p0000019.htm

Examples of the Antarctic region's stamps. To many collectors the region of the Antarctic holds a special fascination; perhaps it is the relative rarity of the stamps, or perhaps it is the history of the region and the way it is represented on the stamps. Much of that history is also described on this comprehensive Web site.

Backgammon FAQ

http://www.statslab.cam.ac.uk/~sret1/backgammon/

Everything you could possibly want to know about backgammon. This site includes the rules, strategy hints, history, how to play backgammon over the Internet, where to find shareware backgammon programs to download, and more.

Bobby Fischer Home Page

http://www.rio.com/~johnnymc/

Exhaustive page on the chess grandmaster that includes a biography, all the moves from 732 of his games over the years, commentaries on the 100 'most notable' games of his career, details of his opponents and an examination of the development of his 'opening repetoire'.

Card Games

http://www.netlink.co.uk/users/pagat/

Descriptions and rules for playing-card, domino, and tile games from all over the world. This site is updated about once a month with new games and is organized in lists by alphabet, type of game, and also by country and region.

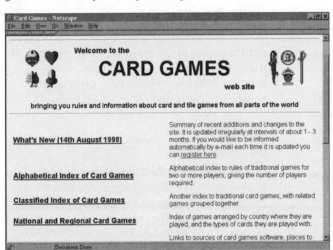

Crossword Puzzles

http://www.primate.wisc.edu/people/hamel/cp.html

Links to puzzles for all ages, difficulty levels, and interest groups. There are details of how to download crossword packages and anagram generators. The solitary agonies of a crossword compiler are also comically described.

Doomgate – Where it all Begins

http://www.gamers.org/doomgate/

Wealth of information on the computer game

> **F**
> **A**
> **C**
> **T**
>
> **COMPUTER GAME (video game)**
> any computer-controlled game in which the computer (sometimes) opposes the human player. Computer games typically employ fast, animated graphics on a VDU (visual display unit) and synthesized sound.

Doom. Frequently updated, it contains advice, a 'Frequently Asked Questions' section, technical details about graphics and specifications, add-on utilities, and links to the large number of *Doom* newsgroups. This site is part of the much larger Gamers Web site which contains details and features on many computer games.

Garry Kasparov's International Chess Master Academy

http://www.chess.ibm.com/meet/html/d.1.html

Profile of the former child prodigy who became the youngest-ever world chess champion. This comprehensive account of Kasparov's career also includes details of his life away from the chessboard.

IllusionWorks

http://www.illusionworks.com/

Heavily interactive site filled with optical and audio illusions to marvel at, be confused by, and fiddle with. The site is well presented as each illusion has a 'Things to do and notice' explanatory section. Some of theses illusions require Java and Shockwave plug-ins, but they can be downloaded from the site.

International Federation of Homing Pigeon Fanciers

http://www.houstonhub.com/page/if/

Information about pigeons. Contents range from veterinary advice and news of events to training tips and 'Lost and found' notices. The site is focused on US pigeon fancying but has links to pigeon sites around the world.

Introduction to Packet Radio

http://www.choisser.com/packet/

Online edition of a book providing a

comprehensive guide to packet radio (used instead of a telephone to communicate between computers). This is part of a series of articles updated to take account of developments in the packet radio network.

Jamba

http://www.jamba.co.uk/

Games, puzzles, and trivia (with prizes). In addition to football and pop music trivia quizzes, games include Catch Phrase, based on the TV quiz show, and film-inspired games such as Armageddon.

Kaleidoscope Heaven

http://kaleidoscopeheaven.org/

Central hub of resources for anyone interested in kaleidoscopes. This page has information on the history of the kaleidoscope, where to find materials to make your own, how to make one, a current educational project, and even an essay on the alleged health benefits of the kaleidoscope.

Ken's Go Page

http://nngs.cosmic.org/hmkw/

Central source of information for go players. Everything about the game can be accessed, including the history, its place in Chinese and Japanese culture, translation of proverbs about go, rules, tactics, and psychological research into the cognitive processes of champion go players. Details are provided of how to play go on the Internet and there are links to a host of go sites in Japan and elsewhere.

MX Boomerangs

http://www.boomerangs.com/

Detailed, illustrated resource about boomerangs, including the techniques involved in throwing, how they are made, and why they come back.

This site also includes information about where to purchase a boomerang, competitions, games, clubs, and boomerang-related organizations.

Pencil Pages

http://www.pencilpages.com/

All you could possibly want to know about pencils. This specialist site for pencil collectors contains articles on the huge variety of pencils found around the world. There is a photo gallery of pencils, a bibliography, information for those wanting to buy and sell, and links to other pencil sites.

Play Draughts Against Chinook

http://web.cs.ualberta.ca:80/~chinook/

Play a game of draughts with Chinook, the world championship draughts program developed by a team of Canadian researchers, find out how well others have performed before you, or follow up some links to related sites.

Quake Perfect

http://quake.perfect.co.uk/

Central source of UK information for devotees of the computer game *Quake*. There is comprehensive news of leagues, players, latest software releases, and other related sites.

Rubik Online

http://www.rubiks.com/

Detailed site about the Rubik's cube. It allows you to play with the cube and learn how to solve the puzzle, and also provides background information about the cube, and other puzzles invented by Erno Rubik. The site also contains competitions, a forum, and a downloadable screensaver.

Science Jokes Archive

http://www.xs4all.nl/~jcdverha/scijokes/index.html

Masses of jokes based around the scientific community. Quite a few gems are included in this vast repository which offers separate sections of jokes on maths, physics, biology, chemistry, scientists in general, mathematicians, physicists, engineers, and academic life.

F A C T

BOOMERANG
hand-thrown, flat wooden hunting missile shaped in a curved angle, formerly used throughout the world but developed by the Australian Aborigines to a great degree of diversity and elaboration.

Scrabble FAQ

http://www.teleport.com/~stevena/scrabble/faq.html

Answers to 'Frequently Asked Questions' about Scrabble, dealing with such topics as the difference between the North American and the UK game, basic tactics, Scrabble records, and paraphernalia. There's also a brief glossary of terms such as 'parallel play' and 'phoney'.

Shogi Page

http://stripe.Colorado.EDU/~leonarm/japan/shogi/

Information about shogi, or Japanese chess, starting with the board and its pieces and progressing to etiquette and breaking the rules.

Stamp Collecting for Beginners

http://www.geocities.com/Heartland/2769/

Simple introduction to stamp collecting, with pages on equipment, starting and enhancing your collection, plus links to related sites.

UK National Lottery

http://lottery.merseyworld.com/

History of the UK National Lottery, with links to the four shareholders who make up Camelot, the consortium licensed to run the lottery. Information is given on how to enter the lottery, and a breakdown is provided of how each pound is spent.

Vegetarian Resource Group Game

http://www.vrg.org/game/

Endless and well-prepared questionnaires from the Vegetarian Resources Group that invite surfers to test their knowledge of the environment and all things ecological and vegetarian.

WebChess

http://www.delorie.com/game-room/chess/

Not much information for beginners, but this site does enable you to play online against a powerful chess computer. There is a series of game options, including who goes first, the size of pieces (from text to 3-D), and limits to the computer's thinking time. Eventually there are plans to charge for longer games, but at the moment it is possible to use all the available game options for free.

Golf

Babe – The Life and Legend of Babe Didrikson Zaharias

http://www.pgatour.com/u/ce/feature/pgatour/0,1977,839863,00.html

Profile of the multi-talented US sporting star. It describes her Olympic athletic successes before concentrating on her golfing career.

Ben Hogan – A Hard Case from Texas

http://www.usatoday.com/sports/sd004.htm

Biography of the diminutive caddie who struggled with adversity to become the world's top golfer. This lively and intimate account of his life on and off the course was written shortly after his death.

Faldo, Nick

http://www.pga97.com/champ97/players/bio01326.html

Biographical details of the British golfer. There is a full list of his tournament victories and year-by-year career earnings.

Faldo, Nick

http://www.europeantour.com/players/bio.sps?playerno=53

Profile of Ryder Cup champion Nick Faldo. The site incorporates a useful browser function, to guide the user through a mine of statistics on Faldo's playing career. It also features a photo gallery, with over 50 photographs of Faldo at work.

Golf Today

http://www.golftoday.co.uk/

European golf magazine with news, features, and coverage of current tours. Other features include a course directory, golf travel information, in-depth tuition from the online golf pro, and a searchable archive.

GolfWeb

http://www.golfweb.com/

Comprehensive golf site that includes news, a library section, an interactive search facility of

over 14,000 courses worldwide, and even an online 'pro shop'.

Greg Norman – For the Record

http://www.golfonline.com/greatwhiteshark/stats.html

Full account of the life and times of the 'Great White Shark', authorized by the golfer. In addition to his golf career, there is a lot of information on Norman's many hobbies and interests.

History of the Ryder Cup

http://www.worldgolf.com/tournaments/rydercup/rydercp.html

Good account of the development of the keenly fought competition between US and European golfers. Statistics are accompanied by text highlighting the great moments in the tournament.

Nicklaus.Com

http://www.nicklaus.com/index1.html

Official source of information from Jack Nicklaus's own company. There is a comprehensive biography, year-by-year account of the 'Golden Bear's' golfing career, a substantial photo gallery and promotional details of his many business activities.

Sky Sports Online Golf

http://www.skysports.co.uk/skysports/golf/

Sky Sports's online forum for news and information on the UK and international golf scene. Site highlights include the European and US PGA calendars, Ryder Cup and Masters tournament statistics and match reports, latest golfing headlines, and television golf schedules.

'Tiger' Woods

http://www.tigerwoods.com/

Constantly updated information on the career of the golfing star. In addition to match results, there are many links to media articles about the young golfer.

Trevino, Lee

http://www.pgatour.com/players/intro/2213.html

Profile of the Mexican-American golf champion. This is a full account of his golfing career

including his continuing success as the highest-earning player on the Seniors Tour.

Vardon, Harry

http://library.advanced.org/10556/english/high/profiles/vardon.htm

Photo and biography of the British golfer. It recounts the main details of his career. Vardon's highly unorthodox playing style is also described.

Zaharias, Babe

http://www.lpga.com/tour/players/bios/zaharias.asp

Biography of one of the greatest sportswomen of the 20th century. This Web site places an emphasis of her golfing career, but also includes details of other parts of her career and a photograph.

Indoor Sports

Snooker Net

http://www.snookernet.com/

Extensive information resource on UK and international snooker. A search engine is included to assist navigation through a massive archive of news, results, fixtures, and statistics. Special features include quizzes, competitions, and an online snooker clinic.

Sport of Gymnastics

http://www.usa-gymnastics.org/gymnastics/

Basic guide to gymnastics from USA Gymnastics Online, with pages on its history, apparatus, scoring, and a glossary of terms.

Tenpin World

http://www.shef.ac.uk/~sutbc/

Complete set of reference material including rules, news, events, and results from all over the world. A good starting point for investigation into the sport.

Terms, Facts, and Rules for Sumo

http://akebono.stanford.edu/users/jerry/sumo/faq.html

Answers to 'Frequently Asked Questions' about

sumo wrestling. There is also a picture archive and some tournament information. If you don't have the capability to display a Japanese character set, some of the text will not display correctly, but all the names are anglicized as well.

USA Weightlifting

http://www.usaw.org/

As well as a history of the sport, this site contains information on the different types of lifts, the way the judging is done, and some common errors to avoid in competition.

Welcome to Cyber Darts

http://www.infohwy.com/darts/index.htm

Constantly updated information on the world of darts. There are details of championships around the world, campaigns to raise the status of the sport, and rules and regulations of the game. The large number of links to other darts sites indicates the global popularity of the sport.

World Wrestling Federation

http://www.wwf.com/

Must for wrestling fans. This brash site provides a complete account of the contests staged by the World Wrestling Federation. There is a host of articles on the Federation and its wrestlers.

Martial Arts

Aiki Web

http://www.aikiweb.com/

Massive source of information on the ancient Japanese martial art. The origins of aikido, its rules, and its spiritual significance are comprehensively explored. Thumbnails help explain techniques and there are links to aikido organizations around the world.

Basic Aikido FAQ

http://ourworld.compuserve.com/homepages/
jemsa/rkshp.htm

Excellent and comprehensive guide to the martial art of aikido from this Wales-based martial arts club, providing an introduction to its history and

principles and the different styles. Information is also provided about competitions, etiquette, training, clothing, and ranking system.

Capoeira

http://www.bnbcomp.net/capoeira/cap1.htm

Capoeira is a cross between a martial art and a dance, performed to music. It originated, and is most common, in Brazil but is practised all over the world. Here you can find a history, pictures and explanations of it, with a glossary, and recordings of typical capoeira rhythms.

Judo Information Site

http://www.rain.org/~ssa/judo.htm

Comprehensive source of judo information providing a guide to the sport for beginners, an illustrated tour of the techniques of judo, history, tournament information, profiles and quotes from judo masters, a humour section, and a short 'black belt' quiz.

Karate CyberDojo

http://www.ryu.com/CyberDojo/

Covering many styles of karate, the CyberDojo aims to develop people's understanding of karate. This is done through an extensive 'Frequently Asked Questions' section, where readers can post their queries and concerns; a searchable terminology database that translates many of the Japanese terms into English; and a detailed bibliography guiding the reader to further study. In addition, the site recommends clubs throughout the world, sorted by style, and includes details of upcoming karate events.

Kendo

http://www.rain.org/~galvan/kndohome.html

Glossary of words and terms used in the sword art kendo. This site also includes information about kendo clubs worldwide, forthcoming events, and the rules and regulations for competitions.

Planet Wing Chun

http://www.wingchun.com/

Dedicated to the Wing Chun style of kung fu, this site contains a history of this style, photographs and animations of students in action, and an extensive list of articles and essays. There is also information about the offshoots of Wing Chun, as well as links to other sites.

Tai Chi Chuan

http://www.spiritweb.org/Spirit/tai-chi.html

Full account of the origins and practice of t'ai chi. There is also a full description of t'ai chi techniques useful for self-defence and spiritual well being. This is an essential site for those wishing to understand this ancient Taoist discipline.

University of Pennsylvania Tae Kwon Do Club

http://dolphin.upenn.edu/~wtftkd/

This site contains background information about the martial art tae kwon do, together with training tips and techniques. An image gallery is available to demonstrate a number of the techniques in practice.

Motor Racing

Alain Prost Grand Prix Home Page

http://www.glink.net.hk/~alanw/welcome.html

Complete and frequently updated profile of the Formula 1 driver. This well organized site has comprehensive information on every race, a library of images, and details of Alain Prost's off-track life.

Ayrton Senna – A Racing Legend

http://public.srce.hr/~mkovac/senna.html

Homage to the legendary Formula 1 ace. The site contains details of his career, photos, and tributes from his fellow racing drivers. The site is in the form of an extended essay.

David Coulthard Official Home Page

http://www.nevis.co.uk/coulthard/intro.html

Officially sanctioned page on the Formula 1 driver that includes a library of images stretching back to 1994, detailed reports on various races, a regularly updated statistics, file and quotes from Coulthard.

Fangio, Juan-Manuel

http://www.ddavid.com/formula1/fangio_bio.htm

Brief sympathetic biography of the Argentine racing legend. There are some good pictures of Fangio.

Häkkinen Net

http://www.hakkinen.net/

As well as a biography and history of this Formula 1 driver, this site includes an extensive multimedia archive, recent news, and a discussion forum for fans.

Indy Racing League

http://www.indyracingleague.com/

Official site of the most popular US motor sport championships. All the latest news, results, team and individual standings, and pit-stop gossip is included. This is an essential site for any Indy fan.

Irv the Swerve

http://www.geocities.com/MotorCity/7864/

Fan site devoted to Northern Irish Formula 1 star Eddie Irvine. The site contains a biography of the Ferrari driver, and a page of statistics on his Grand Prix career.

Mansell, Nigel

http://cool.virtual-pc.com/williams/WGPE/PROFILES/mansell.htm

Brief profile of the first man to simultaneously win the Formula 1 and Indy championships. This

see p 513

site is not simply an eulogy, it raises questions about the extent to which Mansell owed this success to the cars he was driving.

Michael Schumacher Website

http://www.michael-schumacher.org/

Career details of the German Formula 1 ace. There are some photos and an opportunity to send e-mail. There is also a section including the number of titles and races he has won, technical details about the cars he uses, plus some video and audio clips.

Silverstone Circuit

http://www.silverstone-circuit.co.uk/index.htm

Guide to the famous British racetrack, home of the British Grand Prix. This Web site provides a map of the circuit, dates and ticketing information for forthcoming events, a photo gallery, and a guide to Silverstone's facilities.

Sky Sports Online Motor Sports

http://www.skysports.co.uk/skysports/formula1/

Motor racing news, results, and TV schedules from Sky Sports. Coverage includes Formula 1, Indy car racing, superbikes, motorcycle Grand Prix, and speedway.

Outdoor Sports

Archery Index

http://www.rmplc.co.uk/eduweb/sites/
splomas/myarch/archy1.html#British

Home page maintained by a British archery enthusiast, with links to many related topics, events, and statistics. As well as his own best scores, this site includes both indoor and outdoor records for British archery.

Climbing Archive

http://www.dtek.chalmers.se/Climbing/
index.html

Climbing dictionary, a guide to rating systems for climbs, trip reports from places like the Yosemite Big Wall and

the Gower peninsula, climbing songs and poems, techniques and training, and a trivia quiz.

Lawn Bowling

http://www.tcn.net/~jdevons/test1.html

From this Canadian site come articles on the sport of lawn bowling and its history.

National Rounders Association

http://rounders.punters.co.uk/

Official NRA guide to the history and development of the game, its rules, and how to create a rounders pitch. There is also information about known leagues throughout the UK, competitions, and previous winners.

Netball Resources Page

http://www.ucl.ac.uk/~uczcw11/netball.htm

Netball resources including a description of the game, contact information for (and links to) netballing organizations, as well as training drills and exercises. Other features include league results and fixtures and several pre-configured netball searches for use with major search engines.

Orienteering

http://www.williams.edu:803/Biology/orienteering/
o~index.html

Tightly-organized introduction to this outdoor sport, with pages on the use of maps and compasses, and on the layout of a typical orienteering course.

Scottish Highland Games

http://www.saaa-net.org/

Here are basic descriptions and rules for the individual events, such as tossing the caber, plus photographs and some historical articles.

Shinty – Sport of the Gael

http://shinty.com/

Comprehensive information on shinty, from the Camanachd Association, governing body of the ancient Gaelic stick sport. The Web site presents the rules of the game, advice on equipment and details of local clubs for men, women, and children alongside a wealth of fixtures, results, photographs, and other information aimed at promoting shinty in Scotland and beyond.

Tour de France

http://www.letour.fr/

Official site of the Tour de France that includes accounts of past tours and a guide to next year's event. Some pages are only available in French.

UK Climbing.com

http://www.ukclimbing.com/

Extensive information resource for UK climbers. A guide to cliffs and crags in the UK and abroad, a database of climbing walls in the UK, an equipment directory, and links page are among the highlights.

Racket Sports

Badminton Home Page

http://huizen.dds.nl/~anita/badmint.html

Rules of badminton, strategies for playing, and ways of organizing tournaments. This site also includes information on current tournaments, links to other badminton pages, organizations promoting the sport, where to play around the world, and a host of other information for both enthusiasts and novices.

Badminton UK

http://www.ndirect.co.uk/~mark.taylor/badmintonuk/

Information on the British and international badminton scene, with directories of associations and clubs, book and video reviews, a message board, and latest news on the sport. The site contains an online badminton ladder and a useful section on the rules and regulations of badminton.

Internet Squash Federation

http://www.squash.org/

Information about clubs, training, companies, doping policy, hardware, history, management, newsletters, player profiles, rules, and more.

Table Tennis FAQ

http://peacock.tnjc.edu.tw/ADD/sport/faq.html

Comprehensive list of answers to common questions about table tennis, plus sections on rules, terminology, and related associations.

Rugby

Andrew, Rob

http://web.onyxnet.co.uk/TonyKirlew-onyxnet.co.uk/playerRobAndrew.htm

Profile of English rugby player Rob Andrew. This fan page on the Newcastle and England fly-half gives a step-by-step account of his club career and celebrates his world record for the highest number of drop-goals scored in international matches.

Blanco, Serge

http://www.sportszineuk.co.uk/rugbynews/hallnov.htm

Biography of the gifted French rugby union player. Well-written descriptions of his most celebrated tries convey the ingenuity and pace that made him unique. There is also a photo of Blanco and a full review of his career.

Edwards, Gareth

http://www.garethedwards.co.uk/index2.html

Official Web site of the Welsh rugby player. There is a full summary of his career, the innovations he introduced to the game, and his partnership with Barry Johns. With the required plug-in installed, you can also view a video of Edwards.

Gibson, Mike

http://www.sportszineuk.co.uk/rugbynews/halljuly.htm

Profile of the versatile Irish rugby union star. His long career in university and international ruby is described. A photo of Gibson shows his skills as a prolific goal kicker.

Introduction to the Game of Rugby

http://camus.its.anderson.edu/~ade/rugby/index.html

This site contains much useful information on the sport. It details the invention and history of the game, dimensions of the pitch, the different positions and their situation on the pitch (including diagrams), and a rundown of the various terms used in the game.

Irvine, Andy

http://www.sportszineuk.co.uk/rugbynews/hallaug.htm

Profile of the Scottish fullback and his contribution to rugby union. There is an illustrated summary of his career and analysis of his playing style.

Planet Rugby

http://www.planet-rugby.com/

International Rugby Union resource, containing the IBM World Rankings. Highlights include an interactive team guide, a database of player information, match reports, and cuttings from the world's rugby press.

RugbyInfo

http://www.uidaho.edu/clubs/womens_rugby/RugbyRoot/

Comprehensive and well-organized site for rugby union fans. The site contains the rules of the game, tactics and coaching hints, details of the game in various countries, an action page with selected photos and video clips, information on current competitions, and rugby songs and jokes.

Rules, Skills, and Objectives of Rugby League Explained

http://www.senet.com.au/~emjay/rules.htm#

Full description of the rules of rugby league. The scoring system is fully explained, together with the names of the various positions, and the tactical aspects of this contact sport.

Scrum.com

http://www.scrum.com/

Large resource for rugby union fans. Along with all the latest results, this well-designed site includes an explanation of the game, profiles of current stars, a 'Dictionary' which explains all the terminology used in the game, a detailed explanation and history of the women's game, and quizzes and competitions.

Sky Sports Online Rugby League

http://www.skysports.co.uk/skysports/rugbyleague/

Rugby League news, statistics and analysis from Sky Sports. Match reports and details of League games on television are included.

Sky Sports Online Rugby Union

http://www.skysports.co.uk/skysports/rugbyunion/

Sky Sports's online Rugby Union forum. The site provides latest headlines, match analysis, domestic and international fixtures, TV schedules, and UK league tables.

Tennis

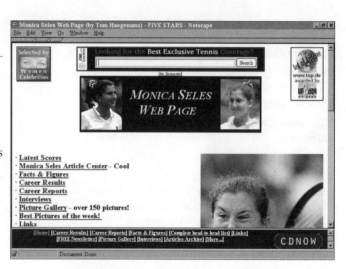

Ashe, Arthur

http://www.cmgww.com/sports/ashe/ashe.html

Profile of US tennis champion Arthur Ashe, from his early playing career to his death from AIDS in 1992. The Web site contains a photo gallery, information on the new Arthur Ashe stadium, and a preview of Ashe's autobiography, published posthumously in 1993.

ATP Tour Official Site

http://www.atptour.com/

Full details of top international tennis competitions and players can be found on this huge and very professional site. A wealth of information, with a search engine, this sites includes player rankings, up-to-the-minute news of current competitions, and tennis statistics.

Borg, Björn

http://www.springhill7.freeserve.co.uk/borg.htm

Biographical information on Björn Borg, the Swedish tennis legend who dominated Grand Slam tennis from his first Wimbledon appearance in 1976. This profile of the unflappable player dubbed 'Ice-Borg' details his string of victories until his retirement at the age of 26.

Boris Becker Profile

http://www.sportsline.com/u/tennis/players/Becker.htm

Biography and career history of Grand Slam champion Boris Becker, the first West German to win the Wimbledon trophy. The Web site lists Becker's career highlights alongside a brief personal history.

Monica Seles Web Page

http://www.geocities.com/Colosseum/7491/index.html

Lots of information about the Yugoslavian tennis player, with archives of articles and pictures, reports on her performances in the major tournaments from 1989 onwards, transcripts of interviews, her latest results, and links to related sites.

Official Site of the Championships – Wimbledon

http://www.wimbledon.org/

Official site of one of the world's most prestigious tennis tournaments. There is a comprehensive history of the championship, explanation of the seeding system, and technical details of how results and images are brought swiftly online. During Wimbledon fortnight there is a constantly updated news service.

Pete's Place

http://www.sampras.com/

Visitors can check Pete Sampras's schedule, follow his career, watch him play on video, and even have a look at his family photo album. The site also includes exhaustive statistics about Sampras's performances with masses of video clips and lengthy explanations of tennis styles. There is, in addition, a summary feature for those lost in the wealth of available information.

Planet Hingis

http://members.xoom.com/hingis_fan/

Dedicated to Martina Hingis, this site is a walk through the life and deeds of the youngest-ever number one in the history of tennis championships, with timelines and video clips of her performances. The site also offers links to the official sites of some of the major Grand Slam Tournaments around the world.

Rod Laver – Smell of Success

http://www.smh.com.au/daily/content/970809/sport/sport11.html

Interesting profile of the legendary Australian sportsman. Written by a journalist, it is the account of a visit to the retired tennis star at his Californian home. Laver answers questions about his career and describes his current life.

Rusedski, Greg

http://freespace.virgin.net/greg.rusedski/

Fan page dedicated to the Canadian-born British tennis star Greg Rudeski. Included is a detailed biography, comprehensive statistics, and an archive containing transcripts of interviews with the player.

Sky Sports' Online Tennis

http://www.skysports.co.uk/skysports/tennis/

News and information on the international tennis scene from Sky Sports. Breaking headlines, feature articles, scores, and results from Grand Slam competitions are presented alongside world player rankings and details of forthcoming fixtures.

Steffi Graf International Supporters' Club

http://www.cgo.wave.ca/~cskelton

Steffi Graf's international fan club brings you all the latest news about the tennis player, her record against other significant players and against her next opponent, highlights of her career, and links to related sites.

Tennis

http://www.cse.unsw.edu.au/~s2213093/tennis.html

Useful and regularly updated site for tennis fans. You can check current world ratings of the top male and female pros and see a complete list of winners of the four major Grand Slam events since 1980. There are links to the official sites of Wimbledon and the US, French, and Australian championships.

Unofficial Andre Agassi Web Site

http://users.ids.net/agassi/

Biography of Andre Agassi, with full details of his tennis career. The information here is complemented with plentiful graphics,and audio and video clips. The site is constantly updated with news of his recent matches.

Welcome to the Real Tennis Web Site

http://www.real-tennis.com/

Comprehensive information on the history, rules, and world of real tennis. The complex rules of the game are explained with the help of useful diagrams. There are articles on many of the world's most famous courts. There is also news of competitions and links to many other sources of information on the game.

Water Sports

British Water Skiing

http://www.britishwaterski.co.uk/

British water skiing's home page, run by the British Water Skiing Association. All branches of the sport are covered here including kneeboarding, wakeboarding, and slalom. The site boasts a chat room as well as sections for beginners, disabled people, and anyone interested in the history of the sport.

Canoeing

http://www.canoeing.co.uk/home.html

Centralized UK-based resource for canoeists that covers the basics of canoeing, as well as the UK system of BCU Star Tests, and links to clubs and retailers across the country.

Mark Spitz – Persistence and Scheduling Mesh Perfectly Seven Times

http://www.usatoday.com/olympics/odxu02.htm

Account of the unparalleled Olympic success of the US swimmer. Spitz and his coach talk of the build-up to the 1972 Olympics and describe the seven races in which he won gold medals. Accusations that Spitz was overly commercial and showed insufficient sorrow when Israeli athletes were killed are also discussed.

Rowing FAQ

http://riceinfo.rice.edu/~hofer/Rowingfaq.html

Answers to 'Frequently Asked Questions' providing a good introduction to the sport of rowing. Various classes of boats, races and regulations, and rowing terminology are clearly explained. There is also advice on technique and sources of further printed and online information.

Swimmers' Guide Online

http://lornet.com/sgol/

Database of over 4,000 full-size, year-round pools available in 47 countries. Each pool has its own description, which includes details about the pool (indoors/outdoors, heated or not, etc) and admission information. Some descriptions include directions and/or links to maps to locate the pools, plus information about programmes and activities offered at the pool. A few have been reviewed.

Waterman

http://www.surfart.com/watrpage.htm

Collection of articles that tells the story of surfing from its Hawaiian roots to its present status as an international sport.

Water Polo

http://www.ausport.gov.au/wpolo/wposp.html

Australian Sports Commission's description of the game's history, rules, and tactics. The site features some action photographs in addition to a lengthy text description of every aspect of the sport.

Wave~Length

http://wavelengthmagazine.com/

Online edition of a popular bimonthly kayaking magazine that has details of kayaking trips, competitions, safety advice, and equipment news from around the world. For anybody interested in the sport this is a good source of current information.

Whitewater Resources Online

http://www.awa.org/awa/online/awa_online.html

Sources of information on how to go boating, when to go boating, who to go boating with, why to go boating, or just fun places to look at if you can't do the real thing.

Windsurfer

http://www.windsurfer.com/

'How to' guide to windsurfing for the beginner or the professional. The site is run by the US Windsurfing Association, but the tips, reviews, and resources are related to wind and water everywhere.

Winter Sports

Figure Skating Page

http://frog.simplenet.com/skateweb/

Latest news stories, information on individual clubs and rinks, regional directories, training camps, and other related links for skaters.

Gretzky, Wayne

http://ww1.sportsline.com/u/fans/celebrity/gretzky2/my_life/biography.html

Intimate profile of the life of the Canadian ice-hockey star. Gretzky's childhood and life on and off the ice is recounted. There are full statistics of his glittering career, and multimedia sections give an insight into the frantic world of professional ice hockey.

Henie, Sonja

http://www.zianet.com/jjohnson/sonja/

Profile of the legendary Norwegian figure skater. It describes how her ballet training helped her to add flair to the sport. Her achievement in becoming the first to win three gold medals in successive Olympics is related. Her successes as a businesswoman, actress, and sponsor of the arts are also described.

International Bobsled and Skeleton Federation

http://www.bobsleigh.com/

Provides the latest news on bobsleighing and tobogganing. It also includes a calendar of events, results from previous years' events, and information about the federation itself. There is also information about the history of the sports, the players, and the equipment.

National Hockey League

http://www.nhl.com/

Official site of the National Hockey League. You will find sections concerning NHL news, statistics, video highlights, scores and recaps, live radio clips, and schedules, plus links to various team sites.

Orr, Bobby

http://schwinger.harvard.edu/~terning/bios/
Orr.html

Profile of the Canadian ice-hockey star. There is a
summary of the career of the dynamic defence
linesman and a dramatic photo of Orr in action.

Sawchuk, Terrance Gordon 'Terry'

http://ucsu.colorado.edu/~norrisdt/bio/
sawchuk.html

Profile of the legendary ice-hockey goalkeeper.
There are biographical details, photos, career
achievements, and season-by-season records. This
is part of a site comparing other great goalkeepers
in the game.

Skating.com – The Skater's Online Magazine

http://www.skating.com/

Inline skating magazine that contains all the news
from the world of skating, as well as reviews of
the latest skating accessories on the market, and
the 'Skate calendar', which allows you to search
all over the world for skate events. There is also a
directory of over 1,600 Web links to related sites.

Technical Figure Skating

http://nsn.nslsilus.org/eakhome/skating/kevinnew/

Get a better understanding of the technical
aspects of figure skating – the jumps, spins, and
jump spins – by studying these video clips and
multiframe images.

US Olympic – PBS Cyberschool

http://www.ibm.pbscyberschool.org/

Series of educational challenges, fun facts, and
educational information based on figure skating,
downhill skiing, and snowboarding. There is also
material for teachers on educational strategies
related to the site and to the Olympics.

Witt, Katarina

http://www.angelfire.com/ia/katarina/witt.html

Tribute to the German skating star Katarina Witt
from a fan. There are several pictures of Witt
together with full details of her life on and off the
rink. There are also frequently-updated details of
her career in films and her official fan club.

Miscellaneous Sports

Contortion Home Page

http://www.contortionhomepage.com/

Complete source of information on contortionism.
There are extraordinary photos of male and
female bodies twisted into the most bizarre
shapes. There is advice for would-be
contortionists, tips on how to limber up, and
news of international contortionist meetings. An
illustrated glossary explains the variety of terms
used by devotees of contortionism.

Feel the Stairs! Catch the Concrete!

http://www.discovery.com/area/shoulda/
shoulda.html

Light-hearted history of skateboarding forty years
after it first took off. This is a good illustrated
account of the ups and downs of the skateboard
craze and its revival with modern competitive
skateboarding.

Fencing FAQ

http://www.ii.uib.no/~arild/fencing/faq/ Top-
view.html

Answers to 'Frequently Asked Questions' about
fencing, such as 'How did fencing originate?' and
– more importantly perhaps – 'Does it hurt?'

First Olympic Games

http://www.orama.com/athens1896/info.html

Dedicated to the first modern Olympic Games,
which took place in Athens in 1896, this site
features primary historical evidence, such as the
manifesto of the Olympic Movement by Pierre de
Coubertin and the history of the Panathenean
Stadium where the 1896 Olympics were held.
There is also additional information about the
organization of the games.

History of the Olympic Games

http://devlab.dartmouth.edu/olympic/history/

Concise presentation of the ancient Greek
Olympic Games. The site describes the birth,

development and significance of the institution in ancient times. It also explores the myths surrounding the games, their prehistory, and other similar events in Greece and as far away as China.

International Professional Rodeo Association

http://www.prorodeo.com/

Latest news from the world of professional rodeo. This site includes details of major championships (and how to hear them over the Internet), upcoming events, latest rankings, and profiles of champion riders.

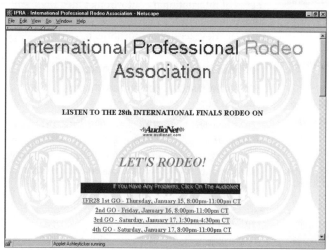

Juggling Information Service

http://www.juggling.org/

Friendly advice and information for jugglers at all levels, from how to juggle two, three, and four balls to juggling torches and the etiquette of passing clubs between jugglers.

Manchester 2002 XVII Commonwealth Games

http://www.commonwealthgames2002.org.uk/2002/

Full details of the 2002 Commonwealth Games, provided by the organizing committee. Games' venues are described and there is general information about the host city, Manchester.

Oxford University Croquet Club

http://users.ox.ac.uk/~croquet/index.html

Look up the 'Coaching notes' section for great information arranged in order of complexity, from basic rules and common misconceptions to advanced cheating tactics. This site also includes the difference between Association croquet and the US six-wicket game.

Regatta – The Oxford–Cambridge Boat Race

http://www.boatrace.co.uk/

Information on the historic race from the providers of the official race programme. This is a complete source of information on the race. There are also links to the site of the race sponsor and to other Boat Race sites.

Schneid's Volleyball Page

http://www.xnet.com/~schneid/vball.shtml

Guide designed for both coach and player, including a glossary of volleyball terms, ways to improve your game, stretching routines, and answers to 'Frequently Asked Questions', plus sections on strategy and skill improvement.

Sportszine UK

http://www.sportszine.co.uk/

Directory of sports in the UK, from athletics to wrestling, with a search engine. Latest sports news, an online bookshop, sporting trivia, and chat are other features of an extensive sports resource.

Sydney 2000

http://www.sydney.olympic.org/

Information on the 2000 Sydney Olympic Games from the organizing committee. This well-organized site provides considerable detail on plans for the games.

US Racquetball Association

http://www.uspra.com/

Everything there is to know about this ancient precursor of many racket and ball games. The rules of rackets are well explained and there is news of US and international championships, and links to other related sites.

Women's Sports Federation

http://www.wsf.org.uk/

The Women's Sports Foundation was set up 'to pursue and promote equity for women in and through sport'. The Web site has information on a wide range of sports, as well as links to other sites.

TECHNOLOGY & COMPUTING

Technology

Advanced Communication Technology Satellite

http://kronos.lerc.nasa.gov/acts/acts.html

Project information on the ACTS project, run by NASA's Lewis Research Centre at Cleveland, Ohio. The site includes detailed descriptions of ACTS spacecraft, operations, and experiments, as well as the latest news and events.

Amateur Holography

http://members.aol.com/gakall/ holopg.html

Features an introduction to the field of holography, as well as a guide to creating your own holograms on a limited budget. There are also numerous links to related Web sites.

Bomb Squad

http://www.pbs.org/wgbh/nova/robots/

Companion to the US Public Broadcasting Service (PBS) television programme *Nova*, this page documents the hazardous duties of the robots that are called upon to perform such tasks as bomb disposal, land mine clearing, and nuclear disaster assessment. Meet the brave robots who tackle such perilous chores and watch video clips of the robots at work. This site also includes an informative interview with Hans Moravec, a principal research scientist at the Carnegie Mellon University Robotics Institute, in which he anticipates the future of robotics. You can also download a transcript of the television programme.

Doors of Perception

http://www.doorsofperception.com/

Site full of commentaries and papers from the five 'Doors of Perception' conferences. These were held to examine the effects of the rapid growth of technology and how we can best use this to improve everyone's quality of life. This is quite a highbrow and hi-tech site, but there are a lot of interesting ideas here.

F A C T

FIBRE OPTICS

branch of physics dealing with the transmission of light and images through glass or plastic fibres known as optical fibres.

Fibre Optic Chronology

http://www.sff.net/people/Jeff.Hecht/Chron.html

Timeline of the history of fibre optics. Starting with the discovery of glass in around 2500 BC and leading up to the late 1970s, this site details every discovery relevant to the history of the fibre optic cables which, among other things, make the Internet possible.

Frequently Asked Questions About GPS

http://www.navcen.uscg.mil/faq/gpsfaq.htm#What's

Good description of the navigational aid known as the 'Global Positioning System'. There is information on the history of the navigation system, how it works, where to learn more about it, and the acronyms used to describe it.

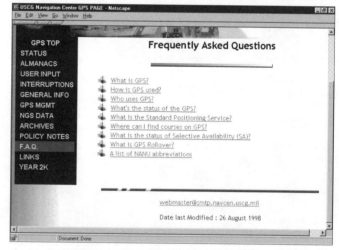

Gas Utilities History

http://www.geocities.com/Athens/Acropolis/4007/gsframe.htm

Despite the irritating frames layout of this Web site it does contain plenty of information on the origins of the natural gas industry. The information database held here is searchable by country, time, or company, and the information pops up in another frame.

History of Radar

http://www.fi.edu/weather/radar/history.html

A brief history of the development of radar, which gives credit to British researchers for their role in the winning of the Battle of Britain.

> **F**
> **A**
> **C**
> **T**
>
> **RADAR (acronym for radio direction and ranging)**
>
> device for locating objects in space, direction finding, and navigation by means of transmitted and reflected high-frequency radio waves.

Morse Code Translator

http://www.soton.ac.uk/~scp93ch/refer/morseform.html

Interactive Web site that allows you to type in words or phrases and it will then translate it into Morse code and even play the sound for you.

QWERTY Connection

http://home.earthlink.net/~dcrehr/

Contains a large amount of information about typewriters, including a description of the very first typewriter, an explanation of why the QWERTY system was invented, and even information about collecting antique typewriters and typewriter ribbon tins!

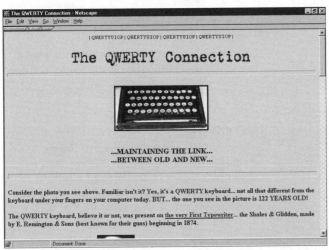

> **F**
> **A**
> **C**
> **T**
>
> **TYPEWRITER**
>
> the earliest known typewriter design was patented by Henry Mills in England in 1714. However, the first practical typewriter was built in 1867 in Milwaukee, Wisconsin, USA, by Christopher Sholes, Carlos Glidden, and Samuel Soulé.

Super Bridge

http://www.pbs.org/wgbh/nova/bridge/

Companion to the US Public Broadcasting Service (PBS) television programme *Nova,* this page introduces us to the four major types of bridges and explains how each is designed to span specific locations. Once you have browsed the site, test your knowledge by linking the right bridge with the right feature. You can also download a transcript of the television programme.

Technology of Compact Discs

http://www.ee.washington.edu/class/ConsElec/cd.html

Introduction to the technology behind the CD player, including music and its relation to frequency, an explanation of the differences between analogue and digital signals, and even why compact discs are so colourful.

Technology Summary

http://www.yahoo.com/headlines/compute/

Daily online magazine specializing in features associated with technology. It includes access to previous issues.

Technology Timeline

http://www.pbs.org/wgbh/pages/amex/technology/techtimeline/index.html

Companion to the US Public Broadcasting Service (PBS) television programme *The American Experience,* this page follows the course of technological progress and invention in the USA from the time of Benjamin Franklin's experiments in the 1750s to the creation of the Hubble Telescope in the 1990s. The information is divided into decades along a timeline. Along the way, you can learn about such inventions as the cotton gin, steamboat, revolver, false teeth, passenger elevator, burglar alarm, barbed wire, skyscraper, dishwasher, zipper, frozen food, electric guitar, atomic bomb, optic fibre, video game, bar code, space shuttle, personal computer, and artificial heart.

Thames Barrier

http://www.highway57.co.uk/tbvc/index.html

Interesting and comprehensive description of the functions of the world's largest movable flood barrier and how it saves London from flooding. There is a comprehensive history of the Barrier, description of how surge tides are generated, and information for visitors.

Toilet Papers

http://members.home.com/doug.graham/toilet.htm

Practical information on how to repair flush toilets. A useful section of 'Frequently Asked Questions' explains, with the help of diagrams, how the toilet works and how to diagnose faults. Easily understandable text tells you how to unblock toilets and repair diaphragms, flappers, and ball-cocks.

Video Cassette Recorder

http://bradley.bradley.edu/~fil/vcr.html

'Point and click' site which answers common questions regarding one of the most confusing of domestic appliances.

Inventors & Industry

Alexander Graham Bell's Path to the Telephone

http://jefferson.village.virginia.edu/albell/homepage.html

Impressive attempt to reconstruct the path towards the invention of the telephone. The presentation aims to communicate the thoughts of Alexander Graham Bell, placing him within the context of other relevant inventions and related ideas. This is achieved mainly through a wealth of graphics retrieved from Bell's experimental notebooks, patents, and other papers accompanied by detailed analysis. An especially worthwhile site for those who are interested in the thought processes behind invention in general, as well as in this particular one.

Big Dream, Small Screen

http://www.pbs.org/wgbh/pages/amex/technology/bigdream/index.html

Companion to the US Public Broadcasting Service (PBS) television programme *The American Experience,* this page tells the story of Philo Farnsworth, David Sarnoff, and the invention of the television. You will also find an interesting section on TV milestones that features numerous photographs, a list of quotes about television, a biography of David Sarnoff, and a list of sources for further reading.

Biography of G Marconi

http://www.nobel.se/laureates/physics-1909-1-bio.html

Presentation of the life and discoveries of Guglielmo Marconi. The site includes sections on his early years and education, and the many patents that he established in the course of his scientific career. Central emphasis is of course given to his development of wireless telegraphy, from the first attempt to send a signal one and a half miles away, up to his successful wireless transmission across the Atlantic in 1901.

Edison, Thomas

http://www.si.edu/lemelson/edison/html/his_life.html

Illustrated biography of the US inventor, plus a chronology and bibliography. It includes sections

F A C T

ELECTRICITY
all phenomena caused by electric charge, whether static or in motion. Electric charge is caused by an excess or deficit of electrons in the charged substance, and an electric current is the movement of charge through a material.

on such topics as his childhood and the electric light.

Forgotten Inventors

http://www.pbs.org/wgbh/pages/amex/technology/forgotteninv.html

Companion to the US Public Broadcasting Service (PBS) television programme *The American Experience*, this page tells the stories of the mostly ignored inventors of useful products we often take for granted. Read about British merchant Peter Durand, inventor of the tin can for storing food, an invention that was soon greatly aided by Ezra Warner's invention of the can opener. Learn what inspired Levi Strauss to invent blue jeans. You can also find information about the inventors of the Frisbee, feather duster, oil burner, and the blood bank.

Gutenberg, Johann

http://www.knight.org/advent/cathen/07090a.htm

Biography of the German goldsmith turned printer. Gutenberg's technical innovations and the lawsuits which dogged his career are set out. The rapid spread of Gutenberg's invention is also described.

Henry Bessemer FRS, An Autobiography

http://www.bibliomania.com/NonFiction/Bessemer/Autobiography/

Full text of Henry Bessemer's autobiography published five years after his death in 1898. This account of the innovative industrialist traces the events of his life up to 1872. A supplementary chapter has examples of many inventions, patents, and correspondence.

How We Made the First Flight

http://www.aero-web.org/history/wright/wright.html

Guide through the processes which the Wright brothers went through in order to create the first powered flight. This site is well-illustrated and written in an engaging first-person tone, with sections such as 'Initial preparations', 'Weight and thrust', and, of course 'Flight!'.

Invention Dimension!

http://web.mit.edu/invent/

All about inventors and inventions. This US-based site includes an 'Inventor of the week' plus

links to many other invention-related Web sites. As well as giving details of the major players in the annual Lemelson-MIT invention awards, the site also includes a list of independent inventors.

Life of Henry Ford

http://www.hfmgv.org/histories/hf/henry.html

Good biography of the car manufacturer from the Henry Ford Museum in Detroit. This comprehensive account of Ford's private and business life provides many interesting and little-known facts about the man. There is a good bibliography and links to other Ford sites.

Oil Industry: Panoramic Photographs, 1851–1991

http://lcweb2.loc.gov/cgi-bin/query/r?ammem/pan:@field(SUBJ+@band(+Oil+Petroleum+))

Part of the Panoramic Photo Collection of the US Library of Congress, this page features approximately 50 panoramic photographs of the US oil industry taken between 1851 and 1991. Most images are of Texas and California. To find a specific image, click on New Search and try a word search. Many of the images include brief notes. Click on the images to increase their size.

Paul D MacCready Profile

http://www.achievement.org/autodoc/page/mac0pro-1

Description of the life and work of the aviation engineer Paul MacCready, best known for his creation of the Gossamer aircraft. The Web site contains not only a profile and biographical information, but also holds a lengthy interview with MacCready from 1991 accompanied by a large number of photographs, video sequences, and audio clips.

Plagiarism Q&A

http://edcen.ehhs.cmich.edu/~mspears/plagiarism.html

Excellent online paper on dealing with plagiarism, particularly relevant in the age of the Internet. The site offers a very clear presentation of the issues and includes examples, links, and suggestions for further reading.

Young, Arthur M

http://www.arthuryoung.com/

Dedicated to the life and ideas of philosopher, cosmologist, and inventor of the Bell helicopter,

Arthur Young. This page features a biography, including a page of comments and an essay about Young. You will also find information about his 'theory of process', including the full-text of essays and journal entries by Young, as well as summaries and excerpts from his books.

Computing & Multimedia

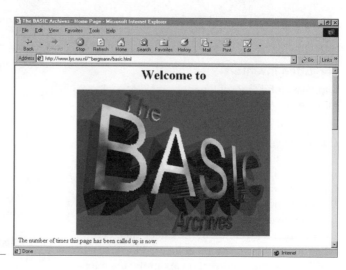

Babbage, Charles

http://ei.cs.vt.edu/~history/Babbage.html

Extended biography of the visionary mathematician, industrialist, and misanthrope. This very full and entertaining account of his life is supported by a number of pictures of Babbage, his plan of the difference engine, and the actual difference engine built by the British Science Museum in 1991. There is a full bibliography.

BASIC Archives

http://www.fys.ruu.nl/~bergmann/basic.html

Detailed guide to this computer-programming language. This site includes an informative 'Frequently Asked Questions', giving tips on such topics as 'how to print graphics with BASIC', 'how to display a BMP or GIF file', and 'how to make an EXE file'. There is also a brief history of the development of BASIC and a number of links to related sites.

FACT

PROGRAMMING

writing instructions in a programming language for the control of a computer. **Applications programming** is for end-user programs, such as accounts programs or word-processing packages. **Systems programming** is for operating systems and the like, which are concerned more with the internal workings of the computer.

Byron, Ada

http://ruku.com/augusta.html

Interesting biography of Ada Byron, the woman credited as the first computer programmer. This page also has links to a range of other online resources about this scientist.

City of Bits

http://mitpress.mit.edu/e-books/City_of_Bits/

Online version of a book by the dean of the MIT School of Architecture in the USA. It describes his vision of cities of the future that don't exist as much in the real world as in the (computing) connections between people. It is a heavily text-based site, but has plenty of hyperlinks to help with navigation.

Club Girl Tech

http://www.girltech.com

Lively site aimed at encouraging girls at school to get involved in technology. It is addressed to girls from the age of about eight and offers sections on art displays, the world of computers, electronic 'Chick chat', trips to museums, and even our solar system. It also maintains separate resource areas for teachers, parents, and the media.

Computer Fraud and Electronic Communication Links

http://jan.ucc.nau.edu/~cvm/computer_laws.html

see p 526

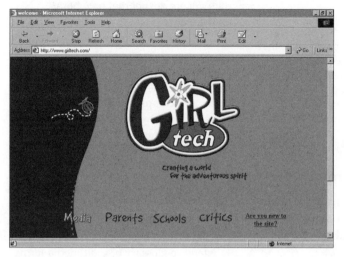

Set of pages attempting to guide 'university and other internet administrators' around the minefield of ethical and legal issues on the Web. There are sections here on copyright, current legal cases, and discussion groups.

Computer Museum

http://www.computerhistory.org/

Well-designed interactive museum, examining the history, development, and future of computer technology. As well as plenty of illustrations and detailed explanations, it is possible to change your route through the museum by indicating whether you are a kid, student, adult, or educator.

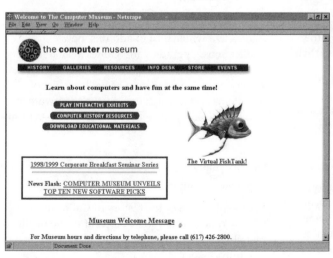

Create Your Own Animated GIFs

http://www.agag.com/howto/how2pc1.html

Beginners' guide to creating animated graphics, known as animated GIFs. It details the relevant software necessary to create animated GIFs and then goes on to describe how to create impressive animated images to liven up a Web site. There are guides for both PC and Macintosh users, as well as a number of advanced tutorials.

Cryptography

http://www.counterpane.com/pitfalls.html

Introduction to the whys and wherefores of encrypting messages. The author introduces various common encrypting systems and explains their relative weaknesses. The site also includes links to other pages that deal more comprehensively with cryptography in the computer age.

Data Powers of Ten

http://www.ccsf.caltech.edu/~roy/dataquan/

Collection of estimates of the quantities of data contained by various magnetic media. Includes interesting facts about the number of books needed to store the same amount of information as on magnetic media.

E-mail: An Introduction

http://www.webfoot.com/advice/email.top.html

Explains e-mail to the uninitiated. There is a good introduction followed by sections on why e-mail is different from paper-based communication. The site also includes information on layout, expressing gestures and intonations, and an appendix of e-mail jargon.

ENIAC's 50th Anniversary

http://www.upenn.edu/almanac/v42/n18/eniac.html

Account of John Mauchly and J Presper Eckert's construction of the first general-

ELECTRONIC MAIL (E-MAIL)

messages sent electronically from computer to computer via network connections such as Ethernet or the Internet, or via telephone lines to a host system. Messages once sent are stored on the network or by the host system until the recipient picks them up. As well as text, messages may contain enclosed text files, artwork, or multimedia clips.

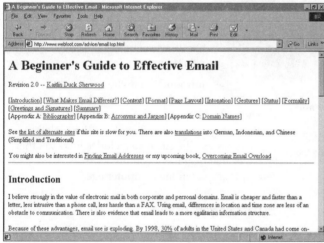

purpose electronic computer, ENIAC. This all-text site explains the importance of this 50-year-old innovation.

Gates, Bill

http://www.pathfinder.com/time/time100/builder/profile/gates.html

Part of a larger archive from *Time* exploring the most influential people of this century, this article highlights the life and work of the US businessman and computer programmer Bill Gates. The profile also features a timeline.

Kasparov v. Deep Blue – The Rematch

http://www.chess.ibm.com/

Official site of the team that produced the first computer able to beat a world chess champion. This is a complete account of the tussle between Deep Blue and Garry Kasparov. There are some thought-provoking articles on the consequences of Deep Blue's victory. There is also some video footage of the games.

Macintosh Tips and Tutorials

http://users.desupernet.net/ohora/index.html

Dedicated to 'less experienced computer users', this site offers a large number of tips for use with Macintosh or iMac computers. The tips are clearly laid out and come complete with illustrations to ease the learning process. Also featured are several tutorials that guide the user through word processing, graphics, databases, and many other subjects.

Multimedia Glossary

http://www.uncg.edu/irc/mm/terms/terms.htm

Extensive glossary of multimedia terms that features illustrations and links to related articles and Web sites. For the uninitiated, there is also a brief explanation of multimedia itself.

Revolutionaries of Silicon Valley

http://www.thetech.org/revolutionaries/

Joint production of the Tech Museum of Innovation and the *San Jose Mercury News*, this site features interviews with many of Silicon Valley's top pioneers of technology. In addition to text of the interviews, you will find audio clips and an area for offering feedback.

Shareware.com

http://www.shareware.com/

Access to a whole host of add-ons, new applications, upgrades, and games available as free downloads from the Internet. There is a wide variety here, so fortunately, as well as a list of new items and a search engine, the shareware is also organized by the most popular requests from the previous week.

Silicon Valley

http://www.internetvalley.com/introduction.html

Brief exploration of the history of California's Silicon Valley, which was named after the brittle metalloid used in the manufacture of microprocessors.

What Is...

http://www.whatis.com/

Useful site for anyone struggling to interpret computer jargon. The site is fully searchable and includes explanations of terms from Accelerated Graphics Port to Zip drive.

What Is Virtual Reality?

http://www.cms.dmu.ac.uk/~cph/VR/whatisvr.html

Text-based introduction to VR and an information resource list. The site covers all major aspects of the subject, and also provides a great many literature and Internet references for further reading.

Windows95 Annoyances

http://www.annoyances.org/win95/

Forum for intermediate to advanced users of Windows 95 who seek answers to annoying questions or have helpful tips they wish to share with others. Troubleshooting techniques, lost files, screen problems, bugs, and other topics are thoroughly discussed in this site. The tips date back to 1996, so not all of the concerns are up-to-date. However, there is still ample valid and important information for Windows 95 users.

F A C T

OPERATING SYSTEM (OS)
in computing, a program that controls the basic operation of a computer. A typical operating system (OS) controls the peripheral devices such as printers, organizes the filing system, provides a means of communicating with the operator, and runs other programs.

Winfiles.com

http://www.winfiles.com/

Well-designed site that contains a wealth of information relating to the Windows operating system. As well as 'Tips and tricks', which include a variety of hints and shortcuts on all aspects of Windows, there is also a comprehensive drivers section, and much more.

ZD Webopaedia

http://www.zdwebopedia.com/

Searchable encyclopaedia of computer

terminology. The definitions are detailed and clear, and there are numerous links from each definition to related Web sites.

The Internet

About the WWW

http://www.w3.org/WWW/

Definition of the World Wide Web and lots of information on what it's all about. This is a good starting point for exploring the Internet as it includes 'talks' by members of the WWW Consortium team, and explains some different aspects of using the Web, such as using newsgroups and how to put up a site, as well as containing a brief history of the World Wide Web.

Beginners' Guide to URLs

http://www.ncsa.uiuc.edu/demoweb/url-primer.html

Guide to Uniform Resource Locators (URLs) that describes what they do and also differentiates between the different types of URL.

Brief History of the Internet

http://www.isoc.org/internet-history/brief.html

Detailed and illustrated history of the Internet. It begins, as one would expect, with the 'Origins of the Internet' and ends with a 'History of the future', dealing with numerous other topics on the way, such as 'Proving the ideas' and 'Commercialization of the technology'.

CNet

http://www.news.com/?ntb.news

Source of up-to-date information about the Internet. This is not so much an introduction to the workings of the Net, as a rich source of current news and issues facing users. There is also a lot of other computing news here, including new programs and games to download, as well as hints for optimizing the use of some common software packages.

Conducting Research on the Internet

http://www.albany.edu/library/internet/research.html

Guide that helps users to conduct research on the Internet. Topics covered include discussion groups, and newsgroups. There is also a comprehensive section on search engines.

Core Rules of Netiquette

http://www.albion.com/netiquette/corerules.html

Excerpted from *Netiquette* by Virginia Shea, this useful guide to Internet etiquette provides explanation of the ten 'rules' of Internet behaviour, aimed at newbies as well as the Internet-savvy.

Electronic Commerce Tutorial

http://webdevelopersjournal.com/columns/ecommerce1.html

Three-part tutorial that shows users how to set up their own electronic commerce site. The information is both detailed and clear, and the topics covered include online catalogues and online purchasing.

Electronic Frontier Foundation

http://www.eff.org/

US-based non-profit organization that aims to protect free speech on the Internet. This site includes a lot of technical legal jargon and the full text of Supreme Court decisions relating to their campaigns. However, there are also a lot of news-style pieces on issues such as encryption, privacy, and free speech which are more accessible to the casual browser.

FAQs about FAQs

http://www.faqs.org/faqs/faqs/about-faqs/

'Frequently Asked Questions' (FAQ) are part of many Web sites and consist of a series of questions and answers. This FAQ answers questions about FAQs themselves and contains information on what FAQs are, how to write one, and how to put it on the Internet.

Global Internet Liberty Campaign

http://www.gilc.org/

Umbrella group campaigning to promote freedom of speech and protection of privacy on the Internet. Its members include the Internet Society. GILC concerns about censorship, cryptography, and privacy are set out. There is news of lobbying and campaigning activities and GILC press releases.

History of the Web

http://dbhs.wvusd.k12.ca.us/Chem-History/Hist-of-Web.html

Transcript of *Birthplace of the Web* by Eric Berger, Office of Public Affairs at FermiLab. The text covers the origins of the Web as a means of communication between scientists at CERN and at FermiLab, and describes how one person's idea in 1991 has brought about a social and cultural revolution in just a few years.

How Can I Send a Fax From the Internet?

http://www.savetz.com/fax/

As its title suggests, this is a tutorial for sending faxes from the Internet. It clearly explains the requirements for sending faxes, and points you to Web sites that allow you to fax over the Internet for free.

How to Search the World Wide Web: A Tutorial for Beginners and Non-Experts

http://204.17.98.73/midlib/tutor.htm

Extensive guide to searching the Internet that describes the various methods of searching. There are also comparisons of the various search engines, as well as a glossary of relevant terms.

Internet Detective

http://sosig.ac.uk/desire/internet-detective.html

Interactive tutorial that teaches users how to evaluate the quality of information they find on the Internet. There are numerous hints and tips, as well as practical examples of the evaluation process. Not only does the tutorial cover standard Web sites, but also electronic journals and mailing lists.

Internet for Beginners

http://diginto.miningco.com/netbasics/

Includes links for exploring the World Wide Web, information on creating your own Web pages, time-saving tips and tricks, and a weekly newsletter to help you get the most out of the Internet.

Internet ScamBusters

http://www.scambusters.org/

Valuable advice on the perils of Internet scams, misinformation, and hype. This is a free and

> ## F A C T
>
> ### INTERNET
>
> global computer network connecting governments, companies, universities, and many other networks and users. Electronic mail, electronic conferencing, educational and chat services are all supported across the network, as is the ability to access remote computers and send and retrieve files.

informative e-zine which might help to save a lot of puzzled newcomers from the small number of people trying to dupe others on the Net.

Internet Starter Kit

http://www.mcp.com/resources/internetsoftware/iskm_frame.html

If you are struggling online then there are worse places to start than this – the full e-text of a recent book that covers everything from advice on getting connected to recommendations about the best shareware. It also includes some information on how to start creating Web pages yourself.

Lightning HTML Editor

http://www.lightningsp.com/HTML_Editor/

HTML editor that teaches you about HTML as you use it. This is a well organized guide to the intricacies of designing Web pages. There is a good list of 'Frequently Asked Questions' and tips and tricks.

Parents' Guide to the Internet

http://www.ed.gov/pubs/parents/internet/

Useful electronic booklet aiming to bridge the gap between children's and parents' knowledge of the Internet. The site introduces the main features of the 'information superhighway' and argues for the benefits of getting connected to the Internet at home. Several sections provide navigation to assist parents' first steps on the Net and give them tips on safe travelling, and advice on how to encourage children's activities at home and at school.

Promoting Your Web Site

http://webdevelopersjournal.com/articles/website_promotion.html

Detailed guide that covers the dangers and

benefits of Web site promotion. The guide shows you the pitfalls of site-promotion services, and explains clearly how to attract more visitors through links and search engines.

Trademarks and Internet Domain Names

http://www.wipo.org/eng/internet/domains/index.htm

Full account of the attempts of the World Intellectual Property Organization to monitor and regulate the use of Internet domain names. The site is text-based and legalistic in tone, but is essential reading for anybody interested in the development of the Web.

24 Hours in Cyberspace

http://www.cyber24.com/htm3/toc.htm?about

Inspiring 'cyberstories' and hundreds of accompanying photos collected by photojournalists from around the world. The site boasts an impressive diversity and over 1000 photos, with features about women of the African Diaspora online, the Net and justice for Vietnam War victims, Arab and Israeli teens bonding over the Internet, cyberspace schooling, propaganda, graffiti, the Net and ancestral lands in Canada, and the great rainforest of the Amazon basin.

Web Building

http://www.builder.com

Guide to HTML, the programming language used to write Web sites. Topics covered here range from the basics – planning your Web site, graphics, and publishing – to more advanced topics, such as JavaScript, commerce over the Internet, and animated graphics. There are also Web site reviews, as well as numerous articles relating to Web design.

World Wide Web Workbook

http://sln.fi.edu/primer/setup.html

Guide for novice Web surfers (limited to users of PCs with Windows). Topics include hypertext, graphics, hypergraphics, imagemaps, and thumbnails. Once the basics have been covered, users are offered a short tour with the help of Spot, the mascot 'Webdog'.

Road (& Off-road) Transport

Alfa Romeo Home Page

http://www.alfaromeo.com

Official Alfa Romeo site in four languages: English, French, German, and Spanish. Not only is there the latest news on Alfa Romeo, there is also a museum and history of the car-manufacturing company. Together with this is information on the latest models, including both photographs and video clips.

Automotive Learning Online

http://www.innerbody.com/innerauto/Default.htm

Fun, interactive, and educational site on the automobile. It is a great training resource for engineering minds but also suited to all those who would simply like to know how their car works. It offers hundreds of images, and animations for Java-compatible browsers.

Beetles Home Page

http://www.geocities.com/MotorCity/1642/

Resource focusing on the legendary German small car. The site includes maintenance and other technical tips, picture archives, links to VW clubs worldwide, and addresses of other VW Web resources. Details of the new VW Beetle model are also available here.

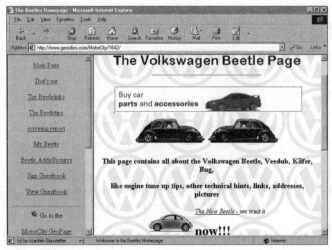

BSM Question Bank

http://www.bsm.co.uk/theory/th_3_f.htm

Test yourself on the driving theory exam using these questions prepared by the British School of Motoring which are based on actual questions used in the test.

Cyberider Cycling Web Site

http://cyberider.us.net/bikes/

This site used to contain more than 50 megabytes of searchable information on cycling equipment, places, and events, with hyperlinks to over 600 other cycling sites. It has recently been hacked and a lot of the information was lost. However, the coordinator of the site has committed himself to rebuilding the site over time. Even at the moment, it still contains advice and news sections, and an archive of older stories, as well as links to many other kinds of cycling resources.

Daimler, Gottlieb

http://www.redhillstudios.com/html/daimler.html

Features an interactive version of German engineer Daimler's workshop. By using the mouse and keyboard, you can explore the whole workshop, zooming in on the first modern automobile and even recreating several of Daimler's inventions.

Early Adventures with the Automobile

http://www.ibiscom.com/auto.htm

Documents the early days of the car and provides three first-hand narratives, including those from the winner of the 1906 Vanderbilt Cup auto race and from the first woman to drive coast-to-coast across the USA. Discover the myriad challenges that she and other drivers of the early 1900s faced in attempting to traverse the country. There is also a list of references.

EV Information Network

http://www.radix.net/~futurev/

Comprehensive information on electrically powered vehicles (EVs). The case against the internal combustion engine is forcefully put. A facts and myths section sets out to prove wrong those who see no role for EVs and to

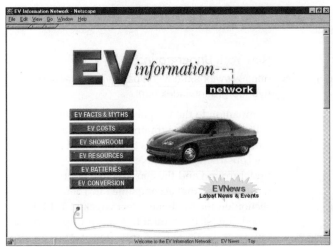

driving the mini, and a section dealing with technical problems and maintenance. Many colour pictures are also to be found here, including one of Sir Alec Issigonis's early design sketches for the mini and a cut away drawing of the engine.

Rat Bike Zone

http://ratbike.org/

Rat bikes are, apparently, motorbikes made to be 'ridden instead of cleaned', and 'maintained at the lowest possible cost'. This site features some of the 'finest' UK and European examples of rat bikes and trikes in its photo gallery, while for aspiring 'ratters' there's a tech section to solve those niggling 'Why won't it run?' questions.

debunk the argument that the environmental and economic costs of generating electricity to run EVs are prohibitive. There is information about electric car events, batteries, and details of manufacturers and suppliers.

Rec.Motorcycles.Reviews Archives

http://rmr.cecm.sfu.ca/RMR/

Plethora of bike (and accessories) reviews, written by motorcyclists and based on their own experiences. These invaluable gems of opinion can also be accessed via anonymous FTP, e-mail server, or by personal request. The site also contains images and access to related discussion groups.

Ferrari

http://www.ferrari.it

Official site with extensive coverage of both the company and the racing team, including a detailed history and a photograph and specification of every car that Ferrari have produced.

What Car Online

http://www.whatcar.co.uk/

UK-based site that contains a wealth of information about second-hand cars. A particularly useful feature is the valuation service which allows you to select the details of your car, and get an instant quote for its current value.

Harley Davidson

http://www.harley-davidson-london.co.uk/

Ultimate site for Harley Davidson fans. There is a complete history of Harleys, details of a newsletter about the bike, and profiles of various models.

Rail Transport

How Two-Stroke Expansion Chambers Work

http://www.motorcycle.com/mo/mcnuts/
em-pipes.html

Part of a larger site called Motorcycle Online, here is a short essay, featuring diagrams, describing the physics of how two-stroke expansion chambers work for motorcycle riders.

Across Russia on the Trans-Siberian Railroad

http://www.ego.net/tlogue/xsib/index.htm

Detailed journal of a trip on the famous railway from Moscow to Vladivostock. A day-by-day account of the 6,000 mile journey is accompanied by a large selection of photographs and useful information for anyone who would like to try it for themselves.

MINI Home Page

http://www.mini.co.uk/timecapsule/1900index.html

Mini information – the design, history, clubs, and events for Sir Alec Issigonis's outstanding small car. The site also includes hints and tips on

City Rail Transit

http://pavel.physics.sunysb.edu/RR/metro.html

Highly informative site about almost every underground railway system in the world. It includes maps, background information, photos, and links to home pages of many railway operators.

Docklands Light Railway

http://www.dlr.co.uk/

Full details of the innovative light railway serving London's Docklands. In addition to a map, route and ticket information, and technical details of how DLR trains operate without drivers, there is a substantial amount of tourist information. The comprehensive history of the London docks is well presented.

European Railway Server

http://mercurio.iet.unipi.it/home.html

Complete source of information about the railways of Europe. The needs of travellers, railway enthusiasts, and students of public transport are provided for. There are links to all of Europe's railway operators and information about real and model trains.

Going Underground

http://victorian.fortunecity.com/finsbury/254/

Forum for sharing thoughts and experiences of the London Underground, with the emphasis on 'fun, and what it's really like to travel on the Tube'.

Iron Road

http://www.pbs.org/wgbh/pages/amex/iron/index.html

Companion to the US Public Broadcasting Service (PBS) television programme *The American Experience*, this page tells the story of the construction of the first US railroad link connecting East and West. It includes information about the harsh conditions that labourers, mostly immigrants, endured during its construction. There is also a list of sources for further reading.

National Railway Museum, York

http://www.nmsi.ac.uk/nrm/html/home_pb/menu.htm

Information for railway enthusiasts. In addition to information about the National Railway Museum and its exhibitions, there is news of railway matters from around the world. There is also a listing of other sites for train buffs.

New York Underground

http://www.pbs.org/wgbh/pages/amex/technology/nyunderground/index.html

Companion to the US Public Broadcasting Service (PBS) television programme *The American Experience*, this page tells the illustrated story of the construction of the New York City underground and the considerable political machinations that accompanied it. There is a section on the Malbone Street wreck of 1918 that killed almost 100 commuters and precipitated the failure of the Brooklyn Rapid Transit. You can also read about Alfred Beach and the fate of the 'secret subway', an early attempt at bringing underground transportation to congested New York City. The programme transcript is available for reading and there is also a list of sources.

Railtrack – The Heart of the Railway

http://www.railtrack.co.uk/home.html

User-friendly Railtrack site which aims to simplify the planning of a railway journey in Britain. Input your destination and time of departure and a schedule rapidly appears. The site also includes corporate information. There are plans to include frequent updates of operational difficulties and advice to travellers.

Steam Engine

http://www.easystreet.com/pnwc/museum/Steam_Locomotive.html

Basic guide to the principles behind the steam engine. It includes a labelled diagram and explanatory text of the engine in its most well-known form – the steam locomotive.

Steel Rails and Iron Horses

http://www.blm.gov/education/railroads/railroad.html

Maintained by the US Bureau of Land Management, this site explores early railroad expansion across the USA and the ways in which new railroad technologies contributed to the development of the West. There is a special feature on how to build a steam engine, and information on experiments that examine such topics as the Doppler effect, energy transformation, and how heat effects the tracks.

UK Rail Travel

http://www.railinfo.freeserve.co.uk/railtravel/index.html

Detailed unofficial information on all aspects of rail travel in the UK, from finding the best route, to taking your bike on board. Sections for enthusiasts include 'UK Railway Frequently Asked Questions', and 'Rolling stock mailing list' for reporting sightings.

Air Transport & Aviators

Airship and Blimp Resources

http://www.hotairship.com/index.html

Information about airships – with the main focus on contemporary development. This site includes sections such as 'Hot news', 'Manufacturer database', 'Homebuilding', and 'Museums'.

Allstar Network – History of Flight

http://www.allstar.fiu.edu/aero/history1.htm

Three-level guide to the history of aviation beginning with the myths and legends which abounded before flight became a reality. The explanations are illustrated throughout and there is a useful 'Knowledge review' at the end of the first level.

Allstar Network – Principles of Flight

http://www.allstar.fiu.edu/aero/princ1.htm

Three-level guide to flight and aviation, involving images, explanations, and experiments to demonstrate the physics behind flight. It begins with an examination of the many uses aircraft are put to and some basic experiments (easy to do at home) with aerofoils and propellers. For more advanced visitors there are sections examining aircraft propulsion and hydraulics in depth.

American Institute of Aeronautics and Astronautics Home Page

http://www.aiaa.org/

Access to the *AIAA Bulletin*. This site also includes details of the institute's research departments,

recent conferences, technical activities, and project updates. If the extensive front page doesn't have what you need, the site is also fully-searchable.

Aviation Enthusiasts' Corner

http://www.brooklyn.cuny.edu/rec/air/air.html

Forum dedicated to furthering interest in aviation-related hobbies. It includes links to museums and displays, features on key events in aviation history, and indexes of aircraft by type and manufacturer.

Balloon Race Around the World

http://www.pbs.org/wgbh/nova/balloon/

Companion to the US Public Broadcasting Service (PBS) television programme *Nova*, this page follows the race to be first to circle the world in a balloon. It documents an unsuccessful 1996–97 expedition and includes articles on the status of current contenders. You will also find articles on the history and science of ballooning which include information on the jet stream, the atmosphere, and more. Looking for an armchair adventure? Take a virtual balloon flight over the Black Rock Desert in Nevada. You can also read an interview with balloonist Steve Fossett and download a transcript of the television programme.

Farnborough International 98

http://www.fi98.com/main/welcfra.asp

Site of the world's foremost showcase for the aerospace industry, suitable for those interested in latest innovations in aeronautic technology. There are a large number of photographs of aircraft, profiles of exhibitors, and also information for visitors to the show.

Faster Than Sound

http://www.pbs.org/wgbh/nova/barrier/

Companion to the US Public Broadcasting Service (PBS) television programme *Nova*, this page commemorates the 50-year anniversary of test pilot Chuck Yeager's breaking the sound barrier in his X-1, the so-called 'bullet with wings'. Hear audio clips of Yeager and others who worked on the project describing those fast-paced days. Learn about the design of the X-1 rocket and the secret history behind the X-1 programme. You can also find out what causes a sonic boom and learn about the latest attempts to beat speed records on land, water, and in the air. You can download a transcript of the television programme, and there is a list of resources.

German Zeppelin Offensive of 1916

http://www.wtj.com/artdocs/zeppelin.htm

This page tells the story of the German airship attacks on England during World War I. Read descriptions of the offensives, learn what the Germans hoped these bombing runs would achieve, and find out about the technology the English devised to bring the zeppelins down. There are a number of photographs of downed airships, plus quotes from German airmen concerning the fear of going down in flames. A brief list of sources follows the narrative.

Great Eastern Balloon Association

http://www.dca.net/geba/geba.htm

How, when, and where to take a flight in a hot air balloon. This site includes information on safety, joining a ballooning society, and also has some pictures of unusual balloons in flight.

Helicopter Aviation Home Page

http://www.copters.com/

Plentiful information on helicopters, including a history of their invention, technical aerodynamic details of what keeps them in the air, a profile of mechanical components, advice to novice pilots, and manuals of various kinds of helicopters. There is also a great number of images of helicopters.

How Do Planes Fly?

http://observe.ivv.nasa.gov/nasa/exhibits/planes/planes_1a.html

Explanation of the whys and hows connected with the flight of an aeroplane. Kids are invited to perform a number of related experiments and the answers are given in a series of fun interactive steps.

International Civil Aviation Organization

http://www.icao.int

Site of the specialized UN agency regulating civil aviation. The role and history of the ICAO are well presented. There is information on rules of the air, international conventions, and standardization of safety standards. The ICAO tries to reassure nervous flyers that air travel is getting safer. There are links to all the online airlines, airports, and pilot training centres in the world.

NASA Dryden Photo Archive

http://www.dfrc.nasa.gov/PhotoServer/

Photographs and information about the research aircraft that have flown from the NASA Dryden Flight Research Centre, California, since the 1940s.

Radio Broadcast of the Hindenburg Disaster

http://www.otr.com/hindenburg.html

Part of a larger site paying homage to the glory days of radio, this site features audio of the chilling, live news coverage of the Hindenburg disaster as the giant airship exploded into flames at Lakehurst, New Jersey, on 6 May 1937. In addition to a seven-minute audio clip, there is a brief article that provides context and a photograph of the Hindenburg engulfed in flames.

Supersonic Spies

http://www.pbs.org/wgbh/nova/supersonic/

Companion to the US Public Broadcasting Service (PBS) television programme *Nova*, this page explores the future of supersonic air travel and offers glimpses of what the next generation of supersonic aeroplanes may look like. Watch a video clip of what NASA

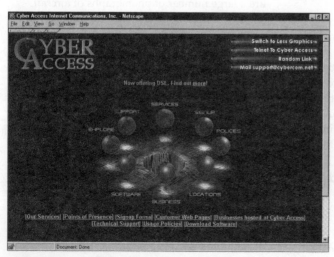

expects tomorrow's planes will look like in flight. Find out about the innovative features that keep the *Concorde* aloft. You can download a transcript of the television programme, and there is a list of resources for further reference.

Welcome to BAA

http://www.baa.co.uk/

Heathrow information provided by the British Airport Authority. It contains all practical information required by travellers, including latest flight arrival times at Heathrow and other British airports. There are, in addition, details of the structure of BAA, its annual report, and comprehensive flight and passenger statistics.

Water Transport

Build a Real Working Hovercraft

http://www.flash.net/~spartech/
ReekoScience/ExpHoverCraft.htm

Instructions on how to build a hovercraft for your pet mouse! This site also includes a brief explanation of the theory.

Canals: Panoramic Photographs, 1851–1991

http://lcweb2.loc.gov/cgi-
bin/query/r?ammem/ pan:(canal)

Part of the Panoramic Photo Collection of the US Library of Congress, this page features more than 70 panoramic photographs of canals, many of the Panama Canal, and most of which were taken at the turn of the 20th century. To find a specific canal, click on New Search and try a word search. Many of the images include brief notes. Click on the images to increase their size.

HMS Jervis Bay

http://www.saintjohn.nbcc.nb.ca/~JervisBay/
jervisbaymon2.htm

Part of a memorial site dedicated to the officers and crew of the *Jervis Bay*. The Web site includes images of the ship, the German ship the *Admiral Scheer* which sunk her, and her Captain Fegen.

The officers and crew were awarded the Victoria Cross for their heroic attack on a foe overwhelmingly stronger in an attempt to allow the convoy they were escorting to escape.

HMS Victory

http://home.att.net/~ronfraser/

Home page for admiral Nelson's flagship *HMS Victory*. The Web site includes several pictures of the famous ship, and also provides a great deal of historical information. For example, it took 27 miles of rigging and 850 men to control the *Victory* at sea, and she remains the world's oldest commissioned battleship. Use the site navigator to move around the Web site and you will find a wealth of information on the ship, her battles, and admiral Nelson.

Introduction to the Trireme *Olympias*

http://www.atm.ox.ac.uk/rowing/ttintro.html

Account of the modern reconstruction of an ancient trireme and of her testing at sea, with illustrations and a glossary of trireme terms.

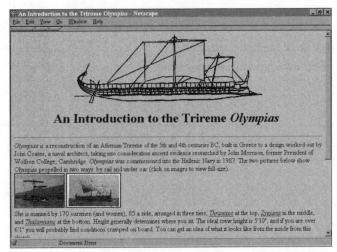

Mary Rose

http://www.cix.co.uk/~mary-rose/

Wealth of information on the *Mary Rose* including a full virtual tour of the Mary Rose Museum. This provides information about historical context as well as detailed pictures of the ship itself. It also includes links to British and global maritime sites.

Mayflower Web Page

http://members.aol.com/calebj/mayflower.html

Lots of information about the *Mayflower* and her

see p 539

RMS Titanic, Inc

http://www.titanic-online.com/

Official site of RMS Titanic, Inc, the company responsible for recovering artefacts from the famous shipwreck. The image gallery offers four categories to choose from: 'Artefacts', 'Expedition', 'Abyss', and 'Archive'. The Titanic Library probes into the ship's history, including details of her construction and accommodation, and gives information about the discovery and recovery operations. Photographs complement the text throughout. A bibliography page also lists more than half a dozen books on the topic.

passengers, the Pilgrims. It includes a history of the ship, a passenger and crew list, transcripts of the passengers' wills, inventories of their belongings, the full texts of books and journals written by the Pilgrims, biographies of Native Americans who played a part in the Pilgrims' early life in Plymouth, and a number of feature articles.

National Maritime Museum

http://www.nmm.ac.uk/Index.htm

Extensive information about the museum's collections. The site contains resources for education, including a wide selection of useful fact sheets, and information about the Royal Observatory at Greenwich, London.

Titanic's Lost Sister

http://www.pbs.org/wgbh/nova/titanic/

Companion to the US Public Broadcasting Service (PBS) television programme *Nova*, this page documents the sinking during World War I of the *Britannic*. You will find information and images about the search and salvage operations, plus a transcript of the *Nova* interview with Dr Robert Ballard, President of the Institute for Exploration. This site provides insight into advances in shipbuilding that followed the wreck of the *Britannic*'s sister ship the *Titanic*, including those safety improvements implemented on the doomed *Britannic* itself, as well as information regarding advances made since World War I. There is also a list of resources for further research.

THOUGHT & BELIEF

Mythology & Oral Narrative

Aadijookaanag, Dibaajimowin: Traditional and True Native American Stories

http://indy4.fdl.cc.mn.us/~isk/stories/stories.html

Stories of Indian experience aimed at sixth form pupils. This interactive site including native tales and legends, tragic and humorous stories, cartoons, the Pocahontas myth as seen by native people, native narratives on information technology, e-texts of Indian books, and short contemporary fiction.

Canaanite/Ugaritic Mythology FAQ

http://pubpages.unh.edu/~cbsiren/canaanite-faq.html

Lengthy description of the religion and mythology of the Canaanite and Ugaritic civilizations. The site describes who the Canaanites were, before describing their deities and cosmology. It features many hyperlinks to fuller descriptions of the characters from the mythologies.

Celtic Myth And Lore

http://www.witchhaven.com/shadowdrake/lore.html

Within these pages there is information about the herbology, astronomy, law, stories, and folk practices of the Celtic people. The site includes many stories and poems, as well as graphics and audio clips.

Classical Mythology Home Page

http://www.princeton.edu/~rhwebb/myth.html

Course materials from the mythology unit of Princeton University's Classics Department. Informative and academically rigorous, but easy for the casual reader to use, the site contains sections such as: 'Gods', 'Titans', 'Monsters', 'Heroes', 'Legends', and 'Women'.

Folklore: An Introduction

http://virtual.park.uga.edu/~clandrum/folklore.html

Access information about folklore at this site by category (oral lore, social and folk custom, and material culture) or by ethnic or social group. Alternatively, just click on one heading for some isolated but interesting examples.

Hittite/Hurrian Mythology

http://pubpages.unh.edu/~cbsiren/hittite-ref.html

Lengthy description of the religion and mythology of the Hittite and Hurrian civilizations. The site describes who the Hittites were, before describing their deities and cosmology. The site features many hyperlinks to fuller descriptions of the characters from the mythologies.

Mayan Folktales

http://www.folkart.com/~latitude/folktale/folktale.htm

Online collection of Mayan folk tales as related by Pedro Miguel Say, a famous Q'anjob'al storyteller from Guatemala, and translated into English by Fernando Peñalosa. This is an evolving site and each month new folk tales will be published.

Mermaids and Other Mythical Sea Beings

http://www.eliki.com/ancient/myth/mermaid/

Mermaid myths and legends. The mermaid's history from the pre-Christian era to the 21st century is documented here, as are definitions and listings of other mythical sea creatures and gods from around the world. The site contains a mermaid art gallery and a section on mermaid poetry.

Mythmedia

http://www-lib.haifa.ac.il/www/art/MYTHOLOGY_WESTART.HTML

Extensive collection of art images related to classical Greek mythology, created by art historians in Haifa University. The site offers a wide range of remarkably clear and fast-loading pictures of deities and heroes from the Homeric world. It also covers ancient iconography and modern art, including an especially rich section on famous episodes of the Trojan War.

Nessie on the Net

http://www.lochness.co.uk/index.html

Official home of Nessie on the Internet. This site includes a host of fun things to do, including sending Nessie postcards, looking for the monster via the Loch Ness Webcam, and lots of pictures to examine. The site also has a history of the creature.

Olympians

http://jcccnet.johnco.cc.ks.us/~jjackson/oly.html

Introduction to the 12 Olympian gods. The deities are presented through the main attributes and incidents of their lives, followed by characteristic passages from ancient texts and links to image repositories.

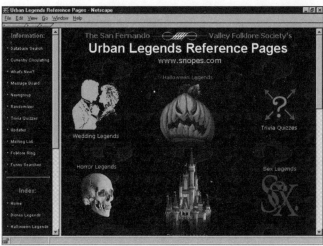

Oral Narratives and Aboriginal Pasts: An Interdisciplinary Review of the Literatures on Oral Traditions and Oral Histories

http://www.inac.gc.ca/pubs/oral/index.html

Interdisciplinary review of the literature written about oral narratives and oral histories from the native past of Canada. The review starts by describing the main methodological premises of the effort, and proceeds with addressing a series of complex matters relating to the (re)construction of the history of relations between Native peoples and newer arrivals to Canada.

Regional Folklore and Mythology

http://www.pibburns.com/mythregi.htm

Links to information about folklore and mythology broken down by cultural and geographical region. This huge site covers almost every part of the world, normally with at least one downloadable story from each region or culture.

Sumerian Mythology FAQ

http://pubpages.unh.edu/~cbsiren/sumer-faq.html

Large Web site describing the religious beliefs and mythology of the Sumerian civilization. The site also deals with Sumerian cosmology and the parallels between Sumerian beliefs and the old testament, including the flood myth.

Urban Legends Reference Pages

http://www.snopes.com/

Huge source of too-good-to-be-true stories culled from the global media but with a US bias. A

search engine allows access to a host of apocryphal tales and Web surfers are invited to add to the list.

Zen Stories to Tell Your Neighbour

http://www.rider.edu/users/suler/zenstory/zenstory.html

Collection of some of the oldest stories in human history. Each tale is followed by the reactions of various people (mostly students and other visitors) and is also linked to other relevant stories and the reactions they have generated. As well as reading the stories, it is possible to contribute a new story, or simply react to the existing ones.

Ancient Religions

Asatru – Norse Paganism

http://www.religioustolerance.org/asatru.htm

Account of the revived Norse pagan faith now recognized as a legitimate religion by the Icelandic government. Nazi attempts to pervert Asatru beliefs are recounted on this site. There is also a description of the faith, its many deities, rituals, and celebration days.

Baal

http://www.knight.org/advent/cathen/02175a.htm

Full account of the variety of religious beliefs and practices associated with the cult of Baal. This history of Baal-worship traces its origins, its development among various Semitic peoples, and the fatal blow dealt to it by the Babylonian invasions of Palestine.

Book of the Dead

http://www.lysator.liu.se/~drokk/BoD/toc.html

Complete translation of this ancient Egyptian text.

Celtic Druidism

http://www.religioustolerance.org/druid.htm

Detailed account of historical Druidism and its contemporary revival. There is a discussion of how Druid beliefs may have evolved from a proto-Celtic faith centred around the Black Sea. Myths around Druidism, in particular that its practitioners engaged in human sacrifice and constructed Stonehenge, are refuted. There is information about current day Druidism and a guide to related Internet sites.

I Ching on the Net

http://www.pacificcoast.net/~wh/Index.html

Source of information on the ancient Chinese divination manual. There are several translations and a large number of commentaries. Further sources of information and details of I Ching software are provided.

Introduction to Dowsing

http://home.interstat.net/~slawcio/dowsing.html

American Association of Dowsers site that includes all the information you might need to make some dowsing rods and how to use them.

Mithraism

http://www.evansville.edu/~ecoleweb/articles/mithraism.html

Comprehensive exploration of the pagan cult dedicated to the worship of the god Mithras, with particular emphasis placed on its manifestation in Persia and ancient Rome. Links are included to other relevant sites.

Christianity

Amish

http://www.religioustolerance.org/amish.htm

Good account of the history, practices, and beliefs of the US-based conservative Anabaptists. The doctrinal basis of their split from other Mennonites is set out. There is also a fascinating account of their lifestyle and ongoing conflicts with the US authorities resulting from Amish insistence on limiting education of their children and the traffic chaos caused by their distinctive black horse and buggies.

Augustine: Confessions

http://ccel.wheaton.edu/a/augustine/confessions/confessions.html

Full text of the famous theological and autobiographical work by St Augustine of Hippo. It traces his childhood, dissolute youth, struggles against evil, and ultimate conversion to Christianity.

F A C T

AUGUSTINE OF HIPPO, ST, (Aurelius Augustinus) (354–430)

One of the early Christian leaders and writers known as the Fathers of the Church. He was converted to Christianity by Ambrose in Milan and became bishop of Hippo (modern Annaba, Algeria) 396.

Book of Mormon

http://www.athenet.net/~jlindsay/BOMIntro.shtml

Produced by a self-professed Mormon, this easy-to-read introduction to the Book of Mormon has a link to the complete text in chapters, as well as attempts to answer some of the most frequently asked questions about the holy book of The Church of Jesus Christ of Latter-Day Saints.

Christian Classics Ethereal Library

http://ccel.wheaton.edu/

Hundreds of classic Christian works in electronic format, brought together by Wheaton College, Illinois.

Church of Christ, Scientist (Christian Science)

http://www.religioustolerance.org/cr_sci.htm

Description of the history, beliefs, and attitudes towards healing of the Church of Christ, Scientist. There is a biography of Mary Baker Eddy and a guide to Christian Science publications and Internet sites. The splits and schisms within the sect are described, together with a presentation of the views of those who condemn Christian Science as a heretic cult.

Church of England   www england-anglican.org

http://www.church-of-england.org/

There is information on the structure of the church, what it means to be an Anglican, and a guide to prayer. There are links to those dioceses that have Web pages of their own and a comprehensive listing of web pages of non-English churches within the Anglican communion.

Cistercians – An Introductory History

http://www.csbsju.edu/osb/cist/intro.html

History of the order written by a Cistercian. It traces the role of Bernard of Clairvaux in saving the order and establishing the structure of its enduring success. The division of the order into the less observant and the more observant (Trappists) is set out. There is also information about the leading Cistercian masters.

Common Prayer, Book of

http://www.church-holy-cross.org/bcp/

Full text of the traditional version of the *Book of Common Prayer* used by US Episcopalians.

Confession of St Patrick

http://ccel.wheaton.edu/patrick/confession/confession.html

Full text of St Patrick's *Confession* plus a version of 'The Shield of St Patrick', a prayer attributed to the saint.

Council of Trent

http://www.knight.org/advent/cathen/15030c.htm

Full details of the ecumenical council called by the Roman Catholic Church to counter Protestant heresies. The national and religious tensions of the early Reformation and how they influenced

the convening and deliberations of the council are well presented at this site.

Development of the Papacy

http://history.idbsu.edu/westciv/papacy/

Part of a larger site on the history of Western civilization maintained by Boise State University, this page provides an introduction to the conflict that existed in the Middle Ages between the church and state. Information is organized into 14 brief articles, each concerning a specific aspect of the conflict surrounding the development of the papacy. You can start at the beginning and work your way through the articles in chronological order or go directly to a page that interests you. Tricky words are introduced with an audio icon to assist with pronunciation. There is also a list of references for further study.

Early Church Online Encyclopedia: The Ecole Initiative

http://www.evansville.edu/~ecoleweb

Online encyclopedia of early church history to the Reformation, created by scholars across the Internet. Here are hundreds of short articles on key figures and movements; longer articles on topics as diverse as Mithraism, Cretan Christianity, and Faustian pacts; translations of primary sources; images; and a two-dimensional chronology that allows the user to view data organized according to both time and place.

Epiphany

http://www.knight.org/advent/cathen/05504c.htm

Detailed account of the post-Christmas festival. The contents include a history of the origin of the festival, various names by which it is known, and details of its spread from the Eastern to the Western church.

Feast of Corpus Christi

http://www.knight.org/advent/cathen/04390b.htm

History of the festival and the role of St Juliana in its inception. The stages by which Corpus Christi became accepted into the Christian calendar are also outlined.

From Jesus to Christ: The First Christians

http://www.pbs.org/wgbh/pages/frontline/shows/religion/

Companion site to a US PBS (Public Broadcasting Service) television programme, this page puts forth controversial historical evidence challenging accepted beliefs and opinions about the life of Jesus and the rise of Christianity. The topics are arranged into five sections, including 'a portrait of Jesus' world', 'the story of the storytellers', and 'why did Christianity succeed?' In addition to commentary from theologians, archaeologists, and historians, you will find maps, charts, ancient texts, images of the archaeological discoveries, a biblical quiz, and audio clips from the television programme.

Gnosticism

http://www.knight.org/advent/cathen/06592a.htm

Extended source of information on the doctrine of salvation by knowledge. Presented by the *Catholic Encyclopedia*, the contents include the etymology of the term, gnosticism's extensive pre-Christian roots in a variety of cultural and historical contexts, and its influence on the development of Christianity.

History of the Christian Altar

http://www.knight.org/advent/cathen/01362a.htm

Complete account of the tabular elevated surface and its significance to Christians throughout the ages. This site includes the many terms that have been used to describe the altar, the material and form of altars, a history of how altars have been consecrated, the origins of the practice of orienting the altar to the east, and notes on surviving medieval altars.

History of the Orthodox Church

http://www.goarch.org/access/Companion_to_Orthodox_Church/History_of_Orthodox_Church.html

Extensive and thorough presentation of Eastern Orthodox Church. The site includes sections on the apostolic era and the persecutions, the heresies and ecumenical councils, the iconoclastic crisis, the relation between the state and the church, and East and the West during the Byzantine era, the Schism, the church under Islam after the conquest of Byzantine empire by the Ottoman Turks, the Orthodoxy facing modern ideology, and the Orthodoxy in the West.

Holy Communion

http://www.knight.org/advent/cathen/07402a.htm

Exposition of Catholic beliefs concerning the Eucharist and its sacramental and spiritual reception. The rules of the church relating to Holy Communion are set out in detail.

Holy Week

http://www.knight.org/advent/cathen/07435a.htm

Detailed analysis of the events of the week leading up to the crucifixion of Christ and their significance. The historical observance of Holy Week is discussed, prior to a description of the main liturgical features of contemporary Holy Week rites.

Iconostasis

http://www.knight.org/advent/cathen/07626a.htm

History of the screen dividing the sanctuary from the rest of the church. The arrangements of icons on this most distinctive feature in Greek Orthodox and Greek Catholic churches is described in detail, together with the attempts at reconciliation with the Western Church over the question of concealment of the altar by the iconostasis.

II Vatican Council

http://www.vatican.va/archive/hist_councils/ii_vatican_council/index.htm

Full text of the constitutions, declarations, and decrees of the II Vatican Council – one of the major reforming moments of the Catholic Church – from the Vatican Archives.

Immaculate Conception

http://www.knight.org/advent/cathen/07674d.htm

Lengthy article from the *Catholic Encyclopedia* asserting the belief that the Virgin Mary was free from original sin. It is admitted that scriptural proof of the dogma cannot be found. The views of leaders of the early church are discussed and challenged, prior to an account of events leading to the formulation of the belief as dogma.

Jesuit Resources

http://maple.lemoyne.edu/~bucko/jesuit.html

Access to information on the Society of Jesus, with information on spirituality and history, as well as access to Jesuit documents, associations, and educational organizations.

Jesus Christ

http://www.knight.org/advent/cathen/08374c.htm

Comprehensive information about the founder of Christianity from the *Catholic Encyclopedia*. There are articles on the origin of his name, a chronology of his life, historical documents mentioning him, his character, the Incarnation, and the Resurrection.

Lent

http://www.knight.org/advent/cathen/09152a.htm

Long article from the *Catholic Encyclopedia* on the origins and significance of Lent. There is a presentation of the evidence from the early church that the modern notion of a 40-day period of fasting and reflection was unknown. The gradual evolution of Lent and agreement on its timing, duration, and dietary restrictions, is described.

Lord's Prayer in Thirty Languages

http://www.christusrex.org/www1/pater

Paternoster presented in English, Latin, and a variety of languages including Basque, Creole, and Tamil.

Luther's 95 Theses

http://www.fordham.edu/halsall/source/luther95.txt

Full text of all 95 theses that Martin Luther nailed on the church door in Wittenberg.

Mennonite Church

http://www.mennonites.org/

Mennonite headquarters site. The contents include a history of the faith, basic beliefs, the current structures of the far-flung Mennonite community, and Mennonite campaigns for peace and social justice. There are links to many Mennonite congregations.

Moravian Church

http://www.moraviansi.com/

Beliefs, history, and structure of the 700,000 strong community of Moravians. The role of John Hus, persecutions in Europe, and the growth of the sect in the USA are described. The tenets of the Moravian faith are set out. There is a bibliography and links to Moravian congregations.

Notre-Dame de Lourdes

http://www.knight.org/advent/cathen/09389b.htm

Information from the *Catholic Encyclopedia* on the famous pilgrimage centre. The 18 apparitions which appeared to the 14-year-old peasant Bernadette Soubiroux are described, together with the process which led the church to declare a belief in their miraculous nature. Statistics on the number of pilgrims and confirmed cures are presented, together with a spirited refutation of those who seek to deny the divine nature of the relief brought to pilgrims.

Order of St Benedict

http://www.osb.org/osb/

Information and news on this ancient monastic order including a geographic index of monasteries around the world, and a hyperlinked and illustrated history of the saint who founded the order.

Oxford Movement

http://www.knight.org/advent/cathen/11370a.htm

Extremely detailed account of the revival of Catholic beliefs within the Church of England. This history, from the *Catholic Encyclopedia*, looks at the post-Reformation structure of the English church by way of explaining the reasons for J H Newman's dissatisfaction with the status quo. The role of Pusey, Keble, and Newman in forging the movement which created Anglo-Catholicism is comprehensively analysed.

Puritan Voices

http://history.hanover.edu/early/puritans.htm

Four examples of puritanical writing. The scripts give some insight into the thoughts of the people who wrote them, and also some idea of the relationship between life and religion at the time. The texts are: Nehemiah Wallington's *Diary*, Josias Nichols' *A Plea for the Innocent*, and two anonymous contributions.

Quietism

http://www.knight.org/advent/cathen/12608c.htm

Lengthy discourse on the doctrine of quietism, by E A Page, and published by the *Catholic Encyclopedia*. It acknowledges the similarity between this Catholic doctrine and that of meditation, familiar to many Eastern religions.

REFORMATION

religious and political movement in 16th-century Europe to reform the Roman Catholic Church, which led to the establishment of Protestant churches. Anticipated from the 12th century by the Waldenses, Lollards, and Hussites, it was set off by German priest Martin Luther in 1517.

Reformation

http://history.idbsu.edu/westciv/reformat/

Part of a larger site on the history of western civilization maintained by Boise State University, this page provides an introduction to Martin Luther, John Calvin, and the Reformation movement. Information is organized into a number of brief articles, each of which deals with a specific aspect of the Reformation and its founders. You can start at the beginning and work your way through the articles in chronological order, or go directly to a page that interests you. There is also a list of references for further study.

Religious Society of Friends

http://www.quaker.org/

Quaker beliefs and ethics are set out here. There is also a detailed history of the faith, and information on Quaker societies throughout the world and their commercial activities.

Reorganized Church of Jesus Christ of Latter Day Saints

http://www.religioustolerance.org/rlds.htm

Objective account of the history, beliefs, structures, and practices of the breakaway group of Restorationists. Their doctrinal points of departure from the Mormons, and the beliefs they have in common, are set out. There is also a bibliography of further points of reference.

Rosary

http://www.udayton.edu/mary/resources/rosdex.html

Comprehensive source of information on the rosary from the International Marian Research Institute. There is detailed advice on how to pray the rosary, a series of rosary images, and a section on the history of the rosary and its place in Catholicism.

Sacrament of Penance

http://www.knight.org/advent/cathen/11618c.htm

Long Catholic exposition on the practice of confession and its history. It argues that the institution is divinely ordained, not a human invention to give the church power over individual consciences. This detailed account outlines the changing role of the rite in various parts of Christendom since the days of the early Church. Protestant perspectives on the importance of penance and confession are also set out here.

Salvation Army

http://www.salvationarmy.org/aboutus.htm

International headquarters of the evangelical mission. There is a history of the Salvation Army, an outline of its structure, and details of the various charitable activities it undertakes in more than a hundred countries.

Seventh-Day Adventist

http://www.religioustolerance.org/sda.htm

Long impartial presentation of the history, beliefs, and practices of the denomination. The role of William Miller and Ellen White in establishing the Seventh-Day Adventists is summarized. Their concerns for healthy living and good diet are set out and interchurch controversies over homosexuality and female ordination are described. Space is also given to the views of theologians who condemn the Seventh-Day Adventists as a cult.

Spiritual Exercises

http://www.fordham.edu/halsall/source/loyola-spirex.html

Excerpts from St Ignatius Loyola's *Spiritual Exercises,* setting out his rules for the Jesuit order and for Christian life, plus a link to the full text of the exercises.

St Patrick's Day

http://www.st-patricks-day.com/

Comprehensive source of information on the legend of St Patrick and the history of celebrations on the 17th March. The significance of the shamrock is also explained. This site also provides regularly updated information on St Patrick's Day celebrations and St Patrick societies in Ireland and around the world.

Trail of Hope: Story of the Mormon Trail

http://www.pbs.org/trailofhope/

Companion to a US Public Broadcasting Service (PBS) television programme, this site documents the Mormons' 1,300-mile journey across the plains to religious freedom in Utah. A series of stories and photos provides insight into what the journey meant to the Mormons, how they prepared for it, and what they encountered along the way.

Unitarian Universalist

http://www.religioustolerance.org/u-u.htm

Even-handed account of a variety of beliefs in the inherent goodness of individuals known collectively as Unitarianism. There is a history of the movement, a listing of the liberal thinkers lauded by Unitarians, and a description of the church structures of those Unitarians who consider themselves as Christians. The principles and ideals shared by all Unitarians are set out, together with a guide to Unitarian Internet resources.

Watchtower Bible and Tract Society (Jehovah's Witness)

http://www.religioustolerance.org/
witness.htm

Long and impartial account of the history, beliefs, organizational structure, and practises of Jehovah's Witnesses. The suffering of German Witnesses who refused to participate in World War II is chronicled. Their contribution, through litigation, to the protection of religious freedom in the US is acknowledged. There is a summary of criticisms levelled at the faith, particularly over their opposition to blood transfusions.

Way of the Cross – Via Crucis

http://198.62.75.1/www1/jsc/TVCmain.html

Virtual tour of the Christian Ways of the Cross. High resolution photographs of the stations are accompanied by text reflecting on the importance of each stage of Jesus' journey to the Crucifixion.

What are Angels? A Biblical Perspective

http://pages.prodigy.net/lgbernard/anglview.htm

Essay giving a biblical perspective on angels. The site describes not only the origins of the word 'angel' but also gives a description of the 'heavenly hierarchy of angels'. The site features a link to every biblical reference to angels, and links to other Internet resources on the topic.

Islam

About Islam and Muslims

http://www.unn.ac.uk/societies/islamic/

UK-based site offering extensive information about the Islamic faith and culture. Facts about the Koran, images, links to newspapers and university sites are all included.

F A C T

ISLAM (Arabic 'submission', that is, to the will of Allah)

religion founded in the Arabian peninsula in the early AD 600s. It emphasizes the oneness of God, his omnipotence, beneficence, and inscrutability. Its sacred book is the **Koran,** which Muslims believe was divinely revealed to Muhammad, the prophet or messenger of Allah.

Dome of the Rock

http://www.erols.com/ameen/domerock.htm

Guide to the Jerusalem landmark. In addition to a history, description, and interior and exterior photographs of the building, there is an analysis (from a Muslim perspective) of how the structure and dimensions of the Dome of the Rock reflect the Muslim world view.

Exploring Ancient World Cultures: Early Islam

http://eawc.evansville.edu/ispage.htm

Illustrated historical guide to early Islam. An introductory article explores similarities between the Islamic faith and both Judaism and Christianity. This site also provides links to the Koran, a chronology, essays, maps, quizzes, and additional Islamic resources on the Web.

Islam at a Glance

http://www.iad.org/books/WAMY1.html

Clear and concise introduction to the key beliefs of Islam. It covers Muhammad, the Koran, prayer, Islam in the modern world, and the Five Pillars of Islam.

Koran

http://etext.virginia.edu/koran.html

Full text of the Koran in searchable SGML format, offered by the Electronic Centre at the University of Virginia, USA.

Ramadhan and Eid ul Fitr

http://www.ummah.org.uk/ramadhan/

Comprehensive account of the significance to Muslims of the fasting month of Ramadan. The site is of interest to Muslims and to those wishing to know more about Islam. There are links to a large number of other Ramadan sites.

Reflections From the Hajj

http://www.erols.com/ameen/hajjexp.htm#kabah

Analysis from a Muslim perspective of the hajj pilgrimage and its spiritual significance. Details of walking around the Kaaba, drinking from the Zamzam well, and prayers at Arafat are supported by photographs.

Shi'ite Encyclopedia

http://www.al-islam.org/encyclopedia/

Detailed exposition of Shi'ite beliefs and practices. The encyclopedia is compiled by a team seeking to bridge differences between Sunnis and Shi'ites and the two perspectives on Islamic theological issues are presented in an even-handed manner.

Judaism

Babylonian Jewry Museum

http://www.babylonJewry.org.il/museum/index.htm

The Babylonian Jewry Museum presents chapters in the history of the Jews of Babylon over a period of 2,700 years, from the time of their exile from the Land of Israel (721–586 BC) until their return to the State of Israel by Operation 'Ezra and Nehemia' (1950–1952).

Babylonian Talmud

http://www.ucalgary.ca/~elsegal/TalmudPage.html

Fascinating and unusual site, presenting a graphic Hebrew page from the Babylonian Talmud. You can click on any portion of the Hebrew and read a commentary on when and where the text was composed – as well as its content, meaning, and purpose – as a starting point to an exploration of the history of Jewish religious literature.

Essenes

http://www.knight.org/advent/cathen/05546a.htm

Comprehensive account of the origins, history, and beliefs of the ancient Jewish sect. The egalitarian and social concerns of Essenes are set out together with their rejection of marriage and practice of adopting children into the sect. The historical legacy of the Essenes and the fascination they have exerted for many Christians are described.

Ethiopian Jewry Home Page

http://www.circus.org/index.html

Introduction to the culture, history, and traditions of the Beta Israel. The links between the Ethiopian Orthodox church and Ethiopian Judaism are stressed. There are a number of photos in a well-presented online 'slide show'. Details are provided of the migration to Israel and the current status of the Jews remaining in Ethiopia.

Hanukkah – Festival of Lights

http://www.ahavat-israel.com/torat/chanukah.html

Comprehensive account of the history of the Jewish festival of lights and its religious significance. Included on this site are a description of the rituals involved and various Hanukkah games as well as the text of some festive songs.

History of the Turkish Jews

http://www.mersina.com/lib/turkish_jews/

Condensed online edition of Naim Guleryuz's lecture on the history of Turkish Jews. The site includes historical information about Sephardic Jews and explores the role of Jews in contemporary Turkish society.

Jewish Culture and History

http://www.igc.apc.org/ddickerson/
judaica.html

Wide-ranging collection of information
on Judaism. The site includes an image
gallery of Polish synagogues, links to
online Hebrew texts, and an introduction
to Judaism.

Jewish Music Network

http://www.jewish-music.com/
listeningstation.htm

Extended Jewish music resource, with recorded
concerts and selected clips available in
RealAudio, as well as reviews and ratings of
current releases, concert listings, and links to the
sites of individual artists. Those with Java-
enabled browsers can also read a section called
'Today's headlines'. You have to register to view
this site, but it's free.

Kabbalah FAQ

http://www.digital-brilliance.com/kab/faq.htm

Thorough introduction to the Jewish mystic
tradition and pointer to further sources of
information. There are full details of famous
kabbalists, the Lesser Banishing Ritual of the
Pentagram, and other arcane mysteries.
Traditional prohibitions on the study of kabbalah
by young people and women are vigorously
refuted.

Monarchy, Exile and Maccabees

http://www.solbaram.org/articles/fn2.html

Online edition of Manfred Davidmann's study
History Speaks: Monarchy, Exile and Maccabees, in
which he provides an analysis of Jewish history
and, more particularly, of what is known about
King Solomon's reign and that of the Maccabean
dynasty.

Passover on the Net

http://www.holidays.net/passover/

Full description of the history and significance of
the Passover festival. In addition there is Passover
music, the foods eaten at the Passover Seder, and
a guide for children celebrating the deliverance of
the Jewish people from Egypt.

**F
A
C
T**

PASSOVER (also called Pesach)

in Judaism, an eight-day spring festival which
commemorates the exodus of the Israelites
from Egypt and the passing over by the Angel
of Death of the Jewish houses, so that only
the Egyptian firstborn sons were killed, in
retribution for Pharaoh's murdering of all
Jewish male infants.

Pharisees

http://www.evansville.edu/~ecoleweb/articles/
pharisees.html

Part of the Ecole Initiative maintained by the
University of Evansville, this page attempts to
shed some light on the Pharisees, one of the
obscure Jewish sects that emerged after the fall of
Judah. The text discusses the scarcity of reliable
information concerning the Pharisees and the
resulting difficulty facing scholars in constructing
an accurate picture of the sect. However, this page
does include a bibliography of over a dozen
sources of further information.

Sadducees

http://www.evansville.edu/~ecoleweb/articles/
sadducees.html

Page attempting to shed life on the Sadducees,
one of the obscure Jewish sects that emerged after
the fall of Judah. The text, part of the Ecore
Initiative maintained by the University of
Evansville, discusses the scarcity of reliable
information concerning the Sadducees and the
resulting difficulty facing scholars in constructing
an accurate picture of the sect. At the bottom of
the page you will find a bibliography of sources.

Eastern Religions

Ahimsa – The Hindu Ethic of Non-Violence

http://www.hinduismtoday.kauai.hi.us/ashram/Res
ources/Ahimsa/AhimsaNonViolence.html

Long and passionate exposition of the universal
values of non-violence and respect for life. The

philosophical roots of the practice of non-injury to others is traced back to Hinduism by the author. There is advice to parents and quotes from respected Hindu thinkers.

Aum Shinrikyo (Supreme Truth)

http://www.religioustolerance.org/dc_aumsh.htm

Good account of the Japanese doomsday cult and its messianic leader. Shoko Asahara's fusion of Buddhist and Christian beliefs and the personality cult around him are described. There is also a section dealing with the Sarin gas attack on the Tokyo underground and Asahara's subsequent trial.

Bhagvat-Gita

http://www.iconsoftec.com/gita/

Fully downloadable text of the most sacred work in the Hindu religion. It is divided into eighteen separate illustrated documents.

Brief Introduction to Taoism

http://www.geocities.com/HotSprings/2426/Ttaointro.html

Good objective introduction to Taoism. The evolution of Taoism within Chinese philosophy is described. The site includes summaries of the various types of Taoism including philosophical, devotional, magical, and alchemical.

Buddha Mind

http://www.abm.ndirect.co.uk/

Well-designed introduction to Buddhism in child-friendly language. The site is divided into 'Left brain' and 'Right brain', sections which take differing approaches to the material and resources available on this site. The various stages of initiation, the main beliefs and practices, meditation, spirituality, and the roots of Buddhist wisdom are explained in simple terms, accompanied by excerpts from the Buddhist scriptures and illustrations.

Buddhist Ethics

http://jbe.la.psu.edu/

Online magazine discussing all things Buddhist. The site is not so much an introduction, as it is full of discursive essays, book reviews, conference reports, and surveys for those with a more in-depth interest in Buddhist studies.

Chinese Religion

http://birmingham.gov.uk/epislive/citywide.nsf/437 194deb01c293b802564d60047624b/e6615e702e 28ffa88025662f00525bc7?OpenDocument#_3vs_

All-text site from Birmingham University containing a lot of information about the three main strands of religion in China – Buddhism, Taoism, and Confucianism. The site also focuses on some of the important religious festivals, including New Year.

Feng Shui and Qi

http://www.spiritweb.org/Spirit/feng-shui.html

Good source of information about this Chinese philosophy. The ancient roots of feng shui are explained in detail. You may learn how your health, business, and love life can be improved by an understanding of the importance of harmony.

Gospel, The

http://magna.com.au/~prfbrown/buddha/index.html

Contains the text of *The Gospel* by Buddha, or Gautama Siddhartha.

Hinduism Today

http://www.HinduismToday.kauai.hi.us/ashram/

Online magazine produced by Sanatana Dharma's Electronic Ashram. It explores India's ancient spiritual path by providing nine informative sections related to Hinduism.

> **F A C T**
>
> **HINDUISM (Hindu *sanatana dharma* 'eternal tradition')**
> religion originating in northern India about 4,000 years ago, which is superficially and in some of its forms polytheistic, but has a concept of the supreme spirit, Brahman, above the many divine manifestations.

His Holiness the Dalai Lama

http://www.nalejandria.com/utopia/english/DalaiLama-eng.htm

Profile of Tenzin Gyatso, the 14th incarnation of the Dalai Lama. It traces his childhood, escape from Tibet, and efforts to preserve Tibetan culture in exile.

Kundalini Resource Centre

http://hmt.com/kundalini/index.html

Large site dedicated to raising public awareness of how kundalini can release psychic and libidinous energy. There is a long explanation of kundalini beliefs and practices. Experiences of devotees are related and there are numerous links to articles, books, and Internet resources.

Outline of Jain History

http://www.cs.colostate.edu/~malaiya/jainhout1.html

Comprehensive pages introducing a timeline of Jain history with parallel events in Indian and World history. Throughout the chronologies there are numerous links to people and events. Click the button at the bottom of the pages to access dozens of Jain resources and images.

Shinto – The Way of the Gods

http://www.trincoll.edu/~tj/tj4.4.96/articles/cover.html

Well arranged guide to Shinto beliefs and practices. The link between Shintoism and Japanese mythology is explained prior to a guide to the main Shinto shrines. Supported by a series of photographs, this site shows the significance of Shinto rituals in modern Japanese life.

F A C T

SHINTO (Chinese *shin tao* 'way of the gods')

the indigenous religion of Japan. It combines an empathetic oneness with natural forces and loyalty to the reigning dynasty as descendants of the Sun goddess, Amaterasu-Omikami.

Sikhism Home Page

http://www.sikhs.org/

Brief overview of the main principles of Sikhism. It also follows the development of the religion,

---

F A C T

SIKHISM

religion professed by 14 million Indians, living mainly in the Punjab. Sikhism was founded by Nanak (1469–*c.* 1539). Sikhs believe in a single God who is the immortal creator of the universe and who has never been incarnate in any form, and in the equality of all human beings; Sikhism is strongly opposed to caste divisions.

---

explores the philosophy and scriptures connected with Sikhism, describes the main religious problems, role models, ceremonies, and religious dates in the life of a Sikh, and provides bibliographic guidance and a glossary of terms.

Vedas and Upanishads

http://www.san.beck.org/EC7-Vedas.html

Thorough source of information on the Hindu mystical texts. Central Hindu precepts and rituals are explained in the course of summarizing, and providing extracts from, the major Upanishad texts. There are also links to English language versions of the full texts of the major Upanishads.

Word, The

http://www.powerup.com.au/~glt/library/buddhism/word1.htm

Contains the text of *The Word* by Buddha, or Gautama Siddhartha.

Zen Buddhism

http://www.iijnet.or.jp/iriz/irizhtml/irizhome.htm

Largest collection of Buddhist primary text materials on the Internet, together with many examples of Zen art, information on Zen centres and masters, a search engine, and bibliography.

Zoroastrianism

http://www.religioustolerance.org/zoroastr.htm

Objective account of the beliefs, history, and practices of the ancient monotheistic faith. Legends associated with Zoroaster and known facts about him are presented. Other sources of information about contemporary Zoroastrianism are indicated.

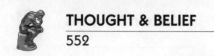

Other Religions

Bahá'í Faith Page

http://www.bcca.org/~glittle/

Introduction to this religion founded in the 19th century. There is an overview explaining the faith (illustrated by maps and charts), and a collection of religious writings. The site also contains access to pages produced by Bahá'í groups around the world.

Corpus Hermeticum

http://www.hermetic.com/

This page provides the text of some of the core documents and figures of the Hermetic religious tradition. Some of the luminaries whose works can be found here include Aleister Crowley, Hakim Bey, Mark Stavish, and Benjamin Rowe.

Druse, Druze, Mowahhidoon

http://www.religioustolerance.org/druse.htm

Good objective summary of the beliefs and practices of those who refer to themselves as the Mowahhidoon. The history of this secretive faith is outlined. There is also an explanation of why others refer to them as Druze.

Hare Krishna

http://www.iskcon.org/

Guide to the philosophy and religious rituals of Hare Krishna from the International Society for Krishna Consciousness.

Hidden Words of Bahá'u'lláh, The

http://www.jps.net/shacoma/texts/hiddenwa.html

Complete text of this work by the Persian religious leader Bahá'u'lláh.

Manichaeism

http://www.knight.org/advent/cathen/09591a.htm

Extensive discussion of the range of beliefs associated with the Iranian prophet Mani. There is a biography of the founder and the formative influences on his childhood. The syncretic mix of the faith he proclaimed, combining elements of Babylonian folklore, Zoroastrian dualism, Buddhist ethics, and Christianity, is described in detail. The long history of rivalry between Christianity and Manichaeism is also set out.

Prayers and Meditations

http://www.bcca.org/~kalantar/writings/authors/bahaullah/pray.meditate/index.html

Text of Baha'u'llah's prayers and meditations which form part of the Baha'i religion.

Proclamation of Bahá'u'lláh

http://www.bcca.org/~kalantar/writings/authors/bahaullah/proc.of.baha/index.html

Full text of the proclamation by which Husayn 'Ali informed the world and its leaders of his mission to usher in an era of peace and spiritual well-being. This document is of central importance to the Baha'i faith.

Scientology

http://www.religioustolerance.org/scientol.htm

Lengthy and non-partisan explanation of scientology beliefs and practices. There is a biography of L Ron Hubbard, a description of the 'Eight Dynamics', a list of publications, and guide to Internet resources. Objections raised by opponents are also set out, together with an account of the church's vigorous legal pursuit of its critics.

Unification Church

http://www.religioustolerance.org/unificat.htm

Even-handed presentation of the history, beliefs, and practices of the Moonies. There is a summary of the criticisms, from fellow Christians and human-rights groups, levelled at the authoritarian cult. There is also a guide to both Moonie and anti-Moonie Web sites.

Voodoo Information Pages

http://www.arcana.com/shannon/voodoo/

General information on the religion of vodoun, more commonly known as voodoo. More than ten sections focus on different aspects of voodoo, including 'Creation mythology' and 'Basic rituals'. These are supported by a glossary, bibliography, and links to other Internet resources.

Waco: The Inside Story

http://www.pbs.org/wgbh/pages/frontline/waco/

Companion to the US Public Broadcasting Service (PBS) television programme *Frontline,* this page tells the story of the violent 1993 siege in Waco, Texas, USA, between agents of the FBI and members of the Branch Davidian religious cult. It includes a chronology of events, a who's who of those involved, and photos, plus a 'Frequently Asked Questions' section and a selection of viewer reactions. You can also download a transcript of the original programme.

The Bible, Old Testament

Aaron

http://www.knight.org/advent/cathen/01003a.htm

Profile of the elder brother of Moses and his role in the journey from Egypt to the Promised Land. This Catholic account of his life takes issue with the Judaic faith in asserting the spiritual powers of priesthood conferred on Aaron's descendants.

Abel

http://www.knight.org/advent/cathen/01035c.htm

Profile of the second son of Adam, who, according to Christian belief, was the first murder victim. Various interpretations of the etymology of his name are discussed, prior to details of his murder at the hands of his brother, Cain. Jewish, Christian, and Islamic theories speculating where the murder took place are also discussed.

Abraham

http://www.knight.org/advent/cathen/01051a.htm

Christian account of the life of the patriarch. The Biblical version of his life is retold, together with discussion of the origin of his name and examination of whether there is any archaeological evidence to support the Biblical and legendary accounts of Abraham.

Absalom

http://www.knight.org/advent/cathen/01058c.htm

Profile of David's favourite son. The story of the fall from grace of the handsome young man with a striking head of hair, his rebellion against his father, and David's grief-stricken reaction to his death, is retold.

Ark of the Covenant Page

http://www.domini.org/tabern/arkcovnt.htm

Detailed description of the Ark of the Covenant. The Ark, its contents (in the form of the two stone tablets of the law), and Aaron's rod that budded are described on this Web site. The page includes a picture of what historians believe the Ark may have looked like. The site also features many hyperlinks to other related religious sites.

Book of Daniel

http://www.knight.org/advent/cathen/04621b.htm

Detailed description of the events related in various versions of the Book of Daniel. The book is assessed as not being a true historical record of the Babylonian Exile, or the life of Daniel, but a source of comfort for God's chosen people undergoing persecution. Various authorship theories are discussed.

Commandments of God

http://www.knight.org/advent/cathen/04153a.htm

Full details of the development and significance of Christianity's fundamental moral and religious precepts. Differences in the ordering and numbering system used by different Christian denominations are explained.

Ecclesiasticus

http://www.knight.org/advent/cathen/05263a.htm

Very detailed commentary on the book of Ecclesiastes. Its maxims on individual morality and family values are presented, together with a history of the writing and translation of this important didactic work.

Elijah

http://www.knight.org/advent/cathen/05381b.htm

Profile of the Hebrew prophet. It examines the sources of information concerning his life, his struggles against the prophets of Baal, and the mystery of his disappearance. Jewish, Moslem, and Druse veneration of Elijah and legends associated with him are also presented.

Eve

http://www.knight.org/advent/cathen/
05646b.htm

Christian analysis of Eve. A retelling of
the few facts about a woman mentioned
only five times in the Bible is
accompanied by a traditional statement of
why Eve, and all women after her, were
sentenced to a life of sorrow and travail
by Eve's transgression in the Garden of
Eden.

Ezekiel

http://www.knight.org/advent/cathen/05737b.htm

Profile of the prophet whose name means 'strong
is God'. It traces how his reputation was built
upon the fulfilment of prophesies he had made.
There is also a discussion of which parts of the
book of Ezekiel are apocryphal.

Gideon

http://www.knight.org/advent/cathen/06402c.htm

Profile of the long life of Gideon, his judgeship
and daring military exploits. Inconsistencies in
accounts of his life and various versions of his
name are discussed.

Hosea

http://www.knight.org/advent/cathen/11337a.htm

Life of the minor Old Testament prophet. The
complex details of Hosea's forced marriage to a
dishonoured woman, and whether it had actual
historical or simply allegorical significance, are
discussed here.

Isaac

http://www.knight.org/advent/cathen/08175a.htm

Profile of the life of the son of Abraham. It traces
the Biblical evidence of how he was taken to be
sacrificed, was miraculously spared, and went on
to live a life of quiet and gentle devotion.

Jacob

http://www.knight.org/advent/cathen/08261a.htm

Profile of the turbulent life of the ancestor of the
12 tribes of Israel. This account from the *Catholic
Encyclopedia* concludes that Jacob was a real
historical figure, a complex mixture of good and
evil chastened by the experience of a long life.

F A C T

JACOB

in the Old Testament, Hebrew patriarch, son of
Isaac and Rebecca, who obtained the rights of
seniority from his twin brother Esau by
trickery. He married his cousins Leah and
Rachel, serving their father Laban seven years
for each, and at the time of famine in Canaan
joined his son Joseph in Egypt. His 12 sons
were the traditional ancestors of the 12 tribes
of Israel.

Jehovah (Yahweh)

http://www.knight.org/advent/cathen/08329a.htm

All there is to know about the Old Testament
name of God. This long article from the *Catholic
Encyclopedia* has information on the pre-Christian
origins, usage, pronunciation, and significance of
the name.

Joel

http://www.knight.org/advent/cathen/08419a.htm

Profile of the minor Old Testament prophet. There
is a summary of the themes of his prophetic
judgements. Various chronological theories trying
to place Joel within known events of Jewish
history are also discussed at this site.

Nahum

http://www.knight.org/advent/cathen/10670a.htm

Profile of the seventh of the minor prophets of the
Old Testament. This site includes a discussion of
the significance of his name, estimation of the
value of non-biblical evidence about him, and
theories concerning his origins. The three
chapters of the Book of Nahum are summarized
with stress on Nahum's obsession with the
impending destruction of Nineveh and its wicked
inhabitants.

Noah

http://www.knight.org/advent/cathen/11088a.htm

Profile from the *Catholic Encyclopedia* of the
improbably long-lived 'second father of the
human race' and his role in rescuing humanity
from the deluge. His 950-year life and also his
discovery of wine is related. The similar
Babylonian version of Noah's tale is also told.

Pentateuch

http://www.knight.org/advent/cathen/11646c.htm

Summary and thorough analysis of the first five books of the Bible from the *Catholic Encyclopedia*. The Pentateuch is presented as the basis for the rules of law and worship of Christians. There is a detailed discussion concerning various theories of authorship.

The Bible, New Testament

Bible Gateway

http://www.gospelcom.net/bible

Full text of six versions of the Bible, including the New International Version, the Revised Standard Version, and the King James Version. These are fully searchable by passage, phrase, or word, and the text includes hyperlinked footnotes and cross-references. The user can choose from five languages (including Latin). Links are also provided to other Bible-related sites.

Epistle of St Jude

http://www.knight.org/advent/cathen/08542b.htm

Summary of the Epistle attributed to Jude. The few hard facts about who Jude was, and when he wrote the Epistle, are related and various theories about the rest of his life are explored.

Epistle to the Galatians

http://www.knight.org/advent/cathen/06336a.htm

Detailed summary of the New Testament epistle and its significance. Historical facts concerning the central Anatolian tribes, known as Galatians, are presented, prior to details of Paul's efforts to win them for the church.

Epistle to the Hebrews

http://www.knight.org/advent/cathen/07181a.htm

Long article on the Old Testament epistle from the *Catholic Encyclopedia*. The practical exhortations in the epistle are stressed. The site shows the stylistic markers which distinguish the text from other, confirmed, writings of St Paul. A summary of the authorship dispute is also included.

John the Baptist, St

http://www.knight.org/advent/cathen/08486b.htm

Long article on the life and ministry of John the Baptist. Various theories concerning his family background and his date of birth are explored. The biblical account of his preaching and death are related, together with an assessment of his influence over later Christians.

Judas Iscariot

http://www.knight.org/advent/cathen/08539a.htm

Portrait of the man who committed the ultimate betrayal, from the *Catholic Encyclopedia*. There is discussion of the meaning of his name, his role as carrier of Jesus' purse, slight differences in biblical accounts of his act of deception, and speculation as to his motives.

Lazarus

http://www.knight.org/advent/cathen/09096a.htm

Article on the two biblical figures called Lazarus. The leprous beggar of the parable told by Luke, and the rewards he received for his stoic acceptance of suffering, are described. There is also an account of the man raised from the dead by Jesus.

Luke, St

http://www.knight.org/advent/cathen/09420a.htm

Extremely detailed source of information on St Luke from the *Catholic Encyclopedia*. A biography of the Greek physician precedes a presentation of the evidence attesting to the authenticity of the Gospel bearing his name. The contradictions and inconsistencies in his writings are defended against those who have criticized him.

Magi

http://www.knight.org/advent/cathen/09527a.htm

Extensive account of historical and Biblical beliefs relating to the magi. There is a description of the development of the Persian priestly caste and Cyrus's reduction of their influence. The Biblical connotation of the magi with magic is discussed, prior to speculation about the number and identity of the mysterious wise astrologers who came to visit the infant Jesus.

Peter, St

http://www.knight.org/advent/cathen/11744a.htm

Ten thousand-word profile of the life and legacy of the martyred first bishop of Rome from the *Catholic Encyclopedia*. The familiar Biblical story of the fisherman who followed Jesus is retold in detail. There is an extensive presentation of the historical facts confirming that Peter was put to death in Rome. There is also a section on how Peter has been represented subsequently.

Pilate, Pontius

http://www.knight.org/advent/cathen/12083c.htm

Portrait of the Roman procurator of Judea whose long period of office overlapped with the ministry of John the Baptist and Jesus. Speculation about his family origins is followed by a description of his actions in endorsing the crucifixion. Ethiopian and Greek Orthodox beliefs that Pilate, struck with remorse, converted to Christianity are rigorously refuted in this article.

St Gabriel the Archangel

http://www.knight.org/advent/cathen/06330a.htm

Profile of the archangel. There are details of the four mentions of Gabriel in the Bible and a summary of the differences between Christian and Jewish beliefs relating to Gabriel.

Worldwide Study Bible

http://www.ccel.org/olb

http://ccel.wheaton.edu/wwsb/index.html

Exhaustive guide to the Bible. The full text of all the books of the Old and New Testaments, synopses of important sections, explanations of the significance of many of the most important aspects, and a biblical dictionary are all provided.

Religious People

Archbishop of Canterbury

http://www.archbishopofcanterbury.org/

Home page of the Archbishop of Canterbury, head of the Anglican church. Alongside a biography of George Carey, the current incumbent, is a description of the role, duties, and history of the post, and information about the archbishop's residence at Lambeth Palace. There are also key articles and speeches, and links to other Anglican sites.

Augustine

http://ccat.sas.upenn.edu/jod/twayne/tabcont.html

Thorough biography of the life and work of St Augustine. It traces his participation in theological disputes, the self-analysis in his famous *Confessions*, and the long dispute over ownership of the Augustinian legacy. There is also a comprehensive bibliography.

Boehme, Jakob

http://www.erols.com/nbeach/boehme.html

Part of the Ecole Initiative maintained by the University of Evansville, this page begins with a biography of German religious mystic Jakob Boehme, then discusses Boehme's principal philosophical and religious ideas, and ends with an evaluation of his contributions to religious thought. The list of sources at the bottom of the page includes works by and about Boehme.

Campion, Edmund

http://www.knight.org/advent/cathen/05293c.htm

Detailed profile of the life of the English Jesuit martyr. It traces his precocious academic career, his growing doubts about having taken the anti-Papist Oath of Supremacy, his barefoot pilgrimage to Rome, the dream in which he foresaw his martyrdom, his return to Britain, and the trial which led to his execution.

Confucius

http://www.confucius.org/main01.htm

Some background information on Confucius and Confucianism as well as images and versions of most of his famous texts on morality. The texts are available in English translation, or the original Chinese, if your browser will support the character set.

Crowley, Aleister

http://www.crl.com/~thelema/crowley.html

Biographical details of the English mystic Aleister Crowley, with links to a description and picture of the Egyptian funerary stele that inspired him, and to the *Book of the Law* that he subsequently wrote.

Francis of Assisi, St

http://www.knight.org/advent/cathen/06221a.htm

Detailed biography of the ascetic founder of the Franciscan order. It traces his privileged upbringing, his renunciation of wealth, the commitment to a life of poverty, which earned him the title of 'the Umbrian *poverello* (poor little man)', and his establishment of the order of mendicant monks. The continuing allure of St Francis, for Catholics and non-Catholics alike, is discussed.

Gurdjieff Home Page

http://www.gurdjieff.org/

Biography and chronology about the Russian occultist and mystic George Gurdjieff. His writings, sayings, music, and key pupils are discussed, and the site contains a number of essays, as well as a bibliography.

Helena, St

http://www.knight.org/advent/cathen/07202b.htm

Biography of the mother of Constantine the Great. It examines her humble childhood, her marriage and divorce, the role of her son in her conversion to Christianity, the energy with which she endowed churches, and the trip to Palestine during which she is said to have discovered the cross upon which Christ was crucified.

Hildegard of Bingen

http://tweedledee.ucsb.edu/%7Ekris/music/Hildegard.html

Extensive presentation of the life and deeds of an extraordinary woman of the Middle Ages. The site discusses all aspects of Hildegard's varied life, with sections on her famous visions, scientific views, liturgical works, and music. It also includes a useful bibliography and discography.

Hus, Jan

http://www.knight.org/advent/cathen/07584b.htm

Biography of the Czech priest, tracing the history of the conflict with Pope Innocent VII which led to his violent death. Huss's support for the English reformer John Wycliffe, and the popular support he received in his native Prague, are also described.

Ignatius of Antioch, St

http://www.knight.org/advent/cathen/07644a.htm

Full biography of the martyred bishop of Antioch. It traces his arrest in Syria, the long journey to Rome during which he composed many epistles, and his violent death. The authenticity of the various documents ascribed to this saint is discussed at length.

International Albert Schweitzer Foundation

http://www.schweitzer.org/english/aseind.htm

Detailed biography and chronology of the theologian, organist, and missionary surgeon Albert Schweitzer. There is information and reviews about a number of his writings, of which many are quoted, and details of his commitment to the disarmament movement.

John Paul II

http://www.vatican.va/holy_father/john_paul_ii/

Official Vatican account of the life, times, and achievements of the current pope. In addition to a biography of Ioannes Paulus PP II, there are full texts (available in eight languages) of the Holy Father's encyclicals, exhortations, apostolic letters, and other pronouncements.

Loyala, St Ignatius

http://www.knight.org/advent/cathen/07639c.htm

Biography of the founder of the Jesuit order. It traces his dissolute life as a young Spanish courtier, the battle wound that began his interest in religion, his visit to the Holy Land, the years of study which led to his ordination in his middle years, and his subsequent work with the Society of Jesus.

Martin Luther (1483–1546)

http://www.geocities.com/Vienna/1667/luther.htm

Introduction to the life and works of the German Christian church reformer, Martin Luther. The page includes links to 'Project Wittenberg', articles on Luther's anti-Semitism, a 'timeline of the Protestant Reformation', and the journal *Semper Reformanda*. Here also, are the words to, and audio clips of, five famous German hymns, and a brief biography of Luther in both English and German, which includes links to contemporary figures.

Mother Teresa

http://www.gargaro.com/mother_teresa/

Huge source of information on the Albanian-born 'saint of the gutters'. This site include a comprehensive biography, pictures and audio clips, news of the campaign to hasten her canonization, and reports of the ongoing work of the Missionaries of Charity.

Patrick, St

http://www.knight.org/advent/cathen/11554a.htm

Extended account of the long life of the patron saint of Ireland, from the *Catholic Encyclopedia*. It relates how his six years as a kidnap victim prepared him for his future apostolic work to convert the Irish. His many journeys in Ireland are described with the help of extracts from Irish texts. His work to build the Irish church is described in detail, together with a summary of his *Confessio*.

Pope Clement VII

http://www.knight.org/advent/Popes/ppcl07.htm

Profile of the turbulent life of the Medici whose papacy was dominated by two disasters for Catholicism. The background to the sack of Rome and the dispute with Henry VIII, which led the English Church to break with Rome, are also related here.

<table>
<tr><td>F
A
C
T</td><td>**POPE**

the bishop of Rome, head of the Roman Catholic Church, which claims he is the spiritual descendant of St Peter. Elected by the Sacred College of Cardinals, a pope dates his pontificate from his coronation with the tiara, or triple crown, at St Peter's Basilica, Rome.</td></tr>
</table>

Pope Gregory XIII

http://www.knight.org/advent/Popes/ppgr13.htm

Profile of the pope who introduced the Gregorian calendar. This account shows this to be one of the few successes of a papacy dogged by misfortune.

Pope Innocent III

http://www.knight.org/advent/Popes/ppin03.htm

Biography of the medieval Pope. It highlights his erudition, the reluctance with which he accepted the papacy, his troubled relationship with King John of England, his launching of the fourth crusade, his struggles against heresy, and his support for St Francis and St Dominic as they established their orders.

Pope John XXII

http://www.knight.org/advent/Popes/ppjo22.htm

Profile of the combative French medieval Pope. It traces his contributions to canon law and his condemnation of the Franciscan assertions that Christ and his disciples owned no material possessions.

Pope John XXIII

http://www.knight.org/advent/Popes/ppjo23.htm

Portrait of the farmer's son, his rise to the papacy, and his summoning of the Second Vatican Council. There are also links to his major encyclicals and speeches.

Pope Julius II

http://www.knight.org/advent/Popes/ppju02.htm

Portrait of the powerful Renaissance pope. It traces his humble origins, his ambitious and twice-thwarted pursuit of the papacy, his championship of the arts, and his vigorous foreign policy.

Pope Leo XIII

http://www.knight.org/advent/Popes/pple12.htm

Profile of the Jesuit pope. It traces his early concerns for social justice and the diplomatic skills with which he countered Italian anticlericalism. The main events of his papacy, his appeasement of Bismarck, persuading French Catholics to accept the republic, and the vigour with which he rebuked uncaring employers, are outlined. All his encyclicals may be accessed at this site.

Pope Paul VI

http://www.knight.org/advent/Popes/pppa06.htm

Profile of the first pope to visit every continent. It traces his upbringing, the poor health that dogged him, his service as a papal diplomat, and his elevation to the papacy. His efforts to internationalize the Curia and to reassert traditional moral beliefs are highlighted. The texts of his encyclicals and speeches may also be accessed at this site.

Pope Pius IV

http://www.knight.org/advent/Popes/pppi04.htm

Profile of the son of a poor Milanese family and his rise to the papacy. His convening of the Council of Trent and his patronage of the arts and learning are highlighted.

Pope Pius IX

http://www.knight.org/advent/Popes/pppi09.htm

Account of the long life of the longest serving pope. It traces how the young epileptic turned to theology after being refused employment in the Vatican as a guard. The account of his papacy highlights the tension in his relations with the Italian state, his compensating successes in spiritual matters, and his affirmation of the infallibility of papal *ex cathedra* pronouncements.

Pope Pius VI

http://www.knight.org/advent/Popes/pppi06.htm

Profile of the unfortunate papacy of Gianangelo Braschi. It traces his difficulties with the Jesuits, Catherine the Great, Joseph II, and the leaders of the French Revolution, and his miserable death in exile as a prisoner.

Pope Pius VII

http://www.knight.org/advent/Popes/pppi07.htm

Biography of the noble Benedictine and his rise to the papacy. His tussles with Napoleon and the turbulence of their relations are highlighted. There is an account of how, despite his previous imprisonment at the hands of Napoleon, Pius VII interceded with the English to treat his old adversary with humanity.

Pope Pius XI

http://www.knight.org/advent/Popes/pppi11.htm

Profile of the humble librarian who became pope in 1922. It describes how his service as papal nuncio in Poland paved the way to the papacy. The description of his papacy highlights his encyclicals on marriage and education and the Lateran Treaty signed with Mussolini which finally resolved the question of the legal status of Rome. The text of his main pronouncements can also be accessed at this site.

Pope Pius XII

http://www.knight.org/advent/Popes/pppi12.htm

Profile of the man, born into a family devoted to papal service, who served as papal nuncio and became pope on the eve of World War II. This account from the *Catholic Encyclopedia* stresses his role in saving Rome from Nazi destruction and sheltering refugees in the Vatican. The text of his main addresses and papal pronouncements can also be accessed.

Pope St Gregory I

http://www.knight.org/advent/cathen/06780a.htm

Extended biography of the influential pontiff from the *Catholic Encyclopedia*. Gregory's achievements as a lawyer, administrator, theologian, and father of the medieval papacy are traced in great, and eulogistic, detail.

Pope St Gregory VII

http://www.knight.org/advent/cathen/06791c.htm

Full biography of Gregory and his long and influential career. His battles to abolish simony and clerical incontinency are related in detail. The account of his lonely death reports his last words: 'I have loved justice and hated iniquity, therefore I die in exile.'

Pope St Leo III

http://www.knight.org/advent/Popes/pple03.htm

Account of the turbulent life of the medieval pope. It describes how the newly enthroned pontiff was abducted, narrowly escaped being blinded, and was rescued by Charlemagne. His relationship with Charlemagne is traced, together with his work to build and restore the churches of Rome.

Pope St Pius V

http://www.knight.org/advent/cathen/12130a.htm

Profile of the ascetic Dominican and his rise to the papacy. His conflicts with the Turks, Elizabeth I, and heretical princes in Germany are highlighted, together with his encouragement of the Inquisition.

Pope St Pius X

http://www.knight.org/advent/Popes/pppi10.htm

Profile of the pious cobbler's son who worked for 26 years as a parish priest before becoming a bishop and succeeding to the papacy in 1903. The account of his papacy highlights his problems with French anticlericalism and modernism. The texts of his pronouncements can be accessed.

Saint Anthony: Father of the Monks

http://pharos.bu.edu/cn/synexarion/Anthony.txt

Extensive biographical article prepared by adherents of the Coptic Orthodox Church on 'the first Christian to live a life of consecrated solitude'. It focuses on his importance to early Christians and his influence in spreading monasticism.

Young, Brigham

http://www3.pbs.org/weta/thewest/wpages/ wpgs400/w4young.htm

Profile of the life and importance of the US Mormon religious leader. The site includes a photograph and links to Joseph Smith, Winter Quarters, Salt Lake Valley, John D Lee, Promontory Point, Utah, and to sections about significant years in Young's life.

Miscellaneous Belief

Astrology Zone

http://astrologyzone.go.com/

Detailed astrology page, including detailed horoscopes which are updated monthly. The site also includes a 'Current planetary trends' feature and a page explaining, to a certain extent, how the astrologer's predictions are made.

Centre for Scientific Creation

http://www.creationscience.com/

Dedicated to researching the case for creation, rather than evolution, as the origin of living species. Most of the evidence is gathered in a book which is heavily promoted on this page. However, the entire book is available online.

Eschatology

http://www.knight.org/advent/cathen/05528b.htm

Extensive treatment of the branch of theology dealing with the 'last things' (*ta eschata*). Eschatological themes in a variety of non-Christian, historical, and traditional cultures are explored, prior to a full description of Christian eschatology, and a statement of Catholic doctrine on the end of time.

Guide to Early Church Documents

http://www.iclnet.org/pub/resources/ christian-history.html

Guide to early church documents including canonical documents, creeds, the writings of the Apostolic Fathers, and other historical texts relevant to church history.

Heaven

http://www.knight.org/advent/cathen/07170a.htm#I

Lengthy exposition of Christian beliefs in the destination of the good from the *Catholic Encyclopedia*. This site includes discussion of the various names given to heaven, beliefs concerning the location of heaven, the supernatural and eternal nature of heaven, and an analysis of beatitude.

Joan's Witch Directory

http://www.rci.rutgers.edu/~jup/witches/

Historical resource about the practice of witchcraft and the persecution of witches in the Middle Ages. The site includes a timeline, details about persecuted witches, a list of references, and links to further relevant information on the Web.

Medieval Sourcebook: Witchcraft Documents

http://www.fordham.edu/halsall/source/ witches1.html

Selection of medieval documents on witchcraft, summarizing the hostility and intolerance against women who were, justly or not, accused of sorcery. The site does not aim to prove or disprove the existence of medieval witchcraft, but it does offer an interesting depiction of this prejudice against women, and a few men, in late medieval times.

Multifaithnet

http://www.multifaith.org/

Run by the University of Derby, this site gives in-depth descriptions of all the main world religions.

Ontological Arguments

http://plato.stanford.edu/entries/ontological-arguments/

Very detailed examination of the history and premises of ontological arguments for the existence of God. There are summaries of arguments, counter-arguments, parodies, and a helpful glossary of terms used in the debate. There is also a comprehensive bibliography and guide to other related Internet resources.

Pantheism

http://plato.stanford.edu/entries/pantheism/

Summary of Pantheistic beliefs from ancient times to the modern day. The dichotomy between immanence and transcendence in Western and non-Western philosophy is exhaustively traced. There is a comprehensive bibliography and guide to Pantheist societies and other Internet resources.

Pentecost (Whitsunday)

http://www.knight.org/advent/cathen/15614b.htm

Account of the origins and variations in observance of the Jewish and Christian festival. Local customs associated with Whitsun in Italy, France, Russia, and England are set out here.

F A C T

PENTECOST
in Judaism, the festival of *Shavuot*, celebrated on the 50th day after **passover** in commemoration of the giving of the Ten Commandments to Moses on Mount Sinai, and the end of the grain harvest; in the Christian church, Pentecost is the day on which the apostles experienced inspiration of the Holy Spirit, commemorated on Whit Sunday.

Places of Peace and Power

http://www.sacredsites.com/

Comprehensive guide to places of pilgrimage across the world. Compiled by an anthropologist, it has details of his journeys, many photos, and analysis of the significance of the sites. There are a large number of articles and links to a wide range of pilgrimage and spirituality sites.

Revelations of Divine Love

http://ccel.wheaton.edu/j/julian/revelations/

Full text of the mystic work for which Julian of Norwich is best remembered. This 1901 annotated edition has notes explaining the meaning of words unfamiliar to the modern reader.

Salem Witch Museum

http://www.salemwitchmuseum.com/

This site is a fascinating source of information on the infamous witch trials of Salem, Massachusetts, which took place in 1692. Read about the history of the trials and check out the 'Frequently Asked Questions' page. You can also take a tour of significant trial sites, which include maps, photographs, and descriptions. You will also find information on the founder of Salem, Roger Conant.

Satanism

http://www.religioustolerance.org/satanism.htm

Detailed objective analysis of what constitutes a satanist. Satanic notions from a variety of cultural and religious standpoints are set out. The modern satanic practices associated with Aleister Crowley are summarized along with the beliefs of the Church of Satan. There are links to the Church of Lucifer and a host of other demonic sites.

Winter Festivals from the Past and Present

http://www.maui.net/~mcculc/xmas.htm

Explains the origins of Christmas and other festivals falling in December. There are descriptions of midwinter festivals in countries as far apart as Tibet, Italy, Japan, Sweden, and Mexico. There are details of some bizarre and fascinating rituals, including a yak-butter sculpting festival.

World Council of Churches

http://www.wcc-coe.org/

Large site of the organization bringing together over 300 Christian churches in 120 countries. It contains comprehensive information on the ecumenical movement, evangelism, and the role of Christian churches in development. There are

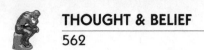

lists of e-mail addresses of churches around the world and of church search engines which are useful in locating the far-flung reaches of Christianity.

World Scripture

http://unification.net/ws/

A good source of scriptural and religious material for scholars and people of all faiths, this site has a comparative anthology of sacred texts containing over 4,000 scriptural passages from 268 sacred texts and 55 oral traditions, organized under 164 different themes. The text is the result of a five-year project involving the collaboration of an international team of scholars representing all the major religious traditions of the world.

Atheism & Hereticism

Articles by Clarence Darrow

http://www.infidels.org/library/historical/clarence_darrow/

This site includes the text of several controversial religious essays written by Clarence Darrow, the titles of which are 'Absurdities of the Bible; Facing Life Fearlessly', which contrasts the pessimistic and optimistic approaches to living life and was initially delivered in a lecture at the University of Chicago; the 'Lord's Day Alliance', which Darrow suggests is a New York society 'engaged in the business of killing pleasure'; and 'Why I Am an Agnostic'.

Atheist Express

http://www.hti.net/www/atheism

Site dedicated to atheism, free thought, humanism, ethics, religious criticism, and state–church separation. It includes history, articles, cartoons, and milestones of and about atheism, as well as a slightly different slant on church history.

Biographical Dictionary of Ancient, Medieval, and Modern Freethinkers

http://www.infidels.org/library/historical/joseph_mccabe/dictionary.html

Full listing and brief biographies of the most famous atheists, agnostics, freethinkers, and opponents of Christian dogma. Among those included are W B Yeats, Mary Wollstonecraft, Peter the Great, Tennyson, Conrad, and Confucius.

Religious Atheism

http://www.hypertext.com/atheisms/

Compilation of non-traditional sources on atheism, including views of the subject according to Christianity, classical atheism, and liberation theology. There are also details and discussion by religious atheists.

Feminism

Andrea Dworkin Online Library

http://www.igc.org/Womensnet/dworkin/OnlineLibrary.html

Large source of information on the life, works, and social concerns of the US feminist writer. Dworkin's major books, articles, speeches, and novels may be accessed, together with an autobiography, bibliography, and reports on moves to outlaw pornography.

Anthony, Susan B

http://www.sba-list.org/

Account of the life and achievements of the US feminist pioneer. This site is run by the group bearing her name that lobbies for increased representation of women in the US Congress. Details of the activities of the Susan B Anthony List are also presented here.

Claim of Englishwomen to the Suffrage Constitutionally Considered (1867)

http://www.indiana.edu/~letrs/vwwp/taylor/suffrage.html

Transcript reprinted from the *Westminster Review*. The text deals with the way in which the first claim of suffrage petition was dealt with by parliament in 1867. The petition was signed by 1,500 women, and its text is a brief proposal that the lack of a right for women to vote was anomalous to existing property laws and other areas of the constitution, and that it should therefore be abolished. The way parliament dealt with the claim is patronizing in the extreme, citing the values of 'motherly virtues' and 'homeliness' as being of equal value in the home as in politics.

Critiques of Feminism – Camille Paglia

http://www.carnell.com/feminism/camille_paglia/

Articles and interviews setting out the views of the combative US antifeminist. The compiler of the selection puts forward his view that the surface glitter of Paglia's prose cannot hide the lack of intellectual content within.

Fawcett Library special Collections: Josephine Butler Society Library

http://www.lgu.ac.uk/fawcett/butler.htm

Pages dedicated to the work of the English social reformer Josephine Butler, and the library where many of the Josephine Butler Society papers are held. Information about the important work of the Society is included, as well as brief biographical details of Butler's life and work.

4,000 Years of Women in Science

http://www.astr.ua.edu/4000WS/

Valuable resource for all those interested in gender studies and particularly women scientists. The site lists over 125 names and offers biographies grouped by subject and century, as well as the usual alphabetical index. It also includes an interactive quiz, photographs, extra links to other photographic galleries, and a 'Did you know?' section with interesting facts on women in science.

Gilman, Charlotte Perkins

http://us.history.wisc.edu/hist102/bios/19.html

Biography of the US feminist. It describes her childhood, early insistence on independence, the marriage-related depression which forever changed her views of the role of women in society, her success as a writer and campaigner, views on housework and household organization, and her suicide.

Goldman, Emma

http://sunsite.berkeley.edu/Goldman/

Comprehensive archive of material on the life and struggles of the feminist. Details of the papers and lecture notes she left behind are set out here and a number of biographies look at her life and ongoing relevance for the feminist movement. Material suitable for school history students is also presented and there is a listing of a large number of publications and Goldman research projects.

Jane Addams – Hull House Association

http://www.hullhouse.org/

Home of the institution founded by social work pioneer Jane Addams. There is a full biography of the first US woman to win a Nobel Prize, extracts from her writings, and details of the institution that continues her work.

Spartacus Educational: The Emancipation of Women 1860–1920

http://www.spartacus.schoolnet.co.uk/resource.htm

Internet encyclopedia on the struggle towards women's emancipation in Britain 1860–1920. Based on excerpts from primary sources of the period, the encyclopedia deals with a wide range of relevant topics. It also offers biographies of a series of women involved in this struggle and a variety of cartoons illustrating the topics discussed.

Stanton, Elizabeth Cady

http://www.govpataki4women.org/eCStanton.html

Interesting biography of the early leader of the US women's rights movement. It describes Stanton's upbringing, efforts to persuade her father to allow her a proper education, commitment to the antislavery movement, her lifelong association with Susan B Anthony, and her hostility to organized religion which antagonized public opinion.

Steinem, Gloria

http://www.greatwomen.org/stnem.htm

Biography of the US feminist writer. The site traces her childhood, the financial hardships of her adolescence, her interest in acting, her political involvement in college, the abortion in Britain which affected her deeply, and the political journalism and involvement in protest movements that have made her famous. There is also a summary of her writing and a bibliography.

Vindication of the Rights of Woman, A

http://www.bartleby.com/144/index.html

Online edition of Mary Wollstonecraft's *A Vindication of the Rights of Woman.*

Votes for Women: Suffrage Pictures, 1850–1920

http://lcweb2.loc.gov/ammem/vfwhtml/vfwhome.html

Part of the American Memory presentation of the US Library of Congress, this page is devoted to images from the campaign for women's suffrage in the USA. The collection features numerous photos of prominent women in the cause, suffrage parades and picketers, plus cartoons commenting on the movement, as well as an anti-suffragette display. The collection can be browsed by keyword, name, or subject. An informative timeline provides an overview to the US suffrage movement.

Who was Fawcett?

http://www.lgu.ac.uk/fawcett/fawbiog.htm

Biography of Millicent Garrett Fawcett, leader of the British campaign for votes for women. The page also includes a black-and-white portrait, an introduction to the Fawcett Library in London where many of her papers are held, and a brief bibliography.

Women on the March

http://www.onf.ca/FMT/E/58/58053.html

Film record of women campaigners at the turn of the century and of the suffragette movement's struggle for equal rights.

Women's National Commission

http://193.128.244.178/wnc/index.htm

Site of the official advisory body charged with ensuring that UK government decisions take into account the views of women. The structure of the commission and the key issues it is concerned with are set out. There is also a full list of the organizations affiliated with it.

Women's Studies: Film Reviews

http://www.inform.umd.edu/EdRes/Topic/WomensStudies/FilmReviews/

Hundreds of films reviewed by the Department of Women's Studies at the University of Maryland, USA. The films themselves are, in the main, not made with feminists in mind, but the reviews generally treat them as if they should have been. The reviews are in plain text format, with no pictures, graphics or any other multimedia content.

Women's Web

http://sfgate.com/examiner/womensweb.html

Coverage of women in business, and women's issues generally. It includes input from *Working Woman, Working Mother,* and *Ms.* magazines.

F A C T

WOMEN'S MOVEMENT

early European campaigners of the 17th–19th centuries fought for women's right to own property, to have access to higher education, and to vote. Once women's suffrage was achieved in the 20th century, the emphasis of the movement shifted to the goals of equal social and economic opportunities for women, including employment.

Women Win the Vote

http://www.inform.umd.edu/EdRes/Topic/WomensStudies/ReadingRoom/History/Vote.html

1995 celebration of the 75th Anniversary of Women's Suffrage in America. The site includes profiles of 75 suffragists, a brief timeline of the suffrage movement, lesser known stories relating to the struggles behind the famous 1920 19th Amendment, and some reflections on the wider significance of that long battle.

Classical Philosophy

Ancient Greek Scepticism

http://www.utm.edu/research/iep/s/skepanci.htm

Good account of the ancient Greek origins of Scepticism. It traces the emergence of Pyrronhism into the more formal Academic Scepticism and its disputation with Stoicism. The controversies of post-academic Scepticism are summarized.

Apology by Plato

http://classics.mit.edu/Plato/apology.html

Plato's account of how Socrates replied to the charges of impiety as he prepared to die. This translation by Benjamin Jowett is linked to comments about the *Apology* and information about other works by Socrates.

Aristotle

http://www-history.mcs.st-and.ac.uk/history/
Mathematicians/Aristotle.html

Biography of one of the most famous philosophers in history. The site includes a portrait taken from a bust of the Greek philosopher and many publication references for further study. The site also has a link to a site at Clarke University, USA, where many of Aristotle's ideas are explained in some depth.

Diogenes of Sinope

http://www.utm.edu/research/iep/d/diogsino.htm

Profile of the ascetic and Cynic philosopher. This site attempts to separate the known facts of his life from fiction and doubt is cast on the famous tale of Diogenes meeting Alexander while sitting in his tub. It is concluded, however, that the philosopher left behind no lasting intellectual legacy.

Discourses, The

http://classics.mit.edu/Epictetus/discourses.html

Text of this work by the Greek philosopher Epictetus.

Heraclitus

http://www.utm.edu/research/iep/
h/heraclit.htm

Profile of the Presocratic Greek philosopher. His aristocratic disdain for mankind is described. His gloomy philosophy and the importance he attached to fire is also set out.

Last Days of Socrates

http://socrates.clarke.edu/

Maintained by the philosophy department at

Clarke College in Iowa, this site uses the works of Plato to describe the last days of Socrates' life and to present the profound philosophical dilemmas he faced before submitting himself to death. To assist in comprehension, the text contains numerous hypertext links to explanatory information. There are also audio clips and a number of sketches, pictures and diagrams that detail where the events are taking place.

Neoplatonism

http://www.utm.edu/research/iep/n/neoplato.htm

Summary of the mystical last development of Greek philosophy. The leading figures of the movement away from scientific rigour are described. The medieval renewal of neo-Platonism is also summarized.

On the Heavens

http://classics.mit.edu/Aristotle/heavens.sum.html

Text of Aristotle's famous work.

On the Nature of Things by Titus Lucretius Carus

http://classics.mit.edu//Carus/nature_things.sum.
html

Full text of the poem by Lucretius. The text is very lengthy, but, to make downloading quicker, the six books of the poem are split into smaller files. The poem is believed to have been written around 50 BC and this translation is by William Ellery Leonard.

On the Soul

http://classics.mit.edu/Aristotle/soul.sum.html

Text of Aristotle's famous work.

F
A
C
T

SOUL
according to many religions, an intangible part of a human being that survives the death of the physical body. Judaism, Christianity, and Islam all teach that at the end of the world each soul will be judged and assigned to heaven or hell on its merits.

Parmenides

http://www.utm.edu/research/iep/p/parmenid.htm

Biography of the Greek philosopher and poet. It

traces how his reputation was established as an exemplary citizen and lawmaker. His innovations in the Ionic prose tradition are described, together with a lengthy summary of his cosmological speculations.

Physics
http://classics.mit.edu/Aristotle/physics.sum.html

Complete translation of Aristotle's work as well as a number of comments written on the piece by readers.

Plato's 'Allegory of the Cave'
http://www.netside.net/~szot/Allegory.html

Online edition of Plato's 'Allegory of the Cave' taken from Book VII of his *The Republic*.

Poetics
http://classics.mit.edu/Aristotle/poetics.sum.html

Text of Aristotle's classic work on tragic drama.

Protagoras
http://www.utm.edu/research/iep/p/protagor.htm

Profile of the life and legacy of the early Sophist. Doubt is cast on the well-known story that he was a poor porter when he met Democritus. The commercial success he gained from the popularity of his teaching is described. His famous maxim that 'man is the measure of all things' is also explained.

Pyrrho
http://www.utm.edu/research/iep/p/pyrrho.htm

Profile of the founder of the school of Scepticism. It traces the formative influence of his participation in the expeditions of Alexander the Great. It describes how he formulated the view that it is impossible ever to arrive at the truth and the effect this had on his personal life. The practical legacy of his philosophy is also analyzed.

Rhetoric
http://classics.mit.edu/Aristotle/rhetoric.sum.html

Full text of Aristotle's analysis of the techniques of persuasion. This W Rhys Roberts translation is accompanied by several commentaries on the *Rhetoric* and links to texts of other works by Aristotle.

Sophists
http://www.utm.edu/research/iep/s/sophists.htm

History of the professional class of Greek pedagogues who became known as Sophists. It describes the function they filled as teachers of rhetoric, politics, grammar, etymology, history, physics, mathematics, and virtue. The author of this site argues that (like modern spin-doctors) truth took a back seat to the presentational skills they imparted to novice politicians.

Stoicism
http://www.utm.edu/research/iep/s/stoicism.htm

Comprehensive account of the Stoic system of ethics. It is stressed that for Stoics pain and pleasure, poverty and riches, sickness and health, were of equal unimportance. The influence of Stoic ideas for the evolution of Greek ethics, physics, and virtue is examined together with an analysis of differences with Cynicism.

Works by Aristotle
http://classics.mit.edu/Browse/browse-Aristotle.html

Downloadable text files containing the full works of Aristotle. Twenty-nine philosophical debates on various subjects make up the collection, each one being in the format of a very large text file. Despite the size of the documents they do not take long to download from this very fast server at the Massachusetts Institute of Technology.

Works by Plato
http://classics.mit.edu/Browse/browse-Plato.html

Twenty five of Plato's works translated into English are available to download as text files from this MIT-run Web site, including possibly his best-known work *The Republic*. The files are complete versions of the works and are therefore large and may take some time to download.

Xenophon: 'The Economist'
http://tom.cs.cmu.edu/cgi-bin/book/lookup?num=1173

Part of the Project Gutenberg e-text collection, this page features the text of Xenophon's essay 'The Economist' – 'A Treatise on the Science of the Household in the form of a Dialogue' between Socrates and Critobulus.

Zeno of Elea

http://www.utm.edu/research/iep/z/zenoelea.htm

Comprehensive account of the life and legacy of the Greek philosopher. It traces his advocacy of the teachings of Parmenides and his love of paradoxes. His classic speculations about the implications for space and time in the flight of an arrow, and later comments on this seeming paradox by Kant, Hume, and Hegel, are analysed in detail.

Medieval Philosophy

Abelard

http://www.nd.edu/Departments/Maritain/etext/abelard.htm

Extended biography (from the Jacques Maritain Centre at the University of Notre Dame) of Peter Abelard, a celebrated and influential philosopher, theologian, and teacher of the Middle Ages.

Avicenna

http://www-groups.dcs.st-and.ac.uk/history/Mathematicians/Avicenna.html

Part of an archive containing the biographies of the world's greatest mathematicians, this site is devoted to the life and contributions of Arabian philosopher and scientist Avicenna. In addition to biographical information, you will find a list of references about Avicenna and links to other essays in the archive that refer to him. The text of this essay includes hyperlinks to the essays of those mathematicians and thinkers who influenced Avicenna. You will also find an image of him, which you can click on to enlarge, and a map of his birthplace.

Bacon, Roger

http://www-groups.dcs.st-and.ac.uk/history/Mathematicians/Bacon.html

Devoted to the life and work of Roger Bacon. In addition to biographical information, you will find a list of 12 references about Bacon and hyperlinks to the essays of those mathematicians

and thinkers who influenced Bacon. You will also find an image of of the man, which you can click on to enlarge, and a map of his birthplace.

Summa Theologica of St Thomas Aquinas

http://www.newadvent.org/summa/

Hypertext edition of the *Summa Theologica,* probably the most famous work of Thomas Aquinas, and one of the earliest general expositions of the Catholic faith.

Thomas Aquinas at Jacques Maritain Centre

http://www.nd.edu/Departments/Maritain/etext/stthomas.htm

Huge, text-based site containing a detailed biography of Thomas Aquinas. There is a large amount of information on his writings and style, and it also details his influence on subsequent philosophers.

Thomism

http://www.nd.edu/Departments/Maritain/etext/thomism.htm

Lengthy exposition of the Scholastic tradition associated with Thomas Aquinas. The contents include the bases of Thomism, the history of its acceptance within the Catholic Church, the decline of Scholasticism in the seventeenth and eighteenth centuries, its revival, and the creation of neo-Thomism. There are also profiles of some prominent Thomists.

16th- & 17th-century Philosophy

Bruno, Giordano

http://es.rice.edu/ES/humsoc/Galileo/People/bruno.html

Biography of the Italian philosopher. It traces the heterodox interests that brought him to the attention of the Inquisition and drove him into exile. This site also contains the revelation that Bruno, burned at the stake for his adoption of Copernican views, was ignorant of astronomy and not well regarded by Galileo and Kepler.

Debate Between Thomas Hobbes and John Locke: A Creative Essay

http://www.yucc.yorku.ca/~rickg/academics/
hobesvlo.html

This page is the 'transcript' of a mock debate on the state of human nature, between philosophers John Locke and Thomas Hobbes held in 2093. The two philosophers are brought back to life in order to debate the state of human nature. A bibliography of sources follows the text.

Discourse on Method

http://cybercom.net/~rbjones/rbjpub/philos/
classics/descarte/index.htm

Complete text of Descartes' work which includes the phrase *'cogito ergo sum'* ('I think, therefore I am').

Erasmus Text Project

http://smith2.sewanee.edu/Erasmus/etp.html

Access to hypertext editions of the work of Desiderius Erasmus. Most of the texts are in English translation, although *Moriae Encomium* is only available in Latin.

Essay Concerning Human Understanding

http://coombs.anu.edu.au/Depts/RSSS/
Philosophy/Texts/LockeUTOC.html

Full text of Locke's influential analysis of the basis of human knowledge. He argues that the mind is born a blank upon which all knowledge is inscribed in the form of human experience.

Ethics (Part I)

http://www.erols.com/jyselman/e1elwes.htm

Complete text of the first part of Benedict Spinoza's most famous philosophical work. This page is part of a larger site, which also contains the remaining parts of *Ethics*, as well as a commentary and a 'Spinoza glossary'.

Malebranche, Nicolas

http://www.utm.edu/research/iep/
m/malebran.htm

Profile of the French Cartesian philosopher. The circumstances of his life are described alongside the attempt to reconcile God's power, knowledge, and goodness with evil which embroiled him in controversy.

Pensées

http://ccel.wheaton.edu/p/pascal/pensees/
pensees.htm

Text of Pascal's famous work.

Pierre Bayle Home Page

http://www.cisi.unito.it/progetti/bayle/

Brief biography of Pierre Bayle; a bibliography that includes a number of dissertations on Bayle; links to related sites, including a link to the e-text of his seminal work *Dictionnaire historique et critique;* and an anthology of additional texts. This site is presented in French and Italian as well as in English.

Robert Burton: Overview of *The Anatomy of Melancholy*

http://www.rc.umd.edu/cstahmer/cogsci/
burton.html

Part of a larger site on cognitive science maintained by the University of California, Santa Barbara, this page provides an examination of Robert Burton's 1621 text *The Anatomy of Melancholy,* described here as 'arguably the first major text in the history of Western cognitive science'. The text includes numerous hyperlinks to additional information.

Spinoza, Benedict de

http://www.orst.edu/instruct/phl302/philosophers/
spinoza.html

Dedicated to Dutch philosopher Benedict de Spinoza, this page provides biographical information, including a timeline of major events in Spinoza's life, and the text of his essay 'Treatise on the Improvement of the Understanding'. You can also read the declaration that officially excommunicated Spinoza from the Jewish faith in 1656. There are also links to related sites and a list of sources.

F
A
C
T

SPINOZA, BENEDICT (1632–1677)
Dutch philosopher. He believed in a rationalistic pantheism that owed much to René Descartes's mathematical appreciation of the universe. Mind and matter are two modes of an infinite substance that he called God or Nature, good and evil being relative.

18th-century Philosophy

Bentham, Jeremy

http://socserv2.socsci.mcmaster.ca/~econ/ugcm/
3ll3/bentham/index.html

Essay, consisting of several letters to friends, in which Jeremy Bentham defends the practice of usury. You will also find an essay in praise of Bentham, written by John Stuart Mill, which originally appeared in the August 1838 edition of *London and Westminster Review,* as well as an annotated bibliography of Bentham's published works.

Berkeley, George

http://www.knuten.liu.se/%7Ebjoch509/
philosophers/ber.html

Devoted to the life and works of the Irish philosopher, George Berkeley. The biography includes an extensive appreciation by the 18th-century writer Joseph Stock. There are also links to his works including 'Treaties including the Principles of Human Knowledge', 'Three Dialogues', and 'The Analyst'. In addition, there are images and a link to another Berkeley site.

Confessions Of Jean-Jacques Rousseau, The

http://eserver.org/philosophy/rousseau-
confessions.txt

Complete text of Rousseau's account of his life.

Giambattista Vico Home Page

http://www.connix.com/~gapinton/index.html

Huge source of information on the influential Italian philosopher. The main events of Vico's life are set out, together with summaries of all of his books, speeches, and lectures. There is information on recent developments in studies of the man and his legacy as well as contact addresses for Vichian scholars.

Godwin, William

http://www.pagesz.net/~stevek/intellect/
godwin.html

Profile of the life and work of the English novelist and philosopher. Godwin's abandonment of his Nonconformist faith is related, together with details of his literary and political activities, his marriage to Mary Wollstonecraft, and his friendship with Shelley.

Hume Archives

http://www.utm.edu/research/hume/hume.html

Comprehensive repository of texts by and about the Scottish philosopher. In addition to the text of everything that Hume wrote, the number of early biographies and commentaries on his work indicate his importance to 18th- and 19th-century philosophy.

Kant, Immanuel

http://www.island-of-freedom.com/KANT.HTM

Extensive discussion and explanation of Kant's philosophy. There are also links to notes which aid understanding of Kant's *Theory of Space and Time, First Antinomy, of Space and Time,* and *Quantum Mechanics.*

Kant's 'Prolegomena'

http://www.utm.edu/research/iep/text/kant/
prolegom/prolegom.htm

Transcript of Kant's paper from 1783 on metaphysics 'Prolegomena'. This Web site divides the paper up into nine sections. The pages are available for downloading in either plain text format or the more elaborate rich text format for import into a word processor.

Leibniz, Gottfried Wilhelm

http://mally.stanford.edu/leibniz.html

Maintained by the Metaphysics Research Lab at Stanford University, this page concerns the life and ideas of philosopher, logician, and mathematician Gottfried Leibniz. It features a timeline of the major events in Leibniz's life, a list of his principle works, a brief examination of his philosophical contributions, and a list of sources for further reading.

Monadology

http://www.utm.edu/research/iep/text/leibniz/
monad.htm

Full text of Leibniz's best-known metaphysical work. This e-text is adapted from George Montgomery's 1902 translation.

Rousseau, Jean-Jacques

http://www.wheaton.edu/polsci/woodiwiss/Rousseau.html

Good biography and summary of the works of Rousseau. It details his interest in music, Catholicism, politics, philosophy, and literature. The end of his life is also described, and there is a listing of all of his works as well as links to further information.

19th-century Philosophy

Bakunin, Michael

http://www.pitzer.edu/~dward/Anarchist_Archives/bakunin/Bakuninarchive.html

Devoted to the founder of Russian nihilism, this site includes a biography and chronology of Bakunin's life, a collection of his writings which features electronic texts of numerous articles and essays, such as 'The Capitalist System', 'God and the State', 'Power Corrupts the Best', and 'Revolutionary Catechism'. You will also find a bibliography of his writings and several contemporary and modern commentaries on Bakunin, plus an image gallery.

'Considerations on Representative Government'

http://english.hss.cmu.edu/philosophy/mill-representative-govt.txt

Text of John Stuart Mill's famous work.

D Anthony Storm's Web Site on Kierkegaard

http://www.2xtreme.net/dstorm/sk/

Devoted to the writings of existentialist philosopher Soren Aabye Kierkegaard, including a biography, bibliography, and image gallery. A number of essays are also provided covering many of Kierkegaard's works.

Evolution and Occultism by Annie Besant

http://slt.pobox.com/besant.toc.html

Full text of essays published by Annie Besant in 1913. These discussions of occultism, materialism, and atheism set out the central beliefs of Theosophy. There is also an interesting modern introduction to this site.

Hegel by Hypertext

http://www.werple.net.au/~andy/index.htm

Provides excerpts from the condensed version of Hegel's book *The Science of Logic,* including chapters on the three subdivisions of logic. You will also find the text of Lenin's notes and annotations to *The Science of Logic,* as well as the text of Engels on Hegel from *Socialism: Utopian and Scientific.* The site includes a glossary, other essays and comments on dialectics, biographical notes on philosophers, additional writings from Engels and Marx concerning dialectics, and more. The texts are helpfully colour-coded to denote degree of difficulty and order of importance.

Hegel, Georg Wilhelm Friedrich

http://plato.stanford.edu/entries/hegel/

Detailed analysis of the life and legacy of the German Idealist. There is a good biography and a history of the influence of Hegel. Metaphysical and post-Kantian views of Hegel's philosophy are set out. There are also commentaries on his major works and a good bibliography.

Man Versus the State

http://socserv2.socsci.mcmaster.ca/~econ/ugcm/3ll3/spencer/manvssta

Full text of Herbert Spencer's well-known work.

Marx/Engels Archive

http://csf.colorado.edu/psn/marx

Several biographies, a large photo gallery, and a number of resources on these two philosophers. There is also an extensive library containing the texts of much of their work, including, among others, *The Communist Manifesto.*

Meinong, Alexius

http://mally.stanford.edu/meinong.html

Maintained by the Metaphysics Research Laboratory at Stanford University, USA, this page includes a brief timeline of the Austrian philosopher Alexius Meinong's life, a list of his major works, and some further references that address Meinong's ideas.

20th-century Philosophy

Nietzsche, Friedrick

http://www.usc.edu/dept/annenberg/thomas/
nietzsche.html

Site on Nietzsche run by the University of Southern California, USA. Designed for a university audience, this site has a strong emphasis on serious academic study, but there is plenty here for the more casual browser, too, including a list of works and detailed biographical information.

On Liberty

http://www.bartleby.com/130/index.html

Online edition of John Stuart Mill's famous philosophical work.

Peirce, Charles S

http://www.peirce.org/

Comprehensive guide to the life and legacy of the US philosopher and scientist. There are photos, a biography, and the texts of many of his most important works. The continuing academic interest in his work is reflected in the extensive guide to current research and the work of the society fostering his beliefs.

Perspectives of Nietzsche

http://www.pitt.edu/%7Ewbcurry/nietzsche.html

Provides Nietzsche's viewpoints on a number of philosophical subjects, including 'will to power', Christianity, truth and knowledge, values and morals, and 'eternal recurrence'. Nietzsche's perspectives on these subjects have been gleaned from several of his books and appear here as quotes with reference given to the particular book from which they were taken. You will also find a list of assorted opinions and maxims, and there is a list of related Web sites.

Proudhon, Pierre Joseph

http://www.pitzer.edu/~dward/Anarchist_Archives/
proudhon/Proudhonarchive.html

This site is devoted to leftist thinker Pierre Proudhon. You will find two biographies of Proudhon: one features a lengthy biography divided into five chapters, including a chapter devoted to the influence of Proudhon; the other provides a more condensed look at his life. There is a collection of Proudhon's writings, including essays, correspondence; a bibliography; and a gallery of photographs.

'André Breton and Problems of 20th-Century Culture'

http://www.socialequality.com/arts/1997/jun1997/
breton1.shtml

Informative, text-only essay on the French writer and poet André Breton. Topics covered here include his relationship with Trotsky and a critical appreciation of his works. There is also a detailed answer to the question, 'what was surrealism?', and finally more general notes on artistic life in France.

Baudrillard on the Web

http://www.uta.edu/english/apt/collab/
baudweb.html

Resource for students of the French cultural theorist. Links are provided to the text of a number of essays by Baudrillard, including excerpts from 'Simulacra and Simulations'. It also includes the text of a number of interviews with Baudrillard, essays about him, and information on other projects on the Internet related to him.

Berdyaev, Nikolai Alexandrovich

http://members.xoom.com/dirkk/berdyaev/

This site features the text of two articles concerning the life and meaning of Russian philosopher Nikolai Berdyaev, as well as the translation of Berdyaev's essay 'Universality and Confessionism', which includes an informative postscript from the translator. You will also find a bibliography of books and writings by and about Berdyaev and a list of related links.

Bertrand Russell Society

http://www.users.drew.edu/~jlenz/brs.html

Links to biographies, images, and discussion of the philosopher Bertrand Russell. There are links to several essays about his philosophical ideas, as well as to the text of a number of his writings, including *The Problems of Philosophy*. There is also information about the Bertrand Russell Society, and its activities.

Carnap, Rudolf

http://www.utm.edu/research/iep/c/carnap.htm

Very comprehensive account of the life and legacy of the German logical positivist. There is an assessment of Carnap's definition of meaningfulness and the analytic-synthetic distinction in logic for which he was noted. His metamathematical contribution to the philosophy of physics is also traced and there is also a detailed bibliography.

Dewey, John

http://www.utm.edu/research/iep/d/dewey.htm

Lengthy account of the life and legacy of the US philosopher. It traces his interest in psychology, epistemology, evolution, and education. His long academic, literary, and public life is described.

Foucault, Michel

http://www.connect.net/ron/foucault.html

Brief presentation of the life and work of Michel Foucault, one of the most celebrated postmodern philosophers of our age. The site takes us through Foucault's early years and education, his academic career, his main philosophical ideas, and the principal influences on his thought.

Heidegger, Martin

http://www.regent.edu/acad/schcom/rojc/mdic/martin1.html

Good profile of the German existentialist. In addition to a biography, there is a full listing of Heidegger's works.

Husserl Page

http://sac.uky.edu/%7Ersand1/husserl.html

Biography and photograph of the philosopher Edmund Husserl. There is also a chronological bibliography, a list of quotations, links to the texts of a number of his works, and information about his contemporaries.

Jacques Derrida Online

http://www.lake.de/home/lake/hydra/jd.html

A number of writings and remarks from Jacques Derrida, including letters, transcriptions of interviews, and essays. The majority of the texts are in English; others are written in German and French. There is also a bibliography of essays for further study.

Karl Popper Web

http://www.eeng.dcu.ie/~tkpw/

Aims to make the philosophy of science more accessible to the general public. This site is very comprehensive, including biographical information and all his major works. You can even join an informal e-mail forum to find out more about Karl Popper's ideas.

Lecture Notes on Wittgenstein

http://www-philosophy.ucdavis.edu/phi001/wittlec.htm

Part of a series of lecture notes concerning reality and knowledge (provided by the philosophy department of the University of California at Davis), this page contains the text of a lecture covering Ludwig Wittgenstein's early ideas on how metaphysical truths could be known. The lecture also investigates the change in Wittgenstein's thinking between the time he wrote *Tractatus* and *Philosophical Investigations*.

Lectures on Heidegger's *Being and Time*

http://caae.phil.cmu.edu/CAAE/80254/Heidegger/SZHomePage.html

Maintained by the philosophy department of the Carnegie Mellon University, USA, this page provides the text of university lectures concerning Heidegger's challenging

The Husserl Page - Netscape

File Edit View Go Window Help

The Husserl Page

Aim: To provide easy access to those net resources pertaining to the life and work of the 20th century philosopher, Edmund Husserl.

Life and Work:
- A Biography of Husserl, 1859-1938
- A Chronological Bibliography
- Secondary Sources
- Quote 'o' Month
- Announcements
- Online Texts
- Links: Specifically Related, Generally Related or Search the Internet

Edmund Husserl 1859-1938

What You Will Not Find Here

Since nowhere in these pages will you find a synopsis, summary, or other such treatise on the phenomenology of Husserl, you may wish to jump to the chronological bibliography of Husserl's writings. Here you may look for citations of the various "introductions" to phenomenology by Husserl himself. The author of this Web site suggests Husserl's *Encyclopaedia Britannica* article on phenomenology as a brief text representing well Husserl's major themes. It is perhaps the most concisely written of all the so-called "introductions." Finished in the years 1927-28 and (in a heavily edited and distorted version) published in the 14th ed. of *The Encyclopaedia Britannica*, this work was intended by Husserl to be a joint project between himself and Martin Heidegger. (This collaboration failed, however, such that Heidegger's contributions were not ultimately incorporated into the article submitted for publication. Hence, the article can serve both as an introduction to Husserlian

Document: Done

philosophical work *Being and Time*. The lectures begin with background information, an overview, and two introductions, before delving into the more complex aspects of Heidegger's thought, including such themes as 'being in the world', 'the problem of truth', 'the problem of death', and 'temporality'.

Martin Buber Home Page

http://www.uni-karlsruhe.de/~uneu/bubere.htm

Biography of the philosopher Martin Buber, as well as a chronology and guide to his works, including an excerpt from his book *I and Thou*. The site also features an essay on him, a detailed guide to further studies, and a number of links to related sites.

Mary Midgley: 'Evolution as a Religion: A Comparison of Prophecies'

http://www.aaas.org/spp/dspp/dbsr/EVOLUT/ midgley.htm

Article written by philosopher and critic of social-Darwinism Mary Midgley. In this article, which first appeared in the June 1987 edition of *Zygon: Journal of Science and Religion*, Midgley compares modern conceptions of evolutionary theory to religious myths and warns against using assumptions about evolution to explain the development of humankind. At the bottom of the page, you will find notes and reference information.

Quine, Willard Van Orman

http://www-groups.dcs.st-and.ac.uk/history/ Mathematicians/Quine.html

Part of an archive containing the biographies of the world's greatest mathematicians, this site is devoted to the life and contributions of the philosopher and logician Willard Quine. In addition to biographical information, you will find a list of references about Quine and links to other essays in the archive that reference him. The text of this essay includes hypertext links to essays on those mathematicians and thinkers who influenced Quine. You will also find an image of him, which you can click on to enlarge, and a map of his birthplace.

Realm of Existentialism

http://members.aol.com/KatharenaE/private/Philo/ philo.html

Guide to existentialist philosophy featuring information about the leading existential thinkers including Nietzsche, Ortega y Gasset, Sartre, Camus, Heidegger, and Unamuno.

Santayana Edition

http://www-phil.tamu.edu/Philosophy/Santayana/

Source of information concerning the writer and philosopher George Santayana. You will find biographical information, a bibliography, and links to related sites.

Sartre, Jean-Paul

http://members.aol.com/KatharenaE/private/Philo/ Sartre/sartre.html

Substantial source of information on the life, work, and legacy of the French existentialist. There is a full biography of Sartre and his literary and political life. There are summaries of all of his novels and critical works, reviews in French and English, and links to further sources of information.

Wittgenstein Think Page

http://ucsu.colorado.edu/~biggus/ludwig/

Numerous quotes from the works, correspondence, and diaries of philosopher and mathematician Ludwig Wittgenstein. Here you will find Wittgenstein's views on God and the meaning of life, excerpts from letters to Bertrand Russell and Ficker, the main outline and preface to *Tractatus Logico Philosophicus*, diary entries from 1937 and 1946, and five sets of fragments from *Philosophical Investigations*.

Writings of Theodor Adorno

http://hamp.hampshire.edu/~cmnF93/adorno.html

This site contains the English translations of three essays written by Theodor Adorno: 'Le Prix Du Progress' and 'The Culture Industry: Enlightenment as Mass Deception', both with Max Horkheimer from the book *The Dialect of Enlightenment*, and 'Culture Industry Reconsidered', from the book *The Culture Industry: Selected Essays on Mass Culture*.

Miscellaneous Philosophy

Centre for Advanced Research in Phenomenology

http://www.flinet.com/~carp/index.html

Essential source of information for those interested in phenomenology. In addition to a beginner's guide to the philosophy there are profiles of leading pioneers of the movement. There is a registry of practising phenomenologists, guide to academic seminars and journals, and an extensive bibliography.

Earthdance: Living Systems in Evolution

http://www.ratical.com/LifeWeb/Erthdnce/erthdnce.html

Philosophical work by Elisabet Sahtouris, based on the Gaia hypothesis, published in 1995 with an introduction by James Lovelock. There are chapters on such topics as 'Problems for earthlife', 'Ecological ethics', and 'Survival: the sustainable society'.

Empiricism

http://www-philosophy.ucdavis.edu/phi001/emplec.htm

Part of a series of lecture notes concerning reality and knowledge (provided by the philosophy department of the University of California at Davis, USA), this page contains the text of a lecture covering empiricism. You can also read lectures that came before and after this one in the series.

Epistemology

http://www.knight.org/advent/cathen/05506a.htm

Analysis of the theory of the nature, origins, and limits of knowledge from the *Catholic Encyclopedia*. A historical outline traces the contribution of ancient Greek, Christian, and modern philosophers to Epistemology.

New Age Dictionary

http://mysticplanet.com/8diction.htm

New Age terms and phrases from 'accupressure' to 'yoga' have definitions and descriptions on this Web site. The site forms a useful resource for those who wish to know exactly what 'wiccan' or 'chakra balancing' are.

Revealing Word: A Dictionary of Metaphysics

http://websyte.com/unity/RVLS2.HTM

Useful guide to the variety of terms used in metaphysics. There are definitions of concepts ranging from 'abate' to 'zeal'.

Social Contract

http://www.utm.edu/research/iep/s/soc-cont.htm

Good summary of various statements of social contract theory. Ideas associated with Plato are presented prior to a long description of Hobbes' views and the arguments of those who disputed them. Post-Hobbesian developments in social contract theory are also summarized.

Solipsism and the Problem of Other Minds

http://www.utm.edu/research/iep/s/solipsis.htm

Long analysis of the development and history of the philosophical position that there is no meaning to the supposition that other individuals have thoughts and experiences. The contribution of leading solipsist thinkers is summarized. There is also an extensive bibliography and guide to other Internet resources.

Towards a More Humane Future – Anthroposophy at Work

http://www.io.com/~lefty/Human_Future.html

Exposition of the mystical philosophy. There is an adulatory biography of Rudolf Steiner and anthroposophical approaches to education, medicine, agriculture, ageing, and the arts are set out.

Universals

http://www.utm.edu/research/iep/u/universa.htm

Detailed examination of the classic problem: whether abstract objects exist in a realm independent of human thought. Plato's theory of universals is summarized, together with Aristotle's response and later views of Augustine and Aquinas. The nominalist solution proposed by William of Ockham is also set out here.

THE WORLD

State of the World

Bathing Water Quality

http://www.environment-agency.gov.uk/s-enviro/
viewpoints/3compliance/5bathing/3-5.html

Regularly updated guide to the state of Britain's
beaches provided by the Environment Agency. A
searchable beach-by-beach index reports the
number of faecal coliforms and salmonella colonies
on every British beach and tells you what levels
are acceptable by European Union standards.

Big Empty

http://www.blm.gov/education/great_basin/
great_basin.html

Sponsored by the US Bureau of Land
Management, this site explores the Great Basin of
the western USA and its desert ecosystem of
plants, animals, and minerals. This site includes
information on the scarcity of water, modern and
environmental challenges, mining, grazing, wild
horses and burros, and a look at methods to
preserve and rehabilitate the ecosystem. Maps
and photographs complement the text.

Biodiversity: Measuring the Variety of Nature

http://www.nhm.ac.uk/science/projects/worldmap/

Exhibition on biodiversity and conservation from
the Natural History Museum in London, with
sections on 'Biodiversity value', 'Rarity and
endemism', and 'Conservation priority and gap
analysis'.

Clean Water – Life Depends on It

http://www.ec.gc.ca/water/en/info/pubs/FS/
e_FSA3.htm

FACT

WATER

the most common element on Earth and vital
to all living organisms. It covers 70% of the
Earth's surface, and provides a habitat for
large numbers of aquatic organisms. It is the
largest constituent of all living organisms –
the human body consists of about 65% water.

Extensive investigation into the quality of the
planet's water (or the lack of it) and the risks
that technological advances have brought about.
The site includes definitions of the major water-
related issues, sections on the self-cleansing of
water, a fact sheet about water quality and the
risks to human health as a result of water
pollution, a detailed presentation of water
quality pollutants, and guidelines delineating
the optimal behaviour towards water and the
aquatic environments.

Effects of Ultraviolet Radiation on Plants and Marine Organisms

http://pooh.chem.wm.edu/chemWWW/courses/
chem105/projects/group2/page7.html

Useful outline of the risks to life on Earth posed
by the build-up of radiation reaching the surface
of the Earth. The information can be understood
by those without a specialized knowledge of
chemistry.

Environmental Effects of the High Dam at Aswan

http://www.gps.caltech.edu/~ge148/1997C/
Reports/148niled.html

Interesting summary of the environmental pros
and cons of building the Aswan High Dam. The
consequences of disrupting historical flow
patterns are clearly set out. There are
recommendations of how to protect the Nile Delta
and avert further environmental degradation.

Environmental Technology is an Ancient Science

http://www.blm.gov/education/technology/
enviro_tech.html

Sponsored by the US Bureau of Land
Management, this site is a cooperative educational
project that focuses on the agricultural and
architectural technologies of the Hupobi Pueblo
who lived along the Rio Ojo Caliente in northern
New Mexico some 500 years ago. Articles
explore the ingenuity of these ancient
peoples in adapting to the dry climate.
Special attention is given to their methods
of dry farming.

Frederick W Taylor: 'The Principles of Scientific Management'

http://socserv2.socsci.mcmaster.ca/
~econ/ugcm/3ll3/taylor/index.html

Part of the Archive for the History of Economic Thought at McMaster University, this page features the text of Frederick W Taylor's 1911 essay 'The Principles of Scientific Management', in which he proffers the remedy for an inefficient US economy: total commitment to a scientific system of management, which would create 'national efficiency'.

Global Warming

http://pooh.chem.wm.edu/chemWWW/courses/chem105/projects/group1/page1.html

Step-by-step explanation of the chemistry behind global warming. There is information about the causes of global warming, the environmental effects, and the social and economic consequences. The views of those who challenge the assertion that the world is warming up are also presented. The graphics accompanying the site are attractive and easy to follow.

Groundwater Quality and the Use of Lawn and Garden Chemicals by Homeowners

http://www.ext.vt.edu/pubs/envirohort/426-059/426-059.html

Extensive information about the problem of keeping groundwater free from garden chemicals. There is a description of groundwater, as well as detailed information on pesticides and their use. There are also notes on applying lawn and garden chemicals, and what should be done with the leftovers.

John Muir Exhibit

http://www.sierraclub.org/john_muir_exhibit/

Full details of the life and legacy of the pioneer US conservationist. Contents include a biography, quotations from his writings, a large selection of pictures, and a comprehensive list of resources available for geography teachers.

Paul Ehrlich and the Population Bomb

http://www.pbs.org/kqed/population_bomb/

Companion to a US Public Broadcasting Service (PBS) television programme, this site details US biologist Paul Ehrlich's crusade to warn and inform people that overconsumption of resources, environmental destruction, and

unchecked population growth will destroy the Earth's ability to sustain life. This site includes detailed information on the world's population situation, a population timeline, and a section on learning exercises.

Problem of ChloroFluoroCarbons

http://pooh.chem.wm.edu/chemWWW/courses/chem105/projects/group2/page5.html

Graphical presentation of the effect of CFCs on the ozone layer. The information can be readily understood by a general reader wishing to learn more about the chemistry of ozone depletion and why more ultraviolet radiation is reaching the surface of the earth.

Rachel Carson Homestead

http://www.rachelcarson.org/

Information on the life and legacy of the pioneering ecologist from the trust preserving Carson's childhood home. There is a biography of Carson, details of books by and about Carson, and full details of the work of the conservation organizations continuing her work.

Sea Empress Oil Spill

http://www.swan.ac.uk/biosci/empress/empress.htm

Overview of the *Sea Empress* oil spill on the coast of South Wales in February 1996. The site contains scientific information about the spill, including its effect on the mammals, birds, and fish in the region. It also contains some good pictures of marine life.

6 Billion Human Beings

http://www.popexpo.net/home.htm

From the Musée de l'Homme in Paris, France, an interactive site about population growth. It explains the causes for the rapid growth of

F A C T

POPULATION

the number of people living in a specific area or region, such as a town or country, at any one time. The study of populations, their distribution and structure, resources, and patterns of migration, is called demography.

population over the last 200 years, and why it might stabilize over the next century. You can find out the world's population in the year you were born, and see a ticking counter of the current population as it approaches the six billion mark.

State of the Environment

http://www.environment-agency.gov.uk/state_of_enviro/index3+.html

UK Environment Agency's page on the environment, with access to data collected and studied by the Agency on the topics of 'Bathing water quality', 'River habitats', and 'River gauging stations'. There is also more general information on the current 'Stresses and strains' on the environment.

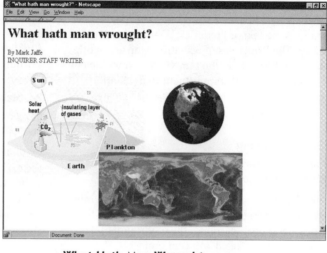

What Hath Man Wrought

http://sln.fi.edu/inquirer/warming.html

Extensive account of the causes and consequences of global warming. It discusses issues as diverse as greenhouse gases, ocean currents, flooded coasts, the fluctuations of the Earth's temperature as far back as 15,000 years ago, and the role of human economic activities in the temperature increase. The site has also incorporated links to a series of space institutes, climate centres, and environmental agencies which conduct related research.

> ### F A C T
>
> **ENVIRONMENTAL ISSUES**
>
> matters relating to the detrimental effects of human activity on the biosphere, their causes, and the search for possible solutions.

Sustainable Eenergy and Anti-uranium Service

http://www.sea-us.org.au/

Information on the campaign to lobby against uranium mining and nuclear energy in general from this Australian organization. There is a lot of material here to support their point of view including a historical overview, details of the nuclear fuel cycle, and information about the techniques used to mine uranium. However, it should be noted that the authors make little attempt to present the other side of the argument.

UNFPA – United Nations Population Fund

http://www.unfpa.org/

Provides news and information on its work assisting developing countries, as well as a section of reports on the state of the world population, and information on the agency's activities, publications, and conferences.

What's it like where you live?

http://www.mobot.org/MBGnet/index2.htm

Aimed at younger children, this imaginative site has sections on different ecosystems from around the world, and includes related activities.

Environmental & Conservation Organizations

Biosphere 2 Centre

http://www.bio2.edu/

All about the Biosphere 2 project in Oracle, Arizona, including a virtual tour of the site. There are full details of the research programmes being

conducted on the 'seven wilderness ecosystems' contained within the dome. The site also contains tailored educational resources for schoolchildren.

Conservation International

http://www.conservation.org/

Non-profit-making organization which uses science, economics, policy, and community involvement to promote biodiversity conservation worldwide.

Countryside Commission

http://www.countryside.gov.uk/

Guide to the work of the Commission and to the attractions of the British countryside. There is information on all of the UK's national parks and officially-designated areas of outstanding beauty. The Commission's work to preserve the countryside is fully explained and there are details of the latest scientific research.

English Heritage

http://www.english-heritage.org.uk/dminterface/dmindex.asp

Site of the public body charged with protecting England's historic environment. The role and structure of English Heritage are described, together with publications and education activities. A clickable map accesses information on historic properties.

English Nature – Facts and Figures

http://www.english-nature.org.uk/facts.htm

Outline of the role of the government agency charged with conserving wildlife and natural features in England. The structure and budget of the agency are clearly presented (with the help of pie charts). There is information about Sites of Special Scientific Interest (SSSIs), national and marine nature reserves, and protection of wetlands.

Environmental Education Network

http://envirolink.org/enviroed/

Collaborative effort to place environmental information on the Internet. It is full of multimedia items, and divided into sections for teachers and students. These are further subdivided into sections such as geology, archaeology, and exploration/travel.

Friends of the Earth Home Page

http://www.foe.co.uk/

Appeal for raised awareness of environmental issues with masses of information and tips for action from environmentalist pressure group Friends of the Earth. The site hosts lengthy accounts of several campaigns undertaken by FoE on climate, industry, transport, and sustainable development. It also maintains an archive of press releases from FoE on some of the most controversial environmental problems encountered in the course of last year around the world.

Katmai National Park and Preserve

http://www.alaskanet.com/Tourism/Parks/Katmai/

Guide to the National Park, which contains the famous Valley of Ten Thousand Smokes, where the 20th century's most dramatic volcanic episode took place.

Recycle City

http://www.epa.gov/recyclecity/

Child-friendly site of the US Environmental Protection Agency designed to help people to live more ecologically. The site includes games and activities to encourage children to think about waste disposal issues.

Schumacher Society

http://www.oneworld.org/schumachersoc/

Report on the activities of the society committed

to continuing the work of the eco-spiritualist E F Schumacher. There are full details of the society's work to foster the spread of ecological and spiritual values, listings of the society's many publications, and links to other Schumacher sites around the world. For a green activist this site is an essential source of information.

Sustainable Development

http://iisd1.iisd.ca/

Tackles a complex issue from many different points of view. There are sections on trade and key topics such as forests and oceans. The site also reports on global initiatives to encourage sustainability. One of the major advantages of this site, though, is that it makes this issue easy to understand for beginners through its 'Contents and principles' section.

United Nations Educational, Scientific, and Cultural Organization

http://www.unesco.org/

This site details UNESCO's work in 186 countries, the organization's structure and history, its programmes and publications, and current events. There are also links to UNESCO's 60 field offices and information on internships and employment with the agency.

World Heritage List

http://www.unesco.org/whc/heritage.htm

United Nations list of 506 sites all across the world that are considered to be an essential part of the 'world's cultural and natural heritage'. This site contains a page on all the sites with a brief description, photo, and the year each one was added to the list.

Worldwide Fund for Nature

http://www.panda.org/

Online base of the international wildlife charity. As well as giving information about current campaigns and encouraging you to join, there is a wealth of well-presented information here about the natural world, including quizzes, interactive maps, and a regularly updated news section.

Renewable Energy

Biomass

http://www.nrel.gov/research/ industrial_tech/ biomass.html

Information on biomass from the US Department of Energy. A graph supports the textual explanation of the fact that the world is only using 7% of annual biomass production. There is a clear explanation of the chemical composition of biomass and development of technologies to transform it into usable fuel sources.

Centre for Alternative Technology

http://www.cat.org.uk/

Dedicated to the Centre For Alternative Technology in Wales, this includes a virtual tour

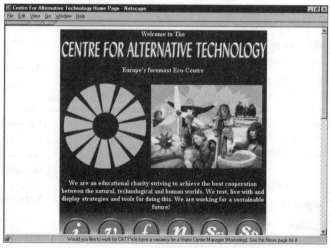

of the site, pictures, and maps. It also includes a quiz, a question forum, and an extensive list of educational resources.

Geothermal Technologies

http://www.eren.doe.gov/geothermal/

Interesting geothermal home page of the US Department of Energy. There is a description of various geothermal energy sources and technologies being developed to exploit them. There is information about a number of energy authorities across the world tapping geothermal energy.

National Wind Technology Centre

http://www.nrel.gov/wind/

Source of information on the importance of tapping wind power and how to do it. This US Department of Energy site has reports on the latest research. For children there is a wind energy quiz and details of educational materials. There is information about a number of authorities generating energy from wind power in various parts of world.

Snowy Mountains Hydroelectric Authority

http://www.snowyhydro.com.au/

Guide to Australia's massive engineering project to harness the waters of the Snowy Mountains. The site contains a detailed history of the Snowy Mountain hydroelectric scheme and an explanation of how it works. There are also educational activities for school children.

Solar Power in the UK

http://www.greenpeace.org.uk/solar/index.html

Greenpeace site campaigning for greater use of solar power. According to this environmental group, solar panels installed on buildings in the UK have the potential to provide the country's total annual electricity consumption.

Wind Turbines

http://www.nrel.gov/wind/turbines.html

Reports on latest wind turbine research. There are technical details of a variety of experimental turbines, information on the work of companies active in research and development, and speculation about the configurations of the kinds of turbines likely to become significant

contributors to energy resources in the next century.

Earth Science & Oceanography

Atlantic Ocean

http://www.umsl.edu/services/govdocs/wofact96/24.htm

Geographical and political details of the second-largest ocean. A downloadable map is also available from this CIA-run Web site. As with all of the sites from the World Factbook, there is a lot of information here, on such things as ports, economy, conflicts, natural resources, and the environment.

British Geological Survey Global Seismology and Geomagnetism Group Earthquake Page

http://www.gsrg.nmh.ac.uk/gsrg.html

Fascinating maps showing the location and relative magnitude of recent UK earthquake activity make up just a small part of this Web site. Also included are historical and archive information, as well as descriptions of felt effects and hazards. Watch out if you live in Wolverhampton!

Byrd, Richard E

http://www-bprc.mps.ohio-state.edu:80

Biography and several photographs of Admiral Richard E Byrd, the famous US polar explorer. The history of the Byrd Polar Research Centre is also detailed, and there is a description of Byrd's pioneering flight across the North Pole.

Cambrian Period: Life Goes for a Spin

http://www.sciam.com/explorations/082597cambrian/powell.html

Part of a larger site maintained by *Scientific American,* this page reports on the research of Joseph Kirschvink of the California Institute of Technology which suggests that the so-called 'Cambrian Explosion' resulted from a sudden shifting of the Earth's crust. The text includes hyperlinks to further information, and there is

also a list of related links, including one to figures, diagrams, and information from Kirschvink's research paper.

Choosing Your Diamond

http://www.gotampabay.com/diamonds/howto.html

Illustrated guide to how diamond brokers choose their diamonds. The site examines each of the four Cs in turn – cut, colour, clarity, and carat-weight.

Cracking the Ice Age

http://www.pbs.org/wgbh/nova/ice/

Companion to the US Public Broadcasting Service (PBS) television programme *Nova*, this page provides information about glaciation, the natural changes in climate over the past 60 million years, the greenhouse effect, global warming, and continental movement. There is also a list of related links.

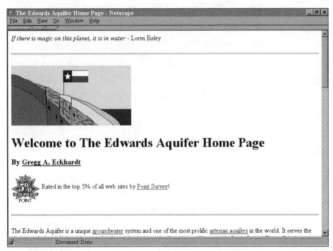

Deccan Traps

http://volcano.und.nodak.edu/vwdocs/volc_images/europe_west_asia/india/deccan.html

Volcanological guide to the vast basalt outflows of the Indian upland. The geological history of the region, and possible connections between volcanic activity and extinction of the dinosaurs is traced. There are also several good photographs.

Earth Introduction

http://www.hawastsoc.org/solar/eng/earth.htm

Everything you ever wanted to know about planet Earth can be found at this site, which contains a table of statistics, photographs taken from space, radar-generated images of the planet, animations of the Earth rotating, and more.

Earthrise

http://earthrise.sdsc.edu/

Earthrise is a growing database of Earth images taken by astronauts from space over the last 15 years. Users can search the image database by keyword, or by clickable topographical and political maps, or just view the highlights.

Earth – the Ever Changing Planet

http://observe.ivv.nasa.gov/nasa/exhibits/rice/rice_0.html

Online exhibit organized by NASA, which highlights some of our planet's changing features from the perspective of Earth orbit. The site offers a unique opportunity to appreciate the constantly changing picture that Earth presents from 'out there'. Exhibits include the lights of night, hurricane shots, and pictures of ocean waves.

Edwards Aquifer Home Page

http://www.edwardsaquifer.net/

Guide to the Edwards Aquifer (a rock formation containing water) in Texas – one of the most prolific artesian aquifers in the world.

Geographia

http://www.geographia.com/

Excellent site for travellers to explore future destinations. The information is divided into five regional sections, with additional special features on selected locations. The text is supplemented by pictures, videos, and sound clips.

Geologylink

http://www.geologylink.com/

Comprehensive information on geology featuring a daily update on current geologic events, virtual classroom tours, and virtual field trips to locations around the world. You will also find an in-depth look at a featured event, geologic news and reports, an image gallery, glossary, maps, and an area for asking geology professors your most

> **F A C T**
>
> **GEOMORPHOLOGY**
>
> branch of geology, developed in the late 19th century, dealing with the morphology, or form, of the Earth's surface; nowadays it is also considered to be an integral part of physical geography.

perplexing questions, plus a list of references and links.

Georges Cuvier – Discourse on the Revolutionary Upheavals on the Surface of the Earth

http://www.mala.bc.ca/~johnstoi/cuvier.htm

Complete original text and English translation of Cuvier's celebrated *Discours sur les révolutions de la surface du globe.* This public domain version has translator's comments and explanatory footnotes to help illustrate Cuvier's argument.

Glaciers

http://www-nsidc.colorado.edu/glaciers/

Comprehensive information about glaciers from the US National Snow and Ice Data Centre. There are explanations of why glaciers form, different kinds of glaciers, and what they may tell us about climate change. There are a number of interesting facts and a bibliography about the compacted tongues of ice which cover 10% of the land surface of our planet.

> **F A C T**
>
> **GLACIAL EROSION**
>
> the wearing-down and removal of rocks and soil by a glacier. Glacial erosion forms impressive landscape features, including glacial troughs (U-shaped valleys), arêtes (steep ridges), and corries (enlarged hollows).

Hawaii: Born of Fire

http://www.pbs.org/wgbh/nova/hawaii/

Companion to the US Public Broadcasting Service (PBS) television programme *Nova,* this page contains interviews with geologists and a biologist from the University of Hawaii, in which

they discuss the formation of the Hawaiian islands, the unique features that produced a wide variety of species, and the nature of lava. There is also a section on two kinds of igneous rock: pumice and granite.

Late Pleistocene Extinctions

http://www.museum.state.il.us/exhibits/larson/LP_extinction.html

Exploration of possible causes of the Late Pleistocene extinction of most large mammals in North America. Different theories are discussed. There is also information on the prehistoric inhabitants of North America.

Mineral Gallery

http://mineral.galleries.com/

Collection of descriptions and images of minerals, organized by mineral name, class (sulphides, oxides, carbonates, and so on), and grouping (such as gemstones, birth stones, and fluorescent minerals).

Multimedia History of Glacier Bay, Alaska

http://sdcd.gsfc.nasa.gov/GLACIER.BAY/glacierbay.html

Virtual tour featuring scenic flights over 3-dimensional glaciers. The multimedia experience combines video footage, computer and satellite images, photos, text, and maps, and includes information on glacial formation. View hand-drawn maps of glaciers that date back to 1794 and watch video of massive ice fronts splitting and splashing into the sea.

National Geographic Online

http://www.nationalgeographic.com

Large and lavishly illustrated Web site. Features include the *Map Machine Atlas,* which allows you to find maps, flags, facts, and profiles for the countries of the world, and discussion forums on a variety of subjects (such as 'Does the millennium matter'? and 'Salem witchcraft hysteria'). Many articles and multimedia items can be accessed for free.

Nature Explorer

http://www.naturegrid.org.uk/explorer/index.html

Wealth of information about water creatures. The presentation is fun and interactive, including a 'Virtual pond dip'.

Ocean Planet

http://seawifs.gsfc.nasa.gov/ocean_planet.html

Oceans and the environmental issues affecting their health, based on the Smithsonian Institute's travelling exhibition of the same name. Use the exhibition floor plan to navigate your way around the different 'rooms' – with themes ranging from Ocean Science and Immersion to Heroes and Sea People.

Ocean Satellite Image Comparison

http://www.csc.noaa.gov/crs/real_time/javaprod/satcompare.html

Maintained by the US National Oceanic Atmospheric Administration, this site is a Java applet which compares satellite images and data about the ocean surface temperatures and turbidity of numerous coastal areas around the USA. The site includes an Image Panner for navigating larger images.

Plate Tectonics

http://www.seismo.unr.edu/ftp/pub/louie/class/100/plate-tectonics.html

Well-illustrated site on this geological phenomenon. As well as the plentiful illustrations, this site also has a good clear manner of explaining the way the plates of the Earth's crust interact to produce seismic activity.

**F
A
C
T**

PLATE TECTONICS

theory formulated in the 1960s to explain the phenomena of continental drift and seafloor spreading, and the formation of the major physical features of the Earth's surface. The Earth's outermost layer, the lithosphere, is regarded as a jigsaw puzzle of rigid major and minor plates that move relative to each other, probably under the influence of convection currents in the liquid mantle beneath.

Royal Geographical Society

http://www.rgs.org/

Mine of information for both geographers and non-specialists, including events organized by the RGS, online exhibitions, field expeditions and research projects, publications, and links to other geographical organizations.

San Andreas Fault and Bay Area

http://sepwww.stanford.edu/oldsep/joe/fault_images/BayAreaSanAndreasFault.html

Detailed tour of the San Andreas Fault and the San Francisco Bay area, with information on the origination of the fault. The site is supported by a full range of area maps.

Some Like it Hot

http://www.blm.gov/education/sonoran/sonoran.html

Sponsored by the US Bureau of Land Management, this site explores the Sonoran Desert, the USA's hottest desert, and the unusual plant and animal life that has adapted to this harsh environment. Articles investigate management challenges facing the area, threatened and endangered species, and Native American cultural areas of the Sonoran Desert.

Virtual Cave

http://library.advanced.org/2974/

Browse the mineral wonders unique to the cave environment – from bell canopies and bottlebrushes to splattermites and stalactites.

Virtual Earthquake

http://vcourseware2.calstatela.edu/VirtualEarthquake/VQuakeIntro.html

US-based site that allows you to simulate an earthquake to learn how they are measured and how they effect the environment.

Volcanoes

http://www.learner.org/exhibits/volcanoes/

Attractive site that contains detailed information about volcanic activity, supported by video clips and other interactive tasks.

Woods Hole Oceanographic Institution Home Page

http://www.whoi.edu/index.html

Site run by a Massachusetts-based oceanographic institute. As well as containing details of their research programmes and an overview of the organization, there is a gallery of marine pictures and videos, and contacts for their education programmes.

World of Amber

http://www.emporia.edu/S/www/earthsci/amber/amber.htm

Everything you need to know about amber is here. There is information on its physical properties, uses, and geological and geographical occurrences, plus fossils in amber, recovery methods, amber myths, museums, and a quiz.

Palaeontology

Dinosaur Extinction Hypothesis

http://www.askeric.org/Projects/Newton/12/Lessons/dinoextn.html

Page dealing with dinosaur extinction hypotheses. The issues behind the hypothesis are outlined and discussed, and there are a number of activities to try.

Dinosauria

http://www.ucmp.berkeley.edu/diapsids/dinosaur.html

Visit this site for a well-researched, illustrated guide to the different dinosaur groups, dispel some myths, and catch up – in Dinobuzz – with recent topics of investigation.

Dinosaur Trace Fossils

http://www.emory.edu/GEOSCIENCE/HTML/Dinotraces.htm

All about the trace fossils left by dinosaurs. The site is divided into several categories of dinosaur fossils: tracks, eggs and nests, tooth marks, gastroliths, and coprolites, and also includes images and descriptions of each one.

Early Dinosaur Discoveries in North America

http://www.ucmp.berkeley.edu/diapsids/dinodiscoveriesna.html

Interesting history of early dinosaur discoveries in North America. Includes a section on the 'feuding paleontologists', Edward Drinker Cope and rival Othniel Marsh, and provides

information on the world's first nearly complete dinosaur skeleton excavated near Haddonfield, New Jersey, in 1858. There are photos and hypertext links to additional information.

Fossil Collections of the World

http://www.geocities.com/CapeCanaveral/Lab/8147/index.html

Comprehensive pages of information about fossils and fossil sites around the world. This is where to find out about geological timescales, the history of fossil-collecting, famous fossil collections and collectors, and maps of sites. There are also links to numerous other related sites.

Fossil Hominids FAQ

http://earth.ics.uci.edu:8080/faqs/fossil-hominids.html

Basic information about hominid species, the most important hominid fossils, and creationist arguments, plus links to related sites.

Ichthyology Resources

http://muse.bio.cornell.edu/cgi-bin/hl?fish

Everything anyone might need for studying fish, including historical information about development, as well as up-to-date listings of currently endangered species. There is also a gallery of fish images and paintings for the less scientifically inclined.

Kevin's Trilobite Home Page

http://www.ualberta.ca/~kbrett/Trilobites.html

Information, photographs, line drawings, and anything else to do with trilobites and the people who study them. The clickable table of contents includes trilobites from different geological periods, a list of trilobite photos available on the Internet, trilobite classification, as well as other more light-hearted aspects of the trilobite world.

Museum of Palaeontology

http://www.ucmp.berkeley.edu/exhibit/exhibits.html

Large amount of detailed information on the subject in a carefully structured and carefully cross-referenced site. You can explore palaeontology through the three areas of phylogeny, geology, and evolution.

Raptor Centre

http://www.raptor.cvm.umn.edu/

Facts, stories, and other information about birds of prey, including multimedia files of raptor images and sounds, a species census, plus information about endangered and threatened birds and the environmental issues affecting them, with a large amount of information on Internet resources and publications.

Set in Stone

http://www.blm.gov/education/paleo/index.html

Sponsored by the US Bureau of Land Management, this site explores palaeontology in the American West, and includes photographs of various sites and activities for students.

World's First Dinosaur Skeleton: Hadrosaurus Foulkii

http://www.levins.com/dinosaur.html

Explores William Parker Foulke's discovery of the first nearly complete dinosaur skeleton near Haddonfield, New Jersey, USA, in 1858. The site is divided into about a dozen sections, dealing with the site as it appears today, finding the bones in 1858, the meaning of the find, the characteristics of the dinosaur, maps of the area, and more. The site is enhanced by photos and drawings.

Weather

Clouds and Precipitation

http://ww2010.atmos.uiuc.edu/(Gh)/guides/mtr/cld/home.rxml

Illustrated guide to how clouds form and to the various different types. The site contains plenty of images and a glossary of key terms in addition to further explanations of the various types of precipitation.

Clouds from Space

http://www.hawastsoc.org/solar/eng/cloud1.htm

This site offers a unique look at clouds, containing photographs of various cloud types taken from space including thunderstorms over Brazil, jet stream cirrus clouds, and a description of how clouds form.

Coriolis Effect

http://www.physics.ohio-state.edu/~dvandom/Edu/coriolis.html

Subtitled 'a (fairly) simple explanation', this site contains a description of the principles involved, and is aimed at non-physicists.

Daily Planet

http://www.atmos.uiuc.edu/

Masses of data and other information on climate around the planet. Among the site's more attractive features is the use of multimedia instructional modules, customized weather maps, and real-time weather data.

Dan's Wild Wild Weather Page

http://www.whnt19.com/kidwx/index.html

Introduction to the weather for kids. It has pages dealing with everything from climate to lightning, from satellite forecasting to precipitation – all explained in a lively style with plenty of pictures.

Earth's Seasons: Equinoxes, Solstices, Perihelion, and Aphelion

http://aa.usno.navy.mil/AA/data/docs/EarthSeasons.html

Part of a larger site on astronomical data maintained by the US Naval Observatory, this site gives the dates and hours (in Universal Time) of the changing of the seasons from 1992 through to

2005. It also includes sections of 'Frequently Asked Questions' and research information.

El Niño Theme Page

http://www.pmel.noaa.gov/toga-tao/el-nino/nino-home.html

Wealth of scientific information about El Niño (a 'disruption of the ocean-atmosphere system in the tropical Pacific') with animated views of the monthly sea changes brought about by it, El Niño-related climate predictions, and forecasts from meteorological centres around the world. It also offers an illuminating 'Frequently Asked Questions' section with basic and more advanced questions as well as an interesting historical overview of the phenomenon starting from 1550.

Hurricane & Tropical Storm Tracking

http://hurricane.terrapin.com/

Follow the current paths of Pacific and mid-Atlantic hurricanes and tropical storms at this site. Java animations of storms in previous years can also be viewed, and data sets for these storms may be downloaded. Current satellite weather maps can be accessed for the USA and surrounding region.

Lightning's Cousins: Sprites and Elves

http://www.sciam.com/explorations/012097sprites/012097explorations.html

Part of a larger site maintained by *Scientific American*, this page examines the phenomena of delicate flashes of colourful light, called sprites and elves, emanating from the tops of clouds during thunderstorms. The site includes hyperlinks to further information, and video clips of red and blue sprites.

Met. Office Home Page

http://www.meto.govt.uk/

Authoritative account of global warming issues such as the ozone problem, El Niño (and the less known La Niña) the tropical cyclones, and forecasting methods. Scientific explanations alternate with images and film clips in an educational site which especially targets teachers and their students.

Questions and Answers About Snow

http://www-nsidc.colorado.edu/NSIDC/EDUCATION/SNOW/snow_FAQ.html

Comprehensive information about snow from the US National Snow and Ice Data Centre. Among the interesting subjects discussed are why snow is white, why snowflakes can be up to two inches across, what makes some snow fluffy, why sound travels farther across snowy ground, and why snow is a good insulator.

Seawave Forecasts for California, Oregon, and Washington

http://facs.scripps.edu/surf/spectrum.html

Maintained by NWS Marine Forecasts and Observations, this site displays wave and surf information for six locations along the Pacific Coast of the USA. Includes a link to bay, coastal, and offshore marine forecasts for selected cities, plus high seas forecasts, and surface observations.

Storm Chaser Home Page

http://www.geocities.com/CapeCanaveral/8546/nc.htm

Set up by an devotee of the sport, this site has swiftly expanded through voluntary contributions of other fans. A vast number of stunning photos and a whole online Tornado Museum are included, to tempt you into this hobby. On the other hand, an extended section of veterans' thoughts on safety may make you think twice. The site also offers severe weather reports for emergencies!

Tornado Project Online

http://www.tornadoproject.com/

All about tornadoes – including myths and oddities, personal experiences, tornado chasing, tornado safety, and tornadoes past and present.

F
A
C
T

WEATHER

Weather differs from climate in that the latter is a composite of the average weather conditions of a locality or region over a long period of time (at least 30 years). Meteorology is the study of short-term weather patterns and data within a circumscribed area.

Welcome to Four Seasons!

http://www.4seasons.org.uk/

Several environment-related Web projects, written by and for teachers. According to the site: 'By using data collected nationally and linking it with locally collected data, using simple equipment, pupils can participate in national projects, while immediately seeing the relevance to their own immediate environment'. The pack also offers valuable background support, with information on National Grid Environmental centres, a calendar of seasonal celebrations, a quiz linked to Web pages that includes the answers to the questions, and guidance for teachers.

World Meteorological Organization

http://www.wmo.ch/

Internet voice of the World Meteorological Organization, a UN division coordinating global scientific activity related to climate and weather. The site offers ample material on the long-term objectives and immediate policies of the organization. It also disseminates important information on WMO's databases, training programmes, and satellite activities, as well as its projects related to the protection of the environment.

Natural Disasters

Avalanche!

http://www.pbs.org/wgbh/nova/avalanche/

Companion to the US Public Broadcasting Service (PBS) television programme *Nova*, this page follows an intrepid documentary team as they set out to film an avalanche. It provides information on the causes of avalanches, as well as details on how the film crew avoided getting swept away by them. There are six video clips of actual avalanches in progress and a number of still photos. You can download a transcript of the television programme.

Avalanche Awareness

http://www-nsidc.colorado.edu/NSIDC/
EDUCATION/AVALANCHE/

Description of avalanches, what causes them, and how to minimize dangers if caught in one. There

is advice on how to determine the stability of a snowpack, what to do if caught out, and how to locate people trapped under snow. Nobody skiing off piste should set off without reading this.

Before and After the Great Earthquake and Fire: Early Films of San Francisco, 1897–1916

http://lcweb2.loc.gov/ammem/papr/sfhome.html

Collection of 26 early films depicting San Francisco before and after the 1906 disaster, including a 1915 travelogue that shows scenes of the rebuilt city and the Panama Pacific Exposition, and a 1916 propaganda film. Should you not wish to download the entire film, each title contains sample still-frames. There is also background information about the earthquake and fire, and a selective bibliography.

Chernobyl: Ten Years On

http://www.nea.fr/html/rp/chernobyl/chernobyl.html

This site examines the disaster at the Chernobyl nuclear reactor in August 1986 and what has happened in the decade since the accident. In addition to learning about the events leading up to the accident, you can find out about the health impacts of the radiation leak, and learn how the nuclear reactors at Chernobyl were meant to work. This official document, produced by the OECD (Organization for Economic Cooperation and Development), contains most recent news regarding the accident and its after-effects.

Decade of Notable Californian Earthquakes

http://209.250.109.195/califneq.html

Details of recent Californian earthquakes with maps, photographs, video clips, and animations. The site title is misleading as there is detailed information on earthquakes from 1980–1995, with official reports to back up the rendering of the seismic shocks in animations and video clips.

Disasters: Panoramic Photographs, 1851–1991

http://lcweb2.loc.gov/cgi-bin/query/r?ammem/pan:
@and(+fires+earthquake+storms+railroad+
accidents+floods+cyclones+hurricane+))

Part of the Panoramic Photo Collection of the US Library of Congress, this page features 144 panoramic photographs of natural and man-made disaster scenes, mostly in the USA, between 1851 and 1991. To narrow your search, click on New Search and enter a specific disaster or location. The images include brief notes. Click on the images to increase their size.

Double Whammy

http://www.sciam.com/explorations/1998/011998asteroid/

Part of a larger site maintained by *Scientific American,* this page explores the catastrophic impact that an asteroid's crashing into the sea would have on civilization and the environment. Animated simulations show the effects of impact and the effect that a tsunami would have on the eastern seaboard of the USA if an asteroid struck the Atlantic Ocean. Learn about the tsunami that struck Prince William Sound, Alaska, in 1964 after an underwater earthquake. The text includes hypertext links to further information and a list of related links.

Dust Bowl

http://www.usd.edu/anth/epa/dust.html

Historical information on the US mid-West dust bowl of the 1930s. The site features period photographs and an MPG video clip of a dust storm taken from original film footage (please beware the lengthy download time for this clip).

Eldfell, Heimaey, Iceland

http://volcano.und.nodak.edu/vwdocs/volc_images/europe_west_asia/heimaey/heimaey.html

Interesting profile of the volcano of Eldfell and its threat to the Icelandic port of Vestmannaeyjar. There is a good account, supported by dramatic photographs, of the 1973 eruption and the concerted efforts which saved the town from destruction.

EqIIS – Earthquake Image Information System

http://www.eerc.berkeley.edu/cgi-bin/eqiis_form?eq=4570&count=1

Fully searchable library of almost 8,000 images from more than 80 earthquakes. It is possible to search by earthquake, structure, photographer, and keyword.

Flood!

http://www.pbs.org/wgbh/nova/flood/

Companion to the US Public

Broadcasting Service (PBS) television programme *Nova,* this page concerns many aspects of flooding. It takes an historical look at floods and examines the measures that engineers have taken to combat them. Three major rivers are discussed: the Yellow, Nile, and Mississippi. In addition to learning about the negative effects of floods, you can also find out about the benefits that floods bestow on farmland. There are many images dispersed throughout the site, plus an audio clip of a flood in progress.

Krakatau

http://volcano.und.nodak.edu/vwdocs/volc_images/southeast_asia/indonesia/krakpics.html

Description and photographs of Indonesia's fiery island. The explosion of 1883 is described. There is also regularly updated information on the current state of Anak Krakatau, the 'son of Krakatoa'.

MTU Volcanoes Page

http://www.geo.mtu.edu/volcanoes/

Provided by Michigan Technological University, this site includes a world map of volcanic activity with information on recent eruptions, the latest research in remote sensing of volcanoes, and many spectacular photographs.

Popocatépetl, Mexico

http://volcano.und.nodak.edu/vwdocs/current_volcs/popo/mar5popo.html

Geological and brief historical information detailing recent volcanic activity of Popocatépetl. Maps, diagrams, and a spectacular photograph of

see p 590

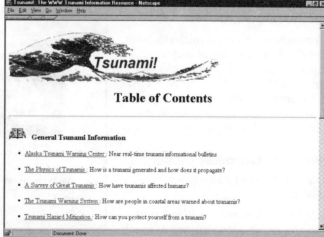

the mountain erupting make up the graphical part of this page.

Tsunami!

http://www.geophys.washington.edu/tsunami/intro.html

Description of many aspects of tsunamis. Included are details on how a tsunami is generated and how it propagates, how they have affected humans, and how people in coastal areas are warned about them. The site also discusses steps you can take to protect yourself from a tsunami and provides 'near real-time' tsunami information bulletins.

Vesuvius, Italy

http://volcano.und.nodak.edu/vwdocs/volc_images/img_vesuvius.html

Site examining the complex geology of Vesuvius and its famous eruption of 79 AD. There are images of the volcano and historical drawings. There is also a link to a local site campaigning for an improved civil defence plan as the volcano prepares once more to explode.

Volcanic Crisis in the Philippines: the 1991 Eruption of Mount Pinatubo

http://vulcan.wr.usgs.gov/Volcanoes/Pinatubo/framework.html

History of the volcanic eruption of Mount Pinatubo in the Philippines. These extensive pages chart the progress of the eruption from April to June 1991. Also included are maps, charts, and colour photographs, as well as links to other related sites.

VolcanoWorld

http://volcano.und.edu

Comprehensive site on volcanoes, with details of the most recent eruptions, currently active volcanoes, a glossary, images and video clips, and even a list of extraterrestrial volcanoes. If you can't find out what you want to know, you can 'Ask a volcanologist'.

Worldwide Earthquake Locator

http://www.geo.ed.ac.uk/quakes/quakes.html

Edinburgh University, Scotland, runs this site, which allows visitors to search for the world's latest earthquakes. The locator works on a global map on which perspective can be zoomed in or out. There are normally around five or six earthquakes a day; you'll find it surprising how few make the news. The site also has some general information on earthquakes.

Exploration

Alive on Everest

http://www.pbs.org/wgbh/nova/everest/

Companion to the US Public Broadcasting Service (PBS) television programme *Nova,* this page follows a team of determined climbers, tracking their mental and physical states, as they ascend from sea level through thin air into the Death Zone on their way to the summit of the tallest mountain in the world. Information on the climb and the condition of the climbers is divided into the four parts. Read articles describing and explaining the deterioration of their physical and mental condition as they move higher and higher. You can also read a timeline history of Everest and its conquerors, from the mountain's birth 60 million years ago to the present, and an interview with veteran climber David Breashears after his fourth ascent of Everest. This site includes several video and audio clips, plus a stunning panoramic photo of the view from the summit with all the surrounding peaks labelled.

Amazon Adventure Home Page

http://www.liverpool.k12.ny.us/Whacked/Intranet Curr/SocialStudies/Amazo nAdventure/index.htm

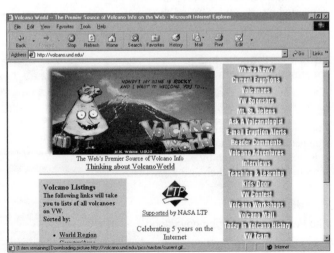

Details of a nine-week expedition up the Amazon River through Brazil and Peru. This site has been specifically set up by the author with schoolchildren in mind. It includes sections on the people, animals, and locations, as well as a travel diary and background information about Amazonia.

Arctic Dawn: Journeys of Samuel Hearne

http://web.idirect.com/~hland/sh/title.html

Travelogue of a journey in the Arctic undertaken in 1768 by Samuel Hearne. As well as being a fascinating historical document, the story is interspersed with images and audio clips of local animals and birds, as well as information about the indigenous American Indian population.

Cavediving

http://www.cavediving.com/home.htm

US Web site run by a cave diving instructor. The site provides all sorts of information for those who wish to swim in cold, dark, underwater caverns. Information on how to and where to cave dive is provided along with news, articles, links, and details of where to learn how to cave dive.

Caves and Caving in the UK

http://www.sat.dundee.ac.uk/~arb/speleo.html

Extensive site on the whys and wherefores of caving in the UK. It includes a map of the best areas and extensively linked text with sections on

caving conservation and legal aspects, as well as how to get started.

Columbus Navigation Page

http://www1.minn.net/~keithp/index.htm

Guide to the history, voyages, and discoveries of Christopher Columbus. This is a heavily illustrated site, and includes details of the types of ships and instruments he would have used, his influence on maritime history, and the debate about where it was that he actually landed in 1492. There are also detailed maps of all his major voyages.

Cook's First Voyage 1768–1771

http://pacific.vita.org/pacific/cook/cook1.htm

Details of Captain James Cook's first voyage of exploration. This very large description of the journey features several sub-pages, including maps, pictures, and quotations from Cook.

DiverNet

http://www.divernet.com/

This massive site, from UK magazine *Diver*, is packed with articles. For the beginner, there's the 'Discover diving' section, with features on getting the gear, where to go diving, getting further training, and basic underwater photography. For the more advanced diver, there are sections on equipment, travel, marine biology, archaeology, wrecks, photography, and much more.

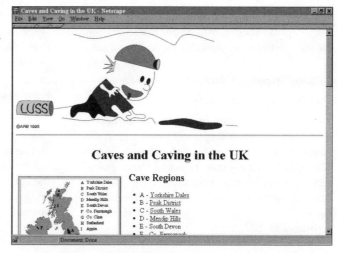

Eirik the Red's Saga

http://www.nlc-bnc.ca/north/nor-i/thule/017e.htm

Saga of Eric the Red, supposedly the first
European to discover Greenland and possibly
North America. This Web site, run by the National
Library of Canada, contains an extract from *The
Norse Atlantic Saga: Being the Norse Voyages of
Discovery and Settlement to Iceland, Greenland, and
America*, by Gwyn Jones.

Endeavour

http://www.barkendeavour.com.au/

Detailed document on a project to retrace James
Cook's most famous voyage over 225 years ago.
There are details of the construction of the ship,
information on where the ship is now, and even
articles written by the current crew.

Everest Quest 96

http://www.pbs.org/wgbh/nova/everest/
expedition96/

This page documents the month-long ascent of
Mount Everest made during April and May of
1996 by David Breashears and his team of IMAX
photographers. Read newsflash reports written
from the mountain by climber and Everest
historian Audrey Salkeld, including a report
concerning the infamous disaster that claimed the
lives of eight climbers. This site includes a virtual
tour of basecamp, a section on the making of the
IMAX film, and an interview with David
Breashears. The sections are arranged by weeks.

Introduction to Mt Fuji Climbing

http://www.sunplus.com/fuji/scott/scott2-1.html

Good general source of information about Japan's
highest peak. There is also practical information
for those wishing to climb the conical mountain.

La Salle Shipwreck Project

http://www.thc.state.tx.us/belle/

Regularly updated site on 'one of the earliest
and most important shipwrecks ever found in
North America'. As well as extensive
illustrations of the excavation and the artefacts
recovered in this year-long project, this site also
contains plenty of historical and contextual
detail about La Salle, and a journal of classroom
resources for teachers.

Letter to the King and Queen of Spain

http://odur.let.rug.nl/~usa/D/1400-1500/columbus/
brf94.htm

Part of a larger site on historical documents, this
page is the text of a letter Christopher Columbus
wrote in around 1494, advocating the
establishment of a Spanish colony in America. A
brief introduction puts the letter in its proper
context.

Lewis and Clark

http://www.pbs.org/lewisandclark/

Incredibly detailed site describing the Lewis and
Clark expedition. The site is run by the film
company responsible for the 'Lewis and Clark'
motion picture. Features of the site include an
interactive story, an archive, a living history
section, and information on the Native Americans
encountered by the expedition.

Missionary Travels and Researches in South Africa by David Livingstone

http://tom.cs.cmu.edu/cgi-bin/book/lookup?
num=1039

Full text of Livingstone's classic account of his
travels in Africa. Written at the request of the
Royal Geographic Society, it was published in
1857. A contemporary review gives a flavour of
how Livingstone's achievements were regarded in
his own day.

Netspedition

http://sunsite.doc.ic.ac.uk/netspedition/

Relive Imperial College's Netspedition to the
Amazon rainforest in 1996. As the team journey
through the Amazon, sounds and images of one
of the most spectacular regions on this planet
were placed onto the Web, allowing the
expedition to be experienced in real time.

Polynesian Voyaging Society

http://leahi.kcc.hawaii.edu/org/pvs/

Home page of a group dedicated to publicizing
and researching the means by which ancient
Polynesians colonized the many tiny islands in
the Pacific Ocean. This site includes maps of the
voyages, details of canoe-building, and views and
opinions of those involved in recreating these
amazing sea journeys.

Explorers

Amundsen, Roald

http://www.south-pole.com/p0000101.htm

Amundsen's trip to the Antarctic is described on this Web site. Along with a lengthy text description of the trip, there are several photographs of the members of the party, their ship, and of other equipment from the 1911 expedition that made Amundsen the first man to reach the South Pole.

> **F**
> **A**
> **C**
> **T**
>
> ### AMUNDSEN, ROALD ENGELBRECHT GRAVNING (1872–1928)
> Norwegian explorer who in 1903–06 became the first person to navigate the Northwest Passage. Beaten to the North Pole by US explorer Robert Peary 1910, he reached the South Pole ahead of Captain Scott 1911.

Around the World in 72 Days

http://www.pbs.org/wgbh/pages/amex/world/index.html

Companion to the US Public Broadcasting Service (PBS) television programme *The American Experience,* this page follows the path of reporter Nellie Bly on her highly publicized, whirlwind tour around the world in 1889. You will also find information on how Nellie Bly affected the course of newspaper reporting and how she came to personify women of the age who did things they 'weren't supposed to do'. Read excerpts from her personal account of her travels and selections from her memoir regarding her consequential undercover work at a mental institution. Listen to an audio clip of the Nellie Bly song and sing along while reading the lyrics. You can read the transcript of the television programme, and there is also a section honouring other female reporters of the age.

Bellingshausen, Thadeus von

http://www.south-pole.com/p0000073.htm

Brief biography and exploration history of the Soviet explorer credited with discovering Antarctica. The Web site includes a small photograph and a reasonable amount of text, and in addition features a section on recommended further reading.

Bonington.com

http://www.bonington.com/4/index2.htm

Web site of Britain's most celebrated mountaineer. There is a full biography of Bonington tracing his career as soldier, explorer, and lecturer. A large number of stunning photographs and news of current expeditions are also to be found.

Cabot Dilemma: John Cabot's 1497 Voyage & the Limits of Historiography

http://etext.virginia.edu/journals/EH/EH33/croxto33.html

Lengthy textual debate on the exact location of Cabot's first landfall in North America. The Web site is a copy of an undergraduate thesis by Derek Croxton, of Charlottesville, Virginia, a first year graduate student at the University of Virginia. The style, in common with many academic papers, is rather dry.

Dampier, William

http://pacific.vita.org/pacific/dampier/dampier.htm

History of the explorations of the English sailor William Dampier. Featuring a map showing his best-known voyage around the Australian North coast and Papua New Guinea, this site describes the journey in detail and also chronicles the life of Dampier.

Dumont d'Urville, Jules Sébastien César

http://www.south-pole.com/p0000077.htm

Story of the world circumnavigation voyage by the French naval expedition of 1837–40, commanded by d'Urville on the Astrolabe and Jacquinot on the Zélée. The expedition visited the South Orkney Islands, South Shetland Islands, the Northwest coast of Antarctic Trinity Peninsula, Orléans Channel, and Joinville Island. This site is mainly text based but does include pictures of d'Urville and the Astrolabe.

Earhart, Amelia

http://www.ionet.net/~jellenc/eae_intr.html

Comprehensive presentation of the life and deeds of Amelia Earhart, America's famous aviatrix. The site takes us through Earhart's early years, focuses

on her growing urge to fly, and follows her years of fame up to her last flight and death.

Explorers of Australia

http://werner.ira.uka.de/~westphal/australia/explore/index.html#contents

Details of 16 explorers of Australia. Of those included, perhaps James Cook, Abel Tasman, and George Bass are among the best known, but the stories surrounding some of the lesser-known explorers are often just as interesting.

Fiennes, Sir Ranulph

http://www.speakers.co.uk/6071.htm

Profile of 'the world's greatest living explorer'. The achievements of his 22 expeditions are summarized, together with his books. There is also a photo of the man described by Prince Charles as 'mad but marvellous'.

Filchner, Willhelm

http://www.south-pole.com/p0000103.htm

Biography of the Swiss-born explorer. This Web site features descriptions of Filchner's voyages to the Antarctic in particular and shows several pictures of Filchner, his vessels, and some of his colleagues.

Franklin, John

http://www.ric.edu/rpotter/SJFranklin.html

Captain Sir John Franklin's disappearance in the Arctic along with two ships and 128 officers and crew was a celebrated mystery in the 19th century, attracting enormous public attention both in the UK and the USA. This site describes what is known of the expedition and the search for the lost expedition party.

Fraser, Simon

http://www.sfu.ca/archives/sf-explorer.html

Portrait and biography of the Canadian explorer. The Web site at the Simon Fraser University Archives, in Burnaby, British Columbia, also describes some of Fraser's journeys, and drops a hint or two about why the University is named after him.

Hakluyt, Richard

http://madhatter.chch.ox.ac.uk/chch/people/hakluyt.html

Profile of the influential early English geographer from his alma mater, Christ Church, Oxford. The main events of Hakluyt's life as scholar, ecclesiast, and unofficial royal adviser are recounted. There is also an analysis of his key role in the promotion of colonization in North America.

Henry the Navigator

http://www.thornr.demon.co.uk/kchrist/ phenry.html

Introduction to the life of the Portuguese explorer Henry the Navigator, concentrating, in particular, on his discoveries and activities with the Order of Christ. The page is illustrated with a portrait of Henry, and there are links to his father, King João, to the Order of Christ, and to bibliographical material.

Hudson, Henry

http://www.georgian.net/rally/hudson/

Well-researched introduction to all aspects of this 17th-century English explorer. The text is illustrated with maps and contemporary illustrations throughout and deals with all four of his major voyages in some detail.

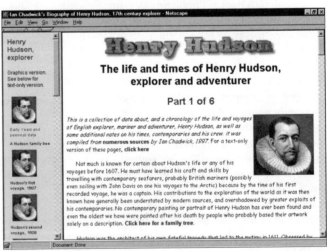

Jason Project

http://www.jasonproject.org

Engaging presentation of the Jason Project, a non-profit organization founded by Dr Robert Ballard after his discovery of the wreck of *RMS Titanic*, in order to allow students and teachers from all over the world to take part in global explorations using advanced interactive telecommunications. Details are posted for schools wishing to join the network.

Jean-Baptiste Charles Bouvet de Lozier

http://www.south-pole.com/p0000067.htm

Brief biography and portrait of the discoverer of Bouvet Island in the South Atlantic. As well as dealing with the personal history of Bouvet, this site describes his explorations and contains a photograph of the island named after him.

La Condamine, Charles Marie de

http://www-groups.dcs.st-and.ac.uk/history/
Mathematicians/La_Condamine.html

Part of an archive containing the biographies of the world's greatest mathematicians, this site is devoted to the life and contributions of geographer Charles La Condamine. In addition to biographical information, you will find a list of references about La Condamine and links to other essays in the archive that reference him. The text of this essay includes hypertext links to the essays of those mathematicians and thinkers who influenced La Condamine. You will also find an image of him, which you can click on to enlarge, and a map of his birthplace.

La Salle, René Robert Cavelier, Sieur de la Salle

http://www.knight.org/advent/cathen/09009b.htm

Profile of the adventurous life of the French fur trader, adventurer, and explorer. It describes how la Salle abandoned early ambitions for the priesthood in order to try to expand French influence in North America from Montreal to Louisiana, an ambition which led to his violent death.

Livingstone – Man of Africa

http://www.rmplc.co.uk/eduweb/sites/blantyre/
living/livmenu.html

Description of the life and exploration expeditions of Dr David Livingstone. The Web site is divided into six subsections, each covering a different section of Livingstone's life. Included are portraits of Livingstone and the journalist Stanley, and also a photograph of Livingstone's birthplace in Glasgow.

Magellan, Ferdinand

http://www.mariner.org/age/magellan.html

Magellan and his remarkable voyage around the world. The Portuguese explorer is credited with making the first circumnavigation of the globe, which is described here. The Web site features several pictures, notably a portrait of Magellan himself, and a map of the journey is also shown. The site also includes descriptions of several of his colleagues and contemporaries.

Nansen, Fridtjof – Scientist, Diplomat, and Humanist

http://www.nrsc.no/nansen/fritjof_nansen.html

Fridtjof Nansen biography. The Norwegian is most famous for his exploration expedition to the Arctic, and later in life, his diplomatic skills. The latter won Nansen a Nobel Peace Prize in 1923, an event which this Web site describes along with his journeys and other aspects of his life.

Nordic Explorers: Bering

http://www.heureka.fi/en/
x/nxpetersenschiorring.html

Description of the life, explorations, and death of Vitus Bering, the famous Arctic explorer. The Web site also deals with an archaeological excavation of Bering's grave on the island named after him, and investigates the possible cause of his death. The standard of English in this Finnish-run page is sometimes faltering, the content is interesting.

Sir Edmund Hillary Profile

http://www.achievement.org/autodoc/page/
hil0pro-1

Description of the life and achievements of Sir Edmund Hillary, the first person to climb Mount Everest. The Web site contains not only biographical information, but also a very lengthy interview with the climber, accompanied by a large number of photographs, video sequences, and audio clips.

Thomas Tew the Pirate

http://www2.prestel.co.uk/orton/family/
thomtew.html

Run by a possible distant descendant of this 17th-century pirate, this site has full descriptions of the life and times of Thomas Tew. There are period pictures of pirates and their ships, and also many links to other pirate sites on the Internet.

Wentworth, William

http://www.effect.net.au/cuddlyk/myworld/history/wentwort.html

Well-written account of the explorer, journalist, and politician, and his role in shaping the development of New South Wales.

William Baffin and Robert Bylot – 1615, 1616

http://collections.ic.gc.ca/arctic/explore/baffin.htm

Outline of the explorations of the 17th-century explorers William Baffin and Robert Bylot. The page lists their accomplishments, as well as a number of interesting facts. There is also a link to a map charting the routes the two men took in 1615.

Maps & Mapmaking

Atlapedia Online

http://www.atlapedia.com/online/map_index_pol.htm

Database of maps which allows you to view a detailed political map for almost any country in the world. You can also choose to see a physical map for the same country. Also included on this site are detailed facts about each of the countries.

Bodleian Library Map Room – The Map Case

http://www.rsl.ox.ac.uk/nnj/mapcase.htm

Broad selection of images from the historical map collection of the Bodleian library. Visitors can choose between rare maps of Oxfordshire, London, areas of Britain, New England, Canada and more. The maps can be viewed by thumbnail and then selected in their full GIF or JPEG version.

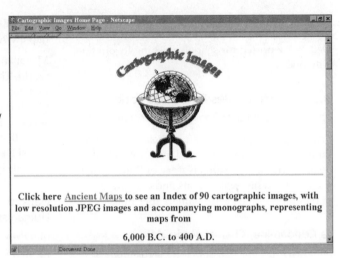

Click here Ancient Maps to see an Index of 90 cartographic images, with low resolution JPEG images and accompanying monographs, representing maps from

6,000 B.C. to 400 A.D.

Cartographic Images Home Page

http://www.iag.net/~jsiebold/carto.html

Treasure trove of cartographic images spanning from 6,000 BC to 1700 AD, put into context with the help of individual or group monographs and a rich bibliography. A valuable and neatly designed resource of astonishing dimensions.

Earth and Heavens – The Art of Map Maker

http://portico.bl.uk/exhibitions/maps/

Excerpts from a major exhibition (now closed) of the British Library on the way maps and mapmaking have been used over the years to make statements about humankind's relationship to the world and the mysteries of the universe.

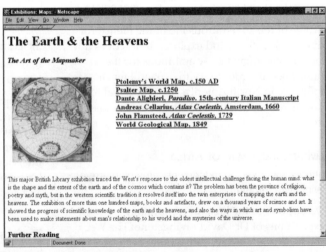

Geographical Study Resources

http://www.m8i.net/

Extensive geographical resource, which includes

outline maps in GIF format, and geographical photographs, both of which are freely available to download. There is also a guide to writing coursework and essays.

Great Globe Gallery

http://hum.amu.edu.pl/~zbzw/glob/glob1.htm

Over 200 globes and maps, showing the earth from all angles, including space shots, political maps, the ancient world, geographical features, and animated spinning globes.

Lebanon from the Sky

http://www.maps.com.lb/maps/photos/menu.htm

Selection of aerial photographs of Lebanon, produced with the help of MAPS geosystems. This geographical survey offers high definition images of urban and rural sites all over this country. The site also provides background information on the technology behind the project.

London Street Maps

http://www.multimap.com/london/

Simple but effective site allowing you to search for any street in the Greater London area. It is quick, and you can see the street and its surroundings at a variety of scales from 1:200,000 down to 1:5,000. The site also allows you to see 'pages' next to your selected street and to choose between colour or greyscale maps.

Mapquest

http://www.mapquest.com/

Features interactive maps of more than 3 million cities worldwide. You can track down businesses and landmarks in Europe and zoom in on street maps. If you've lost your way, 'TripQuest' provides door-to-door driving directions.

Mathematics of Cartography

http://math.rice.edu/~lanius/pres/map/

History of maps and details of the mathematics behind mapmaking. There are maths-related mapping problems to solve and a list of cartographical links.

Mercator, Gerardus

http://www-groups.dcs.st-and.ac.uk/history/
Mathematicians/Mercator_Gerardus.html

Part of an archive containing the biographies of the world's greatest mathematicians, this site is

devoted to the life and contributions of Gerardus Mercator. In addition to biographical information, you will find a list of references about Mercator and links to other essays in the archive that reference him. The text of this essay includes hypertext links to the essays of those mathematicians and thinkers who influenced Mercator. You will also find an image of him, which you can click on to enlarge, and a map of his birthplace.

Ordnance Survey

http://www.ordsvy.gov.uk/home/index.html

Impressive site from the official body responsible for the mapping of Britain. Here you can download a selection of UK maps in a variety of formats. Other features include the 'Education' section which has a selection of teaching resources linked to maps and geography.

Out of This World Exhibition

http://www.lhl.lib.mo.us/pubserv/hos/stars/
welcome.htm

Educational and entertaining exhibition of celestial atlases – highly illustrated scientific books of the post-Renaissance period designed in an effort to capture 'the sweeping grandeur of the heavens, superimposed with constellation figures, in a grand and monumental format'. As well as plenty of images, the site also offers an introductory historical essay and accompanying notes for each image.

Rare Map Collection – Revolutionary America

http://scarlett.libs.uga.edu/darchive/hargrett/maps/
revamer.html

Large collection of maps relating to the American Revolution from the University of Georgia. Included here are maps of both North and South Carolina, Bowles's map of the seat of war, and the theatre of war in North America.

Routeplanner

http://www.cwlease.com/cwlint/index2.htm

If you're thinking of travelling around Europe, you should definitely visit this site first. If you key in a start point and a destination anywhere on the continent, you will quickly be given a map showing a route between the two. You can even choose whether you want the fastest, shortest, or cheapest route. English speakers beware, though – you must type in the local spelling of any place names (for example, München, not Munich).

UK Maps

http://www.multimap.com/uk/

This site allows you to search for maps of towns and cities in the UK. You can view the area in a variety of scales, from 1:50,000 to 1:200,000, and also see 'pages' next to your selected street; you can choose between colour or greyscale maps.

Worldtime

http://www.worldtime.com/

Interactive world atlas featuring information on local time and sunrise and sunsets in hundreds of cities, and a database of public holidays around the world. You can rotate the globe to view areas of daylight and night, zoom in on areas of interest, or display national borders.

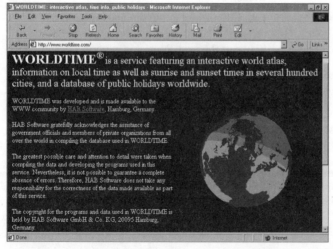

African Countries

About Kenya

http://www.africaonline.co.ke/AfricaOnline/

Social, cultural, and political information about Kenya. This site includes travel-oriented information about this African country, including sections on safaris, national parks, key facts, and even a guide to bus routes.

Abyssinia Cyberspace Gateway

http://www.cs.indiana.edu/hyplan/dmulholl/acg.html

Immerse yourself in the history and culture of Abyssinia – a term used here to bring together the peoples of Djibouti, Eritrea, Ethiopia, Somalia, and Somaliland.

Algeria

http://i-cias.com/m.s/algeria/index.htm

Colourful travelling guide to Algeria and some of its major cities. It includes sections on 'Getting there', 'Visas and passports', 'Climate', 'Health', 'What to buy', as well as a long, illustrated list of places to go.

Angola

http://www.angola.org/angola/

Angola's official Web site has a noticeable pro-government stance, but is well worth looking up for travel information; notes on the country's economy, geography, population, and history; and a virtual tour of Angola's historic buildings.

Angola – A Case Study

http://lcweb2.loc.gov/frd/cs/aotoc.html

Study, carried out by the federal research division of the Library of Congress in the late 1980s, of the dominant social, political, economic, and military aspects of Angolan society.

Benin

http://www.umsl.edu/services/govdocs/wofact96/37.htm

Political and geographical details of Benin are held on this CIA-run Web site. The facts and figures on Benin are quite detailed and can be analysed to give a fairly clear picture of the African country.

Botswana

http://www.umsl.edu/services/govdocs/wofact96/42.htm

CIA world fact book page on Botswana. The information the US intelligence agency holds on this page includes extensive details of the geography, environment, population, government, economy, communications, and defence of Botswana. There are also downloadable files containing brief maps and images of the national flag.

Burundi

http://www.umsl.edu/services/govdocs/wofact96/51.htm

CIA-run site which provides information on almost every aspect of Burundi, from politics to population. The site also includes some downloadable files containing images of the national flag and brief maps of the country.

Cameroon

http://www.umsl.edu/services/govdocs/wofact96/53.htm

CIA world fact book page on Cameroon. The information the US intelligence agency holds on this page includes extensive details of the geography, environment, population, government, economy, communications, and defence of Cameroon. There are also downloadable files containing brief maps and images of the national flag.

Cape Verde

http://www.umsl.edu/services/govdocs/wofact96/55.htm

CIA-run site giving socio-economic details of Cape Verde. The site also includes some downloadable files that hold images of the national flag and brief maps of the islands.

Central African Republic

http://www.umsl.edu/services/govdocs/wofact96/57.htm

CIA world fact book page on the Central African Republic. The information the US intelligence agency holds on this page includes extensive details of the geography, environment, population, government, economy, communications, and defence of Central African Republic. There are also downloadable files containing brief maps and images of the national flag.

Chad

http://www.umsl.edu/services/govdocs/wofact96/58.htm

CIA world fact book page on Chad. The information the US intelligence agency holds on

this page includes extensive details of the geography, environment, population, government, economy, communications, and defence of Chad. There are also downloadable files containing brief maps and images of the national flag.

Congo Page

http://www.sas.upenn.edu/African_Studies/Country_Specific/Congo.html

Concise set of links to resources such as Congo's constitution and a catalogue of its languages. This site also includes a country map, a transcript of Congo's 1992 constitution, and information on the energy resources of this African country.

Djibouti – Overview

http://www.arab.net/djibouti/overview/djibouti_overview.html

Comprehensive introduction to Djibouti, the volcanic desert country near Ethiopia. The presentation includes historical and geographical details, a business section, government pages, and transport advice.

Equatorial Guinea

http://www.umsl.edu/services/govdocs/wofact96/82.htm

Profile of this small West African state. There is information (from the CIA's World Fact Book) on geography, population, and a brief overview of the economy. A map and flag are also included.

Eritrea

http://198.76.84.1/HORN/eritrea/factbook/fb.html

Basic facts and figures for Eritrea from the CIA World Factbook, including area and population statistics, and information about climate, terrain, natural resources, environment, ethnic divisions, language, religion, literacy, government structure, economy, communications, and defence.

Gabon

http://www.umsl.edu/services/govdocs/wofact96/95.htm

Profile of Gabon from the CIA's World Fact Book. There is information on geography, population, and infrastructure and a brief overview of the economy. A map and flag are also included.

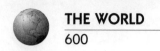

Guinea-Bissau

http://www.umsl.edu/services/govdocs/wofact96/111.htm

Profile of Guinea-Bissau from the CIA's World Fact Book. There is information on geography, population, and infrastructure and a brief overview of the economy. A map and flag are also included.

H-Africa

http://h-net.msu.edu/~africa

Part of the Humanities Online initiative, this site provides a discussion list dealing with the culture and history of the continent. It is a fully searchable site containing journals, images, and contemporary essays.

Home Page of the Republic of Cameroon

http://www.compufix.demon.co.uk/camweb/

Factual data about the country of Cameroon, plus links to a number of associated sites. This site includes a map, an audio clip of the national anthem, and a brief text-only section on tourism in this African country.

Kingdom of Morocco

http://www.mincom.gov.ma/

Morocco's official bilingual window on the World Wide Web. It offers articles on Moroccan identity, lifestyle, and culture, overviews of the different regions of the country, a fauna and flora section, a financial and investment guide, and information on the government.

Leisure Planet Tunisia Travel Guide

http://www.leisureplanet.com/TravelGuides/index.asp?iregionid=5664&strUser=&strPL=LP

This travel guide includes presentations on the different regions and cities of this African country, recommended tours, health and security information, various tips on issues such as travelling for the disabled, business hours, post offices, means of transport, visas and passports, and money. The site also provides ample photographic material and advice on finding a hotel.

Lesotho Page

http://www.sas.upenn.edu/African_Studies/Country_Specific/Lesotho.html

Concise set of resources, including a map, advice for US travellers, a database of Lesotho's languages, and links to further sources of information.

Margaret Rehm's Niger Page

http://www.davison.k12.mi.us/academic/rehm1.htm

Photographic panorama of Niger with photos taken by a volunteer from the Peace Corps. The site is divided into four categories, related to agriculture, village life, livestock, and water.

Nigeria – A Country Study

http://lcweb2.loc.gov/frd/cs/ngtoc.html

Comprehensive pages from the US Library of Congress archives about many aspects of Nigeria's past and present. Click on links to access information about the country's history, land and people, economy, arts, and entertainment.

Republic of Cape Verde Home Page

http://www.umassd.edu/SpecialPrograms/caboverde/capeverdean.html

Information about Cape Verde – its islands, geography and environment, history, culture, and news, plus food aid updates and a 'Did you know...?' section.

Republic of Ghana Home Page

http://www.ghana.com/republic/index.html

Introduction to Ghana, with background notes on its geography, regions, and culture, plus maps of the country, links to newspapers, and tourist information.

Republic of The Gambia

http://www.gambia.com/

Official Web site of The Gambia, with information about the country's history, geography, government, investment opportunities, and economic development, plus a guide for travellers.

Somalia – A Country Study

http://lcweb2.loc.gov/frd/cs/sotoc.html

Extensive presentation of the dominant political, economic, and military characteristics of contemporary Somali society, by the federal research division of the Library of Congress. Topics include an extensive historical overview, analyses of Somalia's social order and religious life, separate entries on foreign relations and security issues, and an account of the history and development of Somalia's armed forces.

South Africa.com – News & Information

http://africa.com/news.html

South African site with general information about, and maps of, the country and links to over ten different newspapers, related organizations, and the South African yellow pages. You can also get hourly weather reports from various weather stations across the country. There are also links back to large sections on 'Travel & tourism', 'Business & finance', and 'Society & culture'.

Sudan – Overview

http://www.arab.net/sudan/overview/
sudan_overview.html

Variety of information on Sudan with extensive historical overviews, maps, pages on the topography, the flora and fauna, and the climate of the country, government, agriculture, and industry presentations, culinary and transport information, and several useful tips and advice on visas, vaccinations, places to visit, shopping, and other issues of interest to potential tourists.

Swaziland Internet

http://www.directory.sz/internet/

Searchable guide to aspects of life in Swaziland today. Type in a word in the search box, or click on links to find out about the country's information technology, food and agriculture, religious organizations, tourism and leisure, and government and diplomatic institutions.

Uganda

http://gaia.info.usaid.gov/HORN/uganda/
cia/uganda.html

Basic facts and figures for Uganda from the CIA World Factbook, including area and population statistics, and information about climate, terrain, natural resources, environment, ethnic divisions, language, religion, literacy, government structure, economy, communications, and defence.

Zaire – A Country Study

http://lcweb2.loc.gov/frd/cs/zrtoc.html

Extensive research on Zaire carried out by the federal research division of the Library of Congress. It focuses primarily on the Zaire of the early 1990s, following the country's attempts to move from President Mobutu's autocratic regime towards a multiparty democracy. The site also includes extensive historical, social, and economic overviews, as well as accounts of security, health, and education matters.

ZimWEB

http://www.mother.com/~zimweb/second.htm

Mini-essays and links to pages about Zimbabwe, its current affairs, business world, education, and tourist attractions.

American & Caribbean Countries

About Guatemala

http://www.tradepoint.org.gt/travelguate.html

Lively window onto Guatemala. The site includes extensive sections on the country's ancient history, colonial times, and modern period. Visitors are also treated to a helpful introduction to the people of contemporary Guatemala with colourful visual material, suggestions for fun and adventure, and a short presentation on the country's flora and fauna.

> **F**
> **A**
> **C**
> **T**
>
> **GUATEMALA**
> country in Central America, bounded north and northwest by Mexico, east by Belize and the Caribbean Sea, southeast by Honduras and El Salvador, and southwest by the Pacific Ocean.

Amigo! Mexico Online

http://www.mexonline.com/

Although a membership-based service, this page also offers lots of free information for the casual

browser – with sections on activities, arts and culture, pre-Columbian history, and help for prospective travellers.

Antigua and Barbuda

http://www.umsl.edu/services/govdocs/wofact96/18.htm

CIA-run Web site describing all aspects of current affairs on the Caribbean islands. The site also includes downloadable files containing images of the national flags and also maps of the region.

Bahamas

http://www.umsl.edu/services/govdocs/wofact96/28.htm

Political and geographical details of the Caribbean islands are available from this CIA-run Web site. An image of the national flag is available for downloading along with a small map of the islands.

Bahamas Online

http://www.bahamas-on-line.com/

One-stop information service for anyone planning to visit the Bahamas, with sections on such topics as Bahamian history, shops and services, places to stay, and things to do.

Barbados – Isle of Dreams

http://www.barbados.org/

Here are facts and figures about Barbados, weather reports, an illustrated history and chronology, a feature on Barbados rum, and links to associated sites.

Belize Online Tourism and Investment Guide

http://www.belize.com/

Designed to attract tourists and commerce to the country, with information grouped under headings such as culture, music, ancient treasures, and news and information.

Bolivia Web

http://www.boliviaweb.com/

Whether you are interested in Bolivian history, music and arts, tourism, or sport, this site should have the information you need. There are plenty of photographs, music to listen to, and links to Bolivian newspapers and radio stations. Most of the site is in English, but some information is only available in Spanish.

Brazil

http://www.umsl.edu/services/govdocs/wofact96/44.htm

CIA world fact book page on Brazil. The information the US intelligence agency holds on this page includes extensive details of the geography, environment, population, government, economy, communications, and defence of Brazil. There are also downloadable files containing brief maps and images of the national flag.

Chile and Easter Island – Lonely Planet Guide

http://www.lonelyplanet.com/dest/sam/chile.htm

Traveller's guide to Chile, with key facts, a slide show, travellers' reports, and sections on the environment, history, economy, and culture of the country.

Colombia

http://www.ddg.com/LIS/aurelia/colombi.htm

General resource on Colombia, with plenty of information on topics such as history, geography, the economy, and politics. There are also two maps to accompany the text.

Costa Rica: Facts

http://www.centralamerica.com/

Costa Rica for tourists. The site provides a summary of Costa Rican history, geography, and politics, as well as information about the actvities you can enjoy in the country.

Costa Rica TravelWeb

http://www.crica.com/info/info_intro.html

Information for the traveller and prospective business investor, with details of Costa Rica's government and political parties, healthcare and medical system, plus an overview of its history and culture.

CubaWeb

http://www.cubaweb.com/

Business library, with background information about Cuba for the prospective business investor, and a culture library, covering Cuban history, art, music, literature, food, sport, and collections of photographs.

Dominican Republic on the Internet

http://www.latinworld.com/countries/
republicadominicana/

Resources about the Dominican Republic – its
news, culture, government, sport, travel
opportunities, and economy, plus links to other
sites. Please note that some of the information is
only available in Spanish.

Ecuador and the Galapagos Islands

http://www.lonelyplanet.com/dest/sam/ecu.htm

Traveller's guide to Ecuador and the Galápagos
Islands, with maps, a slide show, facts at a glance,
and background information about the country's
economy, history, and culture.

El Salvador – Lonely Planet Guide

http://www.lonelyplanet.com.au/dest/cam/els.htm

Traveller's guide to El Salvador, with a map, slide
show, travel information, and sections on the
country's history, economy, and culture.

Honduras.Net

http://www.honduras.net/

Honduran culture, history, and tourist information
Web site. Featuring descriptions of the Honduran
constitution, a brief history, news, and local
recipes, this page has something for everyone
interested in this Central American country.

Introduction to Argentina

http://www.interknowledge.com/argentina/
index.html

Lively, illustrated guide to the six major regions
which make up this country, and sections on such
things as 'History & culture', 'Calendar of events',
and 'Travel tips'.

Luke's South American Diary

http://www.lukemastin.com/diary

Personal travelogue of an expatriate living,
raising a family, and travelling around Venezuela,
Colombia, Ecuador, Peru, Bolivia, Argentina, and
Chile. It is updated with new adventures about
every month, it includes photographs, and can be
searched by date, country, or trip.

Mexico

http://www.trace-sc.com/index1.htm

Wide variety of fully searchable information on
Mexico. It includes pages about the ancient Aztec

culture, including examples of some historical
documents. On a more contemporary note, there
is a current news section, as well as information
on places for the tourist to visit.

Official Guide to Antigua and Barbuda

http://www.interknowledge.com/antigua-barbuda/

Official Web site of Antigua and Barbuda's
Department of Tourism aimed, naturally enough,
at the prospective tourist, with sections on travel
tips, activities, and accommodation.

Oh Canada!

http://www.macabees.ab.ca/canada/canada.html

Aims to define, by means of selected annotated
links, what it is to be Canadian. It includes
information on Canadian history, the constitution,
national anthem, and more.

Panama – A Country Study

http://lcweb2.loc.gov/frd/cs/patoc.html

Comprehensive, if somewhat outdated (1987),
information about the Republic of Panama. The
site takes its visitors through the landmarks of
Panama's history and offers them extended essays
on religious, political, economic, and military
aspects of Panama's society. It includes separate
entries on the ethnic groups of the region, the
penal system and, of course, the Panama Canal.

Peru – A Country Study

http://lcweb2.loc.gov/frd/cs/petoc.html

Extensive study carried out by the federal
research division of the Library of Congress in the
late 1980s on the dominant social, political,
economic, and military aspects of Peruvian
society. The site includes entries on the Andean
societies, the Spanish Conquest, the Colonian
period, the Andean highlands, the Amazonian
tropics, community and Catholicism, and the
trade in cocoa.

Uruguay – General Information

http://www.embassy.org/uruguay/

Comprehensive information about Uruguay.
There are links to a profile of the country
detailing its main features, as well as to its
history, geography and climate, culture, cuisine,
and wine. The site includes a map and a list of
new Uruguay telephone numbers.

Asian Countries

Abkhazia Home Page

http://hypatia.ss.uci.edu/gpacs/abkhazia/

Illustrated tour through Abkhazian history, culture, geography, and current affairs, presented by the School of Social Ecology and Education, University of California.

Administrative Structure Of Vietnam

http://www.batin.com.vn/vninfo/asv.htm

Fascinating insight into Vietnamese government and politics: at times it almost feels as if you are privy to state secrets! There are few multimedia frills on this site, but the colourful propaganda easily makes up for that.

Afghanistan Today

http://frankenstein.worldweb.net/afghan/

Concise 'encyclopedia' of Afghanistan and the Afghans – its society, culture, history, politics, and more. This page is regularly updated and now contains additional sections on food, country and city maps, the armed forces, and Afghan literature.

F A C T

AFGHANISTAN

mountainous, landlocked country in south-central Asia, bounded north by Tajikistan, Turkmenistan, and Uzbekistan, west by Iran, and south and east by Pakistan, India, and China.

Armenia – A Country Study

http://lcweb2.loc.gov/frd/cs/amtoc.html

Handbook on Armenia, one of the 15 new republics created after the break-up of the Soviet Union, describing the pre-Soviet history of the state, its Soviet period, and its development since it declared independence in 1991. The site also includes entries on environmental issues, ethnic minorities, national traditions, religion, the Armenian diaspora, and human rights.

Azerbaijan – A Country Study

http://lcweb2.loc.gov/frd/cs/aztoc.html

Handbook on Azerbaijan, one of the 15 new republics created after the break-up of the Soviet Union, which describes the pre-Soviet history of the state, its Soviet period, and its development since it declared independence in 1991. This site also includes pages on the state's cultural life, social welfare, education system, health provision, industrial activity, and economic reforms.

Bangladesh

http://www.umsl.edu/services/govdocs/wofact96/31.htm

CIA world fact book page on Bangladesh. The information the US intelligence agency holds on this page includes extensive details of the geography, environment, population, government, economy, communications, and defence of Bangladesh. There are also downloadable files containing brief maps and images of the national flag.

Bhutan

http://www.umsl.edu/services/govdocs/wofact96/39.htm

Political and geographical details of Bhutan are provided courtesy of the CIA at this Web site. The facts provided are extensive and cover most aspects of life in the country. An image of the flag is available for downloading, as are some brief maps of the country.

Brunei

http://www.umsl.edu/services/govdocs/wofact96/47.htm

Political, administrative, economic, and geographical details of the Sultanate of Brunei. This CIA-run site covers many aspects of life in Brunei with comprehensive facts and figures. There are also downloadable images containing the national flag and brief maps.

Burma

http://www.umsl.edu/services/govdocs/wofact96/50.htm

CIA world fact book page on Myanmar (Burma). The information the US intelligence agency holds on this page includes extensive details of the geography, environment, population, government, economy, communications, and defence of Burma. There are also downloadable files containing brief maps and images of the national flag.

Cambodia

http://www.umsl.edu/services/govdocs/wofact96/52.htm

CIA world fact book page on Cambodia. The information the US intelligence agency holds on this page includes extensive details of the geography, environment, population, government, economy, communications, and defence of Cambodia. There are also downloadable files containing brief maps and images of the national flag.

China: Subject Guide

http://darkwing.uoregon.edu/~felsing/cstuff/cshelf.html

Treasure trove of information on Chinese life and culture. Extended historical pages are provided, along with pages on information technology and networking, university life, and sports. Military accounts follow pages on education, environment, gender issues, and business. Government and politics reports complement sections on religion, philosophy, and classics in this valuable resource.

China Today

http://www.chinatoday.com/

Complete guide to China, including culture and ethnology, art and entertainment, education, political organizations, and travel. There is also a section on current events and a basic introduction to this country.

Crimean Republic

http://www.geocities.com/Broadway/Alley/5443/crimopen.htm

Coverage of the Crimea, including an overview of its history and a guide to touring its historical cities and villages.

Indonesian Home Page

http://www.uni-stuttgart.de/indonesia/

List of resources relating to Indonesia and its people, with daily news updates, maps, and travel information. The site also contains some general information on this archipelago and regularly updated links to related Indonesian Web sites.

Japan Information Network

http://www.jinjapan.org/index.html

Searchable set of links to resources about Japan – its regions, society, culture, current events, and other aspects of Japanese life.

Kalayaan – A Celebration of the 100 Glorious Years of Philippine Independence

http://www.philcentennial.com/index2.html

Information on the celebrations surrounding the centennial of Philippine independence. The Web site includes information on events taking place during the celebrations and in particular the Mythical Island exhibition site. Two further areas of the Web site which are still under construction describe heroes of the Philippines and provide images of the country.

Kazakhstan

http://www.umsl.edu/services/govdocs/wofact96/137.htm

Source of basic information on Kazakhstan provided by the CIA. There is an overview of political and economic developments since the establishment of Kazakhstan as a state in 1991, together with basic information on population, government, transport infrastructure, communications, and defence. The site includes the flag and a map of Kazakhstan.

FACT

CHINA
the largest country in East Asia, bounded to the north by Mongolia; to the northwest by Tajikistan, Kyrgyzstan, Kazakhstan, and Afghanistan; to the southwest by India, Nepal, and Bhutan; to the south by Myanmar (Burma), Laos, and Vietnam; to the southeast by the South China Sea; to the east by the East China Sea, North Korea, and Yellow Sea; and to the northeast by Russia.

Korea Central News Agency

http://www.kcna.co.jp/

Site of the Korea Central News Agency. This online propaganda from the North Korean regime provides a fascinating insight into the outlook of one of the world's most isolated regimes.

Land and Culture Organization

http://behemoth.compulink.gr/armen-yth/

Armenian international organization intent on preserving the country's monuments and history. As well as providing an Armenian perspective on the history, culture, and sovereignty of this region of Azerbaijan, this site gives information about the organization's campaigns and how the organization operates.

Malaysia Home Page

http://www.sesrtcic.org/DIR-MLY/MLYHOME.HTM

Information about Malaysian history, events, education, economy, politics, tourism, and laws, as well as hyperlinks to other relevant sites.

Mongolia – A Country Study

http://lcweb2.loc.gov/frd/cs/mntoc.html

Handbook on Mongolia prepared by the federal research division of the Library of Congress in 1989. The site focuses on the increasing importance of the country's role in Sino-Soviet relations, the improvement in its relations with the West, and the administrative and political reforms in the country in the 1980s. It also includes historical overviews and entries on the ethnic composition of the society, the position of Mongolian women, and Mongolian national identity.

Mongolia Page

http://www.ozemail.com.au/~mongolei/ENGLISH/engindex.html

Account of the geography, history, politics, and culture of Mongolia. It includes an overview of the country's art, music, and festivals, and a collection of images. This site also has information on travel and even some useful contacts in this country.

My India

http://www.meadev.gov.in/tourism/menu1.htm

Introduction to the politics, history, culture, and society of India. Additional links to relevant sites on the Web are provided. This site is run by the official Indian tourist board and includes descriptions of all the major states, as well as more general background under such headings as 'News', 'Culture', 'Economy', and 'Sport'.

Nepal – A Country Study

http://lcweb2.loc.gov/frd/cs/nptoc.html

Comprehensive examination of the main concerns and features of Nepal in the early 1990s. Emphasis is placed on population issues such as urbanization, migration, castes, ethnicity, and social values. The site also offers an extensive treatment of Nepal's long history, its economy, and its political structures.

Pakistan – A Country Study

http://lcweb2.loc.gov/frd/cs/pktoc.html

Substantial guide to the state of Pakistan from the federal research division of the Library of Congress. It includes extensive discussions of the state's turbulent history, its current social, religious, and financial situation, its political idiosyncrasies and dynamics, the position of women within everyday structures, and the security concerns currently troubling the country.

Philippine History

http://www.tribo.org/history.html

Well organized source of information about Philippine history, with sections on such topics as the islands' ancient past, the colonial period, the Spanish and US occupations, and the Philippine republic.

Russia Alive!

http://www.alincom.com/russ/index.htm

Guide to the new Russia, with links to related sites and a virtual tour of Moscow.

Sakartvelo – former Republic of Georgia

http://www.sakartvelo.com/

Substantial source of data about Georgia – with maps, statistics, images, audio clips, and information about such topics as its history, architecture, and folklore.

Singapore

http://www.mfasia.com.sg/mfasia/tourism/html/singuide.html

Guide to Singapore. History, geography, and travel information, as well as features on festivals, make up the majority of the tourist-oriented information on this site, but there is also information on local transport and a list of useful phone numbers.

Sri Lanka Info Page

http://www.lacnet.org/srilanka/

Host of links grouped under headings such as news, issues, culture, nature, food and cooking, and travel and tourism.

Thailand Information

http://www.bu.ac.th/thailand/thailand.html

Cultural background and tourist information combine with beautiful photographs to make this site the best starting point for a virtual tour of the 'Land of Smiles'. From Thai boxing to road distances, this Bangkok University run site has a whole range of facts about the country.

Tibetan Government's Web Site

http://www.tibet.com/

London-based site set up by the people of Tibet in exile. It contains many aspects of the country's history as well as up-to-date information.

Includes a complete list of the offices representing Tibet around the world.

Tibet in the 20th Century

http://www.tibetinfo.net/tibet-file/chronol.htm

Brief chronology of significant events in Tibet's history over the past century – 1902–90 – prepared by the Tibet Information Network, an independent organization based in the UK and the USA. Click on links at the bottom of the page to access news updates, reports, and basic information.

Turkey

http://www.turkey.org/turkey/

Guide to Turkey and Turkish culture, with links to the country's history as well as a detailed biography of Turkish leader Mustafa Kemal Ataturk.

F A C T

TURKEY

country between the Black Sea to the north and the Mediterranean Sea to the south, bounded to the east by Armenia, Georgia, and Iran, to the southeast by Iraq and Syria, to the west by Greece and the Aegean Sea, and to the northwest by Bulgaria.

Uzbekistan

http://www.umsl.edu/services/govdocs/wofact96/261.htm

Source of basic information on Uzbekistan provided by the Central Intelligence Agency. There is an overview of political and economic developments since the establishment of Uzbekistan as a state in 1991, together with basic information on population, government, transport infrastructure, communications, defence, and environmental issues. The site includes the flag and a map of Uzbekistan.

Vietnam Pictures

http://sunsite.unc.edu/vietnam/

Multimedia archive of Vietnam, including photographs, audio clips, video footage, and text articles covering many aspects of Vietnamese life. The many hypertext links included on this page can take you on a virtual tour of this Southeast Asian country.

Window on Korea

http://www.iworld.net/Korea/

General information about this country with comprehensive sections grouped under the headings 'Politics', 'Economy', 'Culture', 'Society', 'Industry', and 'Travel'. This is not just a tourism-oriented site – it includes information on many aspects of this country.

Australasian Countries

Australia

http://www.umsl.edu/services/govdocs/wofact96/25.htm

CIA world fact book page on Australia. The information the US intelligence agency holds on this page includes extensive details of the geography, environment, population, government, economy, communications, and defence of Australia. There are also downloadable files containing brief maps and images of the national flag.

Fiji Online Home Page

http://www.fiji-online.com.fj

Official Fiji Island Home Page. Visitors will find all the basic facts about the islands, as well as tourism, trade, and finance sections. The site also offers listings of educational institutions, non-profit organizations, and commercial agencies.

Internet Guide to the Republic of the Marshall Islands

http://www.rmiembassyus.org/

Comprehensive official guide to the Micronesian state. The history, culture, cuisine, economy, government services, and democratic system of the Marshall Islands are fully explained with the help of maps and photos. RMI concerns about global warming, from a state whose highest elevation is a mere six metres, are set out.

Nauru

http://www.tcol.co.uk/nauru/naur2.htm

Official guide to Nauru sponsored by the Commonwealth. The site provides information on the geography, history, culture, economy, government, and judicial system of this phosphate-rich island.

New Zealand on the Web

http://nz.com/

Aimed at the prospective visitor, this site includes a virtual tour of New Zealand, a guidebook, and background information on its history and culture. There is also some information about trade and commerce.

Papua New Guinea Information Site

http://www.bellok.freeserve.co.uk/

Guide to Papua New Guinea. The ethnic and linguistic diversity of the country and its complex history are well presented. A clickable map accesses information on each of the country's twenty provinces.

Solomon Islands – Pearl of the Pacific

http://www.solomons.com/

Good source of information on the far-flung islands, atolls, and reefs comprising the state of the Solomon Islands. The contents include a good history, map, and information on the culture, investment opportunities, and government structures. There is also practical information for tourists.

Vanuatu Online

http://www.vanuatu.net.vu/pages/Vanuatu.html

Source of information on the Melanesian state. There is a history of the islands, information on government services, the local economy, and attractions. This is in addition to practical information for tourists which includes a special section for philatelists.

Welcome to Palau

http://visit-palau.com/

Guide to the Pacific state. Information on local history and Palaun culture is supported by good photographs. There is practical information for tourists and for those interested in fishing and diving.

Welcome to the Federated States of Micronesia

http://www.fsmgov.org/

Official site of the four Pacific islands comprising the Federated States of Micronesia. The contents include a good history, information on culture, language, natural resources, and government structures. The tourist attractions of the four states of Micronesia are listed, together with practical information for visitors.

Welcome to the Royal Kingdom of Tonga

http://www.vacations.tvb.gov.to/

Well-presented official guide to the Polynesian monarchy. There is a map, history, and guide to local culture and investment opportunities. The needs of tourists are met with practical information on attractions and accommodation. This site also includes an audio welcome message from Tonga's Crown Prince.

Eastern European Countries

Albanian World Wide Web Page

http://www.albanian.com/main/

Facts, pictures, and maps help you explore Albania and the Albanian-populated regions of the Balkans. Historical, cultural, and travel information is provided, along with a small English–Albanian dictionary. A 'virtual tour' enables you to click on a map and visit places in Albania to find out about their history and tourist attractions.

All About Bulgaria

http://www.cs.columbia.edu/~radev/bulginfo.html

Links to more than 700 Bulgarian-related sites, answers to 'Frequently Asked Questions', and an archive of 200 poems make this an impressive page.

Belarus – A Country Study

http://lcweb2.loc.gov/frd/cs/bytoc.html#by0003

Important and extensive research on Belarus, one of the ex-Soviet Socialist Republics which declared its independence in August 1995. The survey includes extensive historical overviews and political analyses of the effect of *perestroika* on the region. It also examines the current security issues and economy, as well as providing information about Belarusian ethnic composition, religious affairs, education structures, and health services.

Bosnia and Herzegovina

http://www.umsl.edu/services/govdocs/wofact96/41.htm

CIA world fact book page on Bosnia-Herzegovina. The information the US intelligence agency holds on this page includes extensive details of the geography, environment, population, government, economy, communications, and defence of Bosnia-Herzegovina, and also gives a brief status of the regional conflict of recent times. There are downloadable files containing maps and an image of the national flag.

Bosnia Home Page

http://www.cco.caltech.edu/~bosnia/bosnia.html

Political and social news about this troubled country, with photo-essays, a timeline of the conflict, maps of ethnic occupation and military front lines, features on its culture and daily life, and links to other Bosnian sites.

Bulgaria

http://www.umsl.edu/services/govdocs/wofact96/48.htm

CIA world fact book page on Bulgaria. The information the US intelligence agency holds on this page includes extensive details of the geography, environment, population, government, economy, communications, and defence of Bulgaria. There are also downloadable files containing brief maps and images of the national flag.

Cyprus

http://www.stwing.upenn.edu/~durduran/cyprus2.shtml

Site devoted to Cyprus – its news, geography, and culture. Included are picture galleries, Cypriot jokes, and guides to Cypriot and Turkish Cypriot dances.

Czech Republic

http://www.czech.cz/

Root page for the official Czech Republic site, with information on history, geography, and politics. It contains a daily news section, photographs, and Czech music, as well as practical information for tourists.

Estonia Country Guide

http://www.ciesin.ee/ESTCG/

General information and news about Estonia, plus sections on its history, political system, economy, and culture. There is, however, little information of direct use to people wishing to visit the country, except for pages on upcoming events and public transport.

Facts about Croatia

http://www.croatia.hr/contents.html

Presentation of Croatia with a variety of focuses on history, culture and media, financial aspects, political issues and government structure, sections on educational institutions, social and health care, a science fact-sheet, and gastronomic guidance. An extra bonus of the site is its extensive list of Web links on contemporary Croatia, including Web sites of ministries, educational and cultural organizations and networks, tourist associations, and media enterprises.

Hungarian Home Page

http://www.fsz.bme.hu/hungary/homepage.html

Masses of information about Hungary, including a virtual tour of Budapest, Hungarian–English and English–Hungarian dictionaries, and

recipes for dishes from goulash to Transylvanian layered cabbage.

LatviaNet

http://www.latnet.lv/

Bilingual guide to this Eastern European country, including an overview of the Baltic region, as well as plenty of country-specific information on such topics as the environment, communications, government, tourism, and society.

Macedonia – Frequently Asked Questions

http://faq.rmacedonia.org/

Large source of well-presented information on the Balkan state. There is comprehensive information about the Macedonian language, literary heritage, history, cuisine, arts, economy, sports, and religion. This site also has regularly updated news of internal and external affairs.

Russia Today

http://www.russiatoday.com/

Extensive general information magazine on Russia. As well as daily press reviews and business news, the site provides sections on the government, the constitution, and coverage of hot current issues. Russia Today has a reputation for being on top of the news and getting its readers involved: it even offered them a chance to select the next Russian president in a mock election. A must for everyone wanting to make sense of the bewildering developments in the region.

Slovenia – Country Information

http://www.matkurja.com/

Index of pages covering Slovenia. There is information about history, culture, food and

see p 611

drink, and places to visit, as well as Slovenia's economy and government.

SovInform Bureau

http://www.siber.com/sib/index.html

Dedicated to all things Russian, including information about Russian art, culture, humour, politics, communication and technology, travel, and visas. Advice and tools are also offered which enable you to 'Russify' your PC.

Virtual Romania

http://www.info.polymtl.ca/tavi/rom_eng.html

Canadian-based page with a large interactive map, links to news sources, and essays on aspects of Romanian history and culture.

Middle Eastern Countries

Egypt

http://www.arab.net/egypt/egypt_contents.html

Concise but comprehensive source of information about Egypt – with features on its history, from the predynastic period to the current presidency, geography, culture, and a travellers' guide.

Hashemite Kingdom of Jordan

http://www.websofjordan.com.jo/

Unofficial site, with links to documents about Jordan's politics, history and culture, economy, tourism, and education opportunities.

Iranian Cultural and Information Centre

http://tehran.stanford.edu/

First official Web site of Iran, comprising a wealth of information on Iranian culture and contemporary life. Amongst its attractions are included extensive presentations on literature of and about Iran, the Iranian past, cultural events, and travel opportunities. It also offers an impressive photo gallery with images of Iran and Persian art.

Iraq

http://www.arab.net/iraq/iraq_contents.html

Concise but comprehensive information about Iraq's culture, geography, and history – from Mesopotamian times to Saddam Hussein and the invasion of Kuwait.

Israel – A Country Study

http://lcweb2.loc.gov/frd/cs/iltoc.html

Substantial study of the state of Israel by the federal research division of the US Library of Congress. Its long list of features includes exhaustive historical overviews of Israel's diachronic troubles, extensive analyses of its political framework, foreign relations, and security concerns, and illuminating discussions of its social structure, health and education systems, welfare laws, and economic growth. Its main disadvantage is that it doesn't currently include data about the major developments that have been taking place on the political front since the early nineties.

Jordan

http://www.umsl.edu/services/govdocs/wofact96/135.htm

Source of basic information on Jordan provided by the CIA. There is an overview of political and economic developments in recent years, together with basic information on population, government, transport infrastructure, communications, and defence. The site includes the flag and a map of Jordan.

FACT

JORDAN
country in southwest Asia, bounded north by Syria, northeast by Iraq, east, southeast, and south by Saudi Arabia, south by the Gulf of Aqaba, and west by Israel.

Kuwait – Overview

http://www.arab.net/kuwait/overview/kuwait_overview.html

Well-rounded presentation of Kuwait with historical overviews, maps, flora and fauna details, topographical information, extensive business pages on the industrial and agricultural activities in the country, company profiles, separate sections on religion, media, education and language, government and transport information, and a wide range of advice on tourist issues.

Lebanon

http://lcweb2.loc.gov/frd/cs/lbtoc.html

Official guide to Lebanon. There are sections on geography, economy, crafts, education and history. There is practical information for tourists and sightseeing recommendations. This guide has a series of photographs and is an essential stop for anybody planning a visit to Lebanon.

Oman Infoworld

http://Home.InfoRamp.Net/~emous/oman/about.htm

Variety of information on Oman. The site includes a useful fact sheet and a brief overview of the history of the country, sections on its art and architecture, heritage, traditions and customs, fashion and crafts, and sports pages, a presentation of the economic structure including pages on industry, trading, finance, banking, and transport, and a separate tourist information page.

Pictures of Jordan

http://www.geocities.com/TheTropics/Cabana/ 2973/Jordan.html

Impressive collection of photographs from Jordan. This site includes photographs of some of Jordan's most interesting places such as Petra, Mount Nebo, Wadi Rum, The Dead Sea, and Aquaba, as well as an 'Impressions' section.

Qatar Overview

http://www.arab.net/qatar/overview/ qatar_overview.html

Basic facts and figures about Qatar, including population statistics, currency, life expectancy, literacy rates, and religion. The site includes a search engine for concepts or keywords, as well as links to other sections introducing Qatar's history, geography, culture, business, government, and transport.

Syria – A Photographic Journey

http://www.manhal.com/

Photographic journey and a sensitive look around Syria. The itinerary offers marvellous photos capturing Syria's multicultural past and buoyant present. These are accompanied by readings from travellers, writers, and historians.

Syria Overview

http://www.arab.net/syria/overview/ syria_overview.html

Basic facts and figures about Syria, including population profile and density, land area, language, government, and official religion. The site includes a search engine for concepts or keywords, as well as links to other sections introducing Syria's history, geography, culture, business, government, and transport.

Tourism – United Arab Emirates

http://www.ecssr.ac.ae/tourism.html

Guide to the tourist attractions of the United Arab Emirates, with basic practical information for visitors. It is largely text-based but has some good images of local wildlife.

Visitor's Complete Guide to Bahrain

http://www.arab.net/bahrain/bahrain_contents.html

Indispensable one-stop guide for anybody visiting Bahrain, filled with reams of practical information for tourists and business people.

Welcome to Saudi Arabia

http://darkwing.uoregon.edu/~kbatarfi/saudi.html

Links to resources about Saudi Arabia, with maps, recipes, a travel guide, and useful Arabic phrases.

Yemen

http://www.al-bab.com/

Impressive source of comprehensive information on Yemen. There is coverage of history, culture, archaeology, tourism, economics, the political scene, international relations, and the local media. A large number of photographs include some stunning satellite images.

Western European Countries

Belgium: Overview

http://pespmc1.vub.ac.be/Belgcul.html

General information about Belgium, its cities and regions, plus a special focus on its culture, with features on 'typically Belgian things', such as the Belgian character and Hergé's Tintin.

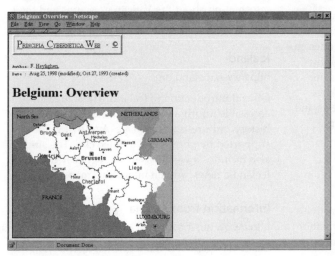

Brief History of Wales

http://www.britannia.com/wales/whist.html

From the Britannia Internet Magazine, a history of Wales in 21 chapters, written by Welsh historian Peter N Williams.

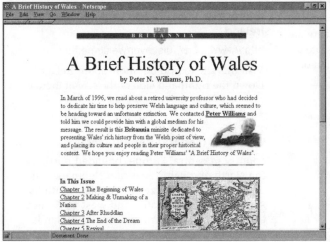

Complete Guide to Ireland

http://members.tripod.com/~AndrewGallagher/ireland/

Guide to the geography, history, and politics of Ireland. The site can be viewed with or without frames and also includes sections on sport, tourism, culture, and the Celts.

Denmark

http://www.umsl.edu/services/govdocs/wofact96/75.htm

Key facts plus links to further information for anyone interested in Denmark. Please note this is not a tourism site, but contains basic information about such things as geography and population, provided by the CIA's *World Factbook.*

Destination England

http://www.lonelyplanet.com/dest/eur/eng.htm

History and tourist attractions of England according to 'Lonely Planet'. This Web site contains something of interest for both the English and the tourist in England. The history of England is briefly described here, starting from the Stone Age and running right through to Tony Blair's election success, but the main focus of the Web site is the many tourist attractions of the country. These attractions have a text description which differs considerably in style from the standard guide book blurb, and the majority of the sections include images of the area under discussion.

Destination Wales

http://www.lonelyplanet.com/dest/eur/wal.htm

'Lonely Planet' guide to Wales. The history of Wales is briefly described, from the Stone Age to the modern day, but the main focus of the Web site is the many tourist attractions of the country. The majority of the texts include images of the area under discussion. Many supporting texts on Welsh culture are also included, such as an article on Tom Jones, and an interactive map of the country is also provided.

FRANCE

country in western Europe, bounded to the northeast by Belgium, Luxembourg, and Germany, east by Germany, Switzerland, and Italy, south by the Mediterranean Sea, southwest by Spain and Andorra, and west by the Atlantic Ocean.

France

http://www.france.diplomatie.fr/france/index.gb.html

Multilingual resource (French, English, Spanish, and German) on this European country produced by the French Foreign Affairs office. It includes an introduction to the country, history, geography, education, science, and culture. All of these are presented in the form of quite in-depth essays. There is also a section on contemporary news and a source of practical information for visitors.

Gateway to Scotland

http://www.geo.ed.ac.uk/home/scotland/scotland.html

Guide to all things Scottish, including an 'active map', a guide to the major cities, and information on the language, as well as sections on famous residents and history.

General Information on the Netherlands

http://www.netherlands-embassy.org/

Well-organized official introduction to Holland from the Dutch embassy in Washington DC. The easily accessed sections include information on the country's history, economy, industry, defense, political structure, social policy, tourism, health, education, environment, and the media. There are a large number of useful links making this site a starting point for finding further information on Holland.

Germany

http://www.bundesregierung.de/

Well-presented official introduction to Germany from the Press and Information Office of the Federal Government. There are thorough overviews of Germany's geography, history, political and judicial system, economy, culture, education, and science. The site also offers links to online versions of information magazines, to federal institutions, and to leading political parties. This is a good first stop for those wanting information about Germany.

Holy See (Vatican City)

http://www.vatican.va/

Multilingual, searchable page, with recent news reports and press releases from the Vatican Information Service. As well as the latest news from the Vatican City State, it also includes information about the Vatican museums and their plans for celebrating the year 2000.

Iceland

http://www.iceland.org/

Official introduction to Iceland. There is easily accessible information on business, education, history, culture, and language. A tourist guide is supported by photos and a video clip. The site also includes a weather report, regularly updated Icelandic news, and an interactive map.

Information from Austria

http://www.austria.gv.at/e/

Easily navigable official guide to Austria from the office of the Chancellor. There is comprehensive information on Austrian foreign policy, as well as education, electoral, parliamentary, and social security systems. There is regularly updated news and foreign ministry press releases. This is an essential first stop for anybody wanting to know about Austria.

Interactive Travel Guide to the Best of Ireland

http://www.iol.ie/~discover/welcome.htm

Visit this site to find out more about Ireland. Down the righthand side of the screen there is an

GERMANY (Federal Republic of)

country in central Europe, bounded north by the North and Baltic Seas and Denmark, east by Poland and the Czech Republic, south by Austria and Switzerland, and west by France, Luxembourg, Belgium, and the Netherlands.

index of places throughout the four Irish provinces. Across the bottom is a list of topics such as 'Accommodation', 'Pictures', 'Business', and 'What's on'.

Internet Guide to Greece

http://www.gogreece.com/

Annotated links to Greek-related resources, under headings such as arts and entertainment, culture, music, food, business and finance, news, and travel information.

Liechtenstein National Tourist Guide

http://www.searchlink.li/tourist/guideeng/index.asp

Official guide to the tiny principality. There is comprehensive information on history, attractions, sporting and recreational pursuits, entertainment, accommodation, and transport. There is a commercial directory, a listing of events, and a guide for philatelists.

Monaco Online

http://www.monaco.mc

Colourful site on the Principality of Monaco. There are sections on all major aspects of life in the principality including the history of Monaco, the Grand Prix, financial advice, a business directory, the annual television festival, and a panorama of impressive shots of the cliffs and shores of Monaco.

Official Documentation and Information from Norway

http://odin.dep.no/html/english/

Well-presented official introduction to all aspects of Norwegian life. There are sections on geography, economy, foreign policy, the political system, the royal family, culture, education, health, sport, and Norway's position within the European Union. Assistance is provided for those wishing to trace their Norwegian ancestry. The site is frequently updated with official Foreign Ministry information and news articles on Norwegian life.

Official Web Site of the Maltese Government

http://www.magnet.mt/

Good source of official information on

the Mediterranean island state. There are sections on the complex history, culture, government services, and the economy. The needs of tourists are also well catered for with a host of practical information.

Principality of Andorra

http://www.xmission.com/~dderhak/andorra.htm

Source of information for the visitor, with sections on such topics as Andorran folklore, festivals, gastronomy, and history.

Small is Beautiful – Welcome to Luxembourg!

http://wwwrzstud.rz.uni-karlsruhe.de/~ujiw/lx.html

Guide to the people, languages, historical background, and culture of Luxembourg. The site is divided into main sections giving general information as well as suggestions of places of interest. There is also a 'Miscellaneous information' section that contains links to various other tourism-related resources for Luxembourg.

Sweden – Provincial Information

http://www.sverigeturism.se/smorgasbord/

Guide to all 27 regions of Sweden from an active map on the home page. Each region contains sections of useful touristic information, such as 'History', 'Culture', 'Events and festivities', 'Family', and 'Major cities'. There is also a separate section called 'Swedish image gallery'.

Switzerland

http://heiwww.unige.ch/switzerland/

'Clickable' map of this central European country, enabling you to navigate around the regions with

your mouse. Nearly all of these are multilingual pages (Swiss-German, English, and German) and contain more general information, as well as being a good resource for the tourist. The site also contains indices of Swiss institutions and forthcoming national events.

United Kingdom

http://www.umsl.edu/services/govdocs/wofact96/258.htm

CIA's world fact book page on the UK. This page links to details held by the US intelligence agency on the UK. The site gives a lot more information than a standard atlas might, including details of international disputes, political inclinations, and economic performance amongst many others. For example, did you know that Britain spent $35.1 billion on defence in 1995?

Virtual Finland

http://virtual.finland.fi/finfo/english/finnmap.html

Set of maps of Finland which include road, rail, and weather, as well as historical maps. There is also an 'active' map which will take you to pages of information about individual towns, cities, and sites of interest.

Virtual Picture Album – Norway

http://carla.acad.umn.edu/VPA/Norway/org_grid.html

Three collections of images of Norway. They are ostensibly designed to be used in language teaching classes, and some help is offered with selecting groups of images for this purpose. However, all the images are freely available for downloading, even if you don't want to use them to learn Norwegian.

Welcome to the Republic of San Marino

http://inthenet.sm/rsm/intro.htm

Good official guide to the world's smallest and oldest nation state. The history of San Marino is interestingly presented. There is a wealth of practical information on attractions, accommodation, and restaurants, as well as coverage of all aspects of political, economic, and cultural life. The pride of the 25,000 Sammarinese shines through this well-organized site.

Windows on Italy – History

http://www.mi.cnr.it/WOI/

Packed with information about the history and culture of Italy's regions and towns. This index leads to pages of information dealing with every major period from prehistoric times to the present day.

INDEX